—— **THE** ——
Which? Hotel
Guide 1994

— THE —
Which? Hotel Guide 1994

Edited by PATRICIA YATES

WHICH?
BOOKS

Consumers' Association

The Which? Hotel Guide 1994 was researched by *Holiday Which?*,
part of the Association for Consumer Research, and published by
Consumers' Association, 2 Marylebone Road, London NW1 4DF

Copyright © 1993 Consumers' Association Ltd
First edition September 1993

British Library Cataloguing-in-Publication Data.
A catalogue record for this book is
available from the British Library

ISBN 0 340 59119 6

Typeset by Rowland Phototypesetting Ltd
Bury St Edmunds, Suffolk
Printed in England by Clays Ltd, St Ives plc

Hoteliers do not pay for entries in *The Which? Hotel Guide*, and the Editor
and her inspectors accept no free hospitality. Consumers' Association
does not permit hoteliers to mention their inclusion in *The Which? Hotel
Guide* in any advertising material.

Warm thanks to Clarissa Hyman, Alison Leach, Andrew Leslie,
Fred Mawer, Diana Vowles and Pat Yale; also to Dick Vine for the
text design and the illustrations; to David Fisher for the maps; to
Paul Saunders for the cover design; to John Parker for the cover
photography; and to Bob Bateman for the chart on pages 8 and 9.
Cover flowers by Andrea Duthie at Cinnamon, Kingston upon
Thames; a selection of props by Dickins & Jones, London W1.

Contents

Introduction

Welcome to the 1994 edition of *The Which? Hotel Guide*. I'm pleased to say that we are bigger than ever this year and have included over 100 more hotels than last year's edition, giving a grand total of over 1,100. So thank you to everyone who has contributed, either by reporting on our previous entries or by suggesting good new places that are worth investigating.

Those of you who have not seen this guide before may not realise that unlike most other guides it is entirely independent – no hotelier can secure an entry by sending us money! – and completely re-written every year, to ensure that it's bang up to date.

Breakfast an optional extra?

As well as finding so many new places for you this year, we have also lost some old favourites for which, sadly, the recession has proved too long and too hard. Times have been difficult for everyone, so we've been scrutinising hotel prices and looking hard at the value they offer. One new wheeze, apparently for keeping room-rates down, is to exclude breakfast and charge extra for it – a relatively new trend which can catch the consumer unawares. I got caught myself recently and paid £14 for the eggs and bacon. The argument in favour of the separate charge is that it's fairer on everyone who just wants a continental breakfast. To me, this doesn't wash. Surely it's an essential part of British hospitality that people can indulge at breakfast and leave with a warm glow that sets them up for the day, rather than being confronted with a priced menu over the newspapers.

The cost of changing your mind

Another area where the unsuspecting consumer could come a financial cropper is the cancellation charge, over which the trade is becoming increasingly militant. Hoteliers are very unhappy about the number of people who simply fail to turn up – or cancel their booking a couple of hours before they are due to arrive. Clearly there may be times when the fates conspire against you and you simply cannot keep your booking, but do remember that when you book a hotel room you enter into a contract, and if you break it the hotelier may be entitled to keep your deposit to cover administrative costs (provided these are reasonable) and loss of profit if he fails to re-let the room. So do be careful to give as much notice as possible if you have to cancel but want to avoid a charge (read the small print in the hotel's brochure to check its policy on cancellation).

A British hotel – the ultimate indulgence?

There is no getting away from the fact that British hotels, by comparison with those of popular foreign destinations, are on the

How room prices compare

£

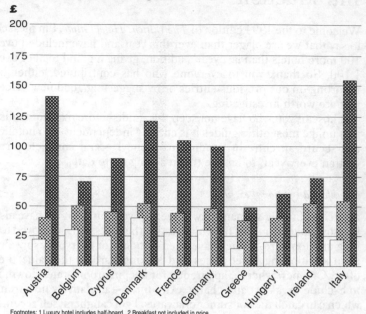

Footnotes: 1 Luxury hotel includes half-board. 2 Breakfast not included in price.

pricey side, and it's no wonder that staying in them is regarded by many as a luxury – affordable only as a special treat or as a business expense.

Many readers write to me comparing UK rates unfavourably with what they pay on the continent or in the USA. As our bar chart of prices shows, it is clear that general perceptions are true: our simple and medium-range hotels are more expensive than anywhere apart from Sweden. Sure enough, across the board, business travellers and conference delegates now make up 60 per cent of hotel guests in Britain compared with 39 per cent in France.

So where does the money go? We asked hoteliers this question and the answers were, first and foremost, to the government, in taxes (17.5 per cent in Britain, as opposed to 5.5 per cent in France) and 'to the bank – to keep them quiet'. French hotels are far more likely to be owned outright and handed down within the family, while British owners often have a hefty mortgage to repay. On the other hand, British hotels benefit from lower staffing costs and lower food bills, but over the last few years lower occupancy rates have made it more difficult for them to cover overheads.

Some hoteliers have sent me very detailed analyses of their accounts. They make sobering reading. One famous name makes 5p profit on a £100 bill ('until three years ago we were profitable'); another shows how he loses £7 per booking, because occupancy rates have fallen by 10 per cent. I've picked out a couple of others – one a B&B and one a hotel, both anonymous but both in the guide you are

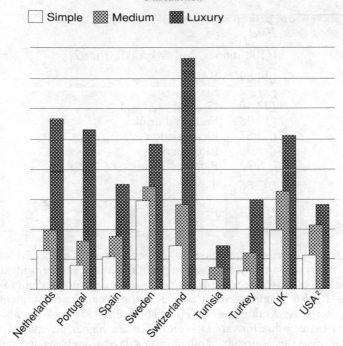

◻ Simple ▨ Medium ■ Luxury

Netherlands Portugal Spain Sweden Switzerland Tunisia Turkey UK USA[2]

reading now – to show you what your money pays for when you pay your bill.

Bed and breakfast	
[Average room rate £55/double]	
£ 8.20	VAT
£ 9.50	Wages
£ 7.80	Services (gas, electricity etc.), insurance and business rate
£ 7.00	Food and drink
£ 5.50	Mortgage
£ 3.80	Finance costs
£ 3.10	Replacements and renewals
£ 3.95	Advertising and publicity
£ 2.55	Laundry
£ 1.00	Ground upkeep
£ 0.50	Toiletries
£ 0.35	Petrol
£ 0.25	Magazines
£53.50	Total cost
£ 1.50	**Profit**

Hotel

[£100 dinner, bed & breakfast for 2]

£14.89	VAT
£21.27	Staff costs
£22.30	General overhead
£19.08	Food and drink
£ 3.83	Depreciation
£ 5.76	Finance costs
£ 8.73	Partners' salaries
£95.86	Total cost
£ 4.14	**Profit**

So there's a vicious circle: low occupancy because of perceived high prices, which in fact yield levels of profit that many another industry would regard as unacceptably poor. One consultant pointed out to us that British hoteliers could take a lesson from their continental counterparts: assume their hotels will be full, set lower prices which offer better value for money – and hope for higher occupancy. In some areas this is already happening on a day-to-day basis, for many hotels are prepared to discount to fill empty beds. 'The published rates are really just a guide to the maximum you should pay,' remarked one chain hotel manager. Certainly it is always worth asking for the best price, particularly if you are booking late in the day. On telephoning several city hotels we found rates dropped from £180 to £100 in a matter of seconds. Of course, it doesn't always work – especially in smaller hotels at peak holiday season – but it's worth a try, and it's a benefit to both the consumer, who might splash out on hotels a little more often if he thought he could afford it, and the hotelier, whose overheads benefit from every extra guest.

Some hoteliers have been outraged that I should suggest that consumers should haggle when they operate on such low margins. Perhaps, however, there are other ways of offering better value for money, such as automatically upgrading customers when the hotel is not full. It really does make guests feel that they've been treated as someone special – far better than that awful (though still widespread) practice of leaving people in the standard room they booked but leaving the doors of all the nicer rooms wide open.

Do you pay your staff?

As is well known, staff salaries in the hotel trade are relatively low, and one way in which this has traditionally been rectified is by the encouragement of tipping. Personally, I find tipping in hotels rather old-fashioned; after all, service is an intrinsic part of what I'm buying.

This seems to be another issue that splits hoteliers too. Many say that they find the practice 'degrading and should be embarrassing to all concerned', and a simple thank-you, on its own, can make their day. Others worry that if there were no tips they might have to pay their staff more, putting the room rates up to compensate. The trend certainly seems to be against tipping, but we'd be interested in your views.

Hotel grading

Crowns, stars, rosettes, moons – yes, there are plenty of systems, but do they really help consumers to choose the best places to stay for the night? I'd say emphatically not. None of the schemes currently in operation covers even half the hotels in Britain, and all the operators make a charge for inspection. The grading systems should be seen for what they are – marketing tools for the hoteliers rather than information services for the consumer. The systems are far from simple to understand. Take the tourist board schemes, for example. The 'crown' systems have now been made even more confusing than they were before since the introduction of 'moons' to cover motor lodges. My complaint is that these schemes are heavily facilities-based – the number of crowns a hotel is awarded depends on what's in the bedroom, and hoteliers are relentlessly pushed into producing standardised hotels with standardised facilities to win their extra crown – particularly irritating, they report, when the goalposts are regularly moved. And it's not necessarily the case that a four-crown hotel is a better hotel than a three-crown: after all, there is much more to a hotel than its facilities.

A few years ago the national tourist boards decided to introduce a quality grading, which is quite different from the schemes which depend on the provision of trouser presses and irons. However, although this was a good idea in theory, it has proved to be deeply flawed in practice. Hoteliers are charged far more for 'quality grading', so many simply don't opt for it – only 30 per cent go for it in Wales, 48 per cent in England, while 100 per cent opt for it in Scotland where it is due to become compulsory in 1995. So if in England or Wales you try to compare two hotels with similar crown ratings, one with and one without a quality rating, you simply cannot know whether the one with no grading has *chosen* not to be graded for quality or has failed to come up to even the lowest standard. So, once again, what's the point? This hotchpotch system should be sorted out: we'd certainly welcome compulsory inspection and obligatory quality grading for all establishments.

Those are the issues that I think are particularly important this year. As ever, we've borne in mind when compiling this guide your wish to get the best value for money possible from your stay, so we have paid particular attention to searching out budget accommodation, indicated by a $\mathscr{L}$ sign. We've also picked out in the entries bedrooms that we liked on our inspection, though I am sure this will lead to more of the sort of comment I received from one hotelier: 'We can easily identify devotees of your Guide, because when they telephone to reserve a room, they always say, "Please don't put us in that bloody awful shack at the back"!'

Please do continue to write in to me, care of Morag Aitken, who keeps all our systems shipshape, with your comments both on hotels in the *Guide* and new recommendations. You'll find report forms at the back, though letters are equally welcome. Remember, *The Which? Hotel Guide* is your guide: it is totally independent and takes no payment from any of the recommended hotels, so we can be absolutely straight in describing them warts and all.

Thank you to those who have sent personal tips and recommendations following the announcement of my new son in the last edition. He's now at the toddler stage and has tried out a few of the hotels in the *Guide* willing to take him. All the stays have proved miraculously easy and, in spite of dire warnings from one hotelier who said she'd rather take a dog, he has not wrecked any decorations with felt-tip pens.

Hope you enjoy the *Guide*, and the hotels in it.

Patricia Yates

Patricia Yates
Editor

Better safe than sorry

With a sigh of relief you reach your hotel after a long and tiring journey. The reception staff are charming and chatty and you can feel yourself relaxing as you complete the registration card. Then you hear the sound of coins dropping round your feet on the marble floor. Automatically you start to pick them up – no one seems to claim them, so perhaps they are yours. Formalities completed, you're ready to go to your room and suddenly you realise your briefcase has disappeared. Yes, you've fallen for one of the oldest con-tricks in the book.

I suppose we all reckon that it will never happen to us. Yet believe me, happen it does. I've sat and watched police videos that showed the few seconds' distraction which is all the light-fingered need to lift your possessions – and even seen one where, when the thief couldn't get close enough the first time, he simply dropped a second lot of coins.

As the police explained, 'The person who has no control over hotel security is the guest, so you must look out for yourself' – and of course not many hoteliers would let guests know that they've had a spate of pilfering. All well and good in theory, but exactly what should you be looking out for? First of all, remember that hotels are nowadays one of the few places that actually encourage people to wander in off the street. Public rooms are just that – public. However relaxing the bar or lounge area, it's not the same as sitting in your own house and you certainly can't be sure that the smart couple sitting next to you are fellow guests.

As my opening paragraph demonstrates your most vulnerable time is at registration – you are in a strange environment, your attention is taken up by booking in, and you have all your luggage on you. A trained thief, possibly working in a team, can take mere seconds to separate you from your bags. One London hotel captured on video a thief entering and leaving the premises: in 30 seconds he had got away with over £3,000. Don't let yourself be distracted. Do be sensible. Among the other tried and tested tricks is ice-cream dropped down the back of your jacket, and even the police laughed when recounting the 'Do you trust me?' routine, in which a fellow guest engages you in conversation for a while, then asks how trusting you are: will you trust him with 50p, £1 for a minute, £5 if he goes out of your sight, your wallet . . . ? Hand it over and you'll never see it again. It sounds unbelievable, I know, but it still works.

Later in the day you may well find yourself chatting with friends in the bar – a good hotel creates the environment to make relaxation easy. Don't forget, though, that however relaxed you feel you are still surrounded by strangers. The hotel bar, again, is prize territory for bag-snatchers (keep your bag on your lap, not discreetly tucked behind the chair) and con-men. One example is the airline pilot who can get you cheap tickets, 'but keep it quiet, because I wouldn't do it for everyone'! And never, whether you are female or male, tell anyone your room number, or leave your key or key card about – one con-man burgled over 500 rooms by simply obliterating the room number on his own key card with correction fluid and writing in someone else's.

As for security in the bedrooms, it is advisable to be familiar with the provisions of the Hotel Proprietors Act 1956. By displaying the terms of this legislation in reception hoteliers limit their liability in the event of any of your possessions being lost or damaged to a maximum of £100, and no more than £50 per item. So if your room door is kicked down while you are at breakfast and your room rifled, the most the hotel will pay you is £100 – and that doesn't go too far nowadays towards the cost of a camera, personal computer or good piece of jewellery. The exceptions to this are if the hotel or staff are negligent, if you have put your property in the hotel safe, or if you've tried to put your property in the hotel safe but the hotel wouldn't take it.

Logically, the first thing to do on arrival is to put in the hotel safe all valuables that you don't intend to use immediately. If you're lucky the hotel will have safety deposit boxes for hire that you can go in and out of easily. If it doesn't, remember that your pet hiding-places aren't likely to prove much of a surprise to the experienced thief, and certainly you should not leave stuff lying around where it may prove too much of a temptation to the many people who may have legitimate reason to enter your room. If people knock at your door and you're not sure who they are, play safe and ring reception to check. One cool female team in London pilfered hundreds of rooms by dressing smartly and pretending to be housekeepers. Modern key cards are far safer than traditional keys – one large hotel says its crime rate fell from 40 thefts a month to 20 a year after they were introduced. Another benefit is that they enable the locks to be recoded. If you are given a traditional key hand it to a member of staff personally when you go out, rather than leaving it on the reception desk where it can easily be taken. And a security-conscious hotel will ensure that reception staff hand single women guests their keys without saying the room number.

But wherever you stay, your most vulnerable possession is likely to be your car and its contents – radio, portable telephone and, above all, the portable computer left in the back. Here the hotelier has no liability at all. The best advice is to choose a well-lit space near the car park and take your valuables with you.

To sum up, follow these simple rules:

1. Keep your luggage in sight – handbags and cameras with the clasp nearest you. Don't drop briefcases or bags on the floor while you check in.
2. Hand all the valuables you don't intend to use immediately to the hotel for keeping in its safe.
3. Empty your car.
4. Never tell strangers, even friendly ones, your room number.
5. Don't leave possessions lying around your room.
6. Always hand your room key to a receptionist, rather than leaving it lying on the desk.

Hotels of the Year

Again, this year we thought we would like to pick out one hotel from each county that had particularly caught our eye. They are not necessarily the most luxurious or expensive – indeed, there are several bed and breakfasts among them – but they all offer individual attention, comfort, a warm welcome – something just a little bit unusual. Not all counties have an award winner.

London

London	Pippa Pop-ins

England

Avon	Queensberry, Bath
Buckinghamshire	Hartwell House, Aylesbury
Cambridgeshire	Chiswick House, Meldreth
Cheshire	White House Manor, Prestbury
Cornwall	Manor Farm, Crackington Haven
Cumbria	New House Farm, Lorton
Derbyshire	Hucklow Hall, Great Hucklow
Devon	Blackaller Hotel, North Bovey
Dorset	Hams Plot, Beaminster
Co Durham	Lumley Castle, Chester-le-Street
East Sussex	Netherfield Place, Netherfield
Essex	Whitehall, Broxted
Gloucestershire	Swan, Bibury
Greater Manchester	Victoria & Albert, Manchester
Hampshire	Gordleton Mill, Lymington
Hereford & Worcester	The Steppes, Ullingswick
Hertfordshire	Hall House, Hertford
Humberside	Winteringham Fields, Winteringham
Isle of Wight	Seaview Hotel, Seaview
Kent	Hancocks Farmhouse, Cranbrook
Lancashire	River House, Poulton-le-Fylde
Lincolnshire	Guy Wells, Whaplode
Norfolk	Morston Hall, Morston
Northamptonshire	Falcon, Castle Ashby
Northumberland	Low Barns, Corbridge

North Yorkshire	White House, Harrogate
Oxfordshire	Upper Green Farm, Towersey
Shropshire	Severn Lodge, Ironbridge
Somerset	Periton Park, Minehead
Staffordshire	Old Beams, Waterhouses
Suffolk	Otley House, Otley
Warwickshire	Caterham House, Stratford-upon-Avon
West Midlands	Jonathans, Oldbury
West Sussex	Angel, Midhurst
West Yorkshire	Wellfield House, Huddersfield
Wiltshire	Old Vicarage, Burbage

Scotland

Borders	The Ley, Innerleithen
Dumfries & Galloway	Riverside Inn, Canonbie
Fife	Peat Inn, Peat Inn
Grampian	Leslie Castle, Leslie
Highland	Tigh an Eilean, Shieldaig
Lothian	28 Northumberland Street, Edinburgh
Strathclyde	Crinan Hotel, Crinan
Tayside	Kinloch House, Blairgowrie

Wales

Clwyd	Starlings Castle, Chirk
Dyfed	Cnapan, Newport
Gwynedd	Ty'n Rhos, Llanddeiniolen
Powys	Monaughty Poeth, Llanfair Waterdine
South Glamorgan	Egerton Grey, Porthkerry

Channel Islands

Guernsey	Idlerocks, St Martin's

Finding your way round the *Guide*

We hope that you will find *The Which? Hotel Guide* easy to use. It is arranged as follows: London, England, Scotland, Wales and the Channel Islands – and alphabetically by the name of the town or village within each region.

The best place to start is with the maps at the back of the *Guide*.

▲ This map symbol marks a place with a recommended hotel that appears in the main part of the *Guide*

△ This map symbol marks a place with a Visitors' Book entry – a more cautious recommendation

□ This map symbol marks a place which has hotels in both the main part of the Guide and in the Visitors' Book section

The index lists each hotel by name.

Symbols

⌣ This denotes somewhere where you can rely on *a good meal* – either the hotel features in the main section of *The Good Food Guide 1994* or our inspectors were thoroughly impressed, whether by particularly competent home cooking or more lavish cuisine

ℒ This denotes that the hotel offers all its twin or double rooms for *less than £25 per person per night including breakfast* at the standard rate. (Many hotels advertise special breaks, and weekend and out-of-season offers, that can mean cheaper room rates than those specifically quoted.)

❧ This denotes that the hotel is in an *exceptionally peaceful situation* where you can be assured of a restful stay

☆ A star placed against the name of an entry denotes that it is *new* to the *Guide* in 1994

Other symbols are used simply to organise our factual information:

◑ *Open and closing periods* of both the hotel and any restaurant

🅩 *Directions* to help you find the hotel and details of *parking* facilities

🛏 Details of the number and type (single, double, four-poster, etc.) of *bedrooms*; *bathrooms*; *shower rooms and other facilities* in the rooms (all rooms have tea/coffee-making equipment unless we specify to the contrary)

◈ Details of the public rooms available and other *special facilities*, including conference facilities (residential and non-residential), babysitting facilities, sports and games at the hotel and/or nearby. We have not inspected hotels specifically from the point of view of disabled readers but pass on as much information supplied by the proprietor as we can about wheelchair access; always telephone the hotel to check

● *Restrictions* of any kind – lack of wheelchair access, restrictions on children, dogs, smoking

▭ Details of *credit cards* accepted

💷 *Prices* that you can expect to pay in 1994 (if 1993 prices are quoted, we state for how long they will last). Unless specified otherwise we give prices *per room per night*, whether for one person in a single room, for one person alone in a twin or double room, or for two people sharing a double room. We also indicate whether the hotel offers special-priced breaks; these can mean a considerable saving on the standard room rate. You will also find details of whether a deposit is required when you book as well as prices of meals in the restaurant, and of breakfast if it is *not* included in the room price. Room prices are rounded up to the nearest £1; meal prices to the nearest 50p

LONDON

LONDON **MAP 11**

Abbey Court

20 PEMBRIDGE GARDENS, LONDON W2 4DU
TEL: 071-221 7518   TELEX: 262167 ABBYCT G
FAX: 071-792 0858

Luxury bed and breakfast in a Victorian home.

The swinging London traditions of Notting Hill and Portobello Road seem to have spawned a small crop of out-of-the-ordinary little hotels. Abbey Court is one of them, a lavish B&B on a Victorian theme. This starts with the bay trees and carriage lamps in the white columned portico and is carried right through with commendable consistency – from the buttonback armchairs, solid oak wardrobes and occasional tables dressed up in floor-length cloths, to good quality prints, scatter cushions and elaborate mirrors (look out for the one with heads of lions and grim bearded men). You can leaf through one of the leather-bound books in the restful, burgundy-toned reception lounge or have a drink or snack in the basement conservatory which leads on to a patio full of flowers. The showpiece bedrooms have four-posters, others have brass beds, all have comfy armchairs, flowery fabrics and – best of all – Jacuzzis.

At the time of inspection the newest addition to the hotel was Mary Ryan, the housekeeper, and it looks as if she will make a big difference. She has a passion for Mrs Beeton-style cookery, which she first gleaned from her grandmother's cook in Ireland, and plans to make her own mucsli, jams and chutney. An American guest ate six of her home-made potato cakes for breakfast, and Peter Mayle, another recent visitor, was regaled with *homage à Provence* – a crêpe with onion sauce, bacon and mushrooms.

◑ Open all year

🔁 Nearest tube station is Notting Hill Gate (Central, District and Circle lines). On-street parking difficult; NCP car park nearby

🛏 6 single, 6 twin, 7 double, 3 four-poster; all with bathroom/WC, exc 1 single with shower/WC; TV, room service, hairdryer, trouser press in all rooms; no tea/coffee-making facilities in rooms

◇ Breakfast room, bar, lounge, conservatory

⊖ No wheelchair access; no children under 12 (exc babies); no dogs

▭ Access, Amex, Diners, Visa

£ Single £83 to £90, single occupancy of twin/double £117 to £130, twin/double £130, four-poster £143 to £160; deposit required. Continental B £7, cooked B £9 (included in room price in low season). Special breaks available

All rooms have tea/coffee-making facilities unless we specify to the contrary.

Abbey House

11 VICARAGE GATE, LONDON W8 4AG
TEL: 071-727 2594

Grand house with simple accommodation in smart Kensington.

The interior architecture of this bed-and-breakfast hotel leaves the visitor with the best memories: a black-and-white tiled grand hall, wrought-iron staircase curving up four floors and lofty rooms leading off. The paintwork is spotlessly white and plants adorn otherwise barren landings. That said, the simple bedrooms, furnished with white chipboard, and the lack of *en-suite* bathrooms, keep the prices remarkably low for such a good address in smart Victorian Kensington. The cheerful red-and-white breakfast room in the basement is the only public place, while the proprietor Albert Nayach or one of his staff presides from a little box-office opening on the first floor.

A reader, while agreeing with the three pluses of price, architecture and location, found the service disappointing during a recent three-night stay there: niggles included a dripping washbasin tap and insufficient pillows, but breakfast was a particular dismay: 'On arrival at the table we were faced by a bowl with a single Weetabix in it; we then ate our hot breakfast (no choices offered here either) to the sight and sound of washing-up in the kitchen. Despite the budget price, a good night's sleep and a restful breakfast are worth more.' More reports, please.

- ◑ Open all year
- ⤤ Nearest tube station is High Street Kensington (District and Circle lines). The hotel is off Kensington Church Street. Parking difficult; public car park nearby
- ⇖ 2 single, 8 twin/double, 5 family rooms; 5 public bathrooms; TV in all rooms; no tea/coffee-making

facilities in rooms
- ◇ Breakfast room; babysitting
- ⊖ No wheelchair access; no dogs; no smoking in public rooms
- ▭ None accepted
- £ Single £30, single occupancy of twin/double £52, twin/double £52, family room £62 to £72; deposit required

Alfa Hotel ☆

78–84 WARWICK WAY, LONDON SW1V 1RZ
TEL: 071-828 8603   FAX: 071-976 6536

Lavish, tasteful décor at rock-bottom prices.

Plant boxes and a good lick of white paint mark the Alfa Hotel out on this busy terraced street of bed and breakfasts, five minutes' walk from Victoria Station. Inside, Howard de Havilland, the interior decorator who has managed the hotel since 1992, has come up with a design that is unusually bold and exuberant for hotels in this price range.

The tone is set in the reception lounge, where you are confronted by a huge black statue of a Greek god, set against the delicate gold stencils and bold colours of the walls. Simple English breakfasts are served in the basement dining-room, a light, airy space which continues the neo-classical theme. Bedrooms in the basement are generally large but can be musty; although their doors look battered, the décor inside is rich and well co-ordinated, picked out here and there with prints, flowers and colourful plates. However, you might well think it is worth paying a little extra for one of the spacious de-luxe rooms on the first floor. Here, Mr de Havilland has really gone to town in rooms like the Emperor, which is furnished with a thickly draped half-tester bed, a chandelier, ornate mirrors and trompe-l'oeil stencils.

◑ Open all year

⤤ Nearest tube station is Victoria (Victoria, Circle and District lines). On-street parking

🛏 14 single, 6 twin, 8 double, 3 triple, I family room, I suite; some with bathroom/WC, most with shower/WC; TV in all rooms

◈ Dining-room, lounge, garden room; conference facilities (max 30 people residential and non-residential); riding, swimming-pool, other sports nearby

⊖ No wheelchair access; no dogs; no smoking in public rooms

▭ Access, Amex, Diners, JCB, Visa

£ Single £39, single occupancy of twin/double £45, twin/double £49, half-tester/triple £55, family room £80, suite £49; deposit required

Aster House Hotel ☆

3 SUMNER PLACE, LONDON SW3 3EE
TEL: 071-581 5888   FAX: 071-584 4925

A horticultural delight in the heart of South Kensington.

As a former London in Bloom award-winner, Aster House's best qualities are on the outside; the white paint of its elegant early-Victorian façade is picked out with all manner of flowers and trees. Rising up to the left of the house, where 1 Sumner Place was bombed out during the war, is a grand first-floor conservatory which is bathed in light and filled with hanging plants and bougainvillaea like a Kew Gardens glasshouse. Healthy buffet breakfasts are served on bone china here amidst the foliage and there are comfy sofas to relax in around a small fireplace. In summer you can take drinks in the back garden, with a fountain, statues and a spectrum of colourful plants for company.

With all this focus on the outdoors, the interior seems to be crying out for a little more attention. Corridors are smart in pink and white, though rather kitsch, and the bedroom furnishings are tasteful and grandiose – all the beds have some kind of swanky overhang. The small, clean bathrooms can, however, be poky and uninviting, and some of the furniture is beyond its sell-by date. Many of the rooms have grand, old-fashioned ceiling fans, and all have a fridge and a safe. All in all, rates are good for an establishment that's only five minutes' walk from South Kensington tube.

◑ Open all year

🔼 Nearest tube station is South Kensington (Piccadilly, Circle and District lines). On-street parking available and public car park nearby

🛏 2 single, 5 twin, 5 double, 1 four-poster; some with bathroom/WC, some with shower/WC; TV, mini-bar, baby-listening in all rooms

◈ Lounge, conservatory

⊖ No wheelchair access; no children under 12; no dogs; no smoking

▭ Access, Visa

£ Single £62, single occupancy of twin/double £80, twin/double £92, four-poster £100; deposit required

Basil Street Hotel

BASIL STREET, LONDON SW3 1AH
TEL: 071-581 3311   FAX: 071-581 3693

A civilised but unstuffy haven in a quiet street just a few steps from Harrods.

The Basil Street Hotel offers old-time elegance, based on traditional virtues of continuity and loyalty: it's still owned by the same family who founded it in 1910 and the manager, Stephen Korany, has notched up 40 years of service here. As a respite from the busy shops of Knightsbridge, the hotel continues to play host to the Parrot Club, a social club for ladies in a room which used to be the ticket office of the underground station.

The exterior resembles a cinema façade and the disjointed reception area is far from impressive, but once you reach the public rooms beyond, you get the feeling that the Basil Street Hotel, with typically English restraint, actually wants to hide its light under a bushel. A grand staircase, dominated by a huge lantern, leads up to the sprawling lounge/bar, where polite service and a comfortable variety of armchairs and sofas provide a tranquil bolthole. What is known as the writing room is in fact a broad, parquet-floored corridor, lined with English antique furniture and, like much of the hotel, dotted with Chinese and Japanese *objets d'art*; here you'll find a row of enticing antique writing tables in a sheltered spot under the window. Opening off the end of the corridor, the green restaurant is vast, elegant and conventional: roast beef is served from a counter and a student from the Royal College of Music plays piano every day.

Bedrooms are traditional too, though brightly decorated in floral patterns. Many have huge baths with chunky taps to match, high beds, and sitting areas where the box armchairs and standard lamps are resolutely pre-'60s in style. Rooms vary widely in size and some suffer from street noise, so it's worth taking a bit of care when booking; those without a private bathroom are a bargain for the hardy. Basilites (regular visitors who have stayed at least five times in five years) receive a discount.

◑ *Open all year*

⤴ *Short walk from Knightsbridge tube station (Piccadilly line). On-street parking (meters) and car park nearby*

🛏 *47 single, 27 twin, 19 double (family rooms and suites available); most with bathroom/WC, some with shower/WC; TV, room service, hair-dryer in all rooms; 6 rooms air-conditioned; no tea/coffee-making facilities in rooms*

◈ *2 restaurants, bar (air-conditioned), 2 lounges,* *ironing-room, drying room; conference facilities (max 40 people residential, 50 non-residential); babysitting*

⊖ *No wheelchair access; no dogs in public rooms*

▭ *Access, Amex, Diners, Visa*

£ *Single £59 to £111, single occupancy of twin/double £133, twin/double £91 to £157, family room £216, suite £239; deposit required. Continental B £5.50, cooked B £11; set L £16, D £19; alc L, D £22/£26. Special breaks available*

The Beaufort

33 BEAUFORT GARDENS, LONDON SW3 1PP
TEL: 071-584 5252   TELEX: 929200 BOFORT G
FAX: 071-589 2834

A small but pricey hotel which offers lavish service and plenty of frills.

Far from clobbering you with hidden extras, the Beaufort lays on more extras than you could ever need and then includes them all in the price of your room. This all-in deal covers continental breakfast and light meals served in your room, drinks from the self-service bar in the sitting-room, and the use of a local health club. In your room you'll find a decanter of brandy, Swiss chocolates, fruit, shortbread, bath robes, an umbrella, a video and a Walkman (tapes for both available from reception), and even a jogging map of Hyde Park. All you need to pay for are phone calls and laundry.

Of course the freebies aren't everything. Within spitting distance of Harrods, the hotel is set in a broad, little-known cul-de-sac off the Brompton Road. Its terraced frontage, facing an attractive line of trees, displays some swanky neo-classical embellishment from the Victorian era and is bedecked with flowers, which form the hotel's main decorative theme – they are scattered around all the rooms, many of the fabrics are floral and the walls are hung with over 400 original English floral watercolours. There's just one public room, a sitting-room lined with comfortable sofas, which has blue-washed walls painted with *trompe-l'oeil* pillars to give the impression of space. 'The outstandingly pretty rooms' reported by one reader are kitted out in a variety of summery, pastel colours; plain-coloured bathrooms are spacious and fitted with power showers, and a profusion of toiletries as you'd expect. Instead of a formal 'Do not disturb' sign, each room is armed with two large bows to hang outside the door, red for no entry and green for go. Indeed, the hotel prides itself on its personal touch: staff are 'very friendly and helpful' and attentive and, beside all the extras mentioned above, the owner provides a constantly updated local restaurant guide.

◑ Open all year, exc 22 to 29 Dec

➔ Nearest tube station is Knightsbridge (Piccadilly line). Parking difficult; car park nearby

🛏 3 single, 5 twin, 13 double, 7 junior suites; all with bathroom/WC, exc singles with shower/WC; TV, room service, hairdryer, baby-listening, air-conditioning in all rooms; tea/coffee-making facilities, trouser press on request

◈ Lounge; riding, swimming-pool, gym nearby

⊖ No wheelchair access; no children under 10 but babies welcome; dogs by arrangement only

▭ Access, Amex, Diners, Visa

£ Single £110, single occupancy of twin/double £120 to £220, twin/double £150 to £220, suite £250; deposit required. Special breaks available

Blakes Hotel

33 ROLAND GARDENS, LONDON SW7 3PF
TEL: 071-370 6701   TELEX: 8813500 BLAKES G
FAX: 071-373 0442

An exotic experience in a peaceful corner of South Kensington.

One shouldn't ask a lady her age, and it seems that Anouska Hempel Weinberg, owner and designer, feels the same way about her famous Blakes. It was opened sometime in the latter seventies, post-Biba but paying tribute to the style – heavy use of blacks and golds, mirrors, Eastern overtones, silky drapery. The hotel sells itself as something very special (it is), emphasising the lavishness, the short taxi distance to Harrods and the glamorous clientele. This can be misleading, for the feel of the place is relaxed and casual, with just a smallish reception lounge – oranges in black bird cages, a love bird, bamboo – as public room, plus the dark and oriental restaurant in the basement that serves modish East-West food at steepish prices. There are some rough edges too, like the badly peeling paint at the back of the building.

The most expensive rooms are true works of art, such as Number 309: decorated in grey, where sculpted swans on the bedhead preside over satiny cushions; or the Franco-Prussian 109, where a gold-embroidered

red drape hangs over a truly regal bed. Humbler doubles have simpler but stunning décor, making good use of hessians and rushmatting, split levels, and maypoles as posts for beds. Detail everywhere becomes an art statement, from the framed vicar's shirts in one bedroom to huge baskets of lavender and symmetrically trimmed little box trees. To help you become part of the décor, bathrobes match each room.

◑ *Open all year*

↗ *Nearest tube station is Gloucester Road (Piccadilly, District and Circle lines). Parking difficult (meters)*

🛏 *14 single, 3 twin, 19 double, 7 four-poster, 9 suites; all with bathroom/WC, exc 4 singles with shower/WC; TV, room service, hair-dryer, mini-bar in all rooms; air-conditioning in some rooms; no tea/coffee-making facilities in rooms*

◈ *Air-conditioned restaurant and bar, lounge; golf, riding, other sports nearby*

⊖ *No wheelchair access; no dogs*

▭ *Access, Amex, Diners, Visa*

£ *Single £135, single occupancy of twin/double £155, twin/double £185, four-poster £300, suite £485 (prices till Sept 93); deposit preferred. Continental B £11, cooked B £16/£23.50; set L, D £36; alc D from £50. Special breaks available*

Bryanston Court

56/60 GREAT CUMBERLAND PLACE, LONDON W1H 8DD
TEL: 071-262 3141   FAX: 071-262 7248

Simple and civilised accommodation; perfect for keen shoppers.

If all you need is modest but civilised and reasonably priced accommodation in the West End, both Bryanston Court and its sister the Concorde, part of the same Georgian terrace, will do the job very nicely. They are particularly good for inveterate shoppers, as Selfridges, Marks & Spencer and the rest of Oxford Street are just around the corner. Both hotels have similar deep-pink wallpapered bedrooms, small but new shower-rooms (mostly) and 'clubby' lounges and bars, leather chesterfields and button-back armchairs, and severe oil portraits that look down on you. Both have the same feel of good old-fashioned, well-run places, but the Concorde's bedrooms look more scuffed and public areas are smaller, so prices are consequently cheaper. Martin and Linda – respective managers and part of the Theodore family who own and run both hotels – emphasised to us that advertised tariff prices are mere fiction in these hard times, and very negotiable.

Included in the price is a buffet breakfast which includes cereal and fruits, cold meats and cheese. Cooked is extra.

◑ *Open all year*

↗ *Nearest tube station is Marble Arch (Central line). On-street parking (metered), public car park nearby*

🛏 *19 single, 24 twin, 7 double, 4*

family rooms; some with bathroom/WC, most with shower/WC; TV, room service, hair-dryer, baby-listening in all rooms

 Breakfast room, bar, lounge; conference facilities (max 20 people); babysitting. Wheelchair access to hotel (2 steps) and 2

ground-floor bedrooms

⬤ None

▭ Access, Amex, Diners, Visa

£ Single £73, single occupancy of twin/double £80, twin/double £90, family room £105; deposit required. Cooked B £6

Cannizaro House

WEST SIDE, WIMBLEDON COMMON, LONDON SW19 4UF
TEL: 081-879 1464   TELEX: 9413837 CANNIZ G
FAX: 081-879 7338   **[see map 9]**

Upmarket Georgian mansion in acres of beautiful parkland.

The seductive sales pitch – 'London's first country-house hotel' – necessarily provokes scepticism, which happily turns out to be unjustified. All the right criteria are satisfied – not only does the hotel have a beautiful position in landscaped parkland on the edge of Wimbledon Common, complete with a sunken garden, an aviary and an ornamental lake, but it is also a fine, cream and pebble-dashed mansion whose first recorded owner was George I's Commissioner of Customs. Furthermore, it has a colourful history: the name comes from an impoverished Sicilian duke who lived here from 1817, and, after passing through the hands of a dashing Indian Maharajah, the house, in the late nineteenth century, played host to such *literati* as Oscar Wilde and Lord Tennyson.

Now owned by the Mount Charlotte Thistle group, the hotel has 46 varied and spacious bedrooms, pleasantly decorated with mostly reproduction furniture and equipped with good marbled bathrooms; many have fine views of the gardens. Downstairs, the central lounge is an impressive affair, with its painted ceiling and intricately carved marble fireplace. There is also a smart bar, with a chandelier dangling from its high ceiling, and a formal restaurant (jackets and ties are required) where the menu changes daily, offering traditional English, French and nouvelle cuisine.

◗ Open all year

⬀ Leave the M25 at Junction 10 (signposted London A3). Follow the A3 for 16 miles and take the Wimbledon/Merton exit to Tibbet's Corner Roundabout. Turn on to the A219 (Parkside Road) and just past the old fountain turn into Cannizaro Road. The second right is West

Side Common. Private car park. Nearest tube station is Wimbledon (District line).

 15 twin, 24 double, 4 four-poster, 3 suites; all with bathroom/WC, TV, room service, hair-dryer, trouser press, baby-listening

 Restaurant, bar, lounge, terrace, 8 private dining-rooms;

conference facilities (max 45
people non-residential and
residential); golf, riding, other
sports nearby; babysitting.
Wheelchair access to hotel,
restaurant and WC (unisex), 5
ground-floor bedrooms and a lift

➖ No children under 8 in
restaurant after 8pm; no dogs in
public rooms

▭ Access, Amex, Diners, Visa

£ Single occupancy of twin/double
£102 to £118, twin/double £118
to £165, four-poster £190 to
£250, suite £225 to £290;
deposit required. Continental B
£7, cooked B £10; set L £17/
£22, D £22; alc L, D £25 (prices
till end 93). Special breaks
available

The Capital

22 BASIL STREET, LONDON SW3 1AT
TEL: 071-589 5171   FAX: 071-225 0011

*This sumptuous, intimate hotel with an excellent restaurant is
under the same ownership as L'Hotel, next door but one – see that
entry.*

◐ Open all year

🡵 Nearest tube station is
Knightsbridge (Piccadilly line).
Private car park

🛏 12 single, 18 twin, 8 suites; all
with bathroom/WC, TV, room
service, hair-dryer, mini-bar,
trouser press, air-conditioning

◈ Restaurant, bar, lounge; hotel
fully air-conditioned; conference
facilities (max 22 people
residential and non-residential)

➖ No wheelchair access; no dogs in
public rooms and by
arrangement in bedrooms

▭ Access, Amex, Diners, Visa

£ Single £149, single occupancy of
twin £179, twin £179 to £220,
suite £250; deposit required.
Continental B £9.50, cooked B
£12.50; set L £21.50; alc L, D
£28 (pre-VAT prices). Special
breaks available.

Concorde Hotel

50 GREAT CUMBERLAND PLACE, LONDON W1H 8DD
TEL: 071-402 6169   FAX: 071-724 1184

*This hotel is under the same ownership as and next door to the
Bryanston Court – see that entry.*

◐ Open all year

🡵 Nearest tube station is Marble
Arch (Central line). On-street

parking (metered), public car
park nearby

🛏 10 single, 12 twin, 3 double, 3

family rooms, 7 annexe rooms, 3 cottages; some with bathroom/WC, most with shower/WC; TV, room service, hair-dryer, baby-listening in all rooms

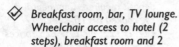 Breakfast room, bar, TV lounge. Wheelchair access to hotel (2 steps), breakfast room and 2 ground-floor bedrooms

⊖ None

▭ Access, Amex, Diners, Visa

£ Single £62, single occupancy of twin/double £65, twin/double £72, family room £85, annexe room/cottage £90; deposit required. Cooked B £6

The Connaught

CARLOS PLACE, LONDON W1Y 6AL
TEL: 071-499 7070   FAX: 071-495 3262

Discreet, traditional English luxury and classic, top-notch French food.

In the heart of Mayfair, this is one hotel that remains reassuringly unchanging in a troubled world, and the limousines keep delivering the affluent guests into its lap of discreet, quintessentially English luxury (some elderly clients leave a suitcase permanently stored at the hotel). An elegant panelled staircase leads to corridors full of paintings and fine antiques, and to bedrooms that are gracious though not flamboyant, each with its own foyer. Prices are strictly on application.

At tea-time, thinly cut cucumber sandwiches are served in the formal lounges or you can have a drink in the dark panelled American bar, but the hotel is deservedly famous for its outstanding food – classic haute cuisine and first-rate wine. Both the restaurant and the cosier green Grill Room serve a similar menu and service is excellent, if a little overwhelming – but, after all, this is what you are paying for.

◖ Open all year

⤢ Nearest tube station is Green Park (Piccadilly, Victoria and Jubilee lines). Parking difficult

🛏 30 single, 36 twin/double, 24 suites; all with bathroom/WC, TV, room service, hair-dryer; no tea/coffee-making facilities in rooms

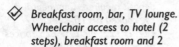 Restaurant, grill room, bar (all air-conditioned), 2 lounges; babysitting. Wheelchair access to hotel (3 steps), restaurant and WC (M), no ground-floor bedrooms but a lift

⊖ No children under 6 in restaurant eves; no dogs; smoking discouraged in restaurant and grill room

▭ Access, Amex, Visa

£ Room prices on application only. Sun L £30; set L £25, D £35; alc L, D from £36 plus 15% service

---

It doesn't matter what you do in the bedroom as long as you don't do it in the street and frighten the horses.

Mrs Patrick Campbell

Cranley Hotel

10–12 BINA GARDENS, LONDON SW5 0LA
TEL: 071-373 0123   FAX: 071-373 9497

Top-notch bed and breakfast with lavish bedrooms.

In a quiet turning off the Old Brompton Road, the Cranley presents an impressive façade: two six-storey Victorian houses of yellow brick and spanking white paint have been knocked together to form the hotel, with the cheery addition of carriage lamps, copious flowers and garden furniture. The interior bears the American stamp of the owner, Bonnie DeLoof, but strives for a very British country-house look which in turn attracts a predominately American clientele.

Antique furniture, dried flowers and lavishly draped pink curtains decorate the comfortable, high-ceilinged lounge, which also shows some modern touches with its spotlights and piped music. Guests can help themselves or be served from the honesty bar; breakfast and light snacks are offered in the bright Petit Salon downstairs, on tables topped with white marble and fresh flowers.

Bedrooms are boldly coloured and many have rich floral wallpaper and ornate swags over the beds. They're not over-designed, however, and manage to create a private residential feel by means of a smattering of antique clocks, oriental fabrics and English oil paintings. Furnished in white with chunky silver fittings, the bathrooms are well up to American standards. Tall bay windows shed plenty of light on rooms at the front; all but three of the bedrooms contain a hidden kitchenette with microwave and fridge.

The Cranley's older sister, One Cranley Place (see entry), lies five minutes' walk away on the other side of the Old Brompton Road. Designed in the same vein, it's not as richly decorated or well-kept as the Cranley, but still offers fair value.

◗ Open all year

◪ Nearest tube station is Gloucester Road (Piccadilly, District and Circle lines). On-street parking and public car park nearby

🛏 3 single, 12 twin, 13 double, 8 suites, family rooms available; all with bathroom/WC, TV, room service, hair-dryer, mini-bar, trouser press

◈ Breakfast room, lounge; babysitting

⊖ No wheelchair access; dogs by arrangement only

▭ Access, Amex, Diners, Visa

£ Single £104, single occupancy of twin/double £104, twin/double £128, family room £177, suite from £198; deposit required. Continental B £9, cooked B £11.50; light meals from £4.50. Special breaks available

---

See the inside front cover for a brief explanation of how to use the Guide.

Dorset Square

39/40 DORSET SQUARE, LONDON NW1 6QN
TEL: 071-723 7874 FAX: 071-724 3328

Gracious living near Regent's Park.

Situated near the smooth expanse of Regent's Park, this Regency terrace hotel conforms to the area's image of classical architecture, gracious living and cricket. The oval, tree-filled square was the site, in 1787, of Thomas Lord's first cricket ground and the theme is discreetly celebrated here, though the lasting impression is left by the bold colours and patterns, the sumptuous draperies, old lace, quality china, fine antique pieces, stripped pine and mixed smells of fresh wax polish and pot-pourri. Guests, we are told, keep returning to luxuriate in yet another of the individually styled bedrooms – you could start in a light, sky-blue 'garret' (Room 401) and work your way down to the giant red wallpaper flowers and plant-filled patio of the grand Room 3 in the basement. Bathrooms are in marble and mahogany with huge mirrors and – oh, bliss – powerful 'massage' showers. Another most laudable feature is the presence of an honesty bar, tucked away in a mahogany cabinet in the Regency-striped lounge. The whole is the creation of Kit and Tim Kemp (who also own the Pelham, see entry) – they seem to have purpose-designed even the staff, who fit perfectly into the ambience, with their Gallic courtesy, neatly elegant uniforms of flowery prints or white cricket sweaters, and ready smiles.

The light basement restaurant has a separate street entrance and is open all day for hearty or light meals or just a drink; the menu is mid-priced and dishes have the nouvelle cuisine sense of aesthetics and combination of flavours. However, the restaurant was empty on a May weekday lunchtime when we sampled there, so it felt rather sad.

◑ Open all year

⤢ Nearest tube station is Baker Street (Circle, Jubilee, Metropolitan and Bakerloo lines). On-street parking

🛏 10 single, 27 twin/double; singles with shower/WC, twin/doubles with bathroom/WC; TV, room service, hair-dryer, mini-bar, trouser press in all rooms; most of the rooms are air-conditioned; no tea/coffee-making facilities in rooms

◈ Restaurant, 2 lounges (all air-conditioned); tennis, swimming-pool, other sports nearby; babysitting

⊖ No wheelchair access

▭ Access, Amex, Visa

£ Single £85, single occupancy of twin/double £110, twin/double £135 to £155; deposit required. Continental B £7.50, cooked B £9.50; set L, D £14.50

I am pent up in frowzy lodgings, where there is not room enough to swing a cat.

Tobias Smollett

The Draycott

24–26 CADOGAN GARDENS, LONDON SW3 2RP
TEL: 071-730 6466   FAX: 071-730 0236

Spacious, luxurious haven with an air of exclusivity.

A discreet brass plaque on the front door announces: 'Private club. Resident members and their guests please ring bell.' Don't be put off, however – all it means in practice is that the Draycott asks for 48 hours' notice before you can stay here. And far from the stiff, traditional formality you might expect from such a place, the atmosphere is friendly, gentle and youthful, attracting a largely American media crowd.

Two huge red-brick terraced mansions in a little-used street behind Sloane Square have been knocked together to form the Draycott. The two houses don't quite match up, which makes for a maze of landings, staircases and stairwells; a lift runs between the floors of the left-hand house. The two public rooms on the ground floor are easy enough to reach: at the front, the homely bar sports rust-coloured wood panelling and an open fire, with black-and-white photographs (which are for sale) to give a modern touch; enticing sofas with beautiful loose covers fill the drawing-room, which overlooks and gives access to Cadogan Gardens, a broad communal lawn shaded by trees.

The best of the bedrooms also face the gardens. The promise that each room has been individually decorated is certainly fulfilled here – interiors are diverse, restrained and tasteful, with an array of antique furniture, woven samplers, plants and prints. Most rooms are ample enough to include a table (upon which breakfast is served) and a small living area around a fire; bathrooms are luxurious, though on the small side. Junior suites consist of only one room and are not much larger than de-luxe doubles, which offer better value.

◑ Open all year

⬏ Nearest tube station is Sloane Square (District and Circle lines). Parking difficult

🛏 6 single, 5 twin, 9 double, 1 four-poster, 4 junior suites; all with bathroom/WC, TV, room service, hair-dryer, mini-bar, baby-listening; no tea/coffee-making facilities in rooms

◈ Bar, lounge; complimentary health club membership nearby; babysitting

⊖ No wheelchair access; dogs by arrangement only

▭ Access, Amex, Diners, Visa

£ Single £100, single occupancy of twin/double £150 to £195, twin/double £150 to £195, four-poster/suites £250; deposit required. Continental B £8, cooked B £11

Hoteliers do not pay for entries in The Which? *Hotel Guide, and the Editor and her inspectors accept no free hospitality. Consumers' Association does not permit hoteliers to mention their inclusion in* The Which? *Hotel Guide in any advertising material.*

Durrants Hotel

GEORGE STREET, LONDON W1H 6BJ
TEL: 071-935 8131   FAX: 071-487 3510

Traditional values at old-fashioned prices.

Step through the columns of Durrants' entrance porch and you'll feel that you've been transported out of London's busy heart into the gentrified hush of a county-town hotel. Standing behind the Wallace Collection and within easy walking distance of Oxford Street, Durrants started life as a coaching-inn on the old Oxford road and, although it now comprises 96 bedrooms, still manages to convey a personalised, home-from-home feel at reasonable prices.

The pine-panelled lobby, with its leather sofa, brass-plaqued post-box and grandfather clock, sets the tone for the whole establishment. Traditional booths and acres of dark oak panels lend an intimate atmosphere to what the management still calls the grill room, though the menu now offers more than just conservative English fare. Elsewhere on the ground floor, you'll find a series of sombre lounges, with sensible chairs awkwardly lining their walls, and a cosy bar staffed by a waiter in starched linen, which has the air of a nineteenth-century gentlemen's club – there's still a separate Pump Room, connected only by a drinks-hatch and hung with paintings of voluptuous nudes, which was once reserved solely for cigar-toting gents. The only discordant note in all this traditionalism is struck by the breakfast room, let down by its cheap-looking blond wood and fluorescent lighting.

An air of English reserve hangs over everything. The hotel has been owned and managed by the Miller family for 72 years, and one reader has written in to praise the staff for being 'friendly and helpful, but not obsequious'. Scattered with antique dressers and wardrobes, the bedrooms are comfortable, plain and subdued, though gradual redecoration is brightening them up. As the building consists of a row of Georgian houses which have been knocked through there's a maze of creaking corridors and the rooms vary widely, those on the front being generally larger and lighter, though slightly noisier.

◑ Open all year

▱ Nearest tube station is Marble Arch (Central line). On-street parking; public car park nearby

🛏 19 single, 40 twin, 31 double, 3 family rooms, 3 suites; most with bathroom/WC, some with shower/WC, some with neither, 3 public bathrooms; TV, room service, hair-dryer in all rooms; trouser press in half of rooms; no tea/coffee-making facilities in rooms

 Restaurant, bar, 3 lounges, breakfast room, smoking room; conference facilities (max 50 people residential and non-residential); tennis, riding, other sports nearby; babysitting. Wheelchair access to hotel (1 step), restaurant and lift, 7 ground-floor bedrooms

● *No dogs*

▭ *Access, Amex, Visa*

⊞ *Single £60 to £85, twin/double £88 to £99, family room £140,*

suite £185; deposit required. Continental B £6, cooked B £8.50; set L, D £18.50; alc L, D £25

For Ebury Court please see Tophams Ebury Court

Egerton House

17–19 EGERTON TERRACE, LONDON SW3 2BX
TEL: 071-589 2412   FAX: 071-584 6540

Elegant formality in a pricey town-house bed and breakfast.

A few yards down a peaceful side-street opposite the Brompton Oratory, Egerton House occupies two immaculately kept six-storey houses, built in red brick in 1880. The interior of the hotel, which was opened in 1990, is similarly spruce and precise, keeping to the Victorian style of the building without becoming too weighty and Gothic. Standards of service are thoroughly 1990s, mixing polite friendliness with professionalism.

The ground-floor hub contains a formal reception lounge, where a graceful pink shell-backed chair stands out; a slightly more homely drawing-room, where you can relax in front of the huge white marble fireplace in a beautifully embroidered armchair, surrounded by oil paintings and antiques; and an adjacent honesty bar, which is as cosy as the hotel gets, decorated in reds and greens and furnished with squashy sofas. Downstairs in the half-basement, the breakfast room is cool, elegant and classical.

Running off narrow, well-lit corridors, the bedrooms vary considerably in size and cost but are all plushly furnished with bold swagged fabrics, antique furniture, stacks of cushions and sturdy marble and granite bathrooms. A hunting theme colours much of the décor, which is co-ordinated with a rather stifling attention to detail – one room has been decked out in green and magenta tartan to match the kilt of a ghillie who stands proudly in a small oil painting on the wall.

◑ *Open all year*

↗ *Nearest tube station is South Kensington (Piccadilly, District and Circle lines). Private car park and on-street parking meters*

🛏 *10 single, 4 twin, 12 double, 1 four-poster, 1 suite; all with bathroom/WC, TV, room service, hair-dryer, mini-bar, air-conditioning*

◈ *Dining-room, bar, lounge (all air-*

conditioned); conference facilities (max 14 people non-residential and residential)

⊖ No wheelchair access; no children under 8; no dogs; no smoking at breakfast

▢ Access, Amex, Diners, Visa

£ Single £95 to £105, twin/double £120 to £135, four-poster £160, suite £195; deposit required. Continental B £7.50, cooked B £12.50; alc L, D £13 to £25 (prices till Sept 93)

The Fenja

69 CADOGAN GARDENS, LONDON SW3 2RB
TEL: 071-589 7333   FAX: 071-581 4958

A-grade bed and breakfast behind Sloane Square.

Occupying a huge red-brick mansion in a turn-of-the-century terrace, the Fenja establishes its individuality by means of an engaging feature: each bedroom is named after a famous artist or writer who lived in Chelsea and is designed to reflect his or her character, with an accompanying biographical note on each dressing-table. This might sound gimmicky, but has been carried out in discreet good taste without taking the idea too literally. The Turner Room, for example, is decorated in every colour of the sun, from the golden swags of the curtains to the intricate marquetry of the headboard, and even has a panel of beige fabric pleated to form a sunburst above the four-poster bed. In contrast, the Sargent room is dark, subdued and masculine, while the Jane Austen room is all floral fabrics and botanical watercolours. The rooms are furnished with antique tables, bureaux and huge wardrobes, and all have good-sized, swanky bathrooms with traditional heavy fittings. All those mentioned above are spacious superior rooms, most of which overlook Cadogan Gardens (to which guests have access), while smaller standard rooms face the back.

The bedrooms run off broad landings hung with eighteenth- and nineteenth-century English paintings and prints, and are decorated in a heavy Victorian fashion that is matched in the formal politeness of the staff. There is only one public area, an elegant drawing-room at the front of the ground floor which is adorned with oil paintings and upright leather armchairs. Breakfast is brought to your room; light meals and drinks (other than those provided on a tray in every room) can also be ordered.

◑ Open all year

⚡ Short walk from Sloane Square tube station (District and Circle lines). On-street parking difficult

🛏 1 single, 7 twin, 4 double, 1 four-poster; most with bathroom/

WC, some with shower/WC; TV, room service, hair-dryer, trouser press, mini-bar in all rooms; no tea/coffee-making facilities in rooms

◈ Drawing-room; conference

facilities (max 12 people residential and non-residential); tennis, riding, heated swimming-pool nearby

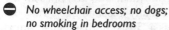 No wheelchair access; no dogs; no smoking in bedrooms

Access, Amex, Diners, Visa

Single £98, twin/double £135 to £195, four-poster £195; deposit required. Continental B £7.50, cooked B £12 (prices till Mar 94)

The Fielding

4 BROAD COURT, BOW STREET, LONDON WC2B 5QZ
TEL: 071-836 8305   FAX: 071-497 0064

A pleasant sleep-only base, well-priced and handy for the Opera.

This is a good example of a London hotel that has resisted dolling up and cashing in on its unbeatable position – virtually across the road from the Royal Opera House, Covent Garden – and has kept its prices extremely reasonable. However, it is not the place to choose if you're looking for more than a room to sleep in. In many of the bedrooms the dark, slightly scuffed wood and the lime green paintwork have been replaced with new pine and sunshine colours; in some, stairs may lead to an extra level with a private little cranny; some are spacious, others are cramped – all are part and parcel of an adapted old London town house. A motley collection of prints on walls and Smokey the parrot (who says 'hello'

THE FIELDING

when he thinks nobody is listening) in the tiny downstairs bar lend the place just enough eccentricity to raise it above the merely pleasant.

Martin Braham the manager presides from the tiny reception office by the entrance; he's assisted by Joel the handyman who also does all the fetching and carrying, while Adele, with chatty husband Paco, runs the basement breakfast room. The room has a '50s suburban décor, but is worth a try if you fancy a traditional British breakfast of bacon and all the trimmings.

One final comment: a single lady reader felt insecure in a ground-floor room with a large window overlooking a back alleyway, while some rooms are at the top of three flights of stairs, so discuss your needs carefully when booking. Rooms are peaceful at night, as the hotel fronts a pedestrian alley next to the Bow Street Magistrates Court.

◐ *Open all year, exc 24, 25 and 26 Dec*

🡒 *Nearest tube station is Covent Garden (Piccadilly line). Opposite Royal Opera House. Limited on-street parking; public car park nearby*

🛏 *11 single, 11 twin/double, 4 suites, family rooms available; some with bathroom/WC, most with shower/WC; TV, room service, hair-dryer, baby-listening in all rooms; hair-dryer on request; tea/coffee-making facilities in some rooms*

◈ *Breakfast room, bar/lounge*

⊖ *No dogs*

▭ *Access, Amex, Diners, Visa*

£ *Single £50 to £68, twin/double £54 to £74, suite £90, family room £98 to £118; deposit required. Continental B £2.50, cooked B £4*

Five Sumner Place

5 SUMNER PLACE, LONDON SW7 3EE
TEL: 071-584 7586 FAX: 071-823 9962

Spotless bed and breakfast in a beautiful South Kensington street.

Part of a white Victorian terrace which is almost wholly given over to hotels, Five Sumner Place is an elegant, white-painted house with a portico over the front door and balconies on the first floor. John Palgan has refurbished the interior in a smart, safe, period style, and maintains it with remarkable attention to detail and cleanliness.

A long pink-papered and chandeliered hall leads through to a gleaming conservatory, where hearty buffet breakfasts, afternoon teas, coffee and snacks are served (there is also a serve-yourself water dispenser). Set against blinding white floor tiles, the dainty tables are covered in yellow and blue cloths and topped with vases of flowers. In summer, you can sit out among the plants in the patio garden.

All the bedrooms offer a wide range of amenities including fridges and have squeaky-clean private bathrooms, which are tiled in grey and white with proper walk-in showers. Room décor is smart and fresh, with floral fabrics, reproduction dark wood furniture and light blue carpets. Mr Palgan has expanded the service he offers to include such things as 24-hour room service and plans to enlarge his conservatory with a bar and lunch room.

◖ Open all year

⤢ Nearest tube station is South Kensington (Piccadilly, Circle and District lines). On-street parking available and public car park nearby

🛏 3 single, 6 twin, 4 double; all with shower/WC, exc 2 twins with bathroom/WC; TV, room service, hair-dryer, trouser press, baby-listening in all rooms; no

tea/coffee-making facilities in rooms

◈ Lounge, conservatory

⊖ No wheelchair access; no dogs; no smoking in public rooms

▭ Access, Amex, Visa

£ Single £61 to £73, single occupancy of twin/double £85 to £99, twin/double £99 to £111; deposit required

---

47 Warwick Gardens

47 WARWICK GARDENS, LONDON W14 8PL
TEL: 071-603 7614 (and fax)

Quiet, discreet bed and breakfast in a smart Kensington home.

There's no sign to show that rooms are available here, because the owner, Mrs Nanette Stylianou, does not accept people calling off the street. Telephone bookings for two or more nights are required, and should be made well in advance as the place gets plenty of regulars. However, don't be put off: Mrs Stylianou, who trained in France and has plenty of experience in the hotel trade, keeps an immaculate, elegant and cheery house.

Most of this large town house, which sits in a Victorian terrace near Holland Park, remains the family home: only three bedrooms in the half-basement are offered, with their own entrance from the street. They are decorated in bright, crisp colours, with whitewood furniture, graceful antique chairs and flower prints. Each has its own well-appointed bathroom: the large double at the front and the twin at the rear have shower attachments over the baths, while the smaller double on the back has a walk-in shower.

English breakfast is served at an antique mahogany table in the classically restrained ground-floor dining-room. When the weather is good, guests can use the fair-sized patio garden behind the house, which teems with pretty flowers in summer. Although Warwick Gardens is a busy thoroughfare during the day the gates at the top of the road are closed at night, which reduces traffic to a trickle.

◑ Open all year

➦ Nearest tube station is Earls Court (District and Piccadilly lines). On-street parking and public car parks nearby

🛏 1 twin, 2 double; 2 with bathroom/WC, 1 with shower/WC; TV, hair-dryer in all rooms

◈ Dining-room, lounge; tennis, riding, other sports nearby

⊖ No wheelchair access; no children under 12; no dogs; no smoking

▭ None accepted

£ Single occupancy of twin/double £50, twin/double £70; deposit required

The Gore

189 QUEEN'S GATE, LONDON SW7 5EX
TEL: 071-584 6601   TELEX: 296244 GORTEL G
FAX: 071-589 8127

Charismatic hotel serving flavoursome food.

Between Kensington and Knightsbridge, the wide avenues leading south from Hyde Park are almost Parisian in elegance and symmetry, with their tall, porticoed and columned Victorian Italianate buildings. One of these is the Gore, a sister to Hazlitt's (see entry), which shares the same insouciantly chic style and the same passion for old prints (over 5,000 adorn its walls) and antique beds. The one in Room 211 is a riot of sculpted gilt curlicues from where you can contemplate the voluptuous reclining *Venus* on the opposite wall; the bed is reputedly Judy Garland's – such decadent extravagance just had to belong to a Hollywood star. For the non-sybarites there is the more severe Tudor room, complete with dark ceiling beams and minstrels' gallery, but even the standard rooms have beds demanding a lie in.

Downstairs, the portrait of a matronly Queen Victoria above the reception desk looks down on the potted palms, oriental rug, mirrors and the extremely lively goings-on in the informal and reasonably priced Bistrot 190 run by chef Antony Worrall-Thompson (he also runs the grander basement restaurant). Unless you're staying at the hotel you cannot book a table, but, if the bistro is full, the young and very friendly staff will do their best to accommodate you at one of the overspill tables in the panelled clubby bar. The food is definitely worth travelling out of your way for: fettuccine with oregano, salmon fishcakes with parsley sauce, or mixed grill of lamb with Moroccan spices and sticky toffee or chocolate fudge for pudding.

◑ Open all year, exc 25 and 26 Dec

➦ Nearest tube station is Gloucester Road (Piccadilly, Circle and District lines). Parking difficult (metered), public car park nearby

🛏 24 single, 4 twin, 18 double, 3 four-poster, 6 suites; most with bathroom/WC, some with shower/WC; TV, room service (with 12½% charge added), hair-dryer, mini-bar in all rooms; no tea/coffee-making facilities in rooms

 2 restaurants, bar, lounge; conference facilities (max 14 people residential and non-residential); tennis, riding, other sports nearby; babysitting by arrangement

 No wheelchair access

Access, Amex, Diners, JCB, Visa

Single £98 to £109, single occupancy of twin/double £136, twin/double £136, four-poster £149, suite £188; deposit required. Continental B £6, cooked B £9.50; alc L, D £15 to £25

The Goring

15 BEESTON PLACE, GROSVENOR GARDENS, LONDON SW1W 0JW
TEL: 071-396 9000   TELEX: 919166 GORING G
FAX: 071-834 4393

An immaculate luxury hotel in a surprisingly quiet location.

Founded in 1910, the Goring claims to have been the first hotel in the world with a private bathroom and central heating in every bedroom, and is now run by a third generation of Gorings (a wooden plaque in the lift showing seventeenth-century Goring House turns out to be a red herring – the house stood on the site of nearby Buckingham Palace but had no connection with the hoteliers). With all that practice behind it, the hotel gives an impression of fine tuning and elegant sophistication, but with a stiff, formal air – apart, that is, from the large model sheep which the present Mr Goring has positioned, on a whim, in the lounge and in some of the bedrooms.

The large, arched reception area gives a crisp, bright welcome with its black-and-white tiled floor and blazing chandeliers. Autumn colours are continued into the main lounge beyond, a formal arrangement of brown leather sofas and stiff balloon-back chairs. Separated by a row of arches from the lounge, the small bar overlooks a lovely ornamental garden which unfortunately is not available to guests. There's also a grand, hushed restaurant offering food that's 'as English as possible' and an extensive wine list.

Running off broad, airy corridors, the bedrooms are neat, luxurious and well-proportioned. Dark wood features heavily, alongside traditionally patterned fabrics in fresh, rich, modern colours. The most sought-after are three rooms with their own large terraces facing the garden at the back.

 Open all year

 Nearest tube station is Victoria (Victoria, Circle and District

lines). Small private car park and on-street parking

28 single, 18 twin, 29 double, 5

suites; all with bathroom/WC, TV, room service, hair-dryer, valet service; no tea/coffee-making facilities in rooms; some rooms are air-conditioned

 Restaurant, bar, 2 lounges; conference facilities (max 60 people residential and non-residential); tennis, riding, other sports nearby; babysitting

 No wheelchair access; no dogs

Access, Amex, Diners, Visa

Single £115, single occupancy of twin/double £130, twin/double £145, suite £180; deposit required. Continental B £8.50, cooked B £11.50; set L £16.50/£19.50, D £25; alc L, D £35

Green Park Hotel

HALF MOON STREET, LONDON W1Y 8BP
TEL: 071-629 7522   FAX: 071-491 8971

Smartly designed, good value for Mayfair and particularly good for business guests and tourist groups.

In Mayfair and a couple of minutes' walk from the park, the Green Park falls within the mid-price range for predominantly business hotels in the heart of London and, consequently, has done rather well out of the recession as corporate clients seek better value for the right comforts and facilities. It occupies a long terrace of neat Georgian town houses on which various designers have been let loose and have done a very good job.

Piped music wafts through the public rooms – lush and rich with their co-ordinating colours and patterns, leaded windows, polished wood, discreet modern lighting and potted greenery. Crisp white table linen and pastel colours make Claude's Restaurant (after Monet the artist) appear bright and smart; Monet's also championed by the water-lily on the entrance mat and prints of his famous paintings. The chef is Eddie Grimes, a new arrival; the intention is to make a name for the restaurant and attract more non-resident diners with simple well-cooked dishes and plenty of fish.

Bedrooms vary in size but are well-designed in pinks, greys and greens and have all the comforts you might need. Thirty-eight of them are for non-smokers and you get automatically upgraded if the hotel is not full.

 Open all year

 Nearest tube station is Green Park (Piccadilly, Victoria and Jubilee lines). On-street parking and public car park nearby

 29 single, 48 twin, 69 double, 1 four-poster, 8 family rooms, 6 suites; all with bathroom/WC,

TV, room service, hair-dryer, trouser press

 Restaurant, bar/lounge (all air-conditioned); conference facilities (max 100 people residential); babysitting

 No children under 7 in

restaurant eves; no wheelchair
access; no dogs

▢ Access, Amex, Diners, Visa

£ Single £94 to £104, single
occupancy of twin/double £104

to £114, twin/double £139 to
£143, four-poster/de-luxe/triple
£147 to £163, family room/suite
£174; deposit required.
Continental B £7, cooked B £10;
alc L, D £12 to £30

The Halkin

5–6 HALKIN STREET, LONDON SW1X 7DJ
TEL: 071-333 1000   FAX: 071-333 1100

Refreshingly modern luxury hotel on a quiet street off Hyde Park Corner.

The Halkin's discreet brick façade conceals a gleaming museum of contemporary design, quite unlike any other hotel in London. With a mix of north Italian chic, small-scale friendly service and state-of-the-art technology, the hotel pulls in a high proportion of business people, many from the worlds of fashion, music and the media. (Though, when even the bell-boys are kitted out in Armani uniforms, the question of what to wear might daunt many people.)

Guests are welcomed at an informal reception desk, a freestanding bar at one end of the small lounge/lobby. Here you'll find a marble mosaic floor, blue leather armchairs and rough grey Cambodian sculptures in an immaculately stylish ensemble, which falls short of being intimidating by virtue of its plants, white-draped arched windows and warm lighting. With more arched windows overlooking a garden at the rear – a delightful backdrop, albeit with no entry to guests – the marbled restaurant continues the radical elegance. The refined Italian cuisine is pricey à la carte, but much better value if you stick to the frequently changing table d'hôte menus.

The bedrooms run off gently curving corridors, lined with black ash-wood; doors are disguised by the wood's soft crenellations which run flush across them. Once inside, you'll find a rich, subtle combination of modernity and three basic natural materials, wood, marble and glass. Korean wooden chests are provided for the TVs, a telephone and fax sits on every antique desk and each bed has a huge, slanting headboard covered in a cream wall fabric. The bathrooms, clad in multicoloured marble, leave nothing to chance: the copious mirrors are even heated to get rid of irksome steam. With control panels for automatic curtains, lighting and air-conditioning which generates an audible hum in the background, the impression is of a soothing hi-tech cocoon.

◗ Open all year; restaurant closed
Sun eve

⤢ Nearest tube station is Hyde
Park Corner (Piccadilly line).

Halkin Street links Grosvenor
Place with Belgrave Square.
Access is via Grosvenor Place,
Chapel Street and Headfort

Place. Private car park and on-street parking

🛏 6 twin, 25 double, 10 suites; all with bathroom/WC, TV, room service, hair-dryer, mini-bar, valet service and fax machine

◈ Restaurant, bar, lounge, private dining-room; hotel is air-conditioned throughout; conference facilities (max 50 people non-residential and residential); riding, heated swimming-pool nearby; babysitting/baby-listening by arrangement. Wheelchair access to hotel, restaurant and WC (disabled), no ground-floor bedrooms but lift

⊖ No dogs; no pipes or cigars in restaurant

▭ Access, Amex, Diners, Visa

£ Twin/double £180 to £225, suite £300 to £350; deposit required. Cooked B £14, continental B £10; set L £18/£24.50, D £24.50/£28.50; alc D from £30

Hazlitt's

6 FRITH STREET, LONDON W1V 5TZ
TEL: 071-434 1771 FAX: 071-439 1524

Inspiring bed and breakfast in Soho, perfect for intellectuals or bathtime hedonists.

Only a very discreet sign reveals this group of three early eighteenth-century houses yards away from Soho Square as a hotel. As a guest you'll have your own key to enter and, unless you stray into the reception or small parlour beyond, you may believe yourself inside a bourgeois home of long-established traditions: the cool silence of the entrance hall, the host of beautiful old prints and sepia photographs, the slightly drunken lino-clad stairs and the assortment of polished wood antiques in the bedrooms. Hedonists can luxuriate in deep, claw-footed baths surrounded by parlour palms and ferns, ceramic ewers and mahogany loo seats (Victorian brass taps come with their original Victorian drips, warns the information leaflet).

The hotel also takes inspiration from its fascinating history – as former lodgings and meeting place for the erstwhile fashionable Soho literati (even the manager, Sture Rydman, has something of the manner of a distinguished literary man). Among the many famous connections are William Hazlitt himself, essayist and painter who died here in 1830, the poetess Mary Blake, and a room named after Jonathan Swift with a crimson sofa with gold-embroidered 'JHS'; the bed has a magnificently sculpted oak headboard.

In the mornings continental breakfast is brought to your room – fresh buttery croissants and coffee from Angellucci's (established 1920) on Frith Street and juice freshly squeezed from oranges bought in Berwick Street Market.

◑ Open all year, exc Xmas period

↗ Short walk from Tottenham Court Road tube station (Northern and Central lines). Parking difficult; public car park nearby

🛏 5 single, 4 twin, 10 double, 3 four-poster, 1 suite; all with bathroom/WC, exc 1 single with shower/WC; TV, room service in all rooms; no tea/coffee-making facilities in rooms

◇ Lounge; sauna, swimming-pool, gym nearby

⊖ No wheelchair access; no dogs

▭ Access, Amex, Diners, Visa

£ Single £95, twin/double/four-poster £115, suite £151; deposit required. Continental B £6

Holland Park

6 LADBROKE TERRACE, LONDON W11 3PG
TEL: 071-792 0216   TELEX: 262167 ABBYCT G
FAX: 071-727 8166

A B&B with good prices, good atmosphere and in a good location.

This is a much humbler sister to the Abbey Court (see that entry), but displays the same flair and, in some respects, has positive advantages: its prices are less than half; the leafy neighbourhood, off Holland Park Road, is delightful; and guests can enjoy a sunny day on the lawn of a secluded garden at the back. This is overlooked by a beautifully proportioned lounge with two large sofas facing each other on a creamy carpet.

Perhaps the one unifying feature of the bedrooms are the candlewick bedspreads (why do modest hotels always have them?); otherwise they are furnished in a mixture of modern furniture and antiques – some in their pre-restoration stage. Plain walls are liberally sprinkled with good quality Victorian prints. Rooms 11 and 15 are the most special, for their beds in particular: a canopied double with walnut fittings in one, mahogany Victorian twins in the other. Bathrooms, with avocado-coloured suites, show their age, but at the time of inspection plans were afoot to spruce up the paintwork. The cheapest rooms share bathrooms.

The manager, Mr Nanji, has grander dreams for the future, to turn Holland Park into London's first theatrical theme hotel where each bedroom will become a stage set and concerts will take place in the garden. Until the dream comes true, enjoy the reasonable prices in a great location.

◑ Open all year, exc Xmas and New Year

↗ Nearest tube station is Notting Hill Gate (Central, Circle and District lines). Parking difficult; public car park nearby

🛏 9 single, 5 twin, 7 double, 2 family rooms; some with bathroom/WC, some with shower/WC, 3 public bathrooms; TV in all rooms

◇ Lounge

⊖ No wheelchair access; no dogs

Access, Amex, Diners, Visa

£ Single £38 to £47, single occupancy of twin/double £47 to £64, twin/double £47 to £64, family room £75 to £90; deposit required. Special breaks available

L'Hotel

28 BASIL STREET, LONDON SW3 1AT
TEL: 071-589 6286   FAX: 071-225 0011

Pastoral retreat offering superior bed and breakfast in the heart of Knightsbridge.

On a quiet residential street just a hundred yards away from Harrods, L'Hotel aims to plunge guests into the ambience of the French countryside. Accordingly the décor, designed by Margaret Levin, the wife of owner David, follows a highly idealised pastoral concept – which, though it may be rather cute for some, is carried off with refreshing panache.

In the bedrooms you'll find bunches of dried flowers, polished Windsor chairs, pine furniture and iron bedsteads. Walls are papered with bright, simple patterns and hung here and there with naïve paintings of farm animals. The hotel's only double bed is in the attic suite; of the twin-bedded standard rooms, three are slightly larger than the others and have ornate leaded fireplaces.

Guests can take breakfast in Le Metro, a functional but stylish wine bar in the basement which has access from the hotel and from the outside. A popular resting place for Knightsbridge shoppers, Le Metro sports a simple but inventive menu of light meals and a highly regarded wine list. There are plans to redecorate Le Metro in August 1993. In contrast to L'Hotel's rural theme, the Capital, its sister hotel two doors away (see entry for details), offers unashamed sophistication. The luxurious bedrooms show great attention to detail, with handmade mattresses, air-conditioning systems disguised in wooden cabinets, and blinds as well as curtains in south-facing rooms. The Capital's small restaurant provides delicately restrained classical cuisine in an ostentatious French setting, decked out by Nina Campbell with huge pink swags and festoons, lavish chandeliers and floral tapestries.

L'Hotel is summarised by one happy reader as 'an excellent base for London shopping and galleries'.

◑ Open all year; restaurant closed Sun eve

↗ Nearest tube station is Knightsbridge (Piccadilly line). Public car park nearby

🛏 11 twin, 1 suite, all with bathroom/WC, TV, breakfast room-service, mini-bar

◈ Air-conditioned restaurant and bar; tennis, riding, other sports nearby; babysitting by arrangement

⊖ No wheelchair access; no dogs in public rooms

☐ Access, Amex, Diners, Visa

£ *Single occupancy of twin £125,
twin £125, suite £145; deposit*

*required. Cooked B £4; alc L, D
£19*

Hotel 167

167 OLD BROMPTON ROAD, LONDON SW5 0AN
TEL: 071-373 3221/0672   FAX: 071-373 3360

A cool, stylish bed and breakfast which strives for an 'arty' look.

Hotel 167 sticks out from the Victorian red-brick of the Old Brompton Road like a sore thumb, with its ground floor covered in green paint and its huge sign written in a distinctive angular script. The stylish modernity continues inside, where the hall invites you in with crisp black-and-white floor tiles, shrubs and friezes of cherubs. Colourful modern oil paintings line the walls here and in the all-purpose public room, which is parquet-floored and subtly spotlit; there's a comfy grey sofa by the reception counter, where you'll receive a relaxed, casual welcome, and stone-topped café tables on which continental breakfasts are served.

The style of the bedrooms ranges from soft Mediterranean (pine beds, wicker chairs and fabric wall hangings) to spiky modern (leather chairs, venetian blinds and spotlights), refreshingly different from the reproduction period style of most London bed and breakfasts. All rooms have fridges and satellite TVs and most have *en-suite* bathrooms, which are mainly small and show signs of wear and tear in places. This part of the Old Brompton Road is busy and quite noisy, but the hotel's windows are double-glazed.

◑ *Open all year*

⤢ *Short walk from South Kensington tube station (Piccadilly, District and Circle lines). On-street parking and public car parks nearby*

🛏 *2 single, 7 twin, 9 double, 1 family room; most with bathroom/WC, some with shower/WC; TV, room service, hair-dryer, mini-bar, baby-*

listening in all rooms

✧ *Dining-room*

⊖ *No wheelchair access; no dogs*

▭ *Access, Amex, Diners, Visa*

£ *Single £54, single occupancy of twin/double £65, twin/double £68 to £75, family room £87; deposit required. Cooked B £5.50; set D £10.50 (before 7pm)*

 Denotes somewhere you can rely on a good meal – either the hotel features in the 1994 edition of our sister publication, The Good Food Guide, *or our inspectors thought the cooking impressive, whether particularly competent home cooking or more lavish cuisine.*

Number Sixteen

16 SUMNER PLACE, LONDON SW7 3EG
TEL: 071-589 5232   TELEX: 266638 SXTEEN G
FAX: 071-584 8615

Relaxing and civilised bed-and-breakfast hotel.

The most luxurious of the many hotels on Sumner Place, Number Sixteen takes up four of the street's immaculate early-Victorian houses. Behind its white-painted porticoes you'll find a warmly lit reception area, an elegant drawing-room decorated in crisp blues and yellows with antique writing tables and comfortable armchairs around an open fire, and a homely library designed in deep reds and greens where you can stock up at the honesty bar. The hotel's best feature, especially in the summer, is at the back: the tranquil walled garden which runs across all four houses includes lawns, a fountain, a fish pond and various nooks and crannies, all of them thick with flowers. There's also a large, well-appointed conservatory which faces south.

Number Sixteen's staff are attentive and friendly. As there is no dining-room, continental breakfasts are brought to your room and served at a small table; a mini-bar stocked with complimentary soft drinks is also provided in every bedroom. The rooms vary widely in size, though none are cramped, and are roughly themed to match their names (Cedar, Garland and Tapestry, for example). They are generally elegant, bright and comfortable, with many antique pieces. Four have their own patios leading to the garden at the back; those on the first floor at the front have french windows and balconies.

◑ Open all year

🡕 100 yards from South Kensington tube station (Piccadilly, District and Circle lines). Parking difficult

🛏 9 single, 27 twin/double; most with bathroom/WC, some with no en-suite facilities; TV, room service (limited), hair-dryer, mini-bar in all rooms; no tea/coffee-making facilities in rooms

◈ Bar, lounge, conservatory; swimming-pool, gym nearby

⊖ No wheelchair access; no children under 12; no dogs; no smoking

▭ Access, Amex, Diners, Visa

£ Single £55 to £95, single occupancy of twin/double £85 to £135, twin/double £85 to £135; deposit required. Cooked B £8

The 1995 Guide will be published in the autumn of 1994. Reports on hotels are welcome at any time of the year, but are extremely valuable in the spring. Send them to The Which? Hotel Guide, FREEPOST, 2 Marylebone Road, London NW1 1YN. No stamp is needed if reports are posted in the UK.

One Cranley Place

1 CRANLEY PLACE, LONDON SW7 3AB
TEL: 071-589 7704   FAX: 071-225 3931

This stylish, upmarket bed and breakfast is under the same management as the Cranley – see that entry.

◑ Open all year

⤴ Off Old Brompton Road. Nearest tube station is South Kensington (Piccadilly, District and Circle lines). Parking difficult

🛏 3 twin, 6 double; most with bathroom/WC, 3 doubles with shower/WC; TV, room service, hair-dryer in all rooms; no tea/coffee-making facilities in rooms

◈ Breakfast room, lounge; tennis, other sports nearby; babysitting. Wheelchair access to hotel, 1 ground-floor bedroom

⊖ Dogs by arrangement only

▭ Access, Amex, Diners, Visa

£ Single occupancy of twin/double £82, twin/double £115; deposit required. Continental B £9, cooked B £11.50

Pelham Hotel

15 CROMWELL PLACE, LONDON SW7 2LA
TEL: 071-589 8288   FAX: 071-584 8444

A small, luxury hotel with exuberant furnishings.

'Like an English gentleman who sports jauntily coloured braces beneath his tweed suit,' reads the brochure, with more than a hint of understatement. Standing opposite South Kensington tube and near the museums, the Pelham's porticoed façade is a brilliant white example of late-Georgian harmony. Inside, the décor is in traditional vein but has been carried off with a daring panache that shows up the soulless Victorian elegance of some country-house-style hotels.

In the reception, your eye is immediately caught by the inlaid tableaux of the grandfather clock and the spidery tree branches of the chandelier. Sunny eighteenth-century pine panelling sets the tone for the drawing-room, which is furnished in rich orange and russet fabrics and hung with a huge scalloped mirror and intricately sculpted dried flowers. The smokers' lounge is darker with acres of mahogany and portraits in oil around a large fire. In the basement, the restaurant has fresh, multi-coloured fabrics and a horseracing theme. Service is attentive, set lunches provide good value and the carefully presented food follows convention with a twist: you may be offered dishes such as mussels with almonds and garlic butter, pork fillet with braised leeks or loin of lamb with jasmine sauce.

Each bedroom is individual, rich in antiques and swathed in colourful, cheery fabrics. Bathrooms are immaculate in mahogany and glazed granite, with good showers. Some rooms on the back are small and rather stuffy; those on the front overlook a busy street but are double-glazed. All rooms have air-conditioning, which can be noisy.

◗ Open all year

⤷ Nearest tube station is South Kensington (Piccadilly, District and Circle lines). On-street parking

🛏 15 twin/king-size double, 21 double, 1 four-poster suite, 1 suite, 1 family room; all with bathroom/WC, TV, room service, hair-dryer, mini-bar, trouser press; no tea/coffee-making facilities in rooms

◈ Restaurant, 2 bars, 2 lounges (hotel fully air-conditioned);

heated swimming-pool, tennis, sauna nearby; babysitting. Wheelchair access to hotel (3 steps), restaurant and WC (M,F), 4 ground-floor bedrooms

⊜ None

▭ Access, Amex, Visa

£ Single occupancy of twin/double £115, twin/double £165, four-poster suite/suite £260, family room £225; deposit required. Continental B £7.50, cooked B £12; set L, D £13.50

Pembridge Court

34 PEMBRIDGE GARDENS, LONDON W2 4DX
TEL: 071-229 9977   FAX: 071-727 4982

An idiosyncratic and comfortable hotel with first-rate housekeeping and the bonus of affordable food in a wine bar-cum-restaurant.

Add together some modern and country-house styles, two big ginger cats, the play on words of a schoolboy's nickname, a Danish lady's taste in theatrical drapery and framed Victoriana displayed like portraits and you come up with Pembridge Court – comfortable, original and very much family-run. Paul Capra's parents bought this white Notting Hill Victorian terrace B&B as an investment in 1969; he took it over for a living, married one of the guests and the rest is history. The original 30-odd bedrooms have been reduced to a mere 21, some positively baronial, decorated in restful peaches and blues with good quality reproduction furniture and bold flowery fabrics that form backdrops like stage curtains to the king-sized beds. Beautiful fans, dolls' clothes and other knick-knacks are displayed on walls. Spencer and Churchill, the resident cats, might greet you on the stairs or in the cosy lounge which has plump sofas and a case full of books.

In contrast to the rest of the hotel, the exposed brickwork in the reception, cellar bar and restaurant feels rather austere. The restaurant is called Caps after Paul's schoolboy nickname and he has taken advantage of the name to decorate the walls with all manner of caps, his son's school blazer and even a boat. The menu is very reasonably priced and the Thai chef may prepare a chicken satay or gado gado.

◑ Open all year; restaurant closed Sun eve

⤢ Short walk from Notting Hill Gate tube station (Central, District and Circle lines). Private parking for 2 cars; on-street parking available

🛏 3 single, 3 twin, 1 four-poster, 2 family rooms, 12 de-luxe rooms; all with bathroom/WC, exc singles with shower/WC; TV, room service, hair-dryer, trouser press, baby-listening in all rooms; no tea/coffee-making facilities in rooms

◇ Restaurant (air-conditioned), bar, lounge (air-conditioned); conference facilities (max 18 people residential and non-residential); sauna/solarium, swimming-pool, gym nearby; babysitting

➖ No wheelchair access; no dogs in public rooms

▭ Access, Amex, Diners, Visa

£ Single £88, single occupancy of twin/double £95, twin/double £115, four-poster £150, family room £160, de-luxe room £135 to £150; deposit required. Alc D £20. Special breaks available

Pippa Pop-ins ☆

430 FULHAM ROAD, LONDON SW6 1DU
TEL: 071-385 2458   FAX: 071-385 5706   **[see map 9]**

A hotel for children, and the only one in this Guide with restrictions for parents.

One night in 1986 Pippa Deakin (27, nursery school teacher, looks like a nineties Mary Poppins) was asked to babysit for seven children, so she took them all into her own home for the night – great ideas are always simple and the hotel (or night nursery) is a roaring success, not surprising in a country where hotels treat children so shabbily.

It is located in a terrace in Fulham Road, and during the day it is a highly professionally run nursery school with a number of flexible services, which include pick-ups from airports. The décor is in the best of home nursery traditions, with lots of colour, things made by children, cheerful wallpapers and bags of toys to suit the ages two to twelve. Upstairs are two pretty twin bedrooms and a dormitory with eight beds; there's a happy bathroom where magic bubble-bath sessions take place for evening guests. Guests also get their own dinner parties and chase fairy gold in the little yard-like garden where several bunnies reside in hutches. The hotel is ideal for parents who come to London for an evening or weekend out (it is solidly booked on New Year's Eve and Valentine's Day). At £25 to £30 per night it is very good value and can work out cheaper than hiring a babysitter; plus the children get a special treat too.

Plans are afoot for expansion – a Pippa Pop-ins will open soon in New York, with Washington, Brussels, Ascot, Bath and Edinburgh also on the agenda.

◐ Open all year

⤢ Nearest tube station is Fulham Broadway (District line). No car park or on-street parking

🛏 Dormitory for 8, 2 twins; 2 public bathrooms

◈ Dining-room, playroom

⊖ No children under 2; no dogs

▭ Amex, Visa

£ £25 to £30 per child; deposit required. Set L, D £2.50

The Portobello

22 STANLEY GARDENS, LONDON W11 2NG
TEL: 071-727 2777   FAX: 071-792 9641

Comfort and originality mixed with a tinge of seventies nostalgia.

Set up some twenty-odd years ago, in the heyday of the nearby Portobello Market, this charismatic hotel still retains much of the free eccentric spirit of the era by using a combination of Victorian and Edwardian antiques, rich oriental touches and a military theme. It's the place that the affluent Sergeant Pepper generation loves coming back to. In the lounge burgundy curtains frame the high windows and potted palms echo the luxuriant greenery of the large residential gardens outside – no access, alas. Walls are adorned with portraits of straight-backed cavalrymen or weepy going-to-war partings; in the basement there's a small conservatory-style bar and restaurant serving simple home-made dishes – steak and kidney pie or hamburgers, perhaps.

   Bedrooms vary greatly in size and flavour: in the appropriately named 'cabins' you can lie in bed and have everything you need within arm's reach (literally); larger doubles and twins have military-style chests and neat shower rooms. The spacious 'specials' are the talking point: there's one, Room 16, where a round bed under a canopy of muslin stands near an Edwardian bath which looks like a Heath Robinson contraption; Number 13 has a massive oak four-poster from where you can contemplate angels floating in a blue sky; the attics (Nos 42 and 43) give a choice of oriental lavishness (floor bed, platform bath) or more Victorian primness (brass bed hung with lace). In all rooms feathery duvets are dressed in silky white Damask cotton.

◐ Open all year, exc 23 Dec to 2 Jan

⤢ Nearest tube station is Notting Hill Gate (Central, District and Circle lines). On-street parking

🛏 9 single, 2 twin, 7 double, 7 suites; all with bathroom/WC, TV, room service, hair-dryer, mini-bar

◈ Restaurant, bar, lounge, drying room; hotel partly air-conditioned

⊖ No wheelchair access; no dogs or smoking in public rooms

▭ Access, Amex, Diners, Visa

£ Single £70, single occupancy of twin/double £100, twin/double £120, suite £140; deposit required. Set L £13, D £15; alc L, D £16

The Savoy

THE STRAND, LONDON WC2R 0EU
TEL: 071-836 4343 TELEX: 24234 SAVOY G
FAX: 071-240 6040

A renowned landmark, combining art-deco elegance and traditional standards of service with modern sophistication.

Grande dame of London hotels, the Savoy trades on its illustrious history and traditions, but has enough streetwise nous to keep itself trim and competitive through constant renewal. Its latest addition is an elegant, impressive fitness gallery (including swimming-pool), built into the roof of the refurbished Savoy Theatre next door.

All the same, bangers and mash will continue to be served for Monday luncheon in the Grill, and the Savoy remains one of London's most famous meeting places for business breakfasts, political lunches and elegant cream teas. Besides the cosy, yew-panelled Grill, you might choose the spacious riverside restaurant; or for lighter meals with nevertheless a strong emphasis on hedonism, Upstairs, the champagne and oyster bar. Personalised cocktails are mixed amongst the mirrored nooks and crannies of the art-deco American Bar, while the hotel's most famous public space remains the Thames Foyer: pink marble columns, pastoral murals, stone stags and floral mirrors create the congenial atmosphere of a rural pavilion, while a pianist or harpist plays over afternoon tea and cocktails.

Bedrooms retain their art-deco doors, mirrors and bedheads, while other features such as curving TV cabinets have been added in the same style. The rooms are individually decorated, but all are spacious and elegant and some of the more expensive have stunning views over the Thames. High standards of service and attention to detail are most clearly manifested in the bell pull by the bath; less obvious are the mattresses and Irish linen sheets which the hotel manufactures itself.

◑ Open all year

⤢ Between the Strand and the Embankment. Nearest tube station Charing Cross (Northern, Bakerloo and Jubilee lines). Private car park

🛏 49 single, 105 twin/double, 48 suites; all with bathroom/WC, TV, room service, hair-dryer, mini-bar, valet service, baby-listening; no tea/coffee-making facilities in rooms

◈ 3 restaurants, bar, lounge; conference facilities (max 500 people non-residential, 30 residential); air-conditioned public areas; sauna/solarium, heated swimming-pool, gym at hotel, other sports nearby. Wheelchair access to hotel and restaurant, no ground-floor bedrooms but a lift; some bedrooms specially equipped for the disabled

⊖ No dogs

▭ Access, Amex, Diners, Visa

£ Single £170, single occupancy of twin/double £195, twin/double £195, suite from £260 to £550; deposit required. Cooked B £16.50, continental B £12; set L £25, D £40 (prices till end 93). Special breaks available

Tophams Ebury Court

28 EBURY STREET, LONDON SW1W 0LU
TEL: 071-730 8147 FAX: 071-823 5966

Old-fashioned refinement in a homely terrace hotel behind Victoria station.

Formerly known as Ebury Court, the hotel has recently enlarged its name to reflect its long family tradition and the continuing expansion of its facilities. Founded in 1938 by Diana Topham (who still lives at the top of the hotel), it's now in the hands of her daughter, Marianne, and son-in-law, Nicholas Kingsford. A new chef with a fine reputation has been taken on, and a patio garden with a large sky-lit breakfast room are soon to be opened up. The owners, however, seem keen to hang on to the cosy but civilised simplicity of the place.

Comprising five attractive and well-maintained Victorian houses, the interior is something of a maze where space is at a premium. The ground-floor lounges have a classically English, country-house feel, with restrained floral fabrics and warm lighting. Many Belgravia residents are enticed by the short but varied à la carte menus on offer in the small yellow-walled restaurant, which is hung with paintings by the family and memorabilia – look out for the cast list of a play showing that a Topham once took the stage with Charles Dickens.

The traditional bedrooms feature pink heavily, along with subdued prints and antique furniture. Eighteen of them have washbasins but no bathrooms; towelling robes are provided for negotiating the corridors to the nine shared bathrooms, which are sombre and old-fashioned but very clean. The hotel is regularly refurbished, although our inspection noted small signs of wear and tear in the bedrooms.

◐ Closed 22 Dec to 2 Jan; restaurant closed Sun eves

↗ 3 minutes' walk from Victoria tube station (Victoria, District and Circle lines). Public car park nearby

🛏 14 single, 10 twin, 13 double, 2 four-poster, 1 family; half with bathroom/WC, 2 with shower, 9 public bathrooms; TV, room service, hair-dryer in all rooms

◇ 2 restaurants, bar, lounge; tennis, riding, other sports nearby; conference facilities (max 16 people residential and non-residential)

⊖ No wheelchair access; no children in restaurant after 8pm; no dogs

▭ Access, Amex, Diners, Visa

£ Single £64, single occupancy of twin/double £72 to £80, twin/double £90 to £112, four-poster £138, family room £150; deposit required. Alc L, D £20. Special breaks available

Standing among savage scenery, the hotel offers stupendous revelations. There is a French widow in every bedroom, affording delightful prospects.
Gerard Hoffnung

Windermere Hotel

142/144 WARWICK WAY, LONDON SW1V 4JE
TEL: 071-834 5163/5480   FAX: 071-630 8831

Spick-and-span rooms at modest prices in a family-run establishment.

A stone's throw from Victoria coach station and very handy for the railway and tube station, the Windermere Hotel consists of two gleaming white early Victorian houses, knocked together and completely refurbished in 1990. The hotel traces its origins back to 1881 when 144 Warwick Way was turned into the Pimlico Rooms, probably the earliest bed and breakfast in the area, and now offers modern facilities in bright, unpretentious surroundings.

The hub of the hotel is the large basement dining-room, which gets plenty of natural light and has been recently redecorated in blues, pinks and white. English and continental breakfasts are served on bone china; you can also have light meals and drinks here (or in your room) throughout the day, or more substantial dishes in the evening. Drinks served from a simple cabinet can be taken with meals or in the ground-floor lounge – a small room on the corner of the hotel, well-stocked with London information and furnished with leather chairs, plants, a chandelier, and swagged curtains in much the same colour scheme as the dining-room.

Bedrooms are predominantly white, neat and well-lit, furnished with flowing curtains and comfortable reproduction chairs, and double-glazed to keep out traffic noise. If you can bear it, rooms without their own bathrooms are a good deal. At the other end of the scale, Superior rooms have extras like a mini-fridge.

◑ Open all year

⤢ Nearest tube station is Victoria (Victoria, Circle and District lines). On-street parking and public car park nearby

🛏 3 single, 5 twin, 11 double, 4 family rooms; some with bathroom/WC, most with shower/WC, 2 public shower-rooms; TV, room service, hair-dryer, trouser press in all rooms; no tea/coffee-making facilities in rooms

◈ Dining-room, lounge; swimming-pool nearby

⊖ No wheelchair access; no dogs; no smoking in public rooms

▭ Access, Amex, JCB, Visa

£ Single £34 to £55, single occupancy of twin/double £44 to £62, twin/double £48 and from £69, family room from £69 and £85; deposit required. Set D £9.50; alc D £13.50

It is always worth enquiring about the availability of special breaks or weekend prices. The prices we quote are the standard rates for one night – most hotels offer reduced rates for longer stays.

Woodville House

107 EBURY STREET, LONDON SW1W 9QU
TEL: 071-730 1048   FAX: 071-730 2574

Cheap and friendly bed and breakfast near Victoria station.

On a terraced Georgian street lined with small hotels and busy with traffic, Woodville House stands out for its flower boxes, elegant railings and smart white paint. Inside, plenty of care has been taken by Ian Berry and Rachel Joplin to provide an opulent but homely atmosphere.

Hearty English breakfasts are served in the ground-floor breakfast room, whose size makes for an intimate, chatty atmosphere in the mornings. It's decorated with deep green wallpaper, plants and huge yellow curtains, but gets plenty of natural light. Beyond is a small, sheltered patio garden where you can sit out in summer. If you want to make hot drinks or light snacks, or do some ironing, head for the neat kitchenette in the basement.

Twelve bedrooms share four bathrooms, one on each half-landing. Be prepared for the rich floweriness of the fabrics, carpets and wallpapers, which some may find overblown. Most of the rooms have white drapes over the beds, small armchairs and reproduction antique clocks; all have washbasins and those at the back of the house are air-conditioned.

◑ Open all year

🔁 Four minutes' walk from Victoria station (Victoria, District and Circle lines). Parking difficult; public car parks nearby

🛏 4 single, 3 twin, 3 double, 2 family rooms; 4 public bathrooms; TV, hair-dryer in all rooms; double rooms are air-conditioned

◈ Breakfast room (air-conditioned), drying room; tennis, riding, other sports nearby; babysitting

⊖ No wheelchair access; no dogs; no smoking in public rooms

▭ Access, Visa

£ Single £32 to £36, single occupancy of twin/double £32 to £36, twin/double £50 to £55, family room £70 to £80; deposit required

ENGLAND

ABBERLEY HEREFORD AND WORCESTER   **MAP 9**

The Elms

STOCKTON ROAD, ABBERLEY, HEREFORD AND WORCESTER WR6 6AT
TEL: GREAT WITLEY (0299) 896666   TELEX: 337105
FAX: (0299) 896804

A business hotel out in the sticks; predictable in places, but well-managed and not without character.

This partially Queen Anne house makes an ideal retreat for small business conferences – although holidaymakers will feel welcome, too, and the dining-room is heavily used by locals. The elms of the title are now actually limes – trees of substantial girth, which line the avenue. Inside, the enormous carved fireplace in the restaurant and the cavernous bookcases in the bar are features well worth studying; they were brought into the house when the original building was extended in the nineteenth century. The bar is furnished more like a sitting-room, while the restaurant is plush and formal, with the cool modern extension looking out on the greenery outside. Food is served in both bar and restaurant. In the latter, you can perhaps enjoy an omelette of sorrel and kidney followed by fillet steak with walnuts and shallots. Bedrooms, some of which are in the old coach-house, vary greatly in size and shape, although all are comfortably furnished. The Studio Suite is palatial enough for chief executives, who can admire themselves in the large semi-circular mirror above the bath.

◐ Open all year

🡖 On the A443 between Worcester and Tenbury Wells, 2 miles after Great Witley. Do not take the turning to Abberley. Private car park

🛏 3 single, 7 twin, 9 double, 1 four-poster, 5 suites (some rooms in annexe); all with bathroom/WC, TV, room service, hair-dryer, trouser press, baby-listening; mini-bar in some rooms; no tea/coffee-making facilities in rooms

◇ Restaurant, bar, drawing-room, lounge; conference facilities (max 75 people non-residential, 25 residential); tennis, putting green, croquet, clay pigeon shooting at hotel, other sports nearby; babysitting. Wheelchair access to restaurant only

⊖ No dogs; no pipes or cigars in restaurant

▭ Access, Amex, Diners, Visa

£ Single £82 to £105, single occupancy of twin/double £82 to £105, twin/double £97 to £128, four-poster £128, suite £140 to £150. Set L £12/£15, D £16/£22; alc L from £3, D £18 to £38; Sun L £15 (prices till end 93). Special breaks available

---

 This denotes that the hotel is in an exceptionally peaceful situation where you can be assured of a restful stay.

ALDEBURGH SUFFOLK   **MAP 8**

Austins

243 HIGH STREET, ALDEBURGH, SUFFOLK IP15 5DN
TEL: ALDEBURGH (0728) 453932   FAX: (0728) 453668

*A small, personal hotel with chatty owners who have a great
interest in the arts.*

'It's just like a production of *The Mousetrap*,' explains co-owner Robert
Selby, who sees many similarities between his former job as theatre
manager and present role as hotelier and restaurateur. 'We set the stage,
put out the props, and it's curtain up at 7.30pm when guests start to
arrive.' Any murders? 'Not yet,' he smiles, 'but I've been tempted.' He
and his partner, Julian Alexander-Worster, share the running of this
small, strawberry ice-cream-coloured hotel which lies a block away from
the sea. A barnacle-encrusted anchor propped up below smart blue
awnings will make the hotel easy to spot if you are a first-time guest.

Inside, the décor is stylish and arty. Signed photos of well-known
guests who monopolise rooms during the Aldeburgh Festival in June
include many of the musicians who come to perform. Robert will regale
you with anecdotes of celebrities who have passed through. Bedrooms
aren't roomy, but the uniformly high standards make up for lack of cat-
swinging space. Bedroom names like Tredinnick, Droxat and Heyworth
demand an explanation and Robert delights in keeping people guessing
by claiming they are anagrams of composers' names. But don't be fooled
– in fact they are simply family names.

Dinner is served in the restaurant (knocked through to merge with a
small lounge and cosy bar). Light blue walls, yellow curtains and wooden
floors make it airy and serene. Julian does the cooking and produces a
substantial fixed-price menu with choices such as black pasta with a
prawn and cream sauce and noisettes of pork with a purée of spiced
lentils. As to breakfast, any variation on the traditional English is served
but the speciality is the 'internationally famous scrambled egg' spoken of
highly in New York and Moscow (or so the owners claim).

◑ Open all year; restaurant closed
Mon eve

🔋 At the south end of Aldeburgh
High Street. On-street parking

🛏 1 single, 1 twin, 5 double; most
with bathroom/WC, some with
shower/WC; TV, room service,
baby-listening in all rooms; hair-
dryer, trouser press on request

◈ Restaurant, bar, 2 lounges;

fishing, golf, tennis, riding nearby

⊖ No wheelchair access; children
at owner's discretion; no dogs in
public rooms

▭ Access, Visa

£ Single £50, single occupancy of
twin/double £50, twin/double
£75; deposit required. Sun L £16;
set D £21. Special breaks
available

Ettington Park

ALDERMINSTER, NR STRATFORD-UPON-AVON, WARWICKSHIRE CV37 8BS
TEL: STRATFORD-UPON-AVON (0789) 450123   FAX: (0789) 450472

A grand hotel and conference venue with expert service and excellent facilities.

As you look across the parkland on your approach to this neo-Gothic extravaganza of a house you know you are in for a treat. The property has been in the same family since before the Domesday Book and parts of it remain from that time; the exterior, however, is relatively recent, having been rebuilt in the nineteenth century. It is a glorious piece of Gothic Revivalism, with tall, narrow windows that are more fitting to a church than a manor house and turrets shaped like Maid Marian's hat. Around the outside, stone bas-relief carvings tell the history of the family, while each generation seems to have left its stamp on the interior either by carving family crests or commissioning elaborate rococo ceilings. From the huge plants in the conservatory at the entrance, to the acres of material at every window, the lofty ceilings and the grand piano dwarfed in the lounge, things here are on an impressive scale. Bedrooms range from simply stylish to fussy, with the emphasis on comfort. Service is expert, as you would expect for the price, though the atmosphere isn't stuffy and children are welcome.

A jacket and tie are required in the dining-room, where the menu is modern English and French – dishes include grilled goats' cheese in orange cream sauce, fillets of red mullet in a peppercorn butter sauce and corn-fed chicken with spinach noodles. There is a huge range of leisure facilities to help you work it all off afterwards.

◑ Open all year

➤ 5 miles south of Stratford-upon-Avon off the A3400. Three-quarters of a mile from Newbold on Stour. Private car park

🛏 8 twin, 30 double, 1 four-poster, 9 suites; all with bathroom/WC, TV, room service, hair-dryer, trouser press, baby-listening; no tea/coffee-making facilities in rooms

◇ Restaurant, 2 bars, lounge, conservatory; conference facilities (max 75 people non-residential, 48 residential); fishing, tennis, riding, sauna/solarium, heated indoor swimming-pool at hotel, other sports nearby; babysitting. Wheelchair access to hotel (ramp) and restaurant, 10 ground-floor bedrooms and lift

⊖ No dogs; no smoking in restaurant

▭ Access, Amex, Diners, Visa

£ Single occupancy of twin/double £115, twin/double £145, four-poster/family room/suite £180; deposit required. Set L £16, D £28; alc D £28. Special breaks available

ALDWINCLE NORTHAMPTONSHIRE   **MAP 5**

The Maltings

MAIN STREET, ALDWINCLE, KETTERING, NORTHAMPTONSHIRE NN14 3EP
TEL: OUNDLE (080 15) 233; changes to (0832) 720233 in Oct 93
FAX: (080 15) 326; changes to (0832) 720326 in Oct 93

Homely bed and breakfast with a lovely garden in a quiet village within easy reach of major motorway routes.

If Northamptonshire is truly the 'county of squires and spires', then Aldwincle is a typical village, surrounded as it is by flat green fields with views for miles. Largely built of yellow limestone, it has two churches of its own and, despite the peacefulness and apparent lack of activity, has managed to keep its post office and village stores open. The Maltings dates from the early 1600s, but, far from being a museum piece, has very much a lived-in feel. Huge stone fireplaces, rugs on parquet floors, antique sideboards and grandfather clocks sound rather grand but there's nothing pretentious about the Faulkners' home. The living-room is a lovely, restful place in pale green with a comfortable sofa and family photographs – a chewed training shoe is evidence that the dog has made himself at home here too. There is one guest bedroom in the main house, with another two in a converted granary a few yards away. Though not luxurious, all are kitted out with radios, torches, large private bathrooms, and cheerful fabrics including pink patchwork duvet covers in two rooms. The granary has skylights which make it particularly sunny, and doors which lead into the garden from a sitting-room that the two bedrooms share.

The garden owes its beauty to the hard work and enthusiasm of Margaret Faulkner: 'The stone wall is my wife's folly,' Nigel tells you. 'She built it singlehandedly.' Open to the public from time to time through the National Gardens Scheme, it has beds of wallflowers, fruit trees leading to a cow meadow, sheltered places to sit, and a huge assortment of stone troughs, pots, buckets and tubs.

◐ Open all year

⤴ In the centre of the village, on the main street between the garage and the village shop. Private car park

🛏 1 twin, 2 annexe rooms; all with bathroom/WC; hair-dryer in all rooms

◈ Dining-room, 2 lounges, drying room; fishing, golf, riding nearby

⊖ No wheelchair access; no children under 10; no dogs; no smoking

▭ Access, Visa

(£) Single occupancy of twin/double £28 to £30, twin/double £39 to £41

ℒ   *This denotes that you can get a twin or double room for £50 or less per night inclusive of breakfast.*

ALSTONEFIELD STAFFORDSHIRE   **MAP 5**

Stanshope Hall

STANSHOPE, NR ASHBOURNE, DERBYSHIRE DE6 2AD
TEL: ALSTONEFIELD (033 527) 278   FAX: (033 527) 470

A peaceful guesthouse in magnificent countryside in the Peak District National Park.

Green hills, stone-walled lanes and trout streams are what you come to expect after a short while in the Peak District, and the area around Stanshope matches its brief. This is beautiful walking country, made famous by Izaak Walton in his bible of fishing, *The Compleat Angler*. Nick Lourie is a keen angler and couldn't have chosen a better spot to set up home, along with his partner Naomi Chambers and their two children. Stanshope Hall is a typical mellow Derbyshire stone building dating from three different centuries – at its newest it is 200 years old. The interior, however, is far from typical. The previous owner, a theatre-set painter, created an entertaining mural of birds, trees and clouds in the living-room, and marble-effect woodwork and a ceiling to mirror the geometric designs of the carpet in the dining-room. 'You can call it *trompe-l'oeil*, but basically it's just false,' is Nick's down-to-earth attitude.

Despite the unusually grand decorations there is nothing formal or intimidating about this house – it's very much a family home. The living-room, with its loose-covered armchairs, exposed floorboards and piano, is an ideal retreat after a day's walking, and though Naomi and Nick have refurbished the three bedrooms they are intriguing and cheerful rather than grand. Best Room is the largest; it has Corinthian pillars painted either side of the windows and a loo with a view in the light, well-equipped bathroom. The Striped and Egyptian rooms have solid antiques and *en-suite* bathrooms. Naomi is responsible for the three-course dinners, which include vegetables from the garden with perhaps lamb in red wine and honey, followed by rhubarb and ice-cream for pudding.

◑ Open all year, exc 25, 26 Dec

↗ From Ashbourne take A515 Buxton road and turn left to Thorpe and Ilam. At Ilam memorial turn right (signposted Alstonefield). Stanshope is 2 miles from Ilam. Private car park

🛏 1 twin, 1 double, 1 family room; all with bathroom/WC, TV

◇ Dining-room, lounge; conference facilities (max 12 people non-residential); walking at hotel, riding nearby

⊖ No wheelchair access; no babies in dining-room eves; no dogs in public rooms; smoking discouraged

▭ None accepted

£ Single occupancy of twin/double £21 to £28, twin/double £42 to £56, family room £56 to £74; deposit required. Set D £16.50 (7.30pm). Special breaks available

Chapel House

KIRKSTONE ROAD, AMBLESIDE, CUMBRIA LA22 9DZ
TEL: AMBLESIDE (05394) 33143

Memorable dinners in a small stone cottage in the oldest part of the town.

The precise age of the two sixteenth-century stone-built cottages that make up Chapel House Hotel is unknown and the origins of its ecclesiastical nomenclature are only a little less obscure. Records suggest that there has been a place of worship in 'Above Stock' (the local name for this old part of Ambleside) since the early 1600s, although St Anne's, which now stands behind the hotel, was not built until 1812. Prevailing wisdom has it that Chapel House started life as a meeting place for worshippers and in a way its function has not entirely changed, though these days it is the devotees of Cumbria's natural beauty and Duncan Hamer's culinary expertise who congregate here.

Duncan provides a no-choice four-course dinner such as pear and cheese salad with walnuts Châtelaine, cream of lettuce soup, poached chicken Edward VII with braised savoury rice, and cream buns served with blackcurrant sauce. The dining-room, with its plain white walls adorned by one or two Lakes prints, provides little to distract.

The lounge is done out with modern, comfortable sofas and armchairs in shades of green and brown. Duncan and Sandra like to join guests for tea and biscuits here at 10pm. The small, cosy bar with its low beams and huge stone fireplace has maintained an authentic country feel, but the bedrooms, though neat and presentable, are unexceptional and tend to be on the small side.

◑ Limited opening Dec; closed Jan, Feb

↗ To the north of Ambleside village. Take the right turn to Kirkstone Pass. On-street parking

🛏 2 single, 2 twin, 5 double, 1 family room; some rooms with shower/WC; no tea/coffee-making facilities in rooms

◈ Dining-room, bar, lounge; water sports, other sports nearby

⊖ No wheelchair access; no dogs; no smoking in bedrooms or dining-room

▭ None accepted

£ Single £30 to £37, single occupancy of twin/double £50 to £62, twin/double £60 to £80, family room £85 to £120 (rates inc dinner); deposit required. Set D £15 (7pm)

Many hotels put up their tariffs in the spring. You are advised to confirm prices when you book.

Drunken Duck Inn

BARNGATES, AMBLESIDE, CUMBRIA LA22 0NG
TEL: AMBLESIDE (05394) 36347

Extra thought has gone into the bar food at this popular and lively pub in an isolated spot near Ambleside.

There are no other buildings near this picturesque whitewashed pub that stands a few miles from Ambleside, but don't be lulled into thinking that this is a sleepy watering-hole for one man and his dog – it isn't. At night it's crowded and the bedrooms that overnight guests retire to are smarter than you might expect of pub accommodation.

The main bar is divided into a number of intimate snugs, and the food shows more imagination than in many pubs. Dishes like chickpeas and mince or chicken in white wine sauce are served up in individual-sized pottery dishes. Due care is also given to puddings, with sticky toffee pudding, a Cumbrian speciality, taking pride of place on the menu. All this can be washed down with a slug of one of over 60 whiskies that stand behind the bar. On Friday and Saturday, dinners are also served in the quieter surroundings of the dining-room. Here guests can try trout caught in the pub's own nearby tarn.

Upstairs, the bedrooms are painted magnolia and decorated with cartoon prints. The bathrooms are brilliant white and have little touches of extravagance such as gold taps and dark wood veneer finishes around the bath. Complimentary soap comes in the shape of a yellow duck.

◑ Open all year; restaurant open Fri and Sat eves only but bar meals always available

↗ Take the A593 out of Ambleside and turn left at Clappersgate on to the B5286 to Hawkshead. After 1 mile turn right immediately opposite the Outgate Inn. The inn is 1 mile up this road. Private car park

⇌ 1 twin, 8 double, 1 four-poster; all with bathroom/WC, exc 1 double with shower/WC; TV, room service, hair-dryer in all rooms

◇ Dining-room, bar/dining areas, bar, lounge, drying room, library; conference facilities (max 12 people residential and non-residential); fishing at hotel, other sports nearby. Wheelchair access to hotel (2 steps), restaurant and 1 ground-floor bedroom

⊖ None

▭ Access, Visa

£ Single occupancy of twin/double £40, twin/double £51 to £65, four-poster £60 to £74; deposit required. Bar lunches from £2; set D £18. Special breaks available

Use the maps at the back of the Guide *to pinpoint hotels in a particular area.*

Rothay Manor

ROTHAY BRIDGE, AMBLESIDE, CUMBRIA LA22 0EH
TEL: AMBLESIDE (05394) 33605 FAX: (05394) 33607

A long-established hotel with a reputation for good food served in genteel surroundings.

Rothay Manor, run by the Nixon family since 1967, is a firmly established country-house hotel where service is formal, polite and friendly. Its large landscaped gardens do much to convince guests that they are in the countryside rather than just off the tricky one-way system around Ambleside, one of the Lake District's busier parts. It's a fine Regency house with a white façade and an unusual wrought-iron verandah on the first floor. The interiors are in keeping with the Regency period, with bold, dark, striped wallpapers and dado rails. The non-smoking lounge is green and the bar is deep red: both have comfortable armchairs.

Meals are taken under the conker-brown ceiling of the dining-room and the menu sticks mainly to formal country-house fare, so you might start with salmon and asparagus terrine, followed by beef Stroganoff, then a plum tart or coconut and lime mousse. The afternoon tea buffet, with its mountain of cream cakes, buns and biscuits, is a special treat.

Good-sized bedrooms are decorated in pinks and pastels and furnished with Regency-style pieces and flowery fabrics. The ones at the front open out on to the verandah.

◑ Closed 2 Jan to 14 Feb

⤢ On the A593 south-west of Ambleside towards Coniston. Private car park

🛏 2 single, 3 twin, 5 double, 5 family rooms, 3 suites; all with bathroom/WC, TV, room service, hair-dryer, baby-listening

◈ 2 dining-rooms (air-conditioned), bar, 3 lounges (1 air-conditioned); conference facilities (max 25 people non-residential, 18 residential); croquet at hotel, other sports nearby. Wheelchair access to hotel (ramp), restaurant and WC (unisex), 6 ground-floor bedrooms, 2 specially equipped for disabled people

⊖ No dogs; no smoking in 1 lounge and dining-rooms

▭ Access, Amex, Diners, Visa

£ Single £69, single occupancy of twin/double £80, twin/double £108, suite £152; deposit required. Sun L £14.50; set D £21/£24/£27; alc L £10. Special breaks available

---

The text of entries is based on unsolicited reports sent in by readers and backed up by inspections. The factual details are from questionnaires the Guide *sends to all hotels that feature in the book.*

Wateredge Hotel

BORRANS ROAD, AMBLESIDE, CUMBRIA LA22 0EP
TEL: AMBLESIDE (05394) 32332 (and fax)

Modern comforts in converted fishermen's cottages with a superb lakeside location.

'A room with a view' proclaims the brochure, though it is not the famous Florentine roofs but a huge expanse of Windermere, the largest and most popular of Cumbria's lakes, that is the object of rapt observation for guests at the Wateredge. Only the neat garden separates the gentle lapping of the lake from the exterior of the two seventeenth-century cottages where a tangle of rosebushes and geraniums in window boxes splash colour against the whitewashed stone walls. Inside, Derek and Pamela Cowap have tried to ensure that while some of the traditional flavour of the original buildings has been maintained it is never at the expense of comfort, space and light. Large arched windows illuminate the main lounge, which has a great lake view, and there is a second lounge area with an open fire as well as a small bar where the atmosphere is a little cosier. The dining-room, set within the original cottages, has oak beams, and a log fire burning in winter. Dinner is a six-course affair and comes with a choice of two starters and two main courses; your meal may include smoked Scottish salmon and horseradish cream, carrot and lemon soup, apple and mint sorbet, roast sirloin of beef with bordelais sauce, honey and walnut roulade and a selection of English cheeses.

Bedrooms are bright and modern with pastel shades and floral patterns, but only about 15 out of the 23 have a lake view so if you're lured by the location make sure to ask in advance. Superior rooms generally have a view of the lake as well as a bit more leg room; the new suites in the annexe are the most spacious, with little balconies or patios. To sum up, some unequivocal praise from a reader: 'All that a small hotel should be – excellent food, friendly attention . . . superb.'

◖ Closed mid-Dec to early Feb

⊡ On the A591 at Waterhead Bay, Ambleside. Private car park

⇔ 3 single, 6 twin, 8 double, 1 family room, 5 half-suites; most with bathroom/WC, some with shower/WC; TV, hair-dryer in all rooms; limited room service

◈ Dining-room (air-conditioned), bar, 3 lounges, TV room, drying room; fishing, rowing (May to Oct), private jetty at hotel, other sports nearby

⊖ No wheelchair access; no children under 7; no dogs in public rooms and by arrangement only in bedrooms; no smoking in dining-room

▭ Access, Amex, Visa

£ Single £55 to £68, single occupancy of twin/double from £69 and £97, twin/double from £94 and £122, suite £140 to £156 (rates inc dinner); deposit required. Alc L from £6.50; set D £24

APPLETHWAITE CUMBRIA   **MAP 4**

Underscar Manor

APPLETHWAITE, NR KESWICK, CUMBRIA CA12 4PH
TEL: KESWICK (07687) 75000   FAX: (07687) 74904

Expensively refurbished Italianate manor house overlooking
Derwent Water. Excellent food served in some style.

Underscar Manor is a recent addition to the already bulky portfolio of
luxury Lake District hotels. The Manor stands in a prime position in the
shadow of Skiddaw overlooking Derwent Water, surrounded by well-
manicured lawns and mature woods. Unusually for the region, the flint
and stone building has Italianate embellishments, with towers topped by
overhanging roofs. The interior design relies heavily on bright colours;
the lounge has conversation-friendly clusters of peach and blue easy
chairs, and fabulous views of Derwent Water are framed in windows
surrounded by acres of trussed curtains.

   Its owners, Pauline and Derek Harrison, bring to the Manor almost 20
years' experience of running a respected restaurant in Manchester,
which is evident from the style and quality of the meals. Food is
smuggled in front of you under a silver dome which is then whipped away
with a flourish. Wine, chosen from a long list, is served from a fiddly,
conversation-provoking silver decanting apparatus. The menu concentrates on red meats served with piquant berry or tomato sauces: you
might have venison with cranberry or beef with a Madeira sauce followed
by a caramelised apple pudding with home-made ice-cream. Service is
proper and formal, but staff are willing to chat if encouraged.

   The pleasing bedrooms are decorated in bright floral colours: green
carpet and yellow and pink striped wallpaper, with a mixture of antique
and reproduction furniture.

○ Open all year

↗ Leave the M6 at Junction 40 and
take the A66 to Keswick for 17
miles. At the large roundabout
take the third exit and turn
immediately right to Underscar.
Private car park

⇌ 11 double; all with bathroom/
WC, TV, hair-dryer

◈ 2 restaurants, 2 lounges,
boardroom, drying room,
conservatory; conference
facilities (max 16 people non-
residential, 11 residential);
fishing, golf, other sports nearby

⊖ No wheelchair access; no
children under 12; no dogs; no
smoking in restaurant

▭ Access, Amex, Visa

£ Single occupancy of double £90
to £125, double £150 to £250
(rates inc dinner); deposit
required. Set L £18.50, D £25;
alc L £18.50, D £28.50. Special
breaks available

Many hotels offer special rates for stays of a few nights or more. It is worth
enquiring when you book.

APULDRAM WEST SUSSEX   **MAP 9**

Crouchers Bottom

BIRDHAM ROAD, APULDRAM, CHICHESTER, WEST SUSSEX PO20 7EH
TEL: CHICHESTER (0243) 784995   FAX: (0243) 539797

Spick-and-span rooms in a tasteful modern extension.

The name may lead you to expect something rustic and wild, but Crouchers Bottom turns out to be a very civilised, meticulously kept small hotel. It lies on the busy A286 just two miles from Chichester, with views of the surrounding fields and orchards and, on a clear day, the South Downs. There is a tidy lawn around a duck pond which is overlooked by the dining-room, a pine-clad extension where crisp white tablecloths dazzle in the ample light pouring in from the tall windows. Hearty English breakfasts, including eggs from the Fodens' free-range hens and a wide selection of teas and coffees, are served here, as well as an appetising dinner menu which changes daily. Guests can also settle into the comfortable sofas of the pretty sitting-room next door, or perhaps play the piano in front of the log fire.

Bedrooms are shielded from the noise of the road in the newly converted coach-house at the back. They're rather box-like, though spacious enough and decorated in smart, jolly colours. One room has been adapted for wheelchair-users.

◑ Open all year, exc 1 week at Xmas

⏩ 2 miles south of Chichester on the A286. Just after the Black Horse pub on the left-hand side of the road. Private car park

🛏 3 twin, 3 double; all with bathroom/WC, exc 1 twin with shower/WC; TV, limited room service, baby-listening in all rooms

◈ Dining-room, lounge; conference facilities (max 15 people non-residential, 6 residential); fishing, golf, other sports nearby. Wheelchair access to hotel, dining-room and 1 ground-floor bedroom specially equipped for disabled people

⊖ Dogs by arrangement only; smoking in lounge only

▭ Access, Amex, Visa

£ Single occupancy of twin/double £49 to £80, twin/double £63 to £80, family room rate on request; deposit required. Set D £18.50. Special breaks available

---

If you make a booking using a credit card, and find after cancelling that the full amount has been charged to your card, raise the matter with your credit card company. They will ask the hotelier to confirm whether the room was re-let, and to justify the charge made.

Amerdale House

ARNCLIFFE, LITTONDALE, NR SKIPTON, NORTH YORKSHIRE BD23 5QE
TEL: ARNCLIFFE (0756) 770250

*Continuing plaudits for the food at this comfortable manor house
with the scenery of the Dales on your doorstep.*

'The food is – after the scenery and tranquillity – the hotel's outstanding
feature,' wrote one satisfied guest after a restorative sojourn at Nigel and
Paula Crapper's immaculate country hotel. It would be invidious to rank
the three ingredients which account for much of Amerdale House's
appeal, but few would quarrel with the contention that it scores very
highly on all three.

The sturdy, mostly Victorian manor stands on the edge of the quiet
village of Arncliffe, where cottages and porched barns skirt a large
oblong green and the views down Littondale to the River Skirfare are
memorable. Inside, the elegance and quality of the furnishings impress
in public rooms that are feminine and neat without being twee. Dainty
stencils in the cheerful but fairly formal dining-room make a welcome
change from the wallpaper borders that seem *de rigueur* in many country
hotels. The lounge is a rhapsody in pink, with large windows, tasteful
drapes and gold-framed mirrors. Since our last edition a couple of
bedrooms have been redecorated and replanned, with fitted furniture to
create more space. All are comfortable and well-equipped, with pretty
bathrooms described by one reader as 'first class'.

Nigel's menus are short but interesting, and the cooking is accomplished and confident. A typical spring menu offered avocado pear salad
with spiced tuna fish mayonnaise, followed by home-made pasta with
smoked ham and Parmesan, roast rack of Dales lamb and soufflé fritters
with cinnamon sugar and warm orange sauce.

◐ Closed mid-Nov to mid-Mar

↗ On the edge of the village of
Arncliffe, 7 miles north of
Grassington. Private car park

🛏 3 twin, 6 double, 1 four-poster,
1 family room; most with
bathroom/WC, some with
shower/WC; TV, room service,
hair-dryer in all rooms; trouser
press in some rooms

◇ Restaurant, bar, lounge, drying
room; fishing, riding, sauna/
solarium, swimming-pool nearby.
Wheelchair access to hotel (2
steps) and 1 ground-floor
bedroom

⊖ No dogs; no smoking in
restaurant

▭ Access, Visa

£ Single occupancy of twin/double
£62, twin/double £103 to £109,
four-poster £109 (rates inc
dinner). Set D £18 (prices till
end 93). Special breaks available

ASHBOURNE DERBYSHIRE   **MAP 5**

Callow Hall

MAPPLETON ROAD, ASHBOURNE, DERBYSHIRE DE6 2AA
TEL: ASHBOURNE (0335) 343403   FAX: (0335) 343624

A well-established, family-run hotel with good food, situated on the edge of the Peak District National Park.

Another year of good reports on Callow Hall, where the Spencer family, who have been involved in the hotel and catering trades in this area for five generations, run a very smooth ship. This large Victorian Gothic manor house is solidly built, with stone-mullioned windows, a 200-year-old yew in the tree-lined drive and views along the wooded valley of Dovedale. Inside, the Spencers are very much in evidence both in front of house, where Dorothy is calmly in control, and in the kitchen, where David is joined by son Anthony. In the ten years they have been at Callow Hall, David and Dorothy have renovated the high-ceilinged rooms – saving some wonderful fireplaces and ornate plasterwork in the process – and kitted them out with heavy gilt mirrors, solid antique furniture and traditional fabrics. The bedrooms, named after family members and long-serving staff, vary in size but not in comfort, and are immaculately kept. All have high-quality furnishings and smart *en-suite* bathrooms; Dorothy is perhaps the grandest, with its four-poster bed with twisted pillars, bird-print wallpaper, walnut dressing-table and glass chandelier. In this hotel luxury is standard, and the rooms have fresh fruit, home-made biscuits, mineral water and flowers, as well as bathrobes and the usual bathroom goodies.

Attention to detail is carried through to the kitchen, too – David gets up early every morning for the markets in Birmingham and there is always a good selection of fish on the menu. One reader was particularly impressed by her breakfast: 'Delicious freshly squeezed orange juice, compôte of dried fruit, yogurt and fresh melon as well as traditional cooked choices.'

◗ Open all year, exc 25, 26 Dec

⤴ Follow the A515 Buxton road through Ashbourne and at the top of hill turn left at crossroads keeping the Bowling Green pub on your left. Take the first right into Mappleton Road. The hall entrance is on the right after the the hump-backed bridge. Private car park

🛏 4 twin, 8 double, 1 four-poster, family rooms available; all with bathroom/WC, TV, room service, hair-dryer, trouser press, baby-listening

◈ 2 dining-rooms, bar, 2 lounges; drying facilities; conference facilities (max 40 people non-residential, 13 residential); fishing at hotel, other sports nearby. Wheelchair access to hotel, dining-rooms and WC (unisex), 1 ground-floor bedroom specially equipped for disabled people

⬤ No dogs in public rooms; no

smoking in dining-rooms

▭ Access, Amex, Diners, Visa

£ Single occupancy of twin/double
£65 to £80, twin/double £90 to
£120, four-poster £120, family

room rate on request; deposit
required. Set L £13.50, D £28;
alc L, D £30. Special breaks
available

ASHBURTON DEVON　　　　　　　　　　　**MAP 10**

Ashburton Hotel ☆　　　　

79 EAST STREET, ASHBURTON, NEWTON ABBOT, DEVON TQ13 7AL
TEL: ASHBURTON (0364) 652784 (and fax)

*A pleasantly refurbished, moderately priced hotel in a street of
Georgian buildings.*

Fred and Carla Van Pylen recently took over the Ashburton Hotel, a
stately grey and cream Georgian town house in a street of other similarly
fine buildings close to Dartmoor National Park. A small and not very
exciting lounge shares the ground floor with an equally small but
nonetheless pleasing restaurant featuring a big marble fireplace and a
piano; the à la carte menu offers plenty of choice (though not for
vegetarians), with Fred's Favourite turning out to be king prawn kebabs,
sautéed in garlic butter and served on a bed of fried cajun-spiced wild
and long-grain rice. On sunny mornings breakfast can be taken in the
attached conservatory.

Upstairs, the bedrooms have been refurbished to a high standard, with
lots of pastel colours, wickerwork and plants. Best are Number Two, a
spacious double on the first floor with a particularly attractive bedstead,
and Number Four, which looks on to the garden and boasts a big cast-
iron fireplace. Unfortunately, traffic flows through Ashburton's narrow
streets at a steady rate, so to be sure of quiet ask for a room at the back.
From mid-November to late April (except bank holidays) guests who
pre-book dinner in the restaurant can stay at the hotel for half the usual
price, provided rooms are available. Parking in the Golden Lion car park
across the road is easily arranged.

◑ Open all year

⤢ Just off the A38 between Exeter
and Plymouth. On-street parking

🛏 1 twin, 3 double; all with
bathroom/WC, TV, room service,
hair-dryer, baby-listening

◈ Restaurant, bar, lounge,
conservatory; conference
facilities (max 12 people non-

residential); fishing, golf, other
sports nearby. Wheelchair access
to restaurant only

⊖ None

▭ Access, Diners, Visa

£ Single occupancy of twin/double
£30, twin/double £44. Cooked B
£4; alc L, D from £6.50

Holne Chase

PRINCETOWN ROAD, ASHBURTON, NEWTON ABBOT, DEVON TQ13 7NS
TEL: POUNDSGATE (036 43) 471   FAX: (036 43) 453

A hotel full of character in remote woodland countryside; suitable for both business travellers and holidaymakers.

A sudden break in Dartmoor's forest reveals Holne Chase, a four-gabled hotel with an immaculately kept lawn spread out in front of it. The Bromages have a wonderful eye for old prints, photographs and cartoons, so there's hardly a square inch of wall that doesn't repay careful inspection. Best of all is the dining-room, where a packet picked up at auction turned out to contain old black and white photos of Egypt. These now hang alongside watercolours of Philae.

Ravenous diners can select two starters from a five-course table d'hôte menu which tends to the substantial rather than the imaginative. Afterwards they can retire to a bar-lounge with log fire or to a drawing-room with small but well-stocked library. Bedrooms are named after local rivers; Ashburn on the ground floor may be suitable for some disabled guests. Upstairs, spacious rooms combine antique and modern furnishings: East Dart has a big four-poster bed and marble fireplace; Velford Brook is a mishmash of a suite, with a sofabed in an outer room, a door straight out to the grounds in the main room and a bright blue bathroom accessible from both bedrooms.

◗ Open all year

⤷ From Exeter take the second exit (marked Ashburton) off the A38. Follow signs to Two Bridges for 3 miles. Private car park

🛏 1 single, 7 twin, 4 double, 1 four-poster, 1 suite; most with bathroom/WC, some with shower/WC; TV, room service, hair-dryer in all rooms; trouser press, mini-bar and baby-listening in some rooms

◈ Restaurant, bar, lounge, drying room; conference facilities (max 15 people residential, 30 non-residential); fishing at hotel, other sports nearby. Wheelchair access to hotel, restaurant and WC (disabled), 1 ground-floor bedroom

⊖ No dogs in public rooms; no smoking in restaurant

▭ Access, Amex, Diners, Visa

£ Single £48, single occupancy of twin/double £63, twin/double £85 to £95, four-poster £115, suite £105. Set L £14.50, D £17.50/£24 (prices till Apr 94). Special breaks available

---

Prices are what you can expect to pay in 1994, except where specified to the contrary. Many hoteliers tell us that these prices can be regarded only as approximations.

ASHTON KEYNES WILTSHIRE   **MAP 9**

Two Cove House

2 COVE HOUSE, ASHTON KEYNES, WILTSHIRE SN6 6NS
TEL: CIRENCESTER (0285) 861221

*Historic home that offers traditional hospitality in a village where
the Thames flows sweetly.*

A large OS map hangs framed and illuminated in the study of Two Cove
House, precisely marked with tourist locations and spheres of interest. It
is a sign of a good military mind at work, and indeed, on our inspection
visit, two Canadian guests were full of praise for Major Hartland's
assistance in planning their sightseeing campaign. The sixteenth-
century house also has military connections – during the Civil War it was
the scene for a tragic tale of fratricide when a Roundhead killed his
Royalist brother. Centuries later the house was requisitioned for American troops, and the occasional GI still revisits.

After 20 years, Elizabeth Hartland is well practised at looking after her
guests with ease and grace. As soon as you arrive at the top of the private
drive that takes you past One Cove House (the manor was divided after
the war) she is there with words of welcome.

It is very much a private family home, full of personal photos, portraits
and heirlooms. The lounge has comfortable seating and a sprinkling of
military memorabilia. Bedrooms are good-sized and homely rather than
smart. Named after birds, they have old furniture, watercolours and
plenty of books. The most unusual is Kingfisher, brightly painted and
with a barrel ceiling and a high sash window.

Three-course dinners feature fresh vegetables from the garden and
local produce. On our inspection an enjoyable meal started with smoked
trout, moved on to excellent home-baked ham (dexterously carved at the
table by Major Hartland), and was rounded off with red fruit crumble.
The small, gracious dining-room looks on to the former carriage yard,
now a delightful walled patio garden and pool.

◑ Open all year, exc Xmas

⤴ Turn west off the A419 Swindon
to Cirencester road towards
Ashton Keynes. At the White
Hart turn left and 100 yards on,
turn left. Private car park

⇌ 2 twin, 1 double, 1 family room;
2 with bathroom/WC, double
with shower/WC, 1 twin with
washbasin only; hair-dryer on
request

◈ Dining-room, lounge, TV room,
drying room; fishing, riding,
water sports nearby; babysitting

⊖ No wheelchair access; no
children under 10 in dining-
room; dogs by arrangement only

▭ None accepted

£ Single occupancy of twin/double
£28 to £34, twin/double £40 to
£48; deposit required. Set D
£16.50 (by arrangement only)

Report forms are at the back of the Guide; *write a letter if you prefer.*

ASKRIGG NORTH YORKSHIRE   **MAP 3**

King's Arms

ASKRIGG, LEYBURN, NORTH YORKSHIRE DL8 3HQ
TEL: WENSLEYDALE (0969) 50258   FAX: (0969) 50635

Refurbishment renders all things bright and beautiful at this atmospheric star of All Creatures Great and Small.

In a county often requisitioned by television and film location scouts, this undulating corner of Wensleydale has become – in tourist board-speak – 'Herriot Country'. At its heart is Askrigg's King's Arms, whose back parlour – a *mélange* of saddle hooks, tack, hunting prints, Victorian cartoons and a sombre notice cautioning hawkers and peddlars – doubles as the Drovers' Arms in the fictional village of Darrowby. A collection of framed photographs celebrates the connection, but despite its fame the bar, a former tack room with a huge inglenook fireplace, avoids becoming a caricature of itself and is a pleasantly rustic venue for innovative bar food offerings such as corn pancake with spiced seafood and salsa. More decorous dining is available in the bistro-style Grill Room or in the formal wood-panelled Club Room, presided over by a large painting of a racehorse. Fish and game are the specialities in a varied menu which might offer a warm timbale of salmon with chanterelle mushrooms and a vermouth and chive sauce, followed by cutlets of venison with a sauce of port and juniper berries, and a bread-and-butter pudding to finish.

Ray and Liz Hopwood are clearly relieved to have arrived at the conclusion of a protracted refurbishment and remodelling of the building, which has created a comfortable lounge with homely furnishings and cottagey fabrics as well as bedrooms with improved facilities and bold modern décor to complement a sprinkling of beams, half-testers and four-posters. Service is friendly and efficient.

◑ Open all year

⤢ ½ mile off the A684 Sedburgh to Leeming Bar (A1) road, between Aysgarth and Bainbridge. Private car park

🛏 1 twin, 2 double, 5 four-poster, 1 family room, 2 suites; all with bathroom/WC, exc doubles with shower/WC; TV, hair-dryer, baby-listening in all rooms

✧ 2 restaurants, 3 bars, 2 lounges, drying room; conference facilities (max 30 people non-residential,

11 residential); fishing, riding nearby

⊖ No wheelchair access; dogs in bars and bedrooms only; no smoking in restaurants and 1 lounge

▭ Access, Visa

£ Single occupancy of twin/double £45 to £50, twin/double £66, four-poster £75, family room £66, suite £90; deposit required. Set L £12.50, D £25. Special breaks available

We mention those hotels that don't accept dogs; guide dogs, however, are almost always an exception. Telephone ahead to make sure.

ASPLEY GUISE BEDFORDSHIRE   **MAP 9**

Moore Place

THE SQUARE, ASPLEY GUISE, NR WOBURN, BEDFORDSHIRE MK17 8DW
TEL: MILTON KEYNES (0908) 282000   FAX: (0908) 281888

An efficient business hotel in a small village near Woburn.

In spite of the fine façade of this red-brick Georgian house with its grand porticoed entrance, you could spend a night in Moore Place and remain totally within a modern hotel. The entrance is at the back of the hotel via the smart conservatory reception and lounge that links the old house to a modern bedroom extension. The décor is primarily in pastel pinks and greens, with good-quality reproduction furnishings reflecting a Georgian style. Public areas are spacious and uncluttered. The canopied conservatory restaurant overlooks the small landscaped garden and waterfall which is floodlit in the evenings and used as a backdrop for photos at summer weddings. One reader complained about the casual attitude of the young staff in the restaurant and the loud pop music playing during dinner and breakfast.

There are some bedrooms in the old house but most are in a simple brick extension at the back. Co-ordinated in yellows and greys, they are light and comfortable, with all facilities. Single rooms are a fair size and there are more than you might expect considering Moore Place's primary use as a business hotel.

◑ Open all year

⚡ Leave the M1 at Junction 13 and follow signs to Aspley Guise. The hotel is in the centre of the village. Private car park

🛏 19 single, 6 twin, 26 double, 2 studio rooms, 1 suite; all with bathroom/WC, TV, room service, hair-dryer, trouser press

◈ Restaurant, bar, lounge, games room, conservatory; conference facilities (max 30 people non-residential and residential); golf, tennis, other sports nearby. Wheelchair access to hotel, restaurant and WC (unisex), 12 ground-floor bedrooms

⊖ No dogs

▭ Access, Amex, Diners, Visa

£ Single £58, single occupancy of twin/double £65, twin/double £75, studio room £95, suite £150; deposit required. Continental B £4, cooked B £7.50; alc L, D from £14. Special breaks available

---

Scottish hoteliers blessed with beautiful soft, peaty water continue to be incensed by guests who complain there must be something wrong with the plumbing because the water's brown. Our advice: if it's good enough for the whisky, it should be OK for your bath.

ASTON CLINTON BUCKINGHAMSHIRE   MAP 9

Bell Inn

ASTON CLINTON, BUCKINGHAMSHIRE HP22 5HP
TEL: AYLESBURY (0296) 630252   FAX: (0296) 631250

Renowned for its restaurant, this old coaching-inn also has charming bedrooms and pretty gardens.

The original coaching-inn, a mellow brick two-storey building, still remains at the heart of this well-established, much-extended restaurant-with-rooms owned by the Harris family for over 50 years and now personally run by Michael and Patsy Harris. It stands just off a busy road, surrounded by high hedges and pretty gardens. It is the restaurant's reputation that draws the guests; a large room, it can be divided with heavy curtains to give diners added privacy. Chef David Cavalier, new to the inn in 1992, produces a classic menu. Comments on the food remain positive. One Christmas guest praised the lamb terrine – 'tiny pieces of lamb in a terrine of aubergines and tomatoes'. However, we have had worrying reports about the service – 'the quality of the service completely detracts from the quality of the restaurant'. Linguistic problems with staff, many of whom are French, to delays with afternoon tea and criticisms of the housekeeping are cited.

The original bar retains a pleasant atmosphere, with a collection of old wood furnishings and a lingering smell of woodsmoke. Reasonably priced bistro-style meals are served here. Bedrooms are in the main building or in the converted stables and old malthouse buildings off the pretty courtyard across a side street. They are all attractive and individually styled in a mix of antiques and interesting furnishings; some have their own sitting-rooms and small garden terraces. A Regency-style white pavilion across the main road houses conference and function rooms.

○ Open all year

⤢ Aston Clinton is set back from the A41 between Tring and Aylesbury. Private car park

🛏 10 twin, 3 double, 2 four-poster, 5 suites, 1 cottage; all with bathroom/WC, TV, room service, hair-dryer, mini-bar, trouser press, baby-listening; no tea/coffee-making facilities in rooms

◇ Restaurant, bar, 2 lounges, library; conference facilities (max 250 people non-residential, 21 residential); croquet at hotel, other sports nearby. Wheelchair access to hotel and restaurant, 2 ground-floor bedrooms

⊖ No dogs in public rooms; no smoking in restaurant

▭ Access, Amex, Visa

£ Single occupancy of twin/double £92, twin/double £107, four-poster/suite £133, cottage £189. Cooked B £12.50, continental B £8.50; set L £18.50, D £22.50; alc L, D £35. Special breaks available

AWRE GLOUCESTERSHIRE   **MAP 9**

Old Vicarage ℒ 🐚

AWRE, NR NEWNHAM, GLOUCESTERSHIRE GL14 1EL
TEL: DEAN (0594) 510282

A very isolated, slightly old-fashioned guesthouse with friendly owners.

Down on the flat borders of the Severn Estuary, by-passed by major roads and lost among the hedges and narrow lanes, Nick and May Bull's guesthouse is unlikely to be full of people who were just passing by and happened to spot it. To reach the red-brick house you must first pass the greenhouses, expanses of vegetables and various ducks and hens, for this seems to be as much a smallholding as a guesthouse. Consequently, you must be prepared for a bit of homely clutter – but equally your welly boots will be welcome in the porch.

Inside, the Georgian proportions of the rooms, and the views towards the river from some of them, combine to give the house an air of elegance. The bedrooms are big, plainly furnished and a little bare. Of the two public bathrooms, there is no doubt that the vicar's original bath (huge, claw-footed and deep) runs away with the prize.

◑ Open all year, exc Xmas; restaurant open weekends only

🡲 1½ miles west of the A48 between Newnham and Blakeney, on the edge of the village of Awre. Private car park

🛏 1 twin, 3 double, 1 double with shower/WC, 2 public bathrooms; hair-dryer on request

◈ Dining-room, drawing-room, study/music room; fishing, golf, other sports nearby

⊖ No wheelchair access; no dogs; no smoking in bedrooms

▭ None accepted

£ Single occupancy of twin/double £18 to £20, twin/double £36 to £40; deposit required. Set D £14.50 (8pm)

AYLESBURY BUCKINGHAMSHIRE   **MAP 9**

Hartwell House

OXFORD ROAD, AYLESBURY, BUCKINGHAMSHIRE HP17 8NL
TEL: AYLESBURY (0296) 747444   FAX: (0296) 747450

A Jacobean stately home converted into a luxurious hotel.

A Grade-I listed building with both Jacobean and Georgian façades, Hartwell House stands in the midst of 80 acres of parkland including lakes, a haha and a ruined church. At the reception you can look at the photo album detailing the painstaking restoration of the house by Historic House Hotels as they converted it from a girls' school into an elegant and sumptuous hotel. From the Great Hall you can make your way through the light, elegant morning-room to the drawing-room or to the library, all of which are graced by handsome fireplaces, elaborate plasterwork, oil paintings and antiques.

You can choose from rooms in the main house or those next to the Spa, with its attractive pool. Bedrooms in the house are spacious and filled with antiques. Those on the second floor are standard rooms and lack the high-ceilinged grandeur of the first-floor rooms – such as Room Six, which has some fine wood panelling and a grand four-poster bed. All are eminently comfortable and spacious.

◑ *Open all year*

▱ *On the A418 Oxford road, 2 miles west of Aylesbury. Private car park*

🛏 *3 single, 20 twin/double, 5 four-poster, 3 suites, 16 Hartwell Court rooms (3 singles, 3 twins, 10 suites); all with bathroom/ WC, TV, room service, hair-dryer, trouser press; tea/coffee-making facilities, mini-bar and air-conditioning in Hartwell Court rooms*

◈ *2 dining-rooms, bar, 4 drawing-rooms, library, drying room, buttery, air-conditioned spa; conference facilities (max 40 people residential, 100 non-residential); fishing (lake), croquet, tennis, sauna/solarium,* *heated swimming-pool, gym, beauty treatments at hotel, other sports nearby. Wheelchair access to hotel (1 step), dining-rooms and WC (unisex), 10 ground-floor bedrooms and lift, 1 bedroom specially equipped for disabled people*

⊖ *No children under 8; no dogs in rooms in house*

▭ *Access, Amex, Diners, Visa*

£ *Single £90, single occupancy of twin/double £108, twin/double £135, four-poster £179, suite £199; deposit required. Continental B £8, cooked B £11; set L £16.50/£22.50, D £38; alc L, D £38. Special breaks available*

HARTWELL HOUSE
– AYLESBURY –

Haigs

KENILWORTH ROAD, BALSALL COMMON, NR COVENTRY, WEST
MIDLANDS CV7 7EL
TEL: BERKSWELL (0676) 533004   FAX: (0676) 534572

*A small business-orientated hotel on a busy main road, lifted by
its reputation for good food.*

Bang on the A452 main road between Coventry and Birmingham, Haigs,
a sandy-coloured pebble-dashed house, is easy to find and convenient
for most of the West Midlands conurbation. An uninspiring house from
the front, it has a large, neat garden at the rear, overlooked by the
restaurant – the chief reason why regulars keep on returning here. With
its pink and yellow décor, red-brick fireplace and large Rosina
Wachtmeister prints, the restaurant itself springs no surprises, but the
food is far more inspired.

   Longstanding chefs Ian Enticott and Paul Hartup produce reasonably
priced meals which bring in non-residents, too. When we visited, the à la
carte menu included prawns marinated with ginger and chilli served on a
bed of crisp lettuce, grilled calf's liver with bacon and onions and sautéed
escalopes of pork with thyme and wild mushroom sauce. Despite its
proximity to major cities with their myriad restaurants, the majority of
John and Jean Cooper's guests choose to eat in. The light, decent-sized
rooms have modern *en-suite* shower rooms and are plain and functional,
with cream woodchip wallpaper and faded cotton bedspreads the norm.

◑ Open all year, exc 26 Dec to 4
Jan; restaurant closed Sun eve

🔀 On the A452, 6 miles south of
Junction 4 of the M6, 4 miles
north of Kenilworth. Private car
park

🛏 8 single, 5 twin; most with
shower/WC, I twin with
bathroom/WC, I public
bathroom; TV, hair-dryer, in all
rooms; trouser press in most
rooms

◈ Restaurant, bar, lounge;
conference facilities (max 24

people non-residential, 18
residential); golf, riding,
swimming-pool nearby.
Wheelchair access to hotel (I
step) and restaurant, 2 ground-
floor bedrooms

⊖ No children under 3; no dogs in
public rooms

▭ Access, Visa

£ Single £25 to £50, single
occupancy of twin £34 to £50,
twin £41 to £57; deposit
required. Sun L £11.50; set D
£16; alc D £13 to £23

Hotels in our Visitors' Book *towards the end of the* Guide *are additional
hotels that may be worth a visit. Reports on these hotels are welcome.*

BANTHAM DEVON **MAP 10**

Sloop Inn

BANTHAM, NR KINGSBRIDGE, DEVON TQ7 3AJ
TEL: KINGSBRIDGE (0548) 560215/560489 FAX: (0548) 560489

Simple accommodation in an off-the-beaten-track seventeenth-century pub.

At the end of a row of thatched cottages, the Sloop Inn, once the haunt of smugglers, is a typical black and white seventeenth-century building. The long car park at the back gives a clue to the popularity of its flagstone-floored public bar with Sunday lunchers, who quickly fill it up to take advantage of a menu featuring pub staples such as scampi and chips topped up with specials chalked on boards on the walls. Those after a longer stay can choose from five fairly basic but moderately priced rooms. Furnishings are rather flimsy and space is sometimes at a premium; in Room Four the wardrobe is actually in the bathroom. There is no residents' lounge, so guests must hope the bar does not get too popular. Still, with the beach just 300 yards away and the surrounding South Hams area offering plenty of unspoilt countryside for walking, visitors are unlikely to be spending much time indoors.

◑ *Open all year, exc last week Dec to end Jan; restaurant closed 25, 26 Dec*

◿ *From the A38, take the A381 to Totnes and Kingsbridge. From Kingsbridge, take Plymouth road through Churchstow, at mini roundabout take Bantham road, follow for 2½ miles. Private car park*

🛏 *3 double, 2 family rooms; all with bathroom/WC, TV, hairdryer*

◇ *Restaurant, bar; laundry facilities; fishing, water sports, other sports nearby*

⊖ *No wheelchair access*

▭ *None accepted*

💷 *Single occupancy of double £26 to £30, double £49 to £54, family room £64 to £70; deposit required. Alc L £3 to £10, D £6 to £15*

BAPCHILD KENT **MAP 8**

Hempstead House ☆

LONDON ROAD, BAPCHILD, SITTINGBOURNE, KENT ME9 9PP
TEL: SITTINGBOURNE (0795) 428020

Plenty of space and facilities in a welcoming family mansion.

Hempstead House is a creeper-covered, early-Victorian brick building which used to be the estate house of a local farm. It is now particularly handy for Channel-crossers, as the A2 – shielded by a high hedge – runs past the bottom of the pretty front lawn. The present owner, Mrs Mandy Holdstock, runs a spruce, easy-going house, paying close attention to details and, as one of our readers has written, treating guests 'as visiting friends'.

As well as lawns, the three-acre grounds contain an attractive heated swimming-pool, and vegetable and fruit gardens which provide the ingredients for much of the food served at dinner. The interior is traditionally decorated, with no great surprises. Pick of the public rooms is the dining-room, done out in pink and green, with a beautifully laid mahogany table and large windows overlooking the garden. The small TV room is homely but rather dowdy, while the formal sitting-room has comfortable sofas in light blue and beige floral patterns and a log fire. Accommodation is in two large suites on the second floor (plans for a third and fourth are well under way), each with a separate dressing area, toilet and bathroom. The décor here is bright and flouncy, and plenty of extras such as mineral water and writing paper are laid on. Breakfast, which includes home-made bread, jams and marmalade, is taken communally on a long wooden table next to the kitchen.

◑ Open all year

⤤ Situated on the A2, 1½ miles east of Sittingbourne. Private car park

🛏 2 twin/double, family room available (4 rooms by 1994); all with bathroom/WC, TV, room service, hair-dryer, baby-listening

◈ 2 dining-rooms, lounge, TV room, drying room, library, conservatory, children's games room; conference facilities (max 20 people non-residential, 4

residential); pitch and putt, heated swimming-pool (May to Sept) at hotel, other sports nearby; babysitting. Wheelchair access to restaurant only

⊝ Dogs by arrangement; no smoking in bedrooms

▭ None accepted

£→ Single occupancy of twin/double £50, twin/double £56, family room from £56. Set L £15 (by arrangement), D £15

BARNSTAPLE DEVON　　　　　　　　　　　　　　**MAP 10**

Lynwood House

BISHOP'S TAWTON ROAD, BARNSTAPLE, DEVON EX32 9DZ
TEL: BARNSTAPLE (0271) 43695　FAX: (0271) 79340

A long-established, family-run restaurant-with-rooms on the approaches to Barnstaple town centre.

From the outside Lynwood House doesn't look much, although the size of its gravel car park suggests the number of diners it expects to attract on a good night. If proprietor John Roberts greets you in his plus-fours it'll be a clue to the general tenor of the interior, which is well-maintained if slightly old-fashioned. There's a small lounge bar with photographs of old Barnstaple life, but the centrepiece of the ground floor is the

restaurant, where authenticity is all; place settings of real silver and
Dartington glasses are laid out beneath a sweeping ceiling fan which
wouldn't look out of place in a Delhi dining-room. The à la carte menu is
especially strong on fish and always includes items suitable for vegetarians; arguably these are a little pricey. In contrast with the downstairs
public rooms, the upstairs breakfast bar, with its stainless steel and
marble tables and anglepoise lights, seems to have strayed from another
building.

The five bedrooms are named after possible views, although the one
called 'Taw' is a little optimistic. 'Park', at the front, has a particularly big
window but could be disturbed by traffic from the road outside. 'Town' is
the smallest, a twin often let as a single. Furnishings vary little from room
to room, but all the doubles have two comfortable seats, and shaver
points in the rooms and *en suite* bathrooms. 'Extras' such as cafetières,
bottled mineral water, Crabtree and Evelyn toiletries and writing kits
complete with stamps can be taken for granted. In the corridors, look out
for John Roberts' collection of witty French dog cartoons and a weird 3D
portrayal of a string quartet.

◐ Open all year; restaurant closed
Sun eve

⤴ From M5, take Junction 27
towards Barnstaple. Turn right to
Bideford at roundabout before
Tesco store, then right at the
next roundabout (follow
Newport sign). Private car park

🛏 5 twin; all with shower/WC, TV,
room service, hair-dryer, trouser
press

◈ Restaurant, bar, breakfast room;

conference facilities (max 60
people non-residential); fishing,
golf, other sports nearby.
Wheelchair access to restaurant
only

⊖ No dogs; no smoking in
restaurant

▭ Access, Amex, Visa

£ Single occupancy of twin £41,
twin £61. Set L £13; alc L, D
£20. Special breaks available

BARWICK SOMERSET   **MAP 9**

Little Barwick House

BARWICK, YEOVIL, SOMERSET BA22 9TD
TEL: YEOVIL (0935) 23902   FAX: (0935) 20908

*A small Georgian dower-house restaurant-with-rooms in restful
surroundings.*

Follow the sign to Barwick church and you'll find Little Barwick House,
an apparent misnomer since you're confronted with what looks like a
sizeable Georgian mansion; inside, however, there are only six bedrooms
for guests. The façade was just starting to show its age, but in the nick of
time a lick of paint has perked it up again. The dining-room, with
terracotta walls and polished floorboards, looks out on the large front
garden where a venerable cedar spreads its branches to shade a bench.

Veronica Colley is in charge of the four-course dinners, which emphasise local produce like rack of spring lamb but include more cosmopolitan dishes such as avocado and chicken tikka salad. It's a bit surprising to have to descend into the bowels of the earth in search of the bar, which is inevitably on the dark and gloomy side; a piano and bridge table suggest it livens up in the evenings.

Upstairs, the bedrooms vary considerably: Number Six is a big double with silky coverlet, a settee with antimacassar, a sizeable bathroom and garden views; Number One is much smaller, with a cubicle for a shower. Throughout, bowls of wood-shavings and cones, fresh flowers and plants bring a touch of countryside indoors.

○ Open all year, exc Xmas and New Year

⤢ From Yeovil take the A37 Dorchester road. After 1 mile turn off left at the Red House pub; the house is ¼ mile on the left. Private car park

🛏 3 twin, 3 double; all with bathroom/WC, exc 1 double with shower/WC; TV in all rooms; hair-dryer, trouser press on request

◈ Dining-room, breakfast room

(both air-conditioned), 2 lounges; conference facilities (max 6 people residential); fishing, golf, other sports nearby

● No wheelchair access; no dogs in public rooms; smoking in lounge only

▭ Access, Amex, Visa

£ Single occupancy of twin/double £47, twin/double £73; deposit required. Set D £23. Special breaks available

---

BASLOW DERBYSHIRE   **MAP 5**

Cavendish Hotel

BASLOW, DERBYSHIRE DE45 ISP
TEL: BASLOW (0246) 582311   FAX: (0246) 582312

A roadside hotel on the edge of the Chatsworth estate, with good food and much-improved bedrooms.

The Cavendish Hotel began life 200 years ago as a lonely inn on the remote turnpike road that crossed this green and wooded part of England, a welcome sight on what is now the eastern edge of the Peak District National Park. Today the area is better served with restaurants and hotels, but the Cavendish Hotel is still a popular refuelling stop. We have had better reports of the food here than the accommodation, though recent refurbishment of all but six of the 24 bedrooms (these to be done by January 1994) has put that to rights. Downstairs, the public rooms are smart, with plain yellows and blues, good-quality fabrics and a large number of oil paintings from owner Eric Marsh's collection. The management team are keen to stress their connection with the Duke of Devonshire's estate, and new carpets, including those in the refurbished bedrooms, have been designed to incorporate the Devonshire coat of arms. Of the new rooms, all of which have cheerful fabrics and a comfortable mix of antique and reproduction furniture, those in the 10-year-old Mitford wing are the nicest. Named after members of the Mitford family, these rooms are light, spacious and have well-equipped bathrooms. The corner rooms are especially peaceful, with views over parkland of the Chatsworth estate.

With the restaurants, however, the Cavendish really comes into its own. The conservatory-style Garden Room offers light meals ranging from sushi to bangers and mash, while the more formal main restaurant serves table d'hôte and à la carte menus which include smoked eel, monkfish sausage, roast ham hock with mustard and honey, Aylesbury duckling with a warm vinaigrette sauce and a good range of puddings. The wine list is long but pricey. A popular idea for foodies is to book the table for two in the kitchen where you get to watch the chef, Nick Buckingham, at work before you sample his creations.

◑ *Open all year*

⤢ *9 miles west of Chesterfield on the A619. Follow signs to Chatsworth House. Private car park*

⇌ *13 twin, 9 double, 1 four-poster, 1 suite, family rooms available; all with bathroom/WC, TV, room service, hair-dryer, mini-bar, baby-listening; trouser press in most rooms*

◈ *2 restaurants, bar, lounge, conservatory; conference facilities (max 18 people residential and non-residential);*

putting green at hotel, fishing, golf, other sports nearby; babysitting

⊖ *No wheelchair access; no dogs; no smoking in restaurants*

▭ *Access, Amex, Diners, Visa*

£ *Single occupancy of twin/double £73 to £83, twin/double £89 to £99, four-poster £99, family room £114, suite £125; deposit required. Continental B £5, cooked B £9; set L, D £25; alc L, D £26 (prices till end 93). Special breaks available*

Fischer's – Baslow Hall ☆

BASLOW HALL, CALVER ROAD, BASLOW, DERBYSHIRE DE45 1RR
TEL: BASLOW (0246) 583259   FAX: (0246) 583818

Pricey accommodation and excellent food in a stylishly furnished house with a curious history.

Built in 1907 in the style of a seventeenth-century manor house, Baslow Hall has an eccentric history as a family home to notable characters. Perhaps the most memorable is Sebastian de Ferranti, a famous electrical engineer and gadget man who installed in the high-ceilinged rooms a heating and lighting system à la Heath Robinson that, fortunately for guests, no longer exists. Since moving here from a successful restaurant business in 1989 Susan and Max Fischer have completely refurbished the house, creating stylish public rooms and pretty, individually designed bedrooms. One trace of previous occupants remains in the form of a stained-glass door leading into the sitting-room which bears the message 'Work and Pray', the motto of the Kenning family who, you can't help feeling, must have lacked a sense of fun.

All the bedrooms overlook the walled garden and are well-equipped, with fruit, mineral water and bathrobes adding to the comfortable environment of antiques and luxurious fabrics. Longshaw, though not large, is perhaps the prettiest, with decorative bows on the peach-coloured upholstered bed-head; Vernon and Haddon have the biggest windows and plenty of space to move around. Haddon's bathroom is extraordinary, housing what is said to be be one of the first showers to be fitted in England. More like the engine room of a submarine than a bathroom, it has a series of pipes leading to control valves with the option to spray, shower or plunge.

Table d'hôte meals in the dining-room are pricey but highly recommended, and include perhaps wild mushrooms with Parma ham, fillet of sea bass with fresh mint, and cherries in port and honey served with cinnamon ice-cream; light meals are served in Café Max, a sunny, less formal room with paper cloths, napkins and a parquet floor. Several readers particularly praise the service; one reports, 'The atmosphere and standard of service were excellent – friendly, courteous and everything a guest could wish for.'

◐ *Open all year, exc 25 and 26 Dec*

↗ *Leave the M1 at Junction 29 and follow signs to Chatsworth on the A623. Baslow Hall is on the right as you leave Baslow village. Private car park*

🛏 *1 twin, 4 double, 1 suite; TV, room service, baby-listening; hair-dryer on request*

◇ *3 dining-rooms, lounge, study; conference facilities (max 25 people non-residential, 6 residential); fishing, golf, tennis,*

other sports nearby. Wheelchair access to restaurant only

⊖ *No children under 10 in dining-rooms eves; no dogs in public rooms; no smoking in dining-rooms*

▭ *Access, Amex, Visa*

£ *Single occupancy of twin/double £70 to £85, twin/double £95 to £120, suite £120; deposit required. Cooked B £4.50; Sun L £20; set L £20, D £34. Special breaks available*

BASSENTHWAITE LAKE CUMBRIA   **MAP 4**

Link House

BASSENTHWAITE LAKE, COCKERMOUTH, CUMBRIA CA13 9YD
TEL: BASSENTHWAITE LAKE (07687) 76291

An informal atmosphere in a large Victorian country house close to the lake.

The prints depicting scenes from Dickens' novels on the dining-room walls and the examples of lacework from the 1820s in the lounge suggest that Brian and May Smith are keen to emphasise the Victorian origins of Link House, a large cream-coloured detached house which sits under the shoulder of the mighty Skiddaw. The conservatory, a recent addition to the house, is very much in keeping, with cane chairs and small oak tables. If this all summons up a rather sedate and staid image, then nothing could be further from the truth: Brian and May have blended the period features with more modern flourishes like bright floral cushions and pastel shades in a way that gives the house a light and breezy feel which reflects the friendly but never overbearing nature of the Smiths themselves. The understated Asiatic theme in the furnishings (china elephants on the lounge mantelpiece, a laughing Buddha on the stairs) adds an extra twist of individuality to the public areas.

The five-course dinner menu leans towards the hearty and traditional: creamed mushrooms may be followed by a chicken casserole or locally produced lamb with a banana split for dessert and though the choice may be somewhat limited it is modestly priced. Service is prompt and cheery, with the grandfather clock that stands in the corner of the front dining-room chiming in regularly. The bedrooms vary considerably in size and not all have a view worthy of the name but they are all nicely furnished, often with pine furniture and vividly patterned duvets.

◐ *Closed Dec, Jan*

↗ *On the A66 from Keswick to Cockermouth; turn right for Dubwath and then bear left. Private car park*

🛏 *2 single, 2 twin, 2 double, 2 family rooms; 1 twin with bathroom/WC, rest with shower/WC, 2 public bathrooms; TV in all rooms*

◇ *Dining-room, conservatory/bar,*

lounge; fishing, riding, swimming nearby

⊖ *No wheelchair access; no children under 7; no dogs*

▭ *None accepted*

£ *Single £20 to £24, single occupancy of twin/double £28 to £32, twin/double £40 to £48, family room rate on request; deposit required. Set D £12.50 (7pm). Special breaks available*

Pheasant Inn

BASSENTHWAITE LAKE, COCKERMOUTH, CUMBRIA CA13 9YE
TEL: BASSENTHWAITE LAKE (07687) 76234   FAX: (07687) 76002

An eighteenth-century pub in a quiet lane in the northern part of the Lake District.

Cars zoom quickly along the A66 past Bassenthwaite Lake and, if they are not careful, past the quiet cul-de-sac where the Pheasant Inn stands. From the outside the inn looks the picture of an English country pub, with its whitewashed walls, black window frames and tubs of geraniums. This impression is confirmed once you step over the threshold. The main bar, with its oak settles and ochre walls, is dark and snug; across the hallway is the main lounge, where rugs are spread out on the parquet floor. Hunting prints hang from the white walls and two rifles have pride of place above the open fire, while dried-flower arrangements and decorative plates add a touch of elegance. A full range of bar snacks is served in here on every day except Sunday, when it is reserved for people eating more formally in the restaurant.

In the evening there is a set dinner with around half a dozen choices for each course – you could have garlic mushrooms with croûtons, breast of chicken stuffed with ricotta and spinach, and strawberry crème brûlée to finish. There is also a cold meat buffet.

The bedrooms are simple and smart, with plain carpets, pine furniture and cream-coloured bedspreads. Those at the front overlook the car park. It should be noted that the entire inn is a television-free zone. The Pheasant has been run for many years by Mr and Mrs Barrington Wilson, and their staff are efficient and courteous.

◐ Open all year, exc 24 and 25 Dec

🔁 The inn is just off the A66, 7 miles west of Keswick on the west side of Bassenthwaite Lake. Private car park

🛏 4 single, 6 twin, 7 double, 3 rooms in bungalow annexe; most with bathroom/WC, 3 with shower/WC; room service, hair-dryer in all rooms; tea/coffee-making facilities in annexe rooms

◈ Dining-room, bar, lounge, drying room; fishing, golf, riding nearby. Wheelchair access to hotel (no steps), restaurant and WC (M,F), 3 ground-floor bedrooms in annexe, I specially equipped for the disabled

⊖ No dogs in bedrooms

▭ None accepted

£ Single £54, single occupancy of twin/double £65, twin/double £92. Set L £11, D £23; alc L £8 to £15. Special breaks available

Riggs Cottage ℒ ❁

ROUTENBECK, BASSENTHWAITE LAKE, COCKERMOUTH, CUMBRIA
CA13 9YN
TEL: BASSENTHWAITE LAKE (07687) 76580

A picture-book cottage in a secluded location close to Bassenthwaite Lake.

Close your eyes and picture the archetypal English country cottage: a tiny whitewashed seventeenth-century building at the end of a winding lane, the stone porch almost hidden under a profusion of wild flowers; inside, solid stone floors and low ceilings with exposed wooden beams and a large open fire. Well, the good news is that it exists and is located just six miles from Keswick – Riggs Cottage is just the thing and Hazel Wilkinson's genuine efforts to provide a home-from-home for her guests round off the idyll neatly. Getting there may be your only problem. Once you have found the turn-off and navigated the bumpy track that leads down to the house, do not waste your time looking for the usual B&B or guesthouse sign: there isn't one. 'I'm not a sign person,' explains Hazel, content with just a welcome horseshoe above the door.

As you enter you encounter one large room which contains both the dining area and the lounge. Meals are served at a single wooden table and are likely to be traditionally based, using local salmon or lamb or even trout from Hazel's own trout pond adjacent to the cottage; the oven-fresh bread is served with home-made jams. The communal atmosphere generated by eating *en masse* is carried over into the sitting-room, where the large sofas around the fireplace provide a snug corner for exchanging those walking anecdotes.

The largest bedroom is a double room with a mezzanine loft housing an extra bed but there is another, slightly smaller room, with its own bathroom. The wooden floors, pine furniture and low beams give the bedroom a rustic feel complemented by modern prints of Lakeland scenes.

◗ Open all year

▱ From the A66 Keswick to Cockermouth road, follow signs to Wythop Mill. Look for the 'Riggs Cottage' sign on the right, ¾ mile after Pheasant Inn, cottage on left-hand side. Private car park

⇌ 1 twin, 1 double, 1 family room (with shower/WC); 1 public bathroom

◇ Dining-room, lounge; fishing, water sports, other sports nearby

⊖ No wheelchair access; no children under 5; no dogs; no smoking

▭ None accepted

£ Twin/double/family room £36 to £44; deposit required. Packed lunches; set D £10 (6.30pm)

BATH AVON   **MAP 9**

Audley House ☆

PARK GARDENS, BATH, AVON BA1 2XP
TEL: BATH (0225) 333110   FAX: (0225) 482879

Peace and privacy in civilised, secluded bed and breakfast.

At night, the only sound to disturb the peace is a tawny owl in the grounds of this fine, detached Victorian house. The silence is particularly remarkable given the proximity of the centre of Bath, and the suburban estates that ring the private acre of garden, lawns and mature trees. Audley House is difficult to find, set back along a steep, private road. Planning regulations do not permit signs, but owners Gordon and Sheila Talbot would not, in any case, wish to have them. This is their private home and they wish to keep it that way, happy to share the tranquillity and comfort with discerning house guests.

A smart but relaxed drawing-room, with a sweep of bay windows, is decorated in shades of blue and terracotta. There are elegant, contemporary sofas, books, paintings and Persian rugs, evidence of many years spent by the Talbots in the Middle East. Double doors open into an equally lofty, well-proportioned dining-room where breakfasts are taken around a polished, round table.

The three bedrooms are reached via a fine central staircase. They are all spacious and beautifully furnished with antique pieces and subtle fabrics in quiet shades. Bathrooms have marble features, thick towels and good toiletries.

◑ *Open all year, exc 10 days at Xmas*

⚡ *Take the Upper Bristol Road (A4) at the western end of Victoria Park. Turn into Park Lane, and then into Park Gardens. Private car park*

🛏 *3 twin/double; 2 with bathroom/ WC, 1 with shower/WC; TV, hair-dryer in all rooms*

◈ *Dining-room, lounge; golf, tennis, other sports nearby*

⊖ *No wheelchair access; no children under 14; no dogs; no smoking*

▭ *Access, Visa*

£ *Single occupancy of twin/double £50, twin/double £68*

Cheriton House

9 UPPER OLDFIELD PARK, BATH, AVON BA2 3JX
TEL: BATH (0225) 429862   FAX: (0225) 428403

Smart bed-and-breakfast accommodation a short distance from the historic centre.

Located in a quiet residential street a gentle ten-minute climb from the city centre, Cheriton House is a large late-Victorian semi-detached house with a coolly elegant interior and views of the city that more than compensate for any leg-weariness you might experience when returning from the Roman Baths or the splendid abbey. Mike and Jo Babbage have been in charge for eight years, during which time they have embarked on a continuous redecoration programme that is now paying dividends. They have produced simple but stylish rooms with an understated classical feel and where they do use ornamentation, such as the brass elephant's head that holds up the dinner gong in the hallway, it seems to be unobtrusively in keeping rather than an attempt to graft on some tenuous individuality. The lounge has a paisley three-piece suite, a deep bluey-grey carpet, large sky-blue drapes and an outlook on to the small rear garden. The breakfast room has the real panorama, though the row of trees outside means that only winter visitors will get the full benefit. A nice pine fire surround and an attractive chandelier are the most striking features of the room, where a full English breakfast is served.

High ceilings give a sense of space in the individually decorated bedrooms, most of which have pine furniture, wicker chairs and pastel shades for the bedcovers and drapes. Views vary but Room Eight probably has the best of the lot.

◐ Open all year, exc Xmas and New Year

◇ Dining-room, lounge; golf, tennis, other sports nearby

⤢ South of Bath, ½ mile up the A367 Wells Road. Upper Oldfield Park is first turning on right. Private car park

⊖ No wheelchair access; children at discretion of management only; no dogs; no smoking in dining-room

⊨ 3 twin, 6 double; most with shower/WC, 2 with bathroom/WC; TV, room service, hair-dryer in all rooms

▭ Access, Visa

£ Single occupancy of twin/double £32 to £38, twin/double £48 to £58; deposit required. Special breaks available

---

Combe Grove Manor ☆

BRASSKNOCKER HILL, MONKTON COMBE, BATH, AVON BA2 7HS
TEL: BATH (0225) 834644

Sports for all at a luxury country-club hotel close to Bath.

A narrow winding drive through acres of private woodland leads to Combe Grove Manor. A handsome seventeenth-century Italianate manor-house is at the centre of the complex, flanked by more recent buildings housing a new bedroom wing, conference suites and a health and leisure club. All the facilities – swimming-pools, tennis courts, golf course and driving range, bowling green, gym, beauty salon and more – are free to hotel guests. Little wonder that this is a popular place for corporate gatherings and the weekend wedding trade.

Combe Grove Manor is a house built around a view, set on a natural scenic terrace high above the Limpley Stoke valley, two miles south of Bath. Many of the rooms take advantage of the panorama. The house has been luxuriously styled from top to toe, with individually designed bedrooms, including two suites with Jacuzzi bath. Rooms on the second floor may be a bit of a climb for non-gym-using residents (no lift), but the willing young porters will carry all the luggage, and even some of the guests, if required. Fresh milk and home-made cookies are provided in each room.

Bedrooms in the Garden Lodge annexe are cheaper and more standardised but still very pleasant. Some of them have sunbathing terraces, rather like Spanish holiday hotels, overlooking the outdoor pool. One advantage is direct access to the health club and indoor pool; the drawback is the need to cross the courtyard to reach the main house, where there is a choice of formal or coffee-shop dining. Umbrellas, however, are provided in each room.

Last but not least, a fully supervised crèche and and playroom is available, plus baby listening and sitting services and cots as required – perfect for parents who wish to go into Bath on their own, or just want to have a private workout in the Nautilus gym.

◐ Open all year

⬀ 2 miles south-east of Bath city centre, just off the A36. Private car park

🛏 29 twin/double, 1 four-poster, 9 family rooms, 2 suites; all with bathroom/WC, TV, room service, hair-dryer, mini-bar, baby-listening

◈ Restaurant, bar, lounge, library; conference facilities (max 100 people non-residential, 40 residential); golf, tennis, sauna/solarium, indoor and outdoor

heated swimming-pools, gym, steam room, aerobics at hotel, other sports nearby; babysitting and crèche facilities

⊖ No wheelchair access; no dogs

▭ Access, Diners, Visa

£ Single occupancy of twin/double £98, twin/double from £130, four-poster £235 to £265, family room from £175, suite from £235; deposit required. Cooked B £6.50; set L £16.50, D £25; alc L, D £30 (prices till end Mar 94). Special breaks available

Fountain House ☆

9–11 FOUNTAIN BUILDINGS, LANSDOWN ROAD, BATH, AVON BA1 5DV
TEL: BATH (0225) 338622   FAX: (0225) 445855

Classy self-contained apartments suitable for families, tourists and business people.

This is the best of both worlds – the services and security of a hotel combined with the seclusion of a private apartment. It is a concept that should be more widely imitated. Built in 1735 for a wealthy merchant, Fountain House is a Palladian mansion on a busy road close to the Assembly Rooms and the Roman Baths. In 1987 it opened as an all-suite hotel, each with one, two or three bedrooms, one or two bathrooms, fully equipped kitchens (everything from corkscrew to dishwasher) and sitting/dining area. It is perfect for those on a long stay, and for those who do not wish to eat out all the time. As a starter pack, each suite comes equipped with a basket of gourmet goodies and the fridge is stocked with staples. Continental breakfast and a newspaper are delivered each morning. There is also a daily maid plus laundry and valet service.

The superior suites are very stylish, with well-chosen fabrics and a mix of antique and contemporary furniture; Number 11 has a large stone fireplace and stairs up to a platform gallery bedroom. The standard suites, while equally well-equipped, are more mass-market modern in design. All the bathrooms are smartly tiled and have good toiletries.

There are no public areas other than the marble-floored entrance lobby. The suites have individual front doors, access by entry phone and the services of a resident concierge.

◐ Open all year

⬀ Take the A36 until you reach the T-junction with the A4. Turn right, and, at the 2nd major set

of traffic lights, turn right again into Lansdown Road. Fountain House is 50 yards to the right. Private car park

🛏 15 suites (2 twin, 4 double, 1 four-poster, 7 family, 1 annexe – 3 beds); all with bathroom/WC, TV, room service, hair-dryer, mini-bar, baby-listening, ironing facilities

◈ Laundry facilities; babysitting by arrangement

⬤ No wheelchair access

▦ Access, Amex, Diners, Visa

£ Single occupancy £92, twin/double £120, four-poster/family suite £168, annexe suite (3 beds) £225; deposit required

---

Haydon House

9 BLOOMFIELD PARK, BATH, AVON BA2 2BY
TEL: BATH (0225) 429862 (and fax)

Lavishly furnished rooms in a stylish Edwardian guesthouse, noted for hospitality, good breakfasts and an exquisite garden.

A mini Kew Gardens surrounds this semi-detached Edwardian villa in a quiet Bath suburb. Evidence of green fingers is all around as you walk up a path bordered with lush vegetation, well-established shrubs and enviable hanging baskets. Magdalene Ashman's talent for creating a civilised retreat from the hustle of the tourist trail also extends within the house: it is an immaculate, sophisticated family home, with high standards of hospitality. There are four bedrooms, three doubles and a twin. Room Four, one of the two smaller doubles, is a pretty pink and white room, with rose chintz material. White louvred doors open up to reveal a minute shower and loo cubicle, a miracle of small-scale logistics. Room Two, the large front twin, is furnished in contemporary apricot fabrics, and has a matching apricot tiled bathroom. As well as the usual choice, all bedrooms have herbal teas, decanters of sherry, sweets and home-made shortbread.

The gracious downstairs lounge is filled with antiques, sofas, books and magazines. Doors lead out on to a patio, where breakfast can be taken in clement weather. More usually, this is served in the elegant dining-room around a polished oval table. Porridge with whisky, and scrambled egg with smoked salmon are popular choices. One visitor wrote ecstatically in the visitors' book that breakfasts at home were never like this – but then he did come from Kiev.

◖ Open all year

⤴ From Bath centre follow signs for the A367 Exeter road and up Wells road for ½ mile. The A367 turns right into a shopping area with the Bear pub on the right. At the end of a short dual carriageway, fork right into Bloomfield Road and second right into Bloomfield Park. On-street parking

🛏 1 twin, 3 double; most with shower/WC, 1 double with bathroom/WC; TV, hair-dryer in all rooms; trouser press on request

◈ Dining-room, lounge, study; golf, tennis, riding, other sports nearby

⊖ No wheelchair access; children by arrangement only; no dogs; no smoking

▭ Access, Amex, Visa

£ Single occupancy of twin/double £40 to £48, twin/double £55 to £65; deposit required. Special breaks available

---

Holly Lodge

8 UPPER OLDFIELD PARK, BATH, AVON BA2 3JZ
TEL: BATH (0225) 424042   FAX: (0225) 481138

Luxurious guesthouse run with professional sparkle, where the style starts at breakfast.

Although Holly Lodge seems in perfect, pristine condition, Carrolle Sellick says she's always doing something new to her de-luxe bed and breakfast. In fact, her regular guests have come to expect it, and tend to greet her on arrival by asking what's changed since their last visit?

During the day, there are good views down the valley to Bath from the detached Victorian house; at night, the terraced garden, gazebo and car park are well lit. Inside, the conservatory, decorated in acid-drop limes and lemons, with white wicker furniture, must be one of the sunniest breakfast spots in town. And when breakfast includes oranges in Cointreau and scrambled egg with smoked salmon, it gets the day off to a doubly cheerful start.

The house is immaculately groomed and styled. However, amongst the antiques, capacious sofas and dramatic floral arrangements, Carrolle seems to have a soft spot for assorted china and stuffed animals. Outsize white elephant lamp-bases, snail pot-plant holders, porcelain cats and eagles reign downstairs, whilst the bedrooms are home to a collection of soft monkeys, lions and dormice. The bedrooms vary in size and shape and are individually designed and very well-equipped. All have 100 per cent cotton bedlinen, and full-sized bathsheets in the chic bathrooms. Room 3 is particularly arresting; a double decorated in navy blue and white, with a hand-crafted, modern Egyptian-styled four-poster. Other bedrooms are more floral – including Room 5, a pretty single in lemon and green chintz.

◑ Open all year

↗ ½ mile south-west of Bath city centre, off the A367 Wells Road. Private car park

🛏 1 single, 2 twin, 3 four-poster; all with bathroom/WC, exc single with shower/WC; TV, room service, hair-dryer, trouser press, baby-listening in all rooms

◈ Breakfast room, lounge, conservatory; golf, tennis, other sports nearby

⊖ No wheelchair access; no dogs; no smoking

▭ Access, Amex, Diners, Visa

£ Single £46 to £48, single occupancy of twin/double £50 to £55, twin/double £70 to £75, four-poster £70 to £85; deposit required

Paradise House

88 HOLLOWAY, BATH, AVON BA2 4PX
TEL: BATH (0225) 317723   FAX: (0225) 482005

Book well ahead for this popular bed and breakfast with commanding views of Bath from the terraced garden.

A fat black cat dozes in the shade, the swallows have returned to nest, and all Bath lies glowing honey-gold at your feet. On a sunny day, Paradise indeed seems close at hand, and it's no wonder that guests regularly return to this delightful eighteenth-century house. The owners, David and Janet Cutting, have worked hard to bring a sense of light and peace to the interior, stripping doors and uncovering fireplaces in their process of restoration. Breakfasts are taken in a pleasant room with lacy cloths, a parquet floor and framed prints. Guests also have the use of a lovely sitting-room that has arched french windows opening on to the lawn.

Some of the well-furnished bedrooms also share the panoramic outlook. Rooms Three and Six are attractive twins, with bay windows that enhance the view and sophisticated colourings. All rooms are *en suite*, except for Room Six, which shares a bathroom with Room Five, making them popular with family groups. Bathrooms vary from cupboard-size to grandiose; Room Three, for instance, has a splendid freestanding bathtub, along with twin washbasins. Plans are still in hand to build an extra garden room.

The house is situated in a quiet cul-de-sac on the site of the ancient Roman Fosse Way where it plunges steeply down towards the city. It is only a seven-minute descent from Paradise, but an uphill task to return. The moral is – take a taxi.

◖ Open all year, exc Xmas period

⚡ Follow A36 Bristol road into Bath. Take A367 Exeter road up hill. Holloway is third turning on left. Then take left fork downhill into cul-de-sac. Private car park

🛏 4 twin, 4 double, 1 family room; most with bathroom/WC, some with shower/WC; TV, room service, hair-dryer in all rooms

◈ Breakfast room, lounge; golf, fishing, other sports nearby

⊖ No wheelchair access; no dogs

▭ Access, Amex, Visa

£ Single occupancy of twin/double £35 to £50, twin/double £48 to £65, family room £70 to £75; deposit required. Special breaks available

---

The Guide *office can quickly spot when a hotelier is encouraging customers to write a letter recommending inclusion – and sadly, several hotels have been doing this in 1993. Such reports do not further a hotel's cause.*

Queensberry Hotel ☆

COUNTY
HOTEL
OF THE
YEAR

RUSSEL STREET, BATH, AVON BA1 2QF
TEL: BATH (0225) 447928   TELEX: 445628 QNSBRY G
FAX: (0225) 446065

Intimate town-house hotel in the heart of Georgian Bath. Modern cooking in the Olive Tree Restaurant.

The Queensberry has just about everything one would want from a town-house hotel. It is particularly welcome in Bath, where it fills a niche between the mega de-luxe and the B&B league.

Built by John Wood in 1772 for the Marquis of Queensberry, the three terraced houses are in a quiet street close by the Assembly Rooms. Stephen and Penny Ross have brought with them the expertise and professionalism of their previous residence, Homewood Park, but have given the Queensberry a much more informal air.

The classical Regency architecture, with original stucco ceilings and ornate cornices, is matched by a cool contemporary décor that mixes period pieces with modern sculpture and prints. A small, clubby bar leads through to a bijou patio garden, lined with lavender and jasmine, that is a sun-filled sanctum from city streets. A front, ground-floor drawing-room is the place for wintry afternoon teas, understated and elegant in urbane cream and greeny/grey tones.

Bedrooms are spacious and decorative, and even the smallest has room for table and sofa. Each is a variation on a theme, softly coloured with draped fabric behind the beds, cream woven spreads, crisp cotton sheets and fresh flowers. Bathrooms are equally well-equipped. Top-floor rooms have lower ceilings and more of an attic feel with sloping walls, but are cosy and pretty. If lucky, you may get to stay in either Room 7 or Room 8. These are the former first-floor drawing-rooms, each with three long sash windows, space for king-size bed, sofa, two armchairs, table, chairs, bureau, outsize wardrobe and still enough room to hold a small cocktail party.

The Olive Tree Restaurant in the basement breathes Mediterranean warmth and colour. Rag-rolled walls, tiled floor and modern, angular wood chairs are the bistro-style setting for simple, unflashy, freshly flavoured and cleanly defined food at sensible prices. The daily-changing set lunch and dinner menus, in particular, offer exceptional value. First courses may offer crab and saffron terrine with tomato and chive vinaigrette, or fish soup, rouille and croûtons; typical main courses may include Tuscan chicken, loin of pork roasted with lemon, garlic and sweet peppers or duck breast with spiced mango. Desserts may include lemon tart, compôte of figs and oranges in port served with Greek yogurt and excellent home-made ice-cream. The wine list is short and sensible.

◑ *Open all year, exc Xmas period*

↗ *Russel Street is just north of the Assembly Rooms, just to the*

north of the centre of Bath. On-street parking

🛏 *11 twin, 11 double; all with*

bathroom/WC, exc 1 twin with shower/WC; TV, room service, hair-dryer, baby-listening in all rooms; no tea/coffee-making facilities in rooms

 Restaurant, bar, lounge; conference facilities (max 16 people residential and non-residential); golf, tennis, other sports nearby; babysitting by arrangement

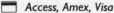 No wheelchair access; no dogs

Access, Amex, Visa

Single occupancy of twin/double £89, twin/double £89 to £149, family room rate £159. Cooked B £7.50; set L £10.50, D £17.50; alc L £15, D £25 (prices till Apr 94). Special breaks available

Royal Crescent

16 ROYAL CRESCENT, BATH, AVON BA1 2LS
TEL: BATH (0225) 319090   TELEX: 444251 ROCRES G
FAX: (0225) 339401

A luxurious re-creation of Regency splendour makes for a memorable if costly stay.

This, of course, is simply the best address in Bath – and, arguably, the best room with the best view at the best address is Room Eight, the first-floor double at the exact epicentre of John Wood's visionary sweep of terraced houses. This exquisitely furnished lemon and green room is the only one with a curved sash window (check from the outside), so that inside one can justifiably claim to be at the very heart of Georgian Bath. Others may argue the merits of suites such as the John Wood, with balustraded steps up to the canopied bed, the Duke of York, with ravishing ceilings, the Jane Austen, with its own conservatory, or the Beau Nash with conservatory and Jacuzzi. But even the standard rooms are impeccably styled.

Much research has gone into the interior design of this superb hotel in order to re-create as much as possible the furnishings and fabrics of the period. The result, whether in the two main linked houses or in the Pavilion and Dower House, makes a formal but unstarchy atmosphere. As one cool guest wrote in the visitors' book, 'Rock on John Wood!'

The lush, mature garden at the back is another surprise; a matchless spot for tea on the lawn, summer cocktails or a dip in the heated plunge pool. Morning coffee can be taken in the front drawing-room, browsing through copies of the *International Herald Tribune* and graciously ignoring the gawking tourists in open-topped double-decker buses and crocodiles of fractious French schoolchildren slowly filing by. Dinners are formal affairs in the Dower House Restaurant. The food is serious, complex, highly rated and expensive.

This is a hotel of some distinction; there can be few others that boast a printed guide to their own art collection. On arrival, aim for the giant magnolia tree rising from the basement and let the uniformed flunkeys do the rest. Luggage and parking, as one reader expressed with satisfaction, will all be instantly and efficiently dealt with.

◑ Open all year

⤴ Close to Bath town centre, on the Royal Crescent. Private car park and on-street parking

🛏 2 single, 11 twin, 13 double, 2 four-poster, 14 suites; all with bathroom/WC (some suites with Jacuzzi), TV, room service, hair-dryer, trouser press, baby-listening; tea/coffee-making facilities on request

◈ Restaurant, bar, 3 lounges, conservatory; conference facilities (max 60 people residential and non-residential); heated plunge pool (May to Oct)

at hotel, golf, tennis, other sports nearby; babysitting. Wheelchair access to hotel (1 step) and restaurant, 4 ground-floor bedrooms, 1 specially equipped for disabled people

⊖ No children under 7 at dinner; no dogs

▭ Access, Amex, Diners, Visa

£ Single £98, single occupancy of twin/double £115, twin/double/four-poster £160 to £195, suite £265 to £325; deposit required. Cooked B £5; set L £14.50/£18.50, D £28; alc D from £35. Special breaks available

Sydney Gardens

SYDNEY ROAD, BATH, AVON BA2 6NT
TEL: BATH (0225) 464818/445362

Convenient access to the city centre makes this artistic, easy-going guesthouse a favourite choice.

Sydney Gardens' brochure description of itself as 'The House in the Park' is a shade disingenuous, as it is also the 'House on the side of the road which runs along the park'. Nonetheless, direct access to the park brings Great Pulteney Street within easy level walking distance, a considerable bonus in a hilly city. It also has the advantage of good views from many of the rooms.

The listed, Italianate Victorian house, run by Stanley and Diane Smithson, makes a restful base for a stay in Bath. The pleasant rooms are given extra interest by Stanley's original paintings and witty wall clock sculptures. The comfortable, well-proportioned, sunny yellow lounge also has a piano, on which visiting concert pianists are able to give impromptu recitals to staff and guests.

Bedrooms are pleasantly furnished with lots of stripped pine and period-style wallpaper. None of the rooms, in Stanley's words, are 'meanly sized'. They all have room for easy chairs, although bathrooms tend to be on the small side. Room 3, an attractive twin with amusing pictures, has the best view over park and city.

○ Open all year, exc 18 to 26 Dec and 2 to 27 Jan

◩ On the A36 ring road in Bath. Near the Holburne Museum. Private car park

🛏 2 twin, 3 double, 1 family room; all with bathroom/WC, TV, hairdryer

◈ Breakfast room, lounge; tennis, riding, other sports nearby

⊖ No wheelchair access; no children under 4; no dogs in public rooms; no smoking

▭ Access, Visa

£ Single occupancy of twin/double £45 to £59, twin/double £55 to £69; deposit required. Special breaks available

---

BATHFORD AVON   **MAP 9**

Eagle House

23 CHURCH STREET, BATHFORD, NR BATH, AVON BA1 7RS
TEL: BATH (0225) 859946

Gracious bed and breakfast in a splendid Georgian house with fine views.

Bathford is a conservation area, so there is no sign to indicate that Eagle House takes guests and first-time arrivals are asked to make sure they don't knock at the private Eagle Lodge nearby. John and Rosamund Napier have worked hard to cultivate relaxed and comfortable surroundings for their guests in this grand house. The hallway is a splendid affair, with a stone floor and sweeping staircase. The top of the stairs is encased by sturdy protective doors, a relic from the house's previous incarnation as a home for young offenders. The bedrooms, which are decorated in light colours and furnished with a mix of pieces, are generally larger at the back of the house, where they also have the better views.

Downstairs, the lounge is huge, with a marble fireplace and light cream carpet. Newspapers and a file of recommended local restaurants and pubs are provided for guests, as is a CD-player and a selection of discs. The view from the lounge is of the garden, which has a large lawn with a child's sandpit; look carefully and you will spot a tree-house as well. At the bottom of the garden is a purpose-built cottage where two double bedrooms share an interesting octagonal sitting-room and small kitchen.

Guests who stay in the main house take breakfast in the yellow and brown dining-room. Cereals are displayed on a dresser and a cooked breakfast is available on request.

○ Open all year, exc 23 Dec to 4 Jan

◩ Leave the A4 ¼ mile east of Batheaston on the A363 to Bradford-on-Avon. Stay only 150 yards on the A363, then fork left up Bathford Hill. After 300 yards turn first right into Church Street. Eagle House is 200 yards along on the right. Private car park

🛏 1 single, 2 twin, 3 double, 1 family room, 1 suite (some in cottages); all with bathroom/WC, exc single with shower/WC;

TV, hair-dryer, baby-listening in all rooms

◇ Breakfast room, lounge; conference facilities (max 14 people residential and non-residential); croquet at hotel, other sports nearby; babysitting

⊖ No wheelchair access; dogs

discouraged in public rooms

▭ None accepted

£ Single £29 to £39, twin/double £42 to £64, family room £56 to £66, suite £70 to £90 (prices till Easter 94). Special breaks available

The Orchard

80 HIGH STREET, BATHFORD, NR BATH, AVON BA1 7TG
TEL: BATH (0225) 858765

A restful house in pretty gardens that makes a good base for exploring Bath.

It is the garden that impresses first as you drive through the wrought-iron gates and up to the front door of this fine Georgian house on Bathford's main street. The square sandstone building stands amid lawn, rose bushes, magnolias and shrubs which are kept in trim by friendly hosts John and Olga London.

The Orchard has the two advantages of Georgian design: high ceilings and large windows. Consequently, the interior is light, bright and airy and the decoration, which is in light shades, helps to emphasise this. The lounge is in pink with easy chairs and a chaise-longue grouped around the fireplace; during summer, french windows are opened on to a small patio where tea is served. Bedrooms and bathrooms are all large and decorated in pinks or beige. There is a further room in the Folly.

Breakfasts are taken together at one table in the dining-room. A full spread which includes home-made muesli, free-range eggs and whole-meal toast will set you up for a day's sightseeing in Bath, just three miles away.

◑ Closed Dec to Feb

↗ Take the A4 to Bathford, go under bridge, and turn left up the hill at the Crown pub. The Orchard is 150 yards beyond the Inn pub on the right-hand side. Private car park

🛏 2 twin, 2 double; all with bathroom/WC, TV; no tea/coffee-making facilities in rooms

◇ Breakfast room, lounge; tennis, riding, other sports nearby

⊖ No wheelchair access; no children under 11; no dogs; no smoking in bedrooms

▭ None accepted

£ Twin/double £47 to £58; deposit required

The Guide *is totally independent, accepts no free hospitality, and survives on the number of copies sold each year.*

BATTLE EAST SUSSEX   **MAP 8**

Powdermills

POWDERMILL LANE, BATTLE, EAST SUSSEX TN33 0SP
TEL: BATTLE (0424) 775511   FAX: (0424) 774540

An elegantly furnished, informal country house with fascinating grounds to explore.

For 200 years Powdermills was the centre of a thriving gunpowder industry until the Duke of Cleveland refused to renew the lease in 1874 because of the constant danger of explosions. Reminders of the mills still dot the grounds, including the remains of a chimney, a cistern and a small outhouse which has been turned into a bar, but you're more likely to notice some of the other features of the 150 acres of parks and woodland: a flock of Soay sheep from the Hebrides, abundant wildfowl, a seven-acre lake filled with carp, a gazebo, statues and columns.

Douglas and Julie Cowpland have furnished their white Georgian manor with a good measure of individuality and flair, even in the recent, harmonious red-brick additions (plans for a further six bedrooms are well under way). An adventurous and reasonably priced three-course menu, with a full vegetarian alternative, is offered in the conservatory-style Orangery, which has large french windows overlooking the terrace and swimming-pool. If you don't want to move from your leather armchair in the Georgian-style library, a light lunch can be brought to you. Correspondents this year praised the bedrooms, the views and the food, but expressed some reservations about the service – slow when the restaurant was full and a slip in standards whilst the owners were away.

◖ Open all year; restaurant closed Sun eve

⚡ Centrally located in Battle. Powdermill Lane leads off the A21 opposite Battle railway station. Private car park

🛏 5 twin, 9 double, 1 four-poster, 1 suite; most with bathroom/WC, some with shower/WC; TV, room service, hair-dryer, trouser press, baby-listening in all rooms; no tea/coffee-making facilities in rooms

◈ 2 restaurants, 2 bars, lounge, TV room, drying room, library; conference facilities (max 60 people non-residential, 16 residential); fishing, unheated outdoor pool (in season) at hotel, other sports nearby. Wheelchair access to hotel (ramp), restaurant and WC (F), 3 ground-floor bedrooms

● No children in restaurant eves

▭ Access, Amex, Diners, Visa

£ Single occupancy of twin/double £40 to £45, twin/double £65 to £70, four-poster £70 to £85, suite £95 to £105; deposit required. Set L £13.50, D £16; alc D £25 to £28. Special breaks available

See our selection of what we consider to be the best hotels in various counties in Hotels of the Year *(page 16).*

Bridge House

3 PROUT BRIDGE, BEAMINSTER, DORSET DT8 3AY
TEL: BEAMINSTER (0308) 862200   FAX: (0308) 863700

*Medium-priced hotel of hotchpotch historic interest. Smart
dining-room but other public rooms lack atmosphere.*

Beaminster is a charming little town and an ideal base for exploring
Thomas Hardy's west Dorset countryside. The privately owned and
well-managed Bridge Hotel dates back, in part, to the thirteenth century.
Tudor mullioned stone windows face on to the main road from solid two
foot-thick stone walls. Bedroom 3 has a blocked-up priests' hole, while
the Georgian, a spacious double, has sash windows dating from the time
'new' extensions were added. These bedrooms are in the main body of
the house, others are in the coach house or the new wing. The latter are
the smartest, decorated in flowery fabrics, with modern bathrooms.
Coach House rooms are cosy but simpler.

    The lounge and bar area are disappointingly plain, with little character
given the historic setting; the uncomfortable suite in the lounge has seen
better days. Dinner in the beamed and panelled dining-room with Adam
fireplace is simply cooked but there can be a tendency towards exces-
sively creamy sauces. Typical offerings might include cauliflower and
Stilton soup, twice-baked crab soufflé, skate in saffron sauce, and pork in
mustard grain sauce. As an alternative to the sugary desserts, there is a
choice of three good regional cheeses. On busy nights, meals are also
served in the conservatory extension, while breakfasts are taken in a small
room overlooking the walled garden.

◐   *Open all year*

↗   *In the centre of Beaminster,
down the hill from the town
square. Private car park*

🛏   *1 single, 4 twin, 8 double, 1
family room; all with bathroom/
WC, exc single and 1 double
with shower/WC; TV, room
service in all rooms; hair-dryer
on request*

◇   *Dining-room, bar, lounge,
conservatory, sun room;
conference facilities (max 14
people residential and non-
residential); golf, tennis, other*

*sports nearby. Wheelchair access
to hotel (no steps) and dining-
room, 4 ground-floor bedrooms*

⊖   *No dogs in public rooms and
accompanied only in bedrooms;
no smoking in dining-room*

▭   *Access, Amex, Diners, JCB, Visa*

£   *Single £31, single occupancy of
twin/double £45 to £55, twin/
double £56 to £80, de-luxe room
£92, family room from £70;
deposit required. Set L £10, D
£16.50; alc L £16.50, D £19.50.
Special breaks available*

See page 817 for other hotels worthy of inclusion in our Visitors' Book.

Hams Plot

6 BRIDPORT ROAD, BEAMINSTER, DORSET DT8 3LU
TEL: BEAMINSTER (0308) 862979

Weekenders, walkers, gardeners and tennis players will all love this charming Regency bed and breakfast.

Hams Plot transports one back to a sunny between-the-wars world of tennis parties and tea with the vicar; one half-expects Miss Marple to cycle down the drive at any moment or Inspector Alleyn to appear through the french windows. Hams Plot (the word is an Anglo-Saxon term for water meadow) used to belong to Giles Dearlove's parents. After a spell in London, he has returned home and is an enthusiastic champion of the attractions of the surrounding Wessex countryside.

The white stucco Regency house, built in the romantic fashion after the Napoleonic wars, with wrought-iron balconies and verandas, stands in two acres of organic grounds. As well as a wildflower garden and mature trees, there is a stream, croquet lawn and swimming-pool. Judy Dearlove is a passionate gardener, and her own dried flowers decorate the house. She also plays regularly on the hard tennis court and has ambitions to restore the grass court.

The interior of the house is quite delightful in an unexpected, charmingly old-fashioned way. Sip a sloe gin in the library and settle back in the solid armchairs to browse through the collection of Hardy novels or plan a ramble from Giles' excellent set of maps and guides; or take tea in the sitting-room, with its Victorian watercolours and Italianate settees, and admire the view of Beaminster's ancient church tower.

The three bedrooms are equally comfortable retreats, with bathrooms converted from former dressing rooms. The good-quality beds have electric blankets and duvets, although blankets can be supplied on request. Burcombe, one of two large front doubles, has a good mahogany wardrobe, Edwardian armchairs and french windows opening on to the balcony that runs the length of the house.

◑ Closed end Oct to end Mar

↗ Hams Plot is down the hill from the market-place, opposite the B3163 to Maiden Newton. Private car park

🛏 1 twin, 2 double; all with bathroom/WC, exc 1 double with shower/WC; hair-dryer in all rooms

◇ Breakfast room, lounge, library; tennis, croquet, unheated outdoor swimming-pool at hotel, other sports nearby

⊖ No wheelchair access; no children under 10; no dogs; no smoking in public rooms

▭ None accepted

£ Twin/double £45 to £55; deposit required

Please let us know if an establishment has changed hands.

Montagu Arms

PALACE LANE, BEAULIEU, HAMPSHIRE SO42 7ZL
TEL: LYMINGTON (0590) 612324 FAX: (0590) 612188

A creeper-clad country hotel in a tourist honeypot.

After starting life as staff accommodation for the nearby abbey, the Montagu Arms became an inn in the eighteenth century. Set in a picturesque village overlooking the Beaulieu River, it can get a little noisy in the daytime because of the stream of tourists visiting the New Forest, the National Motor Museum and Beaulieu Palace House.

With its climbing creepers, leaded windows and hunting-dog statues, the façade leads you to expect a stereotypical country-house hotel – but the interior, fortunately, is more lively and varied than that. Although reception is dark, Gothic and restrained, the lounge is light and airy, with white-painted wood panels around a huge brick fireplace and upright armchairs and sofas. Off the lounge you'll find a colourful library bar with an imposing oak counter, well-stocked with whiskies and books, and a run-of-the-mill conservatory. The formal restaurant overlooking the small terraced garden has low beams, low lighting and crisp white tablecloths, and serves a varied three-course gourmet dinner menu.

Half the oak trees of the New Forest seem to have gone into the bedroom corridors: from the winding staircase to the doors, panels and windowsills, the light, rich wood dominates the décor (although rather perversely each bedroom is named after a different type of wood). Antique furniture, dried flowers and floral patterns embellish the tidy, well-proportioned rooms, and bathrooms are traditional white with the full complement of toiletries. Most singles overlook the garden.

◐ Open all year

⤢ Leave the M27 at Junction 3 and follow signs for Beaulieu. The hotel is on the left as you enter the village. Private car park

🛏 4 single, 3 twin, 9 double, 3 four-poster, 2 family rooms, 3 suites; all with bathroom/WC, TV, room service, hair-dryer, trouser press, baby-listening; no tea/coffee-making facilities in rooms

◇ Restaurant, 2 bars, lounge, library, conservatory;

conference facilities (max 45 people non-residential, 24 residential); fishing, golf, other sports nearby

⊖ No wheelchair access; no dogs in public rooms

▭ Access, Amex, Diners, Visa

£ Single £68, single occupancy of twin/double £76 to £80, twin/double £96 to £110, four-poster/family room £130, suite £166; deposit required. Set L £15, D £19/£24. Special breaks available

*Are you aware of your rights as a consumer when you book into a hotel?
Check them out on page 837.*

BEERCROCOMBE SOMERSET   **MAP 10**

Frog Street Farm ☆

BEERCROCOMBE, NR TAUNTON, SOMERSET TA3 6AF
TEL: TAUNTON (0823) 480430

Attractive Somerset long-house on a working farm in the middle of nowhere.

Frog Street Farm's unlikely name has more to do with the Anglo-Saxon words for 'meeting place' than with any amphibious residents; you'll need good eyesight to catch the small sign pointing to it which highlights the herd of Friesian cows rather than Veronica Cole's small enterprise. In good old farmhouse tradition the porch of a long, low grey stone building dating back to 1436 opens straight into the dining-room with its big fireplace and the smell of cooking wafting from the Aga. Veronica is a dab hand at baking and uses farm produce such as home-grown vegetables, free-range eggs and home-reared beef where possible; the farm is not licensed so you need to bring your own tipple. An even bigger fireplace complete with built-in stone seats features in a lounge which also has a Jacobean panelled screen and a four-seater settee. For greater intimacy, another (smaller) lounge lurks behind the screen.

Of the three bedrooms, the best, a veritable bargain, is really a suite, with the television in the lounge downstairs and twin beds beneath a sloping ceiling upstairs. The other rooms are above the main lounge; one, with an enormous bathroom and adjoining twin room.

◑   *Closed Nov to end Feb*

⤢   *Leave the M5 at Junction 25 and take the Chard/Ilminster road. Leave at Hatch Beauchamp and, by the Hatch Inn, take Station Road for 1 mile. Private car park*

🛏   *3 double; 2 with bathroom/WC, 1 with shower/WC; TV in all rooms*

◈   *Dining-room, 3 lounges, drying-room; fishing, outdoor heated swimming-pool at hotel, other sports nearby*

⊖   *No wheelchair access; no children under 11; no dogs; no smoking*

▭   *None accepted*

£   *Single occupancy of double £27, twin/double £52. Set D £16. Special breaks available*

I was talking to a hotelier in Wales, when she suddenly came out with: 'People don't make their beds themselves any more – it makes a lot of extra work for me, with my bad back.' I suggested, timidly, that perhaps one of the reasons for going away to a hotel was that you didn't have to make your own bed. 'I always do,' she said, 'I like to leave a place exactly as I found it, so I always make the bed and wash the cups out.'

Blue Bell

MARKET SQUARE, BELFORD, NORTHUMBERLAND NE70 7NE
TEL: BELFORD (0668) 213543   FAX: (0668) 213787

A welcoming creeper-clad inn close to the glorious scenery of the Cheviots.

Stencilled bluebells adorn the window boxes that cheer up the sturdy exterior of this traditional eighteenth-century village-centre inn, and there is a chance that you'll find the real thing in the gardens to the rear – a source of the blooms that decorate every part of the hotel. A witty brochure offers 'free of charge spades, forks and hoes to those guests who would like to indulge in a little therapeutic activity!' If your inclinations are rather more sedentary you'll find plenty of places to relax, from the lady-like lounge with its soothing greens and pinks, Adam-style fireplace and sentimental prints to a cosy bar with stuffed birds and a beaten copper chimney-breast. Diners can choose between a cheerful buttery or the more formal Garden Restaurant overlooking the lawns. Crystal and candlesticks gleam on the polished wood of locally crafted tables, setting the tone for a menu that relies heavily on fresh local produce augmented by home-grown fruit and vegetables.

Bedrooms are roomy, well-equipped, and individually decorated in a bright, fresh style, sometimes with reproduction antiques and crown canopies over the beds. Bathroom décor may be less than up to date.

◑ Open all year

🔁 Belford is 1 mile off the A1, 40 miles north of Newcastle upon Tyne. Private car park

🛏 1 single, 8 twin, 7 double, 1 four-poster; most with bathroom/WC, some with shower/WC; TV, room service, hair-dryer, trouser press

◈ 2 restaurants, 2 bars, lounge, games room; conference facilities (max 130 people non-residential, 17 residential);

fishing, golf, other sports nearby. Wheelchair access to hotel (2 steps) and 2 ground-floor bedrooms, 1 specially equipped for disabled people

⊖ No dogs in public rooms

▭ Access, Amex, Visa

£ Single £42, single occupancy of twin/double £54, twin/double £80, four-poster £88, family room £72. Set D £17; alc L £12, D £22. Special breaks available

---

All entries in the Guide *are rewritten every year, not least because standards fluctuate. Don't trust an out-of-date* Guide.

BENENDEN KENT   **MAP 8**

Crit Hall

CRANBROOK ROAD, BENENDEN, KENT TN17 4EU
TEL: CRANBROOK (0580) 240609   FAX: (0580) 241743

A red-brick Georgian country house with caring and attentive hosts.

Don't push or turn the doorbell, pull it! The jangling inside will bring out one of the Sleighs, either Sara or Bill, followed by excited terriers Rosie and Cider. They have been here since the end of 1989 and obviously enjoy welcoming people into their home. Service is definitely personal, with guests dining together round the polished mahogany table in the dining-room; dinner is quite a formal event, with Bill serving and Sara cooking. The menu of the evening is discussed informally in the flagstoned kitchen at breakfast as Sara puts forward some suggestions of what her guests might like. She calls her food 'new English cuisine', a lighter version of traditional local dishes, using local produce as far as possible. One of her favourite menus is avocado, tomato and mozzarella salad, followed by fillet of lemon sole gratinée with coriander and tartare sauce and a dessert of ginger in honey ice-cream.

The lounge is pleasant to relax in, with a pastel marble fireplace, pale lemon walls and antique furniture, while the small, bright and airy conservatory is a good place to sit with a book. Beds are turned down of an evening and the rooms are fresh, in pastel shades. All are homely and have good-sized bathrooms.

◐ Open all year, exc mid-Dec to mid-Jan

↗ As you travel west on B2086 from centre of Benenden, Crit Hall is 1 mile on the left. Private car park

🛏 3 twin; 2 with bathroom/WC, 1 with shower/WC; TV, room service, hair-dryer in all rooms

◇ Dining-room, lounge, TV room, drying room, conservatory; fishing, golf, other sports nearby

⊖ No wheelchair access; no children under 12; no dogs; no smoking

▭ None accepted

💷 Single occupancy of twin/double £28, twin/double £43. Set D £15 (7.30pm)

There is nothing which has yet been contrived by man, by which so much happiness is produced as by a good tavern or inn.

Dr Samuel Johnson

BEPTON WEST SUSSEX   **MAP 9**

Park House

BEPTON, MIDHURST, WEST SUSSEX GU29 0JB
TEL: MIDHURST (0730) 812880   FAX: (0730) 815643

A colourful, sociable country hotel with lots of jolly garden sports.

Almost in the shadow of the South Downs, Park House manages to
attract a highly mixed bag in the summer, as proclaimed by the photos
which line the walls of the small, deep-red honesty bar: actors doing a
season at Chichester Festival Theatre, turf devotees down for Glorious
Goodwood and polo players battling it out at Cowdray Park. The
grounds of this smart, white-painted Victorian house also contain plenty
of opportunity for sporting competition in the form of grass tennis courts,
a putting course, a croquet lawn and a swimming-pool.

The recipe is long-established and clearly successful. Mrs O'Brien,
who has owned and managed the hotel for over 40 years, efficiently
conjures up the relaxed feel of a private residence. Amongst the public
rooms, the star turn is the large drawing-room, filled with comfy sofas
and books, which manages to be both refreshing and elegant in its
primary colours. All meals are served in the soothing red dining-room.
Although the strong colours of their décor look a bit dated, the bedrooms
are generally spacious, well-lit and unfussily comfortable.

◐ Open all year

⤢ Off the Midhurst to Bepton road
(B226). Private car park

🛏 I single, 5 twin, 3 double, I
family room, I suite; most with
bathroom/WC, some with
shower/WC; TV, room service,
hair-dryer, trouser press in all
rooms

◈ Dining-room, bar, lounge, TV
room; putting lawn, tennis,
croquet, heated outdoor

swimming-pool at hotel, other
sports nearby. Wheelchair access
to hotel (2 steps), dining-room
and WC (unisex), I ground-floor
bedroom

⊖ No dogs in dining-room

▭ Access, Amex, Visa

£ Single £52 to £54, single
occupancy of twin/double £52 to
£54, twin/double £90 to £94,
family room/suite £150. Set L
£13.50, D £17.50

BETHERSDEN KENT   **MAP 8**

Little Hodgeham

SMARDEN ROAD, BETHERSDEN, ASHFORD, KENT TN26 3HE
TEL: HIGH HALDEN (0233) 850323

Relaxed country living courtesy of an accomplished hostess.

'A magical place', 'a fairytale cottage', 'a charming building' with 'a
unique flavour' – this is just some of the praise heaped on Little

Hodgeham by our readers. Set among peaceful woods and arable fields, the cottage is almost too good to be true. Roses climb the walls, tulips sprout from the front beds, and the back garden is a riot of colour around a duck pond and fountains (there's also an attractive swimming-pool). But that's not the whole story, for Australian-born owner Erica Wallace presides like a house-party hostess, welcoming guests, cooking their food and entertaining them over dinner. Although looking after a stream of summer guests in this way must be a strain, Erica takes it in her stride: 'A wonderful hostess,' write our correspondents, 'a marvellous raconteur' and 'a first-rate Cordon Bleu chef'.

The country-house ambience is boosted by the style of the 500-year-old cottage. Bedrooms have oak doors and beams, log fires and leaded windows, enlivened by fresh, summery colour schemes. There is one room done out in lilac, with a four-poster bed and, on a platform beneath the sloping roof, two singles. As well as the usual comforts of a hotel, you'll find Crown Derby tea sets, flowers, hand-embroidered pillow slips and extra cushions piled decadently on the beds. But perhaps the most telling remark has come from readers in Australia, who found their hostess to be 'most considerate of all our needs – even those we did not articulate'.

- *Open mid-Mar to 1 Sept*
- *10 miles west of Ashford on the A28 Bethersden road. Turn right at the Bull pub and go towards Smarden for 2 miles; the house is on the right. Private car park*
- *1 twin, 1 double, 1 four-poster; all with bathroom/WC, exc double with shower/WC; hair-dryer in all rooms*
- *Dining-room, lounge, TV room, drying room, library, conservatory; fishing, unheated swimming-pool at hotel, other sports nearby*
- *No wheelchair access; children by arrangement only; dogs by arrangement only*
- *None accepted*
- *Single occupancy of twin/double £58, twin/double/four-poster £95 (rates inc dinner); deposit required. Special breaks available*

BIBURY GLOUCESTERSHIRE   **MAP 9**

Bibury Court

BIBURY, NR CIRENCESTER, GLOUCESTERSHIRE GL7 5NT
TEL: CIRENCESTER (0285) 740337   FAX: (0285) 740660

An old friend – a little battered inside, but a beautiful country house nonetheless and a lovely setting.

The fire which started in the mellow panelled sitting-room in 1992 could have been the end of Bibury Court, but luckily it was snuffed out quickly and by the time you read this the work of restoration should be complete. This magnificent house stands on the edge of Bibury village, surrounded by lawns, trees and river – the very picture of a seventeenth-century

Cotswold manor. Inside, the sitting-room and the curious gilded 1920s-style bar are now supplemented by a conservatory room, built out on to the terrace. Constructed out of green oak and with a closer resemblance to a medieval barn than a kit from the local garden centre, this makes a splendid sunny place to sit, and light meals are now served here. The modern furnishings contrast strangely with the mishmash of chairs, beds and tables scattered throughout the rest of the house, where rooms have both character and comfort but cannot be described as up-to-the-minute in their decoration – not even the two new rooms (30 and 31) up in the attic. One of the best bedrooms is Number 12, which has French 1920s furniture. Most rooms have good views of the grounds.

Dinners are served in the narrow dining-room and adverse reports about the food may be a thing of the past: chef Andrew Parffrey started in 1993, and his menus include such dishes as chicken and walnut terrine with spiced oranges followed by honey-baked breast of duck with caramelised apple.

◑ Open all year, exc 21 to 30 Dec

⤢ Bibury is on the B4425 between Burford and Cirencester. The hotel is behind the church, next to the river. Private car park

⇌ 3 single, 6 twin/double, 7 four-poster, 1 suite, 3 family rooms; all with bathroom/WC, TV, room service, hair-dryer, baby-listening

◈ Dining-room, bar, lounge, TV room, games room, drying room, study, conservatory; conference facilities (max 20 people residential and non-residential);

fishing (1 Apr to 30 Sept) at hotel, other sports nearby; babysitting. Wheelchair access to hotel (1 step), restaurant and 1 ground-floor bedroom

⊖ None

▭ Access, Amex, Diners, Visa

£ Single £55, single occupancy of twin/double £55, twin/double/four-poster £74, suite £95, family room rate on request. Cooked B £5; Sun L £14; alc D £20. Special breaks available

The Swan ☆

BIBURY, NR CIRENCESTER, GLOUCESTERSHIRE GL7 5NW
TEL: CIRENCESTER (0285) 740695   FAX: (0285) 740473

An old inn, recently refurbished to a high standard.

Where Bibury Court has setting and atmosphere the Swan has comfort and style, so this Cotswold village is well served by the two hotels in the Guide. The Swan, which sits by Bibury trout farm, with its own private garden on an island in the River Coln is an old, creeper-covered inn whose interior was gutted and rebuilt before its reopening in early 1992. It is a fairly formal set-up nowadays, with highly polished staff, an obsession with Charles Rennie Mackintosh in the public rooms and extremely comfortable bedrooms. You are, in fact, well-advised to choose your room by its bath rather than its bed, for the designer has gone to town on different bathroom styles and whether your taste is for Victorian-style floral with his 'n' hers basins or for jazzy black and white tiles everywhere, you will find it satisfied here.

The bar, with clubby armchairs, modern panelling and a massive mural depicting the owners and relatives in a modern fantasy pastoral setting, opens into the brasserie (done Miami Beach-style with bright pastels and chrome) with a courtyard beyond for summer eating. There is also a formal, hushed restaurant of some magnificence. Fish comes highly recommended by our readers, especially the trout 'fresh from their own trout stream'. Our inspector dined well in the brasserie on slightly unimaginatively done mussels followed by brilliant home-made fishcakes.

◑ Open all year

⤢ In the B4425 between Burford and Cirencester. Private car park

🛏 1 single, 5 twin, 9 double, 2 four-poster, 1 family room; all with bathroom/WC, exc 1 double with shower/WC; TV, room service, hair-dryer, trouser press, baby-listening in all rooms; no tea/coffee-making facilities in rooms

◈ Restaurant, dining-room, bar, 2 lounges; air-conditioned conference facilities (max 10 people residential and non-residential); fishing at hotel. Wheelchair access to hotel, restaurant and WC (unisex), no ground-floor bedrooms but lift

⊖ Dogs in bar only; 1 no-smoking lounge

▭ Access, JCB, Visa

£ Single £90 to £130, single occupancy of twin/double £130 to £160, twin/double £145 to £170, four-poster £170 to £220, family room £220 to £250; deposit required. Set L £21.50; alc D £40. Special breaks available

---

BIDDENDEN KENT   **MAP 8**

Birchley ☆

FOSTEN GREEN LANE, BIDDENDEN, ASHFORD, KENT TN27 8DZ
TEL: BIDDENDEN (0580) 291413 (and fax)

A beautiful seventeenth-century house set in quiet, well-tended grounds.

As you head up the shady, winding driveway at Birchley, be prepared for a shock – the owner may hurtle past you on his miniature steam engine which he rides along a quarter-mile of track around the grounds. The railway, which took 18 years to build, is Drummond Randall's pride and joy, but the fine lawns and flowerbeds and the large covered and heated swimming-pool have not been allowed to suffer for it. Birchley is now listed to preserve its classic timber framing, intricately leaded windows and earthy wood carving. The interior is largely Jennifer Randall's domain, which she brightens with flower arrangements in almost every corner. Guests can relax by the log fire in the living-room, which is panelled in rich, dark oak, or in the dining-room next door where breakfast (and dinner, by arrangement) is taken at a long table made of highly polished 300-year-old beams in front of a magnificent light oak fireplace, carved with musical cherubs in Italian style. Three huge bedrooms are tastefully decorated, with luxurious pine-furnished bathrooms.

The Randalls are conscientious hosts who pay careful attention to the details. 'The food was excellent and nicely served; second helpings were encouraged. Jennifer is a superb cook and discusses dinner with you at breakfast. One day we asked for fish and she went miles out of her way to obtain fresh haddock as the local supplies were not up to her standard.'

◐ Open all year, exc Xmas and New Year; dining-room open by arrangement only – no evening meal Wed

⤢ From the village green take the A262 signed Sissinghurst and turn left opposite garden crafts nursery. Birchley is 1 mile on left. Private car park

🛏 3 twin/double; 1 with bathroom/WC, 2 with shower/WC; TV, hair-dryer in all rooms; trouser press in 1 room

◈ Dining-room, lounge; sauna, heated swimming-pool at hotel, golf, tennis nearby

⊖ No wheelchair access; no children under 12; no dogs; no smoking

▭ Access, Visa

£ Single occupancy of twin/double £45, twin/double £55 to £65; deposit required. Set D £17.50 (7.30pm). Special breaks available

BIGBURY-ON-SEA DEVON   MAP 10

Burgh Island

BIGBURY-ON-SEA, DEVON TQ7 4AU
TEL: BIGBURY-ON-SEA (0548) 810514   FAX: (0548) 810243

Art deco hotel on an island, accessible by Land-Rover or sea tractor.

Everything about Burgh Island is different: you must telephone ahead for a Land-Rover (low tide) or Spielbergian sea-tractor (high tide) to take you across to it. With its wonderful art deco architecture, fixtures and fittings, Burgh Island is as much a piece of social history as a hotel; in the 1920s it was second only to the Ritz as the place for flappers to spend their weekends, and soon developed a reputation for raciness. Past guests, immortalised in room names, have included Noël Coward, Agatha Christie, Mrs Simpson and the future Edward VIII.

The hotel's current owners, Tony and Beatrice Porter, run it 'like a dream come true,' according to one reader. All our feedback has been glowing. 'A tremendous improvement in room service . . . more professional staff have been added . . . the food is better, more varied and served more quickly.' All agree that style and ambience is excellent and regulars report a good hotel getting better. Lovers of art deco style will think themselves in heaven. This green and white layer cake boasts all the features of art deco design: parquet floors, angled mirrors, shiny black glass, horizontal lines picked out in alternating colours. At its heart is the Palm Court, its domed roof now completely restored, Lloyd Loom chairs grouped round low tables in front of a gleaming bar, terrazzo steps leading up to the sun lounge, a real afternoon suntrap. In the restaurant, its pale orange walls outlined in blue, diners sometimes dress in period style, especially on Saturday nights. The breakfast room, which looks out on the gardens and the sea, has more restrained black and white décor, and stylish director's chairs, but one end is a distinct oddity, even for Burgh Island: a previous owner bought the bridge from the Royal Navy's last sailing flagship, the HMS *Ganges*, creating a jutting out 'Captain's Cabin' effect.

As far as is possible, the Porters have furnished Burgh Island's suites in keeping with the period, which means they're not so much luxurious as interesting; look out for buttons in the walls of some bathrooms which used to be pressed to summon the maid waiting outside each door.

The Pilchard Inn in front is the hotel's private pub. Behind it, Mermaid Pool is a natural rocky inlet which can be closed off with sluice gates; in Burgh Island's heyday the Harry Roy band would be floated out into the middle of the pool to play to dancers on the beach, a custom it's probably too much to hope the Porters can re-create.

◑ Open all year, exc Mon to Thur in Jan and Feb

⤢ Follow signs to Bigbury-on-Sea. At St Ann's Chapel call the hotel from the phone box. Do not drive across the beach to the island. Private car park on mainland

⇌ 2 family rooms, 14 suites; all with bathroom/WC, sitting room, TV, room service, baby-listening; hair-dryer on request

◈ 2 restaurants, bar, drying room, library, conservatory, games room; conference facilities (max 32 people residential, 28 non-residential); fishing, tennis, water sports, sauna, solarium, natural tidal pool, gym, croquet at hotel, other sports nearby

⊖ No wheelchair access; no children under 12 in restaurant eves; no dogs

▭ Access, Amex, Visa

£ Suite/family room £166 to £200 (rates inc dinner); deposit required. Alc L £6 to £19; set D £26 to £28. Special breaks available

---

Use the index at the back of the book if you know the name of a hotel but are unsure about its precise location.

Biggin Hall

BIGGIN-BY-HARTINGTON, BUXTON, DERBYSHIRE SK17 0DH
TEL: HARTINGTON (0298) 84451   FAX: (0298) 84681

Good-value accommodation in a historic manor house with high-standard furnishings and friendly service.

James Moffett and his four fat geese come up to meet you as you approach the collection of mellow stone buildings that make up Biggin Hall, where bees hum in the laburnum and butterflies flicker around the white buddleia. It is a welcome that bodes well for the rest of your stay.

The Moffetts saved the Grade-II listed hall from dereliction 18 years ago and have created a magnificent home where restoration work on the stone-mullioned windows is barely decipherable from the seventeenth-century originals. James did much of the building work himself, while Maria tackled the interior with an obvious talent for selecting fabrics and antiques. Both sitting-rooms are extremely comfortable, with wing-backed and loose-covered chairs, a huge number of books and fascinating bits and pieces that include Civil War breastplates, an ornately carved oak cupboard and dark paintings of severe-looking folk James describes as 'ancestors by purchase' rather than the real McCoy. The dining-room – where evening meals in summer typically include tomato and feta cheese salad, salmon en croûte with hollandaise sauce and queen of puddings with meringue and fresh strawberries – has full-length windows on to the garden.

You have a choice of three types of bedroom. Those in the converted hayloft a few yards from the house have lots of space are the cheapest. The two bedrooms in the Bothy are slightly plainer than those in the main house, which vary in size but not in the high standard of furnishings and comfort. With its prettily draped four-poster bed, characterful beams and gigantic bathroom, the master suite is well worth the supplement.

◑ Open all year

↗ At the end of Biggin village, ½ mile from the A515 midway between Ashbourne and Buxton. Private car park

🛏 2 single, 11 twin/double, 1 four-poster, 2 half-tester, 1 cottage; all with bathroom/WC, hair-dryer; TV, room service and tea/coffee-making facilities in some rooms only

◈ Dining-room, 2 lounges; conference facilities (max 20

people non-residential and residential); fishing, riding nearby

⊖ No wheelchair access; no children under 12; dogs in some rooms only; smoking in lounge only

▭ Access, Amex, Visa

£ Single £23 to £33, twin/double/four-poster/half-tester £45 to £65; deposit required. Set D £14.50 (7pm). Special breaks available

BILLINGSHURST WEST SUSSEX **MAP 9**

Old Wharf

WHARF FARM, NEWBRIDGE, WISBOROUGH GREEN, BILLINGSHURST, WEST
SUSSEX RH14 0JG
TEL: HORSHAM (0403) 784096

*A remote, rural, converted warehouse with canal views and pretty
rooms.*

As you drive up to the square red-brick building you are likely to be met by
Max, the friendly black and white crossbred collie, who will drop stones at
your feet for you to throw. The Old Wharf was formerly a warehouse at the
busy terminus of the Arun Navigation Company, and the old hoist wheel
still dominates the open staircase. Owners Moira and David Mitchell
converted the building into a small bed and breakfast seven years ago.
There are four rooms, named Pink, Blue, Peach and Primrose, and
decorated in pastels accordingly. They are all pretty and well looked after,
with pine furnishings and low beamed ceilings. Primrose, the suite, is the
largest of the rooms, with a tiny sitting area; the others are definitely on the
small side but have pleasing views of the canal and fields. Breakfast is
taken in a small room overlooking the patio, and the little peach-coloured
lounge facing the canal is a pleasant place to relax.

- ◐ Open all year
- ↗ Head west of Billingshurst on the A272 for 1½ miles. The house is on the left-hand side, by the banks of the canal, just after the river bridge. Private car park
- 🛏 3 twin, 1 suite; all with bathroom/WC, TV
- ◈ Breakfast room, lounge; fishing at hotel
- ⊖ No wheelchair access; no children under 12; no dogs; no smoking
- ▭ Access, Amex, Visa
- £ Single occupancy of twin £35, twin £40, suite £55. Cooked B £5

BIRCH VALE DERBYSHIRE **MAP 5**

Waltzing Weasel ☆

NEW MILLS ROAD, BIRCH VALE, VIA STOCKPORT, CHESHIRE SK12 5BT
TEL: NEW MILLS (0663) 743402

Contemporary comfort in a traditional country inn.

Alas, the name does not refer to some arcane High Peak mating ritual,
but was probably brewed up in a burst of Ruddles-fuelled inspiration. It
does, however, indicate an English inn at its best, recommended by
readers as a welcome antidote to so many brewing carbuncles. This
popular roadside local was extended in 1992 to provide high-quality
rooms and restaurant. The bar is still the focal point, but the food attracts

people from afar and the rooms are well patronised by the local business clientele.

The extension has been sympathetically designed in matching local stone by an architect who just happens to live next door. Dining-room, patio and Bedrooms Five and Six have a grand view of Kinder Scout; Rooms One and Two are on the ground floor near the bar, so may either suffer from noise or be handy for a pint, depending on your point of view. All the rooms are furnished with country antiques in soft, subdued colours; the half-tester bed in Room Six is particularly handsome. All rooms and *en-suite* bathrooms make clever use of light and space. The main drawback is the lack of residents' lounge.

Chef George Benham provides plain and plentiful good English cooking. Bar food may include potted trout and game pie, rib of beef, pigeon in puff pastry and treacle tart. There are home-made sausages, Derbyshire oatcakes and local raspberry jam for breakfast.

The atmosphere is open and friendly. As one reader reported: 'The owners do not flunkey, but are invariably available and attentive.'

◑ *Open all year, exc 25 Dec*

▨ *On the A6015, ½ mile west of Hayfield. Private car park*

🛏 *1 single, 2 twin, 4 double, 1 half-tester; all with bathroom/WC, exc single with shower/WC; TV, hair-dryer, trouser press in all rooms*

◈ *Restaurant (air-conditioned), bar, drying room; conference facilities (max 25 people non-residential, 8 residential); fishing, golf, other sports nearby. Wheelchair access to hotel (3 steps), restaurant and WC (M,F), 2 ground-floor bedrooms*

⊖ *No children under 10; dogs at owners' discretion; smoking discouraged in bedrooms*

▭ *Access, Visa*

£ *Single £45, single occupancy of twin/double £58, twin/double £75, half-tester £90; deposit required. Alc L from £12.50; set D £19.50/£23.50. Special breaks available*

BIRMINGHAM WEST MIDLANDS   MAP 5

Asquith House

19 PORTLAND ROAD, EDGBASTON, BIRMINGHAM, WEST MIDLANDS
B16 9HN
TEL: 021-454 5282/6699/0015   FAX: 021-456 4668

A homely small hotel just outside Birmingham city centre – a good alternative to impersonal business accommodation.

Just off the busy Hagley Road, a mile and a half from Birmingham city centre lies Asquith House. This ivy-covered red-brick Georgian-looking house, built in the 1850s, is immaculately kept and has a lovely garden, with huge shrubs and colourful borders, where guests are welcome to have tea in the summer. The public rooms are light and sunny, with plain walls as a backdrop to a great number of painting and sketches; furniture consists chiefly of Victorian pieces that Margaret Gittens has collected over the years. Clocks on the mantelpiece, brass candlesticks and weighing scales are amongst the bric-à-brac that makes the rooms homely, while a tea urn from Marrakech adds to the curiosity factor. The dining-room, with its crystal glasses on polished tables and fresh flower arrangements, is an elegant room for dinner – which can be almost anything from the hotel's large repertoire of mostly modern British dishes such as avocado vinaigrette, roast lamb with red wine and rosemary sauce, and summer pudding.

The bedrooms, named after William Morris designs, are light, cheerful and flowery, with coronet drapes or brass beds, lacy bedspreads or pretty duvets. Those overlooking the garden have the edge for the view and for peace and quiet.

◑ *Open all year; restaurant closed Sun eve*

↗ *Off the main A456 Birmingham to Kidderminster road (Hagley Road), 1½ miles from the city centre. Private car park*

🛏 *2 single, 6 twin, 1 double, 1 family room; all with shower/ WC, exc double with bathroom/ WC; TV, room service, hairdryer, trouser press, babylistening in all rooms*

◈ *2 dining-rooms, bar, lounge, TV room; laundry facilities; conference facilities (max 40 people non-residential, 10 residential); fishing, golf, other sports nearby; babysitting*

⊖ *No wheelchair access; no dogs in public rooms*

▭ *Access, Amex, Visa*

£ *Single £52, single occupancy of twin/double £57, twin/double/ family room £62; deposit required. Set L £14, D £16.50; alc L £17.50, D from £19.50*

Copperfield House

60 UPLAND ROAD, SELLY OAK, BIRMINGHAM, WEST MIDLANDS B29 7JS
TEL: 021-472 8344   FAX: 021-472 8344

A small family-run hotel with functional rooms, handy for the University and Pebble Mill studios.

Copperfield House is very much a family business – John and Jenny Bodycote keep the bedrooms and front of house ticking over while daughter Louise manages the kitchen. In a leafy residential street, away from the hassle of central Birmingham, the Victorian red-brick house is immaculately kept, with neat lawned gardens and mature trees. Inside, the Bodycotes' interest in foreign travel is obvious from the Lebanese prints in the sitting-room and other bits and bobs. Furnishings are functional rather than luxurious but the atmosphere is homely and the visitors' book is full of praise for the friendliness of the staff. The Archers cast often stay while recording at Pebble Mill, so you might find yourself sharing the dining-room with Jill or Shula. Lots of home-made dishes and fresh produce feature on the menu, which Louise (who trained with Prue Leith) changes every day. For a small hotel, food gets lots of attention and as a result many guests choose to eat in. The three-course table d'hôte menu might include home-made tomato and basil soup, grilled lemon sole with prawn and chablis sauce, and a choice of puddings.

Bedrooms are comfortable with white or pine furniture and at present are rather plain, though since they took over in 1991 the Bodycotes have begun to refurbish throughout. The single in the attic has a loo with a view over the university.

◑ *Open all year*

↗ *2 miles from Birmingham city centre. Travel south on the A38 and turn left just past Pebble Mill TV studios. Private car park*

🛏 *6 single, 5 twin, 5 double, 1 family room; all with bathroom/ WC, exc 2 singles with shower/ WC; TV, room service, hair-dryer in all rooms*

◈ *Dining-room, honesty bar, lounge; conference facilities (max 15 people non-residential and residential; weekends only);*

fishing, golf, other sports nearby. Wheelchair access to hotel (1 step or ramp), restaurant and WC (unisex), 3 ground-floor bedrooms

⊖ *No dogs in public rooms; no smoking in dining-room*

▭ *Access, Visa*

£ *Single £45, single occupancy of twin/double £45, twin/double £56, family room £66; deposit required. Set D £15 (prices till Oct 93). Special breaks available*

Swallow Hotel

12 HAGLEY ROAD, FIVEWAYS, BIRMINGHAM B16 8SJ
TEL: 021-452 1144   FAX: 021-456 3442

A grand, luxury hotel with good food near Birmingham city centre.

Swallow hotels don't come cheap, and the Birmingham Swallow is the most expensive of them all. Bang on the massive Fiveways Roundabout, the Swallow has an unpleasantly frenetic position or is convenient for the city centre, depending upon your point of view. Once inside the six-storey Edwardian-style block, however, the opulence is unmistakable. Liveried porters help you with your bags, and business executives gather in huddles against a background of polished mahogany, heavy chandeliers and marble floors. The drawing-room, open to the reception area, is a relatively peaceful place to have tea, and in its décor establishes the hotel's Edwardian theme – a theme continued in the names of the two restaurants: Langtry's is English and informal, while Edward Elgar, with its deep-green walls, lead crystal glasses and dishes arriving under silver cloches, has slightly more ceremony. The atmosphere is far from stuffy – courteous but good-humoured staff see to that. Food is consistently commended, and a three-course à la carte meal might include braised leeks filled with ricotta and dressed with avocado, tomato and basil;

sautéed calf's liver with herbs and trumpet mushrooms; and a choice of classical puddings. The wine list is pricey.

The 98 bedrooms, each with a smart *en-suite* bathroom, are a good size and successfully avoid a 'chain hotel' feel. Facilities you'd expect of a grand hotel include air-conditioning and satellite television, while extra pampering is there too in the form of enormous bathsheets and fresh milk in the mini-bars. In common with most Swallow hotels, this one has a leisure centre – a large pool with Egyptian-style décor and a state-of-the-art gym are to be found in the basement.

◐ *Open all year*

⤢ *Near the centre of Birmingham, at Fiveways where the A456 crosses the A4540. Private car park*

🛏 *14 single, 38 twin, 42 double, 2 four-poster suites, 2 twin suites; all individually air-conditioned, with bathroom/WC, TV, room service, hair-dryer, trouser press, mini-bar, baby-listening*

◈ *2 restaurants, bar, lounge, library; hotel air-conditioned*

throughout; conference facilities (max 100 people residential and non-residential); sauna/solarium, heated indoor swimming-pool, gym at hotel; babysitting

⊖ *No wheelchair access; no dogs in public rooms; some bedrooms non-smoking*

▭ *Access, Amex, Diners, Visa*

£ *Single £110, twin/double £130, four-poster/suite £250; deposit required. Set L from £15.50, D from £18.50; alc L, D £40*

BISHOP'S TAWTON DEVON   MAP 10

Downrew House ☆

BISHOP'S TAWTON, BARNSTAPLE, DEVON EX32 0DY
TEL: BARNSTAPLE (0271) 42497/46673   FAX: (0271) 23947

A remote country-house hotel with extensive grounds.

After the sprawl of Barnstaple it's a relief to find Downrew House, remote even from Bishop's Tawton itself. It's a strikingly attractive black and white house, mainly dating from the eighteenth century, that presides over a sweeping five-hole golf course; you enter through a wooden door so studded with nails you'd think it was intended to repel invaders. In recent years Downrew House has gone through hard times, with several quick changes of ownership, but it is to be hoped that it has now settled down under the stewardship of Clifford Johnson. Certainly the lounge has been completely refurbished, and now features soft damask sofas and chairs, a big log fire, and a window seat with views over rose bushes towards Dartmoor. The elegant restaurant looks out on the back garden through a gently curving window. Set three-course menus change daily, and there's also an à la carte menu.

A pine stairway with deep maroon carpet sweeps up from the flagstoned hall to the bedrooms (each with its own colour scheme); the suite is particularly appealing, the curtains and bedspreads picked out with ferns and flowers, the bathroom boasting a circular window. There are six more rooms in the converted coach-house, which also houses a solarium, billiard room and small conference room; these, however, are fitted out in Identikit pinks and pine.

◐ Open all year, exc Jan

↗ Leave the M5 at Junction 27 and take the North Devon Link Road to Barnstaple. At the first roundabout take the A39 to Bideford and at the next roundabout turn left to Crediton (A377). In Bishop's Tawton turn left by the BP garage and follow the road uphill for 1½ miles. Private car park

🛏 6 twin, 5 double, 1 suite; all with bathroom/WC, TV, room service

◈ Restaurant, bar, 2 lounges, drying room, games room;

conference facilities (max 50 people non-residential, 12 residential); golf, tennis, solarium, outdoor heated swimming-pool at hotel, other sports nearby. Wheelchair access to hotel, restaurant and 3 ground-floor bedrooms

⊖ No dogs in public rooms

▭ Access, Visa

£ Single occupancy of twin/double £36 to £50, twin/double £56 to £90, suite £84 to £110; deposit required. Set L £9, D £18; alc D £24

Halmpstone Manor

BISHOP'S TAWTON, BARNSTAPLE, DEVON EX32 0EA
TEL: BARNSTAPLE (0271) 830321   FAX: (0271) 830826

A surprisingly grand converted farmhouse hotel down a country lane.

Buried in the north Devon countryside, this quiet old three-storey manor well deserves its rating for a peaceful situation. Inside, the ground floor offers strikingly contrasting rooms: the dining-room, all low, dark beams and panelling, is separated from a bright, elegant lounge by a hall with a wonderful oak settle designed to shield occupants from the front door draught. Upstairs, and past a sadly ravaged portrait, it's the dark wood that wins out; the landing boasts a black oak table which would take three men to lift it. Jane Stanbury, a bubbly farmer's wife positively bursting with energy, graduated through offering bed and breakfast for holidaymakers to accommodating business people, and now attracts a happy mixture of the two. Fittings in the five bedrooms, all named after previous house owners, are grander than you might anticipate. Mule and Chichester have four-posters, and a coronet adorns the canopy in Fulke. There is complimentary fruit, flowers, chocolate and sherry in all the rooms. Hawkey has its own dressing-room and a private entrance from the back of the house.

Dinner menus are sophisticated enough to appeal to gourmets: royal Greenland prawns served on a mixed salad might be followed by a champagne sorbet and medallions of venison with poivrade sauce, apple and blackcurrants.

◖ *Open all year, exc Dec and Jan*

⤴ *In Bishop's Tawton, turn left at the garage and continue on this road for 2 miles, then turn right. Private car park*

🛏 *3 twin/double, 2 four-poster; some with bathroom/WC, some with shower/WC; TV, hair-dryer, room service, trouser press in all rooms*

◈ *Restaurant, bar, lounge;*

conference facilities (max 12 people non-residential); golf, riding, other sports nearby

⊖ *No wheelchair access; no children under 12; no smoking in bedrooms*

▭ *Access, Amex, Diners, Visa*

£ *Single occupancy of double £65, double £80 or £100, four-poster £130; deposit required. Set L (by arrangement), D £27.50*

BLACKPOOL LANCASHIRE　　　　　　　　　　　　**MAP 5**

Sunray Hotel ☆

---

42 KNOWLE AVENUE, BLACKPOOL, LANCASHIRE FY2 9TQ
TEL: BLACKPOOL (0253) 51937

An original 1930s guesthouse which still provides classic seaside bed and breakfast.

Although this looks like an ordinary semi in a quiet residential street off the North Shore, the Sunray was actually purpose-built as a guesthouse in the 1930s. The builder, for luck, buried coins of the construction year in the corner of the foundations. It seems to have worked, as guests have been coming back year after year, some since they were children.

This is the very model of a traditional Blackpool bed and breakfast: clean, comfortable and welcoming. Landlady Jean Dodgson takes a motherly interest in her guests' welfare and is particularly caring about children. There are rag dolls and toys for them to play with in the lounge, and she will babysit if needs be. As she says: 'If you make the little ones relaxed, then they'll be much better behaved and everyone will have a nicer time.'

Mrs Dodgson likes her guests to mingle and has a back-to-front clock in the dining-room to get them chatting over the eggs and bacon. She'll cater for special diets and requests. She does a simple, three-course evening meal such as vegetable soup, braised steak and arctic roll, but note that, in good old Northern fashion, dinner is at 5.30pm.

All the bedrooms are simply decorated but there is a choice of duvet or blankets. The *en-suite* bathrooms have extra fan heaters and all the beds are equipped with electric blankets.

◖ *Open all year, exc Xmas and New Year*

⤴ *From Blackpool tower proceed*

north along the promenade for 1 3/4 miles and turn right at Uncle Tom's Cabin. The Sunray is 300 yards on the left. Private car park and on-street parking

🛏 3 single, 2 twin, 2 double, 2 family rooms; all with shower/WC, exc 1 twin with bathroom/WC; TV, hair-dryer, baby-listening in all rooms

◈ Dining-room, lounge; fishing, golf, other sports nearby

⊖ No wheelchair access; no dogs in public rooms

▭ Access, Visa

£ Single £22 to £28, single occupancy of twin/double £22 to £28; twin/double/family room £44 to £56. Set D £10 (5.30pm). Special breaks available

---

BLACKWELL WARWICKSHIRE   **MAP 9**

Blackwell Grange

BLACKWELL, SHIPSTON-ON-STOUR, WARWICKSHIRE CV36 4PF
TEL: ILMINGTON (0608) 682357   FAX: (0608) 682357

A seventeenth-century farmhouse with a comfortable rustic atmosphere and fine home-produced cooking.

Not much disturbs the peace around this small spread-out village with views of the Ilmington hills. As rustic as its surroundings, with flagstone-floors, beams and low ceilings, Blackwell Grange is described by one contented reader as 'lovely, friendly and comfortable'. Fine old oak furniture, horsy pictures and log fires give a homely feel to the sitting-room, where you can slump in a comfortable armchair after dinner with one of the many books that are lying around. With its inglenook fireplace, the dining-room also has its share of character, and we receive consistently good reports about Liz Vernon Miller's cooking. Lots of home-grown produce features in the evening meals, and Liz is flexible enough to provide special food for special diets.

Bedrooms are divided between the farmhouse and a barn conversion. All are well-furnished, with good-quality cottagey fabrics and *en-suite* bathrooms. Rooms in the barn are slightly smaller than the others, but are a perfectly adequate size and share a sitting-room and kitchen – ideal if you want to cater for yourself.

◐ Open all year

↗ Take A3400 towards Oxford from Stratford-upon-Avon. After 5 miles turn right by the church in Newbold-on-Stour. In Blackwell, fork right. Private car park

🛏 1 single, 1 twin, 1 double, 1 cottage; all with bathroom/WC; single with TV

◈ Dining-room, TV/lounge; golf, riding nearby. Wheelchair access to hotel and dining-room, 2 ground-floor bedrooms, 1 specially equipped for disabled people

⊖ No dogs; no smoking

▭ None accepted

£ Single £24, single occupancy of twin/double £27, twin/double/cottage £42 to £48; deposit required. Set D £14.50, supper £10.50 (both by prior arrangement)

BLAKENEY NORFOLK   **MAP 7**

White Horse

4 HIGH STREET, BLAKENEY, NR HOLT, NORFOLK NR25 7AL
TEL: CLEY (0263) 740574

A busy inn turned hotel within a hop and a skip of the harbour.

Blakeney is a part of the North Norfolk 'golden triangle' which extends along the beautiful National Trust-run coastline and into the peaceful countryside inland. This nickname comes not only from the vast spits of yellow sand revealed at low tide where fat seals bask with their cubs, but also from the desirability of property (much of it snapped up for holiday homes). That said, Blakeney is inhabited by enough locals to make it lively year-round, and many find their way to the bar room at the White Horse for a drink and a chat. The flint and brick building (formerly a coaching-inn) lies just up the hill from a busy harbour where sailors prepare their dinghies for fiercely contested local races and hikers tramp over salt marshes. At the turn of the century it was the first hotel in this area; now it is one of many, but competes well on bedroom prices. Only the Harbour Room (a large double with enough room for children's beds) has good views; the others – though comfortable enough and kept in good condition – have none to speak of.

Food is served in the smart bar, the Gallery Room and the family area. Alternatively you can opt to sit in the whitewashed restaurant, converted from an old stable block into an airy room with crisp white tablecloths and pine furnishings. As a resident you can take advantage of a special half-board rate, although many of the main dishes require a supplement. Children are particularly welcomed, with a special menu provided.

◑ Open all year

⤤ Follow signs to Blakeney off the A149 between Cromer and Wells. Private car park

🛏 2 single, 1 twin, 4 double, 2 family rooms; all with bathroom/ WC, exc 1 single with shower/ WC; TV, baby-listening in all rooms

◈ Restaurant, bar, children's room, picture gallery; conference facilities (max 20 people non-residential, 9 residential); golf, fishing, other sports nearby; babysitting. Wheelchair access to bar and restaurant only

⊖ No dogs

▭ Access, Amex, Visa

£ Single £30, single occupancy of twin/double £45, twin/double £60, family room £75; deposit required. Alc L £9, D £13.50. Special breaks available

---

'No rose for you,' boomed the maître d' of a Scottish hotel at a lonesome inspector on Valentine's night, in embarrassing earshot of all the other couples. 'If you're lucky I might treat you to a dram of malt later on.'

Lord Crewe Arms

BLANCHLAND, NR CONSETT, CO DURHAM DH8 9SP
TEL: HEXHAM (0434) 675251   FAX: (0434) 675337

Tradition with a dash of fun in a fascinating old inn.

First of all an apology. Last year we regretted a certain inflexibility on the part of the management – a brickbat that properly belonged to another hotel. We also erroneously reported that this privately owned hotel was company-owned, a mistake for which further apologies are due. Let us hope that the spirit of Dorothy Forster whose ghost is said to haunt this lovely, mellow old inn is now appeased.

The Dorothy Forster legend is part of the quirky character of the Lord Crewe Arms, together with the suits of armour, exposed beams and flagstones which testify to the antiquity of an inn that dates back to the twelfth century. The manicured medievalism infuses the Hilyard Room, with its flagstoned floor, thick walls and theatrically lit priest's hole, and the Derwent Room, where afternoon tea is served in a setting of rugs, settles and the warmth of a blazing fire. It reaches its zenith in the dungeon-like Crypt Bar, with its barrel-shaped walls and heraldic devices. A less distant past is recalled in the large restaurant, where traditional décor, a little dog-eared in places, is ennobled by portraits and tables set with crisp white linen and crystal. Food on a largely English menu – perhaps home-made game pâté with Cumberland sauce, followed by roast best-end of lamb – is competent.

Bedrooms vary in size and style, but are likely to combine modern wallcoverings and chintzy soft furnishings plus every extra you need to make your stay comfortable, from biscuits to hair-dryers.

◑ Open all year

⤢ On the B6306, 10 miles south of Hexham. On-street parking

🛏 8 twin, 9 double, 1 four-poster; all with bathroom/WC, exc 2 doubles with shower/WC; TV, room service, hair-dryer, trouser press, baby-listening in all rooms; ironing facilities on request

◇ Restaurant, bar, 3 lounges, drying room; conference facilities

(max 18 people residential, 30 non-residential); fishing, tennis, other sports nearby

⊖ No wheelchair access; no dogs in public rooms

▭ Access, Amex, Diners, Visa

£ Single occupancy of twin/double £65 to £80, twin/double £75 to £105, four-poster/family room rate £105; deposit required. Alc D £27; Sun L £14.50

'Just picture those balmy summer lunches . . . lazy poolside barbecues à la Cap Ferrat, with grilled langoustines in bubbling garlic butter and ice-cold Muscadet.' – Brochurespeak from, believe it or not, a Scottish Borders hotel

BLAWITH CUMBRIA   **MAP 4**

Appletree Holme

BLAWITH, NR ULVERSTON, CUMBRIA LA12 8EL
TEL: LOWICK BRIDGE (0229) 885618

Self-indulgence in a remote and secluded setting.

Tucked away down a long bumpy track, among low, rolling fells on the
south-western edge of the Lake District, this is the ultimate refuge for
escapists. Not a car to be heard, hardly another building in sight – only
the occasional distant ring of the telephone reminds you of the world
outside. But the great thing about Appletree Holme is that you don't have
to suffer to get away from it all. This is one of the most comfortable
guesthouses we've ever seen. It's a converted two-storey lakeland farmhouse with large rooms (there are only four in all) done out with powerful
colour schemes (pink and green for instance). The bathrooms are a treat
– the one allocated to the Pink Room is almost as big as the bedroom
itself, while the Blue Room has a double bath. Downstairs, there's a
beamed lounge with an open fire and a variety of places to sit – from a
slate bench to a leather chesterfield – and another sitting-room with
books and games. The narrow dining-room, grafted on to the back of the
house, looks out over the terraced lawns. Roy serves a good menu
(there's no choice, but individual preferences and needs are catered for),
which might start with stuffed tomatoes before progressing, via an
orange sorbet, to pork in mustard cream sauce and rounding off with
strawberry meringue and English cheeses.

One report sums up the experience: 'Quite superb in every way – the
warm hospitality of the hosts, the comfort of our accommodation and
last, but not least, the varied, imaginatively presented and most satisfying
of meals.'

◑ *Open all year*

⤴ *Leave the M6 at Junction 36.
Take the A590 to Greenodd,
then the A5092 to Lowick Green
and the A5084 to Blawith. Turn
into the lane opposite Blawith
church, through the farm, taking
the first right and then first left
at sign. Private car park*

🛏 *1 twin, 3 double; all with
bathroom/WC, exc twin with
shower/WC; TV, room service,
hair-dryer in all rooms*

◈ *Dining-room, lounge, drying
room, library; fishing, riding,
other sports nearby*

⊖ *No wheelchair access; no
children under 8; no dogs; no
smoking*

▭ *Access, Amex, Visa*

£ *Single occupancy of twin/double
£51 to £65, twin/double £102 to
£110 (rates inc dinner); deposit
required. Set D £21.50 (8pm)
(prices till Easter 94). Special
breaks available*

All reports are welcome on any hotel, whether or not it is in the Guide.

BLOCKLEY GLOUCESTERSHIRE   **MAP 9**

Crown Inn and Hotel

HIGH STREET, BLOCKLEY, NR MORETON-IN-MARSH, GLOUCESTERSHIRE
GL56 9EX
TEL: BLOCKLEY (0386) 700245   FAX: (0386) 700247

A solid village hotel suitable for an overnight stop.

The Crown is not one of those olde-worlde pubs with creaking floors and
noise from the bar, although it is the focal point of an attractive Cotswold
village. Its coaching-inn origins are betrayed by the archway through
which you drive to the car park, but otherwise the place has been
extensively refurbished and there is only the odd trace of its sixteenth-
century origins – notably the beams that extend from the modern plaster.
It is quite a large hotel, with a bar spreading across two rooms at different
levels, a big grill/fish restaurant and a dining-room under a beamed
ceiling. Bedrooms are comfortable and very sensibly outfitted, although
we have had comments about poor housekeeping – kettles and loo seats
not working quite as they were designed to. Also, a reader mentions, and
our inspector confirmed, that the whitebait in the fish restaurant was
sadly soggy. All in all, though, a good place for a short stay, and with
plenty of local customers for bar and restaurant.

- ◑ Open all year
- ⤢ Off the main A44 Oxford to Evesham road, 1 mile past Moreton-in-Marsh, right turn down into village. Private car park
- 🛏 5 twin, 10 double, 4 four-poster (2 are four-poster suites), 2 family rooms; all with bathroom/WC, TV, room service, hair-dryer; trouser press in some rooms
- ◈ 2 restaurants, 3 bars, 2 lounges;

conference facilities (max 20 people residential, 40 non-residential); golf, fishing, other sports nearby
- ⊖ No wheelchair access; no dogs in some bedrooms
- ▭ Access, Amex, Diners, Visa
- 💷 Single occupancy of twin/double £53, twin/double £78, four-poster £104, family room from £89; deposit required. Set L £14, D £20. Special breaks available

---

BODINNICK CORNWALL   **MAP 10**

Old Ferry Inn ☆

BODINNICK, CORNWALL PL23 1LX
TEL: POLRUAN (0726) 870237

*An attractive pub-hotel on the quieter side of the Fowey Estuary,
with a strong sailing tradition.*

A car ferry plies back and forth between Fowey and Bodinnick, and, as its
name implies, the Old Ferry Inn, a fine black and white sixteenth-

century building, stands beside where it docks on the Bodinnick side, making it the perfect alternative place to stay for those put off by Fowey's congested streets and parking problems. Steps from the tiny hall lead to the first of three public bars, its walls adorned with sailing pictures and stuffed fish (host Simon Farr is a keen sailor); walk through to the third bar (to which parents with children will be directed anyway) and you can examine the exposed rockface where the pub was built into the steep hillside. All three bars have typically English décor, with heavy black oak settles and wheelback chairs, and even in low season they do a roaring lunchtime trade. Should the bars become too crowded, guests can retreat to a spacious and comfortable lounge equipped with lots of books and a pair of binoculars for estuary-watching. The dining-room's best table is slotted into a bay window overlooking the estuary; here, predictably, you can tuck into local trout, crab and prawns, although nut cutlets are available for vegetarians.

A stairway which looks as if it belongs in a rather grander hotel is decorated with huge portraits and old theatre posters. Upstairs the bedrooms turn out to be bigger than you would expect, particularly Room One, a sprawling family room with wonderful views and attractive low beams. Furnishings are simple but adequate, as are the bathrooms; two rooms lack *en suite* facilities.

◑ Open all year (B&B terms only Nov to Mar)

▨ Take the A38 and A390 from Liskeard. At East Taphouse turn left on to the B3359, then after 5 miles turn right on brow of the hill towards Bodinnick. Private car park

🛏 6 twin, 4 double, 1 four-poster, 1 family room; some with bathroom/WC, some with shower/WC, some with neither, 2 public bathrooms; TV, room service in all rooms

✧ Dining-room, 3 bars, lounge; water sports at hotel, other sports nearby

⊖ No wheelchair access; no smoking in dining-room

▭ Visa

£ Single occupancy of twin/double £20 to £47, twin/double £40 to £74, four-poster £40 to £64, family room rate £40 to £90; deposit required. Bar snacks; set D £15; alc D £20 to £25

BOLTON ABBEY NORTH YORKSHIRE　　　　　　　**MAP 5**

Devonshire Arms

BOLTON ABBEY, NR SKIPTON, NORTH YORKSHIRE BD23 6AJ
TEL: BOLTON ABBEY (0756) 710441　TELEX: 51218 DEVARM G
FAX: (0756) 710564

A large, efficiently run former coaching-inn which successfully straddles the business hotel/country-house divide.

'It restored our faith in hotelkeeping,' wrote one visitor who delighted in finding a hotel 'totally lacking in airs and graces' which none the less delivered 'a superb stay'. The hotel's graceful public rooms are due, in no small measure, to the furniture and pictures from Chatsworth, the best-known seat of its owners, the Duke and Duchess of Devonshire.

The original building has a beige pebble-dash extension and throughout the hotel old meets new in sometimes surprising ways, not least in the open-plan reception seating area, with its blazing fire and rug-scattered flagstoned floor from which rise walls of impeccable 1980s smoothness. There are lots of places to sit and relax, from the long lounge beside the restaurant with its old range and stuffed birds to the pleasant day lounge and the classic cocktail lounge, resplendent with striped wallpaper and corner bar.

The Burlington Restaurant is divided into four sections, which successfully masks its size. The overall feel is bright and airy, with white garden-style chairs and an attractive conservatory area. Correspondents have been unanimous in their praise of both the food, 'excellent', and the service, 'friendly but not unctuous'. Dinner is not cheap but was felt to be good value: a well-balanced spring menu offered several choices including fresh mussel soup, sorbet, loin of lamb topped with a mint and apple mousse and a selection of puddings. Less formal food from 'Percy's platter' is available in the Duke's Bar, a sports-themed watering-hole.

Bedrooms in the extension are bright, comfortable and packed with gadgets to make your stay comfortable, but their almost Identikit-look is easily trumped by the gloriously individual rooms in the old section, not least Shepherd with its huge wooden sheep, tapestries, antiques and four-poster. Bathrooms are appositely impressive, and come complete with robes and hot-water bottles.

◑ Open all year

⤢ At the junction of the A59 and B6160, 5 miles north-west of Ilkley. Private car park

🛏 20 twin, 11 double, 8 four-poster, 1 suite; all with bathroom/WC, TV, room service, hair-dryer, trouser press, baby-listening, ironing facilities

◇ Restaurant, 3 bars, 2 lounges, TV room, drying room, conservatory; conference facilities (max 150 people non-residential, 80 residential); fishing at hotel,

other sports nearby; babysitting. Wheelchair access to hotel, restaurant and WC, 17 ground-floor bedrooms, 2 specially equipped for disabled people

⊖ No children under 12 in restaurant; no smoking in restaurant

▭ Access, Amex, Diners, Visa

£ Single occupancy of twin/double £100, twin/double £120, four-poster £135, suite £175. Set L £18, D £28.50; alc L £20, D £32. Special breaks available

---

Some hoteliers will do their utmost to dissuade you from getting them up early: for example, by charging £5 for early-morning tea. On a hotel in Scotland

BOLTON BY BOWLAND LANCASHIRE **MAP 5**

Harrop Fold

BOLTON BY BOWLAND, CLITHEROE, LANCASHIRE BB7 4PJ
TEL: BOLTON BY BOWLAND (0200) 447600

Homely farmhouse hospitality hidden away in remote countryside.

Harrop Fold has a loyal following of 'Old Harropians' who return regularly for the comfort and cheer provided by the hardworking, sociable hosts, Peter and Victoria Wood. The farmhouse, surrounded by its own sheep and cattle farm, dates back centuries and is reputed to be of Viking origin. It is a snug mishmash of styles, a pot-pourri of curiosities. An old mangle stands in the entrance, festooned with artificial flowers and preserves for sale. The upstairs stable/lounge is particularly interesting, dedicated to Victoria's nautical family history and full of seafaring mementoes, including an 1850s ship's bell.

Downstairs, the lounge/bar, formerly the farmhouse kitchen, has plenty of seating, seventeenth-century corner cupboards and old meat hooks hanging from the ceiling. There is a framed Bill Tidy cartoon, drawn in a Theakston-induced glow after a clay-pigeon shooting trip. The dining-room is more simple. Home-made country dinners may include cream of watercress soup, game pâté, salmon fillet or roast duckling with port jelly.

All the furnishings in the named bedrooms have been made by Victoria, who has also done many of the embroidered cushions that are a feature of the hotel. Rooms vary in size and are all *en suite*, although some lack shower. Wardrobe space in some rooms is a curtained-off rail. Rose has an immense bed, perhaps as compensation for the lesser view over the 'fold'. All the rooms are rather fussily decorated in pastel colours, and personalised with little ornaments and knick-knacks.

There are some who may feel hemmed in by the cosiness and feel the house style verges on the twee – on the other hand, there are many who happily return to be cared for and cosseted, Harrop-style.

◑ Closed Jan

⤴ From the A59 Clitheroe to Skipton road, take the turning to Bolton by Bowland. Bear left at the Copy Nook hotel. Turn sharp left to Holden and Slaidburn. In Holden follow the sign to Harrop Fold and go left into the village. The hotel is first on the right. Private car park

⇌ 2 twin, 6 double; all with bathroom/WC, TV, room service, hair-dryer

◈ Dining-room, bar, 2 lounges; fishing, golf, other sports nearby

⊖ No wheelchair access; no children; no dogs; smoking discouraged in bedrooms

▭ Access, Visa

£ Single occupancy of twin/double £41, twin/double £56; deposit required. Set D £16.50. Special breaks available

BOMERE HEATH SHROPSHIRE   **MAP 5**

Fitz Manor ☆

BOMERE HEATH, NR SHREWSBURY, SHROPSHIRE SY4 3AS
TEL: SHREWSBURY (0743) 850295

A distinguished Tudor hall-turned-farmhouse, now an atmospheric guesthouse.

Fitz Manor is not quite miles from anywhere but it is hidden away in an unspoilt section of the Severn Valley, surprisingly high above the banks of the river and surrounded by farmland. The oldest part of the long two-storey building is in the centre, and the whole frontage is being gradually restored as Dawn Baly manages to find the funds.

It is a lovely house, and the interior lives up to the exterior promise, with old panelled hallway, cosy sitting-room and massive dining-room lined with paintings. It is very much a family home too, and there is nothing over-fussy about it: be prepared to be treated as one of the family. In a house of this age *en-suite* bathrooms are too much to expect, but there is plenty of space in the green bedroom, not so much in the small-but-sweet single. Furnishings are plain, but with the odd interesting piece to catch your eye – a huge mirror, for example. Dawn Baly does her own cooking, and is happy to discuss guests' preferences. At the far end of her semi-formal garden lies a sun trap of a swimming-pool – worth remembering for hot days.

◐ Open all year

↗ Take the A5 to Montford Bridge, just north-west of Shrewsbury; then the A4380 to Forton and Fitz. Turn off after 1 mile. The manor's drive is a mile further on. Private car park

🛏 1 single, 2 twin; 2 public bathrooms; room service, hair-dryer, trouser press, baby-listening in all rooms

◈ Dining-room, 2 lounges, TV room, drying room; fishing, riding, croquet, heated swimming-pool at hotel, other sports nearby

⊖ No wheelchair access; dogs by arrangement only; no smoking

▭ None accepted

£ Single £16 to £20, single occupancy of twin £20, twin £32 to £40. Set D £12.50

It is because we put up with bad things that most hotelkeepers continue to give them to us.

Anthony Trollope

BONCHURCH ISLE OF WIGHT   **MAP 9**

Winterbourne

BONCHURCH, VENTNOR, ISLE OF WIGHT PO38 1RQ
TEL: ISLE OF WIGHT (0983) 852535   FAX: (0983) 853056

A peaceful haven with beautiful grounds overlooking the Channel.

Winterbourne received praise from no less a figure than Charles Dickens, who spent the summer of 1849 here composing *David Copperfield*. Writing to his wife of 'a delightful and beautiful house', he enthused, 'I think it's the prettiest place I ever saw in my life, at home or abroad'. Quite a soundbite, but one that would be difficult to contradict today. Standing next to a gnarled eleventh-century church on the edge of the charming village of Bonchurch, Winterbourne shelters in the lee of the steep downs to the north and enjoys a mild, almost Mediterranean climate. Its well-tended landscaped gardens, sloping down towards a shingle beach, are lush with roses, figs and cedars, and contain a secluded, kidney-shaped heated swimming-pool.

The unpretentious bedrooms, which are spread between the creeper-clad stone mansion and a converted coach-house, are named after Dickens' characters. Guests on longer stays are given priority in the allocation of sea view rooms; landward rooms can be tatty and rather dated. Public rooms retain the hushed atmosphere of a genteel resort hotel without being stuffy or formal. The lounge, done out in grey and red with flamboyant pillars and statues, gives on to a scenic garden terrace. Rich, cosy reds also dominate the dining-room, with its chandeliers and fancy balloon-back chairs. Dinner is fairly conventional, based on local fish and vegetables where possible; one reader has complained of indifferent service, and indeed on inspection we felt it was over-fussy and fell down through trying to do too much.

◖ Closed Dec to Feb

⤴ Just off the A3055 Shanklin to Ventnor road, adjoining St Boniface church in Bonchurch. Private car park

🛏 3 single, 5 twin, 8 double, 1 suite (some rooms in annexe); all with bathroom/WC, TV, room service, baby-listening; tea/coffee-making facilities and hair-dryer on request

◇ Restaurant, bar, lounge, verandah; heated outdoor swimming-pool at hotel, other sports nearby

⊖ No wheelchair access; no smoking in restaurant

▭ Access, Amex, Diners, Visa

£ Single £56 to £61, single occupancy of twin/double £91 to £100, twin/double £122 to £132, family room from £122 (rates inc dinner); deposit required. Light lunches by arrangement; set D £15.50

Dog lovers: some hotels not only welcome dogs, but provide gourmet meals for them. Ask.

BOSHAM WEST SUSSEX　　　　　　　　　　　　　　　　**MAP 9**

Millstream

BOSHAM, CHICHESTER, WEST SUSSEX PO18 8HL
TEL: BOSHAM (0243) 573234　FAX: (0243) 573459

Attractive public rooms in this well-established hotel in a pretty village by Chichester Harbour.

Bosham is a pretty little village well known to yachties who spend their weekends at Chichester Harbour, and the Millstream is probably equally well known to them for that rather special romantic dinner. The hotel is easily picked out at the centre of the village, just a couple of minutes' easy walk from the harbour. The downstairs front rooms of the original cottages have been knocked through to provide a charming bar, lounge and restaurant area; the pale yellow bar area has cane chairs, while the lounge is more cosy with grouped chairs and settees predominantly in pink. Dinner is all very pleasant, with a low-level buzz of conversation – though if you want to carry on hearing each other as the evening progresses it may be as well to choose a seat away from the rather exuberant pianist. The table d'hôte menu features English standards such as best end of lamb, roast chicken and roast duck.

Bedrooms are upstairs in the old building or tucked away in the modern extension. All have been refurbished in soft, well-co-ordinated colours since our last edition of the Guide. Although all the staff were professional, a gold star goes to the warm and friendly reception staff, who managed to cope (on an inspection visit) with the myriad demands of a toddler.

◑ Open all year

◪ 4 miles west of Chichester on A259, centrally located in Bosham on Bosham Lane, close to Old Bosham church. Private car park

⇌ 5 single, 9 twin, 13 double, 1 four-poster, 1 family room; all with bathroom/WC, TV, room service, hair-dryer, trouser press, baby-listening

◈ 2 restaurants, bar, lounge; conference facilities (max 20 people residential, 40 non-residential); water sports, golf, other sports nearby; babysitting by arrangement. Wheelchair access to hotel and restaurant, 4 ground-floor bedrooms

⊖ No dogs or smoking in public rooms

▭ Access, Amex, Diners, Visa

£ Single £59 to £69, single occupancy of twin/double £89, twin/double £89 to £99, four-poster/family room £109; deposit required. Set L £12.50, D £17. Special breaks available

---

BOTTOMHOUSE STAFFORDSHIRE   **MAP 5**

Pethills Bank Cottage

BOTTOMHOUSE, NR LEEK, STAFFORDSHIRE ST13 7PF
TEL: ONECOTE (0538) 304277/304555   FAX: (0538) 304575

*An outstanding bed and breakfast with immaculate rooms,
thoughtful hosts and good breakfasts.*

In open moorland five miles east of Leek, with panoramic views and a
silence disturbed only by the calls of various unusual birds, Pethills Bank
Cottage lies just outside the National Park, which gives Yvonne and
Richard Martin freedom from restrictive planning laws. The eighteenth-
century cottage, formerly a stone farmhouse, has been expanded to
include three guest bedrooms, each of them a good size and decorated
with cottagey fabrics. Garden Room on the ground floor is the largest,
and has its own tiny terrace from where you can watch the sun go down.
All rooms, including the small sitting-room, are immaculately kept, but
what lifts this bed and breakfast out of the ordinary is the attention that
Yvonne gives her guests. Each *en-suite* bathroom has a cupboard housing
toiletries, an iron, hot-water bottle, hair-dryer, and a basket of essentials.
In jubilant telegram style, one reader reports that his stay was 'Excellent.
Great attention to detail. Spotlessly clean. Very warm welcome. Excel-
lent breakfasts. The best B&B we have stayed in. Will return.'

◗ Open all year, exc Xmas

▨ Close to the A523, 5 miles
south-east of Leek, 10 miles
north-west of Ashbourne. Turn
into lane opposite the Little Chef
restaurant and follow signs for
½ mile. Private car park

🛏 1 twin, 1 double, 1 suite; all with
bathroom/WC, exc suite with
shower/WC; TV, hair-dryer,
baby-listening; ironing facilities in
all rooms

◈ Dining-room, lounge; golf, riding,
swimming-pool nearby

⊖ No wheelchair access; no
children under 5; no dogs; no
smoking

▭ None accepted

£ Single occupancy of twin/double
£29 to £32, twin/double £34 to
£39, suite £36 to £42; deposit
required. Set D £17.50 by
arrangement only

The 1995 Guide *will be published in the autumn of 1994. Reports on
hotels are welcome at any time of the year, but are extremely valuable in the
spring. Send them to* The Which? Hotel Guide, FREEPOST, 2
Marylebone Road, London NW1 1YN. *No stamp is needed if reports
are posted in the UK.*

BOUGHTON LEES KENT   **MAP 8**

Eastwell Manor

EASTWELL PARK, BOUGHTON LEES, NR ASHFORD, KENT TN25 4HR
TEL: ASHFORD (0233) 635751   TELEX: 966281 EMANOR G
FAX: (0233) 635530

A luxurious architectural deception in huge grounds.

A manor house has stood at Eastwell since the time of Edward the
Confessor, and Queen Victoria was a regular visitor here, but the present
building is steeped in less history than its mullioned windows and lofty
brick chimneys would suggest. It was actually constructed in the 1920s,
although much of the grey stone and elaborately carved oak panelling
was taken from the previous edifice. The mock-Tudor effect of the
building, which is laid out around a flagstoned courtyard, is on the whole
convincing and appealing. At the back, a brick-walled rose garden with a
lily pond and various ornamental terraces gives on to expansive lawns and
box hedges which in turn are surrounded by 65 acres of rough grassland.

The public rooms are suitably baronial. The dining-room has long
windows overlooking the terrace, high-backed leather chairs and a lofty
beamed ceiling hung with chandeliers; the lounge is clad in intricately
worked oak and sports a monumental carved stone fireplace. Standard
bedrooms are grand and airy, decorated in restrained, elegant colours
and furnished with period pieces. More impressive are the bathrooms,
with their pine floors, large dressing-tables and armchairs. Service in the
hotel is courteous and efficient, and the food, though pricey, is elaborate
and adventurous – perhaps goats' cheese salad with tomatoes and
Bayonne ham, followed by a selection of fish couscous and chives, with
Jamaican flan to finish.

◑ Open all year

➹ Take the A251 northwards from
Ashford. The hotel is on the left-
hand side just beyond the sign
for Boughton Aluph. Private car
park

🛏 4 twin, 12 double, 7 suites; all
with bathroom/WC, TV, room
service, hair-dryer, trouser press,
baby-listening

◈ Restaurant, bar, lounge, games
room, drying room; conference
facilities (max 100 people non-
residential, 23 residential);

tennis, archery, falconry, clay
and laser shooting at hotel,
fishing, golf, other sports nearby;
babysitting. Wheelchair access to
hotel, restaurant and WC (M, F),
2 ground-floor bedrooms

⊖ No dogs in public rooms; no
smoking in restaurant

▭ Access, Amex, Diners, Visa

£ Single occupancy of twin/double
£98, twin/double £148, suite
£178; deposit required. Set L
£16.50, D £24.50; alc L, D
£32.50. Special breaks available

---

 *This denotes that the hotel is in an exceptionally peaceful situation
where you can be assured of a restful stay.*

BOUGHTON MONCHELSEA KENT **MAP 8**

Tanyard

WIERTON HILL, BOUGHTON MONCHELSEA, MAIDSTONE, KENT ME17 4JT
TEL: MAIDSTONE (0622) 744705 FAX: (0622) 741998

*A charming medieval country house overlooking the Weald of
Kent.*

Set on a grassy slope with its own lily pond, Tanyard is an idyllic timber-
framed house which was built for a yeoman in the fourteenth century. Jan
Davies, who opened for business here 11 years ago, has furnished the
hotel sympathetically, maintaining its historic atmosphere while introducing a suitable level of luxury.

The natural colours and textures of the lounge's roof-beams, fireplace
and window mullions are matched by the subtle browns and greens of the
sofas, carpets and carved tables. The dining-room has an even larger
stone fireplace, oak floorboards and exposed stone walls, which contrast
beautifully with the gleaming table settings. Plans are afoot to turn this
room into a bar and the current kitchen into a two-tiered dining-room,
which would give the hotel more room to breathe while preserving its air
of rustic chic. One reader has written to praise the 'pleasant and helpful'
staff and to rave about the 'absolutely delicious' set dinner. Bedrooms are
comfortably furnished in restrained, tasteful colours, with some
gorgeous pieces of antique furniture. For a treat, choose the top-floor
suite, which offers a huge double bed under sloping beams, the best
views in the house and a plush gold-trimmed spa bath.

◑ Possible closure 2–3 weeks in
Jan/Feb

↗ From the B2163 at Boughton
Monchelsea turn down Park
Lane, opposite the Cock pub.
Take the first right down
Wierton Lane and fork right –
Tanyard is on the left at the
bottom of the hill. Private car
park

🛏 1 single, 2 twin, 2 double, 1
suite; all with bathroom/WC, TV,
limited room service

◇ Dining-room, bar, lounge; golf
nearby

⊖ No wheelchair access; no
children under 6; no dogs; no
smoking in some public rooms

▭ Access, Visa; Amex, Diners
(subject to surcharge)

£ Single £50, single occupancy of
twin/double £65 to £70, twin/
double £80 to £85, suite £110;
deposit required. Alc D £23

---

*If you have a small appetite, or just aren't feeling hungry, check if you can be
given a reduction if you don't want the full menu. At some hotels you could
easily end up paying £30 for one course and a coffee.*

BOUGHTON STREET KENT   **MAP 8**

Garden Hotel

167–169 THE STREET, BOUGHTON UNDER BLEAN, BOUGHTON STREET,
NR CANTERBURY, KENT ME13 9BH
TEL: CANTERBURY (0227) 751411   FAX: (0227) 751801

A green and pleasant modern hotel, popular with businessmen.

Mentioned by Chaucer as the place where the pilgrims encountered the
Canon Yeoman, Boughton under Blean has long been a handy stopping-
off point on the road to Canterbury and the Channel ports. The Garden
itself is ideally situated on the High Street, with the A2 running along the
bottom of the small back garden – although the drawback of this location
is that traffic noise can be intrusive.

 The building dates from the seventeenth century and has had a
chequered past as a general emporium, a soup kitchen, a school canteen
and an antique shop, but little evidence of its history remains bar the sash
windows in the bedrooms. Any rough edges have been ironed out,
leaving a bright, comfortable, modern hotel. The pine-clad restaurant
has an airy, conservatory-style, with hanging plants and an outdoor
terrace for use in the summer: food is conventional but reasonably
priced. Laid out on two tiers, the bar and lounge are well-lit and freshly
decorated in pinks and greens. This bright, summery feel continues into
the bedrooms, which have modern pine furniture and rich flowery
patterns. Although some rooms are cramped they're immaculately kept,
especially the gleaming white bathrooms.

◑ Open all year; restaurant closed
   Sun eve

↗ Leave the M2 where it crosses
   the A2 Dover to Canterbury
   road. Take left at T-junction into
   village. The hotel is then ¹/₂ mile
   on the right-hand side. Private
   car park

🛏 7 twin, 3 double, family room
   available; all with bathroom/WC,
   TV, room service, hair-dryer,
   trouser press, baby-listening

◇ 2 restaurants, bar, lounge, TV
   room (air-conditioned ground-
   floor rooms); conference facilities

(max 50 people non-residential,
10 residential); fishing, golf,
other sports nearby; babysitting
by arrangement. Wheelchair
access to restaurant only

⊖ No dogs

▭ Access, Amex, Visa

£ Single occupancy of twin/double
   £35 to £45, twin/double £60,
   family room rate £65 to £75;
   deposit required. Set L £10.50, D
   £17; alc L £15, D £20 (service
   charge added to restaurant bills).
   Special breaks available

All entries in the Guide *are rewritten every year, not least because standards
fluctuate. Don't trust an out-of-date* Guide.

BOURNE LINCOLNSHIRE   **MAP 5**

Bourne Eau House

30 SOUTH STREET, BOURNE, LINCOLNSHIRE PE10 9LY
TEL: BOURNE (0778) 423621

A beautifully furnished Wolsey Lodge with a sociable house-party format.

The approach to Bourne, across flat fields dotted with pylons and iron-roofed farm buildings, is not the prettiest in Lincolnshire, though Bourne Eau House itself is a lovely sight. Opposite the twelfth-century church, and bordered by a moat that once marked the boundary of Hereward the Wake's castle – now reduced to a collection of grassy mounds on the other side of the memorial gardens – the Bishops' family home occupies the prime spot in the village, and has a superb setting and a lovely garden with country-cottage borders. The house is red brick and a mix of styles, from Elizabethan chimneys to Georgian casement windows. The interior is beautifully furnished; the Jacobean dining-room, with its flagstoned floor, inglenook fireplace and solid dining table, contrasts with the elegant Georgian drawing-room with pale blue walls, delicate chairs and polished floorboards. Guests meet together here for pre-dinner drinks at 7pm, when the Bishops create a genial house-party atmosphere. A set evening meal in summer might include prawn salad, roast breast of turkey with cranberry sauce and vegetables, strawberries and ice-cream, cheeses, coffee and mints.

The three bedrooms are immaculately kept, with fresh fruit and flowers adding to the luxury of rich fabrics and antiques. The blue Georgian Room is large and smart, with a white modern shower room, while the pale yellow twin is pretty with lacy bedcovers and embroidered pillowcases; our favourite is the smaller, darker Jacobean Room, with a heavy oak carved bed, stone fireplace and enormous, well-equipped bathroom.

◑ Open all year, exc Xmas and Easter

⤢ The concealed entrance to the house is directly opposite the cenotaph in Bourne's Memorial Gardens, in South Street (A15). Private car park

🛏 2 twin, 1 double; all with shower/WC, exc 1 twin with bathroom/WC; TV, room service, hair-dryer in all rooms

◈ Dining-room, lounge, TV room, music room, library; golf, fishing, other sports nearby

⊖ No wheelchair access; children by arrangement only; no dogs; no smoking in bedrooms

▭ None accepted

£ Single occupancy of twin/double £35, twin/double £60. Set D £20

Prices are quoted per room *rather than* per person.

Langtry Manor ☆

26 DERBY ROAD, EAST CLIFF, BOURNEMOUTH, DORSET BH1 3QB
TEL: BOURNEMOUTH (0202) 553887　FAX: (0202) 290115

Sleep in the bed where a king once found his pleasures in this unusual Edwardian hotel.

This Tudor-style cottage on the outskirts of Bournemouth was built in 1877 by Edward VII as a grace and favour residence for his favourite mistress, Lillie Langtry – something that the present owners don't let you forget. The decoration in the public lounge and bar is rather dark, making full use of deep-red carpets, velvet curtains and flock wallpapers. There are occasional wooden beams and these are decorated with Langtry's pithy *bons mots*.

Meals are taken in the dining-room with its minstrels' gallery and stained-glass windows. The menu offers traditional fare such as roast leg of pork, grilled salmon and beef in creamy peppercorn sauce. On Saturdays a six-course banquet is served and staff dress in Edwardian clothes, as do some regular guests. Halfway through the eating marathon, diners pause for a *son et lumière* about the couple.

The grandest bedroom is the Edward VII suite, with its high beamed ceiling and large blue-tiled fireplace. Lillie used to entertain Edward in the massive oak four-poster that still dominates the room. The other rooms exhibit a variety of styles, but decoration is getting a little frayed around the edges. More reports, please.

◑ Open all year

🡒 Turn off the A338 at the railway station, continue over the next roundabout, then left into Knyveton Road. The hotel is at the end, at the junction of Derby Road. Private car park

🛏 2 single, 23 twin/double/four-poster (family rooms and suites available); all with bathroom/WC, TV, room service, hair-dryer, mini-bar, baby-listening

◈ Dining-room, bar, lounge, library/study; conference facilities (max 30 people residential, 60 non-

residential); fishing, golf, other sports nearby. Wheelchair access to hotel (1 step), restaurant and WC, 3 ground-floor bedrooms, 1 specially equipped for disabled people

⊖ No dogs in public rooms; no smoking in dining-room

▭ Access, Amex, Diners, JCB, Visa

£ Single £55, single occupancy of twin/double £70, twin/double/four-poster £89 to £109, suite/family room from £150 (rates inc dinner); deposit required. Set L £12.50, D £20

Porters Hotel ☆

18 HERBERT ROAD, WESTBOURNE, BOURNEMOUTH, DORSET BH4 8HD
TEL: BOURNEMOUTH (0202) 763825

A small 1920s-style hotel, a short drive from the centre of Bournemouth and the beach.

The black-and-white house stands rather unassumingly in a quiet residential area of Alum Chine. Walking into the lounge is like walking on to the set of a Noël Coward play; two brightly coloured sofas face each other, a low coffee table placed between them. In the corner by the inglenook fireplace is a high-backed leather armchair and from the hallway comes the tick-tock of the grandfather clock. Panelled walls and window seats add to the character of the room and wooden beam-like shelves support a mixture of plates and ornaments.

There is a small group of people relaxing in the lounge as our inspector calls. 'We've been coming for the last three years, the food is excellent.' Graham Whitehouse, the proprietor, does all the cooking. There is a set menu every day but it's flexible and requests are noted. An example might be home-made carrot and coriander soup served with hot crusty rolls, followed by chicken en croûte with champagne and mushroom sauce served with Anna potatoes and fresh vegetables. There is a choice of desserts such as profiteroles with chocolate sauce and fresh cream or bananas baked with honey and rum, then if you've got any room left there's the cheeseboard and fresh coffee served with petits fours. The dining-room is small but not cramped and it overlooks the garden and small river.

'We don't put televisions in the rooms,' says Graham. 'We find that people tend to come down to the lounge instead of staying in their rooms all evening.' Nonetheless the bedrooms are pleasant, of average size with old walnut furniture and basket chairs. Carpets are thick and warm and the walls are covered in print wallpaper. Room Eight has a spacious beamed loft bathroom with leaded lattice windows.

On the stairs you are met by a rather life-like full-size china dalmation standing next to an old-fashioned tailor's dummy modelling period costume, completing the transition back in time.

◑ Closed weekdays between Oct and Mar

⤢ A local map is provided on request. Private car park and on-street parking

🛏 1 twin, 7 double; all with bathroom/WC, hair-dryer; trouser press on request

◈ Restaurant, bar, lounge; fishing, golf, other sports nearby

⊖ No wheelchair access; no guests under 18; no dogs; no smoking in dining-room

▭ None accepted

£ Single occupancy of twin/double £25, twin/double £40; deposit required. Set D £12.50

BOURTON-ON-THE-WATER GLOUCESTERSHIRE   **MAP 9**

Coombe House

RISSINGTON ROAD, BOURTON-ON-THE-WATER, GLOUCESTERSHIRE
GL54 2DT
TEL: COTSWOLD (0451) 821966

Keen owners are making a success of this comfortable bed and breakfast.

Bourton-on-the-Water gets packed on hot summer weekends, and if you have been jostling among the sightseers the tranquillity of Graham and Diana Ellis's house on the outskirts of the village will be a welcome relief. Coombe House is an ordinary-looking villa, complete with gravel driveway and small garden, but it makes a good bed and breakfast. Inside, it is extremely spruce – one result of Diana's pride in her business. The sitting-room is formally set out, with showers of leaflets describing local attractions. The breakfast room, warmly furnished in pine, is quite large enough to give you space to breathe. Bedrooms are all comfortably furnished, though they lack character. The most charming, if you like attic rooms, is Number Eight. For hot days there is a sunny balcony on the first floor.

◑ Open all year, exc 24, 25 and 31 Dec

⤢ With the village post office on your right, take the Rissington/ Burford road. The house is signposted and is 300 yards past Birdland, on the left. Private car park

🛏 2 twin, 5 double, family rooms available; most with bathroom/ WC, some with shower/WC; TV, room service in all rooms; hair-dryer on request

◇ Breakfast room, lounge, drying room; fishing, golf, other sports nearby

⊖ No wheelchair access; no dogs; no smoking

▭ Amex, Visa

£ Single occupancy of twin/double from £35, twin/double from £50, family room from £56 to £74; deposit required. Special breaks available

BOVEY TRACEY DEVON   **MAP 10**

Edgemoor

HAYTOR ROAD, BOVEY TRACEY, DEVON TQ13 9LE
TEL: BOVEY TRACEY (0626) 832466   FAX: (0626) 834760

A good rural base on the edge of Dartmoor, within easy reach of the motorway.

This aptly named hotel, a large oblong Victorian brick building covered in creepers and shrubs, sits rather imposingly just outside Bovey Tracey.

At first a little intimidating by virtue of its isolation, the hotel has a warmth that is immediately felt on entering the bar and lounge. Small and intimate with a low black-beamed ceiling and dark wooden furniture with deep-red cushions, the lounge is nicely toasted by the open log fire.

The dining-room is more formal: lace tablecloths with smartly laid glistening silver cutlery, high-backed wooden chairs painted with a hint of pink and windows framed by grey and dusty pink heavy drapes are all combined to elegant effect. The menu is good, and the prawns and mushrooms in garlic we sampled were hot and fresh. Roast duck served with crispy fresh vegetables followed by raspberry meringue was nicely presented and efficiently served by proprietor Rod Day. Both he and wife Pat are always available and willing to help, without being intrusive or over-friendly.

The bedrooms are full of character; each one is different, but bright colours, flowery designs, borders and frills prevail, and thought has clearly gone into colour co-ordination – the heavily lined curtains match the rest of the décor. Room Ten, with its four-poster bed and red velvet chairs, is grand if a little garish.

◐ Open all year

↗ Turn off the A38 on to the A382 Bovey Tracey road. Go straight on at the 1st roundabout and left, towards Haytor and Widecombe, at the 2nd. After ½ mile fork left – the hotel is ½ mile along this road. Private car park

🛏 3 single, 2 twin, 3 double, 3 four-poster, 1 family room; all with bathroom/WC, exc 2 singles with shower/WC; TV, room service, hair-dryer, trouser press, baby-listening in all rooms

◇ Restaurant, 2 bars, lounge, ballroom; conference facilities

(max 100 people non-residential, 12 residential); petanque at hotel, fishing, golf, other sports nearby. Wheelchair access to hotel (2 steps), restaurant and 2 ground-floor bedrooms

⊖ Dogs at manager's discretion; no smoking in restaurant

▭ Access, Amex, Diners, Visa

£ Single £37 to £45, single occupancy of twin/double £37 to £55, twin/double £70 to £85, four-poster £75 to £90, family room from £76 and £92; deposit preferred. Alc L £10 to £13; set D £15.50/£17.50. Special breaks available

---

BOWNESS-ON-WINDERMERE CUMBRIA   **MAP 4**

Lindeth Fell

BOWNESS-ON-WINDERMERE, CUMBRIA LA23 3JP
TEL: WINDERMERE (05394) 43286/44287

Country-house hotel set in lovely gardens on a hill above Windermere, with friendly hosts and simple well-prepared food.

For some, the lakeside views of Windermere have been spoilt by the development and sheer numbers of people that come to visit. The same

LINDETH FELL
- BOWNESS-ON-WINDERMERE -

cannot be said about the view from Lindeth Fell; it stands imperiously above the fray on a hill a couple of miles from the town centre. The drive weaves through gardens before arriving at a large white house with a Union Flag flying proudly beside it. From the front of the hotel you look out over a terrace with a grass tennis court and croquet lawn, past woods to the lake in the distance. Azaleas and rhododendrons grow in abundance and the spring daffodils add their own dash of brilliant colour.

Guests are welcomed in the wood-panelled hall (decorated with old school photos), with a firm handshake and a smile by proprietor Pat Kennedy. One lounge is decorated in light colours, has deep easy chairs and a fine plaster ceiling. Family photos and well-thumbed magazines enhance the friendly atmosphere.

Meals are taken in the pink and red dining-room, or a conservatory extension which makes the most of the views. Menus are usually limited to a couple of choices per course, so dinner will consist of, perhaps, celery soup, boiled ham, followed by a selection of English cheeses – straightforward food that is expertly prepared. Diana Kennedy does the rounds of diners, enquiring if everything is satisfactory.

The bedrooms, with floral wallpapers and a mixture of old and new furniture, are comfortable rather than fashionable and vary in size and outlook. The best lake views are from the top of the house.

◑ *Closed mid-Nov to mid-Mar*

⤢ *1 mile south of Bowness on the A5074 Lyth Valley to Lancaster road. Private car park*

🛏 *2 single, 4 twin, 6 double, 2 family rooms; all with bathroom/ WC, TV, room service, hair-*

dryer, baby-listening; trouser press on request

◈ *2 dining-rooms, 3 lounges, drying room; tennis at hotel, other sports nearby. Wheelchair access to hotel (ramp) and restaurant, 1 ground-floor bedroom specially equipped for disabled people*

● No children under 7; no dogs

▭ Access, Visa

£ Single £40, single occupancy of twin/double £55, twin/double

£79, family room £82; deposit required. Sun L £10; alc L £5 to £7.50; set D £19. Special breaks available

---

Linthwaite House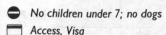

CROOK ROAD, BOWNESS-ON-WINDERMERE, CUMBRIA LA23 3JA
TEL: WINDERMERE (05394) 88600   FAX: (05394) 88601

An unstuffy country-house hotel with great lake views.

Set in 14 acres of garden and woodlands in an elevated position with views of Windermere, Linthwaite certainly has a location to be envied. It was built in 1910 and current proprietors the Bevans made sure that the refurbishment in 1991 retained the Edwardian atmosphere. The recently added conservatory has wicker chairs, a number of plants and a great view that can be appreciated more fully through the pair of binoculars thoughtfully provided. There is a smallish lounge area, supplemented by a cosy bar. Old trunks and suitcases are placed at strategic points for period effect and the pleasant reception area features an old birdcage.

The five-course dinner may typically include warm mousseline of sole in a champagne butter sauce, cream of courgette and cucumber soup, pan-fried breast of duckling with a sauce of clear honey and sherry vinegar, then a home-made brioche crowned with fresh blackberries glazed under golden sabayon, and a selection of British cheeses to finish.

All 18 bedrooms are well-equipped and well-co-ordinated, though only five have a view of the lake. Rates vary according to the size and position of the room but all include free use of a local leisure spa and the hotel's own fishing tarn.

● Open all year

↗ 1 mile from Windermere golf club, on the left as travelling towards the lake. Private car park

🛏 1 single, 5 twin, 8 double, 3 four-poster, 1 suite; all with bathroom/WC, TV, room service, hair-dryer, trouser press, baby-listening

◈ Restaurant, bar, lounge, drying room, conservatory; conference facilities (max 20 people residential and non-residential); fishing at hotel, golf, tennis, other sports nearby. Wheelchair access to hotel (1 step), restaurant and WC (F), 5 ground-floor bedrooms

● No children under 7 in restaurant eves; no dogs; no smoking in bedrooms

▭ Access, Amex, Visa

£ Single £65, single occupancy of twin/double from £70, twin/double from £80, four-poster from £120, suite from £140; deposit required. Set D £25; alc L from £5. Special breaks available

Box House

BOX, WILTSHIRE SN14 9NR
TEL: BATH (0225) 744447   FAX: (0225) 743971

*A pretty Georgian house under new management, moving from
starch formality to a broader family appeal.*

Tim and Kathryn Burnham are new recruits to the hotel business – Tim
is in advertising, while Kathryn used to run a cookery school. They have
chosen Box House for their brilliant new career, taking on an attractive,
classically proportioned Georgian building. They are a casual, rather
laid-back couple, who prefer jazz and soft rock to more conventional
classical Muzak tapes. One of the first changes is to build a children's
play area in the garden.

Bedrooms are mostly spacious, decorated in soft, muted colours.
Northay is a first-floor corner room with elegant sash windows facing in
two directions and a view over Box House's own watercress beds, washed
by natural limestone springs as they slope down towards the trout stream.
Our inspector complained bitterly about the hard bed in Whitewood
during her stay – perhaps an area still to be addressed.

The downstairs rooms are light and airy; the lounge has plenty of easy
sofas, glossy magazines and a stag's head above the corner bar. Despite
the attractive, understated style of the dining-room, dinner was disappointing, judged by our inspector to be clichéd and underflavoured. The
hotel has plans to offer more variety on the menu and to place more
emphasis on food in future. It is, however, early days for the new team –
at the time of our inspection they had only been up and running a bare
two months. By the time this goes to print, who knows, the offending
mattresses may well have been quietly laid to rest. More reports, please.

◑ Open all year

⤢ On the A4 between Bath and
Chippenham. Private car park

🛏 6 twin, 3 double, family rooms
and suites available; all with
bathroom/WC, TV, room service,
hair-dryer, trouser press; tea/
coffee-making facilities on
request

◈ Restaurant, bar, lounge, drying
room; conference facilities (max
50 people non-residential, 9

residential); heated swimming-
pool at hotel, other sports
nearby. Wheelchair access to
public rooms only

⊖ No dogs

▭ Access, Amex, Visa

£ Single occupancy of twin/double
£70 to £85, twin/double £70 to
£85, family room £80 to £95,
suite £80 to £105. Set L £6.50;
alc L £16, D £22. Special breaks
available

All reports are welcome on any hotel, whether or not it is in the Guide.

BRACKENTHWAITE CUMBRIA   **MAP 4**

Pickett Howe

BRACKENTHWAITE, BUTTERMERE VALLEY, CUMBRIA CA13 9UY
TEL: COCKERMOUTH (0900) 85444

A delightfully renovated farmhouse in a peaceful location at the confluence of three valleys.

The only sound you can hear from the courtyard of this small, white-washed farmhouse is the occasional bleating of the Herdwick sheep grazing on the surrounding 15 acres of land belonging to Pickett Howe. The building is Grade-II listed (the oldest parts of the house were built around 1650) and, although many of the original features have survived, Dani and David Edwards have taken care to avoid a period-piece atmosphere by installing modern comforts like whirlpool baths in some of the *en-suite* bathrooms.

'We like to spoil our guests,' says Dani, yet their attentiveness never spills over into intrusiveness. The bar, for example, is self-service and operates on trust, with the guests writing up their measures on the slate in the Jacobean drinks cupboard. Dinner is traditional, with local specialities like devilled rainbow trout seasoned with fresh herbs from the Edwards' garden, followed by a selection of Cumbrian cheeses and rounded off with a Westmorland raisin 'n' nut slice. The breakfast menu is as expansive and imaginative as you could find, with choices ranging from a compôte of apricots, prunes, bananas and raisins cooked and cooled in honey, orange juice and wild raspberry tea to the simple bacon butty.

Instead of being numbered the bedrooms have names, the Georgian Room and the 1730 Room, for example, evoking their origins and emphasising their individuality. What they have in common, apart from the state-of-the-art bathrooms, is the original Victorian bedsteads with white lace bedcovers.

The permanently optimistic barometer in the hallway – fixed on dry – captures the cheerful spirit of David and Dani Edwards' guesthouse to perfection.

- ◑   *Closed Dec to Mar*
- ⬀   *From Keswick take the B5292 Whinlatter Pass to Lorton and then the B5289 towards Buttermere. Private car park*
- 🛏   *1 twin, 3 double; all with bathroom/WC, hair-dryer; TV on request*
- ◈   *Dining-room, 2 lounges, drying*
-   *room, study; fishing, golf, other sports nearby*
- ⊖   *No wheelchair access; no children under 10; no dogs; no smoking*
- ▭   *Access, Visa*
- £   *Twin/double £68; deposit required. Set D £18 (7.15pm). Special breaks available*

Bradfield House

BRADFIELD COMBUST, BURY ST EDMUNDS, SUFFOLK IP30 0LR
TEL: SICKLESMERE (0284) 386301 (and fax)

You'll find a laid-back, relaxed atmosphere at this country-house restaurant-with-rooms.

Food is the priority here: Roy and Sally Ghijben's business had culinary beginnings, but now that a handful of rooms are available to guests, you can spend more than just a meal-time at this seventeenth-century, half-timbered house. Within the two acres of land is a kitchen garden from which Roy gathers fresh ingredients for his dishes, which tend towards traditional English lines combined with a dollop of rural French panache. Praise has been lavished on the avocado with peas in a Stilton and Greek yogurt sauce and the garlic mushrooms with smoked sausage pie was rated 'interesting, in spite of initial doubts'. However, praise comes tinged with a critical observation that the menu remained the same throughout one couple's four-day stay.

There is no doubt that the atmosphere is easy-going. Underlying the careful thought that has gone into each of the bedrooms (all are decorated with interesting furniture and have smart, modern bathrooms) is a relaxed, take-it-or-leave-it approach. For example, on one arrival, Roy handed over a key, waved in the general direction of upstairs and returned to his half-finished job of removing a tree stump from the garden – leaving his guests to unload their car and sort themselves out. Fine, if you're happy to fend for yourself but not so good if you like a little more personal attention. Similarly, toast at breakfast is a do-it-yourself affair – again, no problem if you can't abide toast that arrives too early and is cold by the time you get to it but 'when there's one toaster and several couples at breakfast, it becomes a chore'.

◑ Closed 1 week after Xmas

🡵 Four miles south of Bury St Edmunds on the A134 Sudbury road. Private car park

🛏 1 single, 1 twin, 1 double, 1 four-poster, family room available; all with bathroom/WC, exc single with shower/WC; TV, room service, hair-dryer in all rooms

◈ Restaurant, bar, lounge. Wheelchair access to restaurant only

⊖ No children under 8 in restaurant eves; no dogs; no smoking in restaurant or lounge

▭ Access, Visa

£ Single £50, single occupancy of twin/double £55, twin/double £70, four-poster £85, family room on request; deposit required. Set D £16.50; alc D £17.50/£23.50. Special breaks available

---

All rooms have tea/coffee-making facilities unless we specify to the contrary.

BRADFORD WEST YORKSHIRE   **MAP 5**

Restaurant Nineteen

19 NORTH PARK ROAD, HEATON, BRADFORD, WEST YORKSHIRE BD9 4NT
TEL: BRADFORD (0274) 492559   FAX: (0274) 483827

A justly popular and accomplished restaurant with handsomely decorated bedrooms.

If your vision of Northern mill towns leads you to expect modest terraces of Coronation Street-type houses, this leafy part of Bradford could be an eye-opener, for the sweeping avenue of grand Victorian mansions overlooking the trim lawns and tennis courts of Lister Park looks instantly inviting. Combine this with memorable food and plush, stylish bedrooms, and a business trip to Bradford or a tourist jaunt to visit the National Museum of Photography, Film and Television or the nearby Brontë country begins to look like a serious treat.

The lounge is a rather dark, restrained Victorian parlour, with heavily fringed curtains, china ornaments and the reliable tick of a mantel clock. The open-plan restaurant is, by comparison, an airy wedding cake of a room, with fondant-like green, pink and white décor. Russell Flint's famously *déshabillé* ladies decorate the walls. Stephen Smith's food, served (after a relay of appetisers) by his front-of-house partner Robert Barbour, strives to match the splendour of the surroundings – and succeeds. Flavours are creatively coupled – perhaps a salad of plum tomatoes, buffalo mozzarella, sautéed olive polenta and basil, followed by celery and lovage soup, roast woodpigeon with a celeriac and cheese pudding, and white chocolate ice-cream with warm cherries. The wine-list is wide-ranging, with a dozen house offerings.

You'll share your twin or double room with the Russell Flint lady who gives it its name. Décor in bold modern colours complements her. Rooms are smallish, but you'll be comfortable with the thick quilts, good bathrooms and lots of hanging space for clothes.

◑ Open all year, exc I week Jan and Aug; restaurant closed Sun eve

🔁 Follow the A650 Manningham Lane to the north of Bradford. North Park Road is a left turning just before Bradford Grammar School. Private car park

🛏 2 twin, 2 double; all with bathroom/WC, exc I twin with shower/WC; TV, room service, hair-dryer, trouser press in all rooms; no tea/coffee-making facilities in rooms

◈ Restaurant, lounge; golf, tennis, sauna/solarium, heated swimming-pool, gym nearby

⊖ No wheelchair access; no children under 10; no dogs

▭ Access, Amex, Diners, Visa

💷 Single occupancy of twin/double £60, twin/double £70. Set D £26

BRADFORD-ON-AVON WILTSHIRE **MAP 9**

Bradford Old Windmill

4 MASONS LANE, BRADFORD-ON-AVON, WILTSHIRE BA15 1QN
TEL: BRADFORD-ON-AVON (0225) 866842

Leisurely atmosphere in a friendly windmill conversion.

At a guess, the majority of guests at this unusual, converted old windmill *sans* sails are likely to be *Guardian* rather than *Telegraph* readers. Although most visitors are omnivorous (and bacon is served at breakfast), the ethos of the place is non-smoking, vegetarian and environmentally concerned. No tropical hardwoods are purchased, and recycled wood and stone was used when building the new tower extension. It is the sort of place where you need have no worries about coming down to meals in a Save the Whales T-shirt.

Peter and Priscilla Roberts found themselves moving into the guest-house business as a result of invitations issued and addresses swopped during their world travels. The house is full of mementoes of their wanderings, from Peruvian wall hangings to African seed pods. With only four bedrooms, the house feels like a comfortable, user-friendly country cottage. The circular, beamed lounge has low sofas, books, an open fire and pointed Gothic windows. The shape is mirrored in the Great Spur bedroom, which has a matching round bed and a marvellous view over Bradford. Damsel is another curved room (in the new tower, sympathetically designed by an architect guest) but this time with a water bed (and satin sheets on request). Wallflower is a delightful family room with cabin beds for children on a gallery reached by ladder. Priscilla recommends they are not for under 6-year-olds. There is also an unusual walk-in power shower built into the stone wall of the mill.

Meals are taken communally around a long table, in a cheery room decorated with old agricultural tools. Breakfasts range from English to American (hash browns and short stack), Healthy to Horribly Healthy (vegan wholemeal muffins and devilled mushrooms). Three nights a week, Priscilla cooks vegetarian dinners with an ethnic theme – Thai, Mexican, Caribbean, Nepalese . . .

The windmill is hard to find, down an unmarked drive off a steeply winding main road. On booking, guests will be sent a detailed map.

◐ Open all year; restaurant closed Tues, Wed, Fri, Sun eves

⤧ In Bradford on the A363, find the Castle pub. Go down the hill towards the town centre. After 75 yards turn left into a gravelled private drive immediately before the first roadside house (no sign on road). Private car park

⇔ 2 double, 2 family rooms; double with bathroom/WC, 2 with shower/WC, 1 public bathroom; TV, hair-dryer on request

◈ Dining-room, lounge, drying room; riding, tennis, other sports nearby

⊖ No wheelchair access; no children under 6; no dogs; no smoking

▭ Access, Visa

£ Single occupancy of double £35 to £59, double £49 to £75, family room (3 people) £74 to

£84; deposit required. Set D £19 (8pm); supper tray £7. Special breaks available

---

Priory Steps

NEWTOWN, BRADFORD-ON-AVON, WILTSHIRE BA15 1NQ
TEL: BRADFORD-ON-AVON (0225) 862230   FAX: (0225) 866248

Panoramic views, comfortable bedrooms and home-cooked meals make for a welcoming stay.

Perched on a steep hillside overlooking the old market town, the verdant terraces behind Priory Steps cascade down like Bradford's answer to the Hanging Gardens of Babylon. Do not, however, be tempted to follow the flight of steps that beckon enticingly in the middle of the garden or you will soon end up on all fours, crawling through a secret passage to the former Priory, further down the hill.

Diana and Carey Chapman (and now baby Benedict) quickly move on to first-name terms with visitors to their converted seventeenth-century weavers' cottages. One reader wrote to say: 'We were made so welcome, fed and housed so outstandingly well, that we came away thoroughly relaxed, having had a most enjoyable time exploring the area.'

All five comfortable *en-suite* bedrooms are of a good size and share splendid views over the town and river, looking towards Salisbury Plain. Bathrooms are bright and modern, and have personal details like sea shell collections. One room has a small extra sitting-room which will take a cot or fold-up bed. There are books, games and CDs to enjoy in the library, which has low leather seating. It is a good place to savour a drink before moving into the beamed dining-room for one of Diana's home-cooked dinners. A trained Cordon Bleu cook, she gives her guests, who dine communally in typical Wolsey Lodge style, simple but delicious three-course meals such as smoked haddock and egg mousse, chicken véronique with lots of wholesome vegetables, and Hobson's Choice – the recipe for this delectable dessert of fruit, cream and yogurt was given to Diana by a guest called, yes, Mrs Hobson.

◐ Open all year

↗ Newtown is a left-hand turning, 200 yards to the north of the town centre, off the A363 signposted Bath. Private car park

⇝ 2 twin, 2 double, 1 suite; all with bathroom/WC, TV, hair-dryer

◇ Dining-room, lounge; meetings facilities (max 14 people non-residential)

⊖ No wheelchair access; no dogs; smoking by agreement only

▭ Access, Visa

£ Single occupancy of twin/double £42, twin/double/suite £56. Set D £15 (7.30pm by arrangement)

Woolley Grange

WOOLLEY GREEN, BRADFORD-ON-AVON, WILTSHIRE BA15 1TX
TEL: BRADFORD-ON-AVON (0225) 864705   FAX: (0225) 864059

Civilised, country-house hotel ideal for happy, foodie families.

A pair of tiny green wellingtons stands by the entrance to this beautiful, wistaria-framed Jacobean manor house. A spaniel puppy bounces up, full of slobbering, friendly interest. It sets the tone for a relaxed country-house hotel where children are welcomed as much as their parents.

There are fun and games for all ages here, from tennis, biking, swimming, croquet and badminton to just lazing and loafing around reading all the latest magazines. The children's facilities are exemplary, with play areas, sandpits and a fully supervised Woolley Bears Den. This games room, jammed full of absorbing things like snooker, table tennis, table football, paints and toys, also serves as a dining area to those children who do not want to eat in the main restaurant. With new friends to play with arriving every week, Nigel and Heather Chapman's own four children must be amongst the most envied in Britain.

The hotel itself mixes low-key sophistication with easy comfort. The oak-panelled drawing-room has smart black leather sofas, while the Victorian Gothic conservatory has capacious rattan chairs, a flagged floor and faded Indian rugs. Witty paintings and prints hang throughout.

The bedrooms, all of which can take cots or Z-beds, are beautifully furnished with period beds. There are fresh flowers, home-made biscuits and some also have gas coal fires. All have good bathrooms with Victorian-style fittings, although three are shower only. Six bedrooms are in the Cottage, converted from the old dairy.

Food at Woolley Grange is definitely in the yummy category, from pizzas and fish fingers in the Den to steamed mussels with saffron and spinach, saddle of rabbit with roasted peppers, and white chocolate truffle torte with dark chocolate and espresso sauce on the grown-up's menu. Prices are more in the crikey range, but lighter meals are also available in the conservatory.

◖ Open all year

⤢ On the B3105, ½ mile north-east of Bradford-on-Avon. Private car park

🛏 1 single, 1 twin, 16 double, 2 suites; most with bathroom/WC, some with shower/WC; TV, room service, hair-dryer, baby-listening in all rooms; tea/coffee-making facilities on request

◈ 2 restaurants, 3 lounges, TV room, drying room, conservatory, games room; conference facilities (max 50 people non-residential, 20 residential); tennis, croquet, badminton, heated outdoor swimming-pool (Easter to Oct), nursery, playground at hotel, other sports nearby; babysitting. Wheelchair access to hotel (1 step), restaurant and 1 ground-floor bedroom

⊖ No dogs or smoking in restaurants

▭ Access, Amex, Diners, Visa

(£) Single £80, single occupancy of twin/double £80, twin/double £135, family room/suite £165 to

£185. Alc L, D from £5; set D £28. Special breaks available

BRAITHWAITE CUMBRIA   **MAP 4**

Ivy House

BRAITHWAITE, KESWICK, CUMBRIA CA12 5SY
TEL: KESWICK (076 87) 78338

A cosy hotel with a friendly atmosphere and fine cooking.

Tucked away in the small village of Braithwaite, Ivy House manages to maintain an air of seclusion at the same time as being conveniently placed for the county's main traffic arteries and more scenic touring routes like the nearby Whinlatter Pass. The deep-green Georgian exterior is enlivened by two flower baskets that hang from the lamps on either side of the doorway. Inside, the house oozes an effortless period charm without any dusty museum-piece overtones, and in Nick and Wendy Shill you have hosts who try to ensure that you experience the hospitality of bygone days without its attendant formalities. The lounge is long, but the low ceiling with exposed beams and the log fires at either end ensure a cosy corner even on the coldest days. Bedrooms are of a good size and are generally simply furnished with good-quality modern furniture, though some have antique pieces: Room Five, for example, has a large Victorian four-poster bed and dark wood cupboards and drawers. One reader had some criticisms of Room Three, describing it as 'beside the kitchen', 'poky' with 'ridiculously small bath towels and horrid dried milk sachets'.

The dining-room on the first floor has a fine oak cabinet dating from 1658. The deep greens of the carpeting, walls and ceiling echo the exterior, albeit with a slightly more sombre effect. The four-course dinner has a traditional basis and plenty of choice, with main courses like sirloin steak au poivre or breast of chicken with chasseur sauce following a starter such as mushrooms cooked with Stilton and cream. A selection of freshly made sweets rounds things off before coffee and mints in the lounge.

◑ Open all year, exc Jan

▰ Turn left off the A66 from Keswick on to the B5292 to Braithwaite village. The hotel is in the village centre. Private car park

🛏 2 single, 2 twin, 6 double, 2 four-poster; all with bathroom/WC, exc 1 single with shower/WC; TV, hair-dryer in all rooms

◈ Dining-room, bar, lounge, drying facilities; fishing, riding, other sports nearby

⊖ No wheelchair access; no dogs in public rooms and by arrangement only in bedrooms; no smoking in dining-room

▭ Access, Amex, Diners, Visa

(£) Single £43, single occupancy of

twin/double £53, twin/double
£86, four-poster £98 (rates inc
dinner); deposit required. Set D

£19 (7pm). Special breaks
available

BRAMPTON CUMBRIA   MAP 3

Farlam Hall

BRAMPTON, CUMBRIA CA8 2NG
TEL: HALLBANKGATE (06977) 46234   FAX: (06977) 46683

Top-of-the-market country-house hotel in a wonderful setting.

Farlam Hall has the air of a traditional country home that many hotels
aspire to with differing degrees of success. The original grey stone, ivy-
clad farmhouse is late seventeenth century, but the building was expanded considerably in Victorian times. It is the Victorian influence that
predominates, nowhere more so than in the spacious and elegant dining-
room with its large bay windows and ornate fireplace, the deep-blue
shade of the carpet mirrored in the superb plaster ceiling. The Quinion
and Stevenson families who run the hotel like to maintain an air of
tradition in the evenings, and guests (in jacket and tie) are conducted to
their tables by staff in period attire. The menus are strong on local meat,
game and fish. Confit of duckling leg set on spring leaves and finished
with a raspberry vinegar and walnut oil dressing might be a starter, with a
fillet of halibut or roast Lancashire guinea-fowl as the main course.

  The 13 bedrooms are individually decorated and differ in shape and
size. The Garden Room is a large ground-floor twin with a six-foot four-
poster bed, a deep-green carpet and green and white floral-pattern
wallpaper; the Guest Bedroom is a large double with its own seating area
and a bathroom with a whirlpool bath. All the rooms are attractively co-
ordinated and combine comfort and elegance.

  Readers familiar with Farlam Hall will know that from the moment
they sweep up the drive past the small lake (complete with its own island)
they are entering a world of tradition where they will be pampered; 'I
have never been let down,' reports one regular visitor.

◑ Open all year, exc Xmas to New
Year

↗ 2½ miles along the A689 south-
east of Brampton. Private car
park

🛏 1 single, 6 twin, 5 double, 1
four-poster; all with bathroom/
WC, exc single with shower/WC;
TV, room service (limited), hair-
dryer, trouser press in all rooms;
no tea/coffee-making facilities in
rooms

◇ Dining-room, 2 lounges;

conference facilities (max 13
people residential); fishing, golf,
riding nearby

⊖ No wheelchair access; no
children under 5; dogs in
bedrooms by arrangement only

▭ Access, Amex, Visa

£ Single from £78, single
occupancy of twin/double from
£85, twin/double from £170,
four-poster £196 (rates inc
dinner). Set D £27.50 to £28.50
(8pm). Special breaks available

BRANSCOMBE DEVON   **MAP 10**

Bulstone

HIGHER BULSTONE, BRANSCOMBE, NR SEATON, DEVON EX12 3BL
TEL: BRANSCOMBE (029 780) 446

That rare thing, a hotel for young families in a popular resort area.

The Bulstone is in no doubt about its market – as you pull up in the car park, the big sign proudly declares it a 'hotel for young families'. 'We always point that out to people without children who ring up. It's only fair,' says proprietor Peter Freeman, who has, over a period of ten years, honed the un-English art of accommodating children and their parents to perfection. Here the emphasis is not so much on choosing pretty wallpapers as on decorating rooms to be easily repairable if idle fingers get to work; for that reason, expect furniture and fittings to be attractive but much of a muchness whichever room you choose. There are few ornaments lying around to be broken, and, in the newer wing, windows have higher ledges than normal for safety. Parents can store milk, warm up feeds and wash nappies in a utility room; refreshingly, the poster on the wall is of a father and baby.

Children's teas are served between 4.45pm and 5.30pm at one long table in the dining-room, and the special menus feature favourites like sausage casserole, chicken nuggets and pasta with tomato sauce. An adjacent play area has lots of toys and books, a colourful mural and a carpet with a road layout. In the grounds outside are a tree house, sandpit and climbing frames; a wildflower meadow, newly planted, has yet to flower. While their children play, mums and dads can escape to a sun lounge, television room or main lounge from which their offspring are barred. Tariffs reflect the budgetary constraints of most young families; under-12s stay for half-price, under-fives for free.

◖ Closed Dec and Jan

↗ On the A3052 at a junction called Branscombe Cross. Take the left turning where it indicates that the Bulstone is ¾ mile away. Ignore all other Branscombe turnings. Private car park

🛏 2 double, 4 family rooms, 6 family suites; suites with bathroom/WC, 3 public bathrooms; hair-dryer, baby-listening in all rooms

◈ Dining-room, lounge, TV room, conservatory, playroom; laundry facilities; fishing, golf, other sports nearby; babysitting. Wheelchair access to hotel (1 step), restaurant and 3 ground-floor bedrooms

⊖ No children in dining-room eves; dogs in public rooms only (not dining-room); smoking in lounge only

▭ None accepted

£ Single occupancy of double £21 to £49, double/family room/suite £49 to £69 (children's rates from 30% to 50% of adult prices); deposit required. Set D £15. Special breaks available

The Look Out

BRANSCOMBE, NR SEATON, DEVON EX12 3DP
TEL: BRANSCOMBE (029 780) 262 FAX: (029 780) 272

Ex-Customs and Excise cottages offering an eagle's-eye view of Branscombe beach.

Townies should prepare themselves for a drive through a ford and up a heart-stoppingly steep drive to reach the Look Out, so named because it was from these six nineteenth-century cottages, knocked together in the 1950s, that Customs and Excise officials used to watch for smugglers taking advantage of the isolated bay below. The Look Out lies at the end of Branscombe, a village which spins itself out for miles; fortunately it's floodlit at night so you can't miss it. From the humble exterior you would expect a cottagey interior, but in fact the Look Out is more like a country-house hotel. A long downstairs lounge features flagstone floors and double-angled fireplaces full of dried flowers; the bar is concealed inside what looks like an ordinary cabinet. The dining-room is in turn closed off from the kitchen by solid wooden panelling. Menus change fortnightly and feature a mix of traditional dishes such as fillet of beef with a rich Stilton and port sauce and more exotic starters like stir-fried vegetables with fresh ginger and garlic.

Bedrooms are big and comfortable, with matching capacious bathrooms and huge wardrobes. Your eyrie bed is unlikely to be disturbed by any extraneous noise, but in case the sound of the sea gets too overwhelming, panels slide over the original windows, sealing out draughts as well as sound in what is, anyway, a surprisingly warm building. Baskets of fruit and the contents of the mini-bars will seem particularly welcome if you arrive on a Monday when the restaurant is closed; sandwiches are supposedly available, but on inspection they were keeping a very low profile.

◑ Open all year, exc Xmas week; restaurant closed Mon eve

⤴ Take the road in Branscombe all the way to the beach. Drive through the shallow ford between 'Private access to Look Out only' signs and continue straight ahead and up the cliffside driveway to the hotel. Private car park

🛏 2 twin, 3 double; most with bathroom/WC, some with shower/WC; TV, hair-dryer, mini-bar in all rooms

◈ Restaurant, bar, lounge; fishing, water sports, other sports nearby

⊖ No wheelchair access; no children under 6; no dogs in public rooms

▭ None accepted

£ Single occupancy of twin/double £42 to £49, twin/double £70 to £79, family room £90 to £105; deposit required. Set D £19.50 (prices till Oct 93)

Masons Arms ☆

BRANSCOMBE, NR SEATON, DEVON EX12 3DJ
TEL: BRANSCOMBE (029 780) 300/1   FAX: (029 780) 500

A pub-hotel at the heart of a popular village, with overflow rooms in surrounding houses.

At the heart of Branscombe (if this long, straggly village could be said to have a heart) lies the Masons Arms, slowly awakening from a period of slumber in brewery hands under Carol Inglis' energetic management. Ignore the offputting thatched umbrellas outside; inside, the pub's fourteenth-century origins permeate the public bar where spit-roasts are cooked over a huge log fire on Thursdays. The restaurant, a succession of ever-smaller rooms with exposed stone walls and beamed ceilings, can seat 60 people at a push. Meals can also be taken in the pub; on inspection the leek and potato soup was a little bland, the pan-fried ling disappointingly oily.

Bedrooms over the pub are being gradually updated, and some are bigger than you might anticipate; Number 14 even has an area which can be screened off to provide a baby's room. Branscombe gets busy in summer and rooms in the Masons Arms itself could get noisy. Luckily there are overflow rooms in houses across the street, and more alluring ones in a terrace of thatched cottages above sloping gardens beside it. More recently acquired than the pub, these have newer fixtures and fittings and quirky features like beds whose posts appear to hold the building together. As part of her shake-out, Carol Inglis has just added a suite of conference rooms behind the car park.

◑ Open all year

⤢ Branscombe is signposted from the A3052 Sidmouth/Lyme Regis road. Private car park

🛏 1 single, 4 twin, 11 double, 2 four-poster/half-tester, 2 family rooms; most with bathroom/WC, some with shower/WC; TV, room service, baby-listening in all rooms; hair-dryer on request; no tea/coffee-making facilities in rooms

◈ Restaurant, bar, lounge; drying room; air-conditioned conference facilities (max 80 people non-residential, 25 residential); fishing, golf, other sports nearby.

Wheelchair access to hotel (1 step), restaurant and WC (unisex), 3 ground-floor bedrooms

⊖ Dogs in bar and some bedrooms only; no-smoking area in restaurant

▭ Access, Visa

£ Single £17 to £22, single occupancy of twin/double £21 to £43, twin/double £33 to £74, four-poster/half-tester £48 to £80, family room £65 to £96; deposit required. Sun L £9; set D £16 to £19; bar lunches. Special breaks available

BRAY-ON-THAMES BERKSHIRE   **MAP 9**

Monkey Island Hotel

OLD MILL LANE, BRAY-ON-THAMES, MAIDENHEAD, BERKSHIRE SL6 2EE
TEL: MAIDENHEAD (0628) 23400   FAX: (0628) 784732

A popular, picturesque island setting on the River Thames.

Two low white Regency buildings on an island on the River Thames, surrounded by manicured lawns complete with peacocks, mature willows and chestnut trees – what better place for a hotel? Certainly the surroundings are ideal for a relaxing evening in early summer after a hectic day, but at weekends such chocolate-box surroundings attract the crowds – functions, weddings, Sunday lunches and afternoon teas are all regular features of the hotel's summer season. Still, what Monkey Island has in its favour is space. The Temple houses the bedrooms, the small Wedgwood meeting room and a calm, light breakfast room, which is a good place to linger while you read the papers. The Pavilion, about 200 yards across the lawn, houses the Monkey Room, a small lounge with an eighteenth-century ceiling painting, the terrace bar, a function room and a plush restaurant in greens and pinks. Recent reports commend the food, which includes such dishes as lobster thermidor and poached chicken with king scallops and prawns in a vermouth and chive cream.

Average-sized bedrooms are neatly decorated with some bold fabrics and bathrooms are simple and modern.

Open all year, exc 26 Dec to mid-Jan

Leave the M4 at Junction 8/9 and follow the A308 towards Windsor. The hotel is signposted from Bray village. Private car park

2 single, 13 twin, 7 double, 1 family room, 2 suites; all with bathroom/WC, exc 1 single with shower/WC; TV, room service, hair-dryer, mini-bar, baby-listening in all rooms; trouser press in 2 rooms

Air-conditioned restaurant, bar, lounge, drying room;

conference facilities (max 150 people non-residential, 27 residential); fishing, croquet at hotel, other sports nearby; babysitting. Wheelchair access to hotel (3 steps), restaurant and 12 ground-floor bedrooms

No dogs

Access, Amex, Diners, Visa

Single £74 to £90, twin/double £95 to £116, family room £111 to £126, suite £137 to £158; deposit required. Continental B £6, cooked B £8; set L £14.50/£18.50, D £24; alc L, D from £30. Special breaks available

---

Report forms are at the back of the Guide; *write a letter if you prefer.*

Dove Hotel

18 REGENCY SQUARE, BRIGHTON, EAST SUSSEX BN1 2FG
TEL: BRIGHTON (0273) 779222   FAX: (0273) 746912

*A friendly bed and breakfast where care and attention extends to
younger guests too.*

Peter Kalinke is a most fastidious host; even while he takes your booking
he is already at work, recommending local restaurants, offering dinner
(cooked only on request) and checking the ages of the children of the
family. The Dove is relatively easy to find, set as it is in one of Brighton's
most attractive squares, signposted because it also contains a convenient
underground car park. Outside, the hotel is spick and span, with white
bay windows and black wrought-iron balconies; look carefully and you
can size up the best rooms – definitely those on the first floor, with full-
length windows that you can push up to step on to the small balcony and
smell the sea air. Room Three, just such a room, is beautifully proportioned, high ceilinged and furnished in cool beige and pinks. A leisurely
breakfast ('could not be faulted', remarks one guest) can be taken at the
round table and chairs by the window. Thoughtful touches set the tone –
vases of fresh flowers, a tea-tray (with a proper teapot and jug of milk), a
bowl of fruit. As this room is often let out to families there are
indulgences for children too – boxes of toys and books, a jug of juice and
a little bag of chocolate buttons in a cot. The *en-suite* bathroom is white
and fairly plain, though it does have a nice large shelf for all your
paraphernalia.

One reader complained about a 'poky and claustrophobic' single room
and they are certainly cupboard-sized – better to ask for the small double
(Room Two) that is often let as a single. If you prefer to start your day in
the company of Peter and his wife Deborah, the basement houses a small
breakfast room that is fresh and airy.

◑ Open all year

▰ On the west side of Regency
Square, opposite the West Pier
and 200 yards from the Brighton
Centre. On-street parking and
public car park nearby

🛏 3 single, 2 twin, 5 double; half
with bathroom/WC, half with
shower/WC; TV, room service,
hair-dryer, trouser press, baby-
listening in all rooms

◈ Dining-room/bar, lounge;

conference facilities (max 16
people non-residential, 10
residential); fishing, water sports,
other sports nearby; babysitting

⊖ No wheelchair access; no dogs;
no smoking in dining-room

▭ Access, Amex, Diners, JCB, Visa

£ Single £29 to £38, single
occupancy of twin/double from
£40 and £44, twin/double £48 to
£82; deposit required. Set D
£13. Special breaks available

Topps

17 REGENCY SQUARE, BRIGHTON, EAST SUSSEX BN1 2FG
TEL: BRIGHTON (0273) 729334   FAX: (0273) 203679

An immaculate family hotel with good-sized bedrooms.

Topps is one of the attractive buildings lining Regency Square, right next door to the Dove (see entry). Even from the outside the attention to detail displayed by Paul and Pauline Collins is clear – the hotel is freshly painted, with a riotous display of summer colour sprouting from window boxes. Inside, it is spotless and furnished throughout in browns and cream. Paul Collins was proud to show off every room on inspection, and it is clear there are no hidden horrors here. All the rooms are of a good size, with a sofa to relax into after a busy day shopping or on the beach. There are a couple of four-posters, the most spectacular being in Room 172 – although it looks Elizabethan, according to Paul 'it's a load of old bits and pieces'. Bathrooms too are spacious and colour co-ordinated, many in marble effect.

If you want to eat in there is a small restaurant in the basement that opens five days a week, serving a menu with half a dozen choices (including one for vegetarians). You might opt for fresh salmon pancakes or queen scallops on the half shell in garlic butter, followed by new season's rack of lamb or stuffed chicken breast poached in white wine.

◑ Open all year, exc Xmas; restaurant closed Sun, Wed, and Jan

🔁 Regency Square faces the seafront in Brighton, opposite West Pier and 200 yards from the Brighton Centre. Parking sometimes difficult, hotel has lock-up garage

🛏 1 single, 1 twin, 8 double, 2 four-poster, 2 family rooms; all with bathroom/WC, TV, room service, hair-dryer, mini-bar, trouser press, ironing facilities

◈ Restaurant, lounge; golf, water sports, fishing, other sports nearby

⊖ No wheelchair access; no dogs

▭ Access, Amex, Diners, Visa

£ Single £45, single occupancy of twin/double £59, twin/double £79 to £89, four-poster £99, family room £89; deposit required. Set D £19 (93 prices). Special breaks available

If you make a booking using a credit card, and find after cancelling that the full amount has been charged to your card, raise the matter with your credit card company. They will ask the hotelier to confirm whether the room was re-let, and to justify the charge made.

BRIMFIELD HEREFORD AND WORCESTER **MAP 9**

Roebuck Hotel/Poppies

BRIMFIELD, LUDLOW, SHROPSHIRE SY8 4NE
TEL: BRIMFIELD (0584) 711230   FAX: (0584) 711654

A pub and restaurant which draws praise for service, comfort and food.

'Wonderful! Care and attention of the highest standard,' writes one of Carole Evans's guests at the Roebuck. 'Everything worked like clockwork and staff were a perfect blend of efficiency, friendliness and helpfulness,' echoes another. Reactions such as these explain the popularity of this combination pub and restaurant, and you may have difficulty booking one of the three bedrooms at short notice. The bedrooms are soothing, well-furnished and spacious, though the bathrooms are best described as small but adequate. Most guests, however, come for the food rather than the bathrooms. The fresh produce (much of it organic) served up in Poppies is classed 'excellent' by one satisfied diner. 'On our anniversary night, a special dish was concocted by request; outstanding!' Letters to us inevitably end with the comment 'will return'.

◑ Open all year, exc 2 weeks Feb and 1 week Oct; restaurant closed Sun and Mon eves

↗ Just off the A49, 4 miles south of Ludlow and 7 miles north of Leominster, in the village of Brimfield. Private car park

🛏 1 twin, 2 double; twin with bathroom/WC, doubles with shower/WC; TV, hair-dryer, trouser press in all rooms

◈ Restaurant, bar; conference facilities (max 20 people non-residential); golf, tennis, other sports nearby.

⊖ No wheelchair access; no children under 8; dogs by arrangement only

▭ Access, Amex, Visa

£ Single occupancy of twin/double £40, twin/double £65; deposit required. Alc L, D £27

BRISTOL AVON **MAP 9**

Berkeley Square

15 BERKELEY SQUARE, CLIFTON, BRISTOL, AVON BS8 1HB
TEL: BRISTOL (0272) 254000   FAX: (0272) 252970

Its central position is a bonus for this lively and friendly hotel.

Berkeley Square is a fine Regency square, and if it looks familiar as you draw up it's because you have seen it as the setting for the BBC serial *The House of Eliott*. The hotel makes an ideal base for a break in Bristol. The staff are relaxed, informal and eager to please – car parking is on the meters that surround the square and, in the morning, someone will nip out to feed yours so that you can finish your breakfast in peace.

As you walk in, the art deco restaurant, Nightingales, is on your left. It is red and grey with tables comfortably spread among the marbled pillars. There is a long à la carte menu with the accent on modern dishes, so a typical meal might include squid on saffron noodles, duckling with passion-fruit and the house speciality of fruit pancake. In the corner of the room a spiral staircase descends to the cocktail bar, which is decorated with jazzy black and white photos – a lively joint, especially at the weekends.

All the bedrooms are named after eminent Bristolians, from Billy Butlin to W. G. Grace. They are generally of a good size and are decorated in pinks, blues and beige, sometimes with a sponged or marbled finish. Each is furnished with a sofa and chair.

◐ *Open all year; restaurant closed Sun eve*

↗ *In Bristol city centre, close to the University, City Museum and Art Gallery. Private garaging and on-street parking*

🛏 *25 single, 6 twin, 11 double, 1 suite; all with bathroom/WC, exc 3 singles with shower/WC; TV, room service, hair-dryer, trouser press, baby-listening in all rooms*

◇ *Restaurant, bar; conference facilities (max 12 people*

residential); golf, tennis, gym nearby

⊖ *No wheelchair access; dogs by arrangement only; some bedrooms non-smoking*

▭ *Access, Amex, Diners, Visa*

£ *Single £49 to £73, single occupancy of twin/double £59 to £79, twin/double £69 to £95, suite £88 to £109. Cooked B £8.50, continental B £6; Sun L £10.50; set L, D £14; alc L, D £20*

Downlands   ℒ

33 HENLEAZE GARDENS, BRISTOL, AVON BS9 4HH
TEL: BRISTOL (0272) 621639

There are friendly hosts in this semi-detached guesthouse near the Downs.

Downlands is in a quiet, tree-lined residential street on the edge of Durdham Downs, a couple of miles from the city centre. Bristol University halls of residence are nearby, making this a useful base for parents who are visiting their offspring. There is a pleasing, slightly bohemian touch to the decoration, which makes good use of rugs, potted plants and plenty of knick-knacks. The guesthouse is very much the private home of Peter and Ulla Newman, and visitors are invited to share their lounge where the bookcases are heavy with books and classical music plays gently in the background. In the summer the french windows are thrown open and guests can sun themselves on the enclosed patio at the back.

The bedrooms are of a good size and are decorated in a selection of restful pinks, greens and blues; even the rooms on the second floor, which have sloping ceilings, are spacious. Some of the beds are covered with Ulla's own hand-sewn patchwork quilts. Bedrooms Four and Five have *en-suite* showers. Breakfast is taken in the green and white breakfast room, and a full English fry-up is included in the price.

◐ Open all year

➋ From city centre head towards Westbury on Trym. After 2 miles, Henleaze Gardens is a left-hand turning. On-street parking

🛏 2 single, 3 twin, 5 double; 2 rooms with shower/WC; TV, hair-dryer in all rooms

◈ Breakfast room, lounge; golf, tennis, other sports nearby

⊖ No wheelchair access; no smoking or dogs in public rooms

▭ Access, Visa

£ Single £23 to £34, single occupancy of twin/double £27, twin/double £40 to £46, family room £47; deposit required. Set D by arrangement only

---

BROAD CAMPDEN GLOUCESTERSHIRE   **MAP 9**

Malt House ☆

BROAD CAMPDEN, NR CHIPPING CAMPDEN, GLOUCESTERSHIRE GL55 6UU
TEL: EVESHAM (0386) 840295   FAX: (0386) 841334

An idyllic cottage hotel close to Chipping Campden but well away from the bustle.

Broad Campden is only a mile from Chipping Campden, but is a different world – a tiny strung-out village of only a few houses nestling on the side of a hill. The Malt House lies at the bottom of the hill fronting the (quiet) road, a long low building looking sweetly cottagey. Luckily there is a car park, for there is no room to stop on the road. One of the chief delights of the place is the large garden with a sweeping expanse of lawn whose produce – both flowers and vegetables – you will enjoy during your stay.

The Brown family have done up the interior of the Malt House impeccably, creating, with antique furniture and bright fabrics, a classy piece of Olde England that suits both house and countryside well. Bedrooms – not huge, but with good firm beds – are tranquil and cottagey. Guests eat round one large table, and the food has been described to us as exquisite: 'a crème brûlée out of this world', for example. There is a choice of main course.

◐ Open all year, exc Xmas

➋ 1 mile from Chipping Campden, signed from the B4081, 500 yards beyond the Bakers Arms public house. Private car park

🛏 1 single, 4 twin/double, 1 four-poster, family room available; all

with bathroom/WC, TV, hair-dryer, baby-listening

◈ Restaurant, lounge, drying room; conference facilities (max 5 people residential); croquet at hotel, other sports nearby

⊖ No wheelchair access; no

children under 11; no dogs or smoking in public rooms

▭ Access, Visa

£ Single £38 to £56, single occupancy of twin/double £45 to

£56, twin/double £65 to £85, four-poster £65 to £88, family room £75 to £99; deposit required. Set D £19.50. Special breaks available

---

BROADWAY HEREFORD AND WORCESTER   **MAP 9**

Collin House

COLLIN LANE, BROADWAY, HEREFORD AND WORCESTER WR12 7PB
TEL: BROADWAY (0386) 858354

A pleasing refuge from the crowds a short distance from Broadway.

On its own on the edge of the Vale of Evesham, and away from the rash of guesthouses which inhabit the outskirts of Broadway, Collin House makes a good base for exploring the north-western fringes of the Cotswolds. It is a well-proportioned old farmhouse with dormer windows and a rustic porch, and quite a lot bigger than it looks at first sight. Inside, it is warm and welcoming, with a particularly attractive bar with an open fire and rugs laid over the wooden floor. Drawing-room and dining-room are spacious and hung with interesting paintings; relaxation is the keynote.

The bedrooms are named after flowers and are pleasantly farmhousey, with floral wallpapers, comfortable old furniture and small bathrooms. The single room is definitely small, even for a single, but John Mills has recognised its shortcomings in naming it Weed. The dinner menu, priced according to the main course chosen, is comfortably English – terrine of duck, chicken and pork followed by rack of lamb, perhaps. For hot days there is a secluded outdoor swimming-pool.

◑ Open all year, exc 24 to 28 Dec

◪ One mile north-west of Broadway off the A44. Take a right turn at Collin Lane and the house is 300 yards on the right. Private car park

🛏 1 single, 3 twin, 1 double, 2 four-poster; all with bathroom/ WC, exc single with shower; room service, hair-dryer in all rooms; TV on request

◈ Restaurant, bar, lounge; unheated swimming-pool at

hotel, fishing, golf, riding nearby. Wheelchair access to restaurant and WC (unisex) only

⊖ No children under 8 in restaurant eves; no dogs; no smoking in some public rooms

▭ Access, Visa

£ Single £45, single occupancy of twin/double £60, twin/double £86, four-poster £99; deposit required. Set L £14.50; bar lunches from £3; alc D £15 to £23. Special breaks available

---

Dormy House

WILLERSEY HILL, BROADWAY, HEREFORD AND WORCESTER WR12 7LF
TEL: BROADWAY (0386) 852711   TELEX: 338275 DORMY G
FAX: (0386) 858636

A modernised farmhouse turned into a comfortable mid-range business hotel offering good food and thoughtful service.

As you drive up the side road that leads off the A44 on the steep hill outside Broadway you think that Dormy House is going to be blessed with magnificent views from the escarpment. Alas, although the neighbouring HQ of Group 4 Security get them, Dormy House does not, being positioned just too far back. The old farmhouse this once was now lies buried somewhere in the middle of the sympathetically designed extensions and conversions which go to make up the hotel. The bar is the hub of things; a small cocktail bar is situated next to a longer one where food is also served. However, it would be a pity to miss the excellent food in the main restaurant – a lovely light soft blue room. On inspection, we were presented with an excellent mix of wild mushrooms en croûte, followed by perfectly cooked best end of lamb; the cheese is well-kept, too. The bedrooms are comfortable and spacious, with a good supply of work surfaces, and bathrooms have most of the usual trimmings.

Service is simultaneously to the point and personal. One guest had to make a hasty late-night departure – the bill was ready in seconds, and the hotel refused to charge for the accommodation that had not been used. This sort of attitude is all too rare, so a pat on the back for Dormy House.

◑ Open all year, exc 25, 26 Dec

⤴ From Broadway, join the A44 signposted Moreton-in-Marsh; travel up Fish Hill. Turn first left at sign for 'Group 4', 'Dormy House' and 'Broadway Golf Club'. After ½ mile take the right fork and approach a small crossroads. Turn left, and the hotel is on your left. Private car park

🛏 7 single, 15 twin, 22 double, 2 four-poster, 3 suites (some rooms in annexe); all with bathroom/WC, TV, room service, hair-dryer, baby-listening; mini-bar in suites only; trouser press in all rooms by end 93

✧ Restaurant, 3 bars, 2 lounges; air-conditioned conference facilities (max 200 people non-residential, 49 residential); croquet, putting green at hotel, golf, tennis, other sports nearby; babysitting

⊖ No wheelchair access; dogs in ground-floor bedrooms only

▭ Access, Amex, Diners, Visa

£ Single £55 to £74, single occupancy of twin/double £74, twin/double £100 to £110, four-poster £130, suite from £140/£180. Set L £14/£16, D £25.50/£33; alc L, D £42. Special breaks available

See page 817 for other hotels worthy of inclusion in our Visitors' Book.

Lygon Arms ☆

BROADWAY, HEREFORD AND WORCESTER WR12 7DU
TEL: BROADWAY (0386) 852255   FAX: (0386) 858611

This is what you get when you cross the Savoy with a country inn.

The Lygon Arms is Broadway's poshest hotel and the Cotswold outpost
of the Savoy group. Its strongest appeal is probably to transatlantic
tourists who are used to luxury and want some historic surroundings to
go with it, but since it is the kind of hotel that has everything you could
desire on tap it could be a good choice for a short break (and there are
some quite tempting deals). At heart the Lygon Arms is still the large
coaching-inn it once was, and the present management has sensibly not
attempted to disguise this; there is still the smell of woodsmoke and the
curious little corners that could belong to any ancient pub. There is also a
bizarre barrel-vaulted mock-medieval (actually 1911) hall, complete
with stags' heads, which is now the dining-room. A typically elaborate
meal might comprise smoked oxtail broth with woodland mushrooms,
port and bacon dumplings, a brochette of south-coast lobster in a red
wine and parsley dressing as a main course, with a maple syrup roast pear
to finish. Add to these the smooth service, the extensive leisure centre
with its wonderful galleried swimming-pool and the shop selling classy
souvenirs from Gucci to goats' milk soap, and you can see the sort of
hybrid the Lygon Arms is.

The only point at which the old and the luxurious do not quite mesh is
in the bedrooms, which are well-appointed with antiques and very
comfortable but generally of coaching-inn size. One reader was happy
with 'a very comfortable, soft mattress and pillows'. A bowl of soapflakes
stands alongside the lavish bathroom freebies, but one has to wonder
how many guests here actually wash their own smalls by hand.

◗ Open all year

⤴ On the main street in the centre
of Broadway. Private car park

🛏 2 single, 8 twin, 44 double, 6
four-poster, 2 family rooms, 5
suites; all with bathroom/WC,
TV, room service, hair-dryer,
trouser press, baby-listening; tea/
coffee-making facilities on
request

◈ Dining-room, 2 bars, wine bar, 5
lounges, drying room, billiard
room; conference facilities (max
80 people residential and non-
residential); tennis, sauna/
solarium, heated swimming-pool,
gym, beauty salon, spa bath,
steam room, pool, billiards at
hotel, other sports nearby;
babysitting. Wheelchair access to
hotel, dining-room and WC
(M,F), 9 ground-floor bedrooms

⊖ No dogs in public rooms

▭ Access, Amex, Diners, Visa

£ Single from £88, single
occupancy of twin/double £110,
twin/double £130, four-poster
from £174, family room from
£224, suite from £208; deposit
required. Cooked B £9; set L
£19.50, D £30; alc L from £28,
D from £32 (prices till end 93).
Special breaks available

Old Rectory

CHURCH STREET, WILLERSEY, BROADWAY, HEREFORD AND WORCESTER
WR12 7PN
TEL: BROADWAY (0386) 853729

Constant praise for this large Cotswolds bed and breakfast.

We get more letters about Helen Jones's bed and breakfast establishment in a small village close to Broadway than about any other Cotswolds accommodation, and all of them stress the excellence of the place. One reader lists the plus points as follows: homely feel, helpful owners, excellent breakfasts, lovely garden, detailed brochure describing what each room is like, tasteful décor, plentiful local information, lovely toiletries and satellite TV. It remains for us to add that the dining-room is calm and spacious, with individual tables poised ready for the excellent breakfasts, and that the large sitting-room is comfortable and relaxing, with views over the garden. Bedrooms come in all sorts of different shapes and sizes and are comfortably furnished in a range of styles. Homeliness rather than luxury is the keynote – and that homeliness is much appreciated. 'Combines the excellence of the finest hotels with the warmth of a private home,' writes one guest.

◐ Open all year, exc Xmas

▨ One mile from Broadway on the B4632 Stratford road. Turn right into Church Street at the Bell Inn, Willersey. Private car park

🛏 2 twin, 3 double, 2 four-poster, 1 four-poster suite; most with bathroom/WC, some with shower/WC; TV, hair-dryer, trouser press in all rooms

◇ Dining-room, lounge, drying room, conservatory; golf, tennis, other sports nearby

⊖ No wheelchair access; no children under 8; no dogs; smoking in lounge only

▭ Access, Visa

£ Single occupancy of twin/double £35 to £49, twin/double £50 to £75, four-poster £65 to £85, family room £75 to £95, suite £65 to £85; deposit required. Special breaks available

BROMSBERROW HEATH GLOUCESTERSHIRE   **MAP 9**

Grove House

BROMSBERROW HEATH, NR LEDBURY, HEREFORD AND WORCESTER
HR8 1PE
TEL: LEDBURY (0531) 650584

A conveniently situated Wolsey Lodge.

Grove House is close to the M50, without being disturbed by it, and well situated for visiting Ledbury, walking in the Malvern Hills or exploring the Forest of Dean. This is a large fifteenth-century farmhouse, sur-

rounded by stables and gardens, now run as a stylish Wolsey Lodge by
Michael and Ellen Ross. There is a good mixture of antiquity, elegance
and homeliness here; the low ceilings and oak panelling are complemented by silverware, fresh flowers and the ancient patchwork and
embroidery which decorate the landing. Everyone eats the four-course
dinners round the single long, polished table in the dining-room, after
which they progress to a comfortable sitting-room on the first floor
where there is ample space for relaxing. Two of the three carefully
arranged bedrooms have four-posters and all have spacious bathrooms.

◑ *Open all year, exc Xmas and
New Year*

⤷ *Leave the M50 at Junction 2 and
follow signs to Ledbury. Take
first turning left to Bromsberrow
Heath. In the village turn right
by post office and go up the hill.
Grove House is on the right.
Private car park*

🛏 *I twin, 2 four-poster; all with
bathroom/WC, TV, room service,
hair-dryer; trouser press in twin*

◈ *Dining-room, drawing-room;
conference facilities (max 10
people non-residential); tennis at
hotel, other sports nearby*

⊖ *No wheelchair access; no
children in restaurant eves; no
dogs*

▭ *None accepted*

£ *Single occupancy of twin/four-
poster £45, twin/four-poster £64.
Set D £21 (8pm)*

BROMSGROVE HEREFORD AND WORCESTER   **MAP 9**

Grafton Manor

GRAFTON LANE, BROMSGROVE, HEREFORD AND WORCESTER B61 7HA
TEL: BROMSGROVE (0527) 579007   FAX: (0527) 575221

*Well worth seeking out in suburban Bromsgrove, this stately
Elizabethan manor is family-run and friendly.*

If this hotel were in the Cotswolds, it would be swamped with tourists,
American and otherwise; since it is on the fringes of the Birmingham
agglomeration, holidaymakers are inclined to give it a miss. This is a pity,
for Grafton Manor is an exceptional place. The house is classic Elizabethan – high chimneys, glowing brick, a private chapel and the
beginnings of a formal garden. Furthermore, although its entrance lane
is off a busy road, you could just as well be in deep countryside by the
time you arrive. John Morris, an affectionate bear of a man, runs his hotel
with enormous verve. He turns out to have had a hand in almost
everything you see, even making some of the beds himself, for he counts
welding among his skills. The house is blessed with a proper baronial-
style hall, with decorated ceiling and coat of arms over the fire, which
makes a lovely sitting-room. The bedrooms, scattered all over the house,
vary in size and style, but all are large and well-furnished, and many have
good views. Talbot is the best and biggest, with peacock wallpaper and an
enormous mirror. Son Simon reached the final of the Indian chef of the
year competition and you may well find this talent reflected in the

cooking – though traditional cuisine is also available, as is a good choice for vegetarians.

◑ Open all year

🔁 Leave the M5 at Junction 5 and travel north on the A38 towards Bromsgrove. Then take B4091; Grafton Lane is on the left. Private car park

🛏 1 single, 2 twin, 3 double, 1 four-poster, 2 suites; all with bathroom/WC, TV, room service, hair-dryer, trouser press; no tea/coffee-making facilities in rooms

◇ Restaurant, lounge; conference facilities (max 9 people

residential, 12 non-residential); fishing, croquet at hotel, golf, tennis, other sports nearby; babysitting. Wheelchair access to hotel and restaurant, 1 ground-floor bedroom

⊖ No dogs

▭ Access, Amex, Diners, Visa

£ Single £85, single occupancy of twin/double £85, twin/double £105, four-poster/suite £125. Set L from £17, D from £20

BROXTED ESSEX   MAP 8

Whitehall

COUNTY HOTEL OF THE YEAR

CHURCH END, BROXTED, ESSEX CM6 2BZ
TEL: BISHOP'S STORTFORD (0279) 850603   FAX: (0279) 850385

A self-assured but friendly hotel within a few miles of Stansted Airport.

You won't find long institutional corridors and besuited civil servants at this Whitehall – rather, a large, whitewashed Elizabethan house with distinctive triangular gables overlooking lovely gardens, used as the hotel's trademark on brochures, plates and even painted on the walls of the dining-room. Service is prompt and correct. Used to guests arriving from Stansted (the airport is just 15 minutes away and planes occasionally disturb the peace), a member of staff comes to meet your car when you arrive. In your room, there will be a welcome note and a delicious dish of fresh fruit, as well as mineral water and piles of magazines. Some bedrooms are in the old house, for example Chaureth, painted in muted colours with two large armchairs, an enormous double bed and a big bathroom. Most, however, are in a separate wing and these are named after British prime ministers (a touch of Whitehall after all): whether Gladstone would have liked his tangerine-coloured namesake we shall never know, but it is probable that Churchill would have approved of his – one of the largest rooms in the hotel with a soft sofa to sink into at the end of the day.

Food is a serious subject at Whitchall. Chef Paul Flavell makes it a policy to explain his dishes and philosophy to diners with an enthusiasm that is impossible to fault. First, a carefully prepared plate of amuse-gueules to tickle the palate over a pre-dinner drink is placed in front of you. At the table, a miniature, tongue-in-cheek portion of fish and chips complete with newspaper cone may come before the starter and thereafter each course is no less carefully presented. Most refreshing is the lack of pretension: Paul is just as happy to serve his special Whitehall sausages as other more sophisticated dishes, and delicious they are too.

◑ Open all year, exc 26 to 30 Dec; restaurant open Sun eve by arrangement only

⤴ 10 minutes' drive from Junction 8 (Bishop's Stortford exit) of the M11. Follow signs for Stansted Airport, then signs to Broxted. Private car park

🛏 6 twin, 19 double; all with bathroom/WC, TV, room service, hair-dryer, trouser press, baby-listening; no tea/coffee-making facilities in rooms

◈ 2 restaurants, 2 bars, 2 lounges; conference facilities (max 120 people non-residential, 25 residential); tennis, unheated swimming-pool at hotel, other sports nearby; babysitting. Wheelchair access to hotel (2 steps), restaurant and WC (M,F), 5 ground-floor bedrooms

⊖ No dogs

▭ Access, Amex, Diners, Visa

£ Single occupancy of twin/double £75 to £95, twin/double £105 to £155; deposit required. Set L £19.50, D £29.50; alc L £29.50, D from £29.50. Special breaks available

---

BROXTON CHESHIRE   **MAP 5**

Broxton Hall

WHITCHURCH ROAD, BROXTON, NR CHESTER, CHESHIRE CH3 9JS
TEL: BROXTON (0829) 782321   FAX: (0829) 782330

A half-timbered hotel with atmosphere and antiques.

Ten miles south of Chester, Broxton Hall is popular with middle-management executives and with weekenders who use it as a base for exploring the city while still enjoying the pleasures of the Cheshire countryside. Although it is set on the main Whitchurch to Chester road, the dignified black and white Tudor house carries a sense of its own history that makes it a welcome refuge for the travel-weary.

On cold days, a roaring log fire burns in the panelled entrance hall. A long, polished refectory table mirrors a huge bowl of lilies, and sofas, oil paintings and antiques crowd into the low-ceilinged, beamed room. There is no shortage of comfortable seating in the elegant small-scale drawing-room and the cheerful bar. The Regency-style dining-room has a small conservatory extension (recently enlarged) that opens up on to the garden in summer, and is well-patronised by locals – a sure sign of a good reputation. Dishes on a recent menu included warm vol-au-vent with freshly poached salmon and a lobster sauce, collops of venison cooked in Guinness, onions, mushrooms and thyme and traditional desserts such as profiteroles, bread-and-butter pudding or hot fruit pie and cream. Little girls tend to make a beeline for the collection of Victorian dolls, and may need to be gently discouraged from taking them home.

This is an old house, so nooks and crannies abound and floors slope and creak. The bedrooms vary in size but are all pleasantly decorated with a mix of antique and more modern furniture. Rooms facing south have good views over the rose garden and are full of light on a sunny day, but may get pretty warm in mid-summer. The honeymoon suite has a carved four-poster that dates back to Charles I, a chandelier and a large under-the-eaves bathroom.

◑ *Open all year, exc 25 and 26 Dec*

◪ *8 miles from Chester on A41 towards Whitchurch. Situated at the Broxton roundabout on the left. Private car park*

🛏 *2 single, 3 twin, 5 double, 1 four-poster, 3 family rooms; all with bathroom/WC, TV, room service, baby-listening; trouser press in some rooms; hair-dryer on request*

◇ *Restaurant, bar, drawing-room, drying room, conservatory,*

library; conference facilities (max 35 people non-residential, 14 residential); golf, riding, other sports nearby

⊖ *No wheelchair access; dogs by arrangement only*

▭ *Access, Amex, Diners, Visa*

£ *Single £55, single occupancy of twin/double £60 to £65, twin/double £66 to £70, four-poster £85, family room rate on request; deposit required. Set L £12.50, D £22; alc L £2.50 to £8. Special breaks available*

Frogg Manor

FULLERS MOOR, NANTWICH ROAD, BROXTON, NR CHESTER, CHESHIRE CH3 9JH
TEL: BROXTON (0829) 782629/782280   FAX: (0829) 782238

Characterful country hotel where the whimsy is part of a winning formula.

The trouble with frogs is that they soon multiply, and the frogginess at this comfortable, amusing small hotel is on the verge of getting out of hand. Frogs of all shapes and sizes line corridors, crowd on to tables, spill from cupboards; embroidered frogs, musical frogs, frogs on beakers, frogs furry and fluffy, plastic and porcelain. As Chief Frog John Sykes ruefully explains, guests kindly keep bringing frogs with them, and just what do you do when someone finds their frog has been relegated to the back shelf? Well, that's what comes of calling a hotel after an old girlfriend, even if there is a pond packed with the real thing in the grounds. One can only be grateful her nickname was not Hippo.

Readers continue to sing the praises of Frogg Manor, charmed by the mix of good hospitality, informal atmosphere and the personal attention of the tireless Mr Sykes (six days' holiday in six years, poor man). The tone of the place is set as soon as you enter the slightly shambolic entrance hall that doubles as an office, with its jumble of brollies, hat stands and old English sheepdog. While John Sykes is clearly no conventional hotelier, there is no shortage of creature comforts here. The elegant first-floor lounge has plenty of soft sofas around the open fire; the chandeliered dining-room, divided into smoking and non-smoking sections, serves good dinner-party food to the accompaniment of original '30s music; in summer, a hammock is strung enticingly in the back lawn. There are also facilities for parking horse boxes and for grazing and stabling their occupants.

The *en-suite* bedrooms vary wildly in size and shape, but all have an air of individuality. There are good mattresses, shoe-cleaning kits, irons and ironing-boards that double as trouser presses, and expensive, mega-magnifying shaving mirrors. The most singular room is Wellington, the size of a small ballroom; it has a central, crown-canopied bed, a 50-inch TV set and a secret passage through to the lounge.

The Froggy experience is clearly an international draw – and although one American visitor noted slow service at breakfast, a German lady was happy to write in the guest book: 'I felt very homely here.'

◑ Open all year

↗ Leave the M6 at Junction 16 towards Nantwich, and take the A534 Wrexham road. The hotel is 10 miles along this road on the left, close to the junction with the A41. Private car park

🛏 6 double; most with bathroom/WC, some with shower/WC; TV, room service, hair-dryer, trouser press, baby-listening, ironing facilities in all rooms

◇ Restaurant, bar, lounge,

conservatory; conference facilities (max 25 people non-residential, 6 residential); tennis at hotel, other sports nearby

⊖ No wheelchair access; no children under 5; no dogs in public rooms

▭ Access, Amex, Diners, Visa

£ Single occupancy of twin/double £40 to £80, twin/double £48 to £96. Continental B £3, cooked B £7.50; set L £14, D £17.50; alc D £25. Special breaks available

---

BUCKLAND GLOUCESTERSHIRE   **MAP 9**

Buckland Manor

BUCKLAND, NR BROADWAY, HEREFORD AND WORCESTER WR12 7LY
TEL: BROADWAY (0386) 852626   FAX: (0386) 853557

Expensive, classic country-house hotel.

The setting could hardly be better: a tiny village, a dead-end road, a church next door, and a gabled Elizabethan manor (though the core of the building is earlier) covered with ivy and wistaria. For an extravagant Cotswolds break, or as somewhere to send wealthy transatlantic visitors, Buckland Manor fits the bill perfectly. Inside, nothing jars: the furnishing and the decoration suit the style and period of the house well. Large portraits on the walls, rugs on the polished floors and plenty of panelling help to create the appropriate country-house air. Bedrooms are equally stylish, and each is provided with a bottle of water from Buckland's own spring. The restaurant has a French tinge to it, and is the setting for well-presented food – traditional rather than flash – with good combinations of meat and sauces, and a careful wine list to go with it.

◑ Open all year

⤴ From Broadway, take the A46/B4632 towards Cheltenham; Buckland Manor is off to the left after 2 miles. Private car park

🛏 4 twin, 4 double, 2 four-poster, family room available; all with bathroom/WC, TV, room-service, hair-dryer; trouser press on request; no tea/coffee-making facilities in rooms

◈ Dining-room, 2 lounges; conference facilities (max 10 people residential, 22 non-residential); tennis, croquet, putting, heated outdoor swimming-pool at hotel, other sports nearby. Wheelchair access to hotel (2 steps) and dining-room, 3 ground-floor bedrooms

⊖ No children under 12 as guests, no children under 8 in dining-room; no dogs; no smoking in dining-room

▭ Access, Amex, Visa

£ Single occupancy of twin/double from £135, twin/double from £175, four-poster £270, family room £320 (4 people); deposit required. Sun L £18.50; alc L, D £36

BUCKNELL SHROPSHIRE   MAP 5

Bucknell House

BUCKNELL, SHROPSHIRE SY7 0AD
TEL: BUCKNELL (05474) 248

A pretty house in a pretty stretch of country.

West of Ludlow, where Powys, Herefordshire and Shropshire meet, Bucknell House stands on the edge of the village from which it takes its name. Brenda Davies runs this mellow old vicarage as a friendly, no-frills bed and breakfast. It is the quality of the welcome and the homely atmosphere of a family house which appeal here rather than lavish facilities, although the bedrooms are equipped with TVs and hair-dryers. There is a spacious lounge and a dining-room with a single table where breakfast is served. Brenda also provides guests with a good compendium of information which includes places to eat in the evenings.

◑ Closed Dec, Jan

⤴ Follow A4113 Ludlow to Knighton road, then B4367 towards Craven Arms. The house is on fringe of village. Private car park

🛏 1 twin, 2 double; 1 public bathroom, 2 public WCs; TV, hair-dryer, wash units in all rooms

◈ Dining-room, drawing-room; tennis at hotel, golf, fishing nearby

⊖ No wheelchair access; no children under 12; dogs in bedrooms only; no smoking in bedrooms

▭ None accepted

£ Single occupancy of twin/double £20, twin/double £34

BUILDWAS SHROPSHIRE　　　　　　　　**MAP 5**

Bridge House

BUILDWAS, TELFORD, SHROPSHIRE TF8 7BN
TEL: IRONBRIDGE (0952) 432105

A comfortable bed and breakfast convenient for Ironbridge, with a charming hostess.

Homely knick-knacks fill Mrs Hedges' bed and breakfast near Ironbridge, and everything shines. The golden tractor in the garden of the old coaching-inn is fading a little with the passing years, but the bright-red flooring in the hallway and the sunny personality of the owners cheer things up. The guest lounge is small, with ivy wreathing the mantelpiece and panelling on one wall; the dining-room is peaceful, and the bedrooms immaculate. But this is not altogether an ordinary place – you keep running across things you do not find in other bed and breakfasts. There is the mural of the Greek temple in the narrow corridor in which considerable pains have been taken over the perspective; there is Mr Hedges' collection of swords and bayonets poised (rather worryingly) directly over the bath in Room Six; there are the sloping floors which make you feel you have indulged even when you have not, and the pretty stone fireplace and brass bed in Room Six (again). All in all, an excellent place – and traffic on the road outside dies down at night.

◑ Open all year, exc 3 weeks at Xmas

🔁 On the B4380 Shrewsbury road, 1½ miles from Ironbridge. Private car park

🛏 2 twin, 1 double, 1 four-poster, 1 family room; 1 room with bathroom/WC, 3 public bathrooms

◈ Lounge; fishing, tennis, other sports nearby

⊖ No wheelchair access; no dogs

▭ None accepted

£ Single occupancy of twin/double £22 to £25, twin/double £36 to £38, four-poster £45 to £48, family room £58 to £62; deposit required

---

BURBAGE WILTSHIRE　　　　　　　　**MAP 9**

Old Vicarage

BURBAGE, MARLBOROUGH, WILTSHIRE SN8 3AG
TEL: MARLBOROUGH (0672) 810495　　FAX: (0672) 810663

Two acres of private garden surround this harmoniously restored vicarage in a village near the Savernake Forest.

At one time the Old Vicarage fell into such disrepair that the vicar simply refused to live there anymore. The poor chap was finally rehoused next door (go past the drive marked New Vicarage) and, eventually, the nineteenth-century brick and flint residence passed into the hands of Jane Cornelius and Robert Hector.

All traces of ecclesiastical gloom have long been banished. Instead, the house is light and airy, filled with Jane's hot-house flowers. In the graceful green and white drawing-room, easy chairs are ranged round a table loaded with books and magazines. The dining-room, which looks out on lawns and borders, has striped yellow walls, glazed cotton drapes, family silver and crystal. In the hall, bound copies of *Punch* date back to the turn of the century.

The three *en-suite* bedrooms are smart and comfortable. The small single, decorated in pretty blue floral paper, has teddy bear pictures and a Lloyd Loom armchair. The double is the largest, with a mix of contemporary and old furnishings in apricot and blues, festooned curtains and a mound of scatter cushions on the king-sized bed. It has an unusual, theatrical bathroom painted by a previous owner, the director of a tile company, to resemble the view from his Italian villa. The rather gaudy tiling in the bathroom of the twin also dates from this time. The rooms have china cups and pots, a choice of teas and a tea cosy; we counted four boxes of tissues in one room, along with notepaper, chocolates, mineral water and a supply of hairpins. In the evening, beds are turned down, blinds lowered, and old teabags whisked silently away.

Breakfasts evidence an equally lavish approach – two sorts of freshly squeezed juice, two sorts of milk, exotic fruits, two sorts of butter and three sorts of honey . . . If it is difficult to cope with such decisions in the morning, then at least Jane makes life easier at the other end of the day. Her excellent set dinners are all Aga-cooked and she uses as much home-grown fruit and vegetables as she can. A sample meal might be prawns with lime and coriander in filo pastry, lamb noisettes, rhubarb and ginger yogurt ice and local farmhouse cheeses. During the summer months she also hosts afternoon tea-parties for select groups of Americans, with cucumber sandwiches and Victoria sponge served by 'housemaids' on the lawn. In this perfect English setting, the only thing missing is the vicar.

◑ Open all year, exc Xmas and New Year; dining-room closed Thur and Sun eves

⤢ From Burbage High Street, turn east into Taskers Lane, take 3rd turning on right into Eastcourt; Old Vicarage is on the left. Private car park

🛏 1 single, 1 twin, 1 double; all with bathroom/WC, TV, hairdryer

◈ Dining-room, lounge; conference facilities (max 10 people non-residential, 5 residential); fishing, riding, golf, swimming-pool nearby

⊖ No wheelchair access; no children; no dogs; no smoking

▭ Access, Visa

£ Single £35, single occupancy of twin/double £40, twin/double £60; deposit required. Set L £25 (Sat and Sun), D £25

Andrews Hotel

HIGH STREET, BURFORD, OXFORDSHIRE OX18 4QA
TEL: BURFORD (0993) 823151   FAX: (0993) 823240

A bright, smart bed and breakfast in the centre of this popular Cotswold village.

Daytime traffic trundles down the steep, straight High Street of Burford, past the Tudor-style black and white frontage of this fifteenth-century hotel. Flowering hanging baskets and a large sign entice you into the tea-shop for morning coffee or sumptuous afternoon teas with lots of delicious-looking goodies. Inside, all is bright and fresh. Guests break-fast in the tea-room, where circular wooden tables overlook the street. There is also a lounge in pale green and white from where you can admire the courtyard garden dotted with colourful tubs of flowers. Bedrooms, some with beams, are of a good size. Fabrics are bright, walls are white and in immaculate condition. Bathrooms are smart, some with fresh blue and white tiling. Room 11, with a four-poster bed, has a large bathroom with a bath and separate shower.

- ◑ Open all year, exc 24 to 26 Dec
- ⤢ The hotel is half-way along Burford High Street, beyond the traffic lights on the hill. On-street parking
- ⇤ 2 single, 1 twin, 2 double, 3 four-poster, 1 family room; some with shower/WC, some with bathroom/WC; TV in all rooms; tea/coffee-making facilities on request
- ◈ Breakfast room, 2 lounges; fishing, golf nearby
- ⊖ No wheelchair access; no dogs; no smoking
- ▭ Access, Diners, Visa
- £ Single £45, single occupancy of twin/double £50, twin/double £60 to £70, four-poster £70 to £85, family room £65 to £70; deposit required. Special breaks available

Lamb Inn

SHEEP STREET, BURFORD, OXFORDSHIRE OX18 4LR
TEL: BURFORD (0993) 823155   FAX: (0993) 822228

An old inn in mellow Cotswold stone with civilised, atmospheric bars and simple, pretty rooms.

The Lamb Inn has a good position in Burford, just a couple of minutes away from the busy high street. A row of cottages covered with vines and hanging baskets, the inn is immediately appealing. Inside, the flagstoned bars are full of antiques, old wooden settles, comfy sofas, fresh flowers, and ornaments such as a collection of copper jelly moulds. There is lots of space in the lounge furthest away from the bar. The restaurant to the rear is grand yet restrained, with well-spaced tables, oil paintings and antiques. A typical lunch in March consisted of devilled whitebait with horseradish cream, escalope of salmon with a mussel and prawn sauce, followed by sweets or cheese, then coffee and mints. One reader had a few niggles about breakfast – soft toast and no hot milk provided for the coffee – but was impressed with the 'friendly and efficient service'.

Bedrooms are simple and well-kept, with fresh colour schemes. Malt has striking purple patterned wallpaper and a couple of deep-set windows with plants on the windowsills.

◐ Open all year, exc 25 and 26 Dec

▨ The inn is just off Burford High Street – turn by Tolesey Museum. Private car park

🛏 3 single, 3 twin, 8 double, I four-poster; most with bathroom/ WC, I with shower/WC, 3 rooms with shared facilities; TV, room service, hair-dryer, baby-listening in all rooms; no tea/ coffee-making facilities in rooms

◈ Restaurant, bar, lounge, TV

room, study; fishing, tennis, other sports nearby. Limited wheelchair access to hotel and restaurant, 3 ground-floor bedrooms

⊖ No smoking in restaurant

▭ Access, Visa

£ Single £35 to £38, single occupancy of twin/double £50 to £60, twin/double/four-poster £75 to £80. Sun L £15; set D £18.50 to £24. Special breaks available

---

BURLAND CHESHIRE   MAP 5

Burland Farm

WREXHAM ROAD, BURLAND, NR NANTWICH, CHESHIRE CW5 8ND
TEL: FADDILEY (0270 74) 210

Impressive attention to detail in a comfortable family farmhouse.

Up until the last war Cheshire cheese used to be made in this dairy farm, which has been in the hands of the same family since the 1700s. They have a 'green top' licence and have also started to make frozen yogurt for a national supermarket.

American-born Sandra Allwood brings a touch of Southern hospitality to her relaxed, comfortable family house. There are inviting chairs in the sitting-room, a coal fire, games, books and a piano. The bedrooms are equally enticing, and full of welcoming details such as biscuit tins, herb teas, hand-padded silk hangers, hot-water bottles and a flask of fresh milk (which must be the next best thing to sleeping next to the cow!). A local woodturner has made a four-poster for the Grey Room, while the Billiard Room has quilted satin eiderdowns, a complete Victorian bedroom set and comfortable, old-fashioned armchairs. Sandra provides good, fresh, sustaining farmhouse breakfasts. There might also be extras like fresh salmon cakes, American muffins or prunes marinated with cloves, cinnamon and honey.

The farm is particularly popular as a stop-over with people travelling to and from the Holyhead ferry. Dogs are welcome but no young children as, to quote the owner: 'Farms can be dangerous places for those who don't grow up on them.'

◑ Open all year, exc Xmas and New Year

⤢ 3 miles west of Nantwich on the A534 Nantwich to Wrexham road. Private car park

🛏 1 twin, 2 double; all with bathroom/WC, exc 1 double with shower/WC; TV, hair-dryer in all rooms

◈ Dining-room, lounge, library, games room; conference facilities (max 12 people non-residential); table tennis, croquet at hotel, tennis, swimming-pool nearby

⊖ No wheelchair access; no children under 10; no dogs in dining-room, no smoking in public rooms

▭ None accepted

£ Single occupancy of twin/double £23 to £25, twin/double £40 to £45; deposit required. Set D £12.50

BURNHAM MARKET NORFOLK   **MAP 7**

Hoste Arms

THE GREEN, BURNHAM MARKET, KING'S LYNN, NORFOLK PE31 8HD
TEL: FAKENHAM (0328) 738257   FAX: (0328) 730103

A busy pub near the Norfolk coast which successfully combines tasty food with tasteful rooms.

'Ask to see our beautiful rooms,' announces a blackboard behind the bar. Owner Paul Whittome and his friendly team of staff are justly proud of their 12 bedrooms above the ground-floor bar areas. To reach them you pass the Beresford shell collection – a treasure trove of beach finds displayed in a large glass cabinet. Two rooms have four-poster beds and Number Seven, at the top of the house, could sleep a family of five at a pinch, with a double, a single and two bunk beds. Painted in inoffensive shades of magnolia with neutral carpets and Victoriana bathroom fittings, the rooms are pleasant, well-heated and don't seem to suffer too badly from pub noise.

The Hoste Arms overlooks the green in the peaceful Georgian village of Burnham Market. By night the bow windows are enticingly aglow and most nights (particularly Mondays and Fridays, when jazz musicians or pianists provide entertainment) the bar areas throng with a convivial crowd. Dinner is served between 7 and 9.30pm and you choose either from a blackboard and bar menu or restaurant. There is not a great price difference; the decision mainly rests on your preference of surroundings – either busy and bustling or a little more genteel among the crushed pinks and wood panelling of the small restaurant.

◑ Open all year

⤴ 10 miles north of Fakenham. Hoste Arms is on west side of Burnham Market. Private car park

🛏 3 twin, 6 double, 2 four-poster, 1 family room; all with bathroom/WC, exc 1 double with shower/WC; TV, hair-dryer in all rooms; baby-listening on request

◈ Restaurant, 3 bar/dining areas, bar, lounge; laundry facilities; conference facilities (max 20 people non-residential out of season); golf, fishing, other sports nearby. Wheelchair access to bar/dining areas only

⊖ No smoking in restaurant

▭ Access, Visa

£ Single occupancy of twin/double £40, twin/double £66, four-poster £76, family room £66 (plus £15 per child); deposit required. Bar meals; set D £12.50, £15. Special breaks available

BURY ST EDMUNDS SUFFOLK   MAP 8

Ounce House

NORTHGATE STREET, BURY ST EDMUNDS, SUFFOLK IP33 IHP
TEL: BURY ST EDMUNDS (0284) 761779   FAX: (0284) 768315

A relaxed family home, ideal if you're looking for a friendly retreat close to the town centre.

It's Jenny Pott who runs this austere-looking Victorian guesthouse, but she admits that husband Simon is 'very good at chatting people up'. On a fairly busy residential road, near the Bury St Edmunds' Abbey Gardens and cathedral, Ounce House suits sightseers as well as business travellers eschewing large, impersonal hotels. Ascend the steps which lead up to the front door and you'll discover a smartly decorated house (first built as a merchant's home and later used as a nursery school). The main focus of activity is a knocked-through drawing-room and dining-room, its cool blues brightened with lavish dried-flower arrangements. This is where guests can relax or socialise and it is used in the evenings for communal meals, which Jenny finds often develop into jolly dinner parties. Unless special requests are made, she offers a no-choice menu which might consist of Mediterranean prawns in garlic and Pernod, followed by pork stuffed with pistachio nuts in a red wine sauce, with a pavlova or chocolate pot to finish. There is a choice of red or white French house wine.

Bedrooms are named after places where the Potts have lived at one time or another. Barclay, a large double overlooking the garden, is the nicest. Decorated in bold yellows, it's a cheerful room with an *en-suite* bathroom reached down a couple of steps – 'Not a room to be drunk in,' points out Jenny. Kensington, a twin, is light and airy but overlooks the front of the house and is not recommended for very sensitive sleepers. Broadland is another smart twin, a little smaller than the others, with a narrow bathroom.

◐ Open all year; dining-room open most evenings by arrangement

▱ Approaching Bury St Edmunds from east or west on the A45, leave by the second exit to the town. Turn left at the first roundabout into Northgate Street. The house is at the top of the hill on the right-hand side. Private car park.

🛏 I single, 2 twin, I double; all with bathroom/WC, exc single with shower/WC; TV, room service, hair-dryer, trouser press, baby-listening in all rooms

◈ Dining-room, bar/library, lounge; conference facilities (max 12 people non-residential); golf, tennis, other sports nearby; babysitting

⊖ No wheelchair access; no dogs; smoking in bar/library only

▭ Access, Visa

£ Single £35, single occupancy of twin £40 to £45, twin/double £64 to £70; deposit required. Set D £15 to £18 (by prior arrangement only)

BUTTERMERE CUMBRIA

MAP 4

Bridge Hotel

BUTTERMERE, VIA COCKERMOUTH, CUMBRIA CA13 9UZ
TEL: BUTTERMERE (07687) 70252

A walkers' inn with all the trimmings.

Right in the heart of the hamlet of Buttermere, the Bridge Hotel is on the doorstep of some of the most spectacular Lakeland fells. Haystacks, Red Pike, Grasmoor and Whiteless Edge are all within walking distance. Peter and Janet McGuire have owned the hotel since 1978 and its directors are now Philippe and Catherine Santini. Through combining careful attention to detail with an informal atmosphere, they have established the ideal inn for walkers who want to be sure of a few extra comforts when they stagger back from a day on the fells. Arriving in late afternoon, you stumble straight into the hallway where exhausted hikers sit sprawled in armchairs slurping cups of tea and scoffing cake – all free (to residents only). The rather more formal sitting-room next door is also a good place to relax – without tripping over muddy boots.

Upstairs, the bedrooms – neat and tidy with floral curtains and solid modern furniture – all have bathrooms with gallons of hot water even at peak time, although one reader observes that the bath in Room 21 is 'not much longer than an oversize bidet'. Bedrooms looking south-west have the best views, towards Red Pike. Dinner in the smart dining-room is rather more formal than tea-time, although there is no need to dress up. One five-course menu we sampled began with tomato soup with tarragon, then Whitby prawns before a main course of local lamb. Service is fast, efficient and relaxed to the point of friendly bantering with the guests. One visitor complained about sloppy housekeeping, having been greeted by the previous night's cups, glasses and ashtrays on coming down to breakfast at 8am the next morning. There was no evidence of such a lapse at the time of our inspection.

◑ Open all year

⤴ Leave the M6 at Junction 40 and follow signs to Keswick. Bypass Keswick taking the turning to Buttermere. Alternatively, continue to Cockermouth and follow signs to Buttermere via Lorton. Private car park

🛏 2 single, 8 twin, 10 double, 2 four-poster; all with bathroom/ WC, room service; hair-dryer and baby-listening on request

◈ Restaurant, 2 bars, 2 lounges, drying-room; conference facilities (max 30 people residential and non-residential); fishing, riding nearby

⊖ No wheelchair access; no dogs in public rooms; no smoking in restaurant

▭ Access, Visa

£ Single from £43 and £47, twin/ double from £70 and £78, four-poster from £80 and £88 (rates inc dinner), self-catering cottages from £210 per week; deposit required. Set D £16; bar food at lunch from £3. Special breaks available

---

CALDBECK CUMBRIA   **MAP 4**

High Greenrigg House

CALDBECK, CUMBRIA CA7 8HD
TEL: CALDBECK (06974) 78430

Excellent value and hearty dinners at this restored seventeenth-century farmhouse.

Approaching High Greenrigg House on a blowy autumn evening, you may be reminded of one of those old films where weary travellers are drawn across a desolate landscape to the solitary light that signifies humanity. Affable Fran and Robin Jacobs will be there to welcome you in and make sure that, despite its remote location, their farmhouse will give you a stimulating environment. It's not just the fact that they've converted an old cowshed into a games room with pool table and table tennis; in the house itself there is an abundance of books and board games as well as a piano, surrounded by family photographs.

In the main lounge area, with its exposed beams and flagged floors, you can relax in one of the armchairs surrounding the stone fireplace. Dinner is appropriately unpretentious fare, served buffet-style. You may find a bubbling pot of beef and chickpea casserole alongside stuffed peppers, baked potatoes and vegetables. In the morning, piles of half-oranges and a squeezer tempt you to make your own orange juice before you are served up a traditional cooked breakfast. The bedrooms are simple, with pine bedsteads, bright duvets and Lakeland prints on the walls – and, of course, impressive views.

◑ Closed Jan and Feb

⬏ Take the B5299 west from Caldbeck for 3 miles. Turn left at a minor road signposted Greenhead, Branthwaite and Fellside. The house is ½ mile along on the left. Private car park

🛏 2 twin, 4 double, 1 family room; most with bathroom/WC, some with shower/WC

◈ Dining-room, bar, lounge, TV room, games room; conference facilities (max 16 people non-residential, 7 residential); table tennis at hotel. Wheelchair access to hotel, restaurant and WC (unisex), 2 ground-floor bedrooms specially equipped for disabled people

⊖ No dogs in public rooms; smoking in lounge only

▭ Access, Visa

£ Single occupancy of twin/double £20, twin/double £39; deposit required. Set D £8 (7pm)

Parkend Restaurant

PARKEND, CALDBECK, CUMBRIA CA7 8HH
TEL: CALDBECK (06974) 78494

A popular restaurant in a quiet location with comfortable bedrooms.

This seventeenth-century whitewashed cottage is run as a restaurant-with-rooms by husband-and-wife team Phil and Carol Cornes. There's a small bar where diners mull over the menu before heading into two interconnecting dining-rooms, which have low beamed ceilings and lots of exposed stone walls decorated with plates. On cold evenings, a wood-burning stove keeps the atmosphere cosy. The menu deals in hearty, well-cooked fare such as peppercorn steak or half a chicken in cream sauce. At the end, a sweets trolley does the rounds. Nobody could say portions are small, but just in case there is the 'Parkend Challenge' – successful gourmands who tuck away a mixed grill comprising rump steak, gammon steak, Cumberland sausage, lamb chop, liver, black pudding, tomato, mushrooms, onion rings and chips have their name written in the *Parkend Book of Records*.

The pleasant bedrooms with their light patterned wallpaper, pink bed linen and modern pine furniture are comfortable. On inspection the hot-water supply was not up to the demands of early-evening bathers, although by next morning a piping hot supply had been restored.

◑ Open all year, exc 9 to 31 Jan

⬏ Caldbeck is on the B5299, 1½ miles west of Caldbeck. Private car park

🛏 3 double (family room available); all with bathroom/WC, TV, hair-dryer, baby-listening

◈ Restaurant, bar, lounge, TV room, library; tennis, other sports nearby

⊖ No wheelchair access; no dogs in public rooms; smoking in bar and bedrooms only

▭ Access, Amex, Diners, Visa

£ Single occupancy of twin/double £32, twin/double £48; deposit required. Set L from £3, D £14/ £15; Sun L £8. Special breaks available

CALNE WILTSHIRE MAP 9

Chilvester Hill House

CALNE, WILTSHIRE SN11 0LP
TEL: CALNE (0249) 813981/815785   FAX: (0249) 814217

An informal atmosphere and convivial hosts in a Victorian house with a heated outdoor swimming-pool.

This is a small hotel with a big welcome and service of a sort lacking in many a larger establishment. Gill Dilley, who once worked in the travel industry, will organise theatre tickets and ferry crossings as well as planning routes and sightseeing tours. On booking, guests are sent a personalised, informative letter instead of a brochure. Chilvester is not so much a hotel as the home of a professional family where guests soon become sufficiently relaxed to wander round house and garden with ease.

Pre-dinner drinks are taken in the large, elegant drawing-room. There is also a comfortable sitting-room, filled with family photos and offering a TV and baby grand for entertainment. All round the house are flower show standard pot plants from the greenhouse; on the landing there is an interesting display of Victorian jelly moulds, plus a special collection of old Huntley and Palmer biscuit tins – a touch of family history, as Gill Dilley was formerly a Palmer.

The three guest bedrooms are spacious and attractive. The Blue Room, decorated in co-ordinated fabrics, is perhaps the prettiest, but all the rooms are immaculately turned out and equipped with fresh milk, china cups and flowers. The bathrooms have baths and hand showers. A separate, rather florid, state-of-the-art shower room is available on the ground floor.

Gill's dinners are served in the parquet-floored dining-room around a table set with Royal Worcester china. There may be home-made soup to start, a casserole or corn-fed chicken with tarragon as a main course, and lemon roulade and fresh fruit to finish. Vegetables and salads come from the garden, while breakfasts include Gill's own damson or rhubarb and ginger jam.

◐ Open all year, exc 1 week in Spring or Autumn

↗ ½ mile from Calne on the A4 towards Chippenham. Take a right turn marked Bremhill and Ratford and immediately turn right again through gateposts. Private car park

⇌ 1 twin, 1 double, 1 family; all with bathroom/WC, TV; hair-dryer on request

◇ Dining-room, drawing-room, sitting-room; conference facilities (max 10 people non-residential, 6 residential); outdoor heated swimming-pool in summer,

fishing, golf, riding, tennis nearby

⊖ No wheelchair access; no children under 12; no dogs; no smoking in the dining-room

▭ Access, Amex, Diners, Visa

£ Single occupancy of twin/double £40 to £50, twin/double £60 to £75, family room £81 to £96; deposit required. Set D £18, £22 (8pm)

CALSTOCK CORNWALL   **MAP 10**

Danescombe Valley Hotel

LOWER KELLY, CALSTOCK, CORNWALL PL18 9RY
TEL: TAVISTOCK (0822) 832414 (and fax)

Beautiful Regency hotel on a bend in the River Tamar, close to Cotehele House and Gardens.

Right on the border between Devon and Cornwall, Danescombe Valley Hotel is at the end of a road running alongside the Tamar, just ten minutes' uphill walk away from the National Trust's glorious Cotehele House and Gardens; from the footpath there's a stunning panoramic view back across the Tamar to the hotel, looking rather like a balconied Regency seaside hotel cast adrift in the countryside. Cast adrift is how you too can feel at Danescombe Valley; to help you leave the world's hassles behind, the Smiths have barred televisions and radios from their house, and even newspapers are in short supply. The house has been decorated as far as possible in keeping with its age; even the plates on the hall walls are Victorian bread plates, once used instead of boards for serving bread at tables. Elsewhere, the walls of the lounge, small bar and the stairwell provide hanging space for paintings by local artists.

Personalised letters in the bedrooms welcoming guests and explaining the hotel's facilities are typical of the attention paid to detail. Bedroom furnishings are mainly big, bulky and antique; bathrooms tend to be spacious and interesting – Room Four's is spectacular, approached through double doors from the bedroom and stocked with paperbacks.

The simplest room in the house is the small dining-room where Martin Smith is a ubiquitous and charming host. Four-course dinners, cooked by Anna, don't offer a choice but are absolutely delicious; when we inspected, a starter of tangy onion tart with a mixed leaf salad was followed by excellent roast breast of duck with a sauce of balsamic vinegar and spring onions. But however nice, the orange cake served with honey ice-cream couldn't hope to compete with the stunning array of English cheeses on offer, most of them from minuscule local producers.

◑ Closed Nov to Mar (exc Xmas); restaurant closed Wed and Thurs eves

⚡ ½ mile west of Calstock village

along the river road. Private car park

⇦ 2 twin, 3 double; all with bathroom/WC, hair-dryer; tea/

coffee-making facilities on request; limited room service

◇ Dining-room, bar, lounge, drying room; fishing, golf, riding nearby

● No wheelchair access; no children under 12; no dogs; no smoking in dining-room

▭ Access, Amex, Diners, Visa

£ Twin/double £125, single occupancy by arrangement; deposit required. Set D £30

CAMPSEA ASH SUFFOLK　　　　　　　　　　　　　　**MAP 8**

Old Rectory　　　　　

CAMPSEA ASH, NR WOODBRIDGE, SUFFOLK IP13 0PU
TEL: WICKHAM MARKET (0728) 746524

Renowned local restaurant with comfortable rooms and an inviting garden.

Near the church, screened from the monotony of the surrounding flat countryside by a veil of trees, the Old Rectory is part Tudor with late eighteenth-century additions. Stewart Bassett runs the show and is the creative spirit behind the restaurant. Bedrooms are all different, and the rolling programme of refurbishment includes installation of showers, now in much demand by guests. What will remain intact, though, is the wonderful original plumbing in the *en-suite* bathroom of the Victorian Room, its brass bedstead an added incentive for choosing this room. If you enjoy crazy colours, try the Yellow Room, a twin with sunny walls which make a hearty contrast to the turquoise bathroom; if you prefer the scenery outside the room rather than in (and don't mind eaves) try the Attic Room, reached up a spiral staircase, which has lovely views. Some are colder: the Pink Room has boosters to pump up the temperature – one reader said she found the heating arrangements 'eccentric'.

The cooking is 'autocratic', says Stewart firmly – he produces a set, no-choice menu for guests. But his culinary megalomania can't be that strict because one reader reports happily that her likes and dislikes were taken into account. Certainly the wine list gives you masses of choice – the brochure's boast of an extensive list is something of an understatement, with 300 or so to wade through. An added bonus is the garden, overlooked by the paved conservatory (used for dinners and breakfasts). Are guests free to roam in it? 'Certainly,' replies Stewart, 'they can even weed it if they like.'

◑ Open all year, exc Xmas; restaurant closed some Sun eves

↗ On the B1078, 1½ miles east of Wickham Market. Private car park

⇐ 1 single, 2 twin, 2 double, 2 four-poster; all with bathroom/WC; hair-dryer on request

◇ 2 dining-rooms, bar, lounge, library, conservatory; conference facilities (max 16 people non-residential, 9 residential); golf, riding nearby

● No wheelchair access; no dogs; no smoking

▭ Access, Amex, Diners, Visa

£ Single £30, single occupancy of twin/double £30, twin/double £45, four-poster £55; deposit required. Sun L (occasional) £12.50; set D £18.50

CARBIS BAY CORNWALL   **MAP 10**

Boskerris Hotel

BOSKERRIS ROAD, CARBIS BAY, ST IVES, CORNWALL TR26 2NQ
TEL: PENZANCE (0736) 795295   FAX: (0736) 798632

A family hotel in a quiet St Ives suburb with pleasing public rooms.

For all that Boskerris Hotel is an uninspiring low white building in a not much more exciting suburban street, it nevertheless boasts fine sea views and all the comforts you could want for a family holiday. Although young children are expected, indeed welcomed, the public rooms have a grown-up elegance about them; the lounge has plenty of big, comfortable chairs from where guests can soak up the sea views, while the dining-room is as smart as in any hotel that firmly bars its doors to youngsters. For the sake of fairness, guests staying in the four rooms without views get first pick of the tables by the windows at breakfast and dinner. For the most part dinner menus play safe and English, and vegetarians should certainly mention the fact when booking. All the bedrooms are comfortably furnished, although some are on the small side; Room Ten, a family room, is one of the biggest, with a dressing annexe to its bathroom. Neither of the two singles has *en-suite* facilities. The attractive terraced garden contains a swimming-pool, but the games room in the car park turns out to be little more than a shed with a table-tennis table in it.

◑ Closed Nov to Easter

↗ Take the A30 to St Ives. Upon entering Carbis Bay, take the 3rd turning on the right (signposted to the station). Private car park

🛏 2 single, 4 twin, 9 double, family rooms available; all with bathroom/WC, exc singles; TV, room service, baby-listening in all rooms; hair-dryer on request

◈ Restaurant, bar, 3 lounges, TV room, drying room, games room; outdoor heated swimming-pool

at hotel, fishing, golf, other sports nearby; babysitting

⊖ No wheelchair access; no dogs in public rooms; no smoking in restaurant

▭ Access, Diners, Visa

£ Single £25 to £30, single occupancy of twin/double £37 to £42, twin/double £67 to £72, family room rate on request (rates inc dinner); deposit required. Bar lunches; set D £16. Special breaks available

---

Use the maps at the back of the Guide *to pinpoint hotels in a particular area.*

CAREY HEREFORD AND WORCESTER   **MAP 9**

Cottage of Content

CAREY, HEREFORD AND WORCESTER HR2 6NG
TEL: CAREY (0432) 840242

Away-from-it-all pub with comfortable creaky old rooms.

This is the sort of countryside where you instinctively feel the Archers belong – all cows, tractors and wild flowers in the hedgerows. Carey is about as buried as a village can be; it is little more than a few cottages and a bridge over a stream anyway, and the Cottage of Content is its focal point. Thatched, beamed and atmospheric, the pub stands garnished with climbers and herbaceous flowers – the archetypal picture-postcard. The inside is no disappointment, with beams, bars, locals and all. The bedrooms are excellent for a building of this age, with a fair amount of space, proper bathrooms and some good furniture standing aslant on the sloping floors. Beds are very comfortable. The meals are ambitious for bar food – Javanese chicken or lamb marinated in Pernod, for example, and a wonderful death by chocolate. Breakfast is substantial, but if you want something other than the traditional grill, be sure to say so before it arrives in front of you.

- ◑ Open all year, exc 25 Dec
- ⤴ Turn off the A49 towards Hoarworthy. The pub is 1½ miles from Hoarworthy village. Private car park
- 🛏 4 double, family room available; all with bathroom/WC, TV
- ◇ Dining-room, 2 bars
- ⊖ No wheelchair access
- ▭ Access, Amex, Visa
- £ Single occupancy of double £30, double £45; deposit required. Bar meals £8.50 to £11.50

CARLISLE CUMBRIA   **MAP 4**

Beeches

WOOD STREET, CARLISLE, CUMBRIA CA1 2SF
TEL: CARLISLE (0228) 511962

Homely bed and breakfast in a quiet cul-de-sac close to the city centre.

Known locally as the 'Pink House', the Beeches is a mint-condition Georgian town house located conveniently for the city centre and also for the M6 motorway, which makes it a good base for touring the Lake District, the Eden Valley and the Scottish Borders. Bill and Heather Kilpatrick's 1767 home is a Grade-II listed building in a peaceful cul-de-sac – winner of the 'Quality Street' award from the local council. The Kilpatricks have also notched up some rave reviews, not to mention awards, for their bed and breakfast; one hangs proudly on the wall of the toilet that is shared by the three bedrooms. A self-deprecating gesture perhaps? 'No,' says Bill, 'it is the only place where we're sure everybody will get to see it!'

The bedrooms have a cool, country feel and display a fondness for the styles of Laura Ashley. The Blue Room has rag-rolled walls, pine furniture and china plates on the walls. The Pink Room also has ragged effects, with a floral patterned carpet and two golden cherubs between the beds. The double room is less mannered than the twin rooms – plainer and more rustic with its sloping roof, exposed beams and hand-painted wardrobe. The dining-room is small and homely with one communal table. Bill's collection of china plates adorns the walls alongside a small collection of clay pipes and the inevitable brass bedwarmer.

◑ Open all year

⤢ Leave the M6 at Junction 43. After 1 mile, turn left into Victoria Road (with the Esso station to your right). Turn left when you approach Cellar 5 off-licence on the right. Private car park

🛏 2 twin, 1 double; 1 public bathroom; TV, hair-dryer, trouser press in all rooms

◈ Dining-room; fishing, golf, tennis, other sports nearby

⊖ No wheelchair access; no dogs; no smoking in public rooms

▭ None accepted

💷 Single occupancy of twin/double £20 to £25, twin/double £30 to £35; deposit required

---

CARTMEL CUMBRIA   **MAP 4**

Aynsome Manor Hotel ☆

CARTMEL, NR GRANGE-OVER-SANDS, CUMBRIA LA11 6HH
TEL: CARTMEL (05395) 36653   FAX: (05395) 36016

Elegant manor house with historic connections in the Vale of Cartmel.

When Chris and Andrea Varley took over the management of Aynsome Manor in 1987, the mum-and-dad team of Tony and Margaret Varley was able to relax and take more of a backstage role. You get the impression that there is little the Varleys won't do to make your stay enjoyable, although they accept that some things are just beyond them. When a visitor from South Carolina had stayed in Room Eight, with its four-poster bed and superb views across the valley, she complained that the birdsong was too loud and that there was 'too much scenery'. Many of the bedrooms are similarly cursed and all have been designed with both comfort and tradition in mind, from the attic Room 13 (mind your head on those beams) to the two rooms in the cottage annexe, a converted sixteenth-century stable, with their whitewashed stone walls and pine furniture. The rooms have baths rather than showers due to problems of water pressure; one reader remarked that the only complaint could be that these were on the small side.

The public areas strive to maintain a period feel in their décor without overstating the case. The residents-only lounge upstairs has a fine marble fireplace, where a real log fire will bring a glow to the cheeks of guests making the most of the comfortable sofas or armchairs. The five-course dinner in the elegant Regency dining-room makes use of fresh and local ingredients: smoked haddock, cream cheese and herb roulade served with a tomato and cucumber white wine dressing may be followed by cock-a-leekie soup and then breast of pheasant wrapped with smoked bacon served with a redcurrant and port wine sauce.

The manor house has an interesting history: the bolt-hole in the wine cellar dates from the Reformation, and a passage is said to have lead all the way to Cartmel Priory.

◑ Closed 3 weeks in Jan

🡵 ½ mile north of village, 2½ miles from the A590. Private car park

🛏 1 single, 4 twin, 5 double, 1 four-poster, 2 family rooms; all with bathroom/WC, exc 1 twin with shower/WC; TV, baby-listening in all rooms; limited room service

◈ Restaurant, bar, 2 lounges, drying room; fishing, golf, other sports nearby

⊖ No wheelchair access; no children under 5 in restaurant eves; no dogs in public rooms; no smoking in restaurant

▭ Access, Amex, Visa

£ Single £39 to £51, single occupancy of twin/double £39 to £55, twin/double £77 to £102, four-poster £77 to £102 (rates inc dinner). Set L £10.50, D £18.50. Special breaks available

Uplands

HAGGS LANE, CARTMEL, NR GRANGE-OVER-SANDS, CUMBRIA LA11 6HD
TEL: CARTMEL (05395) 36248

A small and cheerful country-house hotel with great cooking.

Uplands is a relative newcomer to the ranks of Cumbrian country-house hotels, but it has the weight of an already established tradition conferred by its association with Miller Howe. It was opened in 1985 by John Tovey, who brought with him Diana and Tom Peter, his personal assistant and head cook respectively at the highly regarded Windermere hotel.

The lounge area has a plain brown carpet with modern grey sofas and large lamps with peach shades. Drinks are served here, as there is no bar. The dining-room is equally simple and features prints from New York's Metropolitan Museum of Art; there is little to distract attention from the dinner itself, which may typically begin with poached fresh asparagus in puff pastry slice with smoked salmon and hollandaise sauce. A tureen of cucumber and lovage soup might then be followed by a choice of three main courses, such as baked fillet of fresh sea bass with tarragon and chambéry sauce, accompanied by a characteristically imaginative array of vegetables – perhaps deep-fried leek rings, carrots with coriander and salsify in parsley sauce. As at Miller Howe, the wine list has a good selection of wines from the New World.

The five bedrooms are brightly decorated and named after local rivers. We felt that the smallest would be rather cramped as a double, though readers have found the rooms comfortable enough.

◑ Closed 1 Jan to 24 Feb; restaurant closed Mon eve

⤵ From Cartmel village with the Pig and Whistle pub on your right, turn immediately left up Haggs Lane. The hotel is 1 mile up this road on the left. Private car park

🛏 3 twin, 2 double; some with bathroom/WC, most with shower/WC; TV, room service, hair-dryer in all rooms; no tea/coffee-making facilities in rooms

◈ Restaurant, lounge, drying-room; golf, riding, other sports nearby. Wheelchair access to restaurant only

⊖ No children under 8; no dogs in public rooms; no smoking in restaurant

▭ Access, Amex, Visa

£ Single occupancy of twin/double £75, twin/double £128 (rates inc dinner). Set L £14, D £25.50. Special breaks available

---

CARTMEL FELL CUMBRIA   **MAP 4**

Lightwood Farm

CARTMEL FELL, NR BOWLAND BRIDGE, CUMBRIA LA11 6NP
TEL: NEWBY BRIDGE (053 95) 31454

Well-run farmhouse convenient for the Lakes but well away from the crowds.

Lightwood Farm is set on the gentle fells to the east of Windermere – one of the least visited parts of the Lake District where the footpaths are uncluttered and the roads quiet. The large farmyard is clustered with barns and outbuildings, but to find Evelyn Cervetti, whose family has lived on the farm since 1945, continue on to the seventeenth-century farmhouse at the end of the yard. She'll show you to bedrooms either in the main house or in one of the converted barns. The accommodation is fairly simple and some rooms are quite small, but they're neatly decorated with, for instance, flowery wallpaper and pine cupboards. The sitting-room, with its wood-burning stove and loose-fitted sofas, is cosily traditional, as is the low-beamed dining-room. The appetising meals, charmingly served by Evelyn's daughter, are also traditional, with little choice; the wine list is inexpensive and basic. All in all, this is one of the best-value places to stay in the entire National Park.

◑ Open all year, exc Dec

↗ Follow signs for A590 to Newby Bridge, then take the A592 to Fell Foot. Turn right to Kendal; Lightwood is 2 miles on. Private car park

🛏 4 twin, 4 double, 1 family room; some with shower/WC, some with bathroom/WC; room service to all rooms; TV in some rooms; hair-dryer on request

◈ Dining-room, 2 lounges, drying room, conservatory

⊖ No wheelchair access; no dogs; smoking in lounge only

▭ Access, Visa

£ Single occupancy of twin/double £17 to £27, twin/double £33 to £44, family room £65 to £66; deposit required. Set D £11.50 (prices till Easter 94)

CASTLE ASHBY NORTHAMPTONSHIRE   MAP 9

Falcon ☆

CASTLE ASHBY, NORTHAMPTONSHIRE NN7 1LF
TEL: NORTHAMPTON (0604) 696200   FAX: (0604) 696673

Good-value, expertly run inn with luxurious rooms and good food.

A lovely and historic building opposite the village cross in peaceful green countryside, with professional staff, stylish rooms and good food, the Falcon seems to have everything. Since taking over this sixteenth-century inn in 1991 from the Marquess of Northampton's estate, Jo and Neville Watson have followed a programme of refurbishment which is completed now in the main building and will be finished by 1994 in the cottages next door. Rooms in the inn are stylishly kitted out in colours which are far removed from safe pastel shades – turquoise in one, for example, and electric blue in another. Some have good-sized modern bathrooms with power showers, while others have *en-suite* shower rooms. When there's no room at the inn you have to walk 50 yards outside to a cottage annexe, past a tiny post office overgrown with a jungle of wistaria and sweet-smelling clematis. The refurbished bedrooms here are equal in luxury to those in the inn, and the two singles would easily make doubles if the Nevilles didn't put comfort before profit.

The mustard-coloured dining-room is thoughtfully designed so that no one is cramped, and there's an adjoining oval room where groups can eat together. At breakfast, jams and marmalades are all home-made, and the modern-English dinner menu attempts to include as much local produce as possible. When we inspected, asparagus was in season at a local farm, and eight different asparagus dishes were extra to the usual menu, which included baked mushrooms with Brie and white wine, rack of lamb with spring onions, and scallops in chive butter sauce. We thought the silver service a little out of place for a hotel which otherwise has no pretensions. The lounge makes a comfortable place to curl up with a good book, while the invitation to spend Christmas here roasting chestnuts in front of the log fire is equally extended to children and the family dog.

◑ Open all year

⤴ Castle Ashby is signposted from both the A428 and A45. Private car park

🛏 4 single, 3 twin, 6 double, 1 cottage; all with bathroom/WC, exc 1 single with shower/WC; TV, room service, trouser press in all rooms

◈ Restaurant, 2 bars, lounge; conference facilities (max 14 people residential, 20 non-residential); fishing, golf, riding, water sports nearby; babysitting by arrangement. Wheelchair access to hotel, restaurant and WC (M, F), 4 ground-floor bedrooms in cottages

⊖ No young children in restaurant after 8pm; no dogs in restaurant

▭ Access, Amex, JCB, Visa

£ Single £45 to £59, twin/double/cottage room £55 to £73; deposit required. Sun L £13.50; set L, D £18.50; alc L, D £22 to £25 (prices till end 93). Special breaks available

---

CASTLE COMBE WILTSHIRE   **MAP 9**

Manor House

CASTLE COMBE, CHIPPENHAM, WILTSHIRE SN14 7HR
TEL: CASTLE COMBE (0249) 782206   TELEX: 449931 MANOR G
FAX: (0249) 782159

Exclusive and expensive country house on the edge of the Cotswolds.

Castle Combe, on the southern extremes of the Cotswolds, styles itself as the prettiest village in England. Difficult to verify, but if your idea of a

MANOR HOUSE
—CASTLE COMBE—

pretty village is honey-coloured stone cottages with a Jacobean manor house at its heart, then Castle Combe will be on your shortlist. The Manor driveway takes you under the archway cottage and then past a row of labourers' cottages and stables which have been converted for the use of guests – the cheapest available rooms. The Manor itself is surrounded by immaculate formal gardens complete with a croquet lawn.

Decoration in the public rooms of the main house is an expensive mix of Tudor and Victorian. Massive carved fireplaces provide the focal point in the lounges, which have beams, rugs and leather chairs. Staff pad about serving tea or drinks with quiet efficiency. As we have commented before, the rectangular dining-room is something of a disappointment, but as we went to press a decorative overhaul was planned. The menu is classic English fare – guinea-fowl in herbs, salmon in tarragon.

The house bedrooms vary in size, shape and décor, but are uniformly luxurious. One has a freestanding bathtub in the bedroom, another, Lordsmeer, has the bed in the centre of the room with a pink fabric canopy above it like a marquee. Some bathrooms come with their own TV – ostensibly used by high-powered executives to keep up with the news but no doubt equally welcomed by sybaritic guests.

◑ Open all year

⬈ 10 minutes from Junction 17 of the M4. Follow signs to Chippenham, then take the A420 in direction of Bristol. Fork left on to the B4039 to Castle Combe. Private car park

🛏 29 twin/doubles, 5 four-poster, 2 suites (half the rooms in cottages); all with bathroom/ WC, TV, room service, hair-dryer, baby-listening; tea/coffee-making facilities, mini-bar in some rooms

◈ Restaurant, bar, 3 lounges; conference facilities (max 60 people non-residential, 36 residential); fishing (Apr to Oct), tennis, croquet, heated outdoor swimming-pool (summer only), bicycles at hotel, other sports nearby; babysitting. Wheelchair access to hotel (no steps), restaurant and 2 ground-floor bedrooms

⊖ No dogs in public rooms; no smoking in restaurant and bedrooms

▭ Access, Amex, Diners, Visa

£ Single occupancy of twin/double from £95 and £115, twin/double from £100 and £115, four-poster from £175, suite from £195, cottage £295; deposit required. Continental B £8, cooked B £10; set L £17, D £32; alc L, D £45 (prices till Apr 94). Special breaks available

---

Being witness to father and son bickering furiously about how to face recessionary problems in the panelled hall of the grand family room one feared the worst. It was like playing Inspector Morse.

Grey Gables

NORWICH ROAD, CAWSTON, NORFOLK NR10 4EY
TEL: NORWICH (0603) 871259

An informal restaurant-with-rooms where there is a family feel.

There are conflicting reactions to Grey Gables. On the positive side a
reader reports a 'warm welcome, good food and excellent wines', but in
contrast another guest complains that her food was 'a disappointment'
and served on 'stone cold' plates. Since most guests come here on
inclusive dinner, bed and breakfast breaks, the standard of food cannot
afford to fluctuate. However, Rosalind and James Snaith have compiled
a wine list long enough to keep anyone happy, starting with a tongue-in-
cheek catalogue of 'cures' for ailments – perhaps the most appealing
being four glasses of champagne for tuberculosis, rheumatism or fever!
And you won't have to agonise over which dessert to choose, for you can
have a selection of three to try at one go if you can't make up your mind.

There is no criticism of the bedrooms: 'Comfortable and pleasant –
and very good value,' says one happy guest. There are eight to choose
from, all pleasant, with fresh, cottagey décor such as pine furniture and
flowery bedspreads. Perhaps the most appealing quality is the atmosphere of a family home which belies the rather formal red-brick
façade of this former rectory. Rosettes, prep school photos and personal
knick-knacks in the lounge and hallways make it less like a business and
more like a stay at a friend's house.

◗ Open all year, exc 24, 25, 26
Dec

🡕 1 mile south of Cawston village,
near Eastgate. Private car park

🛏 2 single, 1 twin, 4 double, 1
family room; most with
bathroom/WC, 1 double with
shower/WC; TV, room service,
hair-dryer in all rooms

◈ 2 dining-rooms, lounge; drying
and ironing facilities; conference
facilities (max 12 people non-
residential, 8 residential); tennis
at hotel, riding, heated
swimming-pool nearby.

⊖ Wheelchair access to restaurant
and WC (unisex) only

⊖ No children under 5 in dining-
rooms eves; no dogs in public
rooms; no smoking in dining-
rooms

▭ Access, Visa

£ Single £19 to £27, single
occupancy of twin/double £32 to
£40, twin/double £54, family
room £58; deposit required. Set
L £12.50 (by arrangement), D
£10.50 to £15.50. Special
breaks available

---

*The talkative porter of a Scottish hotel: 'Of course she (the owner) has got the
brains and the money.' Later: 'This French suite is absolutely priceless;
(sotto voce) in fact, I've heard it's worth £30,000.'*

CHADLINGTON OXFORDSHIRE   **MAP 9**

Chadlington House

CHAPEL ROAD, CHADLINGTON, OXFORDSHIRE OX7 3LZ
TEL: CHADLINGTON (060 876) 437   FAX: (060 876) 503

A quiet, friendly bed and breakfast suited to an older clientele.

Changes are afoot at Chadlington and 1994 may see bed and breakfast
on a smaller scale than before – Rita and Peter Oxford have enjoyed
running their large Victorian mock-Tudor house as a hotel for the past 18
years but now feel that they want to slow up a little, though they will
continue to operate as a bed and breakfast. The house benefits from
large rooms and a warm, likeable hostess who immediately puts you at
your ease, chatting humorously as she shows you to your room. There is a
homely mix of old-fashioned furniture and rooms are comfortable rather
than stylish, with oranges and browns and velour easy chairs. Views from
the front bedrooms are lovely, over rolling Cotswold countryside. Downstairs there is more than adequate space in the television lounge or, for
fine days, there is a massive garden shaded by mature trees to the rear of
the house. One regular guest commends the welcome and the friendly
service provided by long-serving local staff.

◑ *Closed Jan and Feb; restaurant closed Sun eve*

↗ *Turn off the A361 from Burford. Chadlington is 2 miles south of Chipping Norton. Private car park*

🛏 *2 single, 2 twin, 5 double, 1 four-poster, 1 self-catering cottage/family room; some with bathroom/WC, some with shower/WC; TV, hair-dryer in all rooms*

◈ *Restaurant, bar, lounge, drying room; conference facilities (max 30 non-residential, 10 residential); tennis, riding, other sports nearby; babysitting by arrangement. Wheelchair access to hotel, restaurant and WC, 1 ground-floor bedroom in cottage annexe*

⊖ *No dogs; smoking in bar only and discouraged in bedrooms*

▭ *Access, Visa*

£ *Single £30 to £38, single occupancy of twin/double £45, twin/double £50 to £60, four-poster £60 to £80, family room £60 to £70, cottage room £50 to £60; deposit required. Set D £16.50; alc D £18.50. Special breaks available*

CHAGFORD DEVON   **MAP 10**

Easton Court ☆

EASTON CROSS, CHAGFORD, NR NEWTON ABBOT, DEVON TQ13 8JL
TEL: CHAGFORD (0647) 433469

*Pleasant thatch-roofed hotel with walled garden, close to
Dartmoor.*

Easton Court Hotel is on the A382 before you reach Chagford itself.
The face it turns to the road is deceptively plain, but pass through the
gate into the walled garden and you discover a wonderful stone-walled,
thatch-roofed house dating back to the fifteenth century, prettiest in
autumn when it is swathed in glorious red-and-gold Virginia creeper.
Inside, it is all heavy oak beams, big log fires (an old bread oven is cut into
the side of the one in the lounge), chintzy sofas and deep armchairs,
probably little changed from the days when Evelyn Waugh stayed here
while writing *Brideshead Revisited* in 1944; tradition has it that much of
the writing was done in the bar, a cosy panelled room with lots of dried
flowers and paintings by local artists discreetly for sale on the walls.
Beyond the bar a library full of books positively wills you to sink into its
inviting chairs, if only to watch the television. Meals are served in an airy
rear dining-room with polished dropleaf tables and pretty pink walls.
Menus feature a sensible choice of local dishes like haunch of venison
and foreign imports like Hungarian goulash. Vegetarians need to an-
nounce themselves when booking.

Front bedrooms are double-glazed to seal off noise from the road.
Those at the back offer the best views and the greatest peace and quiet;
sadly, the honeymoon suite with its four-poster bed and lacey coverlet is
one of the noisier rooms, although the exposed stonework is very
attractive. The one ground-floor twin has lovely views from its window
but not from the bathroom, which is a little claustrophobic; other rooms,
however, have spacious naturally lit bathrooms. All the rooms are
comfortably cottagey, with lots of dried flowers.

◗ Open all year, exc Jan

🡵 From the A30 take the A382
exit at Whiddon Down. Follow
the signs to Moretonhampstead.
The hotel is three miles along
this road on the left-hand side.
On-street parking

🛏 2 twin, 3 double, 2 four-poster;
most with bathroom/WC, some
with shower/WC; TV in all rooms

◈ Dining-room, bar, lounge, TV

room, library/study; fishing, golf,
riding nearby

⊖ No wheelchair access; no
children under 12; no dogs in
public rooms; no smoking in
some public rooms

▭ Access, Amex, Visa

£ Single occupancy of twin/double
£44, twin/double £76, four-
poster £82; deposit required. Set
D £22. Special breaks available

Mill End

SANDY PARK, CHAGFORD, NR NEWTON ABBOT, DEVON TQ13 8JN
TEL: CHAGFORD (0647) 432282   FAX: (0647) 433106

Comfortable, long-established country sports hotel in an old mill, across the road from the Castle Drogo estate.

Set at an oblique angle to the road, Mill End Hotel is large and white and shines in the sun. Given the name, it's hardly surprising to find that it used to be a mill; the waterwheel, which continued to turn until 1917, can still be seen in a courtyard outside. There's a pleasant garden in front and the River Teign runs through the grounds but, more importantly for walkers, just across the road is the National Trust's Castle Drogo estate containing an Edwin Lutyens castle.

The hotel is popular with anglers, and the room for storing muddy waders and fishing tackle is suitably full of pictures of the 'it was *this* large' type. In the dining-room, menus are more adventurous than might be expected, and always feature something for vegetarians; most inspirational are the five-course extravaganzas for the regular wine and food weekends. The ground floor accommodates lounges for all tastes: small, large, with and without television. Bedrooms are spacious; the best are the three ground-floor rooms with access to a garden patio.

◖ Closed 10 to 20 Dec and 10 to 20 Jan

▰ From Exeter take the A30 Okehampton road. Turn south at Whiddon Down on the A382 – do not turn into Chagford at Sandy Park. Private car park

🛏 2 single, 3 twin, 10 double, 2 family rooms; most with bathroom/WC, 1 double with shower/WC; TV, room service, hair-dryer, baby-listening in all rooms

◈ Restaurant, bar, lounge, TV room, drying room, hall; fishing at hotel, other sports nearby. Wheelchair access to hotel, restaurant and WC (M,F), 3 ground-floor bedrooms

⊖ No dogs in public rooms

▭ Access, Amex, Diners, Visa

£ Single £35, single occupancy of twin/double £40 to £50, twin/double/family room £80 to £90; deposit required. Alc D £20/£23.50/£26.50. Special breaks available

Charingworth Manor

CHARINGWORTH, NR CHIPPING CAMPDEN, GLOUCESTERSHIRE GL55 6NS
TEL: PAXFORD (0386 78) 555 TELEX: 333444 CHARMA G
FAX: (0386 78) 353

A thoughtfully run Cotswold country-house hotel.

Charingworth Manor lies on the slope of a hill a few miles away from the
star attraction of Hidcote Gardens. It is a big, classic, largely Jacobean
Cotswold manor, well isolated from the humdrum world by its extensive
grounds, and with many of the old agricultural buildings converted into
bedrooms. These do not have the same appeal as the rooms in the old
house, where the heavy beams and uneven floors reflect the periods of
the original building, but are still very comfortable with excellent
bathrooms. There is nothing over-reverential about the decoration,
which consists of bold colours and strong fabrics that fit the place well.
You'll find plenty of places to sit, from the conservatory with its green
wicker chairs to more conventional drawing-rooms, and good views to go
with them. The dining-room, divided up by arches, is a pretty setting for
ambitious modern cuisine. An early summer menu offered grilled baby
crottin with pasta and sun-dried tomatoes, followed by fillet of venison
with cinnamon pear and blueberry sauce and, to finish, Charingworth
cheeseboard with cheese biscuits.

- ◑ Open all year
- ↗ 2½ miles east of Chipping Campden on the B4035. Ignore sign to Charingworth; the manor is 2 miles further on. Private car park
- 🛏 3 twin, 16 double, 2 four-poster, 3 suites; all with bathroom/WC, TV, room service, hair-dryer, trouser press; baby-listening by arrangement; no tea/coffee-making facilities in rooms
- ◈ Restaurant, 3 lounges, conservatory, games room; conference facilities (max 34 people non-residential, 24 residential); tennis, sauna/solarium, heated swimming-pool, steam room, snooker room at hotel, other sports nearby
- ⊖ No wheelchair access; no dogs in public rooms
- ▭ Access, Amex, Diners, Visa
- £ Single occupancy of twin/double £85 to £120, twin/double £110 to £140, four-poster £180, suite £210; deposit required. Set L £15.50, D £27.50

 *Denotes somewhere you can rely on a good meal – either the hotel
features in the 1994 edition of our sister publication,* The Good
Food Guide, *or our inspectors thought the cooking impressive,
whether particularly competent home cooking or more lavish cuisine.*

CHARTHAM KENT   **MAP 8**

Thruxted Oast

MYSTOLE, CHARTHAM, CANTERBURY, KENT CT4 7BX
TEL: CANTERBURY (0227) 730080

Beautifully converted oasthouses set among hop gardens – a good base for Canterbury with the full flavour of Kent.

If hotels won prizes for struggles against adversity, Thruxted Oast would surely be a winner: Tim and Hilary Derouet bought the oast as a gutted shell with no interior walls in 1986, restored its five distinctive chimneys (or cowls, as they say in these parts) and within 14 months managed to open up to guests. The pair warmly welcome guests into their well-maintained home, which also serves as the base for their picture-framing business. Breakfast, which includes home-made jams and marmalades, eggs from the homestead's own hens and fruit from the garden in season, is served communally in the kitchen. Guests can relax in the apricot and green lounge next door, which is charmingly furnished with flowery armchairs, a piano and plenty of attractive, homely clutter. In summer, the back terrace is more popular, with its wooden chairs and tables overlooking a raised lawn and colourful borders.

The three bedrooms, named Chaucer, the Wife of Bath and the Knight, incorporate sloping wooden ceilings and many of the original beams and doors of the oasthouses. Pretty rustic furniture, easy chairs, dried flowers and hops, pictures and old jars complete the pastoral effect, which is complemented by floral wallpaper and fabrics. Every possible convenience with which to pamper guests has been thought of, including hot-water bottles, hand mirrors, bathrobes, sewing kits, writing paper and even a torch by each bed.

◐ Open all year, exc 4 days at Xmas

↗ From Canterbury take the A28 Ashford road. After crossing the bypass, turn left into St Nicholas Road, then right at the T-junction. Continue on this road for 2 miles past the hospital and to a crossroads. Go straight over – the house is near the bottom of the hill, on the right. Private car park

🛏 3 twin; all with shower/WC, TV, hair-dryer

◇ Lounge; walking, riding, golf nearby

⊖ No wheelchair access; no children under 8; no dogs; no smoking in bedrooms and discouraged in public rooms

▭ Access, Amex, Diners, Visa

£ Single occupancy of twin/double £63, twin/double £73

It is always worth enquiring about the availability of special breaks or weekend prices. The prices we quote are the standard rates for one night – most hotels offer reduced rates for longer stays.

Chedington Court

CHEDINGTON, BEAMINSTER, DORSET DT8 3HY
TEL: CORSCOMBE (0935) 891265   FAX: (0935) 891442

*Magnificent views from commodious rooms in classic country house
with terraced garden.*

Chedington Court envelops one in an air of absolute tranquillity; it is the
proverbial place in which to hear a pin drop. As P G Wodehouse might
have put it, the P&Q just takes the biscuit. A mock-Jacobean house built
in 1840, Chedington is a formal country-house hotel with an informal
style (perfect as a romantic bolt-hole) that commands an imperious
three-county view. One reader considers it, 'one of the finest hotels in
England. Relaxed, informal, beautiful, set in lovely gardens with the
most magical views of Dorset . . . really a treat for a country weekend.'

Rooms are spacious, filled with antiques and fresh flowers but the look
is understated; the slightly faded covers have the elegance of worn tweed
jackets and real pearls. Owners Hilary and Philip Chapman provide
discreet, personal service to match. Stone leaded windows look out over
the terraced gardens and ancient yews; the Victorian conservatory is
filled with old roses, jasmine and mimosa trees. The immense panelled
library is the perfect spot in which to fall asleep over a good book.
Bedrooms vary in size, shape and quality, but they all have a homely air
that is far more the real thing than many a sterile, design-dominated
luxury spot. Comfort and ease are the important things here, whether in
the spacious Dorset or Rhododendron rooms, or in the less-imposing
second-floor bedrooms. All have good beds, feather and down pillows,
and armchairs and writing desks wherever possible.

The dining-room has well-set and spaced tables, and has built up a
reputation for good, modern British food. A May set dinner included
duck liver parfait with Cumberland sauce, fillet of brill with two sauces,
noisettes of lamb topped with mushroom and tarragon mousse, sweets
and cheese, but there were alternatives to most courses, including a
vegetarian dish. There is an extensive wine list that includes some
particularly good German wines.

◑ Closed 3 Jan to 3 Feb

⤢ Just off the A356 Crewkerne to
Dorchester road, 4½ miles
south-east of Crewkerne at
Winyard's Gap. Private car park

🛏 4 twin, 5 double, 1 four-poster;
all with bathroom/WC, exc 1
double with shower/WC; TV,
room service, hair-dryer, baby-
listening in all rooms; trouser
press on request

◈ Restaurant, dispense bar, lounge,
drying room, library, billiard
room, conservatory; conference
facilities (max 30 people non-
residential, 10 residential); golf
at hotel, other sports nearby;
babysitting. Wheelchair access to
restaurant, WC (unisex) only

⊖ No children in restaurant eves;
no dogs in public rooms and
unaccompanied in bedrooms

☐ Access, Amex, Visa

£ Single occupancy of twin/double £58 to £71, twin/double £95 to £121, four-poster £121, family

room £117; deposit required. Set D £27.50. Special breaks available

---

CHELTENHAM GLOUCESTERSHIRE   **MAP 9**

Lypiatt House ☆

LYPIATT ROAD, CHELTENHAM, GLOUCESTERSHIRE GL50 2QW
TEL: CHELTENHAM (0242) 224994   FAX: (0242) 224996

A reliable central base in Cheltenham.

Jane and Michael Medforth took over Lypiatt House in the summer of 1992, and have already drawn praise from guests for their friendliness and for their breakfasts. Lypiatt House is a big, bland, self-important Victorian villa in a road full of others of its kind, most of which have now become offices. Inside, it is clean, neat and tasteful, though a bit lacking in character. The conservatory, well-insulated against traffic noise, brightly tiled and furnished with marble-topped tables, is by far the best place to sit. The basement breakfast room is stylishly laid out, with individual marmalade pots on every table. Bedrooms are by and large decent-sized, and bathrooms are well kitted out (though one reader had a minor niggle that the bath towels were rather small). Some of the rooms on the lower floors lack character; those up under the eaves have rather more. Evening meals are served on request. In a town where hotels are apt to be overpriced for what is on offer, here you at least have the quality to justify the price.

◑ Open all year

⬈ Turn off the A46 Bath Road on to the A40 Suffolk Road heading towards Junction 11 of M5. Turn right at the fork after the 1st set of traffic lights into Lypiatt Road. Private car park

🛏 3 single, 4 twin, 3 double; all with bathroom/WC, exc 1 double with shower/WC; TV, room service, hair-dryer in all rooms

◈ Restaurant, bar, lounge, drying room, conservatory; golf, tennis, riding nearby

⊖ No wheelchair access; no dogs; no smoking in restaurant

☐ Access, Visa

£ Single £44, single occupancy of twin/double £50, twin/double £62, king-size room £65; deposit required. Set D (by arrangement only)

Many hotels offer special rates for stays of a few nights or more. It is worth enquiring when you book.

CHESTER CHESHIRE   **MAP 5**

Castle House

23 CASTLE STREET, CHESTER, CHESHIRE CH1 2DS
TEL: CHESTER (0244) 350354

Spick-and-span guesthouse inside city walls; within easy reach of shops, restaurants and tourist attractions.

Castle House was renovated two hundred years ago, when the Regency owner, unable to bear the cost of demolishing and rebuilding his dated Tudor home, slapped on a new Georgian façade instead. The origins of the house only really came to light during more recent restoration work; now the original beams and timbers are to be seen inside, along with exposed wattle and the coat of arms of Elizabeth I above the mantel.

From the outside the street is still Georgian, though there are few private houses left amongst the line of surveyors, solicitors and public houses – only a plaque identifies this small bed and breakfast hidden in the heart of Chester.

The first thing you notice on entering the surprisingly large entrance hall is the smell of polish; the wooden stairs up to the visitors' wing positively gleam. The breakfast-cum-sitting-room is cottagey in style: lots of brasses, a Welsh dresser, a jolly red carpet, a chess set and pot plants. Freshly cooked breakfasts are provided by good-natured Coyle Marl. There are newspapers to read or tourist suggestions to consider.

The bedrooms are neat, cosy and comfortable. The two front rooms may suffer from noise from the pub opposite at closing time. The two singles share a bathroom but the beds are good and family photos lend a homely air. Guests are given keys so they can freely come and go.

◐ Open all year

↗ Within the city walls, next to the castle. Private car park; on-street parking, can be difficult during day

🛏 2 single, 1 twin, 1 double, 1 family room; all with shower/WC, exc singles, 1 public bathroom; TV, room service, hair-dryer, baby-listening in all rooms

◈ Lounge; fishing, golf, tennis, other sports nearby

⊖ No wheelchair access

▭ Access, Visa

£ Single £23, single occupancy of twin/double £34, twin/double £45, family room rate on request; deposit required. Special breaks available

---

 This denotes that you can get a twin or double room for £50 or less per night inclusive of breakfast.

Green Bough Hotel

60 HOOLE ROAD, CHESTER, CHESHIRE CH2 3NL
TEL: CHESTER (0244) 326241   FAX: (0244) 326265

Smartly run small hotel, just outside the city centre, that tries for a turn-of-the-century feel. Not for the mirrorphobic.

The Green Bough stands on a clogged arterial road, lined with small hotels and guesthouses, that runs into the heart of the old walled sandstone city. With plenty of parking space and a bus stop to hand, the Green Bough is a sensible choice for anyone unwilling to brave the maelstrom of Chester's inner ring-road system. Parking is at such a premium here that when the opportunity arose to buy the house next door David and Doreen Castle snapped it up, as much for the extra parking space as for the additional rooms it now provides.

Inside the solid Edwardian house, antiques mingle with bric-à-brac, genuine curios range alongside junk-shop finds. The lounge has comfortable leather chesterfields and a carved wooden fireplace housing a modern gas-effect fire; the bar is a rather full-blown exercise in red velvet and gold. There is a gently ticking grandfather clock on the stairs, an old wind-up gramophone in the hall and a Russian accordian that children can play with.

The bedrooms are full of frills and fripperies, lace and trinkets. Room Six has a toy clown on a trapeze hanging from the canopy of a lacy four-poster. Mirrors line walls and front cupboards to an almost alarming degree – be careful in Room Five not to walk into the bathroom wall. Some may feel the bedrooms tread a narrow line between charm and clutter, but they are all fresh and immaculate. Rooms in the annexe are more subdued and 'masculine', with some good old-fashioned dark furniture, subtler fabrics and smartly tiled bathrooms.

◖ Closed Xmas and New Year

⤴ Leave the M53 at Junction 12 and follow the A56 into Chester. The hotel is ½ mile from the M53 on the right-hand side. Private car park

🛏 1 single, 2 twin, 12 double, 1 four-poster, 3 family rooms (some rooms in annexe); most with bathroom/WC, some with shower/WC; TV, room service, hair-dryer, baby-listening in all rooms

◈ Dining-room, bar, lounge, TV room; conference facilities (max 12 people residential and non-residential); golf, tennis, other sports nearby. Wheelchair access to hotel (2 steps) and restaurant, 5 ground-floor bedrooms

⊖ No dogs in public rooms; no smoking in dining-room

▭ Access, Visa

£ Single £40 to £41, single occupancy of twin/double £43 to £46, twin/double/four-poster £54 to £57, family room £60 to £63; deposit required. Set D £12. Special breaks available

Redland

64 HOUGH GREEN, CHESTER, CHESHIRE CH4 8JY
TEL: CHESTER (0244) 671024   FAX: (0244) 681309

Indulge Victorian Gothic fantasies in this luxurious, antique-filled private hotel.

'It is a model for what hotels of this grade should aspire to,' says a reader who enjoyed a stay at this red-brick detached hotel in a residential area, not far from Chester city centre. Built in the 1860s by the owner of the Redland Brick Company as a wedding present for his daughter, the house seems to have been a vehicle for dreams of ancestral grandeur on the part of the Scottish architect. After acclimatising to the baronial entrance hall, the panelled dining-room and the crypt-like landing, guarded by a knight in shining armour, it is a shock to look out of the windows and see suburban semis and the local golf club instead of craggy mountains and grouse moors.

The proprietrix, Teresa White, has spent five years turning the run-down Redland into a wonderful showcase for her compulsive antique-collecting passion, but she has been careful to keep to the original character of the house. The drawing-room is particularly elegant, featuring a splendid gentleman's resting chair with mechanical features. The dining-room, for breakfasts only, has starched antique lace cloths, an aspidistra in the window and a striking Victorian silver ornamental table stand.

The bedrooms reflect the distinctive style. The Jacobean Suite, in deep crimson and dull gold fabric, is one of three honeymoon suites. The vast, carved four-poster came from Perth Castle and is a bed never to get out of, a mother of all beds, so high you need to take a flying leap or climb the steps at the foot. You re-enter the twentieth century with the corner bath in the glossy new bathroom, or the sauna and sunbed in the basement. Coming right down to earth, a launderette-cum-ironing-room is also available for guests' use.

◐ Open all year

⤢ Leaving Chester, take the A483 Wrexham road and then the A549 Saltney road for 200 yards. The hotel is opposite Westminster Park. Private car park

🛏 3 single, 2 twin, 4 double, 3 four-poster, 1 family room; most with bathroom/WC, some with shower/WC; TV, hair-dryer in all rooms

◇ Breakfast room, bar, lounge, laundry room; sauna/solarium at hotel, golf, other sports nearby

⊖ No wheelchair access; no dogs; no smoking in breakfast room and some bedrooms

▭ None accepted

£ Single £40, single occupancy of twin/double £40, twin/double £55, four-poster £65 to £70, family room £65 to £70; deposit required

CHESTER-LE-STREET CO DURHAM   **MAP 3**

Lumley Castle

COUNTY
HOTEL
OF THE
YEAR

CHESTER-LE-STREET, DURHAM, COUNTY DURHAM DH3 4NX
TEL: 091-389 1111   FAX: 091-387 1437/091-389 1881

A sense of fun and warm-hearted staff in a cleverly restored historic pile.

'No ordinary hotel,' boasts the brochure and, for once, it's not hyperbole. The steep tariff means that Lumley Castle is firmly esconced in the business hotel sector. The splendid building, turreted, crenellated and floodlit at night, has a history dating back to the late fourteenth century which is enthusiastically capitalised upon by the owners, who dress their reception staff in medieval garb and stage weekend Elizabethan banquets in the Baron's Hall.

At the heart of all this Hollywood history is a very good hotel staffed by friendly, unstuffy locals. When we inspected, every sentence seemed to end with a Geordie 'pet', 'love' or 'flower'; the restaurant manageress sang as she straightened a table-setting, and produced a high chair before a couple with toddler had a chance to ask.

Public rooms are appositely grand, decked out with medieval-style furniture and clever repro, and linked by endless corridors and steep stone staircases that seem designed to withstand the angriest cannonball. Pre-dinner drinks can be taken in a library-style bar or an elegant drawing-room with walls draped in pleated blue fabric and bedecked with pictures. Diners are led to the undercroft-style restaurant via a passageway where they file past a row of theatrically lit classical busts. Food, from a three-course table d'hôte menu, is competent but unexciting – perhaps terrine of salmon, duck with orange segments and seven vegetables, and a cheeseboard.

The pricier rooms in the main building have a substantial edge over those in the courtyard and are individually decorated. Our inspector's room was an immaculate single in autumnal colours with heavy print fabrics, reproduction antique furnishings, and everything from cotton wool to a hot-water bottle. The glitzy bathroom was splendidly luxurious, but got the basics right, too, with enormous soft bath sheets.

A huge cold buffet augments the traditional grilled platter, which is served by ladies in mob caps and Victorian flounces – leading one tiny toddler to set up a chorus of 'You're a witch'. Books on shelves scattered around the restaurant include Oliver Wendell Holmes's *Autocrat of the Breakfast Table* – one of the many personal touches that, coupled with the grand setting, make this a memorable hotel.

◗ Open all year, exc 25, 26 Dec and 1 Jan

🔼 Leave the A1 (M) at the exit for Chester-le-Street and follow the

A167 southwards for 3 miles. Private car park

🛏 14 single, 10 twin, 31 double, 8 four-poster, 2 family rooms, 1

suite; all with bathroom/WC, exc
singles with shower/WC; TV,
room service, trouser press,
baby-listening in all rooms; hair-
dryer, mini-bar on request

 Restaurant, bar, lounge, games
room; conference facilities (max
150 people non-residential, 65
residential); fishing, golf, other
sports nearby; babysitting

 No wheelchair access; no dogs

Access, Amex, Diners, Visa

Single £80, single occupancy of
twin/double £80, twin/double
£98, four-poster £125, family
room from £98, suite £160;
deposit required. Set L £13.50, D
£20; alc L, D £25 (prices till
Sept 93). Special breaks
available

CHIEVELEY BERKSHIRE   **MAP 9**

Blue Boar Inn

NORTH HEATH, CHIEVELEY, BERKSHIRE RG16 8UE
TEL: CHIEVELEY (0635) 248236   FAX: (0635) 248506

*An old pub with a modern bedroom annexe, convenient as a stop-
over off the M4.*

Close to the motorway and surrounded by fields, this old country pub is
well placed as an overnight stop-over for travellers on the M4. The
whitewashed, thatched building dates from the sixteenth century and has
a large gnarled tree and a small grassy lawn to the front, edged with tubs
of flowers. A modern whitewashed annexe has been added at the rear.
The central hub of the pub is the long, beamed bar made up of three
interconnecting rooms – a convivial spot in which to grab a bar meal or
while away an evening. Classical music plays in the background and the
bar menu is written up on a blackboard, offering such dishes as onion
soup and gammon steak and chips. A wood-panelled bar with dark
furnishings is a less appealing alternative. Bedrooms are neat and simple,
with plain white walls and modern reproduction furniture; though they
lack homely touches, they are perfectly adequate for an overnight stop.

◑ Open all year; restaurant closed
Sun eve

↗ Leave the M4 at Junction 13 and
take the A34 northbound for 200
yards, then turn left for
Chieveley. Turn left at the
Wheatsheaf pub and turn right
at the T-junction towards
Wantage. The inn is 500 yards
on the right. Private car park

🛏 2 single, 4 twin, 8 double, 1
four-poster; all with bathroom/

WC, singles with shower/WC;
TV, room service in all rooms

 Restaurant, bar; conference
facilities (max 15 people
residential, 20 non-residential)

No wheelchair access; no dogs

Access, Amex, Diners, Visa

Single £37, single occupancy of
twin/double £42, twin/double
£47, four-poster £52. Alc L, D
£17.50. Special breaks available

All reports are welcome on any hotel, whether or not it is in the Guide.

CHIPPERFIELD HERTFORDSHIRE   **MAP 9**

Two Brewers

THE COMMON, CHIPPERFIELD, KINGS LANGLEY, WATFORD,
HERTFORDSHIRE WD4 9BS
TEL: WATFORD (0923) 265266   FAX: (0923) 261884

Olde-worlde charm in a pleasant old pub, now a Forte hotel.

This low, white, traditional English pub overlooking the village green is a pleasant spot for a gentle weekend break. Once used as a training ground for boxing, the cosy pub bar has beams, Windsor chairs, carved settles and a collection of drawings of boxers posing, fists at the ready. The lounge is perhaps less homely but is a little quieter by way of compensation. You can eat either in the bar or the lounge; the menu is varied and includes a vegetarian selection of dishes which are served in generous quantities by cheerful staff.

The bedroom block, overlooking the car park to the rear of the hotel, is connected to the old pub by a corridor filled with plants. The rooms are regularly shaped and of a reasonable size, though a touch lacking in character. Bold fabrics contrast with subtly patterned wallpaper and furnishings are functional.

◑ Open all year

🅰 Leave the M25 at Junction 20. Follow signs to the A41. At the second zebra crossing in Kings Langley turn into Vicarage Lane and follow it for 3 miles until you reach a crossroads. Turn left; the inn is 100 yards on the right. Private car park

🛏 14 twin, 6 double; all with bathroom/WC, TV, room service, hair-dryer, trouser press, baby-listening

◈ Restaurant, bar, lounge; conference facilities (max 25 people non-residential and residential). Wheelchair access to hotel (ramp), restaurant and 10 ground-floor bedrooms

⊖ Some bedrooms are non-smoking

▭ Amex, Diners, Forte, Visa

£ Single occupancy of twin/double £80, twin/double £95. Continental B £6, cooked B £9; set D £17; alc D £26. Special breaks available

CHIPPING CAMPDEN GLOUCESTERSHIRE   **MAP 9**

Cotswold House

THE SQUARE, CHIPPING CAMPDEN, GLOUCESTERSHIRE GL55 6AN
TEL: EVESHAM (0386) 840330   FAX: (0386) 840310

A hotel which manages to be smart and highly individual at the same time.

Cotswold House, once the home of a wool merchant, occupies a prime position in Chipping Campden's tourist-thronged square. It is an effortlessly elegant place: an arch supported by two great pillars frames a graceful spiral stair; there are rugs, cool stone floors and cascades of flowers in the dining-room, plaster mouldings deck the ceiling and Ionic pillars rise above the pale grey tables.

It is in the bedrooms that the quality of the design and the individuality of the hotel show up. The Indian Room uses wood and turquoise, the English Room features William Morris and a reproduction antique radio. By the time you reach French Tarts you expect the flouncy, bouncy fabrics and the prints of busty ladies, but the magnificent Colonial Room may still come as a surprise: a turn-of-the-century American four-poster, complete with pineapple finials, is watched over by severely puritan portraits.

The food is suited to the Cotswolds – English but not too heavy. Smoked fish, crab and avocado might be followed by wild duck and gratin of bananas and mandarin oranges.

◑ Closed 25, 26 and 27 Dec

⬈ 1 mile north of the A44 on the B4081 (between Broadway and Moreton-in-Marsh). Private car park

🛏 3 single, 5 twin, 6 double, 1 four-poster; all with bathroom/ WC, exc 1 single with shower/ WC; TV, room service, hair-dryer in all rooms; tea/coffee-making facilities on request

◈ Restaurant, bar, lounge; conference facilities (max 15 people residential, 18 non-residential); croquet at hotel, other sports nearby

⊖ No wheelchair access; no children under 8; no dogs; no smoking in restaurant

▭ Access, Amex, Visa

£ Single £60 to £70, single occupancy of twin/double from £78 to £85, twin/double £90 to £116, four-poster £140; deposit required. Sun L £15; set D £15; alc D £24.50; brasserie meals from £5 to £10. Special breaks available

---

CHITTLEHAMHOLT DEVON　　　　　　　　　　**MAP 10**

Highbullen

CHITTLEHAMHOLT, UMBERLEIGH, DEVON EX37 9HD
TEL: CHITTLEHAMHOLT (0769) 540561　FAX: (0769) 540492

A huge Victorian country-house hotel at the heart of a complex of suites, swimming-pools, golf course and shop.

The best place to get your bearings at Highbullen is the central tower, from where you get a bird's-eye view of outlying buildings stretching away in all directions. Unlike many big Victorian piles, Highbullen House manages to be light and airy, something you'll appreciate as soon as you turn past the globe of stuffed birds in the porch into the lofty hall. Opening off it, the lounge is vast, with comfortable chairs and sofas clustered beneath a chandelier and more chairs and a table in a huge bay window. The adjacent library with log-burning stove offers greater intimacy. You descend to the basement in search of the restaurant and the bar; there's a second dining-room upstairs which juts out like a ship's prow and offers spectacular views.

Twelve of the 37 rooms are in the house itself; all are strikingly different, the only thing they share being enormous size. Furniture tends to the antique, and indeed anything modern would look lost in these vast spaces. Proprietor Pam Neil has an extraordinary flair with fabrics and most rooms (and corridors) contain at least one exquisitely framed piece of material; in Room 23, a 1930s nightdress has been pressed into service as a lampshade. Room 14, the Hungarian suite, contains a complete set of furniture from Budapest, including a king-size double bed. In the grounds a cowshed and hay-loft have been converted into more rooms.

It would take days to exhaust all Highbullen's attractions, which include two swimming-pools, a billiard room, a gym, a squash court, a Jacuzzi, a golf shop and Pam's own lace and linen shop.

◗ *Open all year*

▨ *Leave the M5 at Junction 27 and take the A361 to South Molton. Then take the B3226 Exeter Road. After 5 miles, turn right up the hill to Chittlehamholt. The hotel is ½ mile beyond the village on the left. Private car park*

🛏 *1 single, 35 twin/double, 1 family room (25 in annexes); all with bathroom/WC, TV, hair-dryer; room service in main house*

◈ *Restaurant, breakfast room, bar, lounge, library, games room, drying room, conservatory; conference facilities (max 20 people non-residential and residential); golf, tennis, sauna,*
solarium, steam room, indoor and outdoor swimming-pools, squash, croquet, table-tennis, indoor putting, billiards at hotel, other sports nearby. Wheelchair access to hotel (2 steps), restaurant and WC (unisex), 3 ground-floor bedrooms

⊖ *No children under 8; no dogs; no smoking in restaurant and breakfast room, and discouraged in bedrooms*

▭ *None accepted*

£ *Single £60, single occupancy of twin/double £60 to £75, twin/double £95 to £140 (rates inc dinner). Cooked B £2.50; set D £17.50; light lunches. Special breaks available*

CHOLMONDELEY CHESHIRE   **MAP 5**

Cholmondeley Arms

CHOLMONDELEY, MALPAS, CHESHIRE SY14 8BT
TEL: CHOLMONDELEY (0829) 720300

Cottage-style rooms in a former village schoolhouse.

Practise the name before you arrive – only tourists pronounce it as it looks: the correct way is 'Chumley'.

The Cholmondeley Arms is the converted Victorian village school, still in use until ten years ago, when they finally ran out of children. It has made a highly successful transformation into a popular pub/restaurant. The vaulted ceiling, washed walls, old military prints, menacing stag's head and mix of wooden furniture make a casual, laid-back setting for an excellent range of home-produced food. The menu lists hot crab pâté and devilled lambs' kidneys, plaice goujons and grilled gammon steaks; daily specials (on the blackboard, of course) include dishes such as braised oxtail and chicken in tarragon and lemon sauce. We can recommend the treacle tart.

The bedrooms are in the former headmaster's house across the playground, now the car park. They are like the spare rooms in someone's modest weekend cottage – that is, they are clean and adequate. *En suite* shower-rooms are neat but basic.

Nonetheless, the tranquillity of the country setting, the good value and the informal atmosphere are attractive enough for people working in Liverpool and Chester to choose to stay out here and commute.

◐ Open all year

⤢ On the A49 between Whitchurch and Tarporley, next to Cholmondeley Castle. Private car park

🛏 1 twin, 2 double, 1 family room; all with shower/WC, TV, hair-dryer

◈ Restaurant, bar; horse-riding nearby. Wheelchair access to hotel, restaurant and 1 ground-floor bedroom

⊖ None

▭ Access, Visa

£ Single occupancy of twin/double £25, twin/double £30, family room £50; deposit required. Cooked B £5; alc L, D £13

CLANFIELD OXFORDSHIRE   **MAP 9**

Plough at Clanfield

BOURTON ROAD, CLANFIELD, OXFORDSHIRE OX8 2RB
TEL: CLANFIELD (036 781) 222   FAX: (036 781) 596

A small-scale Cotswold hotel with personable staff and a restaurant that pleases.

The mellow Cotswold stone house is a welcome sight at the end of the day and the greeting by friendly staff is equally agreeable. A member of the small Hatton Hotels group, the Plough is situated in a small village just off the Swindon road and the hotel too is on an intimate scale, with six bedrooms and a restaurant that attracts local diners. The lounge bar is the hub of the place – an attractive room with a long bar and groups of sofas and armchairs clustered around coffee tables piled with magazines. In the restaurant, background colours are neutral and flowery cushions on padded wooden armchairs brighten up the restrained décor. A salad of mushrooms and pine-nuts might be followed by Dover sole and prawns; vegetable portions are generous and service is attentive.

Bedrooms are on the small side but are well thought out and have large bathrooms, some with whirlpool baths. Tea and coffee trays are provided on request, but otherwise you can enjoy the treat of room service first thing in the morning.

◑ *Open all year*

⤴ *On the A4095 from Witney, 4 miles north of Faringdon. Private car park*

🛏 *2 twin, 3 double, 1 four-poster; most with bathroom/WC, some with shower/WC; TV, room service, hair-dryer, trouser press, baby-listening in all rooms; tea/coffee-making facilities on request*

◈ *2 restaurants, bar, lounge;*

conference facilities (max 10 people non-residential, 6 residential); fishing, golf, other sports nearby

⊖ *No wheelchair access; no dogs; no smoking in restaurant*

▭ *Access, Amex, Diners, Visa*

£ *Single occupancy of twin/double £60, twin/double £80, four-poster £95; deposit required. Set L £11, D £19.50; alc L, D £33. Special breaks available*

CLAPPERSGATE CUMBRIA   MAP 4

Grey Friar Lodge

CLAPPERSGATE, AMBLESIDE, CUMBRIA LA22 9NE
TEL: AMBLESIDE (05394) 33158

A delightfully unstuffy country-house hotel in the heart of the Lake District.

Behind the stern, grey lakeland stone façade of this former vicarage you will find an uncharacteristically informal and homely country-house hotel where you will soon be on first-name terms with the Suttons, Tony and Sheila, for whom 1994 will mark a decade in charge. There is plenty to look at here, whether it is admiring the fabulous views across the Brathay Valley and Park Fell or examining some of the unusual ornaments that enliven the comfortable lounge areas. The inspiration behind the heterogeneous array of bric-à-brac is a genuine collector's curiosity rather than any contrivance: 'We're magpies,' explains Sheila. The bedrooms are carefully and individually co-ordinated, too, with the highlight being Room Three with its four-poster bed carved by Tony's father.

The Suttons, who used to run a restaurant, say they like to infuse their traditionally based dinners with a touch of the exotic, though the menus rarely charter unfamiliar culinary waters. Carrot soufflé with yogurt and watercress may be followed by baked beefsteak and Stilton pudding, with a chocolate pudding in toffee sauce for dessert. The menu carries a suggestion from the wine list which is carefully selected and invariably good value. The audible hum of the daytime traffic on the A593 is soon drowned out by the bubble of bonhomie inside. The Suttons are a gregarious and down-to-earth couple who like to greet you with a real north country welcome – if they are not beaten to the punch by Tom, the bearded collie, springing out to enlist you in some fun and games.

◑ *Closed Nov to Feb*

⤴ *On the A593, 1½ miles west of Ambleside. Private car park*

🛏 *2 twin, 5 double, 1 four-poster; all with bathroom/WC, exc 2 doubles with shower/WC; TV, hair-dryer in all rooms*

◇ *Dining-room, 2 lounges, drying room; fishing, tennis, other sports nearby*

⊖ *No wheelchair access; no children under 10; no dogs; smoking in lounges only*

▭ *None accepted*

£ *Single occupancy of twin/double £28 to £29, twin/double £54 to £57, four-poster £57 to £60; deposit required. Set D £15.50. Special breaks available*

CLEETHORPES HUMBERSIDE   MAP 5

Wellesley Court ☆

40 BRADFORD AVENUE, CLEETHORPES, SOUTH HUMBERSIDE DN35 0BD
TEL: GRIMSBY (0472) 693014   FAX: (0472) 691200

The British seaside fights back! Country-house décor and business-like facilities in a traditional resort setting.

If childhood memories of dingy seaside lodgings have led you to cross British resorts off your list of holiday options, this could be the place to change your mind. The small private hotel has come a long way if Wellesley Court is anything to go by. Situated at the far end of a quiet avenue running off the southern end of Cleethorpes' sea-front, it's a spruce but unremarkable detached brick villa. Interior décor is derived from the modish country-house school, scaled down to suit the proportions of the rooms, but bright, cheerful and elegant in a modern off-the-peg way, with tied-back curtains and flowery fabrics. Drinks are taken in the impeccably neat lounge where pink ripple-effect wallpaper, framed sheet music and prints of Faith, Hope and Charity make a bold impression. Comfy grey sofas are ideal for lounging in while watching terrestrial or satellite TV.

There's more pink and grey in the pretty dining-room, where ruched blinds, stained glass, fresh flowers and silver candelabra set the tone. The short menu has three options at each stage. Food is palatable if unexciting, and cheerfully served in huge portions; April's options included pasta, prawn and apple salad, home-made fish-cakes with herbs, and apple-baked chops.

Make your way up to your room past the caricatures of beekeepers and other Lincolnshire men, and it's there that the surprises really begin; the level of facilities rivals that of many city-centre business hotels, and there are touches – a pot for your tea, biscuits and tissues – that you may not find there. Décor is unfailingly bright – from the snazzy but teenagerish in the preposterously small single Copenhagen to large Regency-style

Salamanca and Waterloo, with its four-poster, antiques and spa bath. Bathrooms are well-kitted out, with extras including cotton wool and disposable razors.

○ Open all year

⤵ Proceed along the seafront until you reach the Kingsway. On the corner of Kingsway and Bradford Avenue, turn right. Private car park

⇌ 2 single, 1 twin, 2 double, 1 four-poster, family room available; half with bathroom/WC, half with shower/WC; TV, room service, hair-dryer, trouser press, baby-listening in all rooms

◇ Restaurant, bar, lounge, TV room, drying room; conference facilities (max 50 people non-residential, 6 residential); fishing, golf, other sports nearby; babysitting. Wheelchair access to hotel (1 step) and restaurant only

⊖ No dogs in public rooms and by arrangement only in bedrooms

▭ Access, Visa

£ Single £30 to £43, single occupancy of twin/double £40 to £55, twin/double £50 to £55, four-poster £65 to £75, family room £55 to £65. Set L £12.50, D £17.50. Special breaks available

---

CLEY NORFOLK   **MAP 7**

Cley Mill

CLEY NEXT THE SEA, HOLT, NORFOLK NR25 7NN
TEL: CLEY (0263) 740209

A sympathetically converted windmill in an unspoilt area that's ideal for walks or birdwatching.

Look around this sleepy place and you may find it hard to believe that Cley was one of the most important East Anglian ports in medieval days, well-known for exports of wool and grain. With the silting-up of the River Glaven in the early seventeenth century and a fire that destroyed many buildings including the Customs House a century later, Cley slowly became the peaceful backwater it is today. The mill was built in 1713 and was used for grinding flour for 200 years before being converted into a holiday home in the 1920s. It became a guesthouse in 1983, but is also open to the public during the summer months – the two upper floors are used as viewing galleries, while the first and second floors house the bedrooms. The Wheat Room and Stone Room are circular in shape, the latter with a balcony around its circumference; the Miller's Room would suit a family, being a double room with single adjacent. Other rooms may disappoint: the Barley Bin, used as single accommodation, is merely small and poky, leaving you with no impression of staying somewhere unique. If you prefer to be independent, the surrounding stables and boat sheds have been converted to self-catering flats, available on a weekly basis.

Breakfast (and evening meals on request) is taken around a long, communal pine table, and by night a log fire is lit in the lounge where guests curl up with a book, play games or watch the television.

◑ Closed 15 Jan to 28 Feb

↗ On the A149 halfway between Wells and Cromer. Private car park

🛏 2 twin, 4 double; most with bathroom/WC, 1 with shower/WC, 1 public bathroom; 2 self-catering flats

◈ Dining-room, lounge, drying room; fishing, water sports nearby

⊖ No wheelchair access; no dogs

▭ None accepted

£ Single occupancy of twin/double £35, twin/double £46 to £56; deposit required. Set D £14.50 (7pm). Special breaks available

---

COLCHESTER ESSEX   **MAP 8**

Red Lion

43 HIGH STREET, COLCHESTER, ESSEX CO1 1DJ
TEL: COLCHESTER (0206) 577986   FAX: (0206) 578207

A historic old inn in the centre of town with good rooms and a house ghost.

Colchester is the oldest recorded town in England and became one of the busiest centres in Roman Britain. There's no evidence that Romans stopped off at the Red Lion for a swift pint before tackling Boadicea's tribes, but it is mentioned as an 'anncyent Inne' in records of 1604. It was said that stage coaches leaving the Red Lion in the morning could reach London by lunchtime – not bad going by mid-eighteenth-century standards. Times have changed and you now enter the inn-turned-hotel between the computer and leather jacket shops that populate Colchester's busy high street. The lounge is little more than a walk-through room, but Alice Miller's Restaurant is in a fifteenth-century hall complete with thick beams and open fire. It is named after a poor woman who was 'cruelly done to death' by her lover in 1632, but despite this treachery refused to leave the Red Lion and still waits for him to return to her. Has manager Barry Medcalf ever set eyes on her? 'No,' he says, 'she knows I'd charge her for staying if I saw her.'

There are 24 bedrooms, all different and many with interesting features such as the exposed wattle and daub in Room Ten, or leaded windows like those in Room Seven (a four-poster). On Friday nights, noise from a nearby nightclub can affect rooms in the old part of the hotel. Dinner is flexible: if the menu doesn't appeal, guests are at liberty to ask for their favourite dish which the chef, David Hart, will prepare if he has the appropriate ingredients. Just leave room for the puddings – it would be a shame to be too full to enjoy the hot toffee bananas or the 'chocolate, chocolate and even more chocolate'.

◑ Open all year

⤢ Centrally located in Colchester High Street, near the town hall. Limited on-street parking, free overnight car park nearby

🛏 10 single, 7 twin, 6 double, 1 four-poster; all with bathroom or shower/WC, exc 2 singles with shower/WC; TV, room service in all rooms, hair-dryer on request

◈ Restaurant, bar, lounge;

conference facilities (max 50 people non-residential, 24 residential); fishing, golf, other sports nearby

⊖ No wheelchair access; no dogs

▭ Access, Amex, Diners, Visa

£ Single £56, twin/double £73, four-poster £90; deposit required. Set D £14; alc L, D £18

COLERNE WILTSHIRE   MAP 9

Lucknam Park

COLERNE, WILTSHIRE SN14 8AZ
TEL: BATH (0225) 742777   FAX: (0225) 743536

De-luxe country-house hotel and conference centre with first-class leisure facilities.

A hotel like Lucknam Park creates its own hermetically sealed world of discreet luxury and privilege. This could be a location for a glossy mini-series; a chauffeur polishes a stretch limo outside the Bath stone mansion, racehorses gallop in the nearby fields, whippet-thin women in dark glasses pass through carrying Bond Street bags, and important men with suntans arrive by helicopter. Lucknam is pukka to the nth degree. The interiors are sumptuous, from the panelled library to the chandeliered drawing-room filled with antiques; legions of staff spring to deal with one's every need. Nothing is forgotten – even a squadron of ornamental fowl parade solemnly to order across the forecourt. All is perfect, down to the hotel cat found deep in feline dreams behind a damask sofa.

Bedrooms and suites, as might be expected, are superbly turned out in individual country-house kit. All rooms have silver carafes of water from Lucknam's own spring and bathrooms are ritzy in white marble. Some suites have wood-burning open fires and four-posters; the Coral Suite is a particularly beautiful room at the front of the house, facing the long, beech-lined driveway and with a huge bay that mirrors that of the drawing-room below. As the guest book full of celebrity names might indicate, it is the most expensive suite, with rates starting at £340 a night (and that includes continental breakfast only!).

However, it is worth inquiring about short breaks, as these, while not cheap, can offer surprisingly good value. They also include memorable à la carte dinners under the painted clouds of the ceiling in the graceful dining-room. Chef Michael Womersley cooks skilfully and inventively, and the set dinner gives some half-dozen choices at each course. The meal might begin with pan-fried scallops set on a bed of confit peppers scented with fresh basil and proceed to roast guinea-fowl larded with Périgord truffles served with Madeira sauce. Desserts are likely to feature several warm puddings such as hot apple and quince soufflés served with a cup of lemon posset. Philippe Pau, the restaurant manager, has a mind-reading ability to provide small plates for those who just wish to sample their companion's choice. When it comes to choosing the wine, this is not the place to look for basement bargains.

All this provides the excuse, if any is needed, to make full use of the leisure spa, set in the walled garden, with indoor pool, gym, steam room, sauna, beauty salon, floodlit tennis courts and trim trail. It equally provides the excuse to sink back into the lap of luxury and do absolutely nothing at all.

◐ Open all year

↱ Leave the M4 at Junction 17 onto the A429 Chippenham road. Before Chippenham, turn right for Bristol on the A420. At Ford (3 miles) turn left to Colerne, and right at the crossroads for Colerne. The hotel entrance is ¼ mile on the right. Private car park

🛏 1 single, 12 twin, 17 double, 1 four-poster, 11 suites (including 7 four-posters); all with bathroom/WC, TV, room service, hair-dryer, baby-listening; no tea/coffee-making facilities in rooms

◈ 2 restaurants, bar, drawing-room, library, conservatory, snooker room; conference facilities (max 100 people non-residential, 42 residential);

tennis, croquet, heated swimming-pool, sauna, solarium, gym, steam room, beauty room, snooker at hotel, other sports nearby; babysitting by arrangement. Wheelchair access to hotel, restaurant and WC (disabled), 16 ground-floor bedrooms. 4 specially equipped for disabled people

⊖ No children under 10 in restaurant eves; no dogs; no smoking in restaurants

▭ Access, Amex, Diners, Visa

£ Single £95, single occupancy of twin/double £125, twin/double £140 to £185, four-poster £215, suites from £225; deposit required. Cooked B £5.50; set L £24, D £39.50. Special breaks available

COLYFORD DEVON · **MAP 10**

Swallows Eaves ☆

COLYFORD, COLYTON, DEVON EX13 6QJ
TEL: COLYTON (0297) 553184

A small, welcoming 1930s hotel that attracts regular guests.

This year several readers have written to recommend the Swallows Eaves, a not particularly beautiful house with a prettier garden and just eight bedrooms. Letters describe the furnishings as of 'good quality' and 'chosen with taste', which means simple and comfortable; there are plenty of extras such as spotlights over the beds, fresh fruit and biscuits. Some rooms have sloping ceilings which could be tricky for the very tall, but the skylights set into them are an attractive feature, scooping up the light and widening the views.

Beyond the rooms, however, what our readers seem to have particularly enjoyed are the meals. One describes the evening meals as 'the best bargain I have found in recent years' and others comment on the liberal servings which mean few can face both the cheese and the dessert. For starters there's always a choice of soup or a dish like mushrooms sautéed with garlic and cream. The main course changes daily but there is no choice, so vegetarians should give some warning. Desserts include such filler-uppers as bread-and-butter pudding with ice-cream.

Jon and Jane Beck seem to have achieved that happy medium of making guests feel cared for yet keeping service unobtrusive.

◑	Open all year
⤴	Opposite the post office in Colyford on the A3052 coast road. Private car park
🛏	4 twin, 4 double; most with bathroom/WC, 2 doubles with shower/WC; TV, room service, hair-dryer in all rooms
◈	Restaurant, lounge; tennis, riding, swimming-pool, other sports nearby
⊖	No wheelchair access; no children under 14; no dogs; no smoking in dining-room and some bedrooms
▭	None accepted
£	Single occupancy of twin/double £31 to £35, twin/double £50 to £59. Set D £16.50. Special breaks available

---

COMBE MARTIN DEVON   MAP 10

Coulsworthy House

COMBE MARTIN, DEVON EX34 0PD
TEL: BARNSTAPLE (0271) 882463

A particularly welcoming family-run ex-farmhouse complete with swimming-pool and private spring.

Coulsworthy House started life as a farmhouse and grew grander as its owners' fortunes improved in the mid-eighteenth century. As you pull up, Blisset the black labrador, the first of many household pets, will rush to greet you; Wendy and Damart, the goats, take more winning over. Inside, the downstairs rooms are thankfully unmodernised, and the lounge fireplace in particular boasts some exuberant plasterwork. Upstairs, in contrast, walls have been knocked down and moved around to modernise the bedrooms; Number 4 has a lethal-looking ceiling hook once used for curing hams. Some rooms are big and feature brass bedsteads and kidney dressing-tables; the shower with seat in Number Ten was made out of an old fireplace. Steep stairs lead to what were once the servants' quarters, now a family room with a ceiling beam artfully retained so that the double bed could be mistaken for a four-poster.

Coulsworthy House's grounds are a veritable nature reserve. Beech trees and Scotch pines provide homes for rooks and buzzards. A small pond incubates frog spawn; a heron stole the fish. A path leads to a spring dispensing a deceptively thin trickle of water; in fact it pours out a steady 900 gallons a day which the Anthonys bottle and serve to their guests. In an all-hands-to-the-pump family enterprise, daughter Alison dreams up dinners which offer more choice than usual; perhaps a twice-baked soufflé, followed by roast wild duck with orange sauce and Brazilian bananas to finish.

◐ Closed 8 Dec to 8 Feb; restaurant closed Sun eve

⤢ Leave Blackmoor Gate on the A399 Combe Martin road. 2 miles from Blackmoor Gate take the right turning signposted Trentishoe and Hunters Inn – the house is 200 yards down this road. Private car park

🛏 2 single, 2 twin, 4 double, 1 family room; most with bathroom/WC, some with shower/WC; TV, hair-dryer, baby-listening in all rooms; no tea/coffee-making facilities in rooms

◇ Restaurant, bar, lounge; tennis, croquet, heated outdoor swimming-pool (in season) at hotel, other sports nearby

⊖ No wheelchair access; no smoking in bedrooms

▭ Access, Visa

£ Single £38 to £50, single occupancy of twin/double £39 to £75, twin/double £50 to £100, family room (4 people) £78 to £150; deposit required. Sun L £15; set D £25. Special breaks available

---

CORBRIDGE NORTHUMBERLAND · MAP 3

Low Barns

COUNTY
HOTEL
OF THE
YEAR

THORNBROUGH, CORBRIDGE, NORTHUMBERLAND NE45 5LX
TEL: HEXHAM (0434) 632408

A smashing guesthouse with enthusiastic hosts and a homely, relaxing atmosphere.

A daffodil-lined drive leads off the Newcastle road to Tom and Sue Jones's 200-year-old converted farmhouse in the heart of some wonderfully unspoilt countryside. Refurbishment has retained the charm and vigour of the old house and married it with modern comfort and a sense of rustic style. Sue, a cheerful and hearty hostess, has created a home that is instantly relaxing and homely, mixing good old furniture with a restrained dash of rustic chintz.

Guests eat in the large, attractive kitchen, with its pine table, Welsh dresser, dried flowers and views over the garden. A stately grandfather clock ticks reassuringly, and framed photographs of the dogs, Drake and Ben, reinforce the feeling that this is a family home. Sue's good-value dinners are likely to feature 'whatever's in season', perhaps kicking off with a home-made soup, followed by salmon or lamb and ending up with rhubarb crumble or Border tart. Most of the vegetables served are home-grown, and eggs and lamb are from local farms. Guests do battle over the bridge table or browse through a pile of magazines and tourist literature in the cosy lounge.

The three bedrooms are all of a good size, spick and span with bright, cottagey décor, rough stone walls and lots of pine. All are generously equipped with electric blankets, tissues and mineral water as well as the usual TV and tea tray.

◐   Open all year

⬈   One mile from Corbridge on the B6530 heading towards Newcastle upon Tyne. Private car park

🛏   2 twin, 1 double; 2 with bathroom/WC, 1 twin with shower/WC; TV, hair-dryer in all rooms

◈   Dining-room, lounge; laundry facilities; fishing, golf, other sports nearby

⊖   No wheelchair access; no dogs; no smoking in public rooms

▭   Access, Visa

£   Single occupancy of twin/double £28, twin/double £40; deposit required. Set D £13.50 (7pm)

CORSE LAWN HEREFORD AND WORCESTER   **MAP 9**

Corse Lawn House

CORSE LAWN, GLOUCESTERSHIRE GL19 4LZ
TEL: GLOUCESTER (0452) 780479   FAX: (0452) 780840

An old coaching-inn which now serves as a reliable base in pretty countryside.

There's a pond complete with ducks in front of Corse Lawn House where they used to wash down the stagecoaches – cheaper than a carwash, no doubt. There is also a swimming-pool round the back and a tennis court to one side, so this establishment is definitely not lacking in facilities. According to one visitor in 1993, however, it is a little lacking in a decent welcome: 'Nobody at reception desk on arrival . . . never a "good morning" . . . no help with luggage.' But no one complains about the well-appointed bedrooms ('excellent, large and well-equipped') or the food ('very good in restaurant and good-value in bistro').

This is a Queen Anne house where modern wings have been added with care to ensure that they blend in well. Bedrooms and bathrooms are good-sized and thought has gone into the extras such as biscuits and fresh milk. The decoration of the public rooms is generally soothing, apart from the striking bar. Baba Hine presides over the kitchen, producing perhaps hot crab tart with a good hollandaise or pigeon breasts baked in a fruity sauce.

◑ Open all year

⤢ From Tewkesbury take the A438 towards Ledbury for 4 miles. Turn left for Gloucester on the B4211 for 1 mile. The hotel is on the left. Private car park

🛏 1 single, 5 twin, 9 double, 2 four-poster, 2 suites; all with bathroom/WC, TV, room service, hair-dryer, trouser press; baby-listening on request

◈ 3 restaurants, bar, 3 lounges, TV room; conference facilities (max 35 people non-residential, 19 residential); tennis, croquet, outdoor heated swimming-pool (May to Oct) at hotel, other sports nearby. Wheelchair access to hotel, restaurant and WC (M,F), 5 ground-floor bedrooms

⊖ None

▭ Access, Amex, Diners, Visa

£ Single £70, single occupancy of twin/double £70, twin/double £90, four-poster £100, suite £110; deposit required. Set L £15.50, D £23.50; alc L, D £20 to £30. Special breaks available

---

COVENTRY WEST MIDLANDS   MAP 5

Crest Guesthouse

39 FRIARS ROAD, COVENTRY, WEST MIDLANDS CV1 2LJ
TEL: COVENTRY (0203) 227822   FAX: (0203) 227244

An immaculate bed and breakfast with caring hosts, right in the centre of Coventry.

A five-minute walk by footbridge from the railway station and just a short journey into the central shopping area of Coventry, this popular bed and breakfast is ideally located if you like to be in the thick of things and don't mind the proximity to the busy inner ring road. Half red-brick and half pebble-dash, the neat exterior with freshly painted blue woodwork gives an indication of standards inside. Sure enough, the open-plan sitting- and dining-room is immaculately clean; large windows at the front and french doors leading into the small garden make the room light and apparently bigger than it is in reality. Fresh flowers on the breakfast table are one of the extra bits of attention the Harveys give their guests. Pastel colour schemes and a mix of modern and old-fashioned furniture are typical of the four well-kept bedrooms, which are comfortably equipped with hair-dryers and hot-water bottles and prettified by dried flowers and frilly duvet covers. Two twin bedrooms have neat shower rooms *en-suite*, while the singles share a public bathroom.

◑ Open all year, exc 25 and 26 Dec

⤢ Turn off inner ring-road at Junction 5, follow city-centre signs. Continue past 1st set of traffic lights and turn immediately left. Private car park

🛏 2 single, 2 twin; the twins with shower/WC; 1 public bathroom; TV, hair-dryer in all rooms

◈ Dining-room, lounge; golf, tennis, other sports nearby; babysitting

⊖ No wheelchair access; dogs by

arrangement; no smoking in
public rooms

☐ None accepted

£ Single £20, single occupancy of
twin £26, twin £40

COWAN BRIDGE LANCASHIRE   MAP 3

Hipping Hall

COWAN BRIDGE, KIRKBY LONSDALE, CUMBRIA LA6 2JJ
TEL: KIRKBY LONSDALE (05242) 71187   FAX: (05242) 72452

*Informal dinner parties in a historic country house on the
Lancashire/Cumbria/Yorkshire border.*

Neither hotel, guesthouse nor bed and breakfast really describe the
relaxed, welcoming atmosphere here that balances domesticity with
professionalism. Perhaps the French term 'logis' or the American 'inn'
come closest to describing an establishment where you have the sense
that you are really a friend on a visit to a private house.

Guests gather for a pre-dinner drink from the honesty bar in the small,
flagged conservatory of this many-centuried house, where conversation
must compete with the shrilling of a pair of love-birds. They do act as
ice-breakers, however, for any especially reserved guest – although, as
Ian Bryant says, by the time the soup course is served, conversation
around the dinner table is usually flowing easily.

The communal dinners take place around the long refectory table
under the minstrels' gallery in the impressive, vaulted Grand Hall.
Jocelyn Ruffle does the cooking, a plain, wholesome five-course dinner
based on local and home-grown produce. A sample dinner comprised
smoked salmon, mushroom soup, chicken breast with Calvados, regional
cheeses and rhubarb tart. For an extra charge, Ian serves a selection of
wine by the glass. Usually, by the end of the meal, guests feel so at home
that they're inclined to feel a touch guilty about not clearing the table or
helping with the washing-up. Instead, they can loll contentedly in the
wide, easy chairs ranged around the open wood-burning stove.

The five bedrooms lack no comfort. All have modern bathrooms,
though one has just a glossily tiled shower cubicle. The beds are high and
firm, the furnishings soft and pretty and there are fresh flowers on the
dressing tables. At breakfast, in the nicely old-fashioned morning-room,
you'll find the bonus of DIY toasters on the sideboard.

◐ Closed Jan

↗ On the A65, 2 miles east of
Kirkby Lonsdale. Private car park

🛏 2 twin, 3 double, 2 suites; all
with bathroom/WC, exc 1
double with shower/WC; TV,
hair-dryer in all rooms

◈ Dining-room, breakfast room,
bar, lounge, drying room,
conservatory; conference
facilities (max 20 people non-
residential, 7 residential);
croquet at hotel

⊖ No wheelchair access; no

children under 12; no dogs in
public rooms; no smoking in
dining-room and some bedrooms

Access, Visa

£ Single occupancy of twin/double
£64, twin/double £75, suite £85;
deposit required. Set D £19.50
(8pm). Special breaks available

CRACKINGTON HAVEN CORNWALL   MAP 10

Manor Farm

CRACKINGTON HAVEN, BUDE, CORNWALL EX23 0JU
TEL: ST GENNYS (0840) 230304

Delightful, hidden farmhouse hotel, ideal for house parties.

Take a wrong turning in Crackington Haven and you could find yourself completely lost in the Cornish countryside, but no matter – once you find it, Manor Farm is the sort of hotel to inspire such eulogies as this from a reader: 'The fact that we have travelled from far-flung countries such as India, Hong Kong and South Korea to stay here on five occasions over 11 years testifies to the enjoyment we receive from returning time and again.' The part-stone/part-whitewashed farmhouse nestles in exquisite grounds above the moors, and, once inside, all the comforts you could hope for come in attractively ancient surroundings: the breakfast room has a beamed ceiling and inglenook fireplace with inset bread and salt ovens; the long, thin dining-room has a display unit created by setting an old wooden window frame into a blocked-up chimney. Externally the house looks deceptively small: in fact, there's ample space for separate summer and winter lounges, a television lounge and a bar. Even so, it's still small-scale enough to be perfect for house parties; the elegant dining table seats eight and the bar runs on an honesty principle.

All the bedrooms are attractively and discreetly decorated and most offer wonderful views; in the older wing beamed ceilings and brass bedsteads make up for limited space. Hotelier Muriel Knight's varied and well-planned menus don't offer a choice but what there is – typically, walnut savoury pie, and crispy breast of chicken in pesto and cream sauce – is delicious.

◐ Open all year

⤢ From the A39 take the B3263 towards Crackington Haven. At the seafront, follow the road up the other side of the valley; turn left before a phonebox on the right. After 100 yards, turn right down a lane. Private car park

🛏 1 single, 1 twin, 3 double; some with bathroom/WC, some with shower/WC; no tea/coffee-

making facilities in rooms

◈ Dining-room, breakfast room, bar, 2 lounges, TV room, games room; fishing, tennis, riding nearby

⊖ No wheelchair access; no children; no dogs; no smoking

▭ None accepted

£ Single £28 to £60, twin/double £56 to £60; deposit required. Set D £12 to £15 (7pm)

CRANBROOK KENT   **MAP 8**

Hancocks Farmhouse ☆

COUNTY HOTEL OF THE YEAR

TILSDEN LANE, CRANBROOK, KENT TN17 3PH
TEL: CRANBROOK (0580) 714645

A half-timbered sixteenth-century farmhouse in beautiful countryside.

'The owners' one aim seems to be that no stone remains unturned in their efforts to care for you and include you in their home.' With such enthusiastic letters arriving from readers we had to visit this well-kept black and white farmhouse with its rambling rose garden.

Entering the farmhouse takes you back to another era. Beamed ceilings and polished floorboards, along with the evidence of Bridget and Robin Oaten's passion for antiques, give a sense of history and indeed the house was first mentioned in a will of 1520, when it was left by a clothier, Thomas Sheaffe, to his son Gervase.

Depending on what time you arrive, you may catch afternoon tea served with fresh home-made cakes or be offered a complimentary sherry before dinner. The lounge, a warm room with an inglenook fireplace, dark mahogany and oak furniture and antique clocks, serves also as the dining-room, where guests are encouraged, but by no means forced, to eat together. The menu offers dishes such as stuffed mushrooms followed by lamb with spices and apricots and a dessert of home-made fresh lime tart or chocolate and coffee roulade. One guest claims to have discovered the true meaning of an English breakfast here and there is no denying that the freshly squeezed orange juice and Bridget's home-baked bread start the day off well.

Bedrooms are large, with fine antique furnishings and fresh flowers in both the rooms and the bathrooms. The four-poster room is rather splendid, with a Cromwellian chest, and one of the twins has a lovely stone fireplace and its own exit to the garden.

◖ Open all year; dining-room closed Sun eve

↗ From Cranbrook take Tenterden road past the windmill on the left. Take the right fork signposted Benenden. Hancocks is up 1st farm track on left, adjacent to farm cottages. Private car park

⤟ 2 twin, 1 four-poster; 2 with bathroom/WC, 1 twin with shower/WC; hair-dryer in all rooms; TV in 2 rooms

◈ Dining-room/lounge; fishing, golf, tennis, swimming-pool nearby. Wheelchair access to hotel (3 steps) and 1 ground-floor bedroom

⊖ Children under 9 by arrangement only; no dogs in public rooms; no smoking

▭ None accepted

£ Single occupancy of twin £22 to £27, twin/double/four-poster £40 to £45; deposit required. Set D £15

Old Cloth Hall

CRANBROOK, KENT TN17 3NR
TEL: CRANBROOK (0580) 712220

A sixteenth-century manor house with a select guest list.

The Old Cloth Hall is a black and white timbered house set in lovely gardens of rhododendrons and azaleas, with a croquet lawn, swimming-pool and tennis courts. Dating from the Middle Ages, it was visited by Queen Elizabeth I, and Katherine Morgan, as current lady of the manor, admits that she is choosy about who she has to stay in her home – 'Gone are the days of the honeymooners, they get confetti everywhere!' The place is a treasure-trove of antiques and beautiful possessions, with lots of mahogany and oak, rugs and beams. In the drawing-room there is an array of family photos, reminding you that Katherine lives here with her family. She plays the hostess superbly, even going for an afternoon dip in the pool with her guests. If people don't know each other they soon make acquaintances over a gin and tonic aperitif in the lounge. Dinner is taken together round the huge mahogany table and Katherine, a Cordon Bleu-trained cook, may serve lamb chops in apple juice, perhaps, chicken in Dijon mustard and orange sauce or boeuf en croûte.

The three bedrooms are tastefully decorated and, in keeping with the rest of the house, have thick carpets, dried flowers and more antiques. The most sought-after (and most expensive) is the large, romantic four-poster room, with its flowery décor and huge bathroom.

◑ Open all year, exc Xmas

⤴ 1 mile out of Cranbrook on the Golford road to Tenterden. Turn right just before the cemetery. Private car park

🛏 1 twin, 1 double, 1 four-poster; 2 with bathroom/WC, twin with shower/WC; TV, room service, hair-dryer, trouser press in all rooms; no tea/coffee-making facilities in rooms

◈ Dining-room, lounge; tennis, unheated swimming-pool at hotel, other sports nearby

⊖ No wheelchair access; children by arrangement; no dogs; no smoking in bedrooms

▭ None accepted

£ Single occupancy of twin/double £45 to £55, twin/double £80 to £85, four-poster £90 to £95. Set D £20

 This denotes that the hotel is in an exceptionally peaceful situation where you can be assured of a restful stay.

CRANFORD NORTHAMPTONSHIRE   **MAP 5**

Dairy Farm

CRANFORD, KETTERING, NORTHAMPTONSHIRE NN14 4AQ
TEL: CRANFORD (0536 78) 273

A peaceful Jacobean farmhouse – cosy, informal and good value for money.

It's iron in the limestone that gives old buildings in this part of Northamptonshire their distinctive deep-orange appearance. Dairy Farm is Jacobean and built of Weldon stone from a quarry nearby; with its mullioned windows and roof thatched with Norfolk reeds, it is the kind of house that oozes history and captivates you immediately. Three centuries after it was built someone went on a tree-planting spree, and the house is now surrounded by mature chestnut and beech trees whose rustling leaves create the only disturbance around here.

Inside, Audrey Clarke keeps a cosy home that is both comfortable and old-fashioned – the shoe-shine box in the hall is the first indication that this is very much a lived-in house. The large, relaxing sitting-room has an open fire, deep sofa and lots of games and books.

Of the five bedrooms, four are in the main house and one is converted from the stablelad's quarters in the barn. More basic than those inside, the latter room is virtually self-contained and is ideal for people who come to hunt or shoot in the area – horses are accommodated too! The other bedrooms include a spacious double (with an *en-suite* bathroom) with a prettily draped four-poster and views over the garden and stone dovecote – an ancient monument. Given prior notice, Mrs Clarke serves inexpensive, well-cooked meals in the evening: soup, perhaps, then a casserole and choice of puddings.

◗ Open all year, exc Xmas period

↗ Leave the A14 (formerly the A604) at the Cranford slip and from the high street take Grafton Underwood road. Turn right into St Andrew's Lane; Dairy Farm is at the end. Private car park

⇌ 1 twin, 1 double, 1 four-poster, 1 family room, 1 annexe room; 2 with bathroom/WC, family room with shower/WC, 1 public bathroom; room service, hair-dryer, baby-listening in all rooms; TV on request

◇ Dining-room, lounge; croquet at hotel, riding nearby; babysitting

⊖ No wheelchair access; dogs by arrangement only; no smoking in public rooms

▭ None accepted

£ Single occupancy of twin/double £18 to £25, twin/double £36 to £40, four-poster room £44; deposit required. Set D £10 (7pm)

L   *This denotes that you can get a twin or double room for £50 or less per night inclusive of breakfast.*

CROOKHAM NORTHUMBERLAND   **MAP 3**

Coach House ☆

CROOKHAM, CORNHILL-ON-TWEED, NORTHUMBERLAND TD12 4TD
TEL: CROOKHAM (0890) 820293

A comfortable, converted Border farm with a friendly, enthusiastic hostess.

'The oldest cottage in North Northumberland, built about 1680 with rare chestnut beams and many interesting features,' noted the listed buildings' surveyor on a recent visit. The original coach-house stands at right angles to the A697 with other buildings forming a square around a sunny courtyard. Gothic windows lend a church-like air, but there's nothing austere about the public rooms of this very friendly guesthouse. The stylish lounge has a modern, uncluttered look that draws all eyes upward to the soaring chimney-breast and the A-framed beamed ceiling. Sit down on one of the beige leather sofas with a glass of sherry from the honesty bar and enjoy the prints of coastal scenes, fresh flowers and plants, or look out through the huge, arched windows. The dining-room in the old dower house sprawls over two rooms, with blue and white wallcovering, Impressionist prints and drawings of Tudor royals for decoration. Four-course dinners served on old tables offer a good choice of starters and desserts and a set main course; perhaps crab pancakes followed by roast gammon with spiced apricots and garden produce, summer pudding and cheese. Special diets are willingly catered for by Lynne Anderson, who has taken a special interest in developing accommodation and facilities suitable for disabled guests.

Courtyard rooms are generally simply decorated, often in a style reflecting the date of conversion in the late 1970s, but have some splendid old furniture, extra-wide doors to accommodate wheelchairs, half-height hanging rails and fridges. Upstairs bedrooms in the dower house have more character, including beams and wall-hung collections of straw hats. They share a huge bathroom. Room Nine has lovely views over the fields, Raphael prints and a sampler embroidered by Lynne to commemorate the Coronation.

◐ Closed Dec to end Feb

↗ On the A697, 5 miles south of Coldstream. Private car park

🛏 2 double, 5 twin, 2 double; most with bathroom/WC, 2 public bathrooms

◇ Dining-room, lounge, TV room, games room; fishing, golf, other sports nearby. Wheelchair access to hotel, dining-room and WC

(M, F), 6 ground-floor bedrooms, 3 specially equipped for disabled people

⊖ No dogs in public rooms; no smoking in dining-room

▭ Access, Visa

£ Single £21 to £31, twin/double £42 to £62; deposit required. Set D £14.50 (7.30pm). Special breaks available

CROSTHWAITE CUMBRIA **MAP 4**

Crosthwaite House

CROSTHWAITE, NR KENDAL, CUMBRIA LA8 8BP
TEL: CROSTHWAITE (05395) 68264

Friendly hosts in a bright and breezy guesthouse offering value for money.

Robin and Marnie Dawson have two simple priorities at Crosthwaite House: to provide good food and a warm welcome. It is a philosophy wholly endorsed by a reader from Dorset: 'Delicious food, the warmest of welcomes . . . an excellent place.' The guesthouse is a neat mid-eighteenth-century building at the edge of Crosthwaite village, just inside the southern boundary of the Lake District National Park. It has been designed with the lightest of touches, eschewing olde-worlde bric-à-brac in favour of a simpler, more homely feel. The lounge has bright modern sofas and one brown leather buttonback settee; there is a stripped pine floor and an attractive old fireplace in the dining-room, where a few china plates and fresh flower arrangements provide the decoration. Dinner is hearty and unpretentious – a typical menu might include melon with fresh lime, spinach soup, chicken breasts in a mushroom cream sauce followed by a choice from the sweets trolley.

The six bedrooms all have *en-suite* facilities but these, like some of the rooms, can be rather small. The bedrooms at the front of the house benefit from a view across the neighbouring fields but also overlook the road, and although it is not particularly busy the back rooms may be a better choice if peace and quiet come top of your list.

◑ Closed Dec to end Feb

⚡ Leave the M6 at Junction 36 on to the Kendal bypass (signed Barrow), then take the A590. Turn right on to the A5074 (signed Bowness and Windermere). Keep on this road and shortly after passing the Lyth Valley Hotel, turn right. Continue up this lane to the T-junction, turn left and the house is on the right. Private car park

🛏 1 single, 2 twin, 3 double; all with shower/WC, TV; 3 cottages (self-catering)

◈ Dining-room, lounge; babysitting

⊖ No wheelchair access; no dogs or smoking in public rooms

▭ None accepted

£ Single £18 to £20, single occupancy of twin/double £18 to £20, twin/double £40, cottage rate £130 to £270 per week. Set D £12 (7.30pm)

The text of entries is based on unsolicited reports sent in by readers and backed up by inspections. The factual details are from questionnaires the Guide *sends to all hotels that feature in the book.*

Whiteleaf at Croyde

CROYDE, NR BRAUNTON, DEVON EX33 1PN
TEL: CROYDE (0271) 890266

A small but welcoming hotel with excellent food not far from the sea in an attractive village.

A 1930s house with pleasant garden, the Whiteleaf at Croyde has a reputation for gourmet cooking, and from ten o'clock in the morning David Wallington can be found hard at work in the kitchen preparing for the night's feasting. Both he and wife Flo are past retirement age and now let only three rooms, so advance booking is advisable. The house is big and airy and Room Five is enormous, with bathroom to match and a garden view. Surprising pieces of Indonesian furniture and art, reminders of David and Flo's years abroad, rub shoulders with the otherwise slightly old-fashioned furnishings; there is a graceful Mandarin cabinet in the lounge and Balinese wall-hangings in Room Five.

The dining-room is very much at Whiteleaf's heart. French windows open on to the garden and there is an amazing circular Flemish table with relief carvings of hunters, perhaps three hundred years old. Sample menus feature such delicacies as rustic rabbit pâté and beef Wallington, complete with 'high rise' Yorkshire pud, rounded off with a mouth-watering choice of desserts such as chocolate and walnut tart. David's note is refreshingly honest: '(The dishes) actually offered depend for variety, comprehensiveness and originality on a number of factors: season, availability, number of guests and not least the health and disposition of the chef!'

◑ Closed 2 weeks in Apr, July and Oct, and Xmas, New Year and Jan

🅿 South-west of Croyde on the B3231 Croyde to Braunton road. Private car park

🛏 1 twin, 1 double, 1 family room; all with bathroom/WC, TV, hair-dryer, mini-bar, baby-listening

◈ Dining-room, lounge, sun lounge; golf, water sports, other sports nearby

⊖ No wheelchair access; no dogs in public rooms; no smoking in dining-room

▭ Access, Amex

💷 Single occupancy of twin/double £35, twin/double £54, family room £65; deposit required. Set D £17.50. Special breaks available

---

 Denotes somewhere you can rely on a good meal – either the hotel features in the 1994 edition of our sister publication, The Good Food Guide, *or our inspectors thought the cooking impressive, whether particularly competent home cooking or more lavish cuisine.*

CRUDWELL WILTSHIRE MAP 9

Crudwell Court

CRUDWELL, NR MALMESBURY, WILTSHIRE SN16 9EP
TEL: MALMESBURY (0666) 577194 FAX: (0666) 577853

A seventeenth-century rectory where the emphasis is on the restaurant rather than the rooms.

Crudwell Court is tucked into the shadow of a pretty village church and stands in three acres of well-maintained gardens with a mix of lawns, rose beds, yew hedges, ponds and a swimming-pool. The building has had conservatory extensions, although this has not detracted from its attractiveness.

Nick Bristow, the affable co-owner (along with Iain MacLean) describes the place as a 'feminine' hotel, and its decoration is light and airy, the atmosphere convivial. The lounge is a delicate yellow and blue, the hallway pink and the dining-room light green, with rattan chairs and some light wood panelling.

The food is good. You could start with a mousseline of brill flavoured with dill, followed by roasted pheasant with bacon and shallots. One reader described his meals as 'delicious and beautifully presented' but complained that the menu was changed only once a week. However, the hotel management tells us that guests who stay a third night are asked to dream up their own choice of dishes.

The bedrooms need (and are receiving) a touch up. They are large and decorated in a range of light blues, yellows and creams. Some have surprisingly large and luxurious bathrooms.

◐ Open all year

⤢ On the A429, 3 miles north of Malmesbury heading towards Cirencester. The hotel is at the end of the village. Private car park

🛏 2 single, 13 twin/double; all with bathroom/WC, TV, room service, baby-listening; trouser press in some rooms; hair-dryer on request

◈ Restaurant, 2 lounges, 2 conservatories; conference facilities (max 45 people non-residential, 15 residential); croquet, heated outdoor swimming-pool (Easter to Sept) at hotel; babysitting on request. Wheelchair access to restaurant and WC (M) only

⊖ No dogs or smoking in restaurant

▭ Access, Amex, Diners, Visa

£ Single £55 to £85, single occupancy of twin/double £55 to £85, twin/double £95 to £120; deposit required. Set L £13.50, D £21.50. Special breaks available

The Guide *office can quickly spot when a hotelier is encouraging customers to write a letter recommending inclusion – and sadly, several hotels have been doing this in 1993. Such reports do not further a hotel's cause.*

Ockenden Manor

OCKENDEN LANE, CUCKFIELD, WEST SUSSEX RH17 5LD
TEL: HAYWARDS HEATH (0444) 416111   FAX: (0444) 415549

*An olde-English house with an abundance of antiques and fresh
flowers and a good village location.*

In 1658 Walter Burrell the ironmaster bought this Tudor house,
originally named after the Okynden family, and had the stone south wing
built. Later the house was occupied by Sir Walter Wyndham Burrell and
his family, who added the Victorian wing and the stable block. The result
is a mixture of architecture and a feeling of history.

Now the hotel is owned by Sandy and Anne Goodman. Anne has
planned the bedrooms, which are all different and are named after
people who have lived in the house: Charles is rather grand, with a four-
poster bed, rich red carpet and dried flowers in the old fireplace;
Raymond, a large double with dark wood antique furniture, overlooks
the nine acres of garden; Edward has matching floral bedspreads and
curtains, armchairs and a beautiful old-fashioned gilt mirror.

Downstairs, the Burrell Restaurant is a fairly small and intimate oak-
panelled room with stained-glass windows and old, gilt-framed portraits
watching over the diners. The table d'hôte menu may offer terrine of
Sussex game studded with pistachio nuts with a chilled port wine
redcurrant sauce, followed by confit of duckling crisped with a sweet and
sour sauce. Dessert may be a choice of strawberry parfait set on sauce
anglaise or crème brûlée with raspberry coulis.

OCKENDEN MANOR
-CUCKFIELD-

There is another restaurant with a magnificent display of dried flowers, huge gilt baroque-style mirrors and a delicate colour scheme of pink and tangerine. The bar is quite small, with dark wood panelling and a low ceiling; fresh flowers and a tapestry peacock brighten it up.

◑ *Open all year*

⬈ *In the centre of Cuckfield, off the A272. Private car park*

🛏 *1 single, 4 twin, 12 double, 4 four-poster, 1 four-poster suite; all with bathroom/WC, exc single with shower/WC; TV, room service, hair-dryer, trouser press, baby-listening in all rooms*

◈ *Dining-room, bar, lounge, conservatory; conference facilities (max 50 people non-residential, 22 residential); golf, tennis, other sports nearby.*

Wheelchair access to hotel, restaurant and WC, 2 suitable ground-floor bedrooms

⊖ *No dogs; no smoking in dining-room*

▭ *Access, Amex, Diners, Visa*

£ *Single £68, single occupancy of twin/double £75 to £85, twin/double £90 to £130, four-poster/family room £145, suite £155; deposit required. Set L from £13.50, D £25.50. Special breaks available*

CULLOMPTON DEVON   MAP 10

Manor House

2–4 FORE STREET, CULLOMPTON, DEVON EX15 1JL
TEL: TIVERTON (0884) 32281   FAX: (0884) 38344

An imposing town-centre pub-hotel, conveniently positioned close to the M5 between Taunton and Exeter.

Once a wool merchant's town house, Manor House dates back to 1603 and its imposing black and white half-timbered façade with an eighteenth-century shell-arched porch dominates Fore Street. Disappointingly, guests approach reception from the sprawling rear car park which quickly dispels the Jacobean atmosphere. The street-facing, elegantly furnished restaurant and the rear carvery currently offer traditional steaks and grills, but the Dodingtons, who only recently took over the management, hope to change the menus to 'something more appropriate to the Manor'. For those in search of less formal dining arrangements, there is also an extensive bar meals menu.

The ten bedrooms are decked out with dark wood furnishings which are pleasing if not quite as distinctive as one might hope. Guests planning to arrive on Sunday afternoons should ring to book as reception is sometimes closed. More reports, please.

◑ *Open all year*

⬈ *Leave the M5 at Junction 28. Follow signs to Cullompton. In Cullompton, turn left at 1st T-junction; Manor House is 200 yards on the right. Private car park*

🛏 *1 single, 2 twin, 5 double, 1 four-poster, 1 family room; all with bathroom/WC, exc single*

with shower/WC; TV, room
service, hair-dryer, trouser press
in all rooms

 2 restaurants, bar, lounge,
games room; conference
facilities (max 50 people non-
residential, 10 residential);
fishing, golf, other sports nearby.
Wheelchair access to bar,

restaurant and WC (unisex)
only

 No dogs

Access, Amex, Visa

£ Single £38, twin/double/four-
poster £45, family room £55. Set
L £8.50, D £10.50; alc L, D £20.
Special breaks available

DARTMOUTH DEVON   MAP 10

Royal Castle

11 THE QUAY, DARTMOUTH, DEVON TQ6 9PS
TEL: DARTMOUTH (0803) 833033   FAX: (0803) 835445

*A three-hundred-year-old quayside pub-hotel with lots of
character.*

As you walk along the Quay, the Royal Castle doesn't immediately stand
out since it is built into a solid row of shops. Cross the road, however, and
look back, and its wonderful black and white façade with slightly
protruding bow windows is very inviting. Most of the ground floor is
taken up with popular public bars, but at the end of the corridor a
receptionist will direct you up an extraordinary stairwell. This stairwell is
the interior's dominant feature and you can linger for ages on the stairs
and landings inspecting all the bits and pieces used to decorate it: a fox's
head, a set of servants' bells, a pair of scales, a dresser full of plates.
Unusually for a hotel, some of the bedrooms face inwards rather than
outwards, a fact reflected in their cheaper prices. Not that the inward-
facing ones are unattractive; indeed, Number Ten has a very impressive
eighteenth-century four-poster bed, a big green sofa, a standing mirror
and a huge wardrobe and dressing-table. All the inward-facing rooms
are air-conditioned.

If you can face a room without a view, there are plenty of alternatives,
including Number Six – a long, thin room where the entrance to a
seventeenth-century priests' hole was discovered in 1959. A large
drawing-room spreads out behind one of the first-floor bow windows;
the Adam Room Restaurant, with a low plastered ceiling, behind the
other. Four-course set dinners are not as fishy as you might expect;
inevitably, the more expensive of the two menus is the more imaginative,
with dishes such as puff pastry filled with tiger tail prawns, scallops and
poached oyster in a saffron sauce.

 Open all year

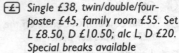 In the centre of Dartmouth
overlooking the inner harbour.
Limited private car parking and

on-street parking facilities. Large
local public car park

4 single, 7 twin, 7 double, 5
four-poster, 2 family rooms;

most with bathroom/WC, some with shower/WC; TV, room service, hair-dryer, baby-listening in all rooms; 4 bedrooms air-conditioned

 Restaurant, bar, 2 lounges, drying room, library; conference facilities (max 40 people non-residential, 25 residential); fishing, riding, watersports nearby; babysitting and crèche facilities

 No wheelchair access; no dogs in some public rooms

Access, Visa

Single £40 to £50, single occupancy of twin/double £60 to £75, twin/double/four-poster/family room £66 to £95; deposit required. Sun L £9.50; set D £15; alc L from £2, D from £15

DEDHAM ESSEX　　　　　　　　　　　　　　　**MAP 8**

Dedham Hall

BROOK STREET, DEDHAM, COLCHESTER, ESSEX CO7 6AD
TEL: COLCHESTER (0206) 323027

A pretty spot, beloved of artists, with homely rooms and an emphasis on food.

On a beautiful spring day, artists set up their easels to paint the tower of the village church which rises above the mature trees of Dedham Hall's grounds. Designated as an Area of Outstanding Natural Beauty, the vale of the River Stour is still very much as Constable painted it and Flatford Mill, the subject of one of his most famous works, is only two miles away. Wendy and Jim Sarton open their house to painting holidays from February to November; a studio has been created from a nearby fifteenth-century barn so work can continue uninterrupted if the weather is bad. For the non-artistic, there are plenty of footpaths to explore and local stately homes and gardens to visit.

Bedrooms are cosy, some with a slight shabbiness that makes them more homely than neglected. With William Morris wallpaper, pine furniture and small, eaved bathrooms, they are comfortable enough, although secondary to the restaurant which occupies much of the ground floor. Decorated in pink, with heavy curtains and a log fire, the dining-room has plenty of space for residents and evening guests. A set menu offers around seven choices per course: perhaps avocado with prawns or fresh dressed crab to start and a peppered sirloin steak or chicken breast with mushrooms in puff pastry as a main dish. Residents can take their coffee in the lounge, which is kitted out with paperbacks and games.

 Open all year

 At the end of Dedham high street, opposite the craft centre. Private car park

 1 single, 3 twin, 2 double, 3 annexe rooms; most with bathroom/WC, some with shower/WC; TV, hair-dryer in all rooms

 2 restaurants, 2 bars, 2 lounges; fishing, golf, tennis nearby. Wheelchair access to annexe

bedrooms and restaurant only

● Dogs in annexe rooms only; no
smoking in some public rooms

▭ Access, Visa

£ Single £34, single occupancy of
twin/double £38, twin/double
£57, annexe room £47 to £57.
Alc L £15.50, D £17.50. Special
breaks available

Dedham Vale/Terrace Restaurant

STRATFORD ROAD, DEDHAM, COLCHESTER, ESSEX CO7 6HW
TEL: COLCHESTER (0206) 322273   FAX: (0206) 322752

A choice between an elegant, luxurious country house (Maison Talbooth) or a cheaper, more cheerful option (Dedham Vale).

Three of Gerald Milsom's mini-empire of hotels and restaurants lie around Dedham Vale; the fourth is the Pier at Harwich (see entry). Le Talbooth Restaurant was the first he acquired – a long, half-timbered building on the side of the River Stour. A courtesy bus transports guests staying at the Dedham Vale or Maison Talbooth hotels (both a few minutes away) to and fro – the idea is to mix and match accommodation and food, and this way guests are encouraged to go further afield without worrying about drink-driving. By all accounts it's worth the trip; one reader reports, 'I have eaten here many times and have never had a bad meal, service or wine.'

So where should you stay – Dedham Vale or Maison Talbooth? The cheaper option is Dedham Vale, a large house lying in three acres of garden in a wooded dale. There are only six rooms here, all *en-suite*, decorated in Laura Ashley sprigs, with large windows and, as a rule, largish bathrooms. Downstairs, the public rooms have a young, lively atmosphere, with breezy décor and modern furnishings. The bar, which lies to the left of reception, is cleverly painted with wall frescoes of balustrades, trees and fluffy white clouds; the Terrace Restaurant, serving lunchtime buffets and traditional evening meals, is conservatory-like in yellows and greens with a ballooning canopy draped over the ceiling like a tent.

By contrast, Maison Talbooth – a ten-minute walk from its sister hotel – is extremely smart, with prices to match. A gravel drive sweeps around a circular fountain in front of the elegant pink façade. Hushed and elegant, with a ticking grandfather clock in the hall, it is hardly the place to march into with muddy boots. A grand piano and fresh flowers in the knocked-through lounge create a refined atmosphere, with beige sofas to sink into with a drink in hand. Bedrooms are named after poets: Wordsworth is one of the principal suites, in pinks and with a large bathroom down a couple of steps; Browning also has a sumptuous bathroom, although its vivid green scheme would not suit everyone. This is the only establish-

ment in Gerald Milsom's triangle of ventures not to have a restaurant –
but because of the courtesy bus it hardly matters.

Service throughout is spot on. 'All the staff are friendly, courteous and
above all take pride in their work,' reports one American guest who also
organised his wedding reception here. 'I would have no hesitation in
recommending the three "gem" establishments to anyone.'

◐ *Open all year*

⤴ *From the A12, about 6 miles north-east of Colchester, take the Stratford St Mary to Dedham road. After 1 mile take the second right-hand turning to Dedham. The hotel is 1 mile along this road on the right. Private car park*

🛏 *2 twin, 4 double; all with bathroom/WC, TV, room service, hair-dryer; no tea/coffee-making facilities in rooms*

◇ *Restaurant, bar, lounge; conference facilities (max 20 people non-residential, 6 residential); golf, tennis, riding nearby*

⊖ *No wheelchair access; no dogs*

▭ *Access, Amex, Visa*

£ *Single occupancy of twin/double £55 to £65, twin/double £70 to £80. Set L, D £19.50; alc L, D £27.50*

Maison Talbooth

STRATFORD ROAD, DEDHAM, COLCHESTER, ESSEX CO7 6HN
TEL: COLCHESTER (0206) 322367   FAX: (0206) 322752

◐ *Open all year*

⤴ *Opposite the Dedham Vale Hotel (see above). Private car park*

🛏 *9 double, 1 family room (suites and twin rooms available); all with bathroom/WC, TV, room service, hair-dryer, mini-bar; no tea/coffee-making facilities in rooms; trouser press, baby-listening on request*

◇ *Lounge, separate restaurant (Le Talbooth) nearby; conference facilities (max 10 people*

residential, 80 non-residential); croquet, giant chess at hotel, other sports nearby; babysitting. Wheelchair access to hotel and restaurant, 5 ground-floor bedrooms

⊖ *No dogs*

▭ *Access, Amex, Visa*

£ *Single occupancy of twin/double £98, twin/double £118, family room £158, suite £138. Cooked B £7.50; set L, D £19.50; alc L, D £20 to £30. Special breaks available*

See our selection of what we consider to be the best hotels in various counties in Hotels of the Year *(page 16).*

Stone Close

MAIN STREET, DENT, NR SEDBERGH, CUMBRIA LA10 5QL
TEL: DENT (05396) 25231

Good-value bed-and-breakfast accommodation in a pretty village on the Cumbrian border.

Though technically in Cumbria the picturesque village of Dent is also in the Yorkshire Dales National Park, which may mean local businesses such as Stone Close are faced with twice the paperwork and slower decision-making. Mind you, the short walk up the quiet cobbled main street to the whitewashed exterior of the two seventeenth-century cottages which make up Stone Close is enough to dispel the idea that anything is hurried around here.

Graham Hudson and Pat Barber offer three rooms above a thriving tea-shop. The rooms are simply furnished and have a genuine country cottage feel with low ceilings, exposed beams and dark wood furniture. Room Three, overlooking the main street, is the largest, while the single room is a little cramped. All the rooms are refreshingly devoid of 'atmospheric' bric-à-brac and share a communal bathroom a short way along the corridor. Dinner is no longer an option but meals are served until 5.30pm in the tea-rooms. The lower of the two rooms has bare stone walls displaying works by local artists and an original cast-iron range shouldering a collection of old beer bottles with names like 'Invalid Stout' and 'Scrumpy Jack'; it is here that guests have breakfasts which one reader hails as 'lavish'. The upper room, with flagged floors and pine tables, also boasts an original range between two contrasting wooden corner units. All sorts of locally produced artefacts are on sale, from brooches to hand-crafted ornamental wellies.

◑ Closed Jan to mid-Feb; tea-shop open weekends only Nov to mid-Mar

⤤ From Sedbergh, Stone Close is the first building on the left on the cobbled street. Public car park adjacent to building

🛏 1 single, 1 double, 1 family room; 1 public bathroom

◈ Dining-room, tea-rooms; golf, riding, fishing, other sports nearby

⊖ No wheelchair access; no dogs in public rooms; no smoking

▭ None accepted

£ Single £17, twin/double £29, family room £36; deposit required. Meals, snacks all day till 5.30pm

Are you aware of your rights as a consumer when you book into a hotel? Check them out on page 837.

DIDDLEBURY SHROPSHIRE   MAP 5

Glebe Farm

DIDDLEBURY, CRAVEN ARMS, SHROPSHIRE SY7 9DH
TEL: MUNSLOW (058 476) 221

*An excellent farmhouse bed and breakfast in a quiet village –
highly recommended.*

Glebe Farm is an ancient half-timbered building covered in roses and
clematis. A stream meanders past its front, sheep graze in the fields to
one side and generations of Diddlebury residents sleep quietly in the
churchyard on the other. For Shropshire tranquillity it is hard to beat.
Adrian and Eileen Wilkes run the bed and breakfast, assisted by one of
their sons. Another son runs the farm. Rooms are either in the main
house or in a cottage annexe. In the main house, you will find a large
sitting-room (garnished with books on Shropshire), a funny little bar and
a spacious breakfast room. Upstairs, Oak is the quaintest room, with fine
oak panelling, while Bridges has the garden view. Cottage rooms have a
little less character, except for Flowers, tucked under the eaves.

The Wilkes no longer serve evening meals but will direct you to the
nearby Crown Inn, where the Thai food is well worth trying. If you decide
to skip supper, you will find the breakfasts at Glebe Farm substantial
enough to fill the gap. 'Clean, solid, respectable,' sums up a reader.

◑ Closed I Dec to I Mar

⚡ On the B4368, 5 miles north-
east of Craven Arms. Private car
park

🛏 I single, 2 twin, 3 double; I with
bathroom/WC, some with
shower/WC; TV, hair-dryer in all
rooms; trouser press on request

◈ Dining-room, bar, lounge; drying
facilities; fishing nearby

⊖ No wheelchair access; no
children under 8; dogs by
arrangement only; no smoking in
dining-room and discouraged in
bedrooms

▭ None accepted

£ Single £20 to £25, single
occupancy of twin/double £22 to
£25; twin/double £37 to £52;
deposit required

DISS NORFOLK   MAP 7

Salisbury House

84 VICTORIA ROAD, DISS, NORFOLK IP22 3JG
TEL: DISS (0379) 644738

*A solid bet on the outskirts of Diss where food takes priority but
bedrooms are no let-down.*

Arrive by day and you are likely to find Barry Davis tidying up the
herbaceous borders and lawn which skirt the solid Victorian façade of

Salisbury House. Come the evening he exchanges gardening tools for culinary tools since he and his wife Sue run what is primarily a first-class restaurant. There are only three bedrooms but they are more than simply somewhere to sleep off a good meal. For those who like privacy, the garden room is the best bet: the four-poster draped in blue fabrics stands where the horses were stabled and the bathroom with exposed flint walls was once the cart-shed. The other rooms are in the main house – the Blue Room decorated in a yellow Regency stripe with a canopied bed and separate bathroom and the Cane Room with a sizeable bathroom and double bed.

Two downstairs rooms are allocated to the restaurant, one used for winter evenings with a roaring fire, the other more summery with ruched curtains highlighting fine bay windows. A monthly menu in neat italic script offers two-course and four-course set meals. A businessman reports very favourably: 'The creamy onion and coriander soup met with approving nods from my colleague and my salmon was beautifully cooked.' And he rates the guesthouse as 'a proverbial oasis', a far cry from the usual 'concrete-block' hotel used by most business people.

◑ Open all year, exc 1 week at Xmas, 2 weeks Aug; restaurant closed Sun, Mon eves

↗ Salisbury House is ¼ mile from Diss town centre on the A1066 heading towards Scole. Private car park

🛏 2 double, 1 four-poster annexe room; 1 with bathroom/WC; TV, room service, hair-dryer, mini-bar in all rooms

◈ 2 restaurants, 2 lounges, conservatory; conference facilities (max 20 people non-residential); croquet at hotel, other sports nearby. Wheelchair access to restaurant only

⊖ No dogs; smoking in lounges only

▭ Access, Visa

£ Single occupancy of double £38 to £50, double £58 to £70, four-poster £65; deposit required. Cooked B £3.50; set L, D £22. Special breaks available

---

DITTISHAM DEVON   **MAP 10**

Fingals

OLD COOMBE, DITTISHAM, DARTMOUTH, DEVON TQ6 0JA
TEL: DITTISHAM (0803) 722398   FAX: (0803) 722401

An off-the-beaten-track hotel with a wonderful swimming-pool and an artistic feel to it.

Fingals, an eighteenth-century house with additions, is isolated in the countryside beyond Dartmouth. You approach across a well-kept lawn and enter through a small bar/bistro where the wall posters and music evoke a continental mood. Behind this lies a much larger dining-room dominated by a wooden rocking-horse and an enormous table; at the heart of the house it is rather dark, so there is also a lighter, wood-panelled breakfast room with blue-checked tablecloths and a statue of St George and Dragon. Hand-written dinner menus offer only limited choice and diners may wind up sitting together at the big table. When we inspected new curtains were going up in a lounge stuffed full of books and magazines; the television is hived off into a smaller back room.

The bedrooms, all completely different, are decorated with furniture and pictures that hotelier Richard Johnston has picked up over the years. The hotel 'aspires to luxury' but 'without excessive plushness'; the huge French bedstead in Room Five is particularly striking, although the risqué painting beside Room Four's four-poster bed wouldn't be to everyone's taste ('I sometimes find it turned to the wall,' Richard commented wryly). Four years ago he added an extension with more rooms, all overlooking the garden; most striking is the huge self-catering barn at the end, an intriguing mass of beams with the beds tucked away behind Japanese screens. Beyond this lies Fingals' other pearl . . . the glorious swimming-pool with removable roof.

◑ Closed New Year to Easter

↗ From the B3207, take the left turning to Dittisham 3 miles before Dartmouth. Turn left by Sportsman's Arms pub, then follow signs to Fingals. Private car park

🛏 2 twin, 6 double, 1 four-poster, 1 family room; all with bathroom/ WC, exc 1 twin with shower/ WC; room service, baby-listening in all rooms; TV, hair-dryer on request

◈ Restaurant, bar, lounge/library, TV room, games room; conference facilities (max 50 people non-residential, 10 residential); tennis (June to Sept), croquet, table tennis, sauna/solarium, heated outdoor swimming-pool at hotel, other sports nearby

⊖ No wheelchair access; no dogs in public rooms

▭ Access, Amex, Visa

£ Single occupancy of twin/double £55 to £60, twin/double £65 to £75, four-poster £80 to £90, family room £125 to £130; deposit required. Set D £25; alc D £20

DODDISCOMBSLEIGH DEVON   **MAP 10**

Nobody Inn

DODDISCOMBSLEIGH, NR EXETER, DEVON EX6 7PS
TEL: CHRISTOW (0647) 52394   FAX: (0647) 52978

A pub-hotel in a remote village on the edge of Dartmoor, with extra rooms in a separate house.

According to legend a weary traveller once stumbled upon the low whitewashed building and tried to find shelter for the night. Receiving no reply, he continued on his journey in the belief that there was nobody in. Luckily today's would-be guests receive a warmer welcome, and there will no doubt be a local propping up the dark, low-beamed bar who will jump at the chance to advise on the virtues of the extensive wine and whisky lists – over 500 and 170 choices respectively. The dining-room overflows its confines to fill the back of the pub, and gets particularly lively at Sunday lunchtimes and for the October to March bi-monthly wine-tasting sessions. Given warning, the chef willingly prepares favourite dishes instead of the standard menu, but don't pass up the chance to sample some of the inn's 30-odd cheeses.

Depending on your tastes you can sleep in one of the four rooms above the pub, which have heavy beams and sloping floors but could be noisy, or in one of the vast, airy rooms of Town Barton, the separate Georgian house 150 yards away across a field where a sound night's sleep is more certain. Pub guests can have continental breakfast brought to their rooms, those in Town Barton can rustle up their own bowls of cereal. Full English fry-ups are served in the pub.

◑ Open all year, exc 25 and 26 Dec; restaurant closed Sun and Mon eves

🡭 Leave the A38 at Devon & Exeter Racecourse (signposted Dunchideock) and follow signs to the Nobody Inn for 3 miles. Private car park

🛏 1 single, 1 twin, 2 double, 3 annexe rooms; most with shower/WC; 1 public bathroom; TV in all rooms; hair-dryer on request

◈ Restaurant, bar, lounge, drying room; conference facilities (max 25 people non-residential, 7 residential); fishing, riding, other sports nearby. Wheelchair access to inn (1 step) and restaurant, 1 ground-floor bedroom

⊖ No children under 14; no dogs; no smoking in restaurant

▭ Access, Visa

£ Single £23, single occupancy of twin/double £28 to £32, twin/double £44 to £53; deposit required. Alc L £8, D £13. Special breaks available

---

DORCHESTER-ON-THAMES OXFORDSHIRE　　　　　**MAP 9**

George

HIGH STREET, DORCHESTER-ON-THAMES, OXFORDSHIRE OX9 8HH
TEL: OXFORD (0865) 340404　FAX: (0865) 341620

A traditional coaching-inn with a popular bar and restaurant and a quiet location.

Dorchester is a quiet village with a few antiques shops near to Oxford and with the benefit of being by-passed by the main road. The George is a well-established pub and restaurant, used by both locals and visitors. The hub of this comfortable old inn is the well-kept bar, with its mix of polished old wood furniture; even on a mid-week winter lunchtime you'll find it busy with diners eating from a limited selection of reasonably priced bar meals served by friendly staff. The restaurant is at the back of the hotel and overlooks a small water garden. The menu is modern and you can choose from dishes such as breast of Barbary duck with orange and lime or grilled fillet of brill with prawns and chive sabayon.

Bedrooms in the main building have beams and sloping roofs, pretty colour co-ordinated fabrics and a mixture of antique and modern fittings. Those in the stable block are less memorable, though comfortable. Single rooms are a little poky.

◖ *Open all year, exc 1 week at Xmas*

▨ *Just off the A423 Henley to Oxford road, 7 miles south of Oxford. Private car park*

⇚ *4 single, 5 twin, 7 double, 2 four-poster; all with bathroom/WC, TV, room service, baby-listening; trouser press, hair-dryer in 9 rooms*

◈ *Restaurant, bar; conference facilities (max 50 people non-*

residential, 18 residential); golf, riding, swimming-pool, gym nearby; babysitting. Wheelchair access to hotel and 6 ground-floor bedrooms

⊖ *No dogs in public rooms*

▭ *Access, Amex, Diners, Visa*

£ *Single £62, single occupancy of twin/double £68, twin/double £75, four-poster £100. Set L £15, D £18/£22*

DOVER KENT   **MAP 8**

Number One Guesthouse

1 CASTLE STREET, DOVER, KENT CT16 1QH
TEL: DOVER (0304) 202007

A homely bed and breakfast which is ideal for ferry travellers.

In a central but fairly quiet location, Number One shines out with its spruce black and gold railings, hanging baskets and frilly curtains. Inside, the Reidys have taken great care with the smart, traditional fittings of their hotel. Adeline Reidy, who used to inspect hotels herself, sets great store by the quality of beds and makes sure that hers have sound mattresses, a choice of feather or foam pillows, and velvet blankets imported from the USA. The décor is rather rich and frilly, making heavy use of flock wallpaper and brown and yellow velvet. Each room has a lace-covered table where breakfast is served (left overnight for those who have an early-morning ferry to catch). Guests also have access to a comfortable lounge with pink wallpaper and red armchairs which leads out to a lovely walled garden. Lock-up garages at the back mean that guests don't have to shift all their luggage on an overnight stop. The affable and attentive Reidys keep a healthy stock of local information for those who are holidaying in Dover, and provide books and toys for their youngest guests.

◖ *Open all year*

▨ *Follow M20, A20 into central Dover. The guesthouse is just*

below the castle. 4 private garages and on-street parking

⇚ *2 twin, 2 double, 2 family rooms;*

all with shower/WC, TV, room
service, hair-dryer

◈ Lounge

⊖ No wheelchair access; no dogs

▭ None accepted

£ Twin/double £32 to £38, family
room (4 people), £52 to £56;
deposit required

DREWSTEIGNTON DEVON   **MAP 10**

Hunts Tor House

DREWSTEIGNTON, DEVON EX6 6QW
TEL: DREWSTEIGNTON (0647) 21228

*A comfortable family home in a particularly pretty Dartmoor
village.*

The discreet eighteenth-century white façade with graceful porch Hunts
Tor presents to the visitor conceals a building dating back in part to the
mid-seventeenth century. Inside, Sue and Chris Harrison specialise in
mirrors on a daunting scale; there's one in the lounge and an even more
intimidating example which ruthlessly exposes every blemish in one of
the bathrooms. They're also keen on art deco, and lovely pieces of
pottery are displayed in the guests' lounge, together with big plants and
three comfortable settees. There's an elegant dining-room at the front of
the house, and another more homely one with big wooden table at the
back. There, too, is a small bar (tiny enough to be a pulpit), made out of
an old cupboard. Above an attractive wood-block floor dried flowers
hang from impressive beams. There are only four bedrooms, one of them
a capacious suite with a huge wardrobe, small Victorian fireplace and
oodles of wickerwork.

   Some of Sue Harrison's recipes have been published in *The Women
Chefs of Britain*; a typical four-course meal might include timbale of
broccoli followed by boned quail stuffed with wild rice and apricots, with
praline parfait to finish.

◑ Closed Dec, Jan

↗ On the village square. On-street
parking and parking on the
village square

🛏 3 double, 1 suite; all with
bathroom/WC; room service,
hair-dryer in all rooms; TV in
suite only

◈ Dining-room/bar, lounge, drying
room; fishing, golf, other sports
nearby

⊖ No wheelchair access; no
children under 14; no dogs in
public rooms; no smoking in
dining-room

▭ None accepted

£ Single occupancy of twin/double
£25 to £30, twin/double £40,
suite £30 to £50; deposit
required. Set D £17 (7.30pm)
(prices till Nov 93)

Prices are quoted per room *rather than* per person.

DULVERTON SOMERSET   **MAP 10**

Ashwick House

DULVERTON, SOMERSET TA22 9QD
TEL: DULVERTON (0398) 23868

A remote Edwardian country-house hotel with galleried hall and glorious grounds; a warm welcome guaranteed.

By the time you near Ashwick House you're in a particularly desolate part of Exmoor, so it's startling to round a bend and spot a quintessential Edwardian weekend cottage surrounded by six acres of manicured lawns and soaring trees. The porch gives on to the turn-of-the-century equivalent of a stone-floored Elizabethan galleried hall, with tall stained-glass windows, huge fireplace and William Morris wallpaper; the little flags representing the nationalities of resident guests are a nice touch. This year readers again describe the 'enthusiasm, friendliness and untiring energy' Richard Sherwood puts into running the hotel and his handiwork is visible everywhere, especially in the handwritten scroll-menus for dinner and the welcome packs laid out on the beds.

Downstairs a billiard room used for making camouflage netting during the Second World War is now a spacious lounge with elegant chaise-longue. The six bedrooms, each named after a tree growing in the garden, are roomy and comfortable; best is the Ash Room, positioned to catch the morning sun and with marvellous views. As well as the standard fixtures, bathrooms come equipped with American 'speak-your-weight' scales, which helpfully warn you how much weight you've put on since you (or the previous resident) last stepped aboard. *Lorna Doone* takes pride of place among the books lined up on bedside tables. Delicious meals, from varied if not wildly imaginative menus, are served in the downstairs dining-room; those who have rabbit-watched from the breakfast terrace may prefer to pass on the rabbit pie.

◑ *Open all year*

⤢ *At the post office in Dulverton take the B3223 signposted Exford & Lynton. Drive over the moor, cross the cattle grid and take a left turn to Ashwick House. Private car park*

🛏 *2 twin, 4 double; all with bathroom/WC, TV, room service, hair-dryer, trouser press; mini-bar in 2 rooms; no tea/coffee-making facilities in rooms*

◈ *Restaurant, bar, 2 lounges, drying room, library; conference facilities (max 12 people non-residential); solarium at hotel, fishing, riding nearby. Wheelchair access to restaurant only*

⊖ *No children under 8; no dogs; no smoking in restaurant*

▭ *None accepted*

£ *Single occupancy of twin/double £51 to £55, twin/double £79 to £84; deposit required. Set L (Sun only) £13.50, D £20; packed lunches. Special breaks available*

Carnarvon Arms Hotel ☆

DULVERTON, SOMERSET TA22 9AE
TEL: DULVERTON (0398) 23302   FAX: (0398) 24022

*A large country-pursuits hotel on the approaches to Exmoor
National Park.*

The fourth Earl of Carnarvon built the Carnarvon Arms in 1874 to
provide for Dulverton Station's passengers; the station has long since
closed but its buildings, some converted into cottages, give the feel of an
open-air museum as you sweep up the drive. Inside, the hotel is the *Field*
come to life, with assorted stuffed animals adorning its walls and
photographs and cartoons highlighting the importance of the huntin',
shootin' and fishin' ethos – 'all catered for, especially fishing, the hotel
being on the Barle and Exe,' reports one reader. That aside, the
Carnarvon Arms manages to be both grand and homely at the same time.
The servants' bells hanging in the hall symbolise the emphasis on good,
old-fashioned service; there are no tea- and coffee-making facilities in
the rooms because proprietor Toni Jones believes that people escape to
hotels to avoid doing things for themselves. In the big front lounge
armchairs are grouped to encourage conversation; across the hall a
library leads to a lighter lounge overlooking the swimming-pool. The
newly decorated basement dining-room features lovely hilly views and
menus with a very English flavour, while the Buttery Bar upstairs serves
standard pub fare as an alternative.

A rolling programme of redecoration means that some rooms are more
modern than others. Front rooms are slightly noisier than those at the
rear, hence their lower prices. Some have excellent views; from Room 14
you can watch the West Somerset Polo Club going through its paces.

The Clock Tower Complex, in an old stable block, means wedding
and sporting parties can be catered for without disturbing other guests.

◗ Open all year

↗ 1½ miles outside Dulverton on
the B3222 Tiverton Road on the
edge of the village of Brushford.
Private car park

🛏 5 single, 13 twin, 4 double, 2
family rooms, 1 suite; most with
bathroom/WC, 1 with shower/
WC; TV, room service, baby-
listening in all rooms; tea/coffee-
making facilities and hair-dryer
on request

◈ Restaurant, 2 bars, 2 lounges;
drying room, library,
conservatory, games room, gun
room; conference facilities (max
120 non-residential, 25

residential); fishing, tennis, livery,
heated swimming-pool, shooting
and croquet at hotel; babysitting.
Wheelchair access to hotel (2
steps) and restaurant, 2 ground-
floor bedrooms specially
equipped for disabled people

⊖ None

▭ Access, Visa

💷 Single from £50 and £60, twin/
double from £94 and £114,
family room rate on request,
suite from £148 and £160 (rates
inc dinner); deposit required. Set
L £10.50, D £20 (prices till end
93). Special breaks available

DUNSTER SOMERSET   **MAP 10**

Exmoor House Hotel ☆

12 WEST STREET, DUNSTER, SOMERSET TA24 6SN
TEL: MINEHEAD (0643) 821268

A small, family-run hotel in the centre of a honeypot Somerset town, close to the church and castle.

Superficially Georgian, Exmoor House Hotel is a fine example of how a building can be transformed with a bit of imagination: the hall used to be an alley separating the main structure from a shop and outhouses, while the television lounge was once a courtyard. Upstairs, pickaxes have been taken ruthlessly to walls, knocking them through to create *en-suite* facilities for most of the bedrooms. Now that the work is finished, the result is a light, airy and very comfortable hotel, run by an enthusiastic and thoroughly welcoming couple, Brendan and Phyllis Lally.

Sitting in the long, thin dining-room (which doubles as a tea-shop), you look through pretty lace curtains to an even longer, thinner lounge with french windows on to the garden. Comfy sofas and armchairs positively invite you to stretch out and relax. The bedrooms have pretty, rather feminine fittings with lots of dried flowers, but are a little small; what look like wardrobes sometimes open to reveal concealed bathrooms. Five face on to the garden and the countryside beyond: rooms at the front could be a little noisy in summer.

◑ Closed mid-Nov to end Jan

↗ Leave the M5 at Junction 25 and take the A39 to Minehead. Leave the road 2 miles from Minehead and take the A396 to Dunster. On-street parking

🛏 3 twin, 4 double; some with bathroom/WC, some with shower/WC; TV, room service, hair-dryer in all rooms

◈ Restaurant, bar, 2 lounges, TV room; fishing, golf, other sports nearby

⊖ No wheelchair access; no children under 12; no dogs in public rooms; no smoking

▭ Access, Amex, Diners, Visa

£ Single occupancy of twin/double £33 to £36, twin/double £49 to £55; deposit required. Bar lunches; set D £14.50. Special breaks available

---

DURHAM CO DURHAM   **MAP 3**

Georgian Town House

10 CROSSGATE, DURHAM, CO DURHAM DH1 4PS
TEL: DURHAM 091-386 8070

A stylish bed and breakfast in the heart of this lovely old city.

Pastel-coloured buildings are not what you expect at the centre of northern English cities, better known for their red-brick terraces. The

Georgian House, simply rendered in white enlivened with colourful baskets of flowers, stands out in the midst of just such an exotic little enclave. Fading gold letters on a green canopy create a hint of dowdiness which is immediately dispelled the second the door is opened and you are led into a hallway where striking stencils of a pillar and leaf motif conjure up images of the Aegean. Comfortable striped and diamond-patterned sofas are ideal for lounging in in the bright front-facing green and white sitting-room, which also accommodates one overspill breakfast table. The main breakfast room is a bright conservatory-style extension over-looking the garden, elegant with bistro chairs and pink table linen. Breakfast is highly regarded; one reader found it 'beautifully served . . . our scrambled eggs decorated with mint leaves looked and tasted wonderful'.

Bedrooms at the top of the steep stairs are individually decorated. One good-sized double has mottled green stencilled walls, bold co-ordinating bed linen, and wicker and basket-weave furniture, giving it a fresh, airy feel. An art deco-style décor complements the room with the slightly decadent corner bath.

◑ Closed 2 weeks over Xmas

🡒 Follow signs in Durham to Crook and Newcastle; go over traffic lights at St Margaret's Hospital and take first turning on right. Go down Allergate to junction with Crossgate. On-street parking

🛏 3 twin, 2 double, 1 family room; all with bathroom/WC; TV

◈ Breakfast room, lounge, conservatory

⊖ No wheelchair access; no dogs; no smoking in bedrooms

▭ None accepted

£ Single occupancy of twin/double £30 to £35, twin/double £40 to £45, family room rate on request; deposit required

---

DUXFORD CAMBRIDGESHIRE   **MAP 8**

Duxford Lodge

ICKLETON ROAD, DUXFORD, CAMBRIDGESHIRE CB2 4RU
TEL: CAMBRIDGE (0223) 836444   FAX: (0223) 832271

A handily placed hotel, near the motorway for convenience but far enough away to be civilised.

Sue and Ron Craddock have had time to settle into this new venture, purchased in December 1991, and it appears that Duxford Lodge has fallen into safe hands. The major change was made almost immediately – namely, gutting and refurbishing the stable block, installing new bathrooms with twinkling gold fittings and, in doing so, losing a room. Two four-posters have been added too, and the overall result is a fresher, bolder look, perhaps lacking in originality but certainly bringing rooms up to favourable standard. The hotel's position near the M11 means that it is popular with business people and travellers who wish to break their journey. It is also close to the Duxford Imperial War Museum and within a short drive of Cambridge, so would make a good weekend base. Discount bed-and-breakfast rates for Friday to Sunday nights (staying a minimum of two) are worth looking into.

Daily menus are good value and the emphasis is on tasty traditional fare. Soup, avocado or pâté starters are followed by roasts, hams, casseroles or fish. An à la carte menu offers duck or chargrilled steaks.

◑ *Open all year; restaurant open Sun eve by prior arrangement only*

⬏ *Leave the M11 at Junction 10; the lodge is just off the A505 Royston/Newmarket road. Private car park*

🛏 *2 single, 1 twin, 10 double, 2 four-poster (some rooms in annexe); most with bathroom/ WC, some with shower/WC; TV, room service, hair-dryer, trouser press, baby-listening in all rooms*

◈ *Restaurant, bar, lounge, TV room, drying room; conference facilities (max 36 people non-residential, 16 residential)*

⊖ *No wheelchair access; no dogs in restaurant*

▭ *Access, Amex, Diners, Visa*

£ *Single £35 to £67, single occupancy of twin/double £35 to £67, twin/double/four-poster £68 to £88. Set L, D £13; Sun L £12; alc L, D from £14.50. Special breaks available*

EASINGTON CLEVELAND   **MAP 3**

Grinkle Park

EASINGTON, SALTBURN-BY-THE-SEA, CLEVELAND TS13 4UB
TEL: GUISBOROUGH (0287) 640515   FAX: (0287) 641278

A late-Victorian industrial magnate's mansion transformed by corporate owners into a friendly, unstuffy country-house hotel.

The castellated tower suggests an antiquity rather greater than Grinkle Park can really lay claim to, but its mock-baronial look is the only phoney note about this comfortable conference and function-oriented member of the country-house school. The 35 acres of grounds, woodland and lake, the long rhododendron-lined avenue and the peacocks all help to add an air of nobility.

Parts of the hotel have a lived-in feel, but the first-floor sitting-room is bright and elegant with lovely views over the grounds, and there is a pretty garden room with lots of bamboo and cane to give a light, summery feel. The bedrooms (named after local moorland and birds) have lots of room and neat, dainty décor in pastel shades or flowery prints. Many have good views. Both the bar and dining-room are traditional in flavour, like the good-value table d'hôte menu, which attracts a number of local diners for appetising fare such as a home-made soup, followed by medallions of pork in a Dijon mustard sauce and farmhouse cheeses. A fairly short but more adventurous à la carte menu is also available.

The friendly staff have cultivated an unpretentious atmosphere that proves that not all corporately owned hotels (this one is part of the Bass empire) need be soulless, and that country-house hotels need not be aloof.

◑ Open all year

↗ 1½ miles south of Easington, on Grinkle Lane, which runs north from the A171. Private car park

🛏 7 single, 6 twin, 5 double, 2 four-poster; all with bathroom/WC, TV, room service, trouser press, baby-listening in all rooms; hair-dryer in some rooms

◈ Dining-room, bar, lounge, snooker room, conservatory; conference facilities (max 60 people non-residential, 20 residential); tennis, snooker, croquet (May to Oct) at hotel, other sports nearby. Wheelchair access to restaurant only

⊖ No dogs in public rooms (and charged for overnight)

▭ Access, Amex, Diners, Visa

£ Single £65, single occupancy rate on request, twin/double £80, four-poster £85. Set L £9/£11, D £15.50; alc D £20. Special breaks available

---

EAST BARKWITH LINCOLNSHIRE   MAP 5

The Grange ☆

TORRINGTON LANE, EAST BARKWITH, LINCOLN, LINCOLNSHIRE LN3 5RY
TEL: WRAGBY (0673) 858249

Good-sized rooms in a well-kept Georgian farmhouse with very accommodating hosts.

Neatly trimmed holly hedges and an immaculately tidy farmyard are the first signs that Anne and Richard Stamp's bed and breakfast and farm businesses are no ramshackle operations. Guests at the red-brick, foliage-clad Georgian farmhouse are welcome to wander around the farm, and the Stamps have created a mile-long farm trail for them to follow. In 1992 they won a national award for wildlife and conservation, and the trail includes a trout lake, bat boxes and grass margins around the fields – Anne and Richard will talk you through it if you ask them.

Inside, the farmhouse is beautifully kept. The restful champagne-coloured lounge is a room for all seasons, with its marble fireplace, magazines and chess set as well as doors out into the garden. Guests have a complimentary sherry here before eating together in the dining-room, where there is an antique sideboard and black-leaded fireplace. A typical set meal in summer might include smoked haddock cream with chives, chicken in sherry and cheese sauce with broccoli, and French apple tart or strawberries and ice-cream. One reader was particularly impressed by breakfast: 'We breakfasted in style, accompanied by a roaring log fire and the 1812 Overture as background.'

The three good-sized bedrooms are solidly furnished with antiques, with décor ranging from heavy 1970s patterns to Laura Ashley country roses. Bathrooms are generously supplied with goodies such as bath oil, cotton-wool balls and shampoo.

◑ Open all year

↗ Turn off the A157 in East Barkwith by the war memorial into Torrington Lane. The Grange is one mile along this lane. Private car park

⇌ 1 twin, 2 double; all with bathroom/WC, exc 1 double with shower/WC; TV, hair-dryer in all rooms; room service on request

◈ Dining-room, lounge, TV room, conservatory; drying facilities; fishing, tennis, croquet, nature trail at hotel, golf nearby

⊖ No wheelchair access; no children under 8; no dogs; smoking in 1 public room only

▭ None accepted

£ Single occupancy of twin/double £21 to £25, twin/double £40; deposit required. Set D £12 (7.30pm, by arrangement)

EAST BUCKLAND DEVON   MAP 10

Lower Pitt Restaurant

EAST BUCKLAND, BARNSTAPLE, DEVON EX32 0TD
TEL: FILLEIGH (0598) 760243 (and fax)

A restaurant-with-rooms in a converted farmhouse in remote Devon countryside.

Every town-dweller's rural fantasy, Lower Pitt Restaurant is in a 400-year-old, sparkling white farmhouse, draped with roses in summer; old farm implements are scattered around outside, some, like the milk churns, offered new life as flower-holders. The church tower beckons over the wall, but you'll have exhausted the village sights, primarily some pretty thatched cottages, in five minutes. Lower Pitt is the sort of place where your hosts, Suzanne and Jerome Lyons, will be at the door to welcome you as you rattle over the cattle grid. Their attention to their guests' needs is unstinting. No television to catch your favourite programme? One can be fetched from the kitchen. Night a touch chilly? Then your electric blanket will have been switched on before you retire to bed.

The three small bedrooms have pine furniture, lots of low lighting and all the little extras that suggest that thought has gone into making them welcoming: fresh milk, a choice of herbal teas, a range of magazines. Downstairs, two big squashy sofas line up between a log fire and a small bar. However, Lower Pitt is a restaurant first and foremost and you can sample Suzanne Lyons' exquisite concoctions either in the original dining-room, partitioned to foster intimacy, or in the conservatory extension. As soon as you see the menu any worries about being in the back of beyond quickly evaporate: on inspection, stir-fried prawns with mushrooms and cashews, Kashmiri lamb with almonds and vegetables and hazelnut meringue gâteau with raspberry cream sauce were just some of the delicious offerings available.

◖ Open all year, exc 25 to 26 Dec

↗ 3 miles north of the A361, signposted East and West Buckland. The hotel is around the corner from the church. Private car park

🛏 1 twin, 2 double; twin with bathroom/WC, doubles with shower/WC; hair-dryer in all rooms

◈ 2 dining-rooms, bar, lounge,

conservatory; golf, water sports nearby

⊖ No wheelchair access; no children under 12; no dogs; smoking in bar only

▭ Access, Amex, Visa

£ Single occupancy of twin/double £35, twin/double £60; deposit required. Alc D £20. Special breaks available

---

EAST GRINSTEAD WEST SUSSEX   MAP 9

Gravetye Manor

NR EAST GRINSTEAD, WEST SUSSEX RH19 4LJ
TEL: SHARPTHORNE (0342) 810567   FAX: (0342) 810080

An aristocratic country house in a peaceful location a little off the beaten track.

As your car sweeps round the gravelled drive running through the bushes and garden, the imposing grey stone manor house is revealed. Camouflaged in creepers, it looks an impressive sight with its numerous chimneys, latticed windows and old tiled roof. If you look closely you will see the initials 'R' and 'K' in stone above the main entrance from the formal garden; Richard Infield had Gravetye built in 1598 for his bride Katherine. Another owner to leave a legacy was William Robinson, who created the wonderful English country-style garden, with its great lawns, rambling woods and beautiful flowers.

It comes as no surprise to learn that bedrooms are named after trees rather than being numbered. With the exception of Larch, all are spacious, with high beds, antique furnishings and tasteful screens hiding the modern intrusion of the television. Public rooms possess an aristocratic, colonial club atmosphere, with panelled walls, polished wooden floors and thick rugs; the leather armchairs creak as you sit down. Fresh flowers in antique vases add a splash of colour.

Dining in the restaurant is a formal affair. A choice of over 400 different wines accompanies the English menu, which has temptations such as noisettes of lamb with fresh garden herbs served with spring vegetables, pan-fried calf's liver and bacon with creamed potatoes or perhaps tournedos of wild Scottish salmon wrapped in bacon and served with light lobster sauce.

◗ Open all year

▨ Off the B2028 between Turners Hill and West Hoathly. Private car park

🛏 1 single, 16 twin/double, 1 four-poster; all with bathroom/WC, TV, room service, hair-dryer, trouser press, baby-listening; no tea/coffee-making facilities in rooms

◈ Restaurant, bar, 2 lounges (1 air-conditioned); conference facilities (max 18 people residential); fishing, croquet at hotel, other sports nearby

⊖ No wheelchair access; no children under 7; no dogs; no smoking in restaurant

▭ None accepted

£ Single £70 to £85, single occupancy of twin/double £85 to £180, twin/double £85 to £180, four-poster £160 to £190. Continental B £7, cooked B £7 to £8; set L £20, D £24; alc L, D £30 to £35

EAST KNOYLE WILTSHIRE   MAP 9

Swainscombe ☆

THE GREEN, EAST KNOYLE, SALISBURY, WILTSHIRE SP3 6BN
TEL: EAST KNOYLE (0747) 830224

Excellent value in a picturesque thatched cottage in a rural hamlet.

As you sit at breakfast in the pretty seventeenth-century cottage you might catch a glimpse of woodpeckers at work in the sheltered garden. It is an atmosphere little changed since Cromwell's men were quartered here while searching for Charles II during the Civil War. Swainscombe is in a tiny hamlet called the Green, about a mile from East Knoyle. It is glorious, unspoilt countryside, ideal for walking and riding. Set in half an acre of grounds, Swainscombe has stabling for guests' horses, and hunting trips as well as clay pigeon shoots can be arranged.

Rex and Joy Orman are cheerful, good-humoured hosts who work hard to maintain high standards of comfort and hospitality. The house has two self-contained wings, although the word may give a misleading impression of scale: this is a cosy cottage with original period features, sloping ceilings, beams and narrow stairs. All the non-smoking bedrooms have good-quality beds and linen, giant bathtowels and electric blankets. Look out for examples of Joy's collection of antique Victorian soap dishes. Bedrooms vary from the decently sized four-poster room, with modern bathroom next door, to two very small singles that share a brand-new shower room and toilet. The east wing has two doubles and a sitting-room, and is suitable for group lets.

At the time of our inspection, Rex was in the process of decorating the sunny guests' lounge. The dining-room has an inglenook hearth and the remains of an old bread oven. Dinners around the period-style table are candlelit, and the table is beautifully set with bone china and silver cutlery. Joy has Cordon Bleu qualifications and cooks a daily changing four-course menu. A typical dinner might be home-made celery soup, lemon sole cooked in spices and tarte normande. There is no alcohol licence, but guests can bring their own wine. Joy and Rex explain that breakfast orders need to be taken the night before, in order that the Wiltshire pork sausages and tomatoes can cook slowly and deliciously in the Aga simmer oven. They also serve local smoked bacon, health-food toast and correctly poached free-range eggs.

◑ Open all year, exc Xmas and New Year

🔁 Turn off the A350 in East Knoyle at Wrens Stores/Post Office. Continue up Wise Lane and over the crossroads at the top of the hill. Enter 'The Green' hamlet and turn right at the red telephone box. Swainscombe is 50 yards on the right. Private car park

🛏 2 single, 2 double, 1 four-poster, 1 suite; some with bathroom/ WC, some with shower/WC, 2 public bathrooms; TV, room service, hair-dryer in all rooms; no tea/coffee-making facilities in rooms

◇ Dining-room, 2 lounges; fishing, golf, other sports nearby

⊖ No wheelchair access; no children under 5; no dogs; no smoking

▭ None accepted

£ Single £20, single occupancy of twin/double £25, twin/double/ four-poster/suite £38 to £40. Set D £13.50 (7.30pm, by arrangement)

EASTON GREY WILTSHIRE　　　　　　　　　　　　　　**MAP 9**

Whatley Manor

EASTON GREY, MALMESBURY, WILTSHIRE SN16 0RB
TEL: MALMESBURY (0666) 822888　FAX: (0666) 826120

Unstuffy country-house hotel with lots of sports facilities.

The long drive, lined with conifers, serves to whet the appetite as you approach Whatley Manor. When it finally comes into view you won't be disappointed by this rambling creeper-clad manor house constructed of weathered limestone with outbuildings and extensions. Although parts of the house go back to the seventeenth century, what you see before you dates from the complete overhaul that it received in the 1920s.

Once through the front door you enter a pine-panelled hall-lounge with its massive fireplace. Just off from this is the darker, larger drawing-room with a red carpet and clusters of easy chairs and sofas. Piles of games and magazines are left around for guests' entertainment.

Peter Kendall and his staff have succeeded in creating a friendly atmosphere. They are helped by the excellent sports facilities: the nearby stable-block houses spa rooms, sauna, solarium and Jacuzzi, as well as table tennis and snooker. There's also a tennis court, croquet lawn and swimming-pool. Guests replace those burned-off calories in the apricot-coloured dining-room. The menu shows a willingness to experiment with international cuisines, so you might have avocado Vermont followed by medallions of beef New Orleans-style or Dover sole Louisiana.

The bedrooms are a good size and are decorated in restful pinks and apricots; objects such as Chinese prints and enormous mirrors add individual touches to their pleasing appearance.

◑ Open all year

⬈ On the B4040, 3 miles west of Malmesbury. Private car park

🛏 6 twin, 10 double, 1 four-poster, 2 family rooms, 10 court-house annexe rooms; all with bathroom/WC, TV, room service (exc court-house rooms), hair-dryer, baby-listening

◈ Restaurant, bar, 2 lounges, 2 games rooms; conference facilities (max 30 people non-residential and residential); Jacuzzi, table tennis, croquet,

fishing, tennis, sauna/solarium, heated swimming-pool (seasonal) at hotel, other sports nearby; babysitting

⊖ No wheelchair access; no dogs in public rooms

▭ Access, Amex, Diners, Visa

£ Single occupancy of twin/double £85 to £96, twin/double £112 to £136, four-poster £136, family room/annexe room £112 to £136. Set L £15, D £28. Special breaks available

---

EAST PORTLEMOUTH DEVON   **MAP 10**

Gara Rock

EAST PORTLEMOUTH, NR SALCOMBE, DEVON TQ8 8PH
TEL: SALCOMBE (0548) 842342   FAX: (0548) 843033

A family hotel on a remote Devon hilltop adjoining National Trust property.

Given its isolated position it's surprising that the Gara Rock is a family-holiday hotel rather than a walker's hidey-hole. Views from the car park are spectacular, with the cliff-face falling away to the sea. Glimpsed side on, the Gara Rock also looks attractive, based as it is on a group of late-nineteenth-century black and white coastguards' cottages; the façade is much less picturesque, as is the rather functional reception area, just past the very necessary 'Shop at the Top' and a table-tennis room.

Rooms here have been designed so that people need only pay for those services they want, through what proprietor Colin Richards calls 'tailor-made tariffs'. The family suites, which can take up to nine people, are big and spacious but with very basic furnishings; the smaller rooms are not much more inspiring. Nevertheless, the hotel aims to provide all those things which will make a family holiday successful; high chairs, cots, a baby-listening service, a clown at Saturday lunchtimes, a mini-club two hours a day, a weekly swimming gala and so on.

With no nearby facilities for eating out, the Gara Rock has to cover every eventuality from brunch breakfasts (any time up to midday) to picnic lunches and early evening fondue sessions. Dinner menus also cater for everyone, with extensive vegetarian selections and special children's dishes. The Gara Rock only takes weekly bookings for the suites, although for the time being you can still book a four-night stay in one of the *en-suite* bedrooms.

◑ Closed Nov to Easter

⬈ At Frogmore turn right, go over bridge and follow signs for East Portlemouth and Gara Rock. Private car park

🛏 I single, 5 twin, 4 double, 22 self-contained suites; most with bathroom/WC, some with shower/WC; TV, room service, baby-listening in all rooms

◈ 2 dining-rooms, bar, lounge, drying room, sun lounge, conservatory, games room; conference facilities (max 60 people residential and non-residential); tennis, croquet, sauna/solarium, gym, heated outdoor swimming-pool, fishing at hotel, other sports nearby; babysitting, adventure playground. Wheelchair access to hotel and restaurant, 16 ground-floor bedrooms

⊖ No dogs in public rooms

▭ Access, Visa

£ 4-day breaks from £80 per room; suites on a weekly basis from £139; deposit required. Continental B £3 to £5.50; bar meals; alc D £15

ECCLESHALL STAFFORDSHIRE   **MAP 5**

St George Hotel

CASTLE STREET, ECCLESHALL, STAFFORDSHIRE ST21 6DF
TEL: STAFFORD (0785) 850300   FAX: (0785) 851452

A popular old inn with a comfortable bar, friendly hosts and variable bedrooms.

There is nothing very extraordinary about Eccleshall. True, it has a castle and a lovely twelfth-century sandstone church famous for its bishops, many of whom are buried here – Bishop Overton, regarded as a dangerous radical by the government of the time and responsible for bringing glass-making to the area, has his tomb near the altar. But mostly Eccleshall is a busy little market town, where locals come to do their shopping and pop into the St George for a drink. The inn used to be called the George and Dragon, as the sign outside suggests, but the previous owner changed it and down-to-earth landlords Gerard and Moyra Slater don't want to confuse things by changing it back. When we visited they were holding a competition to name the new beer they have just begun to brew on the premises. The bar is a spruced-up version of a country pub, with exposed-brick walls, copper-topped tables, logs burning in the fireplace and board games piled above the mantelpiece; the informal bistro-style restaurant, with its deep-green paintwork, overhead rotating fans and tall yukka plants, almost has an art nouveau feel to it. Here you can sample an uncomplicated range of dishes that includes grilled Dover sole, pork fillet in garlic butter with tomatoes and chopped nuts, and steaks.

Relatively upmarket for rooms above a pub (as well as spotlessly clean), the ten modern bedrooms range from plain with muted colours to smart with stripes, bold flowery fabric and an antique bed. Some have bathrooms with Jacuzzis and dated gold taps, while three have gas-flame fires; amongst those with plenty of space is Room Three, a single with its bed in an alcove. The rooms at the back are the quietest.

◑ Open all year, exc 25 Dec

⤢ Leave the M6 at Junction 14 and follow A5013 to Eccleshall. Continue on this road for 6 miles and turn right at the T-junction. At the next crossroads turn right – the hotel is on one corner of the crossroads. Private car park

🛏 4 single, 1 twin, 4 double, 1 four-poster; all with bathroom/WC, exc 2 singles with shower/WC; TV, room service, baby-

listening in all rooms

◈ Restaurant, bar, lounge, drying room; fishing, golf, other sports nearby

⊖ No wheelchair access

▭ Access, Amex, Diners, Visa

£ Single £42, single occupancy of twin/double £42, twin/double/four-poster £55 to £110. Set D from £8; alc D from £15. Special breaks available

---

EDITH WESTON LEICESTERSHIRE   **MAP 5**

Normanton Park Hotel

NORMANTON PARK ROAD, RUTLAND WATER SOUTH SHORE, EDITH WESTON, NR OAKHAM, LEICESTERSHIRE LE15 8RP
TEL: STAMFORD (0780) 720315   FAX: (0780) 721086

Well-equipped rooms in a converted eighteenth-century stable block on Rutland Water.

Normanton Park, on the banks of Rutland Water (Europe's biggest man-made lake), is often busy with sporty people of all types including anglers and clay pigeon shooting parties. Sister hotel to Barnsdale Lodge (see entry), Normanton Park, a converted eighteenth-century stable block, is run on the same efficient lines, aiming mostly at business people but with a careful eye on the leisure market. The Sailing Bar caters well for both. With its exposed stone walls, mezzanine gallery below the rafters and bold striped tablecloths, it is more stylish than your average clubhouse, and serves a good range of bar snacks from lasagne to Rutland trout as well as afternoon teas. Old farm implements, framed butterflies and a collection of old bellows give the public rooms their carefully contrived rustic character.

The bedrooms are quite plush, with good-quality furnishings and modern fabrics. All have *en-suite* bathrooms, and goodies – which include home-made biscuits – are generous. They vary in size though not in price (if you're a light sleeper you'll need to keep your window shut against the chiming of the stableyard clock). You get a view of the lake from the Orangery Restaurant, which is green and leafy and has a menu that lists plenty of fish as well as vegetarian meals. A typical three-course dinner might include coarse country pâté with garlic toast and Cumberland sauce, grilled Dover sole with lemon butter, and pavlova filled with hazelnut ice-cream.

◐ Open all year

⤴ Take the A606 towards Oakham. Turn left for Normanton and RAF Luffenham. The hotel is a mile further on, overlooking Rutland Water. Private car park

🛏 1 single, 3 twin, 5 double, 5 family rooms; all with bathroom/ WC, exc 2 twins with shower/ WC; TV, room service, hairdryer, baby-listening in all rooms

◈ Restaurant, bar, lounge;

conference facilities (max 100 people non-residential, 14 residential), fishing, golf, tennis, other sports nearby. Wheelchair access to hotel, restaurant and 7 ground-floor bedrooms

⊖ No dogs in public rooms

▭ Access, Amex, Diners, Visa

£ Single £50, single occupancy of twin/double £50, twin/double £70, family room £80; deposit required. Alc L from £12, D from £15

ELLESMERE SHROPSHIRE   MAP 5

The Mount   ℒ

ST JOHN'S HILL, ELLESMERE, SHROPSHIRE SY12 0EY
TEL: ELLESMERE (0691) 622466

Quiet hill-top guesthouse in Shropshire's lakeland.

Situated at the highest point of Ellesmere, close to a church, this house looks as if it was built by a Georgian family determined to mark out its social position. Meg Wilkes now runs it as a guesthouse, and a sparkling, homely place it is. The drawing-room is lovely, with plenty of books, comfortable sofas and views over the constantly improving garden down to the countryside beyond. The dining-room is plain, with a single oak table and dresser. Both bedrooms are attractive – new cupboards have gone in this year, and there are flowers to welcome guests. One bedroom has a great deep bath, the other a shower, and there is no need to worry about whether you will get blankets or a duvet for here you have the choice. There is no need to worry about the welcome, either – Mrs Wilkes is keen to provide everything guests could need, and her sense of humour is an added bonus. There are no evening meals, but breakfasts are reported to be very good indeed.

◐ Open all year

⤴ In Ellesmere, follow signs for Tetchill until the corner of Dell's estate agents, then sharp left up St John's Hill. 80 yards up the

hill, turn left into an un-named lane. The Mount is the second house on the left at the top of the lane. Private car park and on-street parking

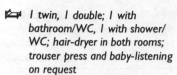

- I twin, I double; I with bathroom/WC, I with shower/WC; hair-dryer in both rooms; trouser press and baby-listening on request
- Dining-room, lounge, drying room; laundry facilities; fishing, tennis, other sports nearby;
- babysitting by arrangement
- No wheelchair access; no dogs; no smoking
- None accepted
- Single occupancy of twin/double £22, twin/double £40; deposit required

ELY CAMBRIDGESHIRE   **MAP 7**

Black Hostelry

THE CATHEDRAL CLOSE, THE COLLEGE, ELY, CAMBRIDGESHIRE CB7 4DL
TEL: ELY (0353) 662612   FAX: (0353) 665658

A bed and breakfast in a medieval building within the cathedral precincts.

Enter the cathedral precincts via the Porta Archway and pass down the narrow Firmary Road to get to this bed and breakfast run by Canon and Mrs Green. Once part of an old monastery where Benedictine monks used to live (they wore black habits, hence the name), the Greens' home now offers peaceful accommodation for secular guests. There are only two rooms, both of which are spacious and one of which has its own sitting-room. Each has a private bathroom. There is no distinctive style but a comfortable mix of old furnishings. Leaflets on the history of the town are thoughtfully provided.

Breakfast is taken at the large polished table in the stone-vaulted undercroft (or those who have the private sitting-room can take breakfast there). Evening meals are not provided but there is a choice of eating establishments just a short walk away across the cathedral green.

- Open all year, exc Xmas
- Turn into Ely Cathedral grounds at the Porta Archway at the end of the Gallery, and follow the road round to the left to the Cathedral car park. Firmary Lane is in the right-hand corner of the car park and the Black Hostelry is second right in Firmary Lane. Private car park
- 2 twin/double, family room

- available; both with bathroom/WC, TV, hair-dryer
- Breakfast room, lounge, drying room; golf, riding, other sports nearby
- No wheelchair access
- None accepted
- Single occupancy of twin/double £23, twin/double £46; deposit required

See the inside front cover for a brief explanation of how to use the Guide.

ETTINGTON WARWICKSHIRE   **MAP 9**

Ettington Manor

ETTINGTON, STRATFORD-UPON-AVON, WARWICKSHIRE CV37 7SX
TEL: STRATFORD-UPON-AVON (0789) 740216

A beautiful, historic manor house with comfortable rooms, an informal house-party atmosphere and good food.

Six miles from Stratford and within striking distance of the Cotswolds, Ettington is an ordinary-looking village – compared with quainter ones nearby – in which the Manor stands out as a particularly beautiful historic building. In an acre of well-tended garden with a croquet lawn, barbecue area and pretty borders, the mellow stone, wistaria-clad manor is chiefly Tudor, with a mix and match set of windows where families over the centuries have made 'improvements' according to their own taste. The drawing-room is positively baronial for a family home, with its huge stone fireplace, Elizabethan panelling, hunting scene tapestry and rich orange curtains. An honesty bar, magazines, gardening books and the informal friendliness of owner Julie Graham keep things on the homely side of grand. Because this is a Wolsey Lodge guests are generally sociable, though if you prefer to be alone Julie is happy to let you use the small sitting-room with its stylish green sofa and poppy fabric. Similarly, you don't have to be chatty over dinner, though most people do choose to eat together around the solid elm dining-table, where inventive evening meals often include game and are rounded off by home-made chocolates. The good-sized bedrooms combine modern power-shower bathrooms with solid antiques or modern pine furniture, lacy duvets and flowery window seats. The four-poster room over the old family chapel is the most characterful, with thirteenth-century timbers.

◑ Closed Dec, Jan

🔁 Ettington village is on the A422 Banbury to Stratford road, 6 miles south-east of Stratford. In the centre of the village turn south into Rogers Lane. The manor is the first driveway on the right. Private car park

🛏 I single, I twin, I double, I four-poster; all with shower/WC, TV, hair-dryer

◈ Dining-room, 2 lounges;

conference facilities (max 24 people non-residential, 4 residential); croquet at hotel, other sports nearby

⊖ No wheelchair access; no children under 12; no dogs; no smoking

▭ Access, Visa

£ Single £35, single occupancy of twin/double £45, twin/double £65, four-poster £70; deposit required. Set D £16 (7.30pm)

All entries in the Guide *are rewritten every year, not least because standards fluctuate. Don't trust an out-of-date* Guide.

EVERSHOT DORSET MAP 9

Summer Lodge

EVERSHOT, DORSET DT2 0JR
TEL: EVERSHOT (0935) 83424   FAX: (0935) 83005

*Bright and attractive country-house hotel run with consistently
high standards.*

Margaret and Nigel Corbett have been running Summer Lodge for the
past 14 years, during which time they have built a solid reputation as
charming hosts at this top-of-the-range country-house hotel. Summer
Lodge was formally a dower house belonging to the Earls of Ilchester. It
stands within a brick-walled garden in the Dorset village of Evershot. As
you pull up along the gravel drive, you are confronted by a cream-
coloured Georgian building with adjoining coach-house that is in tip-top
condition with creepers adding to its attractiveness. Immaculate lawns,
trees and shrubs complete the picture.

The interior has been decorated with the summer/garden theme in
mind. The hallway, in yellow, is like a ray of sunshine, decorated with
floral and wildlife prints. There are abundant sprays of flowers in the
public rooms and the french windows make the most of the garden views.
Each public room is decorated in a different style: the drawing-room is
green and has loose-covered sofas gathered around a large fireplace; the
red smoking-room has rattan chairs on a wooden floor; and the dining-
room (designed by Thomas Hardy) is Wedgwood blue with white
tablecloths. Food is good and local produce is used whenever possible;
perhaps guinea-fowl with garlic croûtons followed by Dorset lamb, with
a caramel soufflé to finish.

The good-sized bedrooms are light and bright and the bathrooms are
decorated with hand-painted tiles. Rooms in the coach-house have their
own private gardens.

◑ Open all year

↗ Evershot is 1 mile from the A37
mid-way between Dorchester
and Yeovil. The entrance to the
hotel is in Summer Lane. Private
car park

🛏 3 single, 13 twin/double, 1 suite;
all with bathroom/WC, TV, room
service, hair-dryer

◈ Dining-room, bar, 2 lounges;
tennis, croquet, heated outdoor
swimming-pool (May to Sept) at
hotel, other sports nearby.

Wheelchair access to hotel
(ramp), dining-room and WC
(M, F), 3 ground-floor bedrooms

⊖ No children under 6; no dogs in
public rooms; no smoking in
dining-room

▭ Access, Amex, Visa

💷 Single £100, single occupancy of
twin/double £125 to £185, twin/
double £125 to £185, suite £235
(rates inc dinner). Set L £17.50,
D £25; alc D £32.50. Special
breaks available

Report forms are at the back of the Guide; *write a letter if you prefer.*

Evesham Hotel

COOPERS LANE, OFF WATERSIDE, EVESHAM, HEREFORD AND WORCESTER
WR11 6DA
TEL: EVESHAM (0386) 765566   FAX: (0386) 765443

A good family hotel with plenty of jokes.

John Jenkinson's 'human-friendly' hotel continues to be as popular as ever, especially with guests who share the off-beat humour that infects the place. Everyone has a favourite memory – perhaps it is the AA man thumbing his nose at the RAC man on the cover of the brochure, the less than flattering descriptions of some of the drinks to be found on the ever-growing, record-breaking bar menu (now relaunched in booklet format) or the experience of a swim in the hotel's swimming-pool, fetchingly done up as Evesham-by-the-Sea. There are even mulberries in the garden (trees rather than bushes) to dance round. Beneath the surface quirkiness, this is an excellently run hotel with good food quickly and efficiently served, a pretty Georgian dining-room and a host of bedrooms in all shapes and sizes including the honeymooners' four-poster – though Mr Jenkinson says he prefers dirty weekenders, who spend more. One of this year's visitors found the total absence of French wine from the otherwise extensive list unsettling; otherwise, there's nothing but praise.

◗ Open all year, exc 25 and 26 Dec

⤢ Coopers Lane is off Waterside (A44) which runs along the River Avon in Evesham. Private car park

🛏 6 single, 11 twin, 22 double, 1 family room; most with bathroom/WC, a few with shower/WC; TV, room service, hair-dryer, iron and board, baby-listening in all rooms

◈ Restaurant, bar, lounge; air-conditioned conference facilities (max 12 people residential, 15 non-residential); croquet, table tennis, heated indoor swimming-pool at hotel, other sports nearby; babysitting. Wheelchair access to public areas and restaurant, 10 ground-floor bedrooms

⊖ No dogs in public rooms; no cigars, pipes in restaurant

▭ Access, Amex, Diners, Visa

£ Single £60, single occupancy of twin/double £66 to £68, twin/double £86 to £96, family room £105 to £110. Alc L £11, D £18. Special breaks available

---

If you make a booking using a credit card, and find after cancelling that the full amount has been charged to your card, raise the matter with your credit card company. They will ask the hotelier to confirm whether the room was re-let, and to justify the charge made.

Waterside Hotel ☆

WATERSIDE, EVESHAM, HEREFORD AND WORCESTER WR11 6JZ
TEL: EVESHAM (0386) 442420

An experience for people who like hotels with verve.

'Don't come here if you want to convalesce,' is David Young's verdict on his own hotel. Evesham seems to breed places to stay that are rather out of the ordinary, and here you will find a different brand of eccentricity from that at John Jenkinson's Evesham Hotel (see above). The Waterside is an unremarkable red-brick building and until you see the restaurant you might think it a fairly ordinary hotel, although the lounge, with its vaguely tropical feeling (river view, rattan furniture), and the extremely well-kept and well-furnished bedrooms are comfortable and have space to spare. But the *pièce de résistance* is Strollers Restaurant, a themed restaurant to beat them all. Not that it is easy to know what the theme is – there are so many. All over the bright brick, brass and wood room hangs a clutter of objects: trombones, stuffed hares with antlers, a huge wooden key, items from circuses and from jails. The food is either 'quickie' (basically American with a touch of Chinese) or else the full menu – largely steakhouse-style with some more adventurous offerings here and there. Waitresses drop on one knee to serve you (they need to in order to get under the pendant lights). All in all, lots of atmosphere and a comfortable night's sleep to follow.

◐ Open all year, exc 25 Dec (though restaurant open)

↗ On the A44 in Evesham. Private car park

🛏 14 double, 2 family rooms, 4 annexe rooms; all with bathroom/WC, TV, room service, hair-dryer, trouser press, baby-listening

◈ Restaurant, bar, lounge, TV room; conference facilities (max 30 people non-residential, 20 residential); fishing at hotel, golf, tennis, other sports nearby. Wheelchair access to hotel (2 steps), restaurant and WC, 2 ground-floor bedrooms

⊖ Dogs in 2 ground-floor bedrooms only

▭ Access, Amex, Visa

£ Single occupancy of double £34 to £48, double £60, family room £70, annexe room £34 to £48; deposit required. Set L, D £7; alc D £12. Special breaks available

---

The 1995 Guide *will be published in the autumn of 1994. Reports on hotels are welcome at any time of the year, but are extremely valuable in the spring. Send them to* The Which? Hotel Guide, FREEPOST, 2 Marylebone Road, London NW1 1YN. *No stamp is needed if reports are posted in the UK.*

Forte Crest

SOUTHERNHAY EAST, EXETER, DEVON EX1 1QF
TEL: EXETER (0392) 412812   TELEX: 42717 THFEX G
FAX: (0392) 413549

*An attractive modern city-centre hotel with leisure facilities and
some good-value leisure break offers.*

The Forte Crest, a mock Georgian/Regency-style modern hotel in the
centre of Exeter, continues to receive positive reports from readers with
praise going to 'delightful, efficient staff'. It is reasonably peaceful in
spite of the large roundabout to the front.

Open-plan public areas are bright, with a mix of mostly reproduction
furnishing peppered with the odd antique or oil portrait. The lounge bar
has a bustling atmosphere at weekends, especially on Sunday afternoons
when lunch guests linger over coffee and afternoon teas are being served.
The restaurant comes in for some criticism from one reader: a request
for lightly poached eggs at breakfast produced 'musket balls', while from
the dinner menu steak chasseur was 'tasteless' and vegetables 'unin-
teresting except for the sauté spuds'.

Bedrooms are well-equipped, with Georgian-style modern furnishings and striped and floral fabrics. They are all pretty much the same,
except for the outlook – ask for a room at the back overlooking the
gardens and with a view of the cathedral. The pool is a popular spot and
the leisure breaks on offer make this a good choice for a weekend.

◑ Open all year

⤴ Follow signs for city centre from
Junction 30 of the M5. The hotel
is 5 minutes from the railway
station. Private car park

🛏 48 twin, 51 double, 6 family
rooms, 5 suites; all with
bathroom/WC, TV, room service,
hair-dryer, mini-bar, trouser
press, baby-listening

◈ Restaurant, bar, lounge,
conservatory (all public rooms
are air-conditioned); conference
facilities (max 150 people non-
residential, 110 residential);
gym, heated swimming-pool,
sauna, solarium, Jacuzzi at hotel,
other sports nearby; babysitting
by arrangement. Wheelchair
access to hotel, restaurant and
WC (disabled), 10 ground-floor
bedrooms, 2 specially equipped
for disabled people

⊖ No dogs in public rooms;
smoking restricted in public
rooms

▭ Access, Amex, Diners, Visa

£ Single occupancy of twin/double
£80, twin/double/family room
£80, suite £120; deposit
required. Continental B £7,
cooked B £10; set L £13, D £18;
alc L, D £10 to £30 (prices till
end 93). Special breaks available

---

*Many hotels put up their tariffs in the spring. You are advised to confirm
prices when you book.*

Oaksmere

BROME, NR EYE, SUFFOLK IP23 8AJ
TEL: DISS (0379) 870326   FAX: (0379) 870051

There's nothing very personal about this country-club hotel, but the rooms are comfy and the garden is a real feature.

While it is part of the Waveney Inns group, this country house has enough distinctive features to make you forget you are staying at a chain hotel. What will strike you immediately is the garden: lime trees form an arrow-straight line on either side of the long driveway and topiary hedges are laid out in weird and wonderful shapes. One semi-circular group of seven yews, huddled together as if in a conspiratorial meeting, is known as the 'seven sisters' after the numerous daughters of a previous owner, Lord Bayning, who lived at Oaksmere in the nineteenth century.

Unfortunately, the attention to detail in the garden is not mirrored in reception. Office filing cabinets and piles of paper greet you by the entrance. Once past this, things improve and you'll be led to your room via a stairwell with a skylight ringed with proverbs taken from the book of Ecclesiastes. The bedrooms are generously furnished with mounds of material – draped over tables, canopied over beds and pleated as pelmets above curtains. Flowery and feminine, some have reproduction four-posters, others half-testers.

There's a choice of eating places: either join the convivial crush in the bar where substantial meals are served on an informal basis – the tiger prawns wrapped in bacon and grilled in garlic are good – or try the large dining-room where dishes are more chi-chi and pricey. Breakfast isn't spectacular – the usual traditional fare is on offer, plus a fruit platter which proved to be less tempting then it sounded.

◑ *Open all year; restaurant closed Sun eve*

↗ *Turn off the A140 Norwich to Ipswich road on to the B1077 to Eye. The hotel is 30 yards on the left. Private car park.*

🛏 *1 twin, 6 double, 4 four-poster; most with bathroom/WC, some with shower/WC; TV, room service, hair-dryer, mini-bar, trouser press, baby-listening in all rooms*

◈ *Restaurant, bar, lounge,*

conservatory; conference facilities (max 80 people non-residential, 11 residential); golf, swimming, riding nearby

⊖ *No wheelchair access; no dogs*

▭ *Access, Amex, Diners, Visa*

£ *Single occupancy of twin/double from £60, twin/double from £75, four-poster from £80, family room rate on request; deposit required. Bar meals; alc L, D from £17.50. Special breaks available*

Hotels in our Visitors' Book *towards the end of the* Guide *are additional hotels that may be worth a visit. Reports on these hotels are welcome.*

Marsh Country Hotel

EYTON, NR LEOMINSTER, HEREFORD AND WORCESTER HR6 0AG
TEL: LEOMINSTER (0568) 613952

An isolated hotel of great antiquity, run much as a friendly home.

This is a rare treat for lovers of old buildings, for the hall of the old fourteenth-century manor has been lovingly restored, with its timber framing, its stone floor and its original windows intact. There is little left of the marsh now except for a pond, but there will soon be a new reed bed – designed not just to look attractive but also to provide an ecological solution to septic tank problems. Jacqueline Gilleland's garden is as much her passion as is her hotel, and her flowers look as well-cared for as her guests. The Marsh is quite a smart place – once you are away from the ancient hall, you will find bedrooms and dining-room decorated with style. The latter is Z-shaped, in soft greys and bright yellows, while bedrooms are distinguished by colourful fabrics and excellent – if small – bathrooms or shower rooms. Five-course set dinners might include asparagus timbale, rabbit terrine and brill and salmon in saffron.

- Open all year
- 2 miles north-west of Leominster. Turn right on to the B4361 to Richards Castle. Turn left after ¾ mile (signposted Eyton and Lucton) and continue to the common. Private car park
- 1 single, 1 twin, 3 double; all with bathroom/WC, exc single with shower/WC; TV, room service, hair-dryer, baby-listening in all rooms
- Restaurant, bar, lounge;

conference facilities (max 24 people non-residential, 5 residential); fishing, golf, riding nearby
- No wheelchair access; no dogs; no smoking in bedrooms
- Access, Amex, Visa
- Single £74, single occupancy of twin/double £74, twin/double £100; deposit required. Set L £17.50/£18.50, D £27.50 (prices till Apr 93). Special breaks available

---

Penmere Manor

MONGLEATH ROAD, FALMOUTH, CORNWALL TR11 4PN
TEL: FALMOUTH (0326) 211411   FAX: (0326) 317588

A large, cheerful hotel on the outskirts of Falmouth, ideal for business travellers but with excellent holidaying facilities as well.

The road to Penmere Manor leads past an industrial estate, so it's a considerable relief to pull into the drive and spot its imposing white façade peeping through the rhododendrons. From the outside the building looks enormous, its original eighteenth-century core having long since expanded sideways; once inside, however, it feels much more manageable, while never quite throwing off the feel of a chain hotel. A small library opens off the hall; it's here that newspapers are laid out in the morning. To reach the spacious bar-lounge you walk straight ahead through bustling, low-ceilinged Bolitho's Restaurant, where the menus offer plenty of choice: on the night we inspected the smoked quail in spicy yogurt sauce with mint and cucumber was wonderful, and a sprinkling of almonds brightened up an otherwise unexceptional cauliflower soup. More disappointing was the main course of turkey fingers, although the scrumptious fudge ice-cream, with real lumps of fudge in it, soon made up for this. (In the morning, however, a request for a soft-boiled egg threw the kitchen into confusion.) After dinner, coffee and a selection of chocolates guaranteed to make anyone abandon a diet are served with panache in the Fountain Bar, through the windows of which you'll spot giant chess pieces outside on the terrace. The bar also offers access to one of Penmere Manor's greatest assets, an 11-metre heated indoor swimming-pool.

Bedrooms in the older part of the hotel are comfortable if not very inspiring. Those in the new part, named after Cornish gardens and with french windows on to Penmere's own garden, are much nicer, with soft peach, yellow and blue décor and light wood furnishings; some are huge, with curtained-off bunk beds and vast two-basined bathrooms.

◑ *Open all year, exc Xmas period*

⤴ *From the A39 turn right on to Gweek and Constantine road. Follow signposts for Budock Hospital, carry straight on for ¾ mile, turn left into Mongleath Road. From Apr 94 take the new link road A39 towards Falmouth. Turn right at Hill Head roundabout, then turn left after 1 mile into Mongleath Road. Private car park*

🛏 *10 single, 10 twin, 7 double, 12 family rooms; most with bathroom/WC, some with shower/WC; TV, room service, hair-dryer, baby-listening in all rooms; trouser press, mini-bar in some rooms*

◇ *Restaurant, bar, 3 lounges (all air-conditioned, exc 2 lounges), games room, library, drying room; conference facilities (max 30 people residential and non-residential); sauna/solarium, 2 swimming-pools, gym, croquet at hotel, other sports nearby. Wheelchair access to hotel (ramp), restaurant and WC (M,F), 14 ground-floor bedrooms*

⊖ *No smoking in restaurant*

▭ *Access, Amex, Diners, Visa*

💷 *Single £53 to £57, single occupancy of twin/double £69 to £70, twin/double/family room £83 to £88, superior room £103 to £112; deposit required. Set D £18, alc L £2 to £6, D £30. Special breaks available*

Use the maps at the back of the Guide *to pinpoint hotels in a particular area.*

Strenneth Farmhouse

OLD AIRFIELD ROAD, FERSFIELD, DISS, NORFOLK IP22 2BP
TEL: BRESSINGHAM (0379 88) 8182   FAX (0379 88) 8260

A former farmhouse, now a friendly guesthouse.

Chances are that Brecken and his mum Carly will come bounding out to meet you when you arrive. No, not the owners, but bouncy bearded collies who greet guests with undisguised enthusiasm. Brenda and Ken Webb offer a welcome just as sincere, if less boisterous, to their red-brick farmhouse which lies in flat countryside about five miles from Diss.

The Webbs operate the sensible system of becoming guests in their own guesthouse during the winter, sleeping two or three nights in each room to check out mattresses, bathrooms and comfort. This way they also avert small but potentially irritating problems like the TV not being visible from the bed or too few hooks for coats. The best room, particularly now that the fine dark oak four-poster bed has been moved in, is Number Nine. It's worth the few pounds extra for the space, mahogany furniture and big 'pharaoh' bath in the light yellow and cream bathroom. Although smaller, the family room, Number Seven, is also a good bet with brass beds and blue décor. A modern extension (attached to the main house by a covered walkway) houses the majority of bedrooms and, although these have less character than elsewhere, the Webbs have tried to make them distinctive: for example, the elegant French bed in Number Two is draped with lace and Number Four has an oval-shaped bath.

The breakfast room is beamed, with ruched pink curtains, a mottled mauve carpet and a redolent whiff of bacon and eggs. There are large tables and the Webbs encourage people to sit together for both breakfast (served between 8 and 9am) and dinner. Ken does the cooking and the evening meal might be plaice florentine, followed by stuffed pork escalopes with apple and sage, with fruit brûlée to finish.

◑ Open all year; dining-room closed Wed eve

⬙ Off A1066, 5 miles west of Diss. Approximately 2 miles through the village. Private car park

🛏 2 single, 2 twin, 3 double, 1 four-poster, 1 family room, most with bathroom/WC, some with shower/WC, 1 public bathroom; TV in all rooms

◈ Dining-room, 2 lounges

⊖ No wheelchair access; no children in dining-room eves; no dogs

▭ Access, Visa

£ Single £21 to £24, twin/double from £37 and £50, four-poster £57, family room on request; deposit required. Set D £13.50 (7.30pm) children's supper £4 (6pm)

See page 817 for other hotels worthy of inclusion in our Visitors' Book.

Manor House

FLAMBOROUGH, BRIDLINGTON, HUMBERSIDE YO15 1PD
TEL: BRIDLINGTON (0262) 850943

A civilised and comfortable Wolsey Lodge scoring highly for value.

It is easy to miss Lesley Berry's restored manor house, tucked away as it is behind a garage, boatshed and small antique shop at the corner of the road leading to Flamborough's famous lighthouse. The building (which dates from the Napoleonic Wars and is the most recent in a succession of manors dating back to the Domesday Book) is plain, though peacocks strutting on the lawns add a touch of grandeur. Once inside, you're struck by an imposing entrance hallway with a noteworthy collection of walking sticks. Décor is restrained and provides a fitting milieu for some very fine period furniture, the spoils of Lesley's antique-dealing skills. Detailed drawings of First World War battleships by Lesley's partner Jeffrey, yachting photographs, trophies and a solid Victorian baby's high chair give a distinctive character to a comfortable sitting- and dining-room warmed by a wood-burning stove.

There are only two letting bedrooms, the larger of which boasts a Portuguese rosewood bed. Our inspector's room teamed light, fresh wallpaper with bold modern fabrics, Chinese and Venetian prints, and a brass-framed bed. Even better is the enormous next-door bathroom with its claw-footed Victorian bath mounted on an elevated platform, a selection of local guidebooks stacked by the loo, and capacious book-shelves loaded two deep in paperbacks that run the gamut from Agatha Christie to *Zen and the Art of Motorcycle Maintenance* via Ian McEwan.

Dinner, served on Coalport china, is by arrangement only, and is likely to be straightforward fare – perhaps egg mousse, followed by chicken roasted and stuffed with apple, then a home-made apple and redcurrant flan and cheese. There's no licence, but you're welcome to bring a bottle. It's worth browsing through the stock in the stable-block antique shop before you leave – even if no *objet d'art* catches your eye you might be tempted by one of the traditional Humber Keel Gansey sweaters, another string to Lesley's bow.

◐ Open all year, exc Xmas

↗ Set back from road on the corner of Tower Street and Lighthouse Road, just past St Oswald's Church on road from Bridlington. Private car park

🛏 1 double, 1 four-poster; both with bathroom/WC, TV, hair-dryer

◈ Dining-room, lounge; fishing, water sports, tennis, golf, boat trips nearby; babysitting by arrangement

⊖ No wheelchair access; no children under 8; no dogs; no smoking in bedrooms and discouraged in dining-room

▭ Access, Visa

£ Single occupancy of double £35, double £51, four-poster £59; deposit required. Set D £19 (by prior arrangement)

FLETCHING EAST SUSSEX   **MAP 9**

Griffin Inn

FLETCHING, UCKFIELD, EAST SUSSEX TN22 3SS
TEL: NEWICK (0825) 722890

*A small, unpretentious, sixteenth-century inn with attractive
rooms.*

The Griffin Inn stands on the high street of Fletching, a sleepy little
Sussex village. A whitewashed low-rise brick building with wooden
beams and an inglenook fireplace, it exudes rural charm. It has been
owned by the Pullan family since 1978 and although it is chiefly a pub and
restaurant it has four pleasant rooms at good prices, making it an
attractive out-of-the-way place to stay.

Bedrooms are named after local landmarks and villages. The three
double rooms have four-poster beds – Fletching is quite grand, with a
brick fireplace and low beamed ceiling. The public rooms are full of
country-pub character, with timbered ceilings and walls; two iron
griffins guard the fireplace in the bar. The restaurant has a sporting
theme, with hunting pictures on the wall and a large gun hanging over the
fire. Readers have complimented the food, which includes fresh fish
from Newhaven every Thursday, a regularly changing à la carte menu
and interesting bar meals. The wine list is diverse and features some
local Sussex wines.

- ◐ Open all year, exc 24, 25 Dec; restaurant closed Sun eve
- ⮔ Take the A22 south from East Grinstead and take a right-hand turning to Fletching at Nutley. Private car park
- 🛏 1 twin, 3 four-poster; 1 with bathroom/WC, the remainder with shower/WC; hair-dryer in all rooms
- ◈ 2 dining-rooms, 2 bars, drying room, games room; conference facilities (max 50 people non-residential); golf, tennis, riding, other sports nearby; babysitting by arrangement. Wheelchair access to restaurant and WC (M, F) only
- ⊖ No dogs in bedrooms; smoking discouraged in bedrooms
- ▭ Access, Amex, Visa
- £ Single occupancy of twin £40, twin/double £45, four-poster £55 to £70; deposit required. Sun L £12.50; alc L, D £15 (10% service charge added to meal prices). Special breaks available

FORD WILTSHIRE   **MAP 9**

White Hart Inn ☆

FORD, NR CHIPPENHAM, WILTSHIRE SN14 8RP
TEL: CHIPPENHAM (0249) 782213   FAX: (0249) 783075

A picturesque pub that serves huge helpings of imaginative food.

The A420 between Bristol and Chippenham is busy, so it's a relief to turn down the steep road to the tiny hamlet of Ford. The White Hart, which dates from the sixteenth century, is made from sandstone bricks and has a gently sagging tiled roof and thick wooden doors. There's even a dovecote on the wall.

Inside, there's a small, spartan public bar. A passageway leads to the saloon bar, which has light wood panelling, red carpets and lots of tables and chairs – testimony to the pub's popularity among diners. Further on, there's a large dining-room which is similarly decorated. Muskets and swords hang from the walls.

It makes no difference where you sit, the menu and price will be the same. Although the menu features its share of regulation pub fare, such as steak and mushroom pie, there are a few surprises. You could try sweetbreads with salad and garlic croûtons, followed by chicken with grapes on a bed of home-made tagliatelle. Servings are huge, especially the puddings. Stay overnight and you'll find, as one reader comments, 'breakfast is enough to feed an army'.

Guests can stay in the converted stable block over the road, where the rooms have brilliant white walls and pine four-posters with linen sheets. Rooms in the main house have more character and are prettily decorated with pinks and yellows with floral bedcovers.

◑ Open all year

↗ On the A420, 5 miles west of Chippenham. Private car park

🛏 I twin, 6 double, 4 four-poster (family room available); most with bathroom/WC, some with shower/WC; TV, room service, trouser press in all rooms

◇ Restaurant, bar; conference facilities (max 14 people non-residential)

⊖ No wheelchair access

▭ Access, Amex, Visa

£ Single occupancy of twin/double £45, twin/double/four-poster £62, family room £80; deposit preferred. Bar meals; alc L, D £15

FOWEY CORNWALL   **MAP 10**

Marina Hotel

THE ESPLANADE, FOWEY, CORNWALL PL23 IHY
TEL: FOWEY (0726) 833315

A small Georgian hotel in a busy street overlooking the Fowey estuary.

Fowey's narrow streets are a mixed blessing for guests at the Marina Hotel; while certainly picturesque, they guarantee that even pausing outside the hotel to drop off your bags before continuing to the public car park can be tricky (fortunately a free mini-bus will run you back there at the end of your stay). Once inside the late eighteenth-century building, however, you will find the Marina a welcoming hotel, and the views from the back quickly make up for the congestion outside the front door. The hallway still boasts some attractive original architectural features, especially the heavy mahogany doors dating from the days when it was the summer residence of the bishops of Truro, but in general the public areas have old-fashioned décor and busy carpet patterns. Fowey's constricted position means that the hotel sometimes seems to be slithering down a hillside; there are stunning estuary views from the dining-room at the back, which is on a level below the hall and feels as if it should be a basement.

Bedrooms are decorated in a light and florally feminine style, with furnishings that look comfortable but occasionally flimsy. Rates reflect the views: those with estuary views and balconies are the most costly. Supplementing an interesting table d'hôte menu, the à la carte dinner menu makes the most of local produce, including Fowey sea trout.

◑ Closed end Oct to mid-Mar

➶ On the Esplanade in Fowey. Take the one-way system through the town and turn right at the start of the shops. Cars are allowed to stop to unload; a public car park is nearby

🛏 5 twin, 6 double; most with bathroom/WC, some with shower/WC; TV, room service, baby-listening in all rooms; hair-dryer on request

◈ Restaurant, bar, 3 lounges, garden room; fishing at hotel, golf, riding, other sports nearby

⊖ No wheelchair access; no children under 6 in restaurant eves; no dogs in public rooms; no smoking in restaurant

▭ Access, Visa

£ Single occupancy of twin/double £40 to £50, twin/double £54 to £80; deposit required. Set D £16; alc D £19 to £25; bar lunches. Special breaks available

---

FRAMPTON DORSET   **MAP 9**

Hyde Farm House

DORCHESTER ROAD, FRAMPTON, DORSET DT2 9NG
TEL: MAIDEN NEWTON (0300) 320272

A country house in a lovely rural setting, with a stylish interior and welcoming hosts.

On the face of it nothing much happens around Frampton, though John Saunders and Jan Faye Schjoll will tell you different: 'We have woodpeckers nesting in our woods, and dippers and kingfishers on the river.' Not action-packed exactly, but a perfect place to retreat to for a few days' break. Apart from Hyde Farm House's own woodland and river banks – where you can also fish – there are lovely walks through rolling green countryside, and plans for a croquet lawn are well under way. With a maximum of eight guests, Hyde Farm House has a house-party atmosphere. You are welcomed with a cup of tea, which you can take in the genteel conservatory with its tangerine and lemon trees and views down to the river or in the art-nouveau sitting-room with its Clarice Cliff collection, beautiful bowed doors, tall plants and open fire.

In the dining-room guests eat all together around the grand oak table where Jan's food is mostly French – no stodgy English puddings here. You can opt to eat separately if you wish. Striking colours and rich fabrics characterise the bedrooms, which vary in size and are well-equipped with plenty of goodies. One, a yellow twin with wicker bedsteads and a walk-in wardrobe, has particularly lovely views.

◗ Open all year

🔁 Frampton is at the junction of the A37 and the B356. Hyde Farm House is on the left-hand side of the road heading out of Frampton towards Maiden Newton. Private car park

🛏 2 twin, I double; all with bathroom/WC, hair-dryer

◈ Dining-room, lounge, TV room, drying room, conservatory; fishing at hotel, golf, tennis, heated swimming-pool nearby

⊖ No wheelchair access; no children under 13; no dogs; smoking in TV room and conservatory only

▭ None accepted

£ Single occupancy of twin/double £23, twin/double £45. Set D £12

GILLINGHAM DORSET   **MAP 9**

Stock Hill House

WYKE, GILLINGHAM, DORSET SP8 5NR
TEL: GILLINGHAM (0747) 823626   FAX: (0747) 825628

A small country-house hotel par excellence, *styled with Victorian extravagance.*

Peter and Nita Hauser defy the trend by advertising 'two for the price of two'; jokes aside, they are adamant that the meticulous standards of their superlative hotel will not fall by even one cotton-wool ball.

This is a very special place to stay, for the Hausers have lavished an immense amount of love and attention on the late-Victorian manor house that was once the home of Osbert Lancaster's grandfather and their guests are equally cosseted. One reader, describing it as his favourite hotel, says, 'There is always someone available to talk to and fulfil any request . . . when the local newsagent failed to deliver the morning paper, Mrs Hauser went down immediately to collect one so that I could read it at breakfast.'

The beech-lined driveway, edged in spring with bluebells and cow-slips and exquisite gardens, lawns, statuary and mature trees, plus the walled kitchen garden, are the province of Peter Hauser, when he is not in the kitchen preparing dinners. Inside the house Nita has created an ornate and opulent Victorian period home, bursting with theatrical exuberance. A pair of nineteenth-century Indian wooden horses rear up in front of a great gilt mirror in the entrance hall, there are carved, painted blackamoors holding wall lights, and an outsize chandelier hangs in the stairwell. The drawing-room is a sumptuous retreat of stuffed chairs and sofas, Victorian objects, box games and vases of flowers.

All the bedrooms are individually and expensively furnished. The snowy white bed linen, towels and bathrobes were all specially made in Austria; fresh flowers are placed daily in both bed and bathrooms; exotic fruit is served on a bed of laurel leaves and Chinese boxes discreetly hold sewing kits, Anadin and tampons. It is hard to choose a favourite room: it may be Room Four, with the high wrought-iron bed that belonged to a Spanish princess, or perhaps Room Two, a chintzy bedroom-cum-sitting-room that looks out onto the lawns and kitchen garden. The new Robin's Nest Suite, converted from the stable block and the prototype for three more currently in the pipeline, is luxurious but lacks the atmosphere and views of the original rooms.

Austrian-born Peter cooks set-price, high-quality dinners, as expansive as his welcome. Classical in technique but wide-ranging in scope, the pan-European offerings in May included Cornish octopus with spinach spätzli, grilled Somerset goats' cheese on cabbage vinaigrette, French guinea-fowl casseroled in paprika, gooseberry and vanilla parfait, and Rehrücken mit Schlag. Well-chosen wines, at a fair price, include Rhône and Loire selections.

◑ Open all year; restaurant closed Sun and Mon eves (exc bank hols)

↗ The hamlet of Wyke is on the B3081, 3 miles south of the A303. Private car park

⇌ 2 single, 3 twin, 2 double, 1 four-poster, 1 suite; most with bathroom/WC, some with shower/WC; TV, room service, hair-dryer, trouser press in all rooms; no tea/coffee-making facilities in rooms

◇ 2 dining-rooms, bar, lounge; conference facilities (max 8 people residential – winter only); croquet, tennis at hotel, other sports nearby. Wheelchair access to hotel (3 steps), restaurant and 1 ground-floor bedroom

⊖ No children under 7; no dogs; no smoking in dining-rooms and discouraged in bedrooms

▭ Access, Diners, Visa

£ Single £60 to £80, single occupancy of twin/double £90, twin/double £110 to £140, four-poster £140, suite £150; deposit required. Set L £18.50, D £26.50

GISLINGHAM SUFFOLK   **MAP 7**

Old Guildhall

MILL STREET, GISLINGHAM, NR EYE, SUFFOLK IP23 8JT
TEL: MELLIS (0379 783) 361

A pretty thatched cottage, once the centre of local government, now a friendly guesthouse.

Facing the school in Gislingham, a lush Suffolk village, the Old Guildhall fits most people's idea of a cute country cottage. It is painted a marshmallow pink, with a roof thatch which flops over its frontage like a horse's forelock and a garden that is bursting with blooms. The beamed interior, pungent with woodsmoke, is equally winning, although low ceilings mean the distinction between snug and cramped blurs in some areas. This is particularly true of the tiny Tudor Rose restaurant which, despite having only four tables, is open to non-residents too. Ray and Ethel Tranter cope with this potential numbers nightmare by organising sittings (residents eat at 7pm, non-residents later). The good-value dinner is along traditional lines – watercress soup or melon followed by duckling à l'orange or breast of chicken in Stilton cheese sauce, then pudding, cheese and a 'bottomless pot' of coffee. The limited though varied wine list is also reasonably priced.

Tall guests would be well advised to pack a crash helmet – low beams in most rooms may give you a permanent stoop. Those in Rooms One and Two ensure lots of character but pose a danger of headbanging. If you are on the lofty side, the best room to opt for is Number Four – but you'll have to be thin, too, since the bathroom is uncommonly narrow.

◐ *Closed Jan*

↗ *In the centre of Gislingham, opposite the village school. Private car park*

🛏 *3 twin, 1 double; all with bathroom/WC, TV*

◈ *Restaurant, bar, lounge, snooker room; fishing, golf nearby*

⊖ *No wheelchair access; no dogs in public rooms; no smoking*

▭ *None accepted*

£ *Single occupancy of twin/double £35, twin/double £70 (rates inc dinner); deposit required. Special breaks available*

GISSING NORFOLK   **MAP 7**

Old Rectory

GISSING, DISS, NORFOLK IP22 3XB
TEL: TIVETSHALL (037 977) 575   FAX: (037 977) 4427

A friendly welcome into this Victorian house where home comforts are a priority.

'Guests don't lose weight here,' smiles Jill Gillam, reeling off a mouth-watering list of sample dishes that she will cook for those who request an evening meal. The puddings are particularly naughty – one of the favourites being profiteroles with lashings of chocolate sauce. Dinners, as well as breakfasts, are served at a long, white-clothed table in a smart dining-room. Jill tries to avoid cooking on Monday and Thursday evenings but can recommend good local pubs instead. Successfully dividing her time between the demands of her guests and those of her young family, she maintains high standards. The three bedrooms are beautifully finished: the cheerful Blue Room has a double aspect, and hot-water bottles are provided as well as dressing-gowns (since the private bathroom is not *en-suite*). The Green and Pink Rooms (both twins) have their own bathrooms, the former being the nicest because of its size, exaggerated even further by a large mirror.

For £4 extra per person per day you can splash around in a sizeable heated indoor pool – although check whether it is open if you plan to stay during the winter period. Alternatively, you can explore the surrounding woodland. In the evening, relax in the spacious lounge filled with magazines and books and warmed by a log fire.

◑ *Open all year; dining-room closed Mon and Thur eves*

🔁 *From Diss take the road to Burston for 4 miles. At Burston, take the first left turn after the crossroads for 1 mile and turn right into Rectory Road, just before the church. Private car park*

🛏 *2 twin, 1 double; 1 with bathroom/WC, 1 with shower/WC; TV, hair-dryer in all rooms*

◈ *Dining-room, drawing-room,*

drying room; conference facilities (max 12 people non-residential); indoor heated swimming-pool at hotel, other sports nearby

⊖ *No wheelchair access; no children under 8; no dogs; smoking in drawing-room only*

▭ *Access, Visa*

£ *Single occupancy of twin/double £34 to £40, twin/double £46 to £54; deposit required. Set D £18 to £20 (7.45pm) by arrangement. Special breaks available*

GLASTONBURY SOMERSET   **MAP 10**

No 3

3 MAGDALENE STREET, GLASTONBURY, SOMERSET BA6 9EW
TEL: GLASTONBURY (0458) 832129

Pleasing Georgian brick building with unexpected Indian touches.

John and Ann Tynan have stamped their personalities all over what might otherwise be a run-of-the-mill, town-centre Georgian hotel. Step into the dining-room and your eye will be caught by the lovely Arthur Maderson neo-Impressionist paintings – for sale should you want a souvenir. Not that they should be allowed to detract from the menus, which feature dishes like pineapple and sunflower salad, and breast of guinea-fowl; as Glastonbury's considered the New Age capital of the UK, there are always dishes like walnut and cashew en croûte for vegetarians, too.

With only three bedrooms in the house, numbers would be super-fluous – suffice to say that one rear bedroom has a half-tester bed, while a front one has a lacy crown canopy. More original are the decorations in the three cottage bedrooms; John Tynan has been visiting India regularly for many years and now helps to fund a Rajasthan tiger-protection scheme, which explains why curtains, bedspreads, even cushion covers are all made from gorgeous Indian fabrics. Most striking of all are glorious star-shaped lamps illuminating the downstairs room.

◗ Open all year, exc Dec and Jan; restaurant closed Sun, Mon, Tues eves

↗ No 3 adjoins the ruin of Glastonbury Abbey. Private car park

🛏 2 twin, 4 double; all with bathroom/WC, TV, room service, hair-dryer

◈ Dining-room, bar, lounge; fishing,

golf, other sports nearby

⊖ No wheelchair access; children by arrangement only; no dogs; no smoking in dining-room

▭ Access, Visa

£ Single £50 to £55, single occupancy of twin/double £50 to £55, twin/double £60 to £75, family room rate £75 to £90; deposit required. Set D £26

GLEWSTONE HEREFORD AND WORCESTER   **MAP 9**

Glewstone Court

GLEWSTONE, ROSS-ON-WYE, HEREFORD AND WORCESTER HR9 6AW
TEL: ROSS-ON-WYE (0989) 770367   FAX: (0989) 770282

Heavily decorated country house with easy-going hosts.

Even if it were not for Christine Reeve-Tucker's decorative talents this would be an interesting hotel, for the huge drawing-room and the massive cedar of Lebanon which stands sentinel on the lawn are both striking in their different ways. It also has the advantage of being well-positioned: it is close to Ross-on-Wye, within easy reach of two main roads, but surrounded by a haven of tranquil orchards. You do not see the scale of the place when you approach for Glewstone Court is hidden behind a red-brick wall at the end of the village, but it reveals itself to be a substantial late-Georgian house. The master bedroom (Victoria) is so large that some may find it daunting; if so, there are others on a more human scale, including the romantically decorated Rose. Christine's skill with stencils, textured paint and arrangements of dried flowers is evident everywhere, except where the walls are covered with ranks of romantic prints and paintings. The style here is distinctly easy-going and children are welcomed, but the hotel shows every sign of being well-run and the menu promises good things (roast rack of lamb with smoked garlic and rosemary gravy, for example).

◗ Open all year, exc 25 and 26 Dec

↗ Glewstone is off the A40 between Ross-on-Wye and Monmouth. Take a right-hand turn 1 mile along the A40 out of Ross-on-Wye. Private car park

🛏 1 single, 4 double, 2 four-poster; all with bathroom/WC, exc 2 doubles with shower/WC; TV,

room service, hair-dryer, baby-listening in all rooms

◈ 2 dining-rooms, bar, lounge; conference facilities (max 20 people non-residential, 7 residential); croquet at hotel, fishing, hot-air ballooning, canoeing, other sports nearby; babysitting. Wheelchair access to restaurant and WC (unisex) only

● No dogs in dining-rooms

▭ Access, Visa

£ Single £45, single occupancy of

twin/double £50, twin/double £78, four-poster £90; deposit required. Set L £15, D £20. Special breaks available

GLOSSOP DERBYSHIRE   MAP 5

Wind in the Willows

DERBYSHIRE LEVEL, GLOSSOP, DERBYSHIRE SK13 9PT
TEL: GLOSSOP (0457) 868001   FAX: (0457) 853354

A traditional guesthouse with good-humoured hosts on the edge of the Peak District National Park.

From huge picture windows in the drawing-room of this early-Victorian house you can look out over Snake Pass, on the edge of the Peak District National Park. Its location is not the only attraction of the romantically named Wind in the Willows: light, airy rooms full of family knick-knacks and the good humour of the Marshes – a mother and son team – are further reasons for staying here.

Comfortable beds, light duvets and plenty of goodies characterise the well-co-ordinated bedrooms with their mix of modern and antique furniture. A Victorian theme runs throughout the house and the two superior rooms, named after Anne's grand-daughters Lucy Anne and Erika Louise, have lovely antique beds – one brass, the other a walnut half-tester. While standard rooms have showers only, Erika Louise has a bathroom with freestanding Victorian bath.

The three-course dinner lacks choice and is pricey, but is competently cooked. A typical meal might include a cheese tartlet, roast English lamb with vegetables, trifle with fresh fruit, and coffee or tea with mint biscuits. Breakfasts are reported to be 'good and traditional'.

◑ Open all year

↗ 1 mile east of Glossop town centre. Turn off the A57 opposite the Royal Oak pub. The hotel is 400 yards on the right just after the golf course. Private car park

⇌ 4 twin, 5 double, 1 four-poster, 1 suite; some with bathroom/WC, most with shower/WC; TV, room service, hair-dryer, trouser press in all rooms

◇ Dining-room, bar, lounge;

conference facilities (max 20 people non-residential, 12 residential); croquet at hotel, other sports nearby

● No wheelchair access; no children under 8; no dogs

▭ Access, Amex, Diners, Visa

£ Single occupancy of twin/double £56 to £75, twin/double £69, four-poster £95, suite £95; deposit required. Set D £17.50 (7.30pm)

Are you aware of your rights as a consumer when you book into a hotel? Check them out on page 837.

GOUDHURST KENT   **MAP 8**

Star & Eagle

HIGH STREET, GOUDHURST, KENT TN17 1AL
TEL: GOUDHURST (0580) 211512/211338

A black and white timbered hotel with rustic rooms and a warm atmosphere.

This hotel has seen a lot of people come and go – in the fourteenth century it was reputedly a monastery, but by the eighteenth century it was not only an inn but also the headquarters of the Hawkhurst Gang, who terrorised the neighbourhood and organised smuggling raids. Nowadays it is popular for its pub-like ambience and its reasonably priced menu. Standing on the main road, centrally placed in the village of Goudhurst, it has lovely views of the surrounding countryside.

The public areas are all quite dark in décor, with beams, brick walls and wooden tables throughout. The restaurant is aglow with horse brasses and copper ornaments, the walls decorated with pictures of birds and hunting scenes. The menu offers a variety of dishes, including mushroom Stroganoff and vegetable curry for non-meat eaters, chicken, ham and mushroom pie served with a creamy leek sauce, and a fisherman's platter served with vegetables and potatoes. The breakfast area is on another level, and the ancient inglenook fireplace promises a warm refuge in winter.

Bedrooms are a reasonable size, with timbered ceilings and latticed windows. Room One has pine furniture and a chocolate-box view of fields, ponies and the local churchyard. Room Two is more flowery and has good views of the countryside, while Five has a heavy dark wooden four-poster, a brick fireplace and a view of the street.

◑ Open all year

⤢ Goudhurst is 2 miles off the A21, on the A262. Private car park

🛏 1 single, 4 twin, 4 double, 2 four-poster; most with bathroom/WC, 1 public bathroom; TV, hair-dryer, trouser press, baby-listening in all rooms

✺ Restaurant, bar, lounge;

conference facilities (max 30 people non-residential, 11 residential); fishing, tennis, golf, riding nearby

⊖ No wheelchair access; no dogs

▭ Access, Amex, Visa

£ Single £30, single occupancy of twin/double £30, twin/double £45, four-poster £55; deposit required. Alc L, D £8

It is always worth enquiring about the availability of special breaks or weekend prices. The prices we quote are the standard rates for one night – most hotels offer reduced rates for longer stays.

GRANGE-IN-BORROWDALE CUMBRIA   **MAP 4**

Borrowdale Gates Hotel

GRANGE-IN-BORROWDALE, KESWICK, CUMBRIA CA12 5UQ
TEL: KESWICK (07687) 77204   FAX: (07687) 77254

Well-run, conventional hotel in superb setting.

Borrowdale Gates is a spruce and efficient hotel tucked away in one of the most stunning corners of the Lake District. The original building, a long-established country hosue, has been greatly extended, giving it a modern feel and a labyrinthine layout; it can be a long walk to some of the bedrooms from the front door. One of the most recent extensions has resulted in a dining-room which floods the hotel with light from its picture windows. In the evenings it's a formal setting (jackets and ties preferred, jeans and T-shirts banned) with efficient service overseen by Terry and Christine Parkinson, who have owned the hotel for three and a half years. One reader wrote to express appreciation: 'We were particularly impressed by the warm and helpful welcome when we arrived and the attention to detail, and guests' comfort and enjoyment, shown by everyone from the lady owner to the chambermaid – exceptional management.' The menu has choices for all four of the courses except the soup. Typical main dishes might be vol-au-vent of scampi thermidor, roast Gressingham duckling or loin of Cumbrian pork, rounded off with perhaps fresh mango mousse or fruit crumble. The wine list extends to around 80 reasonably priced labels.

Bedrooms in the modern wing are larger than in the older part of the house but have less character. Those at the back of the house have some of the best views.

◑ Open all year, exc 3 to 27 Jan

⤴ From Keswick follow the B5289 Borrowdale road for 3½ miles. Turn right over the double humpback bridge signposted Grange. The hotel is 100 yards past the village of Grange, on the right. Private car park

🛏 4 single, 8 twin, 9 double, 2 family rooms; most with bathroom/WC, some with shower/WC; TV in all rooms; hair-dryer, baby-listening on request

◇ Restaurant, bar, 3 lounges, drying room; conference facilities (max 12 people residential only); golf, riding, other sports nearby. Wheelchair access to hotel (ramp), restaurant and WC (M,F), 6 ground-floor bedrooms

⊖ No dogs; no smoking in restaurant

▭ Access, Visa

£ Single £51 to £68, single occupancy of twin/double £75, twin/double £94 to £128 (rates inc dinner); deposit required. Sun L £11.50; set D £19; light lunches. Special breaks available

---

Many hotels put up their tariffs in the spring. You are advised to confirm prices when you book.

GRANGE-OVER-SANDS CUMBRIA   **MAP 4**

Graythwaite Manor

FERNHILL ROAD, GRANGE-OVER-SANDS, CUMBRIA LA11 7JE
TEL: GRANGE-OVER-SANDS (05395) 32001/33755   FAX: (05395) 35549

Friendly, family-run manor house in delightful landscaped gardens.

This ivy-covered establishment set a little way above the main activity of Grange-over-Sands has been owned by the Blakemore family since 1937 and that continuity has done much to ensure a completely authentic English manor-house feel. You enter through a stone arch into eight acres of landscaped gardens with pretty flowerbeds and topiary work leading up to the neat front lawns and the terrace, where guests can relax and take in the view across Morecambe Bay.

Inside, many old features have been maintained but the relaxed and personable nature of the Blakemores undercuts any sense of formality. The bar area has large bay windows and an ornate white fireplace and is furnished mostly with upright chairs upholstered in coppers and golds. The first lounge is a slightly sombre place with a stone fireplace and stained-glass windows, though it is enlivened by some attractive flower arrangements. There is another, more spacious, lounge with a piano and views of the sea at the other end of a long corridor which features mounted stags' heads, a gong and a superb old upright clock that towers above you. Dinner is a fairly traditional six-course affair with main dishes such as fillet of beef Wellington or roast duckling with orange and Grand Marnier.

The bedrooms at the front of the house have the best views but don't go in wholeheartedly for the period touches prevalent in the rest of the hotel; they have a mixture of pine and dark wood furnishings, plain duvets and bedcovers and floral patterns in the curtains and wallpaper.

◑ *Open all year*

⬀ *Fernhill Road leads off the main esplanade road in Grange-over-Sands. Private car park*

🛏 *5 single, 11 twin, 4 double, 1 family room, 1 suite; all with bathroom/WC, exc 2 doubles with shower/WC; TV, room service, baby-listening, hair-dryer in all rooms*

◈ *Restaurant, bar, 2 lounges, drying room, conservatory; conference facilities (max 30 people non-residential, 25 residential); tennis, snooker at hotel, fishing, other sports nearby. Wheelchair access to hotel and restaurant, 5 ground-floor bedrooms*

⊖ *No dogs; 1 non-smoking lounge*

▭ *Access, JCB, Visa*

£ *Single £35 to £45, single occupancy of twin/double £45, twin/double £70 to £90, family room/suite £70 to £110; deposit required. Set L £11, D £18.50. Special breaks available*

White Moss House

RYDAL WATER, GRASMERE, CUMBRIA LA22 9SE
TEL: GRASMERE (05394) 35295

Fine cooking in a comfortable Lakeland house with Romantic associations.

Although William Wordsworth never actually lived in White Moss House, many of his descendants did so and it stayed in the Wordsworth family until the 1930s. It is conjectured that he bought the house in order to secure a vote in the parish of Grasmere against the development of a railway in the area (and as well as providing him suffrage it also gave him a handy porch to rest in on his walks between Rydal and Grasmere). Romantic connections and a position equidistant from Dove Cottage and Rydal Mount have ensured Sue and Peter Dixon a regular flow of devotees to their creeper-covered Lakeland stone hotel over the years.

Peter is a champion of 'real English food' and his menus may include soup of field mushrooms and marjoram followed by fresh Solway salmon soufflé and a main course of roast rack of Lakeland lamb with gooseberry mint sauce, served with baby jacket potatoes, leeks with Pernod, aubergine and pepper casserole and cauliflower with sorrel sauce. There is a choice of three desserts such as bread-and-butter pudding with Calvados. Afterwards guests retire for coffee to the elegant drawing-room with its open fire, soft inviting sofas in bright floral patterns and large Lakeland landscape paintings.

The five bedrooms in the main house are comfortable and stylish, with fresh flowers and sewing kits, but tend to be on the small side. Those at the front of house suffer a little from the proximity of the A591. The Brockstone Cottage suite a short distance away affords more space and has a four-poster room.

◑ Closed Dec, Jan, Feb; restaurant closed Sun eve

↗ On the A591 at the north end of Rydal Water. Private car park

🛏 3 twin, 2 double, 1 cottage suite with four-poster; all with bathroom/WC, TV, room service, hair-dryer, trouser press; no tea/coffee-making facilities in rooms

◈ Restaurant, bar, lounge, drying room; fishing, boating at hotel, other sports nearby

⊖ No wheelchair access; hotel unsuitable for children under 5; no dogs; no smoking in restaurant

▭ Access, Visa

£ Single occupancy of twin/double £79, twin/double/four-poster £128 to £168 (rates inc dinner); deposit required from overseas visitors only. Set D £27 (8pm)

All rooms have tea/coffee-making facilities unless we specify to the contrary.

GRASSINGTON NORTH YORKSHIRE   **MAP 5**

Ashfield House

GRASSINGTON, NR SKIPTON, NORTH YORKSHIRE BD23 5AE
TEL: GRASSINGTON (0756) 752584

A relaxing and unpretentious hotel with memorable food and very friendly hosts.

Grassington is a bustling tourist honeypot with interesting stores and tea-shops, as well as being home to the National Park Information Centre. Stroll a few yards from the main square down one of the pretty cobbled back-alleys or 'folds', and you find yourself in a quiet domain, facing a small mellow-stoned, creeper-clad hotel with a black Burmese cat or two haunting the car park.

Once inside you'll find Linda and Keith Harrison's seventeenth-century house exudes a happy, uncontrived feel for the old country world, with lots of pine furniture, an open fire blazing in a huge inglenook and an oak dresser. A bold modern painting lends a welcome air of the unconventional and provides a good contrast. Another lounge for non-smokers has lots of comfy chairs, plenty of local-interest books and a wood-burning stove. Meals are served in a small, simple, beamed dining-room with a bistro-style blackboard and old photographs on the walls. The short set menu specialises in classic dishes, and the food is highly thought of: perhaps pear and parsnip soup followed by carbonnade of beef, apple and almond tart or home-made ice-cream, and a selection of local cheeses. 'Probably the best food on a three-week tour of northern England . . . the owners are very helpful,' reported one satisfied guest.

Bedrooms eschew the chintz you might expect and combine tasteful modern fabrics with good pine furniture. Number Six, with light flooding in on two sides and an *en-suite* shower room, is particularly attractive.

◗ Closed 7 Nov to 4 Feb

↗ A few yards off Grassington village square; turn left along Ashfield. Private car park

🛏 2 twin, 5 double; all but 1 double with shower/WC, 1 public bathroom; TV in all rooms; hair-dryer on request

◇ Dining-room, 2 lounges (1 with bar), drying room; fishing, golf, riding, swimmng-pool nearby

⊖ No wheelchair access; no children under 5; no dogs; no smoking

▭ Access, Visa

£ Single occupancy of twin/double £27 to £37, twin/double £54 to £81 (rates inc dinner); deposit required. Set D £12.50 (7pm). Special breaks available

---

Many hotels offer special rates for stays of a few nights or more. It is worth enquiring when you book.

The Starr ☆

MARKET PLACE, GREAT DUNMOW, ESSEX CM6 1AX
TEL: GREAT DUNMOW (0371) 874321   FAX: (0371) 876337

A sophisticated restaurant-with-rooms where friendliness is combined with attention to detail.

Swirls and flourishes embellish the Starr's smart sign, well-positioned to catch the motorist's eye. The restaurant-with-rooms occupies a prominent corner of Great Dunmow's old market place and its white façade, brightened by flowery tubs and carriage lamps, is appealing enough to make you want to find out more. Brian and Vanessa Jones have been running this establishment for 14 years and over this period they have added eight rooms to the restaurant, all in a long converted stable block a few paces from the main house. These don't come cheap, but they are reliably good. One of the most expensive – the Oak Room – is an impressive double with a freestanding bathtub in full view of a four-poster bed (if modesty inhibits you from soaking in public, there is a separate shower room too). Peach, named after its colour scheme, is a standard double where you'll find no such surprises but standards that are acceptable on any scale.

Light lunches are served either in the sunny front bar which, on nippy days, is warmed by a glowing wood fire, or in a darker restaurant decorated in soothing greens. Home-made soups, pasta dishes and smoked salmon scrambles can be a meal in themselves or enjoyed as starters before a more substantial main course. The 'pud of the day' is usually guaranteed hot, sticky and served with custard. Dinner menus feature fresh fish combinations and traditional venison, lamb and Dover sole dishes – all pepped up with unusual sauces and accompaniments.

◑ Open all year, exc 3 to 10 Jan; restaurant closed Sun eve

↗ Leave the M11 at Junction 8 and follow the A120 signposted Colchester/Chelmsford. The Starr is in the centre of Great Dunmow. Private car park

🛏 1 twin, 6 double, 1 four-poster; most with bathroom/WC, some with shower/WC; TV, hair-dryer in all rooms

◇ Restaurant, bar; ironing facilities; conference facilities (max 36 people non-residential, 8 residential); fishing, golf, tennis, other sports nearby. Wheelchair access to hotel (1 step), restaurant and WC (M,F), 2 ground-floor bedrooms, 1 specially equipped for disabled people

⊖ No dogs; no smoking in restaurant

▭ Access, Amex, Visa

£ Single occupancy of twin/double £53, twin/double £80, four-poster £110; deposit required. Set D £23 to £35; alc L £15 to £30. Special breaks available

GREAT HUCKLOW DERBYSHIRE   MAP 5

Hucklow Hall

GREAT HUCKLOW, TIDESWELL, BUXTON, DERBYSHIRE SK17 8RG
TEL: BUXTON (0298) 871175

Friendly hosts and good-value food in an old farmhouse in the Peak District National Park.

Bang in the middle of the Peak District National Park, Great Hucklow is a tiny hamlet where idyllic English country gardens are surrounded by fields of sheep. John and Angela Whatley's seventeenth-century farmhouse is set back from the road, and you'll need to keep an eye out for the sign as it is hidden by creepers. One reception room serves as hall, sitting- and dining-rooms and is comfortably kitted out with sofas, a wood-burning stove in the stone fireplace, a mahogany dining-table and plenty of books, many of which reflect John's interest in woodcarving and art. The stairwell, covered in old photographs (some from John's boyhood on the farm), makes an intriguing place to browse.

That the Whatleys enjoy sharing their home with guests is reflected in the consistently good reports we receive. One reader wrote to recommend 'a very warm welcome, help in planning walks and local visits, and the exceptional food, including the best fresh coffee I have tasted since being in Belgium'. Angela's three-course set meals are good value and might include cream of cauliflower soup, chicken breasts stuffed with Stilton and courgettes, and either pears baked in cream or cheese and biscuits.

With their creaky floorboards, farmhouse furnishings and stone-mullioned windows, bedrooms are characterful, but the Low Room perhaps has the edge on account of its low ceiling and view of the hills from your bed.

◑ *Closed Dec to Feb*

↗ *Great Hucklow is signposted from the A623 Chapel-en-le-Frith to Baslow/Chesterfield road. The Hall is at the extreme east end of the village. Private car park*

🛏 *1 single, 1 twin, 1 double; 2 public bathrooms*

◈ *Dining-room, lounge; fishing, golf, other sports nearby*

⊖ *No wheelchair access; no children under 5; no dogs or smoking in bedrooms*

▭ *None accepted*

£ *Single from £18, twin/double from £36; deposit required. Set D £13 (7pm)*

GREAT LONGSTONE DERBYSHIRE   MAP 5

Croft Country House

GREAT LONGSTONE, NR BAKEWELL, DERBYSHIRE DE45 1TF
TEL: GREAT LONGSTONE (0629) 640278

An immaculately kept small hotel with a lovely garden in the Peak District National Park.

Great Longstone, a village of grey stone houses with a green, post office, manor house and church, is about as traditional as you can get – the butcher's shop even has a sit-up-and-beg delivery bicycle parked outside. The long approach to Croft Hotel adds to your sense of retreat – a former occupant collected specimens of flora from all over the world, making the garden surprisingly exotic, and when you arrive you are likely to find Lynne Macaskill and Robert Allan hard at work fighting back the undergrowth. The interior is comfortable without being grand and is immaculately kept by Lynne, who clearly loves her job. The house was chiefly designed by a Victorian engineer, which explains the strange lantern ceiling and galleried landing above the sitting-room, which, despite its slightly warehouse feel, manages to remain a comfortable place to congregate in the evenings. A second sitting-room is cosy in winter with a log fire and plenty of games and books.

Stripped pine doors off the gallery lead to the nine bedrooms, all individual and named after local sights – Ladybower refers to the reservoir where the Dambusters practised their manoeuvres. Marble fireplaces, brass and antique pine beds, lacy tablecovers and ruched curtains make the rooms pretty and Victorian.

The four-course set menu has a choice of starters and puddings, and typically includes fresh crab mousse with cucumber salad, Stilton and celery soup, honey roast lamb and sticky toffee pudding.

◑ *Closed Jan*

▨ *2 miles north-west of Bakewell. From Bakewell take the A6 Buxton road and turn right on to the A6020. After 1 mile turn left towards Great Longstone. Private car park*

↤ *1 single, 2 twin, 6 double; some with bathroom/WC, some with shower/WC; TV, room service in all rooms; hair-dryer on request*

◈ *Restaurant, bar, 2 lounges, drying room; conference facilities (max 25 people non-residential, 9 residential); fishing, golf, other sports nearby. Wheelchair access to hotel (2 steps), restaurant and WC (unisex), no ground-floor bedrooms but lift and 2 bedrooms equipped for disabled people*

⊖ *No dogs; no smoking in restaurant*

▭ *Access, Visa*

£ *Single £58 to £63, single occupancy of twin/double £63 to £68, twin/double £85 to £90; deposit required. Set D £20.50 (7.30pm). Special breaks available*

GREAT MALVERN HEREFORD AND WORCESTER   **MAP 9**

Red Gate

32 AVENUE ROAD, GREAT MALVERN, HEREFORD AND WORCESTER
WR14 3BJ
TEL: MALVERN (0684) 565013

The best sort of guesthouse – comfortable, friendly and full of character.

There are some guesthouses where you instinctively know that everything is going to work, that your fellow guests will be interesting, and that you will want to return. The Red Gate is such a place, and, unsurprisingly, it becomes harder and harder to get a room at short notice. Richard and Barbara Rowan put huge efforts into the business of making their guests feel at home, and the line of thank-you cards on the dining-room mantelpiece is testimony to their success.

The Red Gate is a large, unprepossessing, Victorian town villa blessed with a large garden and situated in a quiet street close to the centre of Malvern. Inside, the Rowans have kept it true to period without being over-fussy: the drawing-room is full of sentimental engravings, for example. The dining-room opens into a small, arched verandah, perfect for breakfasts, while bottles of 'own-label' wine wait on the sideboard. The bedrooms are all pretty, with floral or striped wallpapers, and good beds. Some are definitely on the small side for two people. Number Two is the best room; Three, with a large bay window, is also good, while if you fancy the novelty of having your bath tucked into an alcove of your bedroom, ask for Room One. The three-course dinner menu is straightforward – haddock mornay followed by rhubarb and apple pie, perhaps.

◑ Open all year, exc Xmas and 2 weeks' spring holiday

⬈ Close to Great Malvern Station and Malvern Girls' College, 10 minutes' walk from town centre. Private car park

🛏 1 single, 2 twin, 4 double; most with bathroom/WC, some with shower/WC; TV, room service in all rooms; hair-dryer on request

◈ Dining-room, lounge, drying room; golf, tennis, other sports nearby

⊖ No wheelchair access; no children under 8; no dogs; smoking in lounge only

▭ Access, Visa

£ Single £27 to £28, single occupancy of twin/double £30 to £34, twin/double £50 to £54; deposit required. Set D £13.50

GREAT MILTON OXFORDSHIRE   **MAP 9**

Le Manoir aux Quat' Saisons

CHURCH ROAD, GREAT MILTON, OXFORDSHIRE OX44 7PD
TEL: GREAT MILTON (0844) 278881   FAX: (0844) 278847

Indulge at a price in Raymond Blanc's famous fifteenth-century manor-house restaurant and hotel. A great place for a serious treat.

Diners at Le Manoir aux Quat' Saisons would rarely begrudge the expense of a meal here and the food continues to receive enthusiastic acclaim as guests marvel at how a particular subtle flavour or delicate texture is achieved. Reported niggles about the service in last year's entry provoked one recent honeymoon couple to write a detailed account of their stay, summing up: 'The experience of one night in the Fuchsia Suite and lunch for five cost £1,200 – a lot of money, but it was an experience we will never forget. There was absolutely nothing that could have been improved upon. The staff were so friendly, not at all snooty, and everything was just perfect.'

Some changes have occurred since last year, with redecoration and a change of mood for the restaurant. Designer Michael Priest, who was involved in the interior décor of Le Manoir nine years ago, returned to recreate one of the dining-rooms. Vibrant yellow walls have striking paintings by a former pupil of Matisse, while checked and floral fabrics in blues and yellows cover chairs. An inner panelled room with a rural French feel has rows of chunky preserve jars stuffed with pickled vegetables and fruit. The pink and green conservatory restaurant is unchanged. Other public areas are classic country-house in style, with comfortable sofas and large flower arrangements on mahogany tables.

Bedrooms in the converted stable block are larger than in the house and all are very distinctive. Fuchsia is enormous, with a handpainted four-poster bed and a bathroom with two washbasins and a bath with a waterfall tap. In the romantic Michael Priest Suite, the former dovecote, plaster doves support a light bed canopy in their beaks. Bowls of fruit, fresh flowers and a decanter of madeira are provided in the bedrooms and breakfasts are served here in the morning: breakfast sausages have been described as the best ever tasted and the miniature pastries 'were baked to perfection – wonderful'.

◑ Open all year

⤴ Leave the M40 to Oxford at Junction 7. Turn left on to the A329, and second right after 1½ miles, signposted 'Great Milton Manor'. Private car park

🛏 9 twin/double, 3 four-poster, 7 suites; all with bathroom/WC, TV, room service, hair-dryer, trouser press, baby-listening; no tea/coffee-making facilities in rooms

◈ 2 dining-rooms, 2 lounges, private dining-room, air-conditioned conservatory/restaurant; conference facilities (max 22 people non-residential, 38 residential); tennis, fishing, croquet, outdoor heated swimming-pool (summer only), bicycles at hotel, other sports nearby; babysitting on request. Wheelchair access to hotel (1 step) and restaurant, 6 ground-floor bedrooms, 2 specially equipped for disabled people

⊖ No dogs (kennels in grounds); no smoking in dining-rooms

▭ Access, Amex, Diners, Visa

£ Twin/double/four-poster £165/£235/£275, suite £325/£375; deposit required. Continental B £9.50, cooked B £14.50; set L, D £29.50/£59.50; alc L, D £70. Special breaks available

GREAT RISSINGTON GLOUCESTERSHIRE   **MAP 9**

Lamb Inn

GREAT RISSINGTON, NR BOURTON-ON-THE-WATER, GLOUCESTERSHIRE
GL54 2LP
TEL: COTSWOLD (0451) 820388

A solid Cotswold inn with better-than-average bedrooms.

Close to the wartime airfield of Little Rissington (pieces from a crashed
bomber hang in the bar, together with a memorial to the crew), the Lamb
is the focal point for a tiny village. The pub fronts the village green and
overlooks the Windrush Valley to the rear. The bar is dark, atmospheric
and extensive, with a dining area added on; there is a wide range of bar
food, with the menu chalked up on blackboards. Bedrooms take up most
of the rest of the building. There is a ground-floor suite, small but
beautifully refurbished, and a new attic room with a bathroom the same
size as the bedroom. This will be the quietest room in the inn, as well as
one of the prettiest. Other bedrooms, all well decorated, range from the
small to the medium-sized. Exposed beams and narrow stairs help to
create a suitably traditional atmosphere.

◑ Open all year, exc 25, 26 Dec

↗ Leave the A40 for Burford. Turn
right out of Burford for the
Rissingtons. The inn is in the
centre of Great Rissington.
Private car park

🛏 2 twin, 6 double, 2 four-poster, 2
suites, 2 annexe rooms; most
with bathroom/WC, some with
shower/WC; hair-dryer on
request; TV in suites; ironing
facilities

◇ Restaurant (air-conditioned), bar,
lounge; conference facilities
(max 14 people residential);

heated indoor swimming-pool
(end Apr to Sept) at hotel,
fishing, golf, riding, other sports
nearby

⊖ No wheelchair access; no dogs in
public rooms; smoking
discouraged

▭ Access, Amex, Visa

£ Single occupancy of twin/double
£32 to £38, twin/double £42 to
£48, four-poster £55, suite £72;
deposit required. Set L £10, D
£12.50/£15; alc L £15 to £18, D
£18 to £22.50. Special breaks
available

GREAT SNORING NORFOLK   **MAP 7**

Old Rectory

GREAT SNORING, FAKENHAM, NORFOLK NR21 0HP
TEL: FAKENHAM (0328) 820597   FAX: (0328) 820048

*Buried deep in tranquil English countryside, this idiosyncratic
country house offers old-fashioned hospitality.*

If anywhere should be peaceful it's a guesthouse at this address, and true
to its name you're unlikely to see a soul around. The Old Rectory lies on

the outskirts of the village, facing the church, in its own leafy walled garden. The house is a peculiar mixture of a sixteenth-century hexagonal body with Victorian additions and renovation. The fancy brickwork, elaborate chimneys, mullioned windows and friezes of male and female heads (thought to be the Shelton family for whom it was originally built) makes it a real teaser for architectural buffs. Rosamund Scoles will show enthusiasts other oddities such as a fireplace in one of the doubles which has a window immediately above (the flue bends around the edge of it). For all the singularity of the building, the accommodation is straightforwardly comfortable without being pretentious or unusual. There is little to choose between the rooms, all of which have bathrooms, and instead of tea-making facilities a pre-breakfast drink is delivered to your room whenever you require it.

Dinner, accompanied by a limited wine list, is served in the dining-room, which is dominated by a gently ticking clock. The emphasis is on good home-made cooking with familiar traditional dishes as well as the more unusual: perhaps cornets of smoked salmon filled with cream cheese and prawns to start, followed by roast pheasant (in season) with treacle tart or bananas steeped in rum to round it off. The old-fashioned lounge with red flowers splashed on to the walls and lace coasters on coffee tables is available if you wish to socialise with fellow guests.

○ Open all year, exc 24 to 27 Dec

✈ Great Snoring is 3 miles north-east of Fakenham, signposted from the A148. The Old Rectory is behind the church on the Barsham road. Private car park

🛏 3 twin, 3 double, 5 cottages; all with bathroom/WC, TV, room service; hair-dryer on request; no tea/coffee-making facilities in rooms

◇ Dining-room, lounge; meetings facilities (max 12 people residential and non-residential)

● No wheelchair access; no children under 12; no dogs; no smoking in dining-room

▭ Amex, Diners

£ Single occupancy of twin/double £68, twin/double £88, cottage £220 (min stay of 2 nights). Set D £21.50

GRIMSTON NORFOLK   **MAP 7**

Congham Hall

LYNN ROAD, GRIMSTON, KING'S LYNN, NORFOLK PE32 1AH
TEL: HILLINGTON (0485) 600250   FAX: (0485) 601191

This hotel, set in 40 acres of parkland, succeeds in maintaining high standards in its rooms as well as its restaurant.

Congham Hall has achieved a solid reputation for good cooking as well as being a classic country-house hotel. Endorsement of high standards in the kitchen comes from one guest who found the food 'extremely good'. Not only were the 'set-pieces' at dinner to her liking but 'the simple poached eggs at breakfast were done the old-fashioned way and were

CONGHAM HALL
— GRIMSTON —

absolutely perfect'. There are three evening menus served in the large dining-room overlooking the garden: a light, three-course menu, a four-course à la carte or a set gourmet dinner 'Hobsons' Choice' of seven courses where you sit back and let the chef do the choosing for you.

Bedrooms are elegant, neatly arranged and just-so. If you feel like splashing out, you won't go wrong with Number 16 – a vast suite with lots of space and a glitzy, white bathroom; but if you'd rather spend your money on food, then the standard rooms – although significantly smaller – are perfectly comfortable. The lack of heating caused one reader some grief on a quiet weekend: 'The weather was very cold for the time of year and the heating in the bedrooms was non-existent.'

A large herb garden containing over 300 different varieties reflects a passion of owners Trevor and Christine Forecast; the smell of herbs wafts through the relaxing yellow lounge, where displays of china are highlighted in alcoves.

◐ *Open all year*

⤴ *Go to the A149/A148 interchange north-east of King's Lynn. Follow the A148 to Sandringham/Fakenham/Cromer for 100 yards. Turn right to Grimston. The hotel is 2½ miles further on the left-hand side. Private car park*

🛏 *1 single, 7 twin, 3 double, 1 four-poster, 2 suites; all with bathroom/WC, exc single with shower/WC; TV, room service, hair-dryer in all rooms; tea/*

coffee-making facilities on request

◈ *Restaurant, bar, lounge, drying room; conference facilities (max 12 people residential and non-residential); tennis, croquet, heated outdoor swimming-pool (in season), cricket and stabling at hotel, other sports nearby*

⊖ *No wheelchair access; no children under 12; no dogs; no smoking in restaurant and discouraged in bedrooms*

▭ *Access, Amex, Diners, Visa*

💷 Single £65, single occupancy of
twin/double £72, twin/double
£97, four-poster £113, suite

£150; deposit required. Alc L
£15, D from £19.50. Special
breaks available

GRITTLETON WILTSHIRE   **MAP 9**

Church House

GRITTLETON, NR CHIPPENHAM, WILTSHIRE SN14 6AP
TEL: CASTLE COMBE (0249) 782562 (and fax)

Georgian rectory in a pretty village and with friendly hosts.

Before settling down to live in this eighteenth-century rectory, the
Moores ran a flying doctor service in Africa. If the mood (and means)
takes you, you can arrive by helicopter (a windsock flutters in the meadow
beyond the croquet lawn). Arrival by car will be impressive enough for
most tastes; you draw up on the gravel drive outside a three-storey house
built of Bath stone. It's sandwiched between the church and pub and is
one of the finest houses in Grittleton, a pretty village on the southern
borders of the Cotswolds.

Anna Moore is an energetic and well-informed hostess, full of ideas
on how guests can fill their time. But, as one reader reports, she also
knows when to leave guests to their own devices. Inside, the high-
ceilinged rooms are decorated with mementoes from a life abroad, and
photographs of children are spread around reminding you that this is a
family home not a hotel. Guests eat in a dining-room with a stripped
floor, Adam fireplace and raspberry-red walls. Church House is not
licensed but guests can bring their own wine.

The four comfortable bedrooms are all on the second floor; they are
large and plainly decorated. In some of them the washbasin and shower
are hidden behind a wooden screen.

◐ Open all year

↗ Leave the M4 at Junction 17 and
take the A429 north and
immediately turn left. Grittleton
is signposted 3½ miles. Church
House is between the church and
the pub. Private car park

🛏 2 twin, 1 double, 1 family room;
all with bathroom/WC, exc
double with shower/WC; TV,
hair-dryer in all rooms

◈ Dining-room, drawing-room,
music room; conference facilities
(max 30 people non-residential);

croquet, heated swimming-pool
(Easter to Oct) at hotel, other
sports nearby

⊖ No wheelchair access; no
children under 12 exc babies; no
dogs; no smoking in dining-room

▭ None accepted

💷 Single occupancy of twin/double
£28 to £30, twin/double £45 to
£50, family room £60 to £65;
deposit required. Set D £13.50
(8pm by arrangement). Special
breaks available

HADLEY WOOD HERTFORDSHIRE   **MAP 9**

West Lodge Park

COCKFOSTERS ROAD, HADLEY WOOD, HERTFORDSHIRE EN4 0PY
TEL: 081-440 8311   FAX: 081-449 3698

A large old house with comfortable rooms and spacious grounds.

Just where the sprawl of suburbs meets the green belt that fringes
London within the band of the M25 you will find the West Lodge Park
Hotel. Look north and the view is across farmers' fields; look south and
the houses of Barnet are visible through the trees of the 34 acres of
grounds. Since the Beale family bought the hotel in 1945 they have
created an arboretum that includes the national collection of hornbeam
trees, and the garden is sometimes opened up to the public.

The house is essentially two white blocks linked by a modern extension. The entrance hall-cum-lounge has an open fire and groups of
chairs, and is a welcoming sight even before you reach the reception
tucked away in a corridor. A more private sitting-room is light and bright,
with yellow the predominant colour; it overlooks the gardens, and is a
popular place for afternoon teas. The restaurant is modern, with red-
brick walls, pot plants and pine farmhouse-style chairs. Bedrooms are all
individual and each has a small collection of books, ornaments and
photographs, which add a personal touch. They vary in size and shape
but none are poky and all are well-furnished and comfortable.

◑ Open all year

🔁 Leave the M25 at Junction 24;
the hotel is 1 mile south from
the exit on the A111. Private car
park

🛏 10 single, 20 twin, 16 double, 4
four-poster, suites available; all
with bathroom/WC, TV, room
service, hair-dryer, baby-
listening, trouser press; mini-bar
in some rooms

◈ Restaurant, bar, lounge;
conference facilities (max 40
people residential and non-

residential); putting, croquet at
hotel, golf, tennis, other sports
nearby. Wheelchair access to
hotel (ramp) and restaurant, no
ground-floor bedrooms but lift
and 1 bedroom specially
equipped for disabled people

⊖ No dogs

▭ Access, Amex, Visa

£ Single £80, single occupancy of
twin/double £90, twin/double
£90, four-poster £130, suite
£140. Continental B £6.50,
cooked B £8; set L, D £15

HALIFAX WEST YORKSHIRE   **MAP 5**

Holdsworth House

HOLDSWORTH ROAD, HOLMFIELD, HALIFAX, WEST YORKSHIRE HX2 9TG
TEL: HALIFAX (0422) 240024   FAX: (0422) 245174

An imaginative marriage of the old and the new in a quasi-rural setting a stone's throw from Halifax.

Jacobean houses converted into upmarket hotels have a tendency to become museums, with guests enjoined to talk in whispers, tiptoe around the antiques, and show seemly deference to the antiquity of their surroundings; children are usually banished. Not so at Holdsworth House. In a building that has all the architectural credentials to make it a fully-paid-up member of the killjoy tendency – venerable gables, mullioned windows, a sunken garden and weeping ashes – the Pearson family's philosophy comes as a breath of fresh air; there's even a monthly 'funday' club designed to allow grown-ups to have a leisurely Sunday lunch while youngsters are entertained by qualified nannies in the Stuart Room which occupies one of the house's original barns.

Inside, the genuine and mock-medieval (lots of exposed stone and beams, Jacobean chairs) rub shoulders with modern country-house hotel style – tartan-shaded lamps, rich colours, modish retro-style fabrics and deep sofas. Lounge areas favour the more contemporary look while dining areas, with beams, panelled walls, carved chairs and heavy tables, are more traditional. A long à la carte menu is supplemented by an interesting good-value table d'hôte version with at least three dishes at each stage – perhaps pan-fried guinea-fowl and apple sausage, followed by fillet of brill wrapped in seaweed and rice paper, pan-fried and served with a satay sauce, and caramelised peaches with a champagne sabayon and passion-fruit sorbet. The extensive wine list is fairly priced.

Bedrooms vary from the comfortable and bland to the flamboyant and grand, complete with half-tester or four-poster. All are pretty and well-kept. Expense-account tariffs fall to a more affordable level at weekends, when a programme of special-interest breaks includes courses for devotees of the Brontës, dry-stone walling, vernacular buildings of the West Riding, and seventeenth-century north-country oak furniture.

◐ Open all year, exc 24 to 30 Dec; restaurant closed Sat lunch

↗ From Halifax, take the A629 towards Keighley. After 1½ miles turn right into Shay Lane, signposted Holmfield. The house is 1 mile on the right. Private car park

🛏 20 single, 2 twin, 9 double, 1 four-poster, 3 half-tester, 5 suites; all with bathroom/WC, exc 2 singles with shower/WC; TV, room service (limited), hair-dryer, mini-bar, baby-listening in all rooms; trouser press on request; no tea/coffee-making facilities in rooms

◇ Restaurant, 2 bars, 2 lounges, breakfast room, drying facilities; conference facilities (max 100 people non-residential, 40 residential); golf, riding, other sports nearby; babysitting by arrangement. Wheelchair access to hotel (2 steps), restaurant and WC, 21 ground-floor bedrooms, 2 specially equipped for disabled people

⊖ No dogs in public rooms

▭ Access, Amex, Diners, Visa

£ Single £58 to £70, single occupancy of twin/double £74, twin/double/four-poster £87 to £90, suite £100, family room rate on request (rates inc dinner). Cooked B £5; set L £12.50, D £19.50; alc D £25. Special breaks available

HAMBLETON LEICESTERSHIRE   **MAP 5**

Hambleton Hall

HAMBLETON, NR OAKHAM, LEICESTERSHIRE LE15 8TH
TEL: OAKHAM (0572) 756991   FAX: (0572) 724721

*An expertly managed luxury hotel in beautiful grounds on the
banks of Rutland Water.*

When in 1881 Walter Marshall adopted the Hell Fire Club's motto *Fay
Ce Que Voudras* ('Do As You Please') and had it engraved above the door
of Hambleton Hall, his new hunting-lodge, he was cocking a snook at
Victorian prudishness. The Hall quickly earned a reputation as a place
for pleasure-seekers and indeed its role is not so very different today –
though it has far more respectability and a host of awards, and is more
likely to be featured in travel pages than gossip columns. Tim and Stefa
Hart, who converted the house in 1979, created opulent rooms with
extraordinary attention to comfort, and their staff's efforts are tireless in
maintaining standards. Every bedroom is furnished with antiques and
luxury fabrics in restful colours. Fern, with its stencilled walls echoing
patterns in the curtains and half-tester drapes, is generally considered to
be the best; in common with most rooms, it has wonderful views over
Rutland Water and the gardens. Bathrooms are thoughtfully designed
with deep baths, fluffy towels and bath robes, quality toiletries and
convenient mirrors.

    In 1992 chef Aaron Patterson joined the team, hot-foot from Le
Manoir aux Quat' Saisons, and recent innovations include a new set
menu at two-thirds last year's price. A typical table d'hôte dinner in
summer might be made up of soufflé of salmon on a bed of garden sorrel
and cucumber sauce, Gressingham duck roasted on a bed of dried lime,
orange and lemon grass and served with a jasmine tea sauce, and gratin of
strawberries and rhubarb served with a champagne sorbet and an
elderflower fritter. An extension to the kitchen garden is among the many
improvements recently undertaken, which also include adding a
swimming-pool and creating a lovely English meadow.

◑   Open all year

➦   3 miles east of Oakham, on a
peninsula in the middle of
Rutland Water. Private car park

🛏   10 twin/double, 4 double, 1 four-
poster; all with bathroom/WC,
TV, room service, hair-dryer,
baby-listening; no tea/coffee-
making facilities in rooms; 2
bedrooms with air-conditioning

◈   Restaurant, bar, drawing-room,
private dining-room; laundry
facilities; conference facilities

(max 30 people non-residential,
15 residential); tennis, heated
swimming-pool (late spring to
end Sept), bicycles at hotel,
other sports nearby; babysitting.
Wheelchair access to hotel
(ramp), restaurant and WC (M,
F), no ground-floor bedrooms but
lift

⊖   No dogs in public rooms

▭   Access, Visa

£   Single occupancy of twin/double

£95 to £115, twin/double £95 to £250, four-poster £130 to £160.

Set L, D £26.50/£50; alc L, D £47. Special breaks available

HAMSTERLEY FOREST CO DURHAM   MAP 3

Grove House

HAMSTERLEY FOREST, NR BISHOP AUCKLAND, CO DURHAM DL13 3NL
TEL: WITTON-LE-WEAR (0388 88) 203

A tasteful and lively family home in a gloriously unspoilt spot.

Driving through the Forestry Commission plantation at Hamsterley Forest it is hard not to think of Hansel and Gretel – not least if you're trying to find your way back after dark. By day the golden stone of Grove House glows in the sunshine and, with its pretty garden, the place looks far grander than the tariff would lead you to expect.

Inside, Helene and Russell Close's lively home is informal in character though not in style, with public rooms that are impeccably tasteful and elegant. Family photographs, CDs and other paraphernalia emphasise that this is a family home. Three french windows overlooking forest views allow light to pour into an enormous bar/lounge with autumnal colours, patterned sofas, antique tables, lots of books and games and gleaming sporting trophies. A second small, green, garden-style lounge is a bright spot to sit, and catches the morning sun. The huge, formal dining-room, lined with portraits and ennobled by plasterwork, is set with linen even at breakfast time, when proper bread toasted in thick slices is served together with croissants and brioches to accompany the traditional cooked offering. Dinner was unavailable when we inspected, but Russell's traditional four-course affairs are reputed to be reliable.

Our inspector's room, with neat modern purple and green co-ordinating soft furnishings, a selection of magazines and copies of Van Gogh drawings, would have passed muster as a double but was rather cramped as a twin, leading to unwelcome encounters with the luggage when visiting the public bathroom and the shower room shared by the rooms. Particularly irritating was the fact that the doors of other rooms, larger and unoccupied, were left open, giving a tantalising glimpse of the possibility of greater comfort.

◑ Open all year

� North of West Auckland off the A68. Take the Hamsterley Forest turning to Hamsterley village and then the turning signposted Hamsterley Forest. At Bedburn fork left – the hotel is 3 miles inside the forest on a tarmac road. Private car park

🛏 1 twin, 2 double, 1 self-catering cottage; 2 public bathrooms

◈ Dining-room, lounge, TV room; riding, bicycle hire nearby

● No wheelchair access; no children under 8; no dogs in public rooms; no smoking

▭ None accepted

Single occupancy of twin/double £20, twin/double £40, cottage	from £200 per week; deposit required. Set D £11 (7.30pm)

HANLEY CASTLE HEREFORD AND WORCESTER · MAP 9

Old Parsonage Farm

HANLEY CASTLE, HEREFORD AND WORCESTER WR8 0BU
TEL: HANLEY SWAN (0684) 310124

A spacious comfortable farmhouse with extremely friendly hosts.

The Addisons' farmhouse is extremely well situated for people travelling on the M5 or M50, with views of the Malvern Hills into the bargain. It is a large brick building – not, perhaps, the most attractive of farmhouses to look at from the outside, but bright and peaceful within. Ann Addison's monthly dining club and her husband's interests in the wine trade show where the priorities lie here, but overnight guests are certainly not neglected – in fact, if you can get a room, you will find that the welcome you are given outweighs that in many a pricier hotel. There is plenty of space, too – public areas run to a drawing-room, a television room and a pretty pale yellow dining-room with small tables and old sideboards. The three bedrooms are called by one colour but painted another – the Pink is green and the Yellow is rose-coloured. Only the Red remains red. They are large, sparsely furnished rooms with big bathrooms (one large enough for a wardrobe to inhabit it) and are very good value. The four-course dinners, lovingly cooked by Ann, may include bisque aurore and sole with tarragon, wine and mushrooms. The wine list is extensive and interesting.

Closed mid-Dec to mid-Jan

Take the B4211 out of Upton upon Severn for 1½ miles towards Worcester. Turn left on to the B4209. The farm is 200 yards on the right. Private car park

1 twin, 2 double; all with bathroom/WC; no tea/coffee-making facilities in rooms

Dining-room, bar, lounge, TV room/library, drying room; golf, fishing, riding nearby

No wheelchair access; no children under 12; dogs in lobby only; no smoking in bedrooms

None accepted

Single occupancy of twin/double £27, twin/double £39 to £45; deposit required. Set D £15

HANWOOD SHROPSHIRE · MAP 5

White House

HANWOOD, NR SHREWSBURY, SHROPSHIRE SY5 8LP
TEL: SHREWSBURY (0743) 860414

Complimentary reports continue to roll in for this large guesthouse blessed with skilful hosts.

The village is rather dull, and the White House stands out as about the only attractive building you see from the main road. However, it is not until you reach the large garden sloping down to the river behind the house that you realise what an attractive location the Mitchells have. Poultry, a silent species of peacock and fresh vegetables co-exist happily, and the vegetables (but not the peacocks) are likely to appear on the dinner table, too. The cooking draws high praise: 'It deserves more mention in future editions of the Guide,' writes one reader, with memories perhaps of breast of duck with honey and brown sugar, or grapes in red-wine jelly.

Bedrooms at the White House are on the small side ('little floor space for us and none for our luggage') but are spotless. The public rooms – a peaceful snug of a bar with ticking clock and stone fireplace, a lovely high sitting-room created from an old slaughterhouse and a more conventional lounge – cater for most tastes.

◐ *Open all year; restaurant closed Sun eve*

↗ *From Shrewsbury take the A488 Bishop's Castle road; Hanwood is 1 mile south of the A5 roundabout. Private car park*

🛏 *1 single, 1 twin, 4 double; 1 with bathroom/WC, 1 with shower/WC, 1 public bathroom; hairdryer in 2 rooms; TV in 1 room*

◇ *Dining-room, bar, lounge, TV room; fishing, golf, riding, other sports nearby*

⊖ *No wheelchair access; no children under 10; no dogs; no smoking in bedrooms*

▭ *None accepted*

£ *Single £20, single occupancy of twin/double £30 to £38, twin/double £40 to £50. Set D £12/£15 (7.30pm). Special breaks available*

HARDWICKE HEREFORD AND WORCESTER   **MAP 9**

The Haven

HARDWICKE, HAY-ON-WYE, HEREFORD AND WORCESTER HR3 5TA
TEL: CLIFFORD (0497) 831254

A very civilised guesthouse with everything in the right proportions.

For bookshop-browsers and walkers heading for Hay-on-Wye, the Haven makes an excellent base. The Robinsons' vicarage-turned-guesthouse stands in open country just a short distance from the town. While it is perhaps not the most attractive of vicarages from the outside, the interior, with its bright sitting-room, book-filled library and succession of pretty bedrooms, is immediately relaxing. There are one or two bizarre touches left from previous owners, notably the lavish bathroom in Radnor, where the claret carpet appears to be about to crawl up the walls and the bath would do for an emperor's levée. Clyro, on the ground floor, has been specially done up for disabled visitors.

Dinners, served in the plain dining-room, usually have more than one choice: your meal might consist of pumpkin and tomato soup followed by guinea-fowl and blackberry and apple pudding. The Robinsons put a lot of effort into their business and you are bound to feel welcome.

◑ *Closed Dec and Jan*

⤢ *On the B4348, 2½ miles north-east of Hay-on-Wye. Private car park*

⇌ *I single, 2 twin, I double, I four-poster, I family room; some with bathroom/WC, some with shower/WC, I public bathroom; TV in all rooms; hair-dryer on request*

◈ *Dining-room, lounge, drying room, library; outdoor (unheated) swimming-pool, sauna/solarium*

at hotel, other sports nearby; babysitting by arrangement. Wheelchair access to hotel (ramp) and dining-room, I ground-floor bedroom specially equipped for disabled people

⊖ *No dogs in public rooms; smoking in library only*

▭ *Amex*

£ *Single £21, twin/double £42 to £44, four-poster £52, family room £44; deposit required. Set D £12.50 (7.30pm)*

HAROME NORTH YORKSHIRE   **MAP 3**

Pheasant ✫

HAROME, HELMSLEY, NORTH YORKSHIRE YO6 5JG
TEL: HELMSLEY (0439) 71241; changing to (0439) 771241/770416 in Jan 94

A comfortable family-run hotel in a picture-postcard village.

Harome is less self-consciously pretty than Helmsley, its bustling market-town neighbour, but the Pheasant's location – opposite a church, overlooking a duck pond and with a thatched cottage a couple of doors along – breathes a quintessential Englishness. The building itself is a modern rendering of traditional design in biscuit-coloured stone, and is backed by a pretty garden where ducks waddle when the pond's attraction wanes.

Inside, the hotel is well-maintained and cottagey, achieving a pleasant and relaxing look without embracing any particular style of design. The large lounge, which overlooks the garden, favours autumnal colours, with sofas in green velour or floral patterns, fresh and dried-flower displays, colourful bird prints, copies of *Country Life* and an Adam-style fireplace. The cosy bar with its beamed ceiling and horse brasses might seem a better bet than the rather bland restaurant, but one correspondent in search of a pre-dinner drink found it unstaffed on consecutive nights, and had to ask staff to get hold of a wine list. Other guests have applauded the food from the traditionally slanted menu as 'really good home cooking' and welcomed menus which 'were not elaborate'.

Bedrooms are unusually spacious, with co-ordinating soft furnishings in floral patterns, simple décor and good furniture. Modern bathrooms are also generously sized, and are equipped with extras including bath robes and bottles of Radox. Correspondents are unanimous on the high standards of housekeeping, and welcome the evening tidy-up and turning down of beds. Opinions differ on the Binks family's management style – while most found it 'discreet but helpful', another judged neither management nor the staff particularly friendly.

◐ Closed Xmas, Jan and Feb

↗ Leave Helmsley on the A170 towards Scarborough. After ¼ mile, turn right for Harome. Private car park

🛏 2 single, 5 twin, 4 double, 3 suites, 2 cottages; all with bathroom/WC, TV; room service and hair-dryer on request

◈ Dining-room, bar, lounge, drying room; heated indoor swimming-pool at hotel, fishing, golf, other sports nearby. Wheelchair access

to hotel, restaurant and 1 ground-floor cottage specially equipped for disabled people

⊖ No children under 12; no dogs in public rooms; no smoking in dining-room

▭ None accepted

£ Single £50 to £58, twin/double £100 to £116, suite/cottage £110 to £120 (rates inc dinner); deposit required. Cooked B £8; bar lunches; set D £18.50

HARROGATE NORTH YORKSHIRE   MAP 5

White House

COUNTY HOTEL OF THE YEAR

10 PARK PARADE, HARROGATE, NORTH YORKSHIRE HG1 5AH
TEL: HARROGATE (0423) 501388   FAX: (0423) 527973

An individualistic but reliable hotel a short walk from the centre of this popular spa town.

'This place used to be a furniture repository. It still is,' jokes Jennie Forster of her flamboyantly furnished hotel just behind the Stray, Harrogate's 200-acre arc of open green. A fiendish one-way system makes the hotel (easily identifiable, as it is set amid a row of less extravagant tan buildings) tricky to reach by car. It's worth persevering, although its elaborate frontage, bedecked with flags, balustrades and flashy Victorian architectural devices, appears slightly vulgar to modern eyes. The interior, however, is an unalloyed delight, with wonderful public rooms that speak volumes for Jennie's bold original taste and sly sense of humour – and everywhere there are fine pieces of furniture to admire.

The front-facing library sets the tone, with a coral décor, stripy sofas and not only loads of books but cribbage, boxloads of board games and a globe. The spacious sitting-room, in crisp green and white, has huge windows with bright, modern drapes and lots of family photographs, as well as a giant ceramic frog. The airy restaurant's elegance is enhanced by an ornate plaster ceiling, below which well-spaced tables are set with classic white linen. Menus reveal a willingness to experiment – you might dine on grilled goats' cheese with gooseberry conserve, followed by duck breast on port, wild mushrooms and pink peppercorns, and a bitter chocolate marquise with crème-de-menthe sauce. The bedrooms, generously equipped and sprinkled with antiques, either have woodchip or cheerful modern wallcoverings. Some bathrooms await the removal of avocado suites, but those already refurbished in a bright, stylish way, like the revamped bedrooms, bode well for the future.

◑ *Open all year*

⤴ *Off the A59 between the turning for Wetherby and the Prince of Wales roundabout. Private car park and on-street parking*

🛏 *2 single, 4 twin, 2 double, 1 four-poster suite, 1 half-tester; most with bathroom/WC, some with shower/WC; TV, room service, hair-dryer, baby-listening in all rooms*

◇ *Restaurant, bar, lounge, TV room, library, drying room; conference facilities (max 50*

people non-residential, 10 residential); babysitting

⊖ *No wheelchair access; no dogs; no smoking in bedrooms and restaurant*

▭ *Access, Amex, Diners, Visa*

£ *Single £75, single occupancy of twin/double £85, twin/double £95, four-poster/suite £110, family room £120; deposit required. Set L £15, D £18; alc L, D £24. Special breaks available*

HARTFIELD EAST SUSSEX   **MAP 8**

Bolebroke Watermill

EDENBRIDGE ROAD, HARTFIELD, EAST SUSSEX TN7 4JP
TEL: HARTFIELD (0892) 770425

A converted old mill and barn in quiet surroundings.

If you blink you could easily miss the entrance to the small dirt track to Bolebroke Watermill. 'We haven't put up a big sign,' explains David Cooper, 'because we don't want a lot of tourists turning up.' Bolebroke Watermill was first recorded in William the Conqueror's Domesday Book in 1086 and was used as a working cornmill up until 1948. David and his wife Christine have worked hard to retain the original character of the mill – there are grindstones and internal machinery incorporated into the rustic lounges – and have also placed great emphasis on providing comfort for their guests.

You have to be fairly agile to climb the narrow, steep stairs up to the bedrooms in the Mill, which are reasonable in size and have a frilly pastel décor. The Miller's Barn is a lot easier to negotiate; here you'll find the Honeymooners' Hayloft, with a four-poster bed made from a haywagon.

A decanter of mead awaits in the dining-room, an attractive room with pink walls, a marble fireplace and a view over the garden. For dinner you can expect the taste of a Sussex supper, perhaps pheasant, apple and cider soup followed by smoked chicken and, for dessert, a home-made blackberry and apple pie. Bolebroke is not licensed, so bring your own bottle of wine. Breakfasts vary, perhaps mushrooms with herbs on toast, or a toast basket with bacon. A word of warning – don't eat too much cereal or you may regret not having room for some of the extra surprises!

◐ Closed Dec, Jan and Feb; dining-room closed Wed and Sun eves

↗ Take the A264 from East Grinstead towards Tunbridge Wells for 6 miles to a crossroads, and turn right to Hartfield on the B2026 for 1 mile. Turn left into an unmade lane just past Perryhill Nursery. Private car park.

⇌ 1 twin, 2 double, 1 four-poster; all with bathroom/WC, TV, hair-dryer

◈ 2 dining-rooms, 2 lounges; fishing, golf, tennis, riding nearby

⊖ No wheelchair access; no children under 7; no dogs; no smoking

▭ Access, Amex, Visa

£ Single occupancy of twin/double £45, twin/double £49, four-poster £63; deposit required. Set D £16 (8pm)

HARVINGTON HEREFORD AND WORCESTER   MAP 9

Mill at Harvington ☆

ANCHOR LANE, HARVINGTON, EVESHAM, HEREFORD AND WORCESTER WR11 5NR
TEL: EVESHAM (0386) 870688 (and fax)

An isolated riverside setting and good food in a smartly converted mill.

Simon and Jane Greenhalgh opened in 1989, having turned their mill into a restaurant-with-rooms in best late-Eighties style. This means plentiful pastel colours throughout and careful highlighting of the remaining Georgian features. The red-brick building down on the banks of the Avon is surrounded by rough lawns and shady trees, while a small swimming-pool lies tucked away for hot days. It is not an easy place to find and the approach, past a caravan park and glasshouses, is not promising, but this makes your eventual arrival feel all the more worth-while. And the care continues during the stay, report readers: 'We were treated throughout with such kindness and natural helpfulness that we felt quite comfortable in asking for anything we wished without impos-ing.' The dining-room is soothing, with alcoves full of china, views towards the river, and a pale lilac and peach colour scheme. Bedrooms have adequate space, although the necessity to gut the long mill building for conversion has left them a little bland.

The food, described as a mixture of old-style classics plus some more modern ideas, is well-thought-of. One reader particularly liked the Arbroath smokie tartlets – apparently the secret ingredient was freshly ground nutmeg added at the last moment.

◑ Open all year; exc 24 to 27 Dec

⊠ Turn south off the B439 opposite Harvington village, down Anchor Lane. After 600 yards the hotel driveway is on the left. Private car park

⇔ 3 twin, 12 double; all with bathroom/WC, TV, room service, hair-dryer, baby-listening; trouser press on request

◈ Restaurant, bar/lounge; conference facilities (max 12 people residential and non-residential); fishing, tennis, heated swimming-pool (1 Apr to 30 Sept) at hotel, golf, riding nearby. Wheelchair access to hotel (1 step), restaurant and WC (unisex), 3 ground-floor bedrooms, 1 specially equipped for disabled people

⊖ No children under 10; no dogs; no smoking in restaurant

▭ Access, Amex, Visa

£ Single occupancy of twin/double £54, twin/double £85. Set L £14.50, D £19.50; alc D £22. Special breaks available

HARWICH ESSEX   MAP 8

The Pier at Harwich

THE QUAY, HARWICH, ESSEX CO12 3HH
TEL: HARWICH (0255) 241212   FAX: (0255) 551922

A suitably nautical hotel with a good choice of casual or formal restaurants.

Facing the mouths of the Rivers Stour and Orwell, this large, square hotel topped with a flagpole is painted an unmissable lilac with mouldings picked out in blue. It's a good choice for an overnight stay either before or after a North Sea ferry crossing, partly for its good restaurants and partly for its airy rooms. A nautical theme runs through the public areas and corridors. Original Sealink publicity posters, picked up at Sotheby's, decorate part of the restaurant used by the Ha'penny Pier (the cheaper fish and chip section) which remains here until April, when it moves downstairs to make more space for the formal restaurant during the busier summer months. While you can opt for good-value fish, steak, lasagne or stew in Ha'penny Pier, the restaurant offers set menus and a more expensive à la carte. There are plenty of wines to choose from, with a special list of half-bottles, too.

The pleasantest rooms are those at the front, overlooking the sea and docks. The best is Room Three, which has three large windows giving unsurpassed views, while another favourite is Room Four, which overlooks the heavy machinery of the portside. Neat bathrooms, flowery bedspreads and pictures of boats make all the rooms welcoming.

◑ Open all year, exc 25, 26 Dec

⊠ On the quayside of Old Harwich. Private car park

⇔ 6 double; all with bathroom/ WC, TV, room service, hair-dryer

◈ 2 restaurants, bar; sea fishing, water sports, golf, other sports nearby; ironing facilities.

● No wheelchair access; no dogs

▭ Access, Amex, Diners, Visa

£ Single occupancy of twin/double
£45 to £60, twin/double £63 to

£73; deposit required. Cooked B
£4; Sun L £14.50; alc L £5/£12,
D £5/£16 (10% service is added
to meal prices). Special breaks
available

HASSOP DERBYSHIRE   **MAP 5**

Hassop Hall

HASSOP, NR BAKEWELL, DERBYSHIRE DE45 1NS
TEL: GREAT LONGSTONE (0629) 640488   FAX: (0629) 640577

*Competent management and friendly staff in a historic mansion in
the Peak District National Park.*

Hassop Hall is one of those huge stately homes that have adapted very
well to the role of luxury hotel. Over the past 20 years Thomas Chapman
has created a comfortable establishment that is totally without pretension
and cuts no corners on guest comfort. Most of the bedrooms are
enormous – which makes some standard rooms appear quite small – and
all have views through stone-mullioned windows of the park and the lake
or the formal Italian garden. Some have light cane-look furniture and
modern bathrooms while others are old-fashioned in a grand way, with
antiques, slightly fading fabrics and rise and fall light fittings (weights
and pulleys adjust their height).

  You need plenty of space in your room as breakfast is generally served
in there at the hour of your choice on an immaculate table with a white
cloth, polished glasses and a silver teapot. Dinner is a more sociable
affair. Against a backdrop of grand fireplaces, oil paintings and richly
ornate plaster relief work, the good-value table d'hôte menu might offer
artichoke vinaigrette or smoked trout, grilled leg of lamb with rosemary,
Aylesbury duckling with orange sauce, and home-made puddings.
There are often functions going on at the hall but there are plenty of
places to escape them – the pretty blue sitting-room, for example, or the
low-lit oak-panelled bar. Unaffected by their rather grand surroundings,
Mr Chapman's staff are both efficient and friendly.

◑ Open all year, exc Xmas period;
restaurant closed Sun eve

➚ 2 miles north of Bakewell on the
B6001. Private car park

🛏 7 twin/double, 2 four-poster, 2
family rooms, 1 suite; all with
bathroom/WC, TV, room service,
hair-dryer

◈ 3 restaurants, bar, lounge;
conference facilities (max 60
people non-residential, 12

residential); tennis, croquet at
hotel, other sports nearby.
Wheelchair access to hotel
(2 steps), restaurant and WC
(M,F), no ground-floor bedrooms
but a lift

● No dogs in public rooms and in
bedrooms by arrangement; no
smoking in some public rooms

▭ Access, Amex, Diners, JCB, Visa

£ Single occupancy of twin/double

from £65 to £99, twin/double
£75 to £109, four-poster £75/
£109, family room £95 plus £10
for each child, suite price on

application. Continental B £6,
cooked B £9; set L £13, £15.50,
D £20, £25 (prices till autumn
93). Special breaks available

HATHERLEIGH DEVON   MAP 10

The George Hotel ☆

MARKET STREET, HATHERLEIGH, DEVON EX20 3JN
TEL: OKEHAMPTON (0837) 810454   FAX: (0837) 810901

*A half-timbered, thatch-roofed pub-hotel in the centre of
Hatherleigh.*

You must keep your eyes peeled for the George, not because it is
particularly small but because it is just off a steep hill, with the entrance to
its car park some way below it. Externally, it is a quintessential English
coaching-inn which reeks of local history; records show that it was
originally built by fifteenth-century Tavistock monks. Reception opens
off a central courtyard, beyond which lies the pub which gets particularly
lively at Sunday lunchtimes. Even when rushed off his feet, hotelier John
Dunbar finds time to explain how the cosy lounge-bar with welcoming
log fire used to double up as a hairdresser's-cum-local court on market
days, and how the curious opening cut into the screen separating it from
the dining-room was used to let a farmer watch his mares foaling. Peek
through now and you'll see diners tucking into roasts in a long, thin room
roofed with hefty beams.

   Most bedrooms have attractively sloping ceilings, the bathroom of
Trave'lers Joy boasting the sharpest angles. (Lavender has a disappointing view of the car park.) Despite the space constraints of such an old
building, three rooms squeeze in four-posters. An upstairs lounge is not
as cosy as the downstairs one but may well be quieter.

◐ Open all year; restaurant closed
Sun eve

⤢ From the A30 take the turn-off
to Okehampton. In Okehampton
take a right on to A386
signposted Hatherleigh. Private
car park

⇌ 1 single, 3 twin, 4 double, 3
four-poster; most with bathroom,
some with shower/WC; TV, room
service, baby-listening in all
rooms; hair-dryer on request

◇ Restaurant, 3 bars, lounge,
drying room, games room;
conference facilities (max 11

people residential, 40 non-
residential); outdoor heated
swimming-pool at hotel, fishing,
golf, other sports nearby;
babysitting. Wheelchair access to
restaurant and WC (F) only

⊖ No children in restaurant after
7.30pm; no dogs in public rooms

▭ Access, Amex, Visa

£ Single £29, single occupancy of
twin/double £29 to £50, twin/
double £50 to £68, four-poster
£80, family room rate on
request. Alc D £18. Special
breaks available

Highlow Hall

HATHERSAGE, DERBYSHIRE S30 1AZ
TEL: HOPE VALLEY (0433) 650393

Inexpensive accommodation in a historic farmhouse with an
extremely peaceful location and professional, enthusiastic hosts.

Philip and Julie Wain are young hoteliers worth keeping an eye on.
Having trained in various parts of the country, they have returned now to
the hills near Hathersage to turn Philip's family home into a hotel.
Converting a farmhouse with unused rooms and a mix of antiques and
dated modern furniture into a comfortable hotel is an enterprise the
Wains have entered into with an enthusiasm that shows. They couldn't
have had better raw materials: the sixteenth-century Derbyshire stone
house is square and solid with a castellated roofline, stone-mullioned
windows, a banqueting hall that would sit easily in any baronial manor,
and a simply magnificent location – currently, perhaps, the hotel's
biggest attraction. You can look in one direction over Eyam Moor, land
unaltered for generations with no sign of human habitation. Bang in the
middle of the Peak District National Park, Highlow Hall makes a good
starting point for walkers but is popular with all sorts – especially in the
summer, when you should book ahead.

All six bedrooms have lovely views, light fabrics, solid old-fashioned
furniture and loads of space – except for the single room Philip calls
'extremely single', which is reached through a five-foot latch door and is
more of a priest's hole than a bedroom. Recent improvements mean that
three of the rooms are now refurbished and have *en-suite* shower rooms
– Number Two being the smartest, with its antique brass bed and pretty
blue wallpaper. Downstairs, the sitting-room is somewhat dated but has
a log fire and plenty of comfortable sofas and chairs. The three-course
evening meals, cooked by Julie, might include home-made soup, chicken
provençal and apple pie with cream.

◖ Open all year; dining-room
closed Sun eve

↗ Take the B6001 to Grindleford and
½ mile out of Hathersage turn
right at Abney. The Hall is 1½
miles on the left. Private car park

🛏 1 single, 1 twin, 2 double, 2
family rooms; half with shower/
WC, 2 public bathrooms

◇ Dining-room, lounge (with TV),
function room; conference

facilities (max 30 people non-
residential, 6 residential); fishing,
golf, other sports nearby

⊖ No wheelchair access; no dogs in
public rooms; no smoking in
dining-room and bedrooms

▭ None accepted

£ Single £18, single occupancy of
twin/double £25 to £30, twin/
double £40 to £46, family room
£50 to £56. Set D £12 (7.30pm)

Prices are quoted per room *rather than* per person.

Northleigh House

FIVE WAYS ROAD, HATTON, NR WARWICK, WARWICKSHIRE CV35 7HZ
TEL: WARWICK (0926) 484203

A jolly hostess and comfortable rooms in a guesthouse with a difference.

Sylvia Fenwick is the sort of person who believes in getting things done, being generous and having fun – and her personality is stamped all over her guesthouse. She manages the garden singlehandedly, and has done much of the DIY around the house too. A square turn-of-the-century building on a busy lane surrounded by flat green fields, Northleigh has an unremarkable exterior but inside there is plenty of character. The large sitting-room, with a huge glass-fronted cabinet of books, solid fuel stove and plenty of sofas and comfortable armchairs, has a number of paintings by Sylvia's uncle, which she says are always a great talking point. Another painting, this time by a friend, hangs prominently in the dining-room where guests eat together around three highly polished tables. A recent innovation is dinner party-style evening meals for four or more people by arrangement, provided by a non-resident chef: 'She's a friend of mine, and everyone has great fun,' Sylvia told us. If you'd rather have a light supper on a tray, you can do so.

Sylvia's jolly personality is evident in the décor of the bedrooms, too. Each has a theme which has been carried through with great attention to detail – the ground-floor Blue Room with king-sized bed and space enough for a sofa has only books with blue covers, while Gold, a small double room, has prints, a kettlestand, a door stop and a stained-glass picture all depicting owls. Poppy and the Chinese Room are more restful and are light and sunny. There are facilities for making drinks that go far beyond those offered by most guesthouses – at Northleigh each room has a kitchenette cleverly concealed in a wardrobe.

◑ *Closed mid-Dec to mid-Jan*

⤢ *Take the A4177 for 5 miles north-west out of Warwick to Five Ways roundabout, then turn left towards Shrewley for ½ mile. Private car park*

🛏 *1 single, 1 twin, 4 double; half with bathroom/WC, half with shower/WC; TV, room service, fridge in all rooms*

◈ *Dining-room, lounge*

⊖ *No wheelchair access; no dogs in public rooms; no smoking*

▭ *Access, Visa*

£ *Single £29, single occupancy of twin/double £29, twin/double £40 to £55. Set D £14.50; supper trays (both by arrangement)*

Use the maps at the back of the Guide *to pinpoint hotels in a particular area.*

HAWKRIDGE SOMERSET **MAP 10**

Tarr Steps

HAWKRIDGE, DULVERTON, SOMERSET TA22 9PY
TEL: WINSFORD (064 385) 293 FAX: (064 385) 218

An elegant country-house hotel with wonderful views and a strong sports tradition, next to the Tarr Steps.

Provided you haven't made the mistake of approaching from the road leading inexorably to the ford, a steep drive winds up from the narrow road to the Bronze Age Tarr Steps and deposits guests in front of what is now a primarily Victorian building. Beside the house, tables are laid out on a lawn as for a polite tea-party in keeping with the house's origin in the eighteenth century as Hawkridge's vicarage. The lounge is positioned to take advantage of spectacular views of empty moorland. In season, the hunting community flocks to Tarr Steps; a stag's head gazes down on the bar and the hall walls are decked out with foxy cartoons. Four-course dinners are served in an elegant dining-room split in two by an arch; tables come in a variety of shapes and sizes, but all are dressed up with candles and flowers and menus are hand-written. A typical dinner menu might feature spinach and cream cheese pancakes, chicken breast with tarragon sauce and home-grown vegetables, and oranges in Grand Marnier. Side bedrooms offer the best views, although the few steps down from their doorways could catch out anyone who has oversampled the wine list. Some rooms incorporate old cast-iron fireplaces and big brass beds with lacy counterpanes.

◑ Closed Feb and 1st 2 weeks Mar

⤴ 6 miles from Dulverton. Leave Dulverton on the road signposted Hawkridge. Follow the road to Hawkridge and then signs to Tarr Steps and hotel. Private car park

🛏 3 single, 4 twin, 4 double, 3 four-poster (some rooms in annexe); all with bathroom/WC, exc singles; room service to all rooms; hair-dryer on request; no tea/coffee-making facilities in rooms

◈ Dining-room, bar, lounge, drying room; conference facilities (max 12 people non-residential); fishing, clay pigeon and rough shooting in grounds, other sports nearby. Wheelchair access to hotel, restaurant and WC (M), 1 ground-floor bedroom

⊖ No dogs in public rooms

▭ Access, Visa

💷 Single £38, single occupancy of twin/double £50, twin/double/four-poster £76; deposit required. Sun L £12; set D £21.50. Special breaks available

HAWKSHEAD CUMBRIA **MAP 4**

Grizedale Lodge Hotel

GRIZEDALE, HAWKSHEAD, AMBLESIDE, CUMBRIA LA22 0QL
TEL: HAWKSHEAD (05394) 36532

Comfortable, secluded hotel in the Grizedale Forest yet within easy striking distance of all the tourist traps.

'From Hawkshead follow the brown signs for the Theatre in the Forest – we're the first sign of civilisation you come to.' You get the feeling that life has been made a little easier for Jack and Margaret Lamb since the arrival of the theatre for not only does it provide a great source of local entertainment, from jazz to drama, but it has also been a boon for guests navigating their way to this former hunting-lodge deep in the heart of the Grizedale Forest Park. The warm welcome you receive has been noted by one of our readers and indeed Jack Lamb greets you with a firm handshake like an old friend.

The Lambs have gone in for modern comfort throughout. The bar/lounge has a pub-like seating area built into the bay window as well as a number of armchairs in bright colourful patterns. References to its previous days as a shooting-lodge are unmistakable: stuffed birds, animal prints on the walls, a stuffed squirrel clambering over the optics above the bar and the ubiquitous antlers, two sets of which face each other across the dining-room like enemy squadrons. The dining-room, antlers aside, has a homely feel and Margaret Lamb likes to spice up the traditional Cumbrian menus with some continental dishes. Ratatouille with garlic bread may be followed by chicken in red wine with prawns and mushrooms with a sorbet in between. Vegetarians can be catered for with advance notice. The service tends to be a little rushed though, with hardly a pause for breath between courses when our inspector visited.

The bedrooms are simple and comfortable with a mixture of wood and chipboard furniture. There are two superior rooms, the Beech Suite and the Rowan Suite, both with four-poster beds. Consider avoiding rooms, like Room Six, that look over the nearby cowsheds as the frantic lowing of cattle can disturb that early morning tranquillity.

◑ Open all year, exc Jan

⤢ From Hawkshead take the Newby Bridge road, turn right after 600 yards (signposted Forest Park Centre). Follow this road for 2½ miles; the hotel is on the right. Private car park

🛏 2 twin, 4 double, 2 four-poster, 1 family room; some with bathroom/WC, most with shower/WC; TV in all rooms; hair-dryer on request

◈ Dining-room, bar/lounge, drying room, conservatory; fishing, tennis, water sports nearby. Wheelchair access to hotel (2 steps) and restaurant, 3 ground-floor bedrooms

⊖ No dogs; no smoking in bedrooms

▭ Access, Visa

£ Single occupancy of twin/double £38 to £42, twin/double £60 to £68, four-poster £68 to £80, family room £60 to £68; deposit required. Bar lunches; set D £18. Special breaks available

Are you aware of your rights as a consumer when you book into a hotel? Check them out on page 837.

Highfield House

HAWKSHEAD HILL, AMBLESIDE, CUMBRIA LA22 0PN
TEL: AMBLESIDE (05394) 36344

A spacious and comfortable guesthouse at the heart of the Lake District.

It would be hard to find a better base for making the most of the southern lakes – Windermere and Coniston Water are to the west and east respectively, while Esthwaite Water and the picturesque Tarn Hows are just a short distance away, so whether you are on a nature trail or a literary one you will be well-placed. The elevated position of this late-nineteenth-century Lakeland stone house guarantees splendid views which, according to proprietors Jim and Pauline Bennett, take in the mighty Helvellyn on a clear day.

The atmosphere inside is distinctly unstuffy and the rooms are homely and unpretentious. The large lounge has armchairs beside the fire and two great bay windows; a selection of maps and guidebooks is available to help you plan your days in the surrounding fells (and there are drying facilities should you be caught in inclement weather). There is a small bar where you can enjoy a drop of the local bitter or an aperitif before you head to a dining-room with subtle autumnal shades and extensive views. Dinners always contain a vegetarian choice and – another indication of the Bennetts' thoughtfulness – children's favourites can be prepared for high tea on request. One summer evening's menu included tomato, apple and celery soup and roast loin of pork alsacienne with cider cream sauce. Readers also report a wide choice at breakfast 'including black pudding, Cumberland sausage and Loch Fyne kippers'.

Bedrooms are individually decorated, One and Two being the largest – one reader reports that Room One is 'very well-fitted and comfortable – a good modern bathroom with separate shower cubicles. Lots of space in built-in wardrobes.'

◐ Open all year, exc Xmas

⤴ ½ mile north of Hawkshead on the B5285 Coniston road, on the left-hand side. Private car park

🛏 2 single, 3 twin, 6 double; all with bathroom/WC, exc 2 doubles with shower/WC; TV, hair-dryer in all rooms

◇ Dining-room, bar, lounge, drying room; conference facilities (max 25 people non-residential, 20 residential); fishing, riding, other sports nearby

⊖ No wheelchair access; no dogs in public rooms; no smoking in dining-room

▭ Access, Visa

£ Single £29 to £31, single occupancy of twin/double £36 to £40, twin/double £53 to £59; deposit required. Light lunches; set D £14.50. Special breaks available

---

Report forms are at the back of the Guide; *write a letter if you prefer.*

Ivy House Hotel

MAIN STREET, HAWKSHEAD, AMBLESIDE, CUMBRIA LA22 0NS
TEL: HAWKSHEAD (05394) 36204

A friendly and inexpensive guesthouse in a touristy Lake District village.

This dark green Georgian town house stands in Hawkshead, one of the Lake District's most popular villages. Many visitors come here to see Beatrix Potter's paintings and Wordsworth's grammar school, so parking space is at a premium and Ivy House's car park is a point in its favour.

Inside there is a friendly and relaxed atmosphere, due to the work of the proprietors, the Vaughans: David carries out most of the front-of-house responsibilities, meeting guests, settling bills and serving meals, while Jane works behind the scenes in the kitchen. Meals are taken at a single sitting in the peach-coloured dining-room, which is liberally hung with decorative plates. There is no choice until dessert and you can expect something like soup, roast lamb, mint sauce and roast potatoes, followed by Bakewell tart and custard. Helpings are more than generous. After the meal, guests retire to the lounge with its warming fire for mints, coffee and conversation.

A magnificent curving staircase leads up to the bedrooms, which are functional and neat with modern pine furniture and blue floral duvets. There are more rooms in the annexe at the back, but you would do better to ask for one of those in the main house.

- ◑ Closed Nov to Feb
- ⤢ In the centre of the village. Private car park
- 🛏 2 twin, 7 double, 2 family rooms; most with bathroom/WC, some with shower/WC; TV in 5 rooms
- ◈ Dining-room, lounge, drying room; fishing at hotel, golf, other sports nearby
- ⊖ No wheelchair access; no dogs in public rooms; no smoking in dining-room
- ▭ Access, Visa
- £ Single occupancy of twin/double £28, twin/double £56, family room from £66; deposit required. Set D £9.50 (7pm)

Queen's Head Hotel

MAIN STREET, HAWKSHEAD, AMBLESIDE, CUMBRIA LA22 0NS
TEL: HAWKSHEAD (05394) 36271   FAX: (05394) 36722

A friendly pub with straightforward bedrooms.

Anthony Merrick has been here for five years now, and upgrading continues apace: last year it was central heating, this year two more bedrooms have had *en-suite* facilities added. Otherwise the style remains similar: light, flowery fabrics and plain walls with some stencilling. However, the main attraction of this black and white sixteenth-century pub, in one of the most touristy villages in the Lakes, is the food. After seeing Wordsworth's grammar school and Beatrix Potter's house, and stocking up on woolly sweaters, tourists flock in for a hearty lunch – perhaps a large Yorkshire pudding filled with beef and vegetable casserole or Chinese-style spare ribs. The panelled and beamed bar, hung with plates and signed racing memorabilia, gets pretty crowded, but service is prompt and efficient. The restaurant, also panelled, has daintier lace cloths; its more formal menu runs along the lines of steak, breast of Barbary duck, and chicken suprême. Because the village is pedestrianised there's no parking, but residents are given a ticket for the pay and display car park 100 yards away.

◑ Open all year

⤵ The hotel is in the village square. Free parking at public car park

🛏 3 twin, 8 double, 3 four-poster; some with bathroom/WC, most with shower/WC, 2 public bathrooms; TV, room service, hair-dryer, baby-listening in all rooms

◇ Restaurant, bar; fishing, golf, other sports nearby. Wheelchair access to restaurant only

⊖ No dogs; no smoking in restaurant

▭ Access, Visa

£ Single occupancy of twin/double £32 to £40, twin/double £46 to £58, four-poster £62 to £66; deposit required. Set L from £4; alc D from £12

HAWNBY NORTH YORKSHIRE   **MAP 3**

Hawnby Hotel

HAWNBY, NR HELMSLEY, NORTH YORKSHIRE YO6 5QS
TEL: BILSDALE (04396) 202   FAX: (04396) 417

A peaceful setting and beautiful views tip the balance in favour of this stylishly revamped traditional inn.

On a sunny spring Sunday you'll share your garden table with knapsacked walkers, fluorescent-kitted cyclists and seemingly fearless birds which flit between the visitors on the lookout for crumbs. There is no denying the appeal of the stunning vistas from this creeper-clad inn with green shutters, of the tiny village of honey-coloured stone that lies below it, or of nearby Rievaulx.

Inside, the overwhelming impression is of neatness, with a bright, cottagey style and a penchant for Laura Ashley. Even the bar, with its modern autumnal-shade wallpaper, bird pictures and pot plants, is less grimy than many authentically venerable Yorkshire watering-holes, and a signed photo of Frank Bruno sums up the general air of mateyness encouraged by the friendly staff. Residents can snack here or dine in the Mexborough Room, which combines a modern dining area with a beige lounge and stone fireplace; there are lots of books to browse through.

Bedrooms are bonny, with basketweave chairs and co-ordinating décor in chintzy colours and dainty patterns. Lots of facilities and a decanter of sherry add to the general air of cosiness. Bathrooms are similarly bright and modern, but one reader reported that there was 'so little room that I bruised myself a number of times on the half-wall at the end of the bath that separated it from the loo'.

Our inspector found the choice of food in the bar predictable and unimaginative, and a guest suggested that the limited-choice set dinner in the restaurant 'tasted as if they had had it in the freezer'.

◑ *Open all year, exc Jan, Feb, 25 Dec*

↗ *7 miles north-west of Helmsley off the B1257 Helmsley to Stokesley road. Private car park*

🛏 *4 twin, 2 double; all with bathroom/WC, TV, room service, hair-dryer; ironing facilities*

◈ *Dining-room, bar, lounge; conference facilities (max 20 people non-residential, 12*

residential); fishing, tennis, riding, other sports nearby

⊖ *No wheelchair access; no children under 10; no dogs; no smoking in bedrooms*

▭ *Access, Visa*

£ *Single occupancy of twin/double £40 to £50, twin/double £50 to £70. Bar snacks; set D from £14. Special breaks available*

HAWORTH WEST YORKSHIRE   MAP 5

Weavers

15 WEST LANE, HAWORTH, WEST YORKSHIRE BD22 8DU
TEL: HAWORTH (0535) 643822

A captivating cornucopia of clutter and esoteric ephemera in Yorkshire's most-visited village.

One of the most striking things about this interesting restaurant-with-rooms is its refusal to genuflect to Haworth's most famous daughters; the only references to the 'B' word in its brochure are a terse acknowledgement that the hotel overlooks the house and an instruction to 'look for signs to the Brontë Parsonage Museum'. Instead, the warren-like building celebrates Yorkshire's other great tradition, the textile industry, from the entrance porch with its stacked bobbins and the bar with its hanging spindles and shuttles to an atmospheric low-ceilinged restaurant with exposed stone walls, pine display cases and a framed poster from the Victoria and Albert Museum. Brass, copper, a collection of teapots and a 'Kiss me quick' hat give a quirky feel to the coffee lounge.

The four bedrooms are well-equipped and comfortable, with good old or antique furniture and pleasant classic décor. Attention to detail, from embroidered sheets to proper wooden coathangers, is meticulous.

The food is 'honest northern' and seriously good – perhaps Dales cheese fritters on winter leaves with warm redcurrant and orange dressing, followed by loin of Yorkshire lamb with spicy onion and potato cake, and sticky toffee pudding with whipped cream.

◑ *Open all year, exc 24 Dec for 2 weeks and 2 weeks from end July; restaurant closed Sun and Mon*

◈ *Dining-room (air-conditioned), bar, lounge; golf, riding, heated swimming-pool, other sports nearby*

◪ *In Haworth, follow signs for Brontë Parsonage Museum. Parking in public car park at rear of restaurant*

⊖ *No wheelchair access; no dogs; no smoking in dining-room*

▭ *Access, Amex, Diners, Visa*

⇔ *2 single, 1 twin, 1 double; all with bathroom/WC, TV, room service, hair-dryer, trouser press in all rooms*

£ *Single £45, single occupancy of twin/double £45, twin/double £65; deposit required. Set D £13.50; alc D £20*

HAYES MIDDLESEX   MAP 9

Edwardian International

140 BATH ROAD, HAYES, MIDDLESEX UB3 5AW
TEL: 081-759 6311   TELEX: 23935   FAX: 081-759 4559

Richly decorated Heathrow hotel, owned by the Edwardian group.

This huge and grandiose hotel makes a striking impression as you enter, to the strains of classical music, through a white colonnade into the marbled, chandeliered foyer. The public rooms are glossy and stylish, with thick, boldly coloured carpets to add to the feeling of luxury. The Edwardian theme comes to the fore in Henley's Drawing-Room and Restaurant, where paintings of ladies in bustles decorate the wood-panelled walls. Light meals are served in the bright, mural-clad Brasserie, which overlooks the tiered swimming-pool and waterfall built under a glass dome.

Bedrooms are dominated by strong well-co-ordinated colour schemes, with many unexpected touches of luxury: modern, hand-decorated satinwood furniture, monogrammed pillows and cupboards to hide away the TVs and mini-bars. High standards are maintained in the lavish, marble bathrooms. The A4 on which the hotel stands is noisy but all rooms are double-glazed. You will need plenty of money to stay here, but you will find plenty of helpful staff and ample parking – and it is worth checking if any special deals are on offer.

◑ *Open all year*

◪ *On the main A4 Bath Road, on left-hand side heading towards London. A courtesy coach operates from Heathrow Airport Terminals 1, 2 and 3. Private car park*

⇔ *63 single, 80 twin, 70 double, 7 four-poster, 5 family rooms, 17 suites, 112 executive singles, 105 executive twin/double; all with bathroom/WC, TV, room service, hair-dryer, trouser press,* mini-bar, air-conditioning; tea/coffee-making facilities on request

 2 restaurants, bar, lounge, business centre, drying room; conference facilities (max 500 people residential and non-residential), all air-conditioned; sauna/solarium, health spa, heated swimming-pool, gym at hotel. Wheelchair access to hotel, brasserie and WC (unisex), 82 ground-floor bedrooms

⊖ No dogs in public rooms

▭ Access, Amex, Diners, Visa

£ Single £153, single occupancy of twin/double £153, twin/double £184, four-poster £434, family room £214, suite £434, executive single £184, executive twin/double £215; deposit required. Cooked B £11, continental B £9; set L, D £16.50/£24.50. Special breaks available

---

HAYFIELD DERBYSHIRE   **MAP 5**

Bridge End Guesthouse ☆

7 CHURCH STREET, HAYFIELD, STOCKPORT SK12 5JE
TEL: NEW MILLS (0663) 747321

Comfortable, inexpensive rooms and imaginative food on the edge of the Peak District National Park.

Hayfield village, with its rose-covered cottages, parish church and cricket matches lasting most of the day during summer, is as English as can be. Its position on the edge of the Peak District National Park saves it from the tourist crowds, though it is still pretty busy with walkers delaying their climb up Kinder Scout by browsing around the antique shops or downing a pint in the pub. Bridge End is more of a restaurant-with-rooms than a hotel, and the food is far above standard guesthouse fare. What you save on the inexpensive accommodation is well worth paying towards one of Jonathan Holmes's well-presented dinners, which might be asparagus spears on oyster mushroom sherry sauce, roast saddle of spring lamb with cumin, garlic and red peppers, and the 'Unabridged' pudding which is a bit of everything, including nougatine parfait, mango sorbet, strawberry sable, chocolate mousse and caramelised bananas. Then try climbing one of the peaks!

Though food is lavish the surroundings are not. Stripped pine, dried flowers and wooden floor give the restaurant a café feel, lifted out of the ordinary by paintings by local artists. Bedrooms are equally simple, with pine furniture, plain walls and firm mattresses – welcome after a day's exercise. All rooms have good-sized modern bathrooms which, though they have a slightly unfinished feel, are well-equipped with showers above the bath and plenty of hot water.

◖ Open all year; restaurant closed Sun and Mon eves

 From Stockport take A6 to New Mills, then the Hayfield road.

Bridge End is in the middle of the village, opposite the church. Private car park

🛏 1 twin, 3 double; all with bathroom/WC, TV, room service, hair-dryer, baby-listening

◇ Restaurant, bar, lounge (Nov 93), drying room; conference facilities (max 20 people non-residential, 4 residential); tennis, riding, other sports nearby

⊖ No wheelchair access; dogs by arrangement only; smoking discouraged

▭ Access, Amex, Diners, Visa

£ Single occupancy of twin/double £28 to £30, twin/double £39 to £45. Sun L £13; set D £14; alc D £20

HAYLING ISLAND HAMPSHIRE   MAP 9

Cockle Warren Cottage

36 SEAFRONT, HAYLING ISLAND, HAMPSHIRE PO11 9HL
TEL: HAYLING ISLAND (0705) 464961/464838

Lovingly maintained cottage hotel with its own swimming-pool.

Cockle Warren may be a small hotel, but its owners, David and Diane Skelton, think big. Having started with just one guest bedroom, they have now converted their 15-year-old red-tiled family home to offer five rooms – including one in a stable-block annexe – and have added a conservatory restaurant and a heated swimming-pool. All has been done with tender care and meticulous attention to detail.

The hotel stands about 200 yards back from the beach on the landward side of the seafront road, and, while the view of the sea wall is less than spectacular, the salty tang in the air and the roar of the waves on shingle is unmistakable. Life at Cockle Warren revolves around the lounge, which, thanks to the recent ingenious addition of a dais, has tightly packed seating for all the residents even if the Skeltons have a full house. As well as an old upright piano and reproduction coffee tables, it's furnished with a clutter of horse brasses, plants, carriage clocks and family paintings. The pink velvet three-piece suite and the green walls set the colour scheme which is conscientiously, even slavishly, followed throughout the hotel, even in the tiling of the pool. Breakfasts with home-baked bread, cream teas and carefully prepared set dinners – with good-value house wine by the bottle or by the glass – are served in the smart conservatory at the back of the house.

Besides pink and green, pine features heavily in the pretty but fussy bedrooms. These are crammed with all kinds of details, such as tapestries of old London woven by David's mother and antique phones. Two rooms even have four-poster beds, but don't ask how they were squeezed in. A generous array of extras is also thrown in: decanters of madeira, chocolates, sewing kits, ironing facilities and playing cards.

◑ Open all year

⤢ From A3/M27 to Havant, go over bridge to Hayling Island, south to seafront, turn left ¾ mile along front. Private car park

🛏 3 double, 2 four-poster; all with

shower/WC, exc 1 four-poster
with bathroom/WC; TV, room
service, hair-dryer, trouser press
in all rooms; no tea/coffee-
making facilities in rooms

 Restaurant, lounge, conservatory;
heated swimming-pool (spring to
autumn) at hotel, other sports
nearby; babysitting

 No wheelchair access; no
children under 12 (exc babies);
dogs by arrangement; smoking in
lounges only

Access, Visa

 Single occupancy of double £35
to £55, double £60 to £78, four-
poster £78 to £98; deposit
required. Set D £23.50 (8pm)

HAYTOR DEVON   MAP 10

Bel Alp House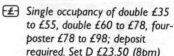

HAYTOR, NR BOVEY TRACEY, DEVON TQ13 9XX
TEL: HAYTOR (0364) 661217   FAX: (0364) 661292

A luxurious and stylish hotel in the middle of Dartmoor.

A fine white Edwardian building, Bel Alp hides down a quiet side road at
the end of a line of properties once owned by the Wills family of tobacco
fame. Inside, its cool elegance is partly derived from the crisp white walls
and arched doorways, partly the consequence of its distinctive fixtures
and fittings: paintings line the hallway, a statue of a naked white nymph
lurks at the foot of the stairs. The whiteness also accentuates the
spaciousness, particularly that of the bedrooms, some of which are the
size of small apartments. Not that the décor is always so restrained; in
one bedroom, for example, the crown canopy above the bed is a dark,
almost funereal navy-blue. In general, the bedrooms are stunning and it
would be hard to think of any comforts that have been overlooked. Some
of the baths are so big they stand in overflow-catching marble trays in
case you get carried away and forget to turn off the taps. Front rooms,
sadly, look out on the car park through their huge windows; those at the
back have the best views.

Hotelier Roger Curnock serves pre-dinner drinks from a small bar in
the corner of one of the lounges, made particularly welcoming in winter
by a roaring log fire. A bigger rear lounge has less character, but boasts
several small paintings by ancestors James Curnock and James Jackson
Curnock; in the dining-room a much larger painting of a blind Roman
flowergirl is harder to overlook. On summer evenings dinners are served
by windows overlooking Dartmoor. Sarah Curnock's set five-course
menus don't offer choices, although a few standbys, including vegetarian
dishes, are listed as possible substitutes; a typical menu might feature
asparagus with melted butter, fennel cream soup, grilled salmon with
avocado sauce and vanilla ice-cream with raspberry liqueur sauce,
rounded off with a selection of Devon cheeses.

The Curnocks also run the hotel on very 'organised' lines, with pre-
assigned tables for dinner (irritating if you land the one by the fire
escape). Some readers have commented on Bel Alp's high prices.

◑ Open all year

⤢ 2½ miles west of Bovey Tracey off the B3387. Private car park

🛏 5 twin, 4 double; all with bathroom or shower/WC; TV, room service, hair-dryer, baby-listening

◇ Dining-room, bar, 2 lounges, games room, drying room; fishing, tennis, other sports nearby. Wheelchair access to hotel (2 steps), dining-room and WC (M,F), 2 ground-floor bedrooms, lift

⊖ No smoking in dining-room and discouraged in bedrooms

▭ Access, Visa

£ Single occupancy of twin/double £72 to £87, twin/double £120 to £150; deposit required. Set D £33

HEACHAM NORFOLK   **MAP 7**

Holly Lodge

HEACHAM, NR KING'S LYNN, NORFOLK PE31 7HY
TEL: HEACHAM (0485) 70790

A colourful guesthouse within easy reach of sandy beaches, five stately homes and good walks.

Entering Holly Lodge is like an encounter with a Neapolitan ice-cream: walls are deep-pink in the entrance hall and chocolate brown in the bar. Strong colours are Lesley Piper's passion and they are used to striking effect throughout the Elizabethan house. Room One, a twin, is a bold yellow with contrasting blue quilts on the beds and Room Three combines peach and terracotta colours with an Aladdin's cave bathroom and a plush canopy over the large double bed. The only disappointment

HOLLY LODGE
–HEACHAM–

is Room Four, where the wallpaper is old-fashioned in comparison with the other rooms, but the four-poster may make up for the mumsy décor.

Dinner is served in a dining-room of racing-car green. The menus offer a good choice: starters of a warm pastry of field and wood mushrooms with cream and basil or perhaps a salad of marinated monkfish, lightly grilled with orange and dill; main courses of oxtail braised in red wine with grapes, fillet steak or grilled Dover sole; and desserts of passion fruit parfait with bitter chocolate sauce or chocolate Saint-Emilion. A small lounge with a bookcase of leatherbound volumes and cosy sofas is a good place to curl up with a coffee.

◑ *Closed Jan, Feb; restaurant closed Sun eve*

⤵ *From King's Lynn turn left off the A149 into Heacham village at the 'Norfolk Lavender' sign. Holly Lodge is 900 yards down the road on the right-hand side. Private car park*

🛏 *1 twin, 3 double, 2 four-poster; all with bathroom/WC; room service, hair-dryer; tea/coffee-making facilities on request*

◇ *Restaurant, bar, lounge, TV room; golf, tennis, other sports nearby*

⊖ *No wheelchair access; no dogs; no smoking in bedrooms*

▭ *Access, Visa*

💷 *Single occupancy of twin/double £55, twin/double/four-poster £85; deposit required. Alc D £22.50*

HELFORD CORNWALL   **MAP 10**

Riverside

HELFORD, NR HELSTON, CORNWALL TR12 6JU
TEL: MANACCAN (0326) 231443   FAX: (0326) 231103

A pretty, whitewashed restaurant-with-rooms overlooking Helford Creek.

It would be hard to imagine a more delightful setting than Riverside's, high up on a terrace above pretty thatched Helford and its creek. What's more, there is little to alert you to the fact that it is a hotel at all, although the excellent restaurant announces itself more loudly. Three-course dinners home straight in on the wonderful local seafood, although there are always a few dishes to satisfy non-fish eaters as well; a typical meal might start with warm local mussels, crab and avocado salad with a dill dressing, move on to salmon in pastry with basil butter and a lemon butter sauce and finish with layered strawberry shortbreads on a raspberry coulis.

A small lounge above the restaurant is supplied with plenty of books and magazines to be read in the morning sun; occasionally it is let as a suite with the adjacent double bedroom, which has a spare single bed tucked away at the back under a sloping ceiling. Other rooms hide in cottages straggling up steps behind the restaurant; guests are given torches to find their way to bed after dinner. All rooms are extremely attractive – even the view of Helford chimneys from the topmost cottage is a winner – and readers particularly like the finishing touches such as fresh milk, home-made shortbread and 'lovely, thick towels fresh every morning'. Edward and Susan Darrell are as hospitable and charming as ever, making their guests feel comfortably at ease.

◑ *Closed mid-Nov to mid-Feb*

⤢ *In Helford, the hotel car park is opposite the public car park*

🛏 *3 twin, 3 double, suite available; all with bathroom/WC, TV, room service, hair-dryer, trouser press, mini-bar*

◈ *Restaurant, bar, drying room; fishing, golf, other sports nearby;*

babysitting by arrangement

⊖ *No wheelchair access; no children under 12 at dinner; no dogs*

▭ *None accepted*

£ *Single occupancy of twin/double £60, twin/double £75 to £95, suite £120; deposit required. Set D £28*

HENLEY-IN-ARDEN WARWICKSHIRE   **MAP 9**

Ashleigh House

WHITLEY HILL, WARWICK ROAD, HENLEY-IN-ARDEN, WARWICKSHIRE
B95 5DL
TEL: HENLEY-IN-ARDEN (0564) 792315   FAX: (0564) 794133

A comfortable guesthouse in a rural setting, convenient for Stratford and the Midlands.

Ashleigh House, with its pebbledash exterior, large, plain windows and red-tiled roof, is a typically unbeautiful Edwardian building, untypically set in farmland. Surrounded by its own neatly lawned garden, well back from the main Warwick road out of Henley-in-Arden, the house is surprisingly peaceful. Since taking over in 1990 Mr and Mrs Jamouse have stamped their own style on the interior, while keeping its Edwardian feel. Glass-fronted cabinets, table tops and chairs are full of antique dolls, of which the Jamouses have a huge collection. Some of them occupy the sitting-room, which is well-kept rather than cosy. The dining-room is light and cheerful with patterned plates and tablecloths.

   There are four cottagey bedrooms in the coach-house annexe, while six more in the main house have a mix of reproduction and antique furniture with some chintzy touches such as shiny wallpaper. The rooms have plenty of space but are light on goodies; Number One, with its large sky-lit bathroom, is the best.

◑ *Open all year; dining-room closed Sun eve*

⤢ *On the B4095 between the A3400 Stratford Road and Warwick. Private car park*

🛏 *4 twin, 6 double (some rooms in cottages); most with bathroom/ WC, some with shower/WC; TV, room service in all rooms, hair-dryer on request*

◇ Dining-room, lounge, conservatory; conference facilities (max 10 people residential); golf, riding, other sports nearby

⊖ No wheelchair access; no children under 15; dogs by arrangement only; no smoking in dining-room and discouraged in bedrooms

▭ Access, Visa

£ Single occupancy of twin/double £36 to £42, twin/double £49 to £55; deposit required. Alc D £15 to £20. Special breaks available

---

HENLEY-ON-THAMES OXFORDSHIRE   MAP 9

Hernes

GREYS ROAD, HENLEY-ON-THAMES, OXFORDSHIRE RG9 4NT
TEL: HENLEY-ON-THAMES (0491) 573245   FAX: (0491) 574645

Classic country-house style and friendly hospitality in a distinctive Wolsey Lodge.

Richard and Gillian Ovey's home is approached up a long, bumpy drive through acres of farmland scattered with grazing sheep and cattle – a mile or so away from Henley-on-Thames – difficult to find unless you have clear instructions. The mellowed brick house, which is in part sixteenth century, has been in the family for around 100 years and the atmosphere is that of a family country house cluttered with interesting objects and portraits acquired through the generations. The Oveys are relaxed and sociable hosts, with several years' experience of welcoming guests to their home. In the evenings guests eat together with Richard and Gillian in the dining-room with its high china cabinet; as there is no licence you may wish to bring your own wine. After dinner you can adjourn to the billiard room, where there is a full-sized billiard table and, in winter, a wood-burning stove alight to keep it cosy.

There are only three guest rooms, two with *en-suite* bathrooms; they all have fine antique furnishings, pretty floral fabrics and interesting ornaments. Tea trays are provided.

◑ Open all year, exc mid-Dec to mid-Jan

⤷ Telephone for directions. Private car park

⇌ 1 twin, 1 double, 1 four-poster; 2 with bathroom/WC, 1 with shower/WC

◇ Dining-room, 2 lounges, TV room, billiard room, drying room; conference facilities (max 10 people non-residential); croquet, outdoor heated swimming-pool (summer only) at hotel, other sports nearby

⊖ No wheelchair access; no children under 13; no dogs; no smoking

▭ None accepted

£ Single occupancy of twin/double £35 to £45, twin/double £55 to £65, four-poster £70; deposit required. Set D from £22.50 (prices till Easter 94). Special breaks available

The Red Lion

HART STREET/RIVERSIDE, HENLEY-ON-THAMES, OXFORDSHIRE RG9 2AR
TEL: HENLEY-ON-THAMES (0491) 572161   FAX: (0491) 410039

An old coaching-inn with refurbished rooms and simple public areas.

Unless you have booked a year in advance it's unlikely you'll find a room in the Red Lion in Henley Regatta week. This old red-brick creeper-clad coaching-inn is in a central position on a busy crossroads, just beside the bridge over the Thames. Owned by the Miller family (who also run Durrants Hotel in London – see entry), the hotel has a restrained decorative style that works better in some areas than others. The Regency Restaurant, where traditional Sunday lunch is cut from the joint on the trolley, has striped upholstered chairs and a dark wood panelled bar; the bar, with black leatherette tub chairs, is more appealing than the small lounge. Refurbishment of the bedrooms has continued throughout 1993 and the results are pleasing – a mix of antiques and modern dark wood furnishings set off by bold fabrics is the style. Of the older-style rooms, Number 103 is a popular choice, with rugs scattered on a stripped wood floor and an oak four-poster bed.

◑ *Open all year*

⤴ *Overlooks Henley Bridge and the River Thames. Private car park*

🛏 *6 single, 10 twin, 8 double, 1 four-poster, 1 family room; all with bathroom/WC, exc 3 singles, 2 public bathrooms; TV, room service in all rooms; hair-dryer in 14 rooms; trouser press in some rooms; no tea/coffee-making facilities in rooms*

◈ *Dining-room, bar, lounge, drying room; conference facilities (max 100 people non-residential, 25 residential); golf, fishing, other sports nearby; babysitting. Wheelchair access to dining-room and WC (F) only (1 step, through back entrance)*

⊖ *No dogs*

▭ *Access, Amex, Visa*

💷 *Single £43 to £70, single occupancy of twin/double £75, twin/double £83 or £95, four-poster £95, family room £125; deposit required. Cooked B £8, continental B £5.50; alc L £10, D £19.50/£22.50. Special breaks available*

HERTFORD HERTFORDSHIRE   MAP 9

The Hall House

COUNTY
HOTEL
OF THE
YEAR

BROADOAK END, OFF BRAMFIELD ROAD, HERTFORD, HERTFORDSHIRE
SG14 2JA
TEL: HERTFORD (0992) 582807

A friendly Wolsey Lodge which gives you the choice of being as sociable or as reserved as you like.

Olive Whiting has visitors who come to stay again and again in her comfortable home, and that's no surprise. The house is in a small hamlet beside a wooded rise just a couple of minutes by car from Hertford. It was rebuilt in 1985 around the original fifteenth-century timber frame and, in spite of the exposed beams in some rooms, the overall impression is of a smart modern home. The wide entrance hall is elegant, with a marble floor, a sweeping curved staircase and a modern chandelier; the sitting-room is formal and ornamental, while the dining-room is more cottagey in style with polished tables. Olive agrees the evening menu with her guests; typical fish dishes include smoked salmon parcels or char poached in butter and dill served with new potatoes, baby squash and french beans. Apple pie, cinnamon crêpes, trifles and summer pudding are popular desserts. If you want wine, Olive is happy for you to bring your own – there is no licence. At breakfast, as an alternative to a cooked meal, Olive provides a delicious fruit platter of, say, strawberries, pineapple and mango.

Bedrooms are cosy and spotless, with pleasing touches such as fresh flowers. Two bedrooms in the cottage across the garden have light floral décor and, just in case you need them, panic buttons that connect with the house.

◐ Open all year, exc Xmas; dining-room closed Sun eve

⬀ On the right-hand side, ¼ mile along the Bramfield road, off the A119 Stevenage road out of Hertford. Private car park

🛏 3 double (2 in cottage annexe); 1 with bathroom/WC, 2 with shower/WC, 1 public bathroom; TV, hair-dryer, trouser press in all rooms

◈ Dining-room, lounge, conservatory; fishing, golf nearby

⊖ No wheelchair access; no children under 14; no dogs; no smoking

▭ Access, Visa

£ Single occupancy of double £45, twin/double £60; deposit required. Set D £20 (7.15pm)

HEXHAM NORTHUMBERLAND   **MAP 3**

Middlemarch

HENCOTES, HEXHAM, NORTHUMBERLAND NE46 2EB
TEL: HEXHAM (0434) 605003

A relaxed and informal but elegant bed and breakfast overlooking the abbey grounds in the centre of town.

The hotelkeeping Elliotts do not, as far as we know, claim kinship with the lady who used the pseudonym George Eliot and wrote the epic novel which shares its name with the splendid cappuccino and cream, listed Georgian building. Instead, their great tradition is one of northern hospitality in a comfortable house that manages to retain the feel of a family home – not least in the downstairs loo, with its photos of family sporting triumphs. A large lounge has comfy chairs grouped in a semi-circle, a display of colourful pottery and endearingly crooked pictures (the house was built on sand and gravel, and daytime traffic thunders past outside), as well as tapestries, caricatures, books, games and tourist literature. Guests eat breakfast at a long refectory table in a large but homely kitchen complete with Aga and the lion from the Booth's gin logo.

Bedrooms are spacious and individually furnished in a bright, uncluttered style, with chintzy décor and the occasional antique; the one room with *en-suite* facilities has a four-poster bed, lovely old furniture and a blue and grey colour scheme. Front-facing rooms may suffer from some traffic noise.

◐ Open all year

↗ From the Abbey take Beaumont Street which leads away from the Abbey to Hencotes. The house is next to St Mary's RC church. Private car park

🛏 1 twin, 1 double, 1 four-poster; 1 with shower/WC, 1 public bathroom; TV, hair-dryer in all rooms

◇ Dining-room, lounge, drying room; laundry facilities; fishing,

golf, tennis, other sports nearby

⊖ No wheelchair access; no children under 10; no dogs in public rooms and by arrangement only in bedrooms; smoking in lounge only

▭ None accepted

£ Single occupancy of twin/double £25, twin/double £38, four-poster £46, family room £54; deposit required

---

HIGH BUSTON NORTHUMBERLAND   **MAP 3**

High Buston Hall

HIGH BUSTON, ALNMOUTH, NR ALNWICK, NORTHUMBERLAND NE66 3QH
TEL: ALNMOUTH (0665) 830341 (and fax)

A distinctive guesthouse, well positioned for exploring Northumbria's coastline and castles.

Tasteful green and gold signs on the road from Alnwick direct you to an anonymous 'country-house bed and breakfast'. Such modesty may avoid the sin of pride, but this particular establishment deserves to blow its own trumpet a little. John and Alison Edwards, a warm and engaging young couple, have furnished this fine, listed Victorian country house in an elegant, interesting style that combines period antiques and *objets d'art* with tasteful décor that has an informal, vaguely ethnic feel. The solid, mellow stone house occupies a commanding, elevated position amid five acres of landscaped gardens and paddock, but the interior is warm and welcoming. A blazing fire sits at the heart of the guests' sitting-room, an airy room with windows on two sides, ornate plasterwork, arts and crafts movement furniture, batik cushions and sofas draped with rugs, as well as lots of books and magazines on subjects of local interest. Guests eat at one large table in a huge dining-room, elegant with gold wallcovering, an antique sideboard and heavy curtains. Set dinners are available by arrangement and after consultation to clarify guests' preferences – perhaps locally smoked salmon with granary bread and butter, followed by baked pork chop with mustard sauce, served with fresh cauliflower, courgettes and new potatoes, apple and raspberry crumble with cream and cheese and biscuits.

The three spacious bedrooms are individually furnished with good period pieces and memorable individual touches such as an embroidered firescreen, willow pattern plates and patchwork quilts. Breakfasts feature kippers when in season, and a cooked vegetarian option is also available.

◐ *Open all year, exc Dec and Jan*

↗ *Just off the B1068 between Warkworth and Alnmouth. The hall is the first house on the right in High Buston. Private car park*

🛏 *1 twin, 2 double; twin with shower//WC; 1 public bathroom; hair-dryer on request*

◈ *Dining-room, lounge, drying room; fishing, golf, other sports nearby*

⊖ *No wheelchair access; no dogs; no smoking*

▭ *None accepted*

£ *Single occupancy of twin/double £30 to £35, twin/double £40 to £55; deposit required. Set D £15. Special breaks available*

HIGHER BURWARDSLEY CHESHIRE   **MAP 5**

The Pheasant Inn

HIGHER BURWARDSLEY, TATTENHALL, CHESHIRE CH3 9PF
TEL: TATTENHALL (0829) 70434   FAX: (0829) 71097

Rooms with a view in a hilltop country pub and restaurant.

On a clear day you can see the twin peaks of Liverpool's two cathedrals way across the Cheshire Plain; at night, the lights of the Stanlow refinery twinkle like distant Christmas trees. This is a favoured stop for real-ale hikers, also ravenous for the real chips and roast beef sandwiches that alone would make the climb worthwhile. The original seventeenth-century country pub has expanded into a cluster of buildings that includes a popular local restaurant, a new conservatory and bedrooms in a converted sandstone barn. David Greenhaugh's pride and joy, a herd of prize-winning Highland cattle, potter round the adjacent field.

Bedrooms are named after local landmarks. Well-insulated by foot-thick walls, most have good views but the décor is disappointingly nondescript; although they are clean, well-equipped and perfectly adequate, the only real imaginative note is the yellow duck in every bathtub. The two rooms above the pub are quite different in character. Eaton, a cheery lemon-coloured room, has the best view of all, while Carden is a family room with old beams and rose-patterned wallpaper. However, these may be noisy when the pub is in full throttle, and the stairs do need careful navigation. At the time of our inspection the small residents' lounge at the back of the bar was due for redecoration.

The timbered bar is noticeable for its two-way open fire, stuffed pheasant and green parrot (live). There is a good choice of bar food. The small restaurant still features the original farmhouse kitchen range, and the menu has daily specials plus standards like tournedos Rossini, escalope of salmon, curry of the day and pheasant in red wine.

◑ Open all year	conservatory; meetings by arrangement; fishing, golf, other sports nearby
⤤ From A41 follow signposts for Tattenhall. From village follow signposts to Burwardsley. At top of hill bear left at the post office. Inn is at top of hill on left. Private car park	⊖ No wheelchair access; dogs in bedrooms only (by arrangement); no smoking in some public rooms
⇥ 2 twin, 5 double, 1 family room; all with bathroom/WC, TV, room service, hair-dryer, mini-bar, baby-listening	▭ Access, Amex, Diners, Visa
◈ 2 restaurants, bar, lounge,	£ Single occupancy of twin/double £40, twin/double £50 to £60, family room £55 to £60; deposit required. Alc L, D £11. Special breaks available

---

HINTLESHAM SUFFOLK   **MAP 8**

Hintlesham Hall

HINTLESHAM, IPSWICH, SUFFOLK IP8 3NS
TEL: HINTLESHAM (0473) 652268   FAX: (0473) 652463

Glossy, polished hotel with welcoming young staff and choice rooms.

There is an entire book devoted to the history of Hintlesham Hall for sale in the reception area of this elegant hotel so real aficionados can swot up on the families who were lucky enough to have lived here over the centuries. The most well-known contemporary occupant, the chef and restaurateur Robert Carrier, moved out as recently as 1984 and since then the hall has been developed into a luxurious hotel efficiently run by general manager Tim Sunderland and his team. The first glimpse cannot fail to impress: before you is a symmetrically proportioned pink and cream façade with two wings on either side of a circular driveway. The 175 acres of land includes an 18-hole golf course (if you take a weekend break you can opt for a complimentary green fee as part of the package). Bedrooms range from enormous (for example, Braganza, a lavish suite with its own drawing-room) via vast (Rosette, refurbished after a fire, has a four-poster and garden views) to merely big (Rialto is a standard room, but still sizeable, with a chaise-longue and chopped-off windows), so whichever you choose space should not be an issue.

There are plenty of public rooms. Dinner is served either in the lilac salon or pine-panelled parlour and the dishes are of a reliably high standard under the direction of chef Alan Ford – although meals do not come cheap if you opt for à la carte. The wine list is lengthy, with a good choice of Chilean, Australian and New Zealand wines as well as European. The most interesting room to take a post-dinner coffee in is the library (reached by walking through the Long Gallery, used as a hospital ward in the Second World War), with its striking red walls, green sofas and zany floor painted with large black circles – refreshing after the studied elegance elsewhere.

◑ *Open all year*

⤴ *4 miles west of Ipswich on the A1071 towards Sudbury. In Hintlesham, just past the church on the right. Private car park*

🛏 *1 single, 9 twin, 17 double, 2 four-poster, 4 suites; all with bathroom/WC, TV, room service, hair-dryer, mini-bar, baby-listening; no tea/coffee-making facilities in rooms*

◈ *3 restaurants, 4 lounges, library, games room; conference facilities (max 80 people non-residential, 40 residential); fishing, golf, tennis, sauna,*

swimming-pool, steam room, spa bath at hotel, other sports nearby. Wheelchair access to hotel, restaurant and WC (M, F), 10 ground-floor bedrooms

⊖ *No children under 10 in restaurants eves; no dogs in public rooms; no smoking in restaurants*

▭ *Access, Amex, Diners, Visa*

£ *Single £85, single occupancy of twin/double £85 to £105, twin/double £97 to £160, four-poster £160, suite £175 to £300; deposit required. Set L £18.50, D £22; alc L, D £28*

HINTON CHARTERHOUSE AVON   **MAP 9**

Green Lane House

1 GREEN LANE, HINTON CHARTERHOUSE, BATH, AVON BA3 6BL
TEL: BATH (0225) 723631

Pleasant bed and breakfast in a pretty village within striking distance of Bath.

There has been a change of ownership since we last visited; the good news is that new owners Christopher and Juliet Davis have made few changes and it is business as usual at this comfortable bed and breakfast.

Three tiny eighteenth-century cottages have been knocked together to make Green Lane House. It is built of sandstone and shelters behind a neatly trimmed hedge on a quiet road just off the fairly busy B3110 that runs through the village and on through undulating countryside to Bath. There are four bedrooms to choose from, but only Rooms Three and Four have *en-suite* showers; Number Four is decorated with a pretty floral wallpaper and light green carpet, while Number Three is pink. The pick of the other two rooms is Number Two, with its cheerful and bright yellow walls.

Downstairs, there is a comfortable lounge with chairs gathered around the exposed stone fireplace. Breakfast is served at separate tables in the dining-room, which is decorated with copper kettles and large bunches of dried flowers.

○ Open all year

⤢ Hinton Charterhouse is on the A36, approx 6 miles south-east of Bath. Turn left at Rose and Crown pub. Private car park

🛏 2 twin, 2 double; 2 with shower/WC, 1 public bathroom

◈ Breakfast room, lounge; golf,

fishing, riding nearby; babysitting

⊖ No wheelchair access; no dogs

▭ Access, Amex, Visa

£ Single occupancy of twin/double £24 to £37, twin/double £37 to £49; deposit required. Special breaks available

Homewood Park

HINTON CHARTERHOUSE, BATH, AVON BA3 6BB
TEL: BATH (0225) 723731   FAX: (0225) 723820

A gracious country-house hotel with fine gardens.

Homewood Park has a tranquil setting in ten acres of parks and gardens on the edge of a pretty Avon village within striking distance of Bath. The long drive takes you past Jacob sheep grazing in the meadow, a tennis court and finally a magnificent croquet lawn before terminating at a Georgian country house with carefully added modern extensions.

The hotel is a family concern. Sara Gueuning, who runs the front-of-house, has given the interior a predominantly formal country-house style but with pleasing individual touches. The yellow hallway has red chairs, a polished wooden floor and a large antique dresser laden with potted fruit; delicate bronze statues, some of which are for sale, stand on the windowsills. The bedrooms are large and comfortable, decoration being mainly in blue or pink with subtle use of stencilling and sponged walls. Many beds are crowned by yards of silky drapes.

Meals are taken in the mauve dining-room. Frank Gueuning, who is in charge of the kitchen and extensive wine list, has produced a rich menu where game is particularly well represented. You could start with salmon and poached quail's eggs, followed by venison and hare in a brandy sauce, with a chocolate crème brûlée to finish. The cosy orange bar has a large selection of cognacs to help round off the evening meal.

◑ Open all year

⤢ Hinton Charterhouse is approx 6 miles south-east of Bath. The hotel is signposted from the A36. Private car park

🛏 8 twin, 7 double; all with bathroom/WC, TV, room service, hair-dryer, baby-listening; no tea/coffee-making facilities in rooms

◈ Restaurant, bar, lounge; conference facilities (max 15 people residential, 20 non-residential); croquet, tennis at hotel, golf, riding nearby. Wheelchair access to hotel, restaurant and WC (unisex), 2 ground-floor bedrooms

⊖ No dogs

Access, Amex, Diners, Visa

£ Single occupancy of twin/double £80 to £90, twin/double £80 to

£125; deposit required. Set L £19.50; alc D £32.50. Special breaks available

HOLDENBY NORTHAMPTONSHIRE   MAP 9

Lynton House

HOLDENBY, NORTHAMPTONSHIRE NN6 8DJ
TEL: NORTHAMPTON (0604) 770777

An Italian restaurant-with-rooms in peaceful countryside, convenient for the M1 and Northampton.

You won't find Muzak in the dining-room of Lynton House; Carol and Carlo Bertozzi have made a career of hotel and restaurant management and have definite ideas about what they want for their guests; peace and quiet to allow conversation and proper appreciation of the food being high on their list. The formula works, for people drive for miles to come for lunch and often linger over coffee. The restaurant is the main thrust of the business, and Carlo makes a very sociable host while Carol is at work in the kitchen. The Bertozzis keep quails in the garden of their red-brick Victorian family house to guarantee a supply of eggs; apart from these, the menu is mostly Italian and includes gnocchi and carpaccio as well as beef with red wine and pepper, grilled Dover sole and a range of rich puddings.

The house is not grand, but is lifted out of the ordinary by its elevated position in the rolling Northamptonshire countryside. Both the dining-room and the majority of bedrooms have restful views over the garden or fields of horses, while a conservatory, acting as overspill, makes a lovely lunch spot in summer. The watercolours in the bar and dining-room, of churches, harbours and various sites in Italy, have been painted by Carlo. Each of the five bedrooms has a shower room and is comfortably kitted out with dark wood reproduction furniture, a pretty quilt cover and mineral water and fresh-cut flowers. Though they are modern and immaculately kept, like the public rooms they are essentially quite plain. Rooms Two and Three, facing east, have the best views. One reader thought Lynton House excellent value for money – but found dim lighting made reading difficult.

◑ Open all year, exc 2 weeks in the summer; restaurant closed Sun eve

↗ The hotel is just to the east of Holdenby on the East Haddon to Church Brampton road. Private car park

🛏 2 single, 1 twin, 2 double, suite available; all with shower/WC,

TV, room service, hair-dryer, trouser press, baby-listening

◈ Restaurant, bar, lounge, conservatory; conference facilities (max 20 people non-residential, 6 residential); golf, tennis, riding nearby. Wheelchair access to restaurant only

⊖ No wheelchair access; no

children under 6; no dogs; no cigars or pipes in restaurant

Access, Amex, Visa

£ Single £53, single occupancy of twin/double £53, twin/double £58, suite £58. Set L £15; alc L, D £25

HOPTON CASTLE SHROPSHIRE   MAP 5

Park Cottage

HOPTON CASTLE, CRAVEN ARMS, SHROPSHIRE SY7 0QF
TEL: BUCKNELL (05474) 351

An isolated, attractive country guesthouse.

The castle after which Hopton Castle is named stands gaunt, grey and ruined in a nearby field. It brings one or two enthusiasts to the village, but otherwise Hopton Castle is the kind of place you stumble across only by chance – just a few scattered houses among fields and quiet valleys. Park Cottage, a substantial black and white cottage surrounded by a rambling, sunny garden, is on the outskirts. It used to be a gamekeeper's residence, but contains some rather grand panelling in the dining-room which suggests a long history. Two bedrooms are set aside for the use of guests – both fairly simple, but bright and comfortable. Josephine Gardner runs a welcoming home, and serves substantial and imaginative food. This is a good place to tuck yourself into for a couple of days' walking in the Welsh Marches.

◐ Open all year

⤴ At Knighton, turn on to the B4367 towards Hopton Heath. Hopton Castle is signposted from Hopton Heath. When in the village, take a left turning to Bedstone. Private car park

🛏 1 twin, 1 double; twin with private bathroom, double with en-suite shower; TV in both rooms; tea/coffee-making facilities on request

◈ Dining-room, lounge, conservatory; fishing, riding nearby

⊖ No wheelchair access; no children under 7; no dogs; no smoking in dining-room

▭ None accepted

£ Single occupancy of twin/double £30; twin/double £47; deposit required. Alc D £18 (by arrangement)

HOPTON WAFERS SHROPSHIRE   MAP 5

Crown Inn

HOPTON WAFERS, CLEOBURY MORTIMER, NR KIDDERMINSTER, HEREFORD AND WORCESTER DY14 0NB
TEL: CLEOBURY MORTIMER (0299) 270372   FAX: (0299) 271127

A pub with plenty of character and smashing bedrooms.

There is plenty to savour in this old coaching-inn, notably the fact that
the bar is as dark, untouched and rustic as you could wish, while the
restaurant just next door is fresh and bright, with yellow tablecloths and a
large fireplace. Best of all, the bedrooms, while retaining what you might
expect by way of beams and sloping walls and floors, are modern,
peacefully decorated in peach, lavender or claret, and singularly well-
appointed. Room Seven is perhaps the best, but if you are worried about
traffic noise (and there is some) try one of the rooms at the back – Room
11, perhaps. There is food at the bar (and plenty of space to eat it in), as
well as the full menus in the restaurant.

● Open all year; restaurant closed
Sun and Mon eves, but bar food
every evening

⊅ On the A4117 between Cleobury
Mortimer and Ludlow. Private
car park

🛏 2 twin, 6 double; all with
bathroom/WC, TV, room service,
baby-listening; hair-dryer on
request; trouser press in some
rooms

◈ Restaurant, bar; fishing, golf,
riding nearby

● No wheelchair access; dogs by
arrangement only

▭ Access, Visa

£ Single occupancy of twin/double
£38, twin/double £60; deposit
required. Set D £21; alc D £21;
bar meals. Special breaks
available

HORLEY SURREY   **MAP 9**

Chequers Thistle Hotel

BRIGHTON ROAD, HORLEY, SURREY RH6 8PH
TEL: HORLEY (0293) 786992   TELEX: 877550 CHQURS G
FAX: (0293) 820625

*A pleasant hotel that's handy for Gatwick, with free parking and
courtesy transport to the airport.*

Named Chequers after the Earl de Warrene's coat of arms, the hotel
began its career as a beer house known as Bolters. It then became a
coaching-inn, a halfway halt between London and Brighton for the mail
and stage coaches – hence the name of the Halfway Halt brasserie. Here,
in a pleasant pub-like ambience, ploughman's, chillis, curries, Cumberland sausages, burgers and sandwiches are served. The restaurant is
more formal (though not overly so), with a warm pink and green décor,
bookshelves lining the walls and fresh flowers on the tables. A main
course may be something like port fillet stuffed with Stilton, wrapped in
bacon and flavoured with Calvados, or magret of duck basted with honey
and thyme, finished with a Drambuie sauce. There is a choice of 55
different wines, including English ones.

   Bedrooms are fairly uniform, of standard size, modern and perfectly
comfortable for an overnight stop. However, the asset that lifts this hotel

above the other chains around Gatwick must be the professional management and very friendly staff.

◑ Open all year

⤴ On the A23, 2½ miles from Gatwick Airport, off Junction 9 of the M23. Private car park

🛏 1 single, 44 twin, 31 double, 2 family rooms; all with bathroom/WC, TV, room service, hair-dryer, trouser press, baby-listening

◈ 2 restaurants (1 air-conditioned), 2 bars, air-conditioned lounge; air-conditioned conference facilities (max 60 people residential and non-residential);

heated outdoor swimming-pool (Apr to Sept) at hotel, other sports nearby. Wheelchair access to hotel and restaurant, 39 ground-floor bedrooms

⊖ Dogs by prior arrangement only

▭ Access, Amex, Diners, Visa

£ Single/single occupancy of twin/double £79, twin/double £89, family room rate on request; deposit required. Continental B £6.50, cooked B £8.50; set L £11.50, D £17; alc L, D from £21. Special breaks available

Langshott Manor

LANGSHOTT, HORLEY, SURREY RH6 9LN
TEL: HORLEY (0293) 786680   FAX: (0293) 783905

A family-run hotel in a peaceful, romantic setting and convenient for Gatwick.

Langshott Manor is a beautiful red-brick restored Elizabethan manor house run by the Noble family. It exudes rustic charm, with an abundance of beamed ceilings, wooden floorboards scattered with rugs, dried flowers in the old fireplaces and birds obligingly chirping in the gardens, which encompass a man-made lake with two resident swans.

The fresh, bright bedrooms are named after children in the family and are individually decorated: Charlotte has a bathroom tucked away up a small staircase, while Gregory boasts a luxuriously large pink and black tiled bathroom. An ancient rocking horse dominates the spacious Nursery. The Cook's and Butler's rooms are smaller and cheaper but still pleasant.

In general, public rooms are tasteful yet homely. Family photos and personal possessions decorate the lounge, making you feel that you're staying with friends rather than in a hotel. In the dining-room, menus offer fare such as cream of courgette soup with lovage and Stilton, chicken in wine with tarragon cream, and meringues with Jersey cream on a fruit sauce.

◑ Open all year

⤴ From the A23 Horley Chequers roundabout, take Ladbroke Road to Langshott. The manor is ¾ mile on the right. Private car park

🛏 1 twin, 6 double; all with bathroom/WC, TV, room service, hair-dryer; no tea/coffee-making facilities in rooms

◈ Dining-room, bar, lounge, drying

room, function room; conference facilities (max 12 people non-residential, 7 residential); croquet at hotel, fishing, golf, other sports nearby. Wheelchair access to hotel (1 step), dining-room and WC (unisex), 2 ground-floor bedrooms

● No children under 10 (exc babies); no dogs; no smoking in bedrooms

▭ Access, Amex, Diners, Visa

£ Single occupancy of twin/double from £78, twin/double from £90; deposit required. Cooked B £8, continental B £5; set L £22, D £25. Special breaks available

---

HORNDON ON THE HILL ESSEX   **MAP 8**

Bell & Hill House

HIGH ROAD, HORNDON ON THE HILL, ESSEX SS17 8LD
TEL: STANFORD-LE-HOPE (0375) 642463   FAX: (0375) 361611

A successful combination of hotel and pub in a flowery rural village.

Between Basildon and the M25, in a rural village lying well off the beaten track, you will find the flowery façade of Hill House Hotel (recently re-named Bell & Hill House) overlooking a narrow high street just a few paces from sister establishment the Bell Inn. Christine and John Vereker run both businesses with a shrewd eye for convenience. Guests can pop out for a drink and bar meal in the Bell and it will appear on their hotel bill the next morning. Alternatively, set menus are served daily except Sundays and Mondays in the pink-walled restaurant-cum-breakfast room, a sizeable place stencilled with urns, tassels and pillars to add a frivolous touch. There is plenty of choice included in the menu, though vegetarians might be advised to mention their preference when booking.

The Verekers opened rooms to guests in 1986. Three bedrooms in a converted outbuilding overlook the car park, and are not as appealing as the rooms in the old staff quarters; matching curtains and bedspreads, brickwork fireplaces and modern ceiling lights make these the best choice. Number One, with a 'feminine touch' of pinks and oranges (which John confesses is not his favourite), has a spa bath, as has Number Six. A self-contained stable conversion with small lounge, and spiral staircase up to the sleeping area, is best suited to guests who like their independence and the chance of cooking facilities.

◑ Open all year, exc 25 Dec to 30 Dec; restaurant closed Sun, Mon eves

↗ Take Junction 30/31 from the M25, signed Tilbury, Thurrock, Lakeside and A13. Then the B1007 to Horndon. Private car park

🛏 3 twin, 6 double, 1 family room, 1 suite; most with bathroom/WC, some with shower/WC; TV, room service, hair-dryer, trouser press in all rooms

◈ Restaurant, bar; golf, fishing nearby. Wheelchair access to hotel (1 step), restaurant and 1

ground-floor bedroom

● No dogs in some bedrooms

▭ Access, Amex, Visa

£ Twin/double from £40, family room £55, suite £60. Cooked B £6, continental B £3; set L £18, D £19

HORTON DORSET   **MAP 9**

Northill House

HORTON, WIMBORNE, DORSET BH21 7HL
TEL: WITCHAMPTON (0258) 840407

An unpretentious farmhouse set in open countryside.

There are regrettably few small hotels that consider the needs of disabled people in such detail as Northill House. Courtney and Joy Garnsworthy won a national award for the room they have equipped specially in their Victorian farmhouse hotel in rural Dorset. This ground-floor room, converted from an old outhouse, has parking directly outside, hand grips, easily operated taps and shower controls, an adapted shower unit and many other features which make it suitable for wheelchair travellers. In addition, Courtney suggests, the two-bedroomed family room in the courtyard block could be used not just by parents with children over eight years, but by grown-up children bringing elderly parents with them. All the *en-suite* bedrooms have a mix of furniture and are individually decorated; all have particularly comfortable beds, fresh milk in thermos flasks and tins of home-made shortbread.

The house was built by the great reformer Lord Shaftesbury for a tenant farmer, and his crest can be seen above the porch and on the original floor tiling in the hall. Northill is family run and has an unaffected, down-to-earth atmosphere; the lounge is decorated with William Morris-style wallpaper and is a homely, easy place to sit and have after-dinner coffee. There is also a simple little bar area.

Meals are served either in the light, modern dining-room or in the conservatory – good for watching the birds in the sheltered garden. The tables are set with Portmeirion china and flowers from the garden; evening meals are equally wholesome and straightforward, with dishes such as melon with port, lamb chops and rhubarb crumble or trifle. Breakfasts include home-made bread and marmalade.

◑ Open all year, exc 20 Dec to 15 Feb

↗ Six miles north of Wimborne on the B3078. Halfway between Horton Inn and the village. Private car park

🛏 4 twin, 4 double, 1 family room; most with bathroom/WC, some with shower/WC; TV in all rooms

◈ Dining-room/conservatory, bar, lounge, drying room; fishing, golf, riding nearby. Wheelchair access to hotel (1 step), restaurant and WC (unisex), 4 ground-floor bedrooms, 1 specially equipped for disabled people

● No children under 8; no dogs; no smoking in dining-room

▭ Access, Amex, Visa

£ Single occupancy of twin/double £36, twin/double £63, family room £30 per person; deposit required. Set D £13 (7.30pm); bar meals from £2. Special breaks available

HOVINGHAM NORTH YORKSHIRE — MAP 3

Worsley Arms Hotel

HOVINGHAM, YORK, NORTH YORKSHIRE YO6 4LA
TEL: MALTON (0653) 628234   FAX: (0653) 628130

A stylish and sophisticated roadside coaching-inn with highly regarded food.

The roadside position and the frontage of mellow golden stone and colourful flower boxes suggest a typical Yorkshire coaching-inn, but one American correspondent reported being 'very pleased to find that behind its nineteenth-century front, the Worsley Arms is far from a small-town operation', its pretty village setting notwithstanding.

The lounge areas are divided into sections, modern prints adding an unexpected element to fairly traditional rooms with lemon walls, lots of sofas in classic patterns, hunting prints and Chinese plates; display cases offer Victorian and Edwardian jewellery and silverware for sale. The graceful morning-room is often used for conferences and private dinner parties. Crimson walls and dog prints complement the conservative feel of the residents' bar, while the public Cricketer's Bar is made more cheerful by plants, fresh flowers on the tables and lots of sporting memorabilia. The large front-facing restaurant is unusually bright, thanks to a bank of windows and green décor in the modern classic country-house style. 'Dinner was so good that we asked for the menu as a souvenir (and got it),' reported one guest. 'In addition to the outstanding food, the service was excellent.' The set menu sometimes adopts a national or regional theme – Italian, Mexican or oriental – or embraces a well-judged cosmopolitanism; you may find salad of smoked duck breast with orange segments, followed by baby fillet of beef en croûte with a rich madeira sauce, then strawberry cheesecake.

Bedrooms are individually and tastefully furnished, with careful co-ordination and good old furniture joining the shiny reproduction to add character. The immaculate bathrooms are equally recommendable.

◑ *Open all year*

↗ *From York take the A64 to Scarborough and follows signs to Castle Howard. Hovingham is mid-way between Helmsley and Malton on the B1257. The hotel is in central Hovingham, opposite the village green. Private car park*

🛏 *3 single, 2 twin, 9 double, 8 cottages; all with bathroom/WC, TV, room service, hair-dryer, baby-listening*

◇ *Restaurant, 2 bars, 3 lounges, function room; conference facilities (max 45 people non-residential, 22 residential); tennis, squash at hotel, other sports nearby; babysitting. Wheelchair access to hotel,*

restaurant and 4 ground-floor
bedrooms

● No dogs in public rooms

▣ Access, Amex, Visa

£ Single £55 to £62, single

occupancy of twin/double £62 to
£72, twin/double £84, cottage
£84; deposit required. Set L
£12.50, D £18.50; alc L £15, D
£25. Special breaks available

HUDDERSFIELD WEST YORKSHIRE MAP 5

Lodge Hotel ☆

48 BIRKBY LODGE ROAD, BIRKBY, HUDDERSFIELD, WEST YORKSHIRE
HD2 2BG
TEL: HUDDERSFIELD (0484) 431001

An astonishing temple of art nouveau in a quiet suburban location.

'Welcome ever smiles' promises the motto on the flamboyant stained-glass door of this converted and listed Victorian gentleman's residence, parts of which date from 1847. Most of the house, however, was built in 1900 and it is the carefully restored art nouveau features of the public rooms that make the deepest impression. The owners, Garry and Kevin Birley, are knowledgeable about the history of the house and will deliver a discourse on it at the drop of a hat.

The bar glories in wood panelling, an ornate ceiling, an overmantel with a classical scene and an arched door with inlaid silver platework. The restaurant occupies the original billiards room and is pretty with blue and pink fabrics, plates on the picture rail and flowers on the tables as well as on the prints that decorate the walls. The more masculine walnut-panelled library with leaded windows is often used for private dining. The food is highly thought of; your meal might consist of Dublin Bay prawns and queen scallops in a shellfish sauce under a puff pastry case, French onion soup with Gruyère croûtons, braised breast of Yorkshire pheasant in a brandy cream and muscatel sauce, and sticky toffee pudding with walnut and butterscotch sauce.

Bedrooms are attractively decorated in a modern cottagey style which, though fresh and cheerful, generally fails to match the exuberance of the splendid public rooms. However, the furniture is often in period, purchased from local antique shops, then stripped and handwaxed. Particularly fine are Room Seven, a single, and the bridal suite with its four-poster. Bathrooms have been tastefully refurbished.

◖ Open all year, exc 25 and 26
Dec; restaurant closed Sun eve

⚡ Leave M62 at Junction 24 and
follow signs to Huddersfield on
the A629. Turn left at the 1st set
of traffic lights, then right after
Nuffield Hospital. The hotel is

100 yards on the left. Private car
park

🛏 4 single, 3 twin, 3 double, 1
four-poster, family room
available; all with shower/WC,
TV, room service, hair-dryer,
baby-listening

Restaurant, bar, lounge, library, 2 private dining-rooms, games room; conference facilities (max 40 people non-residential, 11 residential); fishing, golf, other sports nearby. Wheelchair access to hotel (1 step), restaurant and WC (unisex), 3 ground-floor bedrooms specially equipped for disabled people

 Dogs by arrangement only; no smoking in bedrooms

Access, Amex, Visa

Single £40 to £50, single occupancy of twin/double £40 to £50, twin/double £50 to £60, four-poster £70, family room £100 to £120; deposit required. Sun L £12; set D £20.50; alc L £12. Special breaks available.

Wellfield House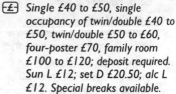

33 NEW HEY ROAD, MARSH, HUDDERSFIELD, WEST YORKSHIRE HD3 4AL
TEL: HUDDERSFIELD (0484) 425776

Comfortable rooms, friendly hosts and excellent food in a lovely Victorian house an easy drive from the town centre.

There is nothing from the outside to suggest that this substantial but rather plain sandstone house just off the A640 is particularly remarkable. Inside, the public rooms of John and Polly Whitehead's tasteful small hotel are an essay in high Victoriana, though there's nothing at all bombastic in the welcome which sees your bags swept up to your room, with tea and home-baked cake offered to help you settle in.

Dawdling over a pre-dinner drink or coffee gives you a chance to admire the fascinating lounge with its ornate plasterwork and overmantel with beaten copper panel. Feminist hackles may rise at the motto 'Man for the field and woman for the hearth' and be sent into orbit by its partner above the door, which reads 'Man with the head, woman with the heart'. However, this ornamentation certainly provides a talking point among the guests. A blue velour suite adds a homely note to the operatic splendour of the room. The dining-room is equally memorable, not only for its oak panelling and absence of Muzak, but for the inventiveness and quality of the food served there at astonishingly modest cost. There are two options at each stage, and the inspection meal – Malmsey mushrooms, followed by duck in a honey sauce with grapefruit, then hot banana in a rum and butterscotch sauce – was most enjoyable. An imaginative breakfast menu included apples poached in honey as well as the usual fare.

The large, comfortable bedrooms are simple in comparison to the public rooms but have lots of items to engage your interest, from a collection of Royal Wedding and other mugs above the pelmet to a wealth of magazines from *Good Housekeeping* to the *Dalesman*. Bathrooms are modern with good, fluffy towels.

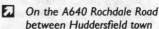 Open all year, exc 24 Dec to 2 Jan

On the A640 Rochdale Road between Huddersfield town

centre and Junction 23 of the M62 (there is no exit from the M62 when coming from the East). Private car park

🛏 1 single, 2 twin, 1 double, 1 family room; all with bathroom/ WC, TV, room service, hair-dryer

◇ Dining-room, bar, lounge; conference facilities (max 20 people non-residential, 5 residential); golf, tennis, other sports nearby. Wheelchair access to dining-room and WC (F, unisex) only

⊖ No dogs; no smoking in dining-room

▭ Access, Visa

£ Single £40, single occupancy of twin/double £40, twin/double £55, family room £65. Set L £12.50, D £15.50. Special breaks available

HUNGERFORD BERKSHIRE   MAP 9

Marshgate Cottage

MARSH LANE, HUNGERFORD, BERKSHIRE RG17 0QX
TEL: HUNGERFORD (0488) 682307 FAX: (0488) 685475

A family-run hotel in a pretty canalside position.

Marshgate Cottage is in a rural position on the edge of Hungerford with a view of the Kennet and Avon Canal and ducks and geese waddling around in the surrounding fields. Elsebeth and Mike Walker have extended and knocked together three small cottages to create their small hotel. Firmly Scandinavian in style (Elsebeth is Danish), the hotel has tiled floors, lots of pine and is simply furnished with the motif of ducks and geese appearing throughout. The small sitting-room with open coal fire has family ornaments, a stereo and magazines. It links with the breakfast room, where pine tables overlook the canalside walk and a small honesty bar occupies one corner. Elsebeth and Mike used to offer evening meals but now limit this to groups as they find that most of their guests set out along the tow-path on the 15-minute walk to the pubs and restaurants of Hungerford.

A couple of bedrooms in the old cottages are quite small: those in the single-storey extension are larger and some have doors to small terrace areas, brightened up with flowering baskets and troughs, where you can sit out. All have pine furniture and light flowery fabrics.

◑ Closed Xmas

↗ From Hungerford High Street turn at railway bridge into Church Street, cross over stream (½ mile) and immediately right into Marsh Lane. Private car park

🛏 1 single, 3 twin, 3 double, 1 four-poster, 1 family room; most with shower/WC, 1 with bathroom/WC; TV, hair-dryer in all rooms

◇ Breakfast room, bar, lounge; meetings facilities (max 10 people residential); fishing, water sports, other sports nearby. Wheelchair access to hotel (ramp) and restaurant, 7 ground-floor bedrooms

⊖ No children under 5; no dogs;

smoking in some bedrooms only

▭ Access, Amex, Visa

£ Single £26 to £36, single
occupancy of twin/double £26 to

£36, twin/double £40 to £49,
four-poster £49, family room
from £56 to £60; deposit
required

HUNMANBY NORTH YORKSHIRE   MAP 3

Wrangham House Hotel

10 STONEGATE, HUNMANBY, NORTH YORKSHIRE YO14 0NS
TEL: SCARBOROUGH (0723) 891333

*A cosy and unaffected hotel with a traditional feel, well placed for
exploring Yorkshire's dramatic coastline.*

The name honours Francis Wrangham, sometime vicar of this parish
and avid reader, who added a substantial new wing and renovated the
mainly seventeenth-century house in 1803. A tablet in Latin reveals that
he did this at a cost of £1,200. The Reverend Wrangham was noted for
his philanthropy, and to this day prices at Wrangham House are kind.
The red-brick pantiled house with a well-integrated courtyard wing
stands behind All Saints Church and was judged 'quiet apart from the
church clock' by one guest. An attractive wooded garden makes it a
popular venue for wedding receptions.

Public rooms are lady-like, traditionally decorated and furnished with
an eye to comfort rather than innovative design. Autumnal colours
predominate and the overall impression is light and neat. Log fires blaze
when the temperature calls for it. Bedrooms are feminine and embrace a
more co-ordinated look, with individual touches – beams in some rooms,
stencilling in others – to give each its own character. Lovely oak and pine
furniture mingles with basketweave and velour. All are cosy and irreproachably well-groomed.

Set and carte menus offer lots of choice, with the table d'hôte sticking
to the straightforward. 'Dinner was simple but well-cooked with some of
the best lamb chops I have had in a long time . . . interesting local
cheeses were so good we bought some in the village when we left.'
Breakfasts with '*the* most delicious home-made marmalade' were similarly appreciated. Staff are reported to be friendly and helpful: 'By the
end of the stay we felt as if we belonged,' wrote one guest.

◗ Open all year

⤴ From the main A64 road follow
the A1039 to Filey, turning right
after Flixton on to Hunmanby
Road. The hotel is behind All
Saints Church in Hunmanby
village. Private car park

🛏 2 single, 4 twin, 7 double; some
with bathroom/WC, most with

shower/WC; TV, room service,
hair-dryer in all rooms

◈ Dining-room, bar, lounge, drying
room, conservatory; conference
facilities (max 30 people non-
residential, 13 residential); golf,
riding, other sports nearby.
Wheelchair access to hotel,
restaurant and WC, 2 ground-

floor bedrooms, I specially equipped for disabled people

● No children under 12; no dogs; smoking in bar only

▭ Access, Amex, Diners, Visa

£ Single £28 to £37, single occupancy of twin/double £28 to £37, twin/double £56 to £74. Set D £13; alc D £19 (prices till Apr 94). Special breaks available

HUNSTRETE AVON   MAP 9

Hunstrete House

HUNSTRETE, CHELWOOD, NR BRISTOL, AVON BS18 4NS
TEL: HUNSTRETE (0761) 490490 FAX: (0761) 490732

Bright and cheerful country-house hotel with fine grounds and a deer park.

The ambience sought, and achieved, by the Clipper Hotel group who run Hunstrete House is that of a comfortable country-house hotel minus the stuffiness. Two things contribute to their success: the service from the young, friendly staff and the decoration which is light and bright. The lounge and library are decorated in green or yellow and have red striped chairs and sofas. Chess and Scrabble sets are left out for guests and modern oil paintings hang from the walls. There are two restaurants, one being reserved for smokers. The main one is light and bright with a high plaster ceiling and views out on to the Italianate courtyard with its statues and fountains. The menu is classic English country-house, so you might have pheasant breast with a raspberry sauce or pan-fried brill. Many vegetables and herbs come from the house's own gardens.

The bedrooms are either in the main house or the converted stable block which is attached to the main house. There's little to choose between them. They are large and comfortable and decoration is in cheerful colours like Sudbury yellow and Wedgwood blue. Furniture is a mix of authentic and reproduction antique pieces and TVs are hidden in closed cabinets. Generally, the rooms in the main house have the better views of the surrounding 92-acre grounds. If you are tempted outside there are areas of woodland, with maps of circular walks provided, as well as a croquet lawn and walled garden with swimming-pool.

◑ Open all year

⤢ From Bristol, take the A37 (Wells road) to Chelwood village. Turn left at the traffic lights in Chelwood on to the A368. The hotel is 2 miles along this road on the left-hand side. Private car park

⇌ I single, 18 twin, 2 double, 2 four-poster, I suite; all with bathroom/WC, TV, room service, hair-dryer, trouser press; no tea/coffee-making facilities in rooms

◈ 2 restaurants, bar, lounge, library; conference facilities (max 24 people residential, 45 non-residential); tennis, heated outdoor swimming-pool at hotel, other sports nearby. Wheelchair access to hotel (no steps) and

restaurants, 1 ground-floor bedroom

● No children under 10; no dogs; 1 no-smoking restaurant

▭ Access, Visa

£ Single £95, twin/double £150, four-poster £195, suite £170; deposit required. Set L £16, D £29.50; alc L £30, D £40. Special breaks available

HUNTSHAM DEVON MAP 10

Huntsham Court

HUNTSHAM, NR BAMPTON, DEVON EX16 7NA
TEL: CLAYHANGER (039 86) 365 FAX: (039 86) 456

A vast Victorian mansion with enormous rooms: ideal for house parties.

A stay at Huntsham Court is a real experience. As you wander into the Great Hall with its polished wooden floor, panelled ceiling, marble columns and huge log fire, your mind fills with thoughts of Dracula movies, Hallowe'en and murder weekends. Twelve years ago Andrea and Mogens Bolwig took a rotting Gothic pile in remote countryside and turned it into a spectacular homage to music: rooms are named after famous composers, there's a CD player in the hall pulpit, and guests can choose from over 10,000 records.

Of the 14 bedrooms the most stupendous is Beethoven, with a grand piano in the bedroom and not one but two freestanding tubs in the bathroom. Brahms has a bathroom organ, Handel a piano by the bed, and all the rooms come equipped with old-fashioned wirelesses. Depending on your taste you'll either love or hate the high-Victorian fixtures and fittings – but cosily intimate the rooms are not: 'An American couple arrived and left straight away, saying they wanted something smaller,' says Andrea.

In keeping with Huntsham Court's motto, *dulce nihil facere* (how sweet it is to do nothing), breakfast in bed can be ordered any time up to noon. Then, after a hard day on the croquet lawn or tennis court or just playing billiards, you can settle down to a five-course dinner at a table which seats 28. Teas and coffees are thrown in free, and the bar operates on a friendly 'drink now, settle up later' basis.

Huntsham Court fills with guests at weekends, but is quieter during the week. A quarterly newsletter provides details of opera festivals and wine-tasting weekends.

◑ Open all year

▤ Leave the M5 at Junction 27 and take the exit to Sampford Peverell. Turn right over the bridge at Sampford Peverell. Follow signs to Uplowman and then to Huntsham. Private car park

🛏 2 twin, 8 double, 1 four-poster, 3 family rooms; all with bathroom/ WC, hair-dryer, room service on request; no tea/coffee-making facilities in rooms

◇ Dining-room, bar, 2 lounges, games room, library, drying

room; conference facilities (max 20 people residential, 60 non-residential); tennis, croquet, table tennis, sauna, gym at hotel, other sports nearby; babysitting by arrangement

⊖ No wheelchair access; no dogs;

no smoking in dining-room

▭ Access, Amex, Visa

£ Single occupancy of twin/double £75, twin/double/four-poster £110, family room £125; deposit required. Set D £27.50

HURSTBOURNE TARRANT HAMPSHIRE   MAP 9

Esseborne Manor

HURSTBOURNE TARRANT, ANDOVER, HAMPSHIRE SP11 0ER
TEL: HURSTBOURNE TARRANT (0264) 76444   FAX: (0264) 76473

A small, secluded hotel offering country-house elegance and adventurous cooking – but problems with service persist.

Esseborne Manor stands in an exposed spot on the Hampshire Downs, and the orderliness of its lawns, driveway and hard tennis court stands out sharply from the woods and ploughed fields around. The Victorian main building is similarly spruce in its coat of cream paint, although it presents a functional, four-square aspect in keeping with the windswept landscape of its setting. Behind its bay windows, the main sitting-room is a treat: bright and airy, with a crisp colour scheme of yellow and light blue sitting easily with the homeliness of loose-covered armchairs and shelves of books. A tiny, fluorescent-lit bar in floral red and blue adjoins the intimate pink restaurant, where good-value set dinners featuring dishes such as home-made ravioli and provençal beef stew are served (gentlemen are required to wear a jacket).

Bedrooms in the main house are bright and florid – you're better off asking for one of the large modern rooms in the converted stable block at the back, where you'll find pelmeted beds, antique mirrors and a couple of rubber ducks thrown into the spacious bath for good measure. Reports have been mixed this year, focusing particularly on service: complaints about the lack of help with luggage on arrival have cropped up again. More positively, one couple wrote to say that their suite (Chichester) provided every luxury.

◑ Open all year

↗ On the A343 between Newbury and Andover. 1½ miles north of Hurstbourne Tarrant. Private car park

🛏 5 twin, 6 double, 1 four-poster; all with bathroom/WC, TV, room service, hair-dryer, trouser press; no tea/coffee-making facilities in rooms

◈ Dining-room, bar, lounge, drying room; conference facilities (max 12 people residential and non-residential); tennis, croquet at hotel, other sports nearby. Wheelchair access to hotel (no steps), restaurant and WC (M,F), 1 ground-floor bedroom specially equipped for disabled people

- No children under 12; no dogs
- Access, Amex, Diners, Visa
- Single occupancy of twin/double

£84, twin/double £112, four-poster £125. Set L £17.50, D £19.50; alc D £30

HUXLEY CHESHIRE   **MAP 5**

Higher Huxley Hall ☆

HUXLEY, CHESTER CH3 9BZ
TEL: HUXLEY (0829) 781484

Croquet, cows and a charming Cheshire family welcome.

The distinctive three-storey old white manor house looks across the Cheshire Plain to the castles of the Peckforton Gap. This is a working family farm, where they breed Holsteins and hunters; the land has been farmed for 800 years and parts of the house date back to the thirteenth century. Huxley land is even referred to in the Domesday Book.

The three guest rooms are on the top floor, reached by the Elizabethan staircase. All have been furnished with care and comfort and each has a convenience drawer providing everything from aspirins to tampons; there are new posturepaedic beds in old brass frames. Beware, though, low Tudor beams. An ironing and utility room is also available.

The Marks are a friendly and engaging couple with small children and a knack of making guests feel one of the family. It is indeed very much a family home, comfortable and spacious, full of attractive things but with lived-in rather than looked-at rooms. Pauline Marks cooks an optional five-course dinner – there might be carrot and orange soup, smoked salmon timbales or local pheasant shot by her husband. Farm milk and butter and free-range eggs are on the table at breakfast.

A new conservatory overlooks the croquet lawn and there is a heated 40-foot swimming-pool. The only drawback is that real farms mean real muck – and when the wind is in the right direction, there is the unmistakable scent of the countryside in the air.

- Open all year
- Leave the M6 at Junction 16 and take the A500 towards Nantwich, then the A51 towards Chester. After Tilstone Fearnall turn on to A49 and after ¾ mile turn right to Huxley. In Huxley, pass the Farmers Arms and turn right at the T-junction. Private car park
- 1 twin, 2 double; 1 with bathroom/WC, 2 with shower/WC; TV, hair-dryer in all rooms; ironing facilities on request
- Dining-room, lounge, conservatory; conference facilities (max 12 people non-residential); fishing, heated indoor swimming-pool, croquet at hotel, golf nearby
- No wheelchair access; no children under 10; no dogs; no smoking
- Visa
- Single occupancy of twin/double £31 to £40, twin/double £60 to £70; deposit required. Set D £12/£20

ILKLEY WEST YORKSHIRE

MAP 5

Rombalds Hotel

WEST VIEW, WELLS ROAD, ILKLEY, WEST YORKSHIRE LS29 9JG
TEL: ILKLEY (0943) 603201   FAX: (0943) 816586

Great food, superb service and a wonderful location compensate for uninspiring bedrooms in this bright, family-run hotel.

Ilkley combines an air of Victorian grandeur with the bracing prospect of its famous moor – and Rombalds, a honey-coloured Georgian edifice on a slope twixt the two, allows you to enjoy the best of both worlds. Owner Ian Guthrie came to hotelkeeping late in life after a business career, and has brought to his new vocation a clear understanding of what the customer wants, gleaned from decades on the other side of the reception desk. Staff are trained to share his vision and do him proud; our inspector arrived late after a long drive and asked if there was time to bathe before dinner. Assurances were given, luggage was fetched from the car park, and enquiries were made as to whether a drink should be brought to the room. The restaurant is highly regarded locally and is an elegant room with blue and pink décor, floral displays and formally laid tables. Food is fairly traditional; perhaps smoked salmon wrapped around a smoked trout mousse, followed by breast of guinea-fowl and then a hazelnut and honey parfait with whisky and ginger sauce. Staff are friendly and adaptable – after a superb avocado, orange and mango salad in walnut dressing our inspector asked to opt out of the main courses on offer, and the requested omelette, a fluffy, well-filled specimen, was served with grace. Solo diners will be pleased to encounter a wine-list with a decent range of half-bottles. Breakfasts are equally good and include a wide selection of leaf teas. The Sunday Edwardian Brunch is an opportunity for a self-indulgent blow-out on a massive scale, Buck's Fizz and all.

The comfortable lounge has high windows, lemon-striped walls and a predominantly blue theme enlivened by prints of French vineyard scenes. Bedrooms are the only disappointment, with haphazard co-ordination and a distinctly spare-roomish quality. No one would deny, however, that they are neat, tidy and comfortable – or that, given the unusually high standards set in the rest of the hotel, they rather let the side down.

◗ Open all year, exc 27 to 30 Dec

⤢ From the A65 traffic lights in the town centre, travel up Brook Street, cross the Grove into Wells Road; the hotel is 600 yards on the left. Private car park and on-street parking

⇌ 4 single, 2 twin, 4 double, 1 family room, 4 suites (3 self-contained flats); some with bathroom/WC, most with shower/WC; TV, room service, hair-dryer, trouser press, baby-listening in all rooms

◈ Restaurant, bar, lounge; air-conditioned conference facilities (max 40 people non-residential, 15 residential); fishing, golf, other sports nearby; babysitting. Wheelchair access

to restaurant and WC (unisex) only

⊖ No dogs in public rooms; no smoking in restaurant

▭ Access, Amex, Diners, Visa

£ Single £58 to £72, single occupancy of twin/double £72 to

£84, twin/double £84 to £110, family room £84 to £110, suite £120 to £140, flats £235 to £320 per week; deposit required. Set L £10.50, D £14; alc L to £14, D to £24. Special breaks available

---

INGLEBY GREENHOW NORTH YORKSHIRE — MAP 3

Manor House Farm

INGLEBY GREENHOW, NR GREAT AYTON, NORTH YORKSHIRE TS9 6RB
TEL: GREAT AYTON (0642) 722384

A house-party atmosphere at this rural retreat on a working farm.

Ornithologists will be ready to bale out, binoculars at the ready, at the first glimpse of the 300-year-old duck pond, home to 21 breeds of duck, geese and swans and one of the first attractions to grab the attention of visitors to Martin Bloom's working farm in the foothills of the Cleveland Hills. Others will enjoy the journey past the very grand manor house along the splendid wooded drive that leads to the low-slung eighteenth-century stone farmhouse. The lounge, warmed by a Norwegian log stove, is simply but neatly furnished, with flowery easy chairs, various knick-knacks, a wall of books and a TV. Dinner, served at 7pm in the blue and white dining-room, is mandatory to help encourage a house-party atmosphere. Cuisine is international – your meal might consist of deep-fried mushrooms filled with Brie and chopped ham, followed by roast Lunedale duckling served crispy with a fruity stuffing and cherry sauce, and cheese. The wine list majors on France and Germany.

All three good-sized bedrooms have neat, simple décor, private facilities, clock-radio alarms and tea/coffee machines.

◐ Open all year, exc 15 to 30 Dec

↗ Ingleby Greenhow is 10 miles south of Middlesbrough. Take the B1257 at Stokesley to Great Broughton, and turn off for Ingleby. The entrance to Manor House Farm is opposite the church in Ingleby. Private car park

⇖ 2 twin, 1 double; 2 with bathroom/WC, 1 public bathroom

◈ Dining-room, lounge, library; fishing, shooting at hotel, other sports nearby

⊖ No wheelchair access; no children under 12; no dogs; no smoking

▭ None accepted

£ Single occupancy of twin/double from £30, twin/double from £60 (rates inc dinner); deposit required

---

All reports are welcome on any hotel, whether or not it is in the Guide.

Belstead Brook Hotel ☆

BELSTEAD ROAD, IPSWICH, SUFFOLK IP2 9HB
TEL: IPSWICH (0473) 684241   FAX: (0473) 681249

*Slick hotel that is favoured by business travellers and pays
particular consideration to guests' needs.*

At long last we have found a hotel in Ipswich that merits inclusion in the
Guide. Although mostly used by business people and wedding parties,
the Belstead Brook also makes a good base for holidaymakers keen to
explore Ipswich and nearby Constable country. Bargain weekend rates
make it all the more attractive.

Since the hotel lies in the quiet, leafy outskirts of the town it is too far
to walk easily to the centre, but if you don't have a car it's only a short
journey in a taxi. The mature gardens are a major selling point: new
residential buildings nearby are screened by the trees which cluster
around velvety lawns. On first approach the elegant Jacobean house does
not seem large enough to offer 91 rooms, but these are housed in a long
extension at the back of the building. There is a considerable regard for
particular needs that guests may have: special rooms equipped for
disabled people have wide doors, low furniture and alarms to reception.
Ladies' bedrooms are provided with a spy hole and security chain on the
door, plus an ironing board, cotton wool and plenty of magazines.

Dinner is served in the oldest part of the house, where the Jacobean
wood panelling and herringbone brickwork remain intact. Again, if you
have particular needs you should find these catered for: not only is there
a separate vegetarian menu, but diabetic and gluten-free menus are
available too. The accompanying wine list runs to 10 pages with a list of
'Belstead Brook Bin Ends' flagged as exceptional value for money.

◑ Open all year

↗ At the A12/A45 interchange
roundabout take the A1214
towards the town centre. At
Tesco's Superstore roundabout
turn right, and right again at the
mini-roundabout. At the next
roundabout take the 2nd exit
into Belmont Road. Turn right
into Ellenbrook Road and left
into Belstead Road. Private car
park

⇌ 8 single, 25 twin, 47 double, 1
four-poster, 2 family rooms, 8
suites; all with bathroom/WC,
exc singles with shower/WC; TV,
room service, hair-dryer, mini-
bar, trouser press, baby-listening
in all rooms

◇ Restaurant, bar, lounge, 8
meetings rooms; conference
facilities (max 60 people
residential and non-residential);
laser shooting at hotel, fishing,
golf, other sports nearby;
babysitting. Wheelchair access to
hotel, restaurant and WC
(unisex), 23 ground-floor
bedrooms, 2 specially equipped
for disabled people

⊖ No dogs in public rooms

▭ Access, Amex, Diners, Visa

£ Single £50, single occupancy of
twin/double £60, twin/double

£60, four-poster £85, family room £70, suite £85; deposit required. Cooked B £7,

continental B £5; set L, D £8.50/£14; alc L, D £15/£25. Special breaks available

IRONBRIDGE SHROPSHIRE   MAP 5

Severn Lodge

COUNTY HOTEL OF THE YEAR

NEW ROAD, IRONBRIDGE, SHROPSHIRE TF8 7AS
TEL: IRONBRIDGE (0952) 432148

A remarkably refreshing and enthusiastically run bed and breakfast.

Severn Lodge is built on the side of the steep Ironbridge gorge, only a couple of minutes' walk from the centre of town but uphill from the main road and away from the tourist throngs. Its virtues as a place to stay are many: the bedrooms are kitted out to a standard found in much pricier places, the water is hot and the baths deep, while the breakfast (at whatever time you wish) is lavish and comes with newspaper, and coffee as strong as you want it. These things alone would make it well worth its place in this guide, but it is lifted to a higher standard still by the care which Alan and Nita Reed lavish on their guests. Restaurants are suggested for evening meals or are highlighted in the folder of local information which they provide, and there is a torch on hand to help you find your way through the steep garden down to the street below. There's a small residents' lounge furnished with books (consult Alan's geology and geography texts if you are feeling academic) and the garden is a lovely place to take advantage of on a sunny day. You will definitely feel cosseted here, and the bill will consequently seem remarkably cheap.

◑ Open all year

⤢ A few minutes' walk from the Iron Bridge. With the bridge on your left, New Road is the right turn immediately before the Malthouse restaurant. Private car park

🛏 1 twin, 2 double; doubles with bathroom/WC, single with shower/WC; TV, room service,

hair-dryer in all rooms

◇ 2 dining-rooms, lounge, TV room, drying room

⊖ No wheelchair access; no children under 12; no dogs; no smoking

▭ None accepted

£ Single occupancy of twin/double £35 to £44, twin/double £44; deposit required

ISLEY WALTON LEICESTERSHIRE   MAP 5

Park Farmhouse

MELBOURNE ROAD, ISLEY WALTON, CASTLE DONINGTON,
LEICESTERSHIRE DE74 2RN
TEL: DERBY (0332) 862409   FAX: (0332) 862364

Comfortable accommodation in an informal farmhouse handy for Donington Park.

Situated just outside the competitors' entrance to Donington Park race circuit, Park Farmhouse has seen more peaceful days in its 300-year history. To be fair, the black and white farmhouse, surrounded by green open fields and with no visible neighbours, is in a quiet enough spot when there isn't an event on, though for most people the lively pub atmosphere is the main attraction. Pine furniture, plain walls, plenty of space and immaculate bathrooms characterise the well-kept bedrooms, which now include three adjoining rooms in the attic that are ideal for families. With their low doorways, beams and chimney, they have the most character.

John and Linda Shields' flexible attitude means that meals in the half-panelled residents' bar are served pretty much when demanded (except that they don't do lunches). Up to around 9pm, or later if there's a crowd, you can take your choice from the short blackboard menu, which usually includes steaks and casseroles in generous portions. (There's always soup, too, though it may not have been written up on the board.) If it's busy and you want to hide away, the large sitting-room with a walnut grand piano and Dutch marquetry bureau makes an elegant retreat.

◑ Open all year, exc 2 weeks at Xmas; reduced service Sun eves in winter

🔁 7 miles north-east of Ashby de la Zouch. At Isley Walton on the A453, take the Melbourne turning. The house is ½ mile on the right, the only black and white building. Private car park

🛏 1 single, 4 twin, 3 double, 2 family rooms, 1 annexe room; some with bathroom/WC, some with shower/WC, 2 public bathrooms; TV, hair-dryer, trouser press, baby-listening in all rooms

◈ Dining-room, bar, lounge; conference facilities (max 10 people residential and non-residential); golf nearby. Wheelchair access to farmhouse, dining-room and WC (unisex)

⊖ No dogs in public rooms

▭ Access, Amex, Diners, JCB, Visa

£ Single £35 to £49, single occupancy of twin/double £35 to £49, twin/double £45 to £60, family room £55 to £70, annexe room £110 to £120; deposit required. Alc D £15

KEMERTON HEREFORD AND WORCESTER   **MAP 9**

Upper Court

KEMERTON, NR TEWKESBURY, GLOUCESTERSHIRE GL20 7HY
TEL: OVERBURY (0386) 725351   FAX: (0386) 725472

A welcoming Wolsey Lodge in a well-situated manor house.

The village of Kemerton snuggles under the slopes of Bredon Hill, an outpost of the Cotswolds that acts as the endstop to the Vale of Evesham. It is an excellent place from which to explore in all directions – Evesham and Cheltenham are both within easy driving range – and the Herford family's Georgian manor, with its large grounds, lake and pretty gardens, makes an excellent base. The facilities, which include croquet, tennis, fishing and a heated swimming-pool, might befit an expensive country-house hotel, but here you have the advantage of being in a family home – one that is furnished with antiques and offers pretty, well-appointed bedrooms, two of them containing four-poster beds. There is also self-catering accommodation in the converted coach-house. Mrs Herford's cooking, 'simple dinner party' in style, sounds just right for those who like fresh, imaginative food. Jams are home-made and vegetables come straight from the garden.

◑ Open all year, exc Xmas

⤤ From Cheltenham travel north on the A435/B4079. 1 mile after the A438 crossroads, turn right to Kemerton. Turn off the main road at the war memorial. Private car park

🛏 2 double, 3 four-poster; all with bathroom/WC, TV, hair-dryer

◈ Dining-room, bar, lounge, drying room; conference facilities (max 16 people non-residential, 5 residential); fishing, tennis, heated outdoor swimming-pool (in season), croquet and table tennis at hotel, other sports nearby; babysitting. Wheelchair access to hotel, dining-room and WC, 2 ground-floor bedrooms

⊖ No children in dining-room eves (there is a ground-floor room with kitchen for families with children); no dogs in public rooms and in ground-floor bedrooms only

▭ Access, Visa

£ Single occupancy of double £50, double £75, four-poster £75, master room £105; deposit required. Set D £21

KENDAL CUMBRIA   MAP 4

Lane Head House

HELSINGTON, KENDAL, CUMBRIA LA9 5RJ
TEL: KENDAL (0539) 731283/721023

Unpretentious hillside hotel sited at the gateway to the Lakes.

While Kendal is the gateway to the Lake District, you wouldn't choose to make it your holiday base for the Lakes. However, after a long slog up the M6, the thought of pulling up at this cheerful guesthouse is most enticing. It's a cream pebble-dashed house, standing next to a working farm at the end of a long drive.

The interior has been confidently decorated with cheerful modern patterns and the bedrooms, with bright carpets and coffee and cream Formica furniture, are spacious and equipped with all mod cons. Some bedrooms have showers only – and these can be small.

If you don't fancy heading back into town for an evening meal you can dine at Lane Head. The menu features a couple of choices such as venison in red wine or lamb in redcurrant sauce – simple enough fare, but on the night our inspector dined standards were variable. Also, breakfast places were already set at the empty tables – hardly an encouragement to take a slow, leisurely meal. After the meal coffee is served in the lounge, which has large windows looking down on the twinkling lights of Kendal below.

◗ Open all year

🔁 Take the A6 southbound from Kendal to the town boundary. The house is up a country lane almost opposite the BP garage. Private car park

🛏 3 twin, 2 double, 1 family room, 2 suites; most with bathroom/WC, some with shower/WC; TV, limited room service in all rooms; hair-dryer on request

◈ Dining-room, lounge; golf, riding, other sports nearby

⊖ No wheelchair access; no dogs; no smoking

▭ Access, Amex, Visa

£ Single occupancy of twin/double £35 to £40, twin/double £50 to £60, suite £55 to £65, family room £60 to £70; deposit required. Set D £15.50 (7.30pm). Special breaks available

---

KENILWORTH WARWICKSHIRE   **MAP 5**

Castle Laurels

22 CASTLE ROAD, KENILWORTH, WARWICKSHIRE CV8 1NG
TEL: KENILWORTH (0926) 56179   FAX: (0926) 54954

Small hotel opposite Kenilworth Castle, convenient for exploring the Midlands and blessed with obliging hosts.

You can hear the thunder of cannon fire as costumed soldiers bring the English Civil War back to Kenilworth, though from this hotel the

CASTLE LAURELS
-KENILWORTH-

sandstone castle itself is obscured by trees. Special events at the castle have boosted weekend trade for the Glover family, who have run Castle Laurels for nearly a decade. The red-brick Victorian hotel provides a comfortable base if you're visiting the Midlands, and though there's nothing luxurious about this establishment it is well-run, with comfortable rooms and a *laissez-faire* atmosphere. The ground-floor bedroom is the prettiest, and perhaps the most comfortable, with a blue plaster-relief ceiling, wooden panelling, a floral duvet cover with matching cushions and a full bookshelf. Other rooms are plainer, with those on the third floor reached by a steep staircase that is unsuitable if you're unsteady on your feet. All rooms are no-smoking and, if not stylish, are neat and clean with spotless shower rooms. Those facing west overlook Abbey Fields Park and the old High Street with restaurants and pubs dating back to the fourteenth century. If you want to eat in you can – the Glovers offer a simple menu, some of which is home-made, including beef and mushroom pie, chicken wings and chilli con carne. Serving times are flexible, indicating the Glovers' willingness to please.

◑ Open all year, exc 10 days over Xmas; dining-room closed Sun eve

🡕 Opposite Kenilworth Castle and overlooking Abbey Fields Park in old Kenilworth. Private car park

🛏 3 single, 3 twin, 5 double, 1 family room; all with shower/ WC, TV, room service; hair-dryer on request

◈ Dining-room, lounge/bar; tennis, swimming-pool, other sports nearby

⊖ No wheelchair access; no dogs; smoking in lounge only

▭ Access, Visa

£ Single £29, single occupancy of twin/double £34, twin/double £45, family room £57. Alc D £7.50 to £15. Special breaks available

---

KESWICK CUMBRIA   MAP 4

Brundholme Hotel

BRUNDHOLME ROAD, KESWICK, CUMBRIA CA12 4NL
TEL: KESWICK (07687) 74495   FAX: (07687) 73536

An elegant country-house hotel with memorable views.

Brundholme's location off a quiet country road just a few minutes from Keswick gives it the best of both worlds: proximity to local services and a sense of rural isolation. The fell views are superb – the area brought poetic tributes from both Coleridge and Wordsworth, who, with his sister Dorothy, was a guest here in 1794 when the house was known as Old Windebrowe and was the home of the Calvert family. The existing sand-coloured edifice dates mostly from the nineteenth century, when it was extended in the style of Nash.

Nowadays, Ian and Lynn Charlton relish the challenge of maintaining Brundholme's air of grandeur while providing the comforts and relaxed atmosphere sought by its contemporary visitors. The lounge has peach and lime sofas, heavy velvet drapes and a mantelpiece with pretty vases; the bar area has a more masculine feel, with an imposing wooden bar, pictures of the Blencathra hunt and a wall-mounted deer's head. The south-facing stone-floored conservatory is a good place to relax.

The dinner menu is where the Charltons like to inject a note of innovation. Terrine of venison, pheasant and pigeon with a light liver mousse served with raspberry vinaigrette and toasted brioche is a typical starter; soup and sorbet courses may be followed by a gently steamed sea bass on a bed of roasted fennel enhanced with chervil and Pernod. Coffee and home-made chocolates round off the occasion after the dessert and cheeses.

The individually decorated bedrooms tend to emphasise the traditional character of the house and all have splendid views. Room Five is possibly the pick – a large four-poster room with a mixture of dark wood and pink furniture, a pink carpet and bright floral curtains.

◑ Open all year, exc Dec and Jan

⤢ Leave the A66 at the Crosthwaite roundabout and take the Keswick road. Turn left after Crosthwaite Garage for ½ mile, and left again down Brundholme Road. The hotel is ¼ mile on the right. Private car park

🛏 2 single, 2 twin, 5 double, 2 four-poster; all with bathroom/WC, exc 2 singles with shower/WC; TV, room service, hair-dryer in all rooms

✧ 2 restaurants, bar, lounge, drying room, conservatory; conference facilities (max 20 people non-residential, 10 residential); fishing, golf, other sports nearby. Wheelchair access to restaurant and WC (M) only

⊖ No children under 12; no dogs in public rooms; no smoking in restaurant

▭ Access, Amex, Visa

£ Single £40, single occupancy of twin/double £50, twin/double £80, four-poster £100, cottage £230 to £300; deposit required. Alc D £15 to £30. Special breaks available

The Grange

MANOR BROW, KESWICK, CUMBRIA CA12 4BA
TEL: KESWICK (07687) 72500

An elegant and welcoming hotel with magnificent fell views.

Duncan and Jane Miller run a tight ship at the Grange: high housekeeping standards and attention to detail are the order of the day. It has not gone unnoticed by readers, one of whom spoke of the 'very relaxing atmosphere – easy to settle into'. The Lakeland stone house was built in the 1840s and commands fine views of the surrounding fells – most notably in the dining-room, from where Skiddaw, Grizedale Pike and Catbells are all within view. With such a panorama available, it is not surprising that Duncan and Jane have kept the room delightfully uncluttered. The five-course dinner has a choice of two starters and main courses, possibly beginning with celery, apple and cashew-nut salad before roast loin of pork with apricot and herb stuffing. There is a Scottish slant to breakfast, with traditional oatmeal porridge, kippers and oatcakes on the table.

The high ceilings in the public areas create a sense of space and the finely detailed plasterwork adds an extra touch of elegance to rooms like the lounge, where there is a pleasing combination of old and new seating styles. The bar is for residents only but has a good pub feel and a choice of 25 malt whiskies. Bedrooms are decent-sized, individually decorated and equipped with *en-suite* facilities; romantics will go for those with half-tester beds. One reader thought that the shower cubicle was a bit of a squeeze, and indeed the demand for *en-suite* facilities has led to the creation of some cupboard-like bathrooms – although this was the only quibble to set against a long list of good points.

◖ *Closed Nov to end Nov*

⬈ *From Keswick take the A591 towards Windermere for ½ mile. Take the first right – the hotel is 200 yards on the right. Private car park*

🛏 *3 twin, 5 double, 2 half-tester; half with bathroom/WC, half with shower/WC; TV, room service, hair-dryer in all rooms*

◈ *Dining-room, bar, 2 lounges, drying room; conference facilities*

(10 people residential); fishing, golf, other sports nearby.

⊖ *No wheelchair access; no children under 7; no dogs; no smoking in dining-room and bedrooms*

▭ *Access, Visa*

£ *Single occupancy of twin/double £42 to £45, twin/double £69 to £74, half-tester £74 to £79; deposit required. Set D £17. Special breaks available*

Swinside Lodge

GRANGE ROAD, NEWLANDS, KESWICK, CUMBRIA CA12 5UE
TEL: KESWICK (07687) 72948

A smartly furnished Victorian house in a peaceful rural setting.

Swinside Lodge is not exactly off the beaten track, in fact it's a very short drive from Keswick, but you could be forgiven for thinking that you were a long way from the nearest living beings. Set in its own small grounds, backed by woodland with Catbells rising up ahead, the hotel is spoiled for scenic beauty and tranquillity – 'I met four roe deer just 100 yards from the house,' remarks one reader. Inside, Graham Taylor's choice of pale blues, pinks and greens in the décor and furnishings and the light pouring in through the large bay windows enhance the restful effect. The bedrooms, each named after a different flower, all have *en-suite* facilities. Lilac is a capacious twin with a large bay window that gives fine views of the surrounding fells. The furniture is modern and the pale blue marble-effect walls are hung with a few bright prints of flowers. The rooms have more than the usual share of little extras such as chocolates, mineral water and a generous supply of toiletries. The biscuits in the bedroom were declared 'delicious' by one reader.

Dinner might be a chicken and spinach pancake followed by roast sliced port in a Dijon mustard sauce with fresh vegetables. When you reach the dessert course you are offered a choice of treats; the cheese-board has a selection of British farmhouse cheeses. If you like a glass of wine with your meal you should bring your own as the hotel is unlicensed.

After dinner, guests are served coffee in the larger of the two lounges. It has a deep-pink carpet and blue and green sofas which are subtly angled towards each other to maximise the social aspect of the room.

Graham Taylor is an unobtrusive but attentive host who seemed genuinely touched when departing guests enthused about their stay.

◑ *Closed mid-Dec to mid-Feb*

⬈ *3 miles south-west of Keswick. Take the A66 towards Cockermouth and turn left at Portinscale. Follow the road towards Grange for 2 miles. Private car park*

🛏 *2 twin, 7 double; most with bathroom/WC, some with shower/WC; TV, hair-dryer in all rooms*

⬦ *Dining-room, 2 lounges; fishing, golf, other sports nearby*

⊖ *No wheelchair access; no children under 12; no dogs; no smoking*

▭ *None accepted*

£ *Single occupancy of twin/double £38 to £50, twin/double £59 to £76; deposit required. Set D £22 to £24 (7.30pm). Special breaks available*

KILVE SOMERSET   **MAP 10**

Meadow House

SEA LANE, KILVE, BRIDGWATER, SOMERSET TA5 IEG
TEL: HOLFORD (0278) 741546   FAX: (0278) 741663

A quiet, secluded Georgian hotel close to the sea and the Quantocks.

Meadow House is a typically stark yet graceful white Georgian house, situated just across the road from a duck pond surrounded by a myriad daffodils in spring. The Wyer-Robertses, who bought the house two years ago, are keen gardeners, and the back bedrooms, dining-room and lounge look out on banks of flowers. Large, comfortable bedrooms full of antique-looking furniture contrast with modern bathrooms with pine and porcelain fittings and lots of cruelty-free toiletries on offer. Service in the dining-room is attentive and menus feature a choice of two or three dishes per course. After dinner the cosy smoking-room with log fire provided a venue for lively debate about the meal. Our conclusion? Much the same as the reader who wrote that the food is 'good but not gourmet', and the price a little on the steep side. Breakfast kippers, however, are marvellous, and the roast duck in black cherry sauce receives rave reports from another reader.

As night falls the only sounds come from sheep, jackdaws and the little stream across the road. Even greater peace and quiet can be found in the adjacent cottage-suites, especially in the Coombe, apart from the others and slightly up a hill. With their own bathrooms and sitting-rooms, these represent particularly good value for money.

Sea Lane continues past St Mary's church and the ivy-clad ruins of a chantry chapel (to which an underground passage leads from Meadow House) to emerge by the sea and provide access to long clifftop walks.

◑ *Open all year exc 25, 26, 31 Dec, 1 Jan*

▷ *Take the A39 from Bridgwater. Once in Kilve, turn right just before the Hood Arms pub into Sea Lane. Meadow House is ½ mile on the left. Private car park*

🛏 *1 twin, 4 double, 1 half-tester, 4 cottage suites; most with bathroom/WC, some with shower/WC; TV, room service, hair-dryer in all rooms*

◈ *Dining-room, 2 lounges, library/ study, conservatory; conference facilities (max 30 people non-residential, 10 residential); croquet at hotel, other sports nearby; babysitting*

⊖ *No wheelchair access; dogs in cottage suites only; smoking in bedrooms and study only*

▭ *Access, Amex, Diners, Visa*

£ *Single occupancy of twin/double £55 to £60, twin/double from £75, half-tester £70, cottage suite from £80; deposit required. Set D £21*

KINTBURY BERKSHIRE   **MAP 9**

Dundas Arms

53 STATION ROAD, KINTBURY, BERKSHIRE RG15 0UT
TEL: KINTBURY (0488) 58263   FAX: (0488) 58568

An old-fashioned canalside pub with good food.

The Dundas Arms is just beside the canal bridge facing on to the Kennet and Avon Canal with the small station of Kintbury beyond; to the rear is the River Kennet. This small pub has been run by David Dalzell-Piper for around 25 years and has built up a good reputation for its food. In the bar with its old oak tables you can sit undisturbed with a drink and watch passers-by on the towpath (look out for the woman who takes her pet sheep for a walk). Bar meals are tasty and include dishes such as thick parsnip soup with a hunk of brown bread or dressed crab. The restaurant, with its green upholstery bench seating and colourful paintings by Margaret Loxton, has a pleasant outlook over pretty private gardens; the menu includes home-cured gravad lax, rack of lamb with rosemary sauce, sea trout with sorrel sauce and maybe summer pudding to follow. Breakfast is served in a small ante-room to the restaurant which is also used as an overflow from the restaurant or bar.

The peaceful, slightly old-fashioned bedrooms are on the ground floor, with french windows opening on to a terrace beside the River Kennet overhung with shrubbery and weeping willows. Each room has matching wallpaper and bedspreads and a comfortable armchair.

◑ Open all year, exc Xmas to New Year; restaurant closed Sun and Mon eves

⤢ 1 mile off the A4 between Newbury and Hungerford. Private car park

🛏 2 twin, 3 double; all with bathroom/WC, TV

◈ Restaurant, bar; fishing, golf, riding nearby. Wheelchair access

to hotel (2 steps), restaurant and WC (M,F), 5 ground-floor bedrooms

⊖ Dogs by arrangement only

▭ Access, Amex, Diners, Visa

£ Single occupancy of twin/double £55, twin/double £65; deposit required. Set L £16.50; alc D £17

KIRKBY LONSDALE CUMBRIA   **MAP 3**

Courtyard   ℒ

5 FAIRBANK, KIRKBY LONSDALE, CUMBRIA LA6 2AZ
TEL: KIRKBY LONSDALE (05242) 71613

Friendly, good-value bed and breakfast in a mellow Cumbrian village.

Tim and Gill Grey, who have been offering bed and breakfast here for about six years, eschew any overt guesthouse paraphernalia in favour of an authentically homely atmosphere. It certainly has the desired effect inside the house, where guests are made to feel like friends of the family, but it may result in the odd problem for the navigationally challenged, as the small plaque which announces 'The Courtyard' can be easily missed as you drive out of the centre of the village. The entrance to this stone-built listed Georgian property is actually around the side, so guests drive under an archway along a narrow path into the courtyard. The house owes its existence to the needs of a wealthy nineteenth-century land-owner who had it built while reconstruction work was carried out at his mansion. A wooden beam in the top-floor bathroom is inscribed with the building's date of birth: 1811.

The interior is simple, with stone floors in the hall and stone stairs leading to the bedrooms. These have old pine furniture, plain carpets and a few carefully selected prints; one boasts a four-poster bed.

◑ Open all year

⤢ From the Market Square, exit via New Road – the 1st right down the hill. Left at the bottom. Private car park

🛏 1 single, 2 twin, 1 four-poster; 1 twin with bathroom/WC, 2 public bathrooms; TV, room service, hair-dryer, trouser press, baby-listening in all rooms

◇ Breakfast room, lounge, drying room; fishing, riding, other sports nearby

⊟ None accepted

⊖ No wheelchair access; no children under 10; no dogs; no smoking

£ Single £15, single occupancy of twin/double £18 to £20, twin/double £40, four-poster £35; deposit required

KIRKOSWALD CUMBRIA   **MAP 4**

Prospect Hill

KIRKOSWALD, PENRITH, CUMBRIA CA10 1ER
TEL: LAZONBY (0768) 898500

Charmingly converted farmhouse in the heart of the unspoilt Eden Valley.

That John and Isa Henderson spent the best part of a decade of hard graft turning an old farmhouse and its disused outhouses into a lovely hotel is there for all to see: photos throughout the hotel vividly chronicle its development and dates carved into wood or stone – in the breakfast room, the bar and sundry other nooks and crannies – mark the end products of the Henderson labour. Of the finished article, one Vancouver couple left the encomium, 'the best yet', in the visitors' book.

Before dinner you can have a drink in the cosy bar which was inhabited by cows in its former life; breeds of sheep are now delineated on prints on its stone walls. The dining-room is a cavernous former barn with a beamed ceiling and old hay barrows for decoration. Dinners are traditional and unpretentious: chicken liver and mushroom pâté with Cumberland sauce may be followed by baked salmon and cucumber sauce. It is all well prepared and presented, with prompt but easy-going service.

Bedrooms vary in size and style. The newest additions, 10 and 11 in the coach-house annexe, are perhaps the simplest and most rustic; Room Four, the largest in the house, has a more Victorian feel with its brass bedstead and chaise-longue. The hotel also has a comfortable television lounge with a real fire, and another small lounge with an old safe in the corner now housing nothing more precious than a few boardgames. Hard-working John and Isa try to foster a homely feel in their tranquil corner of the valley. However, one reader has remarked that on days when the hotel is being used for weddings several of the bedrooms may be unpleasantly noisy late into the night and you will be pointed in the direction of the village pub for your dinner.

◑ Open all year, exc 24, 25, 26 Dec

▨ Leave the M6 at Junction 41 and take the A6 to Lazonby. Go through Lazonby and Kirkoswald on B6413 and travel up the hill to the hotel. Private car park

⨝ 2 single, 4 twin, 4 double, 1 family room; some with bathroom/WC, 2 public bathrooms; hair-dryer on request

◇ 2 restaurants, 2 bars, lounge, TV room, drying room; conference facilities (max 40 people non-residential, 11 residential); cycling at hotel, fishing, riding, swimming, other sports nearby; babysitting. Wheelchair access to restaurant only

● No dogs; smoking discouraged in bedrooms

▭ Access, Amex, Visa

£ Single £20, single occupancy of twin/double £28 to £40, twin/double £44 to £57, family room £63 to £73; deposit required. Set D £13.50; alc D £8 to £16; Sun L £7 (prices till Mar 94). Special breaks available

KNUTSFORD CHESHIRE　　　　　　　　　　**MAP 5**

La Belle Epoque ☆

KING STREET, KNUTSFORD, CHESHIRE WA16 6DT
TEL: KNUTSFORD (0565) 633060　FAX: (0565) 634150

An art nouveau restaurant-with-rooms.

For a moment, as you sit by the ground-floor window eating brioche and home-made preserves while the small shops of Knutsford open for the day, you have the sense of being in a small, classic restaurant-with-rooms in provincial France. And that, indeed, is the model for La Belle Epoque.

The establishment takes its name from its special architectural heritage. One of the sights of Knutsford, it was built in 1907 in art nouveau style by a local millionaire for use as a temperance coffee house and meeting hall. It spills astonishingly into the narrow Georgian street in a flourish of Italianate towers and turrets, rustic balconies and little winding stone staircases. Much interior detail remains unchanged; the bar-cum-foyer (where breakfasts are taken) still has the original Venetian glass mosaic floor, helmeted copper fireplace, painted mural and period furniture, now mixed with more modern cane seating.

The dining-room has an air of exotic theatricality, with swathes of indigo and sea-green drapes, marble columns, flamboyant statues, dark beams and parquet flooring. Residents are gently encouraged to dine here as a trade-off for the favourable room rates. The meals, however, are expensive and ambitious: the long à la carte menu changes regularly but may include rillettes of duck, terrine of fresh salmon, a brace of boned quails, coq au vin, boned saddle of rabbit or pigeon and potato pie. There is a sound wine list, priced fairly overall.

The size and shape of the rooms reflect the unconventional character of the hotel; all are comfortable and furnished in a varying selection of styles. Room Seven is particularly spacious with an equally large bathroom, and a door leading out on to the patio roof garden.

There is a family feel to Nerys and Keith Mooney's operation and a number of readers have commented on the friendly atmosphere. One guest so favoured the lack of formality he even faxed the *Guide* an enthusiastic recommendation from Osaka.

◑ Open all year, exc 1st week Jan;
   restaurant closed Sun eve

⬀ 2 miles from Junction 19 of the
   M6, in the middle of Knutsford.
   On-street parking

🛏 1 single, 2 twin, 4 doubles; all
   with bathroom/WC, TV

◈ Restaurant; conference facilities

(max 10 people residential)

⊖ No wheelchair access; no
   children under 14; no dogs

▭ Access, Amex, Diners, Visa

£ Single £35 to £40, single
   occupancy of twin/double £35 to
   £40, twin/double £45 to £50.
   Cooked B £5; alc D £25

Longview Hotel

51 & 55 MANCHESTER ROAD, KNUTSFORD, CHESHIRE WA16 0LX
TEL: KNUTSFORD (0565) 632119   FAX: (0565) 652402

*Appealing, Victorian terrace hotel in busy market town. Bedrooms
lack period charm of main rooms.*

We do not know if Mrs Gaskell ever visited, but we do know she lived in
the house, just visible, across the open heath. The Longview is a small,
hospitable terraced hotel, where the owners have gone to much trouble
to match the Victorian building with corresponding style and atmosphere. The hotel, in fact, is in two parts, separated from each other
by a dance academy.

Pauline and Stephen West enjoy collecting antiques, and the public
rooms are full of their acquisitions and heirlooms. The reception area,
once the back kitchen, still has the old, black-leaded range in full
working order and fired up of an evening; the desk is made from an old
'mule' chest, relic of the textile trade. The period dining-room has
recently acquired a Victorian chandelier, in keeping with the paisley
curtains, sentimental pictures and glass case of stuffed dippers. There is
an upright piano in the comfortable cellar bar for guests' use.

En-suite bedrooms vary in shape and size, but are similarly decorated
with a stock blue-and-pink print. They are agreeable but feel disappointingly standardised after the flourish of full-blown Victoriana downstairs.

The restaurant is open to non-residents and offers a mix of traditional
and adventurous dishes, often using local produce such as Tatton
venison. There is also a vegetarian menu including a 'medley' that gives
you a little bit of everything. Good selection of medium-priced wines.

◑ Open all year, exc Xmas and
   New Year; restaurant closed Sun
   eve

⬀ Leave the M6 at Junction 19 and
   take the A556 towards Chester/
   Northwich to the traffic lights,
   turn left to Knutsford. At
   roundabout, turn left and

Longview is 200 yards up on the
right. Private car park

🛏 6 single, 7 twin, 9 double, 1
   family, 2 self-catering cottages;
   all with bathroom/WC, TV, room
   service, hair-dryer, trouser press,
   baby-listening

◈ Restaurant, bar, lounge, drying

room; conference facilities (max 16 people residential); golf, tennis, other sports nearby; babysitting

⊖ No wheelchair access; no dogs or smoking in public rooms

▭ Access, Amex, Visa

£ Single from £33 and £48, single occupancy of twin/double from £42 and £55, twin/double from £58 and £70, family room from £70 and £80 (3 people); cottage £275 per week; deposit required. Set L £13.50 (by arrangement), D £15.50. Special breaks available

LACOCK WILTSHIRE   MAP 9

At The Sign Of The Angel

6 CHURCH STREET, LACOCK, NR CHIPPENHAM, WILTSHIRE SN15 2LA
TEL: CHIPPENHAM (0249) 730230   FAX: (0249) 730527

There are period rooms with plenty of nooks and crannies in this hotel in a heavenly National Trust village.

The house used to belong to a fifteenth-century wool merchant, and angels were the coins used to pay for the wool. Nowadays, the Levis family prefers guests to settle their accounts in more conventional currency. The hotel is basically an inn-with-rooms, except there is no bar, and it is run as a private hotel and restaurant rather than a pub.

Grade-I listed, the Angel is strong on atmosphere and genuine character, with lots of low ceilings, curiously shaped rooms, thick beams, creaking floors and twisty, turny stairs. Bedrooms, by necessity, vary in size, and some of the smaller rooms feel overcrowded with dark, carved, period furniture. Room Three, at the front, has a magnificent Spanish carved bed, once belonging to Brunel, that practically fills the room. Duck, if you're over 5' 2", when entering the bathroom (though the lintel is padded in case you forget). The *en-suite* bathrooms have baths and handshowers, but are looking dated. Rooms in the annexe at the bottom of the garden are reached by a footbridge across a little brook. Similarly furnished to the main house, they are bigger, lighter and more peaceful, with smart, modern bathrooms. Residents have a small, panelled lounge, with easy chairs and a cosy fire, on the first floor above the dining-room.

A good choice of traditional English food is available in the small candlelit dining-rooms. Many of the vegetables are from the garden. Lighter bistro meals are also available. However, mixed reports continue to come in to us. One reader, for example, found the service attentive, the wine good but the food disappointing.

◑ Open all year, exc 22 Dec to 30 Dec; restaurant closed Mon eve

⤵ Leave the M4 at Junction 17 and follow signs for Chippenham and Warminster. 3 miles south of Chippenham on the A350,

Lacock is signposted on the left. Follow 'Local Traffic' signs into village. Church Street is at the bottom of the village. Private car park

🛏 2 twin, 5 double, 2 four-poster, 1

family room (3 in cottage annexe); all with bathroom/WC, TV, hair-dryer

3 restaurants, lounge; fishing, golf, riding nearby

No wheelchair access; no children in restaurant eves; no dogs in public rooms

Access, Amex, Visa

Single occupancy of twin/double £55 to £70, twin/double £75 to £93, four-poster £75 to £93, family room £100 to £120; deposit required. Sun L £20; alc L £20.50, D £32.50. Special breaks available

---

LANCASTER LANCASHIRE   **MAP 5**

Edenbreck House

SUNNYSIDE LANE, LANCASTER, LANCASHIRE LA1 5ED
TEL: LANCASTER (0524) 32464

Popular guesthouse in a reproduction Edwardian villa on the edge of town.

An Englishman's home may be his castle, but for the Houghtons it is an Edwardian villa, Tudor-beamed banqueting hall, ranch kitchen and dream-movie boudoir rolled into one. Ten years ago, they literally built themselves their ideal home in the garden of their old house next door.

There are those who may find the rooms overfurnished, but they are undoubtedly comfortable, bright and warm. The Master Suite has a four-poster and links into an equally large bathroom with a sensational, freestanding pink Jacuzzi, 'probably the only one in Lancaster,' Mrs Houghton announces. She makes all the furnishings, and was in the process of DIY redecorating at the time of our inspection. All she would say regarding her colour scheme was that she was trying to get away from too much pink. The criticism in last year's *Guide* that there was no pay phone has now been rectified.

Mr Houghton was formerly in the meat trade, so presumably knows where to get a good breakfast sausage. A Weight Watchers' breakfast is also on offer. However, make sure you fill in the choice card the night before or, as one irate reader found, you will miss out on breakfast altogether. As she said, surely a curious system for a bed and breakfast with only five bedrooms?

This same correspondent also experienced a not uncommon difficulty in finding the house. There are in fact three houses called Edenbreck, all next to each other. The trick is to go through the common entrance, carry on past the two villas on your right, and follow the drive as it curves round towards Edenbreck House itself.

Open all year

From the city centre, follow signs for the British Rail Castle station. Go past the station and turn left into Ashfield Avenue which leads to Sunnyside Lane. Private car park

2 twin, 2 double, 1 four-poster; all with bathroom/WC, TV

◈ Dining-room, lounge, conservatory

⊖ No wheelchair access; no smoking or dogs in public rooms

▭ Access, Visa

£ Single occupancy of twin/double £26, twin/double £35 to £40, four-poster £40 to £50; deposit required (prices till Mar 94)

LANGAR NOTTINGHAMSHIRE   **MAP 5**

Langar Hall

LANGAR, NOTTINGHAMSHIRE NG13 9HG
TEL: HARBY (0949) 60559   FAX: (0949) 61045

A well-run country-house hotel with beautiful furnishings and cheerful staff.

Langar Hall is a solidly built nineteenth-century house with large casement windows and grounds that encompass a croquet lawn, medieval fishponds and pretty country-cottage borders. Readers report that Imogen Skirving manages to make it feel 'much more of a visit to a country house than a stay in a hotel'. The house is beautifully furnished, with antiques, chandeliers, fresh flower arrangements and pictures, pictures everywhere – Imogen was formerly a picture restorer. The study in particular is a room to linger in, with its treasure chest, painting of a glum student and glass-fronted bookcase of books that are not just for show. Dinner in the pillared dining-room would be a grand affair except

LANGAR HALL
- LANGAR -

for the informal atmosphere that the cheerful staff create. A typical dinner in summer offers a choice of five starters, main courses and puddings, and might include toasted scallops with runner beans and mint, pot-roast leg of lamb with lentils and baby aubergines, and apricot and caramel delight. One reader praised 'all courses reaching equal excellence, a very rare experience'.

Bedrooms are good-sized and furnished to the same high standard as elsewhere. Those in the main house have the edge for character, but all have well-equipped bathrooms and a page of good-humoured instructions to ensure a sound night's sleep. Notes in Brownlow – our favourite for its restful colours, lovely views in two directions and picture of a sticky moment in a croquet match – warn that the switch for the television is yards away by the door, and point out the dressing-room to which you can escape if your partner snores.

◑ *Open all year; restaurant closed Sun eve*

🔌 *Signposted off the A46 mid-way between Leicester and Newark, and off the A52 mid-way between Grantham and Nottingham. The hotel is behind the church in Langar. Private car park*

🛏 *2 twin, 9 double, 1 four-poster, family rooms available; all with bathroom/WC, exc 1 double with shower/WC; TV, room service, hair-dryer in all rooms; trouser press and baby-listening on request*

◈ *Restaurant, lounge, TV room, study, drying room; conference facilities (max 20 people non-residential, 12 residential); golf, tennis, other sports nearby; babysitting by arrangement. Wheelchair access to hotel (1 step), restaurant and 3 ground-floor bedrooms*

⊖ *No children under 12 in restaurant eves; dogs by arrangement only; no smoking in bedrooms*

▭ *Access, Amex, Visa*

£ *Single occupancy of twin/double £60 to £80, twin/double £80 to £110, four-poster £120, family room £80 to £100; deposit required. Set L from £10, D £20. Special breaks available*

LANGDALE CUMBRIA   **MAP 4**

New Dungeon Ghyll ☆

LANGDALE, AMBLESIDE, CUMBRIA LA22 9JY
TEL: LANGDALE (05394) 37213

Isolated but comfortable hotel in one of the most picturesque parts of the Lake District.

The Langdale Pikes, which provide some of the region's most dramatic scenery, are popular with both climbers and walkers – and this newly refurbished Victorian grey slate building stands at a prime location for providing rest and sustenance.

Service is efficient and friendly without being too relaxed in this family-run hotel. You can take a bar meal – pies, fish and chips washed down with a couple of pints of bitter in the walkers' bar with its stone floor and mountain pictures on the wall. Otherwise, there is a dining-room, decorated with thick Anaglypta paper and a russet carpet, where the menu features a few choices per evening such as venison in cherry sauce, roast lamb or grilled trout. After a meal, most guests flop in one of the chairs gathered around the large log-burning fire in the residents' lounge. Coffee is also served here. The bedrooms, which have modern pine or dark wood furniture and green duvets, are comfortable but lack charm – although the views across the Pikes more than compensate.

◐ Open all year

⤴ From Ambleside follow the B5343 to Langdale for 6 miles. Private car park

🛏 2 single, 5 twin, 10 double, 1 four-poster; all with shower/ WC, exc 2 twins with bathroom/ WC; TV, hair-dryer in all rooms

◈ Dining-room, bar, drying room; conference facilities (max 18

people residential and non-residential)

⊖ No wheelchair access; no dogs in public rooms

▭ Access, Visa

£ Single £30 to £35, single occupancy of twin/double £30 to £35, twin/double £56 to £60, four-poster £60 to £66; deposit required. Set D £17.50; alc L £5.50

LANGHO LANCASHIRE   **MAP 5**

Northcote Manor

NORTHCOTE ROAD, LANGHO, NR BLACKBURN, LANCASHIRE BB6 8BE
TEL: BLACKBURN (0254) 240555   FAX: (0254) 246568

Enterprising country hotel that has turned overnight stops into luxury gastronomic events.

North-south travellers charging up and down the M6 would do well to venture ten miles off the motorway at Junction 31, should they be in need of a pit stop that provides high-grade gourmet fuelling. Manager Craig Bancroft and chef Nigel Haworth describe their country-house hotel as 'compact'. This is slightly misleading, as the late-Victorian red-brick house, built by a local cotton family, has now been seamlessly extended to provide a total of 13 bedrooms plus a private dining/conference suite and a bay-fronted enlargement of the main dining-room. With heart-warming optimism, the dynamic young pair are embarking on a 15-year plan to redesign the garden, greenhouses and grounds. This will help blot out the proximity of traffic on the nearby bypass.

Northcote has built a considerable reputation, though, as a high-powered restaurant destination in its own right. Swiss-trained Nigel makes everything on the premises, down to the last bread roll. Modern European food mixes with traditional English and there is an increasing tendency to present dishes based on old Lancashire recipes, on the model of French provincial hotel cooking. Typical of this new vein are Pendle lamb shank, pot-roasted with onions on a crisp layer of potatoes; Hindle Wakes chicken; collared pork (an old eighteenth-century Manchester dish); and Bury black pudding and buttered pink trout with mustard and nettle sauce. The wide-ranging wine list is likely to suit most tastes and pockets. All this to be enjoyed in the elegant lemon-and-navy dining-room, with its crisply starched napery.

The bedrooms have an air of comfortable affluence. All are furnished with carefully chosen pieces and have smart bathrooms. Throughout, there are beautiful fabrics from a mill in nearby Burnley, as befits the former home of a Lancashire textile magnate.

◑ Open all year, exc 1 Jan

↗ Leave the M6 at Junction 31 and take the A59 Clitheroe road for 9 miles. The hotel is on the left-hand side before the 1st roundabout. Private car park

🛏 1 twin, 12 double, 1 four-poster; all with bathroom/WC, TV, room service, hair-dryer, trouser press, baby-listening

◈ Restaurant, bar, 2 lounges; conference facilities (max 30

people non-residential, 14 residential); golf, tennis, other sports nearby; babysitting. Wheelchair access to hotel, restaurant and WC (unisex), 4 ground-floor bedrooms

⊖ No dogs

▭ Access, Amex, Diners, Visa

£ Single occupancy of twin/double £59, twin/double £70, four-poster £90; deposit preferred. Set L £14; alc L, D from £25. Special breaks available

---

LANGLEY MARSH SOMERSET   **MAP 10**

Langley House

LANGLEY MARSH, WIVELISCOMBE, SOMERSET TA4 2UF
TEL: WIVELISCOMBE (0984) 23318   FAX: (0984) 24573; changing to 623318 (tel) and 624573 (fax) Oct 1993

An elegant country-house hotel offering classy food and drink.

At first glance Langley House is a not particularly striking eighteenth-century building in pretty gardens. Inside, however, it is an oasis of quiet luxury with a bold use of colour: deep terracotta walls in the front lounge, canary-yellow ones in the back dining-room (used for small conferences) and strikingly vivid fabrics in the bedrooms. Space, too, is important: a shallow arch nominally divides the huge lounge in two; gentle pastel-coloured armchairs and sofas hug the walls, making a feature of the rug laid over the polished floorboards. The dining-room sharply reduces the scale, creating a more cottagey atmosphere accentuated by the swag of dried flowers running along the chimney breast.

Peter Wilson's four-course dinners are carefully served by his wife Anne, although it doesn't pay to be in a hurry. On inspection, the fanned dessert pear marinated in walnut oil with a herb savoury and the smoked salmon soufflé were dreamy, although the mignons of Angus beef fillet came too rare for some tastes, a fault quickly rectified but one which could have been avoided by checking individual preference first. Since there is only a choice of dessert, vegetarians could be caught napping unless they discuss the menu when booking. The wine list is obviously a great hit with regulars.

Upstairs the bedrooms, although not particularly large, are a delight, the bright yellow paper tea roses running round the top of the wall in one being typical of the thoughtful finishing touches. Beds are turned down at night, and hot-water bottles are provided.

◑ Closed Feb

↗ On an unclassified road signposted Langley Marsh that leads from the centre of Wiveliscombe. Private car park

🛏 1 single, 2 twin, 3 double, 1 four-poster, 1 family room; all with bathroom/WC, exc 1 double with shower/WC; TV, room service, hair-dryer, baby-listening in all rooms; no tea/coffee-making facilities in rooms

◇ Restaurant, bar, 2 lounges, drying room, conservatory; conference facilities (max 8 people residential, 18 non-residential); croquet at hotel, other sports nearby; babysitting. Wheelchair access to restaurant and WC only

⊖ No children under 7 in restaurant eves; no dogs in public rooms

▭ Access, Amex, Visa

£ Single £58 to £65, single occupancy of twin/double £58 to £65, twin/double from £79, four-poster £95 to £105, family room £115 to £130; deposit required. Set D £22.50. Special breaks available

---

LASTINGHAM NORTH YORKSHIRE   **MAP 3**

Lastingham Grange

LASTINGHAM, YORK, NORTH YORKSHIRE YO6 6TH
TEL: LASTINGHAM (0751) 417345/417402

A classic of its kind – comfortable, confident, unperturbed by the diktats of style gurus and wholeheartedly committed to pampering its guests.

The scene is timeless: a stone-walled seventeenth-century farmhouse, festooned with veils of creeper and converted into a fine country hotel with the delights of the North Yorks moors all around it. Small wonder that battalions of regulars return year after year, sinking into a mellow atmosphere that must have all the joyful familiarity of an old slipper.

Public rooms are reassuringly traditional. A dresser, antiques and elephant and dalmatian ornaments set the tone in reception, presided over by a bust of Churchill. More elephants feature in the resolutely English L-shaped lounge, which is swaddled in autumnal colours with plenty of chairs and sofas and a bank of windows overlooking the lovely gardens. The dining-room has dark wood antique tables set with crystal and red napkins, an Adam-style fireplace and a Canaletto print. Tariffs include morning coffee and afternoon tea, and menus – as traditional as the surroundings – have been praised for avoiding repetition while sticking to the tried and tested; perhaps pâté maison, followed by lemon sorbet, roast sirloin of beef and Yorkshire pudding – 'exceptional', according to one visitor.

Bedrooms complement the rest of the house, with traditional patterns and solid old furniture prevailing. Modern bathrooms deliver piping hot water. Guests leave relaxed, well-satisfied and ready to sing the praises of the owners: 'Mr and Mrs Wood and all their staff deserve the highest praise for their total dedication to the comfort and welfare of their guests . . . the care and attention they lavish is genuine,' concluded one correspondent.

🌓 Open all year, exc Jan, Feb and Dec

🚹 3 miles north of the A170 (between Pickering and Kirkbymoorside). Private car park

🛏 2 single, 7 twin, 3 double, family rooms available; all with bathroom/WC, TV, room service, hair-dryer, trouser press, baby-listening

◈ Dining-room, lounge, drying room; fishing, golf, other sports nearby

⊖ No wheelchair access; no dogs in public rooms; no smoking in dining-room

▭ None accepted

£ Single £57 to £60, single occupancy of twin/double £57 to £60, twin/double/family room £105 to £110. Set L from £13, D from £21.50

LAVENHAM SUFFOLK   MAP 8

Angel

MARKET PLACE, LAVENHAM, SUFFOLK CO10 9QZ
TEL: LAVENHAM (0787) 247388   FAX: (0787) 247057

No surprises, but you can't go wrong with this solid pub and the welcome is sure to be enthusiastic.

Of the three recommendations we make in Lavenham, the Angel is the lightest on the pocket. It is well-situated on the wide market place of this pretty medieval wool town and is handy for a visit to the old Guildhall (run by the National Trust) opposite. Benches, tables and window boxes brim on to the pavement in front of the old whitewashed inn, tempting strollers to stop for morning coffee. Reports continue to come in of the warmth of the welcome offered by the joint owners – the Whitworths and the Barrys. 'From the moment we arrived, we encountered friendliness and helpfulness – a very welcoming atmosphere,' says one happy guest. Bedrooms are unextraordinary, verging on the simple, but, as the same guest put it, 'all one could desire'. Creamy walls, beams, cane furniture, a fireplace, perhaps a view on to the garden – you'll be guaranteed a comfortable night. A lovely residents' lounge, with a ceiling resembling an iced cake, overlooks the square.

Meals are served in the restaurant behind the bar area. Prices are reasonable and dishes included tomato and mozzarella salad, steak and kidney pie, chocolate brandy torte and strawberry pavlova on inspection. And who could resist the coffee and home-made fudge to round it off? Go back to the bar and you may also be tempted by the substantial list of malt whiskies chalked on a blackboard.

◐ *Open all year, exc 25 Dec*

▨ *On A1141, 2 miles east of A134 between Sudbury and Bury St Edmunds. Turn left from Lavenham High Street into Market Place. Private car park and on-street parking*

🛏 *1 twin, 5 double, 1 family room; some with bathroom/WC, some with shower/WC; TV, room service; hair-dryer, baby-listening on request*

◈ *Restaurant, bar, lounge; golf,* *riding, other sports nearby. Wheelchair access to hotel (1 step), restaurant and WC, 1 ground-floor bedroom*

⊖ *Dogs in bar, and bedrooms by arrangement only*

▭ *Access, Visa*

£ *Single occupancy of twin/double £40 to £50, twin/double £50 to £60, family room £60 to £70; deposit required. Alc L £6 to £10, D £12 to £17. Special breaks available*

Great House

MARKET PLACE, LAVENHAM, SUFFOLK CO10 9QZ
TEL: SUDBURY (0787) 247431

The combination of a solid, English town house run with French style is a recipe for success.

'Bon appétit,' murmurs the waitress as she places a plate of fresh asparagus with hollandaise sauce in front of you and for a moment you might imagine yourself holidaying in France. However, at the Great House there's no need to feel guilty about the standard of your rusty French – although it is French-owned and run by a friendly French team, their English is fluent enough to make you feel very welcome.

The house, which overlooks the central medieval market place, is originally fifteenth century, built by the Causton family who were wealthy local weavers. Three hundred years later it was given a Georgian face-lift and in the 1950s the poet Stephen Spender moved in, hence the well-fingered volume of his work which may lie next to your bed. The emphasis is firmly on the cuisine but this doesn't mean to say that the bedrooms have been overlooked. The four bedrooms are furnished with heavy antiques and thick rugs cover polished floorboards. A couple have separate sitting-rooms – Room Three comes with a cosy two-seater sofa and lots of space. Half-timbered walls and wonky floors add character.

Dinner is served in the rich terracotta dining-room with old maps of Lavenham on the wall and a large log fire. The menu offers a good choice, relying on seasonal ingredients, and the service is carefully attentive. If the weather permits, meals are also taken in the central paved courtyard among brimming pots of flowers.

◖ *Open all year*

⤴ *Lavenham is on the A1141, 2 miles east of the A134 between Bury St Edmunds and Sudbury. The hotel is in Lavenham's market place. On-street parking*

🛏 *2 twin, 1 double, 1 family room; all with bathroom/WC, exc 1 twin with shower/WC; TV, room service, hair-dryer, baby-listening in all rooms*

◈ *Restaurant, bar, lounge,* *conservatory; conference facilities (max 15 people non-residential); tennis, riding, other sports nearby*

⊖ *No wheelchair access; no dogs in public rooms*

▭ *Access, Amex, Visa*

£ *Single occupancy of twin/double £50, twin/double £68 to £78, family room rate on request; deposit required. Set D £15; alc L £2 to £8, D £18/£20*

Swan

HIGH STREET, LAVENHAM, SUFFOLK CO10 9QA
TEL: SUDBURY (0787) 247477   FAX: (0787) 248286

Slick service in a hotel whose history can be traced back centuries.

St Valentine's dinner dance, Mothering Sunday, Hollywood revisited, Burns Night supper . . . you name it, the Swan devotes an evening to it. The rooms in this fifteenth-century building tend to be costed by their period features. Skelton offers not only beams but a fireplace too; Lindsey, a lovely four-poster room, also has a large fireplace and a curtained dressing-room, whereas poor Shimpling, a standard double, limps behind a little with few features and a very small window.

There are no fewer than five log fires burning in the downstairs public rooms to make the atmosphere cosy and welcoming; there are lots of places to sit and the two bars serve local and real ales. A pianist regales diners in the restaurant and the evening menu may start with warm chicken liver salad among the starters and Swan Stroganoff among the main courses, with a wide selection of desserts to round the meal off.

◖ *Open all year*

⤴ *In Lavenham on the A1141. Private car park*

🛏 *9 single, 14 twin, 19 double, 2 four-posters, 3 suites; all with bathroom/WC, TV, room service, hair-dryer, mini-bar, trouser press, baby-listening*

◈ *Restaurant, 2 bars, 5 lounges; conference facilities (max 80 people non-residential, 50 residential); riding, tennis, other sports nearby; babysitting. Wheelchair access to hotel, restaurant and WC, 8 ground-floor bedrooms*

● No dogs in public rooms; no smoking in restaurant

▭ Access, Amex, Diners, Visa

£ Single £85, single occupancy of

twin/double £95, twin/double £110, four-poster £135, suite £145. Continental B £6, cooked B £8; set L £15, D £19. Special breaks available

LEAMINGTON SPA WARWICKSHIRE   **MAP 9**

Flowerdale House

58 WARWICK NEW ROAD, LEAMINGTON SPA, WARWICKSHIRE CV32 6AA
TEL: LEAMINGTON SPA (0926) 426002   FAX: (0926) 883699

A bed and breakfast with peaceful public rooms, cheerful bedrooms and friendly hosts.

Barbara and Bill Powell's Victorian red-brick house has a commanding position on the junction of the Rugby Road and Warwick New Road since developers demolished the house next door. One of the nicest features about this bed and breakfast, apart from the genuine friendliness of the owners, is the conservatory with its black and white tiled floor and eight-foot avocado plant – a wonderful leafy retreat if the weather's not good enough for sitting in the walled garden. The breakfast room leads into the house from here and, like the lounge, is a restful room with muted colours. Dried flowers in the grate and ruched curtains give the lounge the edge on prettiness.

The relaxed, homely feel also extends to the bedrooms. Each has a good-sized bathroom and fresh, hectically patterned walls and fabrics. An assortment of furniture collected over the years means that your room might have a lovely marble washstand alongside an old-fashioned television. Huge windows at the front of the house make these rooms light and cheerful, while those at the back are quieter and overlook the garden. A sunny yellow single room in the attic suits people looking for a longer stay.

◑ Open all year

↗ On the junction of Warwick New Road (B4099) and Rugby Road (B4453), opposite the headquarters of Guide Dogs for the Blind. Private car park

↤ 1 single, 3 twin, 2 double; most with bathroom/WC, some with shower/WC; TV in all rooms; hair-dryer on request

◇ Breakfast room, bar, lounge, drying room, conservatory; ironing facilities; golf, fishing, other sports nearby

● No wheelchair access; no children under 12; no dogs or smoking in public rooms

▭ Access, Visa

£ Single £22 to £26, single occupancy of twin/double £28 to £32, twin/double £36 to £42; deposit required

See the inside front cover for a brief explanation of how to use the Guide.

Lansdowne

87 CLARENDON STREET, LEAMINGTON SPA, WARWICKSHIRE CV32 4PF
TEL: LEAMINGTON SPA (0926) 450505   FAX: (0926) 421313

*A well-run small hotel in central Leamington Spa with
enthusiastic staff and smart rooms.*

The Lansdowne is just about as central as you could hope to get in
Leamington Spa. The square, pale green Regency town house is well
cared for on the outside and immaculate within, where David and Gillian
Allen run a very tidy operation. Guests returning from the tourist fray
pass by the picture of the Queen in the hall and head to their rooms to
freshen up, or to the sitting-room with its fussy curtains and comfortable
sofas. Smart, well-chosen wallpaper and fabrics ensure that every
bedroom is well co-ordinated, with Laura Ashley-style patterns and pine
furniture in most rooms. Pot plants, dried flowers and lace lend a hint of
Victoriana. All rooms are double glazed to cut down on street noise and
bathrooms, though not large, are well-equipped. Single rooms suffer
from lack of space, but large windows give those on the sunny side of the
house plenty of light.

The Allens' enthusiastic young chef offers table d'hôte menus which
might include home-made mushroom and burgundy pâté served with
walnut bread, poached mixed seafood in a light pastry case with a fresh
herb, wine and cream sauce, and griddled prime Aberdeen Angus steak.
David Allen's interest in wine is obvious from the bottles lined up on the
marble mantelpiece in the bar – where he dispenses pre-dinner drinks
and canapés – and the wooden wine case plaques that cover one wall in
the dining-room; his extensive wine list is predominantly French.

◐ Open all year

↗ In the centre of Leamington Spa,
at the junction with Warwick
Street. Private car park

🛏 7 single, 5 twin, 3 double; some
with bathroom/WC, most with
shower/WC, 3 public bathrooms;
TV, hair-dryer in all rooms; baby-
listening on request

◇ Restaurant, bar, lounge; golf,
tennis, other sports nearby;
babysitting by arrangement.

Wheelchair access to hotel (1
step) and restaurant, 2 ground-
floor bedrooms

⊖ No children under 5; no dogs; no
smoking in restaurant

▭ Access, Visa

£ Single £29 to £49, single
occupancy of twin/double £29 to
£49, twin/double £39 to £58;
deposit required. Set D £17;
alc D £22. Special breaks
available

---

*Use the index at the back of the book if you know the name of a hotel but are
unsure about its precise location.*

York House

9 YORK ROAD, LEAMINGTON SPA, WARWICKSHIRE CV31 3PR
TEL: LEAMINGTON SPA (0926) 424671

A small, friendly, family-run hotel opposite the Pump Room gardens.

Cheerfulness is the name of the game at York House, and the severe expressions in a series of Victorian family photographs in the hall seem out of place. Just across a quiet residential street from the River Leam and Pump Room gardens, this three-storey red-brick Victorian house with wrought-iron balconies, heavy in summer with clematis and colourful hanging baskets, occupies one of the nicest spots in Leamington. The interior is immaculately clean and neat, with a mix of Victoriana and modern furnishings. Unusual door panels embossed with figures, urns and flowers add character to rooms furnished with functional Dralon sofas and plain fabrics. The dining-room, with its collection of plates and bric-à-brac and white table cloths, is an informal place where, with half an hour's notice, Robert and Sue Davis serve light suppers from the 'snacks list' – omelettes, chicken salad or lasagne, perhaps. Photographs of the Davises' family and friends – who include Andrew Sachs of *Fawlty Towers* fame – complete the friendly atmosphere.

Bedrooms are modern and well-heated, with an assortment of furniture; pink predominates and pale flowery duvets are the norm. The modern *en-suite* bathrooms are not very large but are spotlessly clean. The single rooms are quite cramped; if you prefer lots of space, rooms on the third floor at the front are best, though those at the back are sunnier.

◐ Open all year, exc 24 Dec to 1 Jan; dining-room closed Sun eve

↗ From main parade in Leamington Spa turn right into Dormer Place, left into Dale Street, then left into York Road. The hotel overlooks the River Leam. Private car park

🛏 2 single, 4 twin, 2 double, family rooms available; some with bathroom/WC, some with shower/WC, some neither; TV, room service, hair-dryer, baby-listening in all rooms

◈ Dining-room, lounge; golf, tennis, other sports nearby; babysitting

⊖ No wheelchair access; dogs by arrangement only; smoking in lounge and 4 bedrooms only

▭ Access, Amex, Visa

£ Single £20 to £26, single occupancy of twin/double £25 to £36, twin/double £36 to £50, family room £50 to £60; deposit required. Set L from £6.50, D £10.50; alc D £16.50. Special breaks available

---

It is always worth enquiring about the availability of special breaks or weekend prices. The prices we quote are the standard rates for one night – most hotels offer reduced rates for longer stays.

LECK LANCASHIRE   **MAP 3**

Cobwebs

LECK, COWAN BRIDGE, KIRKBY LONSDALE, LANCASHIRE LA6 2HZ
TEL: KIRKBY LONSDALE (05242) 72141 (and fax)

Charming Victorian guesthouse with high standards of food, wine and comfort.

Cobwebs is just off the A65, halfway between the Lake District and Yorkshire Dales in the lovely Lune Valley, justly celebrated by John Ruskin. It is a small country house run in tandem by Paul Kelly and Yvonne Thompson. Decorated with William Morris-style wallpaper, it verges on the fussy, but effectively creates a mood of modern nostalgia.

Rooms are not numbered; instead, guests' names are inscribed on each door, a detail that gives a pleasing moment of self-importance. All five bedrooms are a decent size, except for one small double at the back, which has a separate bathroom and toilet. Rooms are individually furnished with Edwardian and Victorian pieces, pretty fabrics and wallpapers and frilly spreads. Bathrooms are modern, with yellow ducks and towelling robes.

In comparison to the two small parlours, the size of the conservatory restaurant reflects the important role dinner plays at Cobwebs. It has well-spaced tables with heavy pink cloths and decorative china, and there are maps of wine-growing regions on the wall. The windows open only to the garden, fells and the gaze of passing sheep in the next field.

The multi-course set dinner, with just a choice of starter, changes daily (chef Yvonne will check any particular dislikes when you book). It is well-executed modern British cooking, prone to certain conceits; two soups in one bowl have become Yvonne's particular signature. There is a serious, well-priced wine list, strong on New World and Alsace wines. A spring menu consisted of chilled lettuce and cucumber soup together with hot broccoli and apple soup, a trio of smoked fish roses with warm wild salmon and tomato confit, marinated breast of guinea-fowl set on a kumquat and pink peppercorn sauce, a fine selection of local cheeses and a trio of desserts. After such a meal, one needs little encouragement to climb into a neatly turned down, immensely comfortable bed and enjoy the sweet dreams wished in the note left on the pillow.

◐ *Closed Jan to mid-Mar*

⤴ *Leave the M6 at Junction 36 and travel east for 8 miles on the A65. Turn left at Cowan Bridge. Private car park*

🛏 *2 twin, 3 double; most with bathroom/WC, some with shower/WC; TV, room service, hair-dryer in all rooms*

◈ *Restaurant, 2 lounges, drying room; fishing, golf, tennis nearby. Wheelchair access to restaurant only*

⊖ *No children under 12; no dogs; no smoking in restaurant*

▭ *Access, Visa*

£ *Single occupancy of twin/double £40, twin/double £65; deposit required. Set D £25. Special breaks available*

LEDBURY HEREFORD AND WORCESTER **MAP 9**

Hope End

HOPE END, LEDBURY, HEREFORD AND WORCESTER HR8 1JQ
TEL: LEDBURY (0531) 633613   FAX: (0531) 636366

A secret domain, ideal for dreaming or contemplation.

Beyond the suburban fringes of Ledbury where neat villas clump together on the edge of small lanes, the childhood home of Elizabeth Barrett Browning lies deep in a hollow, surrounded by magnificent bluebell-strewn woodland. The house, sunny in ochre brick, is low and unassuming, but the curious minarets and pillars topped with urns that rise from the courtyard walls give it an air of mystery – you half-expect it to be the home of an alchemist or astrologer. Instead it is the abode of John and Patricia Hegarty, who have turned it into a comfortable and efficient hotel where friendliness is combined with the right degree of formality to ensure that your peace is undisturbed. The public rooms are bright and modern, with much use of wood and colourful fabrics; oil paintings add colour where needed. The drawing-room upstairs is a particularly pleasant place to relax. Bedrooms, with plentiful stripped pine and exposed beams, vary in size and price; modern fabrics, thick carpets and silence are their chief virtues. The food, much of it organically grown in the estate's walled garden, consists either of a light supper two nights a week or a five-course dinner on the other evenings.

- ◑ Closed mid-Dec to mid-Feb
- ⤢ 2 miles north of Ledbury, just beyond Wellington Heath. Private car park
- 🛏 3 twin, 6 double; all with bathroom/WC
- ◈ Dining-room, 3 lounges, library/study; conference facilities (max 10 people residential)
- ⊖ No wheelchair access; no children under 12; no dogs; no smoking in dining-room
- ▭ Access, Visa
- £ Single occupancy of twin/double £87, twin/double £99 to £143; deposit required. Set D £30. Special breaks available

---

LEE DEVON **MAP 10**

Old Vicarage ☆

LEE, NR ILFRACOMBE, DEVON EX34 8LW
TEL: ILFRACOMBE (0271) 863195

A quiet family home with extensive grounds, suitable for house parties.

Set in three acres of partly wooded, partly cultivated garden, this nineteenth-century building used to house the cleric assigned to the adjacent church. One reader describes its décor as 'traditional and sympathetic . . . refreshingly devoid of the work of snooty interior designers' – which is not to say that it isn't clean, fresh and modern throughout; stencilling brightens up the lounge and some of the bedrooms. The Old Vicarage can accommodate up to ten people at a time, in four rooms upstairs and one room downstairs; the dining-room has a table that can be extended to seat all the guests together, after which they can adjourn to a comfortable lounge with log-burner, sofas and window-seat. Drinks are dispensed from a hall cabinet on an honesty basis.

Susan and Philip Hungate pride themselves on offering their guests peace, quiet and good old-fashioned service for very reasonable prices. There is no television in the house; instead you amuse yourself watching the antics of three Manx sheep.

○ Open all year

⤴ Take the A361 towards Ilfracombe, then the B3343 towards Lee. Private car park

🛏 1 twin, 2 double, 2 family rooms; some with bathroom/WC, some with shower/WC, 1 public bathroom; room service to all rooms; hair-dryer, baby-listening on request

◇ Dining-room, bar, lounge, drying room; fishing, golf, other sports

nearby; babysitting. Wheelchair access to hotel (3 steps), dining-room and WC (unisex), 1 ground-floor bedroom

⊖ No dogs; no smoking in bedrooms

▭ None accepted

£ Single occupancy of twin/double £18 to £44, twin/double £36 to £50, family room £36 to £50; deposit required. Alc D £13

LEEDS WEST YORKSHIRE   MAP 5

42 The Calls

42 THE CALLS, LEEDS, WEST YORKSHIRE LS2 7EW
TEL: LEEDS (0532) 440099   FAX: (0532) 344100

Innovative minimalist design in a memorable waterfront hotel.

If you can't imagine why you would need a bedroom with three telephones 42 The Calls is probably not the place for you, though there's no denying that it serves its chosen constituency – expense-account turbo-thrusting young businessfolk – exceedingly well. Design statements abound in this state-of-the-art converted grain warehouse, from the striking black and white entrance and the smart, lofty reception area to the minimalist bar with its vaguely Japanese feel – the overriding impression is of a high-tech design ethos where the Conran shop meets Charles Rennie Mackintosh. A mezzanine-level lounge combines coral sofas, bold striped wallpaper and rattan-backed wood-framed chairs. The black and white motif reasserts itself in the breakfast room overlooking the river where spindly metal-framed chairs partner black tables and jazz, Robert Doisneau and James Dean posters line the white walls.

Bedrooms are individually designed and planned with serious business use in mind: the uncluttered look leaves plenty of room for meetings and desks are the sort you can really work at, with lights and power points in the right places. Superior rooms even have fax machines. Continental breakfast can be dropped off through a hatch without disturbing the occupant. If all this sounds too cell-like and bound by the work ethic, the TV has satellite channels and there's a stereo system complete with CD-player (choose your discs from the library at reception) to soothe the soul.

Staff are young and friendly, and the tariff (calculated on the basis that businessfolk travel solo) lets partners stay for a nominal £5 extra charge. Thoughtful billing arrangements with designated restaurants, including next-door Brasserie 44 co-owned by 42's proprietor Jonathan Wix, let you charge restaurant accounts to your hotel bill.

- ◑ Open all year, exc 5 days at Xmas
- ↗ In the centre of Leeds; detailed instructions sent upon booking. Private car park and on-street metered parking
- ⊨ 6 single, 32 twin/double, 3 suites; all with bathroom/WC, TV, room service, hair-dryer, mini-bar, trouser-press, baby-listening
- ◈ Restaurant, breakfast room, bar, lounge; conference facilities (max 55 people non-residential, 39 residential); golf, riding, other sports nearby; babysitting. Wheelchair access to hotel, restaurant and WC (unisex), 1 bedroom specially equipped for disabled people
- ⊖ Dogs by arrangement only; no pipes/cigars in restaurant
- ▭ Access, Amex, Diners, Visa
- £ Single £77, single occupancy of twin/double £95, twin/double £100, suite £135 to £195; deposit required. Cooked B £10, continental B £7; set L £7.50; alc L, D £24. Special breaks available

---

Haley's ☆

SHIRE OAK ROAD, HEADINGLEY, LEEDS, WEST YORKSHIRE LS6 2DE
TEL: LEEDS (0532) 784446   FAX: (0532) 753342

An elegant conversion of late-Victorian houses in a quiet suburb close to the university and the cricket ground.

The name is a tribute not to the veteran singer who used to rock around the clock but to a master stone mason active in turn-of-the-century Leeds. The building is a blonde sandstone villa in its own grounds, much-extended and revamped, with witches' hat turrets and mock-Tudor strapping. Inside, the décor leans towards the country-house school, but there is less chintz than usual and the public rooms are attractively designed with bright modern fabrics and wallcoverings to make the most of original design features that survived the recent transformation to create the present hotel. The overall effect is not particularly stylish, but is undeniably comfortable and cheerful. In the light, airy restaurant, more modern in feel than the bay-windowed drawing-room, the menu aims at traditional English rather than a cosmopolitan bistro-style; perhaps a salad of lambs' sweetbreads, followed by grilled sirloin steak with red cabbage and fresh thyme, and a selection of English and French cheeses with home-made biscuits and walnut bread.

Bedrooms are individually decorated in a light modern style but with lots of nods to design classics – in various places we saw striped wallpaper, paisley bedspreads and tartan-covered chairs. Bathrooms are smart and robes are provided as well as the usual basket of toiletries.

◑ *Open all year, exc 26 to 30 Dec*

⤢ *Just off the A660 Leeds to Otley road, 2 miles north of the city centre and just before the Arndale shopping centre. Private car park*

🛏 *8 single, 4 twin, 10 double, suites available; all with bathroom/WC, TV, room service, hair-dryer, trouser press*

◈ *Restaurant (air-conditioned), bar, 2 lounges, library, private dining-room (air-conditioned); conference facilities (max 25*

people non-residential, 22 residential); fishing, golf, other sports nearby; babysitting by arrangement. Wheelchair access to restaurant only

⊖ *No dogs*

▭ *Access, Amex, Diners, Visa*

£ *Single £95, single occupancy of twin/double £102, twin/double £112, suite £165; deposit required. Set L from £14, D from £19; alc L, D £22. Special breaks available*

LEICESTER LEICESTERSHIRE   **MAP 5**

Spindle Lodge

2 WEST WALK, LEICESTER, LEICESTERSHIRE LE1 7NA
TEL: LEICESTER (0533) 551380   FAX: (0533) 543076

Competently run, good-value small hotel near the centre of Leicester and convenient for the university.

West Walk is typical of the nineteenth-century Leicester streets of red-brick houses which were built on the back of the boot, shoe and textile industries which were then booming in this part of the Midlands. Once the home of a well-to-do haberdasher, Spindle Lodge is now surrounded by departments from the nearby university. Architectural plans for the original building hang on the wall, and the Cottons are justly proud of having preserved many original Victorian features – not merely preserved, in fact, but positively treasured: the pine doors with brass fittings, the finely etched glass in the front door and the patterned tiled hallway floor are all gleaming. Immaculate housekeeping extends to the rest of the house, too. Angie Cotton has an eye for colour, and has co-ordinated smart paper and fabrics stylishly. Knick-knacks include a collection of dolls' straw hats in the dining-room, and an advert for children's boots and scouring flannels on the staircase. The 13 bedrooms range from plain to pretty with good-quality furnishings. Though not large – one single is particularly tiny – they are comfortable, and better equipped than you might expect in a small hotel.

◑ *Open all year, exc 24 Dec to 1 Jan; restaurant closed Fri, Sat and Sun eves*

↗ *From Leicester BR station, turn left on to the A6 London road and take the first turning right into De Montfort Street. Carry on to the traffic lights and turn left and first left again into West Walk. Private car park*

↜ *5 single, 3 twin, 3 double, 2 family rooms, some with shower/ WC, 3 public bathrooms; TV, room service, hair-dryer, baby-*

listening in all rooms

◈ *Dining-room, bar, lounge; golf, tennis, other sports nearby*

⊖ *No wheelchair access; dogs in bedrooms only by arrangement; no smoking in dining-room*

▭ *Access, Visa*

£ *Single £26 to £36, single occupancy of twin/double £31, twin/double £46 to £56, family room £60; deposit required. Bar lunches £1.50 to £5; alc D £7 to £14*

LEICESTER FOREST EAST LEICESTERSHIRE   **MAP 5**

Red Cow

HINCKLEY ROAD, LEICESTER FOREST EAST, LEICESTER, LEICESTERSHIRE
LE3 3PG
TEL: LEICESTER (0533) 387878 (and fax)

Friendly service in a good-value converted pub with special facilities for families and a handy location for the M1.

The Red Cow was established in the days when pubs were pubs and drinkers were locals plus a few stray travellers winding their weary way. The seventeenth-century gaolers who used to leave their charges in the cellars here while they nipped upstairs for a jug may be turning in their graves at the state of the Red Cow today; others might applaud the enterprising spirit of Everards brewery, out of which has been born a complex of good-value, well-equipped rooms and reliably good facilities.

The fact that this 300-year-old building is thatched, ivy-clad and has the original stone mounting block outside its door is largely irrelevant now that the old part is swamped by a huge new extension at the back and a separate red-brick bedroom annexe to one side. Nor does the interior hold any surprises: the restaurant, with its light-wood clothless tables, barely padded dining chairs and exposed brick walls has an austere hostelry feel, while the low-lit bar has only old photographs of the area and prints of rural scenes and prize-winning stock to give it atmosphere. The annexe has 31 almost identical bedrooms, which are well-coordinated with light floral-print fabrics and peachy-coloured wall-paper. Both the bedrooms and their fully tiled bathrooms have plenty of space to move around in and are well-equipped; each room has a sofa-bed, which makes them especially economical for families. The conservatory too is ideal for children, with low tables, a half-portion half-price menu and access to the garden, which has an adventure playground area complete with padded mats. Food in the restaurant is more imaginative – and more expensive – than in the bar; it includes Chinese-style duck, paella, and steak prepared in various ways.

◑ *Open all year*

⤴ *On the A47 between Leicester and Hinckley. Leave the M1 at Junction 21 or 22 and follow outer ring road. Private car park*

🛏 *4 twin, 27 double (family rooms available); all with bathroom/WC, TV, hair-dryer, trouser press*

◈ *Restaurant, bar, drying room, conservatory; golf, heated swimming-pool, other sports nearby. Wheelchair access to*

hotel (ramp), restaurant and WC (disabled), 16 ground-floor bedrooms

⊖ *No dogs*

▭ *Access, Amex, Diners, Visa*

£ *Single occupancy of twin/double £29 to £40, twin/double £29 to £40; deposit required. Cooked B £5, continental B £2.50; set L, D £10; alc L, D £20 (prices till end 93). Special breaks available*

LEINTWARDINE HEREFORD AND WORCESTER　　　　　**MAP 5**

Upper Buckton Farm　

LEINTWARDINE, CRAVEN ARMS, SHROPSHIRE SY7 0JU
TEL: LEINTWARDINE (05473) 634

An excellent away-from-it-all farmhouse, with the added bonus of good food.

This is a fine place for a stay in peaceful, totally unspoilt countryside. Tucked away in the area where Herefordshire and Shropshire meet Wales, Upper Buckton is a large three-storey Georgian farmhouse. Hayden and Yvonne Lloyd manage to look after their guests in parallel with looking after their farm, and the two operations dovetail together without apparent strain – even extending to allowing children to help with the animals. The four guest bedrooms are scattered over the house; they are large, and plainly furnished with good solid wardrobes and good solid beds (plus electric blankets). The huge, fluffy towels are a notable bonus point. Three bathrooms and a shower room go with the bedrooms, and although you may have to wander about a bit before finding them, they are rewardingly large.

However, the ins and outs of Upper Buckton are less important than the quality of the hospitality. One guest writes enthusiastically of the warm welcome, the superb and plentiful food (including special efforts on Yvonne Lloyd's part for a vegetarian guest), the welcome extras such as early-morning tea, and, above all, of the excellent value, which she describes as 'almost as cheap as being at home'.

◑ Open all year

↗ Take the A4113 from Ludlow towards Knighton. Turn right at Walford crossroads for Buckton, 2nd farm on left. Private car park

🛏 2 twin, 2 double; 3 public bathrooms; no tea/coffee-making facilities in rooms

◈ Dining-room, lounge, games room, TV; fishing, golf, tennis, riding nearby

⊖ No wheelchair access; no children under 4; no dogs; no smoking

▭ None accepted

£ Twin/double £32 to £40; deposit required. Set D £14

LEWDOWN DEVON   **MAP 10**

Lewtrenchard Manor

LEWDOWN, NR OKEHAMPTON, DEVON EX20 4PN
TEL: LEWDOWN (056 683) 256/222   FAX: (056 683) 332

A stunning early seventeenth-century manor house in isolated Devon countryside.

As you cross the threshold of Lewtrenchard Manor you get a surprise as what looked from the outside like a nineteenth-century mansion turns out to be an early seventeenth-century one, with stunning Jacobean woodwork. The puzzle is solved when hotelier James Murray explains how it once belonged to the Reverend Sabine Baring-Gould (writer of 'Onward Christian Soldiers'), who turned it into a subtle amalgam of Jacobean and Victoriana. The second surprise is to discover that this quintessentially English manor house is actually owned by South Africans, which explains the other little quirks: the leopard skins in the hallway, the African ebony heads in the Long Gallery, the quantity of South African labels on the wine list.

This is a breathtaking building. When you have dragged yourself away from the lounge fire you can inspect the breakfast room, with its magnificent plastered ceiling, wood-panelled walls and carved female figures of Latin virtues like 'Harmonia'; only 'Valor', above the doorway, is male. After this the dining-room is comfortingly small, with a plainer plaster ceiling and lots of portraits; a typical no-choice dinner might start with fish, move on to breast of maize-fed chicken with forcemeat stuffing and prune sauce and end with an iced raspberry terrine in a tulip basket filled with exotic fruit salad and mango cream sauce.

A grand staircase leads to a stunning Long Gallery, low and dark with a plastered ceiling which is part original, part perfect copy. The bedrooms opening off it are as marvellous as you would expect, all of them named after Baring-Gould hymns: Noningham has a half-tester bed, two armchairs, its own fireplace, a huge wardrobe and a vast bathroom; Melton boasts a magnificent original four-poster bed; and Hornsea has stained-glass windowpanes depicting scenes from Aesop's Fables.

◑ Open all year

⬈ Take A30 from Exeter for 26 miles, then take old A30 for 6 miles when Lewdown is signposted. At Lewdown turn left at the sign for Lewtrenchard and follow this road. Private car park

🛏 5 twin/double, 2 four-poster, 1 suite; all with bathroom/WC, TV, room service, hair-dryer; no tea/coffee-making facilities in rooms

◈ 2 dining-rooms, bar, 2 lounges, ballroom; conference facilities (max 50 people non-residential, 8 residential); fishing at hotel, riding, water sports nearby. Wheelchair access to dining-rooms and WC (unisex) only

⊖ No children under 8; no dogs in public rooms and by arrangement only in bedrooms; no smoking in dining-rooms

▭ Access, Amex, Diners, Visa

£ Single occupancy of twin/double from £75, twin/double from £98, four-poster from £125, suite £135; deposit required. Set L £18/£25, D £25; alc D £34. Special breaks available

---

LEWES EAST SUSSEX   MAP 9

Millers ☆

134 HIGH STREET, LEWES, EAST SUSSEX BN7 1XS
TEL: LEWES (0273) 475631

A charming and off-beat town-centre bed and breakfast, run with endearing enthusiasm.

The plain brown door in the white-painted sixteenth-century façade gives no indication of the bed and breakfast you'll find once you get inside Millers. The entrance lounge resembles a farmhouse kitchen, with oak beams, a pine dresser, a bare tiled floor in front of a massive stone fireplace, and everywhere the most extraordinary clutter of antiques, dried flowers and samplers – there is even a carved wooden harmonium in one corner. Breakfast, served at a long wooden table here, embodies the friendly care and individual style that Teré and Tony Tammar bring to everything. Big jugs of freshly squeezed fruit juice are laid on for the health-conscious, and you can proceed with an excellent fry-up and toast with a choice of a dozen preserves. In summer, guests can enjoy the rambling, pretty garden at the back, which is lazily patrolled by the three resident cats.

The immaculate bedrooms have monumental double beds and are stuffed with all kinds of fascinating treasures, arranged in a loose, appealing harmony; bathrooms are tasteful and maintained to a high modern standard. The two front rooms get some road noise, but they are double glazed and the traffic is only heavy in the middle of the day.

◑ Open all year, exc Xmas and New Year

⬈ In central Lewes, just uphill from Shelley's Hotel

🛏 2 double, 1 four-poster; all with bathroom/WC, exc 1 double with shower/WC; TV in all rooms

◈ Dining-room/lounge; fishing, golf, other sports nearby

⊖ No wheelchair access; no dogs; no smoking

▭ None accepted

£ Single occupancy of twin/double £34 to £40, twin/double £39 to £45, four-poster £45

LICHFIELD STAFFORDSHIRE   **MAP 5**

Oakleigh House Hotel

25 ST CHAD'S ROAD, LICHFIELD, STAFFORDSHIRE WS13 7LZ
TEL: LICHFIELD (0543) 262688/255573

A small family-run hotel with a popular conservatory restaurant and a quiet residential location.

Near to Stowe Pool, in a peaceful residential area a mile from the centre of Lichfield, Oakleigh is an ordinary enough Edwardian house with a red-brick and pebble-dash exterior and a small but pretty garden. The interior is modern and neat, with five bedrooms in the main house and five more (four of them good-sized singles) in an annexe in the garden. Well co-ordinated and comfortable, with bathrooms or shower rooms *en suite*, the bedrooms in the house are on the whole bigger and lighter than those in the annexe, with large windows giving views of the park opposite.

In 1991 the MacGregors franchised the restaurant side of the business to young chef Martin Daniels, whose qualifications line the sitting-room walls. His conservatory restaurant, with its pink tablecloths and striking Villeroy and Boch plates, is the venue for good-value table d'hôte dinners which might include shellfish broth flavoured with star anise and finished with cream and parsley, English lamb with port, redcurrant and fresh mint sauces, crème brûlée with fresh fruits and coffee and home-made petits fours. The à la carte menu is even more adventurous and twice the price.

◑ Open all year, exc 27 Dec to 2 Jan; restaurant closed Sun and Mon eves

⤢ Behind the cathedral at the bottom end of Stowe Pool. Telephone for directions. Private car park

🛏 4 single, 4 twin, 2 double; some with bathroom/WC, some with shower/WC, 1 shared bathroom; TV in all rooms; hair-dryer, room service on request

◈ Restaurant (air-conditioned), bar/lounge; conference facilities; fishing, golf, heated swimming-pool nearby. Wheelchair access to hotel (2 steps), restaurant and 5 ground-floor bedrooms

⊖ Children by arrangement; no dogs in public rooms

▭ Access, Visa

£ Single £35, single occupancy of twin/double £36 to £40, twin/double £36 to £55. Sun L £13.50; set D £12.50; alc D £25

LIFTON DEVON   **MAP 10**

Arundell Arms ☆

LIFTON, DEVON PL16 0AA
TEL: LIFTON (0566) 784666   FAX: (0566) 784494

*A large hotel suitable for business travellers and holidaymakers
and very popular with the fishing fraternity.*

Now that Lifton has been bypassed by the A30 peace has once again
descended on the roadside Arundell Arms, which announces its fishy
interests as soon as you enter the slate-floored reception area where
panels of fishing flies and piscine pictures decorate the walls. A narrow
corridor, which quickly fills with delegates when a conference is on, runs
back to the lounge and split-level bar before spreading out in front of a
huge, high-ceilinged restaurant overlooking the gardens; once again,
hunting pictures on the wall furnish a clue to the type of clientele who
particularly favour the Arundell Arms. Despite the two- and three-
course set lunches on offer here, bar lunches (anything from sandwiches
to hot dishes) are probably more popular; three-course dinner menus
play it safe, though one reader thought the quality of the food 'exceptional'. Conscious that holidaymaking guests can quickly feel overwhelmed by a hotel full of delegates, hotelier Anne Voss-Bark restricts
residential conferences to the winter months.

Bedrooms in the main hotel are reasonably spacious and, as a reader
puts it, 'sensibly furnished', with lightish colour schemes and plenty of
chairs for relaxing at the end of a hard day's fishing. The four rooms
overlooking the road are all double-glazed against any traffic noise; the
others overlook the garden where the small building which now houses a
rod room used to be a cockpit. One business traveller wrote that 'the
availability of a trouser press would have been more useful than a ghillie',
but in fact laundry bags can be found in drawers and irons are available.
Overflow rooms in a converted stable block are smallish, with uninspiring bathrooms given their relative newness – stick with the main
building if you can.

◑ Open all year, exc 2 nights over
Xmas (restaurant remains open)

🔁 In Lifton, just off the A30. Private
car park

🛏 8 single, 9 twin, 7 double, 5
annexe rooms; most with
bathroom/WC, some with
shower/WC; TV, room service,
hair-dryer, baby-listening in all
rooms

◈ 2 restaurants, 2 bars, lounge,
drying room, games room;

conference facilities (max 100
people non-residential, 29
residential); fishing (Mar to Oct),
shooting (pheasant and snipe
Nov to Jan) and skittles at hotel,
other sports nearby. Wheelchair
access to restaurants and bars
only

⊖ No dogs or smoking in
restaurants

▭ Access, Amex, Diners, Visa

£ Single £54 to £57, single

occupancy of twin/double £54 to £57, twin/double £88 to £92, annexe room £74 to £77;

deposit preferred. Bar meals; set L £15, D £23; alc L, D £28. Special breaks available

LINCOLN LINCOLNSHIRE   **MAP 5**

D'Isney Place Hotel

EASTGATE, LINCOLN, LINCOLNSHIRE LN2 4AA
TEL: LINCOLN (0522) 538881   FAX: (0522) 511321

A hotel with no public rooms but an ideal location near Lincoln Cathedral.

Just over an aisle's length from the cathedral in the ancient upper part of the city, D'Isney Place does away with the conventions of most hotels and has no public rooms, only bedrooms. Nor does the smart hallway really qualify as a reception area, but if you don't mind the impersonal feel and lack of community with other guests, this hotel makes a convenient base for exploring Lincoln. The bedrooms, divided into smoking and non-smoking, are well kitted out with a mix of reproduction and antique furniture, good-quality fabrics and fresh milk to go with the drinks-making facilities. It is worth asking for a de-luxe room as these have more space – useful in the morning, when breakfast is served in your room. Numbers 38 and 22 have the most room to move around in. Modern bathrooms are well-equipped with fluffy towels and goodies such as bath oil. One reader reports that he had a comfortable stay and staff were particularly helpful, but parking was not easy.

◑ Open all year

⤢ By the cathedral. Private car park and on-street parking

🛏 1 single, 3 twin, 10 double, 1 four-poster, 1 family room, cottage rooms; most with bathroom/WC, some with shower/WC; TV, room service, hair-dryer, baby-listening in all rooms; trouser press on request

◇ Wheelchair access to hotel (ramp) and 9 ground-floor bedrooms only

⊖ No dogs or smoking in public rooms

▭ Access, Amex, Diners, Visa

£ Single £40, single occupancy of twin/double £48, twin/double £60, four-poster/family room £70, suite £120, cottage £210 per week; deposit required. Special breaks available

---

The 1995 Guide *will be published in the autumn of 1994. Reports on hotels are welcome at any time of the year, but are extremely valuable in the spring. Send them to* The Which? Hotel Guide, FREEPOST, 2 Marylebone Road, London NW1 1YN. *No stamp is needed if reports are posted in the UK.*

LITTLE BEDWYN WILTSHIRE MAP 9

Harrow Inn ☆

LITTLE BEDWYN, MARLBOROUGH, WILTSHIRE SN8 3JF
TEL: MARLBOROUGH (0672) 870871   FAX: (0672) 870401

A village-owned pub and restaurant with cheerful rooms and imaginative bar food.

When the freehold inn at Little Bedwyn closed down, the regulars were so upset that they clubbed together to purchase the property. Louize Juniper's father persuaded her and her Australian husband Sean to take over the management and supervise the renovation of the Victorian brick building.

Both are trained chefs (Louize used to cook directors' lunches in London), and they have introduced a modern menu. Their unconventional pub grub is attracting a following, and bookings are advised for dinner. For all those disappointed to find no scampi in a basket there are plenty more keen to try the corn chowder, fig and parma ham salad, oxtail with dumplings or baked skate with a herb crust. There is a good choice of New World wines plus Hook Norton beer.

Louize and Sean have created a lively, up-to-date setting for their food. The bar and restaurant consist of three small open-plan rooms that are colourfully furnished. A jolly mural depicts the village, which stands in a pretty valley by the Kennet and Avon Canal. The outsize wheel from a racing yacht hanging beside the bar was a gift from one of the shareholders.

The three bedrooms are bright and warm, resourcefully decorated on a limited budget. The smallest is the yellow room, with a sunny burst of primary paint that contrasts with the royal blue duvet cover; it has pine furniture and a small modern bathroom. The green standard twin is similar to the pink superior twin, except the latter is larger, looks out over the front and has a more spacious bathroom.

◐ Open all year; dining-room closed Sun to Tues (though snacks served Tues eves)

↗ Take the A4 to Marlborough; Little Bedwyn is signposted from there. Private car park by arrangement; on-street parking

⇌ 1 single, 2 twin; all with bathroom/WC, TV

✧ Dining-room, bar, lounge, drying room; fishing, golf, other sports nearby

⊖ No wheelchair access; no dogs in bedrooms

▭ Access, Visa

£ Single £25, twin £35 to £40. Alc L £6, D £15

  This denotes that you can get a twin or double room for £50 or less per night inclusive of breakfast.

LITTLEBURY GREEN ESSEX   **MAP 8**

Elmdon Lee

LITTLEBURY GREEN, NR SAFFRON WALDEN, ESSEX CB11 4XB
TEL: ROYSTON (0763) 838237

A relaxing farmhouse with spacious rooms and good home cooking.

Although lying near the M11 which connects London and Cambridge, this eighteenth-century farmhouse surrounded by 900 acres of farmland seems a world away from both. Behind its creeper-clad flint façade are beautifully proportioned rooms with high ceilings and lots of space. The biggest bedroom, which overlooks the garden, is known as Twelve Acres because of its vast dimensions. Opt for this one, however, and you will sacrifice an *en-suite* bathroom. The nicest *en-suite* room is the Laura Ashley room (so-called because of its curtains); it is snugger and smaller than the others, with a large, airy bathroom to make up for any deficiencies in bedroom size.

Elmdon Lee is part of the Wolsey Lodge group and so evening meals are taken together in the impressive dining-room with stripped floors and large bow windows. The owner, Diana Duke, does the cooking and may serve home-made soups or smoked fish pâté as a starter, followed by roast pork or salmon cutlets and finished off by a gooseberry pie or fruit brûlée. You can take coffee or relax after walks in the cool green sitting-room in front of a log fire.

◑ Open all year, exc Xmas

↗ 16 miles south-east of Cambridge. Travelling on the M11 from the north, leave at Junction 10; from the south, Junction 8. Elmdon Lee is on the outskirts of Littlebury Green. Private car park

🛏 1 single, 2 twin, 1 double; all with bathroom/WC, TV, hair-dryer

◈ Dining-room, breakfast room, lounge; conference facilities (max 6 people non-residential and residential)

⊖ No wheelchair access; no children in dining-room eves; no dogs; no smoking in bedrooms

▭ Access, Visa

£ Single £25, single occupancy of twin/double £28, twin/double £50; deposit required. Set D £15.50

LITTLE PETHERICK CORNWALL   **MAP 10**

Molesworth Manor

LITTLE PETHERICK, WADEBRIDGE, NR PADSTOW, CORNWALL PL27 7QT
TEL: RUMFORD (0841) 540292

An ex-rectory converted into a very reasonably priced and comfortable bed and breakfast near Padstow.

Don't be fooled by Molesworth Manor's gabled Victorian façade; behind it lurks a building dating back to 1620. Its present immaculate condition is entirely thanks to the restorative efforts of Peter Pearce and Heather Clarke, who even stripped layers of varnish off the banisters to reveal the splendid Molesworth coat of arms; their latest baby is the conservatory extension to the breakfast room, decked out with a huge mirror rescued from an old pub. It's fortunate that the rooms are so large or there wouldn't be enough space to accommodate all their finds, which include a pair of lounge chairs with one long seat for a man and another shorter one for a woman and a Charles II oak chest in the guests' music room. The bedrooms favour huge Victorian fixtures and fittings: His Lordship's Bedroom has a double brass bedstead and claw-foot bathtub, while the South Bedroom has a lovely walnut bedstead and a pair of old coal scuttles cunningly disguised as bedside tables. While modern central heating is welcome, it's still interesting to be able to inspect the three-way Victorian ventilation system surviving in several rooms.

◑ Open all year, exc Nov

⤢ On the A389 from Wadebridge to Padstow. Once through St Issey and Little Petherick you will find the manor 200 yards up the hill on the right. Private car park

🛏 1 single, 1 twin, 5 double, 2 four-poster, 1 family room, 1 cottage; most with bathroom/WC, some with shower/WC; tea/coffee-making facilities, hair-dryer, room service, baby-listening on request

⬦ Dining-room, bar, 2 lounges, TV room, drawing-room, library, study, conservatory; fishing, golf, other sports nearby

⊖ No wheelchair access; no children in dining-room; no dogs; no smoking

▭ None accepted

£ Single £19, single occupancy of twin/double £20 to £26, twin/double £32 to £39, four-poster £47, family room £52, cottage £100 to £200. Cooked B £4

LITTLE SINGLETON LANCASHIRE   **MAP 5**

Mains Hall

MAINS LANE, LITTLE SINGLETON, NR BLACKPOOL, LANCASHIRE FY6 7LE
TEL: POULTON-LE-FYLDE (0253) 885130   FAX: (0253) 894132

A historic royal love-nest hideaway, now an executive bolt-hole for upmarket wining and dining.

Even in the eighteenth century, the royal family needed privacy for a spot of illicit wooing; Mains Hall, built by monks in the sixteenth century, is most noted for the fact that it was here that the Prince Regent secretly courted Maria Fitzherbert. The small, Grade-II listed manor house is discreetly tucked away in a flat stretch of farmland just outside Blackpool. In former days, access would have been via the River Wyre at what is now the rear of the house. Today, the back garden is now the front garden, and the house is approached down a long, private lane.

Mains Hall is slowly being taken upmarket by relatively new owners, Roger and Pamela Yeomans, who aspire to establish a select country-house hotel with a gourmet reputation. Room Two is probably the most atmospheric, with an old oak four-poster and tapestry-style fabrics. It has a good view over the garden, and there are extras such as fresh fruit, mineral water, electric blanket and a chocolate on the pillow.

The downstairs rooms are mostly charming. There is a pretty sitting-room with green leather chesterfields, lemon rose-patterned drapes and a priest's hole beside the fireplace. The entrance hall is panelled, with oak furniture and a Bechstein. The main dining-room has open views over the river and the historic dovecote, and is a good setting for chef Simon Dobson's mannered, modern food based on seasonal produce. Typical dishes might include warm mousse of lemon sole and scallops, roasted ballotine of quail, saddle of Highland venison and pan-fried suprême of maize-fed chicken. Good breakfasts include fresh, exotic fruit salad and home-made lemon curd.

◑ Open all year

↗ From Junction 3 on M55, follow signs to Fleetwood (A585) for 5 miles. Ignore signs to Singleton; Mains Hall is ½ mile past second set of traffic lights. Private car park

🛏 3 twin, 3 double, 3 four-poster; some with bathroom/WC, some with shower/WC, 2 public bathrooms; TV, room service, hair-dryer, trouser press, baby-listening in all rooms

◇ 2 dining-rooms, bar, lounge, library, conservatory; conference facilities (max 80 people non-residential, 12 residential); golf, fishing, other sports nearby. Wheelchair access to hotel (2 steps) and dining-rooms, 2 ground-floor bedrooms

⊖ No dogs in public rooms and some bedrooms; no smoking in bedrooms

▭ Access, Amex, Visa

£ Single occupancy of twin/double £50 to £60, twin/double £70 to £90, four-poster £120, family room £95; deposit required. Sun L £11.50; set D £25. Special breaks available

---

LITTLE WALSINGHAM NORFOLK	**MAP 7**

Old Bakehouse

33 HIGH STREET, LITTLE WALSINGHAM, NORFOLK NR22 6BZ
TEL: WALSINGHAM (0328) 820454

A small high-street restaurant-with-rooms where the welcome is friendly.

The entrance is right on the narrow high street in the centre of this historic town and, once past the threshold, you step directly into a high-ceilinged restaurant, once the old bakery. Pine furnishings and lots of greenery, plus nostalgic touches like the old bakery scales hanging from a bracket, make this a pleasant and unusual dining-room. The old ovens are still *in situ*, embedded in the exposed brick walls of a smaller overflow area which is decorated with bird prints. Here, overnight guests take breakfast. Chris Padley does the cooking (the restaurant is open in the evenings only) and will gladly omit the cream or alcoholic additions if you prefer your food plain. For the sinful majority, there are calorific temptations along the lines of pigeon breasts in a prune and Armagnac sauce or fillet steak stuffed with Stilton cheese in a sherry sauce to choose from. The residents' dinner menu of three courses plus tea or coffee is very reasonably priced.

There are just three bedrooms, two doubles and a twin, with only the double having *en-suite* facilities. This is not to say that the accommodation side of the business is a low priority – each room is nicely furnished and equipped with a television.

◑ Closed 3 weeks in Jan/Feb, 1 week each June and Nov; restaurant closed Mon and Sun eves Easter to Oct, and Sun to Wed eves Nov to Easter

↗ In the centre of Little Walsingham, 5 miles north of Fakenham. On-street parking and public car parks nearby

🛏 1 twin, 2 double; 1 double with shower/WC, 1 public bathroom; TV in all rooms

◈ Restaurant, bar/lounge; fishing, riding, other sports nearby

⊖ No wheelchair access; no children under 8 in restaurant; no dogs; smoking in bar only

▭ Access, Visa

£ Single occupancy of twin/double £23 to £25, twin/double £35 to £40; deposit required. Set D £12.50 (residents only); alc D £20 to £27 (Sat only)

LIVERSEDGE WEST YORKSHIRE　　　　　　　　　　**MAP 5**

Lillibet's Restaurant & Rooms

64 LEEDS ROAD, LIVERSEDGE, WEST YORKSHIRE WF15 6HX
TEL: HECKMONDWIKE (0924) 404911　FAX: (0924) 404912

Good food and comfortable rooms in a suburban setting.

The West Yorkshire conurbation of Leeds, Bradford, Halifax, Huddersfield and Dewsbury linked by a seemingly endless coil of ribbon development might not seem the most obvious place to take a holiday, but to anyone interested in industrial heritage the combination of Victorian mills with glorious scenery is a clear winner – and if you find yourself in the Spen Valley, whether on business or in search of the locations of *Shirley*, Charlotte Brontë's 'trouble at t'mill' novel, you'll be well looked after at Liz and Martin Roberts's well-established restaurant-with-rooms. The building is a sooty, honey-stoned villa with various additions including a sympathetic recent bedroom extension. A rich blue and gold monogrammed carpet runs through most of the house, and into a neat china blue and pink-walled lounge/bar/reception with stripped light wood furniture and modern blue Queen-Anne-ish chairs in rather formal groupings. Modern, uncluttered bedrooms are plain and comfortable, cheered up by chintzy soft furnishings.

Bright yellow walls, wall-mounted lamps and flower-bedecked alcoves make the restaurant a cheerful place. Residents can opt for the mainstream menu or save on a short, rather conservative, but good-value carte offering perhaps cream of mushroom soup, followed by grilled escalope of salmon served with a white wine sauce. The style is Anglo-French, and the cooking is usually reliable. We are assured that the deficiencies of service and management style noted last year are a thing of the past.

◑ Closed Xmas, New Year; restaurant closed Sun

🡕 On the A62, halfway between Leeds and Huddersfield; near Junctions 25, 26 and 27 from the M62. Private car park

🛏 6 single, 2 twin, 5 double; most with bathroom/WC, some with shower/WC; TV, room service (limited), trouser press, baby-listening in all rooms; hair-dryer on request

◈ Restaurant, bar/lounge; conference facilities (max 20 people non-residential, 16 residential). Wheelchair access to hotel (3 steps) and restaurant, 3 ground-floor bedrooms

⊖ No dogs

▭ Access, Amex, Visa

£ Single and single occupancy of twin/double £46 to £49, twin/double £65. Set L £13, D £18/£23.50

LONGFRAMLINGTON NORTHUMBERLAND MAP 3

Embleton Hall

LONGFRAMLINGTON, NORTHUMBERLAND NE65 8DT
TEL: LONGFRAMLINGTON (0665) 570249/570206

A spacious family-run hotel with considerable character, spoilt for some by the initial welcome.

There is no denying the appeal of the stately hall, with its eighteenth-century ancestry and the six acres of grounds and pretty gardens in which it is set. 'The public rooms are the hotel's glory,' reports one reader, and indeed the elegance of the formal drawing-room with its windows on three sides and marble fireplace is beyond reproach. 'For residents the small breakfast room is homely and during our stay a real log fire was always here to welcome us,' was another comment.

Management style has come in for some comment: while the overall verdict of one reader was 'relaxed and friendly, but also professional in coping with large inflows of dinner guests without neglecting the residents', another reader found his welcome 'chaotic' and an American couple entered the hall of the old country house to be met by no one at all. 'Eventually Mr Trevor Thorne appeared and showed us to our room,' they wrote. In fact their stay then improved considerably as Trevor Thorne upgraded them to the Fenwick suite at the same rate.

Bedrooms are large and tastefully furnished with good old furniture, lots of knick-knacks and fresh, often chintzy décor. Our American friends were charmed by the airy room and its fine views but perplexed by the plumbing – 'the toilet was loose on the floor and all the drains made a powerful gurgling sound'.

The dinner menu is described as 'conventional and servings are both copious and well cooked. Roast duck was provided in such quantity as to call for a doggy bag, but we were assured that the local canines, including a friendly if ageing labrador, would cope.' Home-grown vegetables have also been highly praised.

◑ Open all year

⤴ On the A697 road from Morpeth to Coldstream, at the northern end of Longframlington village. Private car park

🛏 2 single, 3 twin, 3 double, 2 four-poster; all with bathroom/ WC, TV, room service, hair-dryer, baby-listening in all rooms; trouser press in most rooms

◇ 2 dining-rooms, bar, lounge, drying room, children's games room; conference facilities (max 30 people non-residential, 10 residential); tennis, croquet, resident Shetland pony at hotel, other sports nearby; babysitting. Wheelchair access to public rooms only

⊖ No dogs in public rooms; smoking discouraged

▭ Access, Amex, Diners, Visa

£ Single £55, single occupancy of twin/double £55, twin/double £75, four-poster/family room £90. Set L £11.50, D £19.50. Special breaks available

---

LONGHORSLEY NORTHUMBERLAND   **MAP 3**

Linden Hall

LONGHORSLEY, MORPETH, NORTHUMBERLAND NE65 8XF
TEL: MORPETH (0670) 516611   FAX: (0670) 788544

Attractive grounds, comfortable bedrooms and a glitzy new leisure complex in an upmarket business hotel in a rural setting.

Our correspondents' views of this establishment are mixed. One enthusiastic regular felt it offered 'everything you would expect from a country-house hotel without the rather hushed, aloof atmosphere other superior hotels can adopt' and castigated us for being churlish in questioning the practice of ringing rooms after you arrive to check that everything is satisfactory. Another guest confirms that the practice persists and found it 'a little irritating – I would tell them if it wasn't OK'.

Unanimity was restored over the splendour of the noble Georgian mansion which is the heart of the hotel and the lovely gardens and woods that surround it.

Leisure-seekers were certainly outnumbered by executives at the time we arrived (when a charming porter dispelled any unfavourable impression created by a terse receptionist). The grand reception hall with its flagstoned floor, classical fireplace and leather chesterfields gives way to a softer look in the bright, elegant drawing-room with its seemly pastels and moulded ceilings. Both the library and the southern part of the restaurant were being refurbished when we visited. The northern section of the Dobson Restaurant is graced by lofty gilded and moulded ceilings, and has views over the paddock to the rear. Our correspondents were all satisfied with the quality of the food, though one found it irksome to have to wait over an hour to be taken into dinner because of the demands of a function.

Bedrooms are individually decorated in modish country-house style, with those in the old house scoring over extension rooms for character. All are of at least a reasonable size, and the most expensive rooms are very spacious. Reports agree on the attentiveness of the staff and their willingness to help, but while one guest found the atmosphere 'heavy' and 'formal' another described her regular stays as 'wonderfully relaxing and a real treat for one not "to the manor born"'.

◑ Open all year

⤢ 1 mile north of Longhorsley on the A697. Private car park

🛏 9 single, 21 twin, 14 double, 5 four-poster, 3 suites; all with bathroom/WC, TV, room service, hair-dryer, mini-bar, trouser press, baby-listening

◈ 2 restaurants, 2 bars, lounge, games room, library, conservatory; conference facilities (max 300 non-residential, 52 residential); tennis, croquet, fishing, heated swimming-pool, gym, sauna/solarium, Jacuzzi, steam room, beauty treatments at hotel, other sports nearby; babysitting. Wheelchair access to hotel (ramp), restaurant and WC (M, F), 20 ground-floor bedrooms, 3 specially equipped for disabled people

⊖ No dogs in public rooms

▭ Access, Amex, Diners, Visa

£ Single £85, single occupancy of twin/double £95, twin/double £115, four-poster £160, family room rate on request, suite £185 to £200; deposit required. Set L £17, D £21.50; alc L, D £30 (prices till mid-Dec 93). Special breaks available

---

LONG MARSTON WARWICKSHIRE   MAP 9

King's Lodge

LONG MARSTON, STRATFORD-UPON-AVON, WARWICKSHIRE CV37 8RL
TEL: STRATFORD-UPON-AVON (0789) 720705

Comfortable bed-and-breakfast accommodation in a historic house on the Charles II escape route.

The smell of baking and the sound of lawn-mowing greeted our inspector when we visited King's Lodge this year, a reflection of how hard the Jenkinses work at keeping this restored manor house up to scratch. Hospitality has always been the name of the game here – in September 1651 Charles II, fleeing the Battle of Worcester, stayed the night disguised as manservant Will Jackson. The dining-room (perhaps the grandest room, with its solid wooden dining-table and leather dining-chairs) was once the kitchen; the stone inglenook fireplace still exists where King Charles was shouted at by the kitchenmaid for failing to 'wind up the jack' properly. Today the house is immaculately kept, which doesn't in any way detract from its homeliness. The panelled guests' lounge is small and snug with plenty of armchairs to help you make the most of the books which lie around, or you could struggle through a history of the house in old English. One of the three bedrooms is *en suite*, with an ancient carved double bed and modern bathroom; the other two have hand-basins but share a good-sized bathroom along the landing. The twin room is the most modern, with pretty pink and white bedspreads, while the third room feels more historic, with its alcove fireplace, spindly antique chair and four-poster bed – which was actually made only 16 years ago from elms formerly growing in the garden.

Angela Jenkins finds there's not much demand for evening meals, though she's happy to provide light suppers on request and has compiled a 'where to eat' folder.

◐ Closed Dec and Jan

↗ Leave the B439 Stratford to Evesham road at Welford and continue to Long Marston. Private car park

🛏 1 twin, 1 double (with bathroom/WC), 1 four-poster; TV on request

◈ Dining-room, TV lounge; fishing nearby

⊖ No wheelchair access; no dogs or smoking in public rooms

▭ None accepted

£ Single occupancy of twin/double £19, twin/double £36 to £48, four-poster £40; deposit required. Light suppers £5 to £6 (by arrangement)

LONG MELFORD SUFFOLK   **MAP 8**

Black Lion/Countrymen Restaurant

THE GREEN, LONG MELFORD, SUFFOLK CO10 9DN
TEL: SUDBURY (0787) 312356   FAX: (0787) 374557

Lots of personal touches in this well-placed hotel where food and wine are taken seriously.

Long Melford pulls in many trippers who pause to visit Melford and Kentwell Halls (sixteenth-century rivals) and the wealth of antique shops in the village. If you decide to spend more time in this picturesque spot, the Black Lion and Countrymen Restaurant is a good place to stay and eat. The seventeenth-century, L-shaped building, formerly a coaching-inn, overlooks a broad green tract of common land. The business is run by Janet and Stephen Errington, who bought the premises in 1989, and their policy is to make their guests feel as much at home as possible. Most bedrooms overlook the road at the front, but traffic noise shouldn't be a problem. They are either standard or de-luxe (the only difference is size) and most have pretty patchwork quilts, pine furniture and little touches like sewing boxes which match the curtains. Room Five is particularly good for families – the children's area is separate and is equipped with bunk beds.

Stephen uses predominantly local ingredients in his cooking. His set menus offer plenty of choice: soups, pâtés or terrines to start, then cannelloni della casa or Countrymen coupe preceding the main course of steaks, poultry or vegetarian dishes. Cheeses or puddings round off the meal. Janet is in charge of wines and is happy to give advice if you have trouble choosing. The restaurant, peppered with jelly moulds, horse brasses and plate displays, dominates the ground floor, but there is also a lounge with plenty of saggy sofas and a small bar with pew seats.

◐ Open all year; restaurant closed Sun and Mon eves

On the village green, 2 miles north of Sudbury on the A134 towards Bury St Edmunds. On-street parking

⚲ 2 twin, 3 double, 2 four-poster, 1 family room, 1 suite; all with bathroom/WC, TV, room service, hair-dryer, baby-listening

◇ Restaurant, bar, lounge, TV room, library; conference facilities (max 16 people non-residential, 9 residential); golf, tennis, other sports nearby

⊖ No wheelchair access; no dogs in public rooms

▭ Access, Visa

£ Single occupancy of twin/double £50 to £60, twin/double £65 to £90, four-poster £75, suite/family room £90; deposit required. Set L from £9.50, D from £12.50. Special breaks available

---

LONGNOR SHROPSHIRE   MAP 5

Moat House

LONGNOR, SHREWSBURY, SHROPSHIRE SY5 7PP
TEL: DORRINGTON (0743) 718434 (and fax)

A medieval house, beautifully converted into a stylish Wolsey Lodge.

The Moat House lies at one end of the straggling village of Longnor, close to, but utterly isolated from, the main A49 road. The outside of the black and white house, with its skilfully blended-in modern extension, looks much like many another old Shropshire building, and it is not until you get inside that its antiquity is really brought home. In the old hall upstairs the fifteenth-century roof has been uncovered, with some of the old timbers not only intact but decoratively carved too. Here you eat Peter and Margaret Richards' four-course dinners by the light of candles in a setting which is unlikely to be surpassed. Downstairs, the old parlour, now the drawing-room, is totally relaxing, padded with thick carpets and plush grey chairs. One bedroom is in the newer part; the others are more in keeping with the antiquity of the house – especially where the original windows have been cleverly glazed.

◑ *Closed Dec, Jan, Feb*

↗ *8 miles south of Shrewsbury on the A49, take east turn signed Longnor. Go through village past school and shop. Turn left into lane signposted 'No Through Road'. Where lane turns left the Moat House is straight ahead. Private car park*

🛏 *1 twin, 2 double; all with bathroom/WC, exc 1 double with shower/WC; TV in 1 room*

only; hair-dryer on request; no tea/coffee-making facilities in rooms

◈ *Dining-room, lounge; golf, tennis, other sports nearby*

⊖ *No wheelchair access; no children; no dogs; no smoking in bedrooms*

▭ *Access, Amex, Visa*

£ *Single occupancy of twin/double £37, twin/double £62; deposit required. Set D £19 (8pm)*

LORTON CUMBRIA   **MAP 4**

New House Farm ☆

 COUNTY HOTEL OF THE YEAR

LORTON, COCKERMOUTH, CUMBRIA CA13 9UU
TEL: COCKERMOUTH (0900) 85404

Enthusiasm and charm are the keynotes in this carefully restored farmhouse set in breathtaking scenery.

John and Hazel Hatch are a young couple who deserve to succeed. Enthusiastic, charming and good-natured, they have worked wonders in transforming this old black and white farmhouse into a delightful away-from-it-all retreat.

They are helped by a stunning natural setting in the Vale of Lorton, surrounded by heather-clad fells. Here they have created a tiny, informal hotel, tailormade for easy-going walkers (not hikers) and leisurely Lakeland explorers. One of life's simple pleasures must be to return to the comfort of New House Farm at the end of day and lie on the bed watching the sun set over Low Fell.

The house dates from the seventeenth century and careful renovation has uncovered the original oak beams and rafters, open fireplaces and flagged floors. There are modern armchairs and sofas, sepia family photographs and unusual dried-flower and feather arrangements. The bedrooms have fine views and are fresh and spruce with twin beds that zip into king- or queen-size doubles.

Dinner provides the focus for most of the evening's entertainment. John, waiting at table during Hazel's traditional, five-course English meals, will tell stories and encourage guests to chat and unwind. He was awarded a spontaneous round of applause when he brought in a game pie, made from venison, pheasant and grouse he had shot personally within sight of the farm.

- ◑ Open all year
- ⤢ On the B5289 between Lorton and Loweswater, 6 miles south of Cockermouth. Private car park
- 🛏 3 twin/double; 2 with bathroom/WC, 1 with shower/WC; room service, hair-dryer in all rooms; no tea/coffee-making facilities in rooms
- ◈ Dining-room, 2 lounges, TV

room, drying room; fishing, golf, other sports nearby
- ⊖ No wheelchair access; no children under 12; no dogs in public rooms; no smoking
- ▭ None accepted
- £ Single occupancy of twin/double £55 to £65, twin/double £45 to £55; deposit required. Packed lunches; set D £20

LOWER BEEDING WEST SUSSEX   **MAP 9**

South Lodge ☆

BRIGHTON ROAD, LOWER BEEDING, WEST SUSSEX RH13 6PS
TEL: HORSHAM (0403) 891711   FAX: (0403) 891766

A fine Victorian house with plush public areas, spacious bedrooms and rural surroundings.

Smothered with creepers and various foliage, the large grey brick house stands amid wonderful gardens for it was built as a family home for Frederick Ducane Godman, a noted explorer and botanist. His passion for flowers, trees and shrubs is still in evidence, there being over 260 varieties of rhododendron and many other interesting flowers.

Inside, much care has been devoted to providing luxurious comfort. Public areas are wood-panelled affairs with a clubby feel. Thick pink and cream rugs cover the polished wooden floor in the lounge; leather chairs, chandeliers, a grandfather clock and a grand piano are framed by the tooled leather cherub border on the walls.

The restaurant is renowned for its excellent, sophisticated cuisine and is not cheap. A sample starter could be home-made ravioli of fresh langoustines with a lobster vinaigrette, followed by a main course of a whole partridge pot-roasted with smoked bacon, button onions and mushrooms and glazed with port.

Bedrooms are large, with the exception of the Ronnie Corbett room, which is small and sweet with steps leading to an upstairs bathroom. Rooms in the stable wing have more of a country feel than the ones in the main house, which are traditional in style.

◐ *Open all year*

↗ *On the A281 at Lower Beeding, just south of Horsham. Private car park*

🛏 *2 single, 9 twin, 24 double, 2 four-poster, 2 suites; all with bathroom/WC, TV, room service, hair-dryer; baby-listening by arrangement; no tea/coffee-making facilities in rooms*

◈ *Restaurant, bar, lounge, library/study, games room; conference facilities (max 85 people non-residential, 40 residential); tennis, croquet, putting at hotel, fishing, golf, other sports nearby;*

babysitting. Wheelchair access to hotel (1 step), restaurant and 9 ground-floor bedrooms, 1 suitable for disabled people

⊖ *No dogs; no smoking in restaurant*

▭ *Access, Amex, Diners, JCB, Visa*

£ *Single £90, single occupancy of twin/double £110, twin/double £110, four-poster £205, family room £155, suite £205; deposit required. Continental B £7.50, cooked B £10; set L £15, D £25; alc D £35. Special breaks available*

LOWER BRAILES WARWICKSHIRE   **MAP 9**

Feldon House

LOWER BRAILES, NR BANBURY, OXFORDSHIRE OX15 5HW
TEL: BRAILES (0608) 85580; changing to (0608) 685580 autumn 1993

Imaginative, good-sized bedrooms and creative cooking in a small country-house hotel.

Tucked underneath the belltower of the village church in the higgledy-piggledy group of buildings that make up Lower Brailes, Feldon House is tricky to spot from the road and hard to define. The Withericks' red-brick part-seventeenth-century, part-Victorian home is a peaceful place to stay, and is made much more than a guesthouse by the high standard of furnishing and Allan's keen interest in food. Bold, stylish colours, such as raspberry and deep orange, characterise the public rooms, along with log fires and comfortable sofas where you are quite likely to be joined by one of the family cats. Victorian features include the decoratively tiled entrance hall and the large dining-table around which all guests eat together. There is no choice for dinner, though you are consulted beforehand, and Allan's cooking is inventive and delicious. A four-course dinner in winter might include leek and almond soup, sole in Pernod, breast of chicken stuffed with pâté, lemon meringue roulade, coffee and home-made petits fours.

The four bedrooms all have plenty of space and are imaginatively decorated. Those in the main house have private bathrooms, while the slightly dearer rooms in the coach-house at the bottom of the pretty walled garden are more luxurious and worth the supplement. One has dragon-patterned fabric and an enormous double bed, along with a small television room.

◑ Open all year, exc 2 weeks in autumn; restaurant closed Sun eve

⬚ On the B4035 between Shipston on Stour and Banbury. Private car park

🛏 1 twin, 2 double, 1 four-poster (2 rooms in the coach-house annexe); all with bathroom/WC, TV, hair-dryer

◈ 2 dining-rooms, 2 lounges; conference facilities (max 5

people residential, 8 non-residential); croquet at hotel, golf nearby

⊖ No wheelchair access; no children under 11; dogs by arrangement only

▭ Access, Amex, Visa

£ Single occupancy of twin/double £32, twin/double £46, four-poster £60, annexe room £56. Set L £18, D £23. Special breaks available

---

LOWER SLAUGHTER GLOUCESTERSHIRE   MAP 9

Lower Slaughter Manor

LOWER SLAUGHTER, NR CHELTENHAM, GLOUCESTERSHIRE GL54 2HP
TEL: COTSWOLD (0451) 820456   FAX: (0451) 822150

A lovingly cared for country-house hotel, made more personal than most by the careful choice of paintings and furniture.

This is a very curious-looking building. At heart it is seventeenth-century, replacing an earlier nunnery, but it was played around with a good deal in Victorian times and the roof juts out well over the walls, making it look as if the roof of a Swiss chalet has been grafted on to a Cotswold manor. Inside, all is serene and harmonious. The first thing to come to notice is the huge bowl of fresh flowers in the hallway, their scent infiltrating the whole house. Next, the magnificent ceiling in the main drawing-room will catch your eye as plaster pigeons gaze down at you. If this disconcerts, there are two other sitting areas – head for the one on the first-floor landing if you like views while you relax. Since last year the dining-room has switched from yellow to rose, but its ceiling and the collection of excellent modern paintings (of which there are more in the drawing-room) are unchanged. We cannot speak for the food at the moment as chef Julian Ehlers was a recent arrival on our inspection visit – reports on his modern French cuisine (such as shallot and parsley ravioli with langoustine, fillet of lamb in pastry) would be welcome.

The bedrooms, under the judicious eye of Peter Marks, live up to the high standard of the rest of the house. The most interesting are probably those on the top floor, with sloping ceilings – the bigger, more luxurious rooms on the first floor are actually not so characterful. It is worth mentioning the deep (uniformly 7' 6") swimming-pool in the old chapel.

◑ Open all year, exc 2 weeks in Jan

↗ Lower Slaughter is off the A429, 3 miles south of Stow-on-the-Wold. The Manor is on the right-hand side of the lane approaching the village centre. Private car park

🛏 14 twin/double, 2 four-poster; some rooms in coach-house; all with bathroom/WC, TV, room service, hair-dryer, trouser press; no tea/coffee-making facilities

◈ 2 dining-rooms, lounge, study; conference facilities (max 30 people non-residential, 16 residential); tennis, croquet, heated indoor swimming-pool, sauna at hotel, other sports nearby

⊖ No wheelchair access; no children under 10; no dogs; no smoking in dining-rooms

▭ Access, Amex, Visa

£ Single occupancy of twin/double £100 to £170, twin/double £120 to £170, four-poster £200; deposit required. Alc L £16, D £29.50. Special breaks available

---

Washbourne Court ☆

LOWER SLAUGHTER, NR CHELTENHAM, GLOUCESTERSHIRE GL54 2HS
TEL: COTSWOLD (0451) 822143   FAX: (0451) 821045

A comfortable and pleasing family-run hotel – not bad value for the Cotswolds, either.

'It is so good that for the first time we are writing to you in order to recommend it,' starts the letter that brought us to the Penders' old grammar school-turned-hotel on the edge of one of the Cotswolds' most attractive villages. The building is not obviously beautiful, although the old school, surrounded by outbuildings, has low beams and flagstones to give it character. Public rooms are on the small side, with the sitting area in front of the fireplace opening into the long bar, but there is enough space in the restaurant for you not to feel cramped.

The bedrooms in the main building are spruce and slightly cottagey, without going over the top into full-blown rusticity; the suites in the outbuildings are smart and modern, with the bedrooms under the eaves giving them some character.

Neal Birtwell's food is described as traditional English and draws praise, and he does well in providing a full vegetarian menu as an option. The wine list is not wildly extensive, and perhaps needs more thought.

◑ Open all year

↗ 3 miles south of Stow on the Wold in the centre of Lower Slaughter. Private car park

🛏 1 twin, 7 double, 1 family room, 6 cottage suites; most with bathroom/WC, some doubles with shower/WC; TV, room service, hair-dryer, baby-listening in all rooms

◈ Restaurant, bar, lounge; conference facilities (max 25 people residential and non-residential); fishing, golf, other sports nearby. Wheelchair access to hotel, restaurant and 2 ground-floor bedrooms

● No dogs in public rooms; no smoking in restaurant

▭ Access, Amex, Visa

£ Single occupancy of twin/double

£65 to £75, twin/double/family room £85 to £95, cottage suite £120; deposit required. Set L from £3.50, D £19.50. Special breaks available

---

LOXLEY WARWICKSHIRE **MAP 9**

Loxley Farm

LOXLEY, WARWICKSHIRE CV35 9JN
TEL: STRATFORD-UPON-AVON (0789) 840265

A lovely old thatched farmhouse with rooms in a converted barn.

Loxley, just outside Stratford and only six miles from the M40, is a surprisingly peaceful village with an eighth-century Saxon church, a rookery and views across green fields; Loxley Farm, a thatched, half-timbered cruck farmhouse dating from the fourteenth century, is an American tourist's dream. A pity then that guests don't get to stay in the main house – except in emergencies or when the children aren't at home – but are exiled to a converted seventeenth-century barn at the top of the pretty English country garden. However, the Sheiling, with its thatched roof, timbered walls, and french windows looking out to mature trees, stone troughs spilling over with pansies and perhaps a cockerel strutting around, makes a very pleasant haven for a weekend. Sharing a small kitchen and sitting-room, the two double bedrooms are a cross between pretty and rustic, with beams, stripped pine furniture and flowery bedspreads. Each has its own modern tiled bathroom. You can cater for yourself or have breakfast in the house, which is full of character with its dark antiques, low beams and flagstoned floors. The Hortons don't serve evening meals, but there are local pubs that do.

◑ Open all year, exc Xmas

↗ In Loxley village, 3½ miles south-east of Stratford-upon-Avon. Private car park

🛏 2 double, 1 family room; all with bathroom/WC, hair-dryer

◈ TV room

● No wheelchair access; no dogs in public rooms

▭ None accepted

£ Single occupancy of twin/double £28 to £30, twin/double £39 to £42; deposit required

---

LUDLOW SHROPSHIRE **MAP 5**

Number Eleven

DINHAM, LUDLOW, SHROPSHIRE SY8 1EJ
TEL: LUDLOW (0584) 878584

High-class accommodation in Ludlow.

For immaculate Georgian town-house accommodation, look no further. Guy Crawley and his partner Michael Martin fled the metropolis and the antiques trade for this lovely and historic town, bought Number Eleven, close to the old castle, and plunged with enthusiasm into the business of looking after guests. It is not so much the interior of the house itself that impresses as the way it has been decorated and furnished. It is not a place for the easily daunted or the high-spirited, for the stern gaze of the Victorian matriarch who adorns the wall of the beautiful sitting-room may wither the former, while the latter may feel that the beds are just too splendid to be bounced on. From morning-room to dining-room, everything is precise and pleasing. The bedrooms are quite plain by contrast, though all are a fair size. The master bedroom, where you need the bedsteps provided to climb into the magnificent brass bed, and the tiny attic room have the most character. As for Michael's food, spicy mushroom terrine, duck and cranberry soup, salmon, pecan and apple pie and elderflower sorbet appeared on the menu one night in spring.

◑ Open all year, exc Feb

↗ Leave Castle Square along Dinham. The house is on the dog-leg opposite the castle walls. Private car park and on-street parking

🛏 4 twin, 1 four-poster; most with bathroom/WC, some with shower/WC; tea/coffee-making facilities, TV, room service, hair-dryer on request

◈ Dining-room, drawing-room, TV room, drying room; conference facilities (max 10 people non-residential and residential); bowls, ballooning at hotel, fishing, golf, other sports nearby

⊖ No wheelchair access; no children under 12; no dogs; no smoking

▭ Access, Visa

£ Single occupancy of twin £28 to £30, twin £50, four-poster £56. Set D £12.50 (7.30pm). Special breaks available

LYDFORD DEVON   **MAP 10**

Castle Inn

LYDFORD, OKEHAMPTON, DEVON EX20 4BH
TEL: LYDFORD (082 282) 242   FAX: (082 282) 454

A charming village pub-hotel beside ruined Lydford Castle and close to Lydford Gorge.

The sixteenth-century Castle Inn's bright pink façade looks as if it has strayed from one of the Suffolk wool villages, and is in striking contrast to the dark wood and low ceilings of the interior. Arrive at lunchtime and you will find the public bar crammed with locals and walkers tucking into substantial pub lunches; the minestrone alone is served with such a sizeable hunk of brown bread that it will keep you going for the rest of the day. With very little space to spread out, the wooden benches, pictures and grandfather clock struggle for space; you may need to move chairs around to get at a table – it simply adds to the character. Things are a little calmer at the back, where a snug bar has wooden settles with backs so tall they could almost be walls. Beyond them the restaurant is as 'woody' as the bars, its walls and beams hung with enough plates to give a Greek itchy fingers. It would be odd if the menu did not feature equally traditional English dishes such as chicken in cider and treacle tart, but Clive and Mo Walker, who took over two years ago, have not been able to resist breaking out with the odd curry, too.

Upstairs, the corridor walls are rough-hewn and the bedrooms are inevitably on the small side – in Rooms Five and Seven the beds all but fill the rooms. The biggest is the Castle Suite, which somehow manages to shoehorn in a four-poster bed, chintzy armchairs and a huge wardrobe. If you are prepared to forego an *en-suite* bathroom, Room Two has a wonderful walnut bedstead with matching bedside cabinets.

◑ Open all year

⤢ Leave the A30 at Sourton and turn on to the A386 towards Tavistock. After 4 miles turn off this road where Lydford is signposted. Castle Inn is next to the Castle and opposite the public car park. Private car park

⇌ 7 single/twin/double, 1 four-poster (family room available); most with bathroom/WC, some with shower/WC; TV, room service in all rooms; hair-dryer, baby-listening on request

◇ Restaurant, bar, drying room;

conference facilities (max 12 people residential and non-residential); golf, riding nearby. Wheelchair access to restaurant and WC (M, F) (1 step) only

⊖ None

▭ Access, Amex, Visa

£ Single £25 to £35, single occupancy of twin/double £25 to £35, twin/double £38 to £48, four-poster £53, family room from £53; deposit required. Bar meals; set L £9.50, D £14.50; alc D £19.50 (prices till end 93). Special breaks available

LYME REGIS DORSET   **MAP 10**

Alexandra Hotel

POUND STREET, LYME REGIS, DORSET DT7 3HZ
TEL: LYME REGIS (0297) 442010   FAX: (0297) 443229

A seaside hotel with fine views from a hill above the town.

The hotel occupies a fine position on a hill above this much-visited town on the Dorset coast. There is little to look at from the front – just a compact car park and the main road; the best views are saved, rightly, for guests who view the hotel from the well-kept gardens. This fine white building, originally built in the eighteenth century as home to a princess, also has a conservatory extension so that guests can enjoy the view out to sea as the evenings draw in.

The Alexandra is run with a great deal of pride by Mr and Mrs Haskins who are usually on hand to welcome you in the pink reception decorated with nautical barometers and model galleons. Staff throughout the hotel are courteous and friendly and there's an air of old-fashioned comfort. Meals are taken in a large peach and green dining-room, and a reasonably priced menu features dishes such as chicken suprême or lambs' kidneys in herbs and cream.

The bedrooms are decorated in confident reds, pinks and yellows, with co-ordinating duvets and curtains; some rooms have large bay windows which show off the view to its best advantage.

◑ Closed Xmas to last week Jan

↗ On the sea side of main street. Private car park

🛏 2 single, 4 twin, 11 double, 8 family rooms, 1 annexe twin; all with bathroom/WC, exc 1 single with shower/WC; TV, room service, hair-dryer, baby-listening; trouser press on request; 3 bedrooms with air-conditioning

◈ Restaurant, bar, lounge, drying room, conservatory; golf, riding, other sports nearby. Wheelchair access to hotel (3 steps), 3 ground-floor bedrooms but 5 steps to restaurant

⊖ No children in restaurant eves; no dogs in public rooms and some bedrooms; some public rooms non-smoking

▭ Access, Amex, Diners, Visa

£ Single £37 to £40, single occupancy of twin/double £40 to £55, twin/double £60 to £70, family room £94 to £100, annexe twin £80 to £90; deposit required. Set L £10, D £17.50; alc L, D £22.50. Special breaks available

---

LYMINGTON HAMPSHIRE   **MAP 9**

Gordleton Mill ☆

 COUNTY HOTEL OF THE YEAR

SILVER STREET, HORDLE, LYMINGTON, HAMPSHIRE SO41 6DS
TEL: LYMINGTON (0590) 682219

An excellent French restaurant-with-rooms set in a pastoral idyll.

The most pressing reason for staying at Gordleton Mill is to sample Jean-Christophe Novelli's cooking at the Provence Restaurant down-stairs, but even if the restaurant were suddenly washed away in the adjacent millstream the hotel would remain a powerful draw in itself. For a start, the setting is gorgeous: the river running through the small, quiet valley forks around a tiny grassy island before feeding a water wheel which can still be seen turning in the old part of the hotel; white wooden bridges connect the island and the beautiful lawns on both banks, which are dotted with birches and weeping willows and inhabited by ducks and temperamental geese. The converted mill houses a smart but informal reception area and two bright rustic reading rooms, furnished with squashy armchairs beneath low beams. Bedrooms are on the first floor of a very French country villa (pink plaster, small balconies and red roof-tiles) which has been added on to the mill house. Here you can stay in rich pastoral luxury, enjoying a successful combination of traditional and modern styles. Some might find the bathrooms a little camp – scalloped basins and loos, a Jacuzzi option in the bath and dressing-room lights around the mirrors – but few could object to the lavish attention to detail.

Naturally, the same high standards of service are found in the restaurant, a crisp, luxurious room which is lit by full-length windows overlooking the river at lunchtime and warm spotlights confidently directed at the centre of each table at dinner. Menus feature meat and fish which has been smoked or cured on the premises and some highly involved, adventurous dishes such as lamb noisettes and scallops in a foie gras sauce; the cooking subtly and deliciously matches up to such high ambitions.

◑ Possible closure for 2 weeks in Jan; restaurant closed Sun eve (closed all day Sun during low season)

↗ Take the A337 from the M27 through Lyndhurst to Lymington. Cross the 1st mini-roundabout in Lymington, then 1st right. Gordleton Mill is 2 miles along this road on the right. Private car park

🛏 3 twin, 4 double; all with bathroom/WC, TV, hair-dryer

◈ Restaurant, 2 lounges, conservatory; conference facilities (max 30 people non-residential, 7 residential); fishing at hotel, golf, tennis, other sports nearby

⊖ No wheelchair access; no children under 7; no dogs; 1 smoking lounge and some bedrooms for smokers

▭ Access, Amex, Diners, Visa

💷 Single occupancy of twin/double £50 to £65, twin/double £70 to £80; deposit required. Set L £17.50, D £25

Stanwell House

HIGH STREET, LYMINGTON, HAMPSHIRE SO41 9AA
TEL: LYMINGTON (0590) 677123   FAX: (0590) 677756

A smart, corporately owned hotel on the steep slope of Lymington High Street.

Now owned by the Clipper Hotels chain, Stanwell House presents a smart, cream-painted Georgian frontage to shoppers toiling up and down the High Street. The location is good – just three minutes from Lymington quay – and the interior, though not as characterful as the façade, is immaculately kept, making this a safe if unimaginative choice. Public rooms – a bar, a lounge and a small library with buttonback armchairs – are neat and efficient, done out mostly in cool blues and pinks; Railings Restaurant is an airy, attractive space, decorated in summery greens and beiges, with 20 or so tables covered in crisp white linen and a view over the patio and garden at the back.

The hotel has 35 *en-suite* bedrooms upstairs and in the new annexe at the back. Decorated in bright combinations of colours, they are all large enough to contain a writing desk and most a velvet-covered armchair. Cream-coloured bathrooms provide a touch of luxury, although on our last inspection visit the tiling was looking tatty in places.

◑ Open all year

⤢ In the centre of Lymington. On-street parking and free public car parks nearby

⇌ 6 single, 11 twin, 16 double, 1 four-poster, 1 suite; all with bathroom/WC, TV, room service, hair-dryer, trouser press; baby-listening by arrangement

◈ Restaurant, bar, lounge, library; conference facilities (max 20 people residential and non-residential); tennis, golf, other sports nearby; babysitting by arrangement

⊖ No wheelchair access; no dogs

▭ Access, Visa

£ Single £73, twin/double £98. Set L £12.50, D £18.50; alc D £25 (prices till Apr 94). Special breaks available

---

LYNMOUTH DEVON   **MAP 10**

Rising Sun Hotel

HARBOURSIDE, LYNMOUTH, DEVON EX35 6EQ
TEL: LYNTON (0598) 53223   FAX: (0598) 53480

A picturesque, thatch-roofed hotel overlooking the harbour, with a honeymoon suite once occupied by Shelley.

It's impossible to miss the Rising Sun, a glistening, whitewashed terrace of buildings that straggle up an incline immediately opposite Lynmouth Harbour. Out of season, on-street parking won't be a problem; in July and August, however, you may be forced to use a public car park. The Rising Sun dates back in part to the fourteenth century and once through the door into the public areas you enter a world of low oak beams, wooden panelling and uneven floors. Mirrors make the dining-room look bigger than it really is, and diners can tuck into more imaginative fare than the olde-worlde atmosphere might suggest: the three-course menu changes daily, but features surprises like deep-fried Somerset Brie and large tiger prawns; even the roast breast of Exmoor duck comes in a cassis sauce with pink grapefruit. Bedrooms vary enormously, depending on how recently they have been refurbished and whether they are in the older or newer parts of the complex, but most favour pine fittings; the best have wonderful harbour views. Expect the bar to get busy, and noisy, at the height of the season.

For something that bit more special there's Shelley's Cottage, a perfect thatched cottage with roses round the door and its own garden where the poet honeymooned with 16-year-old bride Harriet in 1812. Predictably it has a four-poster bed and stunning views. Even more predictably, it's popular at weekends; you'll need to book ahead.

- **◑** Open all year
- **↗** Leave the M5 at Junction 23 signposted Minehead. Follow the A39 to Lynmouth; the hotel is next to the harbour. On-street parking (restricted in high summer)
- **⇌** 1 single, 3 twin, 10 double, 1 half-tester, 2 family rooms, 1 cottage; some with bathroom/WC, most with shower/WC; TV, room service, baby-listening listening in all rooms; hair-dryer on request
- **◈** Dining-room, bar, lounge, drying room; fishing at hotel, tennis, riding, golf nearby
- **⊖** No wheelchair access; no children under 5; no dogs in public rooms; smoking in bar and some bedrooms only
- **▭** Access, Amex, Diners, Visa
- **£** Single from £40, single occupancy of twin/double from £55, twin/double from £79, half-tester £95, family room £110, cottage £110 (2 nights); deposit required. Set L £15.50, D £21.50; alc L £25.50, D £28.50. Special breaks available

Tors Hotel ☆

LYNMOUTH, DEVON EX35 6NA
TEL: LYNTON (0598) 53236   FAX: (0598) 52544

A comfortable Victorian seaside hotel in a dominant position above Lynmouth Harbour.

'When people see the hotel they assume it will be too expensive for them,' the housekeeper says, and certainly the Tors Hotel's grand external appearance and dominant position on a hill above the harbour do suggest it will be expensive. In fact, the hotel aims to offer a range of rooms to suit all pockets: the most expensive are big and recently decorated, with balconies and crown-canopy beds, the least expensive are smaller with shabbier décor, although some do have sea views. One regular recommends the resident manager and his wife, Gary and Marilyne Hayward, on the basis that they 'run this hotel on friendly and informal lines and in our opinion the warmth of the welcome and the genuine interest in you far outweighs any possible niggles'.

The Tors Hotel's position places it above the worst of the choking day-trip traffic clogging harbourside streets in summer. Despite the physical limitations of the hillside, it has its own heated swimming-pool so guests can escape the strong sea currents below. There's even space for a breakfast terrace with views.

The elegant lounge and restaurant overlook the harbour, and long-stay guests will find their dinner table adjusted so everyone gets a chance at the best view. Adventurous dishes such as pan-fried chicken in a lightly curried white wine, mushroom and cream sauce are available alongside such solid English staples as roast sirloin of beef. Although Tors Hotel is very popular with older guests, children are catered for, with early teas and special menus. A vast family suite can accommodate five people in a jigsaw of double, single and curtained-off bunk beds.

◑ Closed Jan and Feb

↗ On the A39 in Lynmouth. Private car park

🛏 14 twin, 12 double, 9 family rooms; all with bathroom/WC, TV, room service, baby-listening; hair-dryer and trouser press in some rooms

◈ Restaurant, 2 bars, lounge; laundry facilities; conference facilities (max 80 people non-residential, 35 residential); heated outdoor swimming-pool, table tennis and pool at hotel, fishing, golf, other sports nearby. Wheelchair access to hotel (ramp), restaurant and WC (M,F), no ground-floor bedrooms but lift

⊖ No dogs in restaurant

▭ Access, Amex, Diners, Visa

£ Single occupancy of twin/double £37 to £77, twin/double £64 to £94, family room rate on request; deposit required. Sun L £10; set D £16; alc D from £18.50. Special breaks available

---

LYNTON DEVON   **MAP 10**

Valley House ☆

LYNBRIDGE ROAD, LYNTON, DEVON EX35 6BD
TEL: LYNTON (0598) 52285

A small family-run hotel offering a warm welcome and stunning sea views.

It takes a nifty way with the first gear to get into Valley House Hotel's almost vertical drive from Lynbridge Road; luckily, once you've settled in, a footpath over the hills and down to Lynmouth lets you forget about the road. The approach to the house continues through a luxuriant, rhododendron-filled garden, oddly evocative of an Indian hill station. Valley House, when you finally reach it, has that odd style of architecture favoured by the Victorians, part tile, part brick, part wood. In what is still very much a family house, the downstairs rooms will be too homely for some tastes. Upstairs, however, bedrooms have been thoroughly modernised and some have *en-suite* facilities. The best are Rooms Two and Four, with spectacular sea views from precarious balconies; at night, bats swoop and dip in front of them and the only noise comes from a waterfall cascading down behind the house.

Refugee teachers Russell and Joan Herbert have taken to their new careers as hoteliers like ducks to water. The welcome they provide is summed up in the following comments by a satisfied guest: 'They offered to drive us to the starting point of various walks. When our car broke down and was taken to a garage 20 miles away, they insisted on taking us there in their own car to collect it.' Russell takes care of the cooking, which, to judge by visitors' book comments such as 'fab food' and 'who needs Floyd?', is equally satisfactory.

◑ Open all year

🔁 On the B3234 Lynmouth to Barnstaple road, 5 minutes' walk from Lynton. Private car park

🛏 4 double, 1 family room; some with bathroom/WC, some with shower/WC; TV, room service, hair-dryer, baby-listening in all rooms

◈ Dining-room, bar, lounge; drying facilities; fishing, tennis, riding, water sports nearby

⊖ No wheelchair access; no children under 9 (exc babies); dogs by arrangement only; no smoking in public rooms

▭ Access, Amex, Visa

£ Single occupancy of twin/double £17 to £33, twin/double £34 to £44, family room from £51 and £56; deposit required. Set D £12 (7.30pm)

MADELEY SHROPSHIRE   **MAP 5**

Madeley Court

MADELEY, NR TELFORD, SHROPSHIRE TF7 5DW
TEL: TELFORD (0952) 680068   FAX: (0952) 684275

An eager-to-please hotel with some fine bedrooms, but a bit of a mix overall.

Modern extensions and conversions surround the Elizabethan core of this large mansion house. The modern work has been most tastefully done (an old mill has just been reopened as a rather splendid banqueting suite), but the place can't help reminding you of an old lady surrounded by rather garish grandchildren. The chief virtue of the hotel is its eagerness to please; the chief drawback is the difficulty of creating a comfortable multi-purpose hotel from a house that was never designed to be used as one. This is most noticeable in the lack of sitting space (one reader wrote that he was hard put to find anywhere at all to drink his after-dinner coffee even though the dining-room was not full) and in the rather poky bathrooms in the main house. Bedrooms are extremely varied. The oldest (known as the 'historics') are magnificent, with beams, an oak-roofed four-poster perhaps and plenty of space.

The food draws praise (though we've heard that the service is a little over-attentive at dinner) and you have the choice of eating in the undercroft bistro if you do not want the full works available in the old hall upstairs. Breakfast offers a fine selection (black and white pudding, sautéed kidneys, kedgeree of fresh cod, grilled kippers, finnan haddock and all the usual eggs, sausages and bacon) and 'brisk, efficient and cheerful' service.

◑ Open all year; restaurant closed Sun and Mon eves

🔁 4 miles from Junction 4 of the M54. Private car park

🛏 9 single, 3 twin, 18 double, 2

four-poster; all with bathroom/WC, TV, room service, hair-dryer, trouser press, baby-listening

◈ Restaurant, brasserie, 2 bars, 3

lounges, TV room, drying room; conference facilities (max 100 people non-residential, 30 residential); fishing in grounds, other sports nearby. Wheelchair access to hotel, restaurant and WC (unisex), 12 ground-floor bedrooms

● No dogs

▭ Access, Amex, Diners, Visa

£ Single £75, single occupancy of twin/double £90, twin/double £90, four-poster £110. Alc D £10 to £30. Special breaks available

MAIDENHEAD BERKSHIRE MAP 9

Fredrick's Hotel

SHOPPENHANGERS ROAD, MAIDENHEAD, BERKSHIRE SL6 2PZ
TEL: MAIDENHEAD (0628) 35934   FAX: (0628) 771054

A plush suburban hotel for well-heeled business executives.

The suburban surroundings are perhaps not what you'd expect for an executive-style business hotel, and nor does the exterior of this red-brick gabled house hint at the style and standards of the interior. Swiss-born Fredrick Losel opened his doors around 16 years ago – 'a realisation of a dream', as the glossy brochure says – and with family involvement in all aspects of the business, he has created a meticulously run good-quality hotel. Reflective gold pillars, gilt and glass coffee tables, chandeliers and a central waterfall decorate the lobby overlooking the lush garden. Staff are professional and discreet. The subtly decorated, luxurious bedrooms have king-sized beds and are fully equipped.

Dinner in the plush restaurant is a serious business. Besuited businessmen discuss deals across the table over pricey à la carte dishes such as fillets of sole with shrimps and oysters on a curry and mango sauce or veal with scampi in Pernod. The table d'hôte menu offers a slightly cheaper option.

◐ Open all year, exc 24 to 30 Dec; restaurant closed Sat lunch

� Near the centre of Maidenhead, close to the railway station. Private car park

🛏 11 single, 11 twin, 9 double, 6 suites; all with bathroom/WC, exc 4 singles with shower/WC; TV, room service, hair-dryer, mini-bar, trouser press, baby-listening in all rooms; no tea/coffee-making facilities in rooms

◈ Restaurant (air-conditioned), bar (air-conditioned), lounge, winter garden/patio; air-conditioned conference facilities (max 140 people non-residential, 25 residential); croquet at hotel, other sports nearby. Wheelchair access to hotel (1 step) and restaurant, 13 ground-floor bedrooms

● No dogs

▭ Access, Amex, Diners, Visa

£ Single £120 to £130, single occupancy of twin/double £120 to £130, twin/double £155 to £165, suite £165 to £230; deposit required. Set L £19.50, D £28.50; alc L, D £33 to £48 (prices till Oct 93)

Cottage in the Wood

HOLYWELL ROAD, MALVERN WELLS, HEREFORD AND WORCESTER
WR14 4LG
TEL: MALVERN (0684) 573487   FAX: (0684) 560662

The views are the great attraction in this comfortable hotel.

Some cottage! With 20 bedrooms to play with most cottage-dwellers might consider reclassifying their house, but doubtless the cosiness of the name draws guests to what is in fact a Georgian dower house high on the slopes of the Malvern Hills. After the initial shock at the size of the place they are unlikely to be disappointed, for the position, with the Severn Valley spread out below the windows, is superb. The sitting-room and dining-room both have the best of the view, as do the front bedrooms. The rooms are generously decorated, some with antique furniture and modern bathrooms, but may be on the small size – it is worth discussing your requirements when you book, especially since some of the rooms are in the separate Coach House and adjoining cottage (especially convenient for muddy walkers). The Cottage in the Wood usually has something adventurous on its menu or its wine list, and we have noted kangaroo, monkey-gland steak and Texan Gewürztraminer in the past. However, there is plenty for the less daring eaters and drinkers too.

◐ Open all year

↗ Leave the M5 at Junction 8, taking the M50 to Junction 1. Follow the A38 towards Worcester but turn into Upton-on-Severn. Turn right over river bridge on to the B4211, then left on to the B4209 after 1 mile. Continue through Hanley Swan and on to T-junction in Wells Road (A449). Turn right and immediately left. Private car park

🛏 2 single, 4 twin, 11 double, 3 four-poster (some rooms in cottages); all with bathroom/WC, TV, room service, hairdryer, baby-listening

◈ Restaurant, bar, lounge; conference facilities (max 14 people residential and non-residential); golf, riding, other sports nearby

⊖ No wheelchair access; no dogs in public rooms or some bedrooms; no smoking in restaurant

▭ Access, Amex, Visa

£ Single £58 to £74, single occupancy of twin/double £68 to £74, twin/double £95 to £115, four-poster £115 to £130. Set L £10; alc L, D £22 to £26; Sun L £13. Special breaks available

Old Vicarage

HANLEY ROAD, MALVERN WELLS, HEREFORD AND WORCESTER WR14 4PH
TEL: MALVERN (0684) 572585

Fairly simple bed-and-breakfast accommodation in a house with lots of character.

The Victorian Gothic Revival period was good for vicarages, the pointed doors and crucifix windows leaving no doubt as to their function. This one now operates as Michael Gorvin's bed and breakfast and is usefully close to the centre of Malvern Wells, as well as being good value in an area where accommodation usually carries a mark-up because of the scenery.

This is a clean, well-cared-for house, with books in the lounge, prints in the sweetie-pink dining-room, and comfortably large bedrooms – some of them plain, some of them elaborately papered. Bathroom facilities vary considerably and it is worth checking what is available when you book. Evening meals can be had by arrangement in advance, but most guests will probably choose to eat out and a list of local restaurants is on hand. Breakfasts are help-yourself buffet affairs plus cooked dishes.

◐ *Open all year; restaurant closed Sun eve*

⤢ *From Malvern take the A449 Wells Road. Turn left down the B4209 Hanley Road to Upton-on-Severn. The hotel is close to the Three Counties Agricultural Showground. Private car park*

🛏 *2 twin, 3 double, 1 family room; half with bathroom/WC, half with shower/WC; TV in all rooms; hair-dryer, baby-listening on request*

◇ *Dining-room, lounge; golf, riding, other sports nearby; babysitting by arrangement. Wheelchair access to hotel (ramp) and restaurant, 1 ground-floor bedroom*

⊖ *No dogs in public rooms; no smoking in dining-room*

▭ *None accepted*

£ *Single occupancy of twin/double £30 to £34, twin/double £44 to £48, family room £50 to £56 (3 people); deposit preferred. Set D £14.50 (7.30pm). Special breaks available*

MANACCAN CORNWALL   **MAP 10**

Tregildry Hotel

GILLAN, MANACCAN, HELSTON, CORNWALL TR12 6HG
TEL: MANACCAN (0326) 231378   FAX: from 1994 (0326) 231561

A small, moderately priced family-fun hotel close to the Cornish coastal footpath.

Sleeping policemen crossing the road to Tregildry Hotel prepare you for the generally slowed-down pace of life in this quiet part of Cornwall close to the coastal footpath. Tregildry Hotel itself is an unexciting low white building where the light femininity of the bedrooms contrasts with the darker, more masculine feel of the downstairs public areas, with rather unlikely shades of mustard dominating the bar and dining-room carpet and furnishings. Some of the bedrooms have sloping ceilings and fine views of Gillan Creek and Helford River, with boats bobbing up and down on them. Furnishings are simple but adequate, and the lightly sprigged wallpapers and pinky, peachy colours help to make small rooms seem larger.

Dinner menus offer limited choice and favour tried and tested English favourites such as steak and kidney pie. Given a bit of notice, though, the friendly Nortons are happy to cater for vegetarians as well.

◑ *Closed Nov to end Feb*

🔀 *From Helston, take the St Keverne road. Turn left towards Helford/Manaccan. Once through Manaccan follow signs to Gillan. Private car park*

🛏 *4 twin, 4 double, 2 family rooms; all with bathroom/WC, exc 1 twin with shower/WC; TV in all rooms; hair-dryer, baby-listening on request*

◈ *Dining-room, bar, lounge, TV room; sea fishing, water sports at hotel, golf, riding nearby*

⊖ *No wheelchair access; no dogs in public rooms; no smoking*

▭ *Access, Visa*

£ *Twin/double £54 to £60, family room £110 to £120; deposit required. Set D £17; bar lunches. Special breaks available*

MANCHESTER GREATER MANCHESTER   **MAP 5**

Charterhouse Hotel

OXFORD STREET, MANCHESTER M60 7HA
TEL: 061-236 9999   FAX: 061-236 0674

A bold conversion of a city-centre landmark where the setting sometimes dwarfs the guests.

To Mancunians it will always be the Refuge, because for over 90 years the imposing building with its distinctive, Italianate clock-tower was the headquarters of the Refuge Assurance Company.

The reworking has been sensitive, displaying to advantage the original Victorian tiling, pillars and plasterwork. The public areas are open-plan; a tiled fountain and scattered modern seating are framed by dark raspberry and teal-green drapes. It is a huge, striking, sound-stage of an interior; empty, it can seem cavernous and cheerless. Lounge service can be excruciatingly slow, and gauche and forgetful when it arrives. Reception needs to be snappier all round.

The spacious bedrooms are conventionally well-equipped but lack enticing armchairs and sofas. Contract cabinets and muted floral prints make a tasteful, if bland, mix.

Parking is a major problem – there is none, only a nearby NCP and dubious streets. Outside the entrance there are double yellow lines and bus stops. As the hotel lacks both doorman and drive-in bay, luggage-laden arrivals in rush hour can be fraught.

Manchester's first Mongolian restaurant has opened in the basement, to be joined by a health club. The trick will be to pep up the atmosphere without downgrading the style.

◐ *Open all year*

⤴ *In the centre of Manchester, 5 minutes' walk from Piccadilly railway station. Private car park and public car parks nearby*

🛏 *23 twin, 22 double, 13 suites; most with bathroom/WC, 2 rooms with shower/WC; TV, room service, hair-dryer, mini-bar, trouser press, baby-listening, air-conditioning in all rooms*

◇ *Restaurant, coffee-shop, bar, lounge; conference facilities (max 180 people non-residential,*

58 residential); sauna/solarium, heated swimming-pool, gym nearby; babysitting. Wheelchair access to hotel (2 ramps) and restaurant, no ground-floor bedrooms but lift

⊖ *No dogs in public rooms*

▭ *Access, Amex, Diners, Visa*

£ *Single occupancy of twin/double £90 to £110, twin/double £120, suite £125. Cooked B £4; set L £13, D £17.50. Special breaks available*

Etrop Grange

OUTWOOD LANE, MANCHESTER AIRPORT, MANCHESTER M22 5NR
TEL: 061-499 0500   FAX: 061-499 0790

A classy airport hotel that redefines the term.

The futuristic, cantilevered glass and steel K2 terminal at Manchester International Airport faces square on to Etrop Grange; a bleak, low-rent housing estate laps at the rear perimeter; the Georgian core is subsumed by its own multi-million pound, neo-Georgian redevelopment – modern Britain in microcosm.

Etrop Grange is smartly designed in country-house-comes-to-airport style. The reception area, part of the original house, has a pretty pale blue-tiled fireplace, classical Muzak and a glossy photo and framed letter of thanks from John Major. During the week, the hotel caters mostly for corporate business and conference trade; junior execs may be spotted earnestly tapping their lap-tops on low-slung sofas. There are eight self-contained business suites, one of the most popular meeting-rooms being the mahogany-panelled library with copies of *Punch* dating back to 1841. At weekends, when room rates are considerably cheaper, weddings and functions tend to take over.

The hotel enlargement (from eight to 40 rooms) was sympathetically planned, with the result that the bedrooms have character. They are attractively furnished with hand-picked fabrics and individual antique pieces; Cholmondeley, for example, has intriguing Victorian painted tin headboards. Bathrooms are small but de-luxe, in repro-Edwardian style with power showers behind lace curtains. Each bedroom is named after a

Cheshire village, which is depicted in specially commissioned water-colours.

Light meals and snacks are served in the conservatory that looks out on to the airport. The restaurant, seamlessly fashioned from the ruins of the house next door, serves expensive, stylish meals with a wine list to match.

◖ Open all year

⤢ Leave the M56 at Junction 5 and take the first left at the roundabout, signposted to the hotel – which is 250 yards further on. Private car park

🛏 3 single, 4 twin, 24 double, 7 four-poster, 2 suites; all with bathroom/WC, TV, room service, hair-dryer, mini-bar, trouser press, baby-listening

◈ 2 restaurants, bar, 2 lounges, conservatory; conference facilities (max 80 people non-residential, 40 residential); tennis, golf, other sports nearby.

Wheelchair access to hotel (ramp), restaurant and WC, 8 ground-floor bedrooms, 1 specially equipped for disabled people

⊖ Dogs by prior arrangement only

▭ Access, Amex, Diners, Visa

£ Single £55 to £95, single occupancy of twin/double £55 to £95, twin/double £55 to £95, four-poster £80 to £105, suite £90 to £130; deposit required. Continental B £7, cooked B £9; set L £14.50, D £28. Special breaks available

Holiday Inn Crowne Plaza ☆

PETER STREET, MANCHESTER M60 2DS
TEL: 061-236 3333   TELEX: 667550 CPLAZA G   FAX: 061-228 2241

Former grand railway hotel restored to glory.

This great terracotta monument of a hotel has a special place in Mancunian history. Most famously, it was here that Rolls met Royce and decided to go into partnership. A former flagship of the old Midland Railways Hotels, it is still the focal point for much of the city's social life – guests have ranged from royals to footballers, pop stars to Pavarotti. The Octagon Terrace, descendant of the Winter Garden, is still the place for *tout* Manchester to gather on a Saturday night after the theatre to see and be seen.

Built in 1903 on the site of the Peterloo massacre, it covers an enormous 6½ acres, has 3½ miles of marble-clad corridors, two full-time florists and its own tour guide. Construction in the shape of a figure 8, around two huge, tile-covered light wells, meant that even inner rooms were given an unusual degree of lightness.

Holiday Inn went to great pains to restore many of the period Edwardian features that had not been lost in earlier phases of modernisation. Twenty-two layers of paint had to be stripped off the old wood panelling in the gilded French restaurant, for example, and beautiful green German tiles were discovered lining a stairwell.

The bedrooms are all one would expect from the de-luxe end of the international chain in terms of style, comfort and facilities. And, if you walk through the mezzanine one night and see a lady in grey, it's only the hotel ghost, a 1930s resident who swore she would never leave.

◑ *Open all year*

⤢ *In the city centre, just north of Oxford Road and adjacent to the G-Mex Centre. Nearby car park*

🛏 *70 single, 226 twin/double, 7 suites, family rooms available; all with bathroom/WC, TV, room service, hair-dryer, mini-bar, trouser press, air-conditioning*

◈ *3 restaurants, 2 bars, lounge, ironing-room (all public areas air-conditioned); conference facilities (max 200 people residential and non-residential); heated indoor swimming-pool, Jacuzzi, gym, health club, hair and beauty salon at hotel, other sports nearby; babysitting. Wheelchair access to hotel (ramps), restaurants and WCs (disabled), no ground-floor bedrooms but lifts, 1 bedroom specially equipped for disabled people*

⊖ *None*

▭ *Access, Amex, Diners, Visa*

£ *Single £78 to £114, single occupancy of twin/double £78 to £120, twin/double £78 to £126, family room rate £78 to £138, suites £199 to £399; deposit required. Cooked B £11; set L from £10, D £32; alc L, D from £10. Special breaks available*

Victoria & Albert Hotel ☆

COUNTY HOTEL OF THE YEAR

WATER STREET, MANCHESTER M60 9EA
TEL: 061-832 1188   FAX: 061-834 2484

Luxury conversion of a riverside waterhouse into a TV-themed city-centre hotel.

You don't have to be a TV addict to stay here, but it helps you to spot the references. Granada has built an upmarket hotel from an old warehouse on the banks of the spruced-up River Irwell, adjacent to both its studios and the Granada Studio Tours complex; each room is named after a Granada TV programme, be it current, fondly remembered or long forgotten. What could have been a crass concept in themed hotel design actually transcends its own gimmickry and succeeds surprisingly well. In the public areas as well as the bedrooms, clever use has been made of the original brickwork, iron pillars and wooden ceilings and beams. Character is given by a décor that includes old programme props and artefacts, production stills, old movie cameras and so on. All the bedrooms share a smart, subdued blue-and-brick colour scheme, are well-equipped and have glossy bathrooms.

The suites are probably the most fun. Jewel in the Crown has ornate Moghul furniture and nets over the bed; Weatherfield is Stan and Vera's idea of heaven and includes Hilda Ogden's flying ducks on the wall. Café Maigret is a pastiche brasserie with French posters and music, while the

Sherlock Holmes Restaurant and Watson's Bar are pseudo-Victorian, with some amusing features such as a glass swan and a bubbling mock chemistry lab outfit. One singular feature is the dining table, laid with what looks like a complete plastic replica of a meal. For once, though, life imitates art; this is real food cooked to display a sample restaurant menu.

The food is ambitious and expensive, and the à la carte also includes a selection of traditional Victorian dishes. On inspection a lunch at the Café Maigret was attractively presented but fell disappointingly short on real taste and texture.

◑ Open all year

↗ In the city centre beside the River Irwell and the Granada Studios. Private car park

🛏 14 single, 23 twin, 86 double, 3 family rooms, 4 suites, 2 disabled; all with bathroom/WC, TV, room service, hair-dryer, mini-bar, trouser press, baby-listening

◈ 2 restaurants, 2 bars, lounge, 2 conservatories, snooker room (all air-conditioned); conference facilities (max 200 people residential, 350 non-residential); sauna, solarium, multi-gym, heated swimming-pool at hotel, other sports nearby; babysitting on request. Wheelchair access to hotel, restaurant and WC (unisex), 2 bedrooms specially equipped for disabled people

⊖ No dogs

▭ Access, Amex, Diners, Visa

£ Single £115, single occupancy of twin/double £115, twin/double/family room £115, suite from £220; deposit required. Continental B £8.50, cooked B £10.50; set L £10 to £15, D £20 to £30; alc L £20, D £30. Special breaks available

---

MARAZION CORNWALL　　　　　　　　　　　　**MAP 10**

Ennys

ST HILARY, MARAZION, PENZANCE, CORNWALL TR20 9BZ
TEL: PENZANCE (0736) 740262

A small, remote farmhouse hotel with interesting bedrooms and lovely gardens.

Ennys is a seventeenth-century stone farmhouse with a lovely rose- and clematis-clad façade which you approach via an avenue of flowering cherry trees; somewhere outside you'll probably spot Sue or John White tending the extensive gardens. A flagstoned hall opens on to a lounge where Eartha Kitt, the cat, is very keen to befriend guests. Opposite is a dining-room with polished wooden tables where Sue's sophisticated and wonderful meals are served; 'You'll need to watch your figure,' a satisfied guest assured our inspector. Typical starters might include asparagus soup and prawns in garlic, with seafood pancakes or pheasant in red wine with chestnuts to follow.

Upstairs, the bedrooms, named after other local farms, are more luxurious than you might expect: Tregembo and Trewinnort both have four-poster beds, while Trainack has a big bathroom with claw-foot bathtub. The stable and hayloft have been converted into two family suites, one containing a stunning 1920s art-nouveau bedstead. When we inspected Sue and John were putting the finishing touches to an outdoor swimming-pool.

◑ *Open all year, exc 25 and 26 Dec*

⤢ *Take the A30 to Marazion and the 2nd left out of town. Turn left into Trewhella Lane after 2 miles. Private car park*

🛏 *1 twin, 2 four-poster, 2 family suites; some with bathroom/WC, some with shower/WC, 2 public bathrooms; TV, hair-dryer, baby-listening in all rooms*

◈ *Dining-room, lounge, drying room, games room; conference facilities (max 5 people residential); tennis, heated*

swimming-pool at hotel, fishing, golf, other sports nearby; babysitting

⊖ *No wheelchair access; no children under 5; no dogs; no smoking in bedrooms*

▭ *None accepted*

£ *Single occupancy of twin £25 to £30, twin £40 to £45, four-poster £48 to £50, family suite from £50 to £70; deposit required. Set D £13.50; alc D £19.50 (7pm). Special breaks available*

MARKET DRAYTON SHROPSHIRE   **MAP 5**

Goldstone Hall

MARKET DRAYTON, SHROPSHIRE TF9 2NA
TEL: CHESWARDINE (0630 86) 202/487   FAX: (0630 86) 585

A relaxed country-house hotel given spice by an interesting calendar of events.

Whether it is Clive of India or Candlemas that is being celebrated there is usually something in the offing nowadays at Goldstone Hall. Energy and enterprise are the keynotes of the hotel – why stop at three courses for dinner when you can offer five? – but relaxation is not hard to come by either, for not only is the surrounding countryside peaceful and well away from through-routes, but the hotel is blessed with three sitting-rooms, an orangery (well, conservatory) and a lovely walled garden. The general air of well-being extends to the furnishing – nothing stiff or pompous, but plenty of big chests, carved chairs, rugs and polished wood. The bedrooms are stylish and comfortable, with the four-poster room much in demand. Dinners are taken seriously, with traditional Shropshire dishes, home-baked bread and a good range of cheeses.

◑ *Open all year*

⤢ *4 miles south of Market Drayton off the A529, signposted Goldstone. Private car park*

🛏 *2 twin, 4 double, 1 four-poster; all with bathroom/WC, TV, room service, hair-dryer, baby-listening; tea/coffee-making facilities on request*

Restaurant, bar, 3 lounges, snooker room, conservatory; drying facilities; conference facilities (max 60 people non-residential, 7 residential); croquet at hotel, other sports nearby; babysitting by arrangement

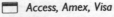 No wheelchair access; no dogs in bedrooms

Access, Amex, Visa

Single occupancy of twin/double £58 to £65, twin/double £75, four-poster £85. Set L £15, D £20; alc L £10 to £20, D £15 to £30. Special breaks available

MARKINGTON NORTH YORKSHIRE   MAP 5

Hob Green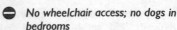

MARKINGTON, HARROGATE, NORTH YORKSHIRE HG3 3PJ
TEL: HARROGATE (0423) 770031   FAX: (0423) 771589

A small, friendly country-house hotel with high standards of service and an attractive setting.

The hotel stands alone beyond the tiny village of Markington in 870 acres of farm and woodland, and the traditional low-rise building is backed by 'wonderful vegetable gardens', according to one guest. Décor throughout the house lacks originality and sticks fairly rigidly to middle-of-the-road country-house school. Yellow-striped floral patterned wallpaper sets the tone in the lounge, where an ornate fireplace, grandfather clock and armoire-style cabinet deserve better than the grey shell-shaped modern sofas and armchairs that they get. For all that, the room is bright and comfortable and there is plenty to read. The wallpaper in the dining-room is scruffy in places but the situation is redeemed by prompt and courteous service, which includes the serving of crudités and canapés while you wait. Our inspection meal included medallions of pork with wild mushroom and spring onion sauce, served with vegetables from the garden including broccoli, carrots and new and duchesse potatoes, and generous slabs of Stilton and Wensleydale.

Bedrooms are neatly decorated and furnished with bold modern prints and fabrics. Modern tiled bathrooms have huge bath sheets, face flannels, classy toiletries, cotton wool and hand lotion.

After our adverse comments in 1992 we found service exemplary this year – luggage is carried to your room, beds are turned down and rooms are tidied while you dine. Reports have been unanimous on the friendliness of the staff.

 Open all year

Turn off the A61 Harrogate to Ripon road at Wormald Green and continue towards Markington. Hob Green is 1 mile through the village. Private car park

3 single, 5 twin, 2 double, 1 four-poster, 1 suite; all with bathroom/WC, TV, room service, hair-dryer, mini-bar

Restaurant, lounge; conference facilities (max 12 people non-residential and residential);

croquet at hotel, golf, riding, other sports nearby. Wheelchair access to restaurant and WC (unisex) only

No dogs in public rooms

Access, Amex, Diners, JCB, Visa

£ Single £70, single occupancy of twin/double £78, twin/double £80 to £90, four-poster £98, suite £110. Set L £12; alc D £19. Special breaks available

---

MARLOW BOTTOM BUCKINGHAMSHIRE   **MAP 9**

Holly Tree House

BURFORD CLOSE, MARLOW BOTTOM, BUCKINGHAMSHIRE SL7 3NF
TEL: MARLOW (0628) 891110   FAX: (0628) 481278

A suburban bed and breakfast close to Marlow with modern facilities and a friendly welcome.

Tina Woods is now into her fourth season running her house as a bed and breakfast; guests visiting local businesses and preferring a more personal base than a hotel make up much of her business. Previously an air hostess, Tina has travelled widely and she has used her experiences of hotels to create a comfortable establishment. A conservatory lounge overlooks a terrace with a small pool from where there are views over the trees and rooftops to the valley below. There are piles of glossy magazines and daily papers on the table and a stack of videos for rainy days; for information on the area there are maps, guidebooks and tourist leaflets in the hall.

Tea trays in the bedrooms are the only places you'll find a portion pack, though fresh milk is available. The rooms are light and well-kept, with neutral colours and pine furnishings.

Open all year

1½ miles north-west of Marlow, just off the A4155. Private car park

1 single, 4 double; all with bathroom/WC, TV, room service, hair-dryer, trouser press, ironing facilities

Dining-room, lounge/conservatory; conference facilities

(max 9 people residential and non-residential); heated outdoor swimming-pool at hotel (May to Sept), other sports nearby

No wheelchair access; no dogs in public rooms and by arrangement only in bedrooms

Access, Amex, Visa

£ Single £55, double £68 to £73

MASHAM NORTH YORKSHIRE   **MAP 3**

King's Head

MARKET PLACE, MASHAM, NORTH YORKSHIRE HG4 4EF
TEL: RIPON (0765) 689295

An easy-going hotel with pretty bedrooms.

Among Masham's claims to fame is that it is home to Theakston's Old Peculier brewery. It is fitting, then, that in the bar of the King's Head you find a genuine country pub – not an advertising copywriter's sanitised version but the real thing, complete with a real fire, collections of walking sticks and old bottles, a smoky atmosphere, marked old tables and lots of locals. Although the air of informality pervades the whole place (despite the words 'Excise Office' still just discernible above the doorway), the traditional beamed restaurant moves things a tad upmarket with its stained glass, tiffany lamps, dresser of piratical toby jugs and white linen napkins. Food is good-value straightforward fare; perhaps deep-fried mushrooms in a beer batter followed by baked local trout.

Room Two is a lovely big double with twin windows, faded blue floral pattern soft furnishings, bright chintzy wallpaper and a good old pine dressing table. The *en-suite* shower room is simple and adequate.

Given Masham's pronounced country feel (with horsy locals in checked jackets and jaunty caps), it is surprising that it is only 10 minutes from the Thirsk exit of the A1, making it a good bet for anyone breaking a journey to or from Scotland.

◑ Open all year

⤤ 15 minutes off the A1 from the Thirsk/Masham turn-off. The hotel is in Masham's market square. On-street parking

🛏 2 single, 1 twin, 6 double, 1 four-poster; most with bathroom/WC, 2 with shower/WC; TV, hair-dryer, trouser press in all rooms

◈ Restaurant, bar; conference facilities (max 50 people non-residential, 10 residential); fishing, golf, tennis, riding nearby. Wheelchair access to restaurant only

⊖ No dogs

▭ Access, Amex, Diners, Visa

£ Single £43, single occupancy of twin/double £43, twin/double £55, four-poster £65. Sun L £8; alc D £10 to £20

MATLOCK DERBYSHIRE   **MAP 5**

Riber Hall

MATLOCK, DERBYSHIRE DE4 5JU
TEL: MATLOCK (0629) 582795   FAX: (0629) 580475

A family-run hotel with luxurious rooms and lovely gardens.

Riber Hall is a magnificent building in a peaceful position above the tourist towns of Matlock and Matlock Bath, close by the ruins of Riber Castle. The mellow stone hall, part of which dates back to the 1400s, is mostly Elizabethan. Reproductions mix happily with solid antiques in most rooms but the prevailing character is Jacobean, especially in the dining-room, where the dark oak table legs and chair backs are ornately carved. The lunches served here are substantial, while the evening menu is modern English with plenty of game and a good range of fish. Nine of the 11 bedrooms – all of which are in a separate block from the main house – sport four-poster beds, which indicates Alex and Gill Biggin's drive for grandeur since they rescued the property from dereliction in the early 1970s. As each room is luxurious, with muted colours, light fabrics, lots of space and facilities, there is little to choose between them – although the hoop-top bed in Room Eight is particularly unusual and makes this our favourite, while Room Ten has the edge on space and the bonus of its own steps down into the superb walled garden. We found there to be an intrusive number of signs advising you of this and that both in the bedrooms and around the exterior of the hotel, but otherwise all is peaceful.

◑ Open all year

↗ 1 mile off the A615; in Tansley, turn left at the Murco filling station and follow road to hotel. Private car park

🛏 2 double, 9 four-poster; all with bathroom/WC, TV, room service, hair-dryer, trouser press, mini-bar

◈ 2 dining-rooms, bar, lounge, drying room, conservatory; conference facilities (max 16

people non-residential, 12 residential); tennis at hotel, other sports nearby

⊖ No wheelchair access; no children under 10; no dogs

▭ Access, Amex, Diners, Visa

£ Single occupancy of twin/double £78 to £92, double/four-poster £92 to £137 (prices till end Mar 94); deposit required. Cooked B £7.50; set L £14.50; alc D £25 to £30. Special breaks available

---

MATLOCK BATH DERBYSHIRE   **MAP 5**

Hodgkinson's

150 SOUTH PARADE, MATLOCK BATH, DERBYSHIRE DE4 3NR
TEL: MATLOCK (0629) 582170

A striking, museum-like atmosphere in this well-run hotel with friendly hosts.

Don't be put off by the plain exterior of Nigel Shelley and Malcolm Archer's four-storey hotel. The main street of Matlock Bath through which tourist traffic hurtles is not an ideal location for a peaceful break, nor is the building itself, an eighteenth-century flat-fronted town house, particularly appealing – but stick to your guns, because the interior is a real treat. Each of the bedrooms is furnished with antiques that Malcolm has collected over the years and the décor is by Nigel, a trained interior designer. Light fittings are a particular curiosity; you'll find everything from fine glass gas mantles to a monstrous copper and brass contraption in Room Five – the biggest and perhaps grandest room with its lacy white bedspread, tiled washstand, oriental lacquer table and purple Dralon sofa. All rooms have immaculate modern shower rooms with luxurious towels and smart gold taps. Everyone will have a favourite room; our inspector liked Room One, with its marble fireplace, French cradle bed and walnut Pullman carriage doors leading into the bathroom.

The hotel is not only a museum of antiques and inspired ideas, however. The ground-floor sitting-room makes a comfortable place for lounging around with books, and in good weather you can sit among foxgloves and flags in the garden. Developing the garden is an ongoing project for Nigel, who also does most of the cooking. Four-course table d'hôte meals in the restaurant might include soup, baked avocado stuffed with cheese and herb pâté wrapped in bacon, fillet of lamb with honey and lavender sauce, and a choice of puddings.

◑	Open all year		fishing, riding, other sports nearby
⬀	On the main A6 Derby to Manchester road, 1½ miles south of Matlock. Private car park	⊖	No wheelchair access; no dogs in public rooms
🛏	1 single, 6 double; all with shower/WC, TV, room service; hair-dryer on request	💳	Access, Amex, Visa
◈	Restaurant, bar, 2 lounges, hairdressing salon at hotel;	£	Single £25 to £30, single occupancy of twin/double £30 to £60, twin/double £40 to £80; deposit required. Set D £22.50. Special breaks available

---

MAWNAN SMITH CORNWALL   **MAP 10**

Budock Vean

MAWNAN SMITH, NR FALMOUTH, CORNWALL TR11 5LG
TEL: FALMOUTH (0326) 250288   FAX: (0326) 250892

A monumental country-house hotel in sprawling grounds, perfect for golfing holidays.

The grand entrance gate and magnificent drive leading to Budock Vean are pointers to the monumental size of this hotel which began life in the nineteenth century and put out expansive tentacles in the 1930s and 1960s. Size robs the lounges of much intimacy, although the Pendennis Room, where afternoon tea is served in front of a log fire, is cosier provided you don't mind the stuffed animal heads gazing down from the walls. The Duchy Restaurant is big enough to double as a ballroom and sports a minstrels' gallery; as usual it is the tables by the windows that are the most inviting. The five-course dinners boast some imaginative touches (like half a galia melon filled with strawberries and flaked almonds soaked in Grand Marnier), and there is a cold buffet as an alternative to the hot main course.

The head of a Lord Derbyshire giant eland dominates the grand stairwell leading to bedrooms that can hardly be faulted for comfort or luxury; indeed, one golfing reader wrote that Budock Vean was for us 'as near to perfect as we are ever likely to get'. Particularly appealing is Room Eight, with a half-tester bed and a curtained arch leading to a sitting area; sadly, it overlooks the car park at the front of the hotel rather than the 9/18-hole golf course at the back. Given golf's importance to Budock Vean it is not surprising to find a golf-shop decked out with golfing cartoons on the ground floor. There is also a spectacular indoor swimming-pool under a dome.

◑ *Closed Jan and Feb*

⤴ *From Truro take the A39 for 7 miles, then the A394 for 1 mile. Follow signs to Mabe, Argal and Mawnan Smith. At the Red Lion pub fork right, signposted Budock Vean. Private car park*

🛏 *10 single, 28 twin, 15 double, 2 four-poster, 3 suites; all with bathroom/WC, TV, room service, hair-dryer, baby-listening; tea/coffee-making facilities on request*

◈ *Restaurant, 2 bars, 4 lounges, drying room, games room, conservatory; conference*

facilities (max 50 people residential and non-residential); golf, tennis, heated indoor pool at hotel, other sports nearby

⊖ *No wheelchair access; no children under 5 in public rooms eves; no dogs in public rooms and charged for in bedrooms*

▭ *Access, Diners, Visa*

£ *Single £58 to £85, single occupancy of twin/double £87 to £127, twin/double/four-poster £116 to £169 (rates inc dinner); deposit required. Set D £16.50; alc D from £16.50; bar snacks. Special breaks available*

Meudon Hotel

MAWNAN SMITH, NR FALMOUTH, CORNWALL TR11 5HT
TEL: FALMOUTH (0326) 250541   FAX: (0326) 250543

A large hotel in a quiet corner of Cornwall with a wonderful hanging garden.

It's unfortunate that the original early twentieth-century building (encompassing two seventeenth-century coastguards' cottages) was added to in the 1960s, resulting in a brutalist annexe. Could you but approach from the other side you would be greeted by one of the finest hotel gardens in Cornwall, believed to have been laid out by Capability Brown and falling away steeply into a ravine. So lush is the vegetation that flourishes in the mild climate that you'll spot oddities like Australian tree ferns and Brazilian giant rhubarb growing happily alongside the more usual magnolia and azaleas. A path leads down through the garden to a private beach. Not surprisingly the best tables in the dining-room, with its distinctive granite pillars, are the ones that look out on the garden. The four-course table d'hôte menus stick with conventional dishes (the scallops may well have been plucked from the seabed by owner Mark Pilgrim). There are two lounges, both of them comfortable and both with garden views, although neither can hope to match the spectacular panorama offered from the otherwise uninspiring 'bridge' lounge linking the hotel's old and new parts.

The bedrooms, all looking on to the garden and all with different colour schemes, have mundane furnishings; for more modern décor you should opt for a room in the new part, which boasts several attractive suites. The Pilgrims pride themselves on offering guests a high standard of service; beds are turned back at night and shoes are cleaned.

◐ Closed Dec, Jan

🔀 From Truro take the A39 for 7 miles, then the A394 for 1 mile. Follow signs to Mabe, Argal and Mawnan Smith. Fork left at the Red Lion pub. The hotel is 1 mile on the right. Private car park

🛏 4 single, 25 twin/double, 1 family room, 2 suites; all with bathroom/WC, TV, room service, hair-dryer, trouser press; tea/coffee-making facilities on request

◈ Restaurant, bar, 3 lounges, drying room, conservatory, games room; fishing, riding, water sports, private beach at hotel, free golf, other sports nearby

⊖ No wheelchair access; no children under 5; no dogs in public rooms

▭ Access, Amex, Diners, Visa

£ Single £75 to £85, single occupancy of twin/double £75 to £85, twin/double/family room £130 to £150, suite £200 (rates inc dinner); deposit required. Set L £12.50, D £18; alc L £17, D £26 (prices till Mar 94). Special breaks available

---

Nansidwell

MAWNAN SMITH, NR FALMOUTH, CORNWALL TR11 5HU
TEL: FALMOUTH (0326) 250340   FAX: (0326) 250440

A luxuriously comfortable and stylish country-house hotel with a subtropical garden.

Nansidwell Country House is so thickly blanketed in clematis and wistaria that almost all you can see of the building are the striking stone window mullions that label it a turn-of-the-century edifice. Inside, spacious, comfortable bedrooms have stylishly designed décor and big beds; the stone windows often make attractive features, framing armchairs and round tables positioned to take advantage of garden views. Room 24 has a particularly large bathroom with arched ceiling, while Room 10 has pretty marbled walls and cupboards. The two ground-floor lounges are full of, but never swamped by, pictures, photographs, books and magazines; one offers stunning views across the garden to the just-visible sea. A pleasing dining-room features dried-flower trees on either side of a fireplace, window seats to take advantage of more views, and a plethora of plates decorating the walls. The three-course table d'hôte menus offer limited choice; a typical dinner might start with cream of celery and Stilton soup, move on to roast fillet of pork with orange and walnuts, and end with the chef's pudding of the day. After dinner there are nine acres of beautiful gardens to stroll in and a path leading down to the sea.

◑ *Closed Jan*

⤢ *From Truro take the A39 for 7 miles, then the A394 for 1 mile. Follow signs for Mabe, Argal and Mawnan Smith. At the Red Lion in Mawnan Smith fork left – the hotel is on the right. Private car park*

⇌ *12 twin/double; all with bathroom/WC, TV, hair-dryer, trouser press*

◈ *Dining-room, 2 lounges, drying room; tennis at hotel, other*

sports nearby. Wheelchair access to hotel (1 step), restaurant and 2 ground-floor bedrooms

⊖ *No children under 6 in dining-room eves; no dogs in public rooms*

▭ *Access, Visa*

£ *Single occupancy of twin/double £95, twin/double £186 (rates inc dinner); deposit required. Cooked B £4; set L £15, D £23; alc D £28. Special breaks available*

MAXSTOKE WARWICKSHIRE   **MAP 5**

Old Rectory ☆

CHURCH LANE, MAXSTOKE, WARWICKSHIRE B46 2QW
TEL: COLESHILL (0675) 462248   FAX: (0675) 481615

Home-from-home Victorian rectory that is convenient for the NEC.

As an alternative to large modern hotels, the Old Rectory attracts many business people looking for a taste of traditional England. The early nineteenth-century sandstone house, built within the walls of a ruined Augustinian priory, couldn't be more English with its view over green fields and its colourful rambling garden with carp pools, moorhens and geese. The Pages' border collie will probably keep you company if you fancy a half-mile stroll round the grounds past the tiny mill and the monks' bread ovens and beehives.

Inside the house, the décor takes you back to the 1970s with huge floral prints and mock-leather settees. Two of the three bedrooms are enormous and comfortably equipped, sharing a large modern bathroom; the third was being converted to *en suite* when we visited. The dining-room with its grand walnut dresser overlooks one of the carp pools and surrounding fields, and is a lovely room for breakfast. Dinners are served by prior arrangement. The lounge too has views of the garden and there's plenty of information on local places, along with a reasonable selection of books. If you would rather chat than read, the Pages' obvious enjoyment of sharing their house means that they are perfectly happy to sit together with guests in the evenings.

◑ *Open all year, exc 2 weeks at Xmas*

⤢ *Leave the M42 at Junction 6. Follow the A45 south for 2 miles.*

Turn left by the Little Chef and continue for 3 miles to a T-junction. Turn left, and the entrance is at the bottom of the hill on a bend through a gateway to the left. Private car park

🛏 I twin, I double, I family room; twin with bathroom/WC, remainder with shower/WC; TV in all rooms

◈ Dining-room, lounge; golf nearby

⊖ No wheelchair access; no dogs in public rooms and in bedrooms by arrangement; smoking in lounge only

▭ None accepted

💷 Single occupancy of twin/double £26, twin/double £41, family room £59

MELBOURN CAMBRIDGESHIRE   MAP 9

Melbourn Bury

MELBOURN, NR ROYSTON, HERTFORDSHIRE SG8 6DE
TEL: ROYSTON (0763) 261151   FAX: (0763) 262375

Civilised, formal country house surrounded by stunning grounds.

The grounds are the first thing that impress when you sweep into the gravel driveway belonging to this gracious Wolsey Lodge. Mature chestnuts, copper beeches, trimmed lawns and a pond momentarily divert the eye from the imposing white building with its castle-like crenellations and cross design over a pillared porch. Although parts of the house date from the sixteenth century most of it is Victorian and Sylvia Hopkinson, the owner, remembers visits to her grandmother who lived here earlier this century. Her ancestors arrived in the middle of Queen Victoria's reign and there are antiques and heirlooms around the house. There are just three bedrooms, but these are large and airy. Otherwise the Hopkinsons concentrate on conferences and receptions, and the formal atmosphere may make you feel more comfortable in smart clothes than jeans.

Guests eat together (faithful to the Wolsey tradition) in style. Sylvia is a devotee of home-made soups and may serve dishes such as smoked loin of pork with madeira and cream sauce or duck with honey and ginger sauce as main courses. Ice-creams, too, are a favourite – also home-made. A new herb garden, recently constructed, makes a pleasantly perfumed place to wander.

◑ Open all year, exc Xmas and Easter

↗ Leave Royston on the A10 northbound and take the first exit to Melbourn. The entrance to the house is 300 yards on the left after the turn. Private car park

🛏 I single, 2 twin; all with

bathroom/WC, exc I twin with shower/WC; TV, room service in all rooms; hair-dryer on request; tea/coffee-making facilities on request

◈ Dining-room, lounge, billiard room, library, conservatory; conference facilities (max 50 people non-residential)

⬤ No wheelchair access; no children under 8; no dogs; no smoking in bedrooms

▭ Access, Amex, Visa

£ Single £47 to £50, single occupancy of twin £47 to £50, twin £75 to £80. Set D £15.50 (8pm)

MELDRETH CAMBRIDGESHIRE MAP 9

Chiswick House

MELDRETH, ROYSTON, HERTFORDSHIRE SG8 6LZ
TEL: ROYSTON (0763) 260242

A successful combination of comfort and history in a bed and breakfast that's convenient for visiting Cambridge.

This 500-year-old timber-framed house isn't only a good base for exploring Cambridge (eight miles away), it's also a history lesson. The fine Jacobean oak panelling in the lounge dates from the period when King James I used the building as a hunting-lodge and his coat of arms, now faint, tops the fireplace in the ground-floor twin room. In the same room are fourteenth-century etched beams, decorated by medieval travelling artists, carefully protected by thick curtains.

If you've ever wondered how the Powder room got its name, stay in Room Three, a cosy double. Proprietors John and Bernice Elbourn will explain the history of the snug, windowless bathroom which was once used for powdering wigs. All the rooms are comfortable, but the best are those in the converted stable block a few paces from the house. With peachy décor and pine furnishing, they are light, airy and have the added advantage of separate access.

The traditional breakfast, served on a help-yourself basis, is taken communally either at a long oak table in the lounge or in the conservatory, which is filled with geraniums.

◖ Open all year

↗ Meldreth village is 1 mile west of the A10, 8 miles south of Cambridge and 3 miles north of Royston. Private car park

🛏 2 twin, 4 double (some rooms in stable annexe); 1 with bathroom/WC, remainder with shower/WC; hair-dryer in all rooms; TV on request

◇ Breakfast room, lounge, drying room, conservatory; golf, tennis, riding, heated swimming-pool nearby. Wheelchair access to hotel (1 step), breakfast room and 4 ground-floor bedrooms

⬤ No dogs in public rooms; no smoking

▭ None accepted

£ Twin/double £38; deposit required

All entries in the Guide *are rewritten every year, not least because standards fluctuate. Don't trust an out-of-date* Guide.

Sandridge Park

MELKSHAM, WILTSHIRE SN12 7QU
TEL: BATH (0225) 706897   FAX: (0225) 702838

A hilltop country house with elegant reception rooms and individual, well-furnished bedrooms.

For Annette Hoogeweegen every guest is a VIP, and her visitors could hardly be better looked after or in finer surroundings. Set in 30 acres with magnificent views towards both Salisbury Plain and the Mendips, Sandridge Park was built in 1850 of Bath sandstone. It had fallen into virtual dereliction when Annette and Andrew took it over about 10 years ago, since when they have worked immensely hard to make this a stylish, relaxed country house. Apart from creating a delightful herb and kitchen garden, Annette has done much of the interior design herself – including the original vestibule, lined with striped material on walls and ceiling to give a marquee effect.

The house is full of antiques, interesting paintings and sculptures. The well-proportioned drawing-room has plenty of comfortable seating around the open fire. A table laden with old glassware stands by the window. Pre-dinner drinks are taken in here before you move into the dramatic dining-room, which has glazed red walls, gilt mirrors, a carved wooden fireplace and a huge gong. In Wolsey Lodge style, dinners are taken around a candlelit polished table set with silver cutlery and old china. Annette ran her own catering company for many years, so the standard of cooking is high. A four-course dinner one evening consisted of chicken liver pâté, poussin with honey and lemon, home-grown vegetables, chocolate profiteroles and cheese. The excellent breakfasts include bacon and sausages from a nearby farm and Annette's own bread, croissants and preserves.

All the bedrooms are charmingly furnished and of good size; views are either over the walled garden or front lawns. There is one bedroom-cum-sitting-room on the ground floor suitable for the elderly. Some *en-suite* bathrooms have an extra shower cubicle; all are comprehensively equipped, right down to plastic ducks.

◑ *Open all year, exc Xmas and New Year*

⤴ *From Melksham take the A3102 towards Calne. The hotel is 2 miles along this road on the left. Private car park*

🛏 *1 twin, 2 double; all with bathroom/WC, TV; trouser press in 1 room; hair-dryer on request*

◈ *Dining-room, lounge, TV room; conference facilities (max 20 people non-residential); fishing, golf, other sports nearby. Wheelchair access to hotel, restaurant and 1 ground-floor bedroom*

⊖ *No children; no dogs; no smoking in bedrooms*

▭ None accepted

£ Single occupancy of twin/double £40, twin/double £70; deposit required. Set D from £20 (8pm, residents only). Special breaks available

---

Shurnhold House

SHURNHOLD, MELKSHAM, WILTSHIRE SN12 8DG
TEL: BATH (0225) 790555

Excellent and relaxed accommodation in a licensed B&B.

As one satisfied customer wrote in the visitors' book: 'This is a helluvanice place to stay!' That is the general consensus about this well-restored Jacobean manor house just outside Melksham. Although on the main road, the house and gardens (look out for the sign) are screened by trees. Unusually, for a B&B, there is a small licensed bar for guests. This gives an air of relaxed sociability, clearly much appreciated by many of Sue Mead's devoted weekday business clientele. As she says: 'Why shouldn't people be able to have a drink when they come back here?'

It is not hard to feel at home in this elegant home, furnished to show off its fine proportions and old timbers. The stone-flagged lounge has an open hearth and a huge sofa, fresh flowers, magazines, books and interesting ornaments. The breakfast room is attractively decorated in grey and white. Evening meals are not available, but Sue will advise on eating out in the area, and will obligingly rustle up a plate of filling sandwiches for anyone staying in.

The large bedrooms have equally generously sized bathrooms, some with corner baths. A self-contained apartment has a spacious lounge with an Elizabethan fireplace, and a narrow spiral staircase up to a below-the-eaves bedroom. It is an ascent that may be difficult for the tipsy.

◑ Open all year

⚡ Shurnhold is just off the A365, 1 mile from Melksham, 10 miles from Bath. The driveway is well signposted. Private car park

🛏 1 twin, 3 double, 2 four-poster, 1 family room, 1 annexe room, 1 cottage; all with bathroom/WC, exc cottage room with shower/WC; TV, room service, hair-dryer, baby-listening in all rooms

◇ Dining-room, bar, 2 lounges;

croquet at hotel, golf, tennis other sports nearby

⊖ No wheelchair access; dogs by arrangement in bedrooms only; smoking in bar and lounge only

▭ Access, Visa

£ Single occupancy of twin/double £42 to £45, twin/double £58 to £68, four-poster £68, family room £78, annexe room/cottage £68; deposit required. Cooked B £3.50, continental B £1.50

All rooms have tea/coffee-making facilities unless we specify to the contrary.

Toxique

187 WOODROW ROAD, MELKSHAM, WILTSHIRE SN12 7AY
TEL: BATH (0225) 702129

Expect the unexpected in this outré *restaurant-with-rooms.*

Do not be deterred by the black front door and ominous-sounding name – think rather of exotic or intoxicating, for this is a restaurant with accommodation as striking as the food. This is the alternative approach to country living, the antithesis of floral frills and pastel flounces. Whatever it is, it is lots of fun. Even locals come and stay the night.

As soon as you enter the low, seventeenth-century farmhouse, you know you are in for the unconventional. This is a very dark restaurant – midnight blues, deep burgundies and dusky draped fabrics covering low, plastic garden chairs set the style. Unframed paintings by owner Peter Jewkes hang around the walls. A second dining-room, recently opened, is brighter and more Mediterranean in feel, with a showy wall mural and stout white candles in terracotta plant pots.

Each of the four bedrooms is differently themed. The Desert Suite is a study in lemon and turquoise, with a tented brocade ceiling above the boxed-in double bed; the Attic Suite is Spanish-villa style with white walls and covers and atmospheric paintings; the Oriental Room has Indian carved wood, wall hangings and muslin drapes. It also has a Jacuzzi and a rock floor sculpture (well, it helps to hide the carpet join). The Rococo Suite is dimly lit and romantic, with red walls, green velvet and heavy brocade. All the rooms have built-in circular baths, with high surrounds edged in either sand or pebbles. They look amazing, but could be hazardous on bare bottoms.

Peter's partner, Helen Bartlett, prepares the meals. A set dinner might typically include skewered monkfish with black-bean sauce, tarragon and lime; pistachio-crusted loin of lamb with honey and mustard glaze; and rhubarb strudel with vanilla sauce.

◑ Open all year, exc hols in Jan or Feb; restaurant closed Sun and Mon eves

↗ From the mini-roundabout in the town centre, take the Calne road. After ⅓rd mile turn left into Forest Road. Toxique is ¾ mile along on the left. Private car park

🛏 I double, 3 four-poster; all with bathroom/WC, room service; further facilities on request

◈ 2 dining-rooms, lounge; fishing, golf, tennis nearby. Wheelchair access to restaurant only

⊖ No dogs; no smoking in dining-room

▭ Access, Visa

£ Single occupancy of double £64, double/four-poster £108 (rates inc dinner). Set L £16.50, D £24

See page 817 for other hotels worthy of inclusion in our Visitors' Book.

Chetcombe House ☆

CHETCOMBE ROAD, MERE, NR WARMINSTER, WILTSHIRE BA12 6AZ
TEL: MERE (0747) 860219

Personal attention makes this small hotel a good base for touring the area.

Colin and Susan Ross have received enthusiastic recommendations for their sensibly priced, detached 1930s guesthouse. It does have drawbacks, principally the location on a slip road off the busy A303 by-pass; nor is the house much to look at externally, hemmed in slightly as it is on either side. Inside, however, it is nicer and more peaceful than one might expect. As one reader wryly wrote, it is 'unpretentious and well recommended by a usually cynical traveller'. Another reader insisted we mention the intimate atmosphere: 'It is small enough for Colin Ross to introduce guests to each other; we got on so famously with a Canadian couple on vacation we invited them home!' The Ross's have also been praised for their care in looking after guests and have been described as 'friendly, helpful and attentive owners full of advice and information'.

The comfortable lounge, where guests gather before and after dinner, has french windows that give on to a pleasant garden with fields behind. The dining-room is light and pleasant, with well-spaced tables, hanging ferns and a large bay window. A small bar in the entrance hall doubles as reception desk.

The better bedrooms, with the views, are at the back of the house. Rooms facing towards the road are less sunny and traffic noise may intrude for some. They are all freshly but simply decorated. Some of the modern *en-suite* bathrooms have shower only.

Much praise has also been given to the food. Dinners are freshly cooked, menus change daily and guests sit down to eat together at 7pm. One reported to us in detail: 'The cheese soup was the best we've had . . . chicken with tarragon melted in the mouth . . . the apple tartlets were of the crisp, sweet flan pastry my wife has always wished she could master.' Breakfasts, too, win praise: 'Fabulous scrambled eggs à point, super local (all meat) sausages and bacon, excellent cafetière coffee.'

- ◑ Open all year
- ⊠ Just off the A303, before reaching Mere (from the east). Private car park
- ⇤ 1 single, 1 twin, 2 double, 1 family room; 2 with bathroom/WC, 3 with shower/WC; TV in all rooms
- ◈ Dining-room, bar, lounge; baby-listening
- ⊖ No wheelchair access; no dogs in public rooms; smoking in lounge only
- ▭ Access, Amex, Visa
- £ Single £28, single occupancy of twin/double £32, twin/double £48, family room £63; deposit required. Set L, D £12.50 (by arrangement). Special breaks available

Forest of Arden

MAXSTOKE LANE, MERIDEN, COVENTRY, WARWICKSHIRE CV7 7HR
TEL: MERIDEN (0676) 22335   FAX: (0676) 23711

A large, modern hotel and country club with excellent facilities.

Over the treeline of the park that surrounds the Forest of Arden Hotel you can just see the lights of Coventry. Except for that, you feel completely cut off from the outside world in this huge complex of restaurants, bars, bedrooms, tennis and squash courts encircled by an 18-hole golf course. The plain modern low-rise building is uninspiring, but comfort and facilities are the name of the game here, not aesthetics. Similarly, inside you'll find efficient service rather than ceremony, air-conditioning rather than fresh flowers. A large sitting-room, with dozens of slate blue sofas and views of the golf course, is well divided up to prevent an 'airport lounge' feel and in the restaurant solo diners and couples are seated away from business groups so that they don't feel swamped. Natural colours, dried flowers and exposed rafters give the restaurant a rustic feel which, along with slick service and reliable food, make dinner an enjoyable experience whatever your reason for being here. The short à la carte menu lists Stilton and apple soup, fillet of monkfish, escalopes of veal and Barnsley chops amongst the mainly modern English dishes.

Light ash furniture, cool colours and leafy patterns characterise the bedrooms, which are a good size and extremely well-equipped. The radio pipes into the bathroom so you can combine a bath with the Archers at the end of a heavy day.

◑ Open all year

▰ Take Junction 6 from the M42 and follow the A45 towards Coventry. Carry straight on to Stonebridge Island and after ¾ mile turn left into Packington Lane. The hotel is 2 miles on the left. Private car park

🛏 75 twin, 75 double, 2 suites; all with bathroom/WC, TV, room service, hair-dryer, trouser press, baby-listening

◈ 2 restaurants, 3 bars, lounge, games room; all public areas air-conditioned; conference facilities (max 200 people non-residential, 120 residential); children's activities; fishing, golf, tennis, sauna/solarium, heated indoor swimming-pool, gym, beauty salon, spa bath, dance studio, snooker, squash at hotel; babysitting. Wheelchair access to hotel (ramps), restaurant and WC (M,F), 50 ground-floor bedrooms, 2 specially equipped for disabled people

⊖ No dogs

▭ Access, Amex, Diners, Visa

£ Single occupancy of twin/double £80 to £110, twin/double £95 to £125, suite rate on request; deposit required. Set L, D £19; alc L, D £30. Special breaks available

MEVAGISSEY CORNWALL   **MAP 10**

Mevagissey House

VICARAGE HILL, MEVAGISSEY, CORNWALL PL26 6SZ
TEL: MEVAGISSEY (0726) 842427

Small and welcoming family-run hotel.

A sweeping drive conceals Mevagissey House, an early Victorian ex-vicarage attached to an older white farmhouse, from the road, but the downstairs lounge offers fine views over four acres of grounds to Mevagissey itself. The bar and sun-lounge on either side of it have colonial-style wicker chairs from which you can appreciate the views. In the smallish dining-room a big fireplace is disappointingly fitted with an electric fire, which rather destroys the period impression given by the Holbein prints adorning the panelled walls. Here three-course table d'hôte dinners offer a limited choice of standard English fare such as soups, hotpots and pies; the à la carte and vegetarian menus look more inspiring. A big stairwell acts as a showcase for unusual Sierra Leonean carvings, and upstairs the six bedrooms are adequately if rather functionally furnished, with lots of chipboard cupboards. Should you land one of the rooms without *en-suite* facilities you'll be able to take advantage of a bathroom as big as many of the bedrooms. The warm welcome and very reasonable rates offered by Diana and John Owens should keep you happy.

- ◗ Closed Nov to Feb
- ⤴ Take the B3272 St Austell to Mevagissey road. In Pentewan pass the caravan park, turn left at the top of the hill, then two right turns. Private car park
- ⊨ 1 twin, 3 double, 2 family rooms, 3 cottages; some with bathroom/WC, some with shower/WC, 1 public bathroom; TV, room service in all rooms; hair-dryer on request
- ◈ Dining-room, bar, lounge, drying room, conservatory; fishing, water sports, other sports nearby
- ⊖ No wheelchair access; no children under 7; no dogs; smoking in bar and conservatory only and restricted in bedrooms
- ▭ Access, Visa
- £ Single occupancy of twin/double £20 to £28, twin/double £28 to £46, family room £44 to £46, cottage £38 to £46; deposit required. Set D £12; alc D from £9.50

MIDDLEHAM NORTH YORKSHIRE   **MAP 3**

Greystones

MARKET PLACE, MIDDLEHAM, NORTH YORKSHIRE DL8 4NR
TEL: WENSLEYDALE (0969) 22016

A neat and welcoming Georgian guesthouse where the food – and in particular the baking – scores highly.

Once inside Greystones there is no doubting that you've struck gold. Frances and Keith Greenwood's guesthouse is one of those places where you feel instantly at home, not least because tea and home-made cake is immediately offered to help you settle in. The homely lounge with its real fire, green leather sofa, family photos, piano and library of books plus local prints does the rest. There is good old furniture in the sweet little dining-room, which has views over the market square as well as trophies testifying to Keith's skill at quoits. The four tables – one for each of the rooms – are close enough to allow conversation to flow between them. The dinner itself is likely to be one of the talking points, for although there is no choice at the main-course stage, few can leave the table unsatisfied after a meal that might feature Wensleydale cheese tart with apple salad followed by breast of chicken in honey, thyme and cream, sticky toffee pudding with vanilla sauce, and local cheeses with grapes and oatmeal biscuits.

Bedrooms combine chintzy soft furnishings with solid old furniture and pleasant *en-suite* facilities. The nibbles in the biscuit tin, like the bread served with dinner and the biscuits that accompany the cheese, are home-baked.

◑ Closed 1 Nov to mid-Feb, exc Xmas and New Year

⤢ From the A1 turn on to the B6267 to Masham and follow this road to Middleham. On-street parking

🛏 1 twin, 2 double, 1 family room; all with shower/WC, exc 1 double with bathroom/WC; room service, hair-dryer, baby-listening in all rooms

◈ Dining-room, lounge, drying room; fishing, golf, riding nearby

⊖ No wheelchair access; no dogs; smoking in lounge only

▭ None accepted

£ Single occupancy of twin/double £35, twin/double £55, family room £65; deposit required. Set D £12.50 (7pm)

Millers House

MARKET PLACE, MIDDLEHAM, NORTH YORKSHIRE DL8 4NR
TEL: WENSLEYDALE (0969) 22630　FAX: (0969) 23570

A friendly hotel tucked behind Middleham's cobbled square in the heart of the Dales.

The miller who lived here must have been a bit of a plutocrat – a mill owner rather than a chalky-faced, flour-under-the-fingernails chap with a strong back for heaving bulging sacks – for Judith and Crossley Sunderland's well-run small hotel has loads of Georgian elegance, from the clean lines of its grey façade set back from the market square to the grandeur of its four-poster bedroom.

MILLER'S HOUSE
-MIDDLEHAM-

For all that, the bar/lounge with its reproduction furniture and muted walls is a simple, almost spartan room, though it is decked out with pleated drapes of a classic Regency design and a co-ordinating sofa around which modern curved-back chairs are arranged in a conspiratorial grouping. The pictures of racehorses above the log fire point to this area's abiding passion – early risers might see a string of horses from local stables parade past ready for their morning exercise. The dining-room is elegant below its moulded ceiling, with coral-striped wallpaper, fresh floral displays and pink table linen. The short menu finds room both for the audacious and the traditional; perhaps chilled leek and avocado vichyssoise, followed by noisettes of lamb with a lemon and mint sauce, then mango and cardamom gâteau and cheese.

Bedrooms vary in size, and there is still some white woodchip to be replaced. Refurbished rooms score highly for pleasant décor: attractive old or pine furniture and an irreproachable neatness. Huge Wensleydale is dominated not by its four-poster bed, but by a centre-stage claw-footed bath. Modest souls can perform their ablutions behind a traditional screen.

'We will certainly be returning,' concluded one visitor, pronouncing himself happy with the accommodation, cuisine and warmth and friendliness of the welcome.

◑ Closed Jan

⤴ As Greystones entry above. Private car park

🛏 1 single, 3 twin, 2 double, 1 four-poster; all with bathroom/WC, exc single, 1 public bathroom; TV, room service in all rooms

◈ Dining-room, lounge/bar, drying room; limited conference facilities (max 8 people non-residential and residential);

croquet at hotel, other sports
nearby

 No wheelchair access; no
children under 10; no dogs; no
smoking in dining-room and
bedrooms

 Access, Visa

Single £34, twin/double £67,
four-poster £82; deposit
required. Set D £17/£19.50;
picnic hampers. Special breaks
available

MIDDLE WALLOP HAMPSHIRE   **MAP 9**

Fifehead Manor

MIDDLE WALLOP, STOCKBRIDGE, HAMPSHIRE SO20 8EG
TEL: ANDOVER (0264) 781565   FAX: (0264) 781400

*An historic manor-house hotel with attractive gardens and a fine
restaurant.*

In the shadow of the Iron Age fort on Danebury Hill and a short drive
from Stonehenge, Fifehead Manor is centred on a medieval building of
mullions and lattices with foundations dating from 1042. A highly
recommended restaurant, the hotel's main attraction, now occupies a
wonderfully enticing room on the ground floor of this section, complete
with huge stone fireplaces, low oak beams and warm, restrained décor.
Both the *carte* and the set menus are adventurous and reasonably priced;
you may be offered dishes such as pork fillet in a caraway beer sauce with
herby dumplings or lamb fillet with spinach and pine-nuts, as well as a
daily choice of fish from the market.

The other public rooms, scattered with flowers and paintings, are pale
in comparison, though the lounge with its log fire and richly carved
furniture is airy, uncluttered and very comfortable. A broad staircase
(showing signs of wear and tear in places) leads up to the spacious, plain
and unfussy bedrooms; bathrooms are well-fitted. Traffic on the busy
A343 can be noisy during the day.

Open all year, exc 2 weeks at
Xmas

On the A343, 5 miles south of
Andover. In Middle Wallop, 5th
house on the right after the
crossroads. Private car park

6 single, 10 twin/double; all with
bathroom/WC, exc singles with
shower/WC; no tea/coffee-
making facilities in rooms

Restaurant, bar, lounge, drying
room; conference facilities (max
20 people non-residential, 16
residential); croquet at hotel,

fishing, golf, other sports nearby.
Wheelchair access to hotel,
restaurant and WC (unisex), 2
ground-floor bedrooms specially
equipped for disabled people

No dogs in public rooms

Access, Amex, Diners, Visa

Single £50, single occupancy of
twin/double £70, twin/double
£75 to £95; deposit required. Set
L £18, D £25; alc L £25, D £30
(service charge added to meal
prices). Special breaks available

MIDHURST WEST SUSSEX   **MAP 9**

Angel ☆

COUNTY HOTEL OF THE YEAR

NORTH STREET, MIDHURST, WEST SUSSEX GU29 9DN
TEL: MIDHURST (0730) 812421   FAX: (0730) 815928

A traditional coaching-inn, run with some panache.

As befits its history as a sixteenth-century coaching-inn the Angel is slap on the main road to Midhurst, its freshly painted cream and green façade difficult to miss. Peter Crawford-Rolt and Nicholas Davies have shaken the place up since they bought it in 1992, and all their hard work leaves one with the feeling that here is an establishment that is a success.

Let's start with the food. Next door to a bar is a simply furnished brasserie serving the sort of menu that attracts locals and delights the casual guest – for example, oysters and cracked crab with herb mayonnaise and caponata, lambs' sweetbreads and wild mushrooms in pastry leaves, and desserts such as banana tart flamed with rum or dark chocolate terrine with caramelised oranges. If you'd like to dine a touch more formally, try the elegant dining-room furnished in yellow and blue. The only time this smooth operation fell apart on our inspection was at breakfast – it's simply no good toast arriving after you've finished the bacon and eggs. It didn't just happen to us, either, for all around the room guests started being very precise about when they wanted things to appear.

Bedrooms are freshly done up with floral fabrics and wonderful old furniture. Tariffs vary considerably, and the standard doubles, though reasonably priced and stylish, are fairly small. Our inspector stayed in the family room (Five) overlooking the street and wasn't bothered by the noise, though light sleepers may prefer a rear-facing room. Huge dark wood furniture including a mirrored chest of drawers would have dwarfed many a modern room. Bathrooms are fashionably white and brass, and have baths rather than showers. Residents have a small lounge, cosily furnished in dark reds and greens, right next to the bar so that you still feel part of the place.

◑ Open all year

↗ Situated on the A272, the main road through Midhurst. Private car park

🛏 4 twin, 10 double, 1 four-poster, 2 suites; all with bathroom/WC, TV, room service; hair-dryer and trouser press on request; no tea/coffee-making facilities in rooms

◇ 2 restaurants, bar, lounge; conference facilities (max 70 people non-residential, 21 residential); golf, tennis, other sports nearby. Wheelchair access to restaurants and WC (M) only

⊖ No dogs

▭ Access, Amex, Diners, Visa

£ Single occupancy of twin/double £40 to £50, twin/double £50 to £80, four-poster/suite £95 to £105; deposit required. Set L, D £15 to £20. Special breaks available

Spread Eagle

SOUTH STREET, MIDHURST, WEST SUSSEX GU29 9NH
TEL: MIDHURST (0730) 816911   FAX: (0730) 815668

A creaking, characterful inn with harmonious extensions.

The Spread Eagle offers a comfortable stay rather than luxury, but the real reason for coming here is to steep yourself in the history of this museum piece: its 500-year existence has left it with sloping, creaking floors, medieval ships' timbers (one beam is said to date from the thirteenth century), Tudor bread ovens, seventeenth-century Flemish stained glass, and a window bricked up to avoid tax. Conscious of this legacy, the Goodmans, whose family have owned the place for 37 years, have exposed a section of the original wattle-and-daub outside wall behind a glass window on the first floor.

The heart of the hotel is the broad fireplace in the restaurant, above which hang copper pans and maturing Christmas puddings – the management put these up for Yuletide guests in readiness for their next visit. On one side lies the original tavern, now the Lounge Bar, dark and rich with oak floorboards, leather armchairs and Windsor chairs. The sloping-ceilinged residents' lounge above is more airy and comfortable, fitted with upholstered armchairs, a sofa and a clavichord.

This lounge gives on to the hotel's most expensive room, the Queen Elizabeth I Suite, with a large sitting-room and a four-poster bed; the leaded windows overlooking the street have seen better days and the bathroom is tiny, but the suite does come with its own wig-powder closet. The old part of the hotel also contains a few characterful standard bedrooms, but most are in a new annexe across the small courtyard.

🌓 Open all year

🔼 In the centre of Midhurst, overlooking South Pond. Private car park

🛏 2 single, 17 twin, 17 double, 5 four-poster; most with bathroom/WC, some with shower/WC; TV, room service, baby-listening in all rooms; no tea/coffee-making facilities in rooms

◇ Restaurant, 2 bars, 2 lounges; conference facilities (max 70

people non-residential, 40 residential); fishing, golf, other sports nearby; babysitting by arrangement

⊖ No wheelchair access; no dogs or smoking in restaurant

▭ Access, Amex, Diners, Visa

£ Single £59, single occupancy of twin/double £59 to £85, twin/double £78 to £98, four-poster £130; deposit required. Cooked B £4; set L £16, D £26

MILDENHALL SUFFOLK   MAP 7

Riverside Hotel

MILL STREET, MILDENHALL, BURY ST EDMUNDS, SUFFOLK IP28 7DP
TEL: MILDENHALL (0638) 717274   FAX: (0638) 715997

An imposing town hotel, best visited in the summer when the garden comes into its own.

This large, red-brick hotel was originally built in 1720 as a house for the owner of the local mill. As its name suggests, pretty gardens and a croquet lawn lead to the gently flowing River Lark where guests can wander, fish or take boats. The Terrace Restaurant in a glass extension at the back of the hotel takes full advantage of the grounds, spilling out from a peachy interior on to an open paved area where diners can enjoy *al fresco* meals. Lunch and dinner are good value and with four or five choices per course, the table d'hôte menu may include seasonal seafood salad with caviare mayonnaise in the starters, pan-fried suprême of chicken with a tangy red wine sauce in the main courses and a traditional rhubarb crumble or steamed syrup sponge as a dessert. In contrast with the garden freshness of the restaurant, the next-door bar seems fusty.

If you prefer high-ceilinged rooms and large windows, ask for a bedroom on the first floor, as they get lower the higher up the building you go. However, all are *en suite* and comfortable, with a number of luxury rooms reserved for quixotic couples who opt for a special Romantic Weekend Break.

◑ Open all year

⤢ Take the A1101 to Mildenhall. At the mini roundabout turn left along the High Street and then into Mill Street. Private car park

🛏 4 single, 5 twin, 5 double, 1 four-poster, 4 family rooms, 4 cottages; all with bathroom/WC; TV, room service, hair-dryer, trouser press, baby-listening

◇ Restaurant, 2 bars, lounge, drying room; conference facilities (max 50 people non-residential,

18 residential); fishing, boules, croquet, putting, row boats at hotel, other sports nearby

⊖ No wheelchair access; no dogs in restaurant

▭ Access, Amex, Diners, Visa

£ Single £50, single occupancy of twin/double £59, twin/double/cottage room £75, four-poster/family room £87; deposit required. Set L £15, D £16; alc L, D £15 to £25. Special breaks available

---

MINEHEAD SOMERSET   **MAP 10**

Periton Park

COUNTY HOTEL OF THE YEAR

MIDDLECOMBE, NR MINEHEAD, SOMERSET TA24 8SW
TEL: MINEHEAD (0643) 706885 (and fax)

A luxurious country-house hotel on a hill overlooking Minehead.

In grand isolation at the top of a succession of hairpin bends, Periton Park is a haven from the bustle of Minehead below. Externally the hotel is a smart if not particularly beautiful Victorian country house surrounded by rhododendrons and azaleas. Inside it is an immaculately kept family home. Bedrooms are spacious, some having built-in window seats offering views over Minehead and Exmoor; there are also striking fabrics and plumply upholstered seats. Bathrooms come with gallons of water so hot it necessitates a warning notice. While filling your bath, you will have trouble resisting the biscuits provided with the tea-making facilities.

The restaurant, once a billiard room, is discreetly elegant, with wood-panelled wainscoting giving way to smooth salmon-coloured walls with prints showing the Quorn Hunt in action. Richard Hunt provides excellent service, and the food is highly praised. One reader writes, 'On the first evening my husband enjoyed his venison so much that he chose it again the following evening.' Our inspector felt similarly about the salmon Periton Park – strips of salmon, prawns, artichoke bottoms and mushrooms bound together with double cream and served on a tomato and basil coulis. Desserts, too, are delicious; the apricot ice-cream in a tuile basket was light enough to follow even the most filling main course. After-dinner coffee is served in a roomy lounge.

◐ Open all year

⤴ On the south side of the A39 Minehead to Porlock road. Private car park

🛏 3 twin, 5 double, 4 double; most with bathroom/WC, some with shower/WC; TV, room service, hair-dryer in all rooms

◈ Restaurant, lounge, drying room; conference facilities (max 24 people non-residential, 8 residential); riding at hotel, other sports nearby. Wheelchair access

to hotel (2 steps) and restaurant, 1 ground-floor bedroom specially equipped for disabled people

⊖ No children under 12; dogs in 1 bedroom only; no smoking in dining-room and 2 bedrooms

▭ Access, Amex, Visa

£ Single occupancy of twin/double £64, twin/double £88; deposit required. Alc D £19; lunch by arrangement only; prices till end 93. Special breaks available

---

MITHIAN CORNWALL   **MAP 10**

Rose-in-Vale ☆

MITHIAN, ST AGNES, CORNWALL TR5 0QD
TEL: TRURO (0872) 552202   FAX: (0872) 552700

A small, elegant Georgian hotel in a quiet village inland from Perranporth.

Built in the 1760s as the winter home of a local tin-mine captain, Rose-in-Vale was at first a glorified two-up, two-down in 11 acres of grounds on the banks of a stream. Now, although it still retains its well-proportioned Georgian façade, it has been enlarged with the addition of a suite of bedrooms at the back. Tony, Vanda and Allison Arthur deserve much praise for making the hotel the comfortable, stylish place it is now; their imagination is vividly illustrated by the reception desk honed out of a pulpit rescued from a redundant Methodist chapel. In addition to the completely refurbished lounge and new bar/lounge, there is a long, thin dining-room with fine garden and pool views; the à la carte menus look more interesting than the table d'hôte.

The most modern bedrooms are in the extension and include three ground-floor bedrooms, one specially adapted for disabled guests; while not particularly spacious, all have garden views and Room 15 has a fine mahogany four-poster bed. Not surprisingly, one of the best rooms in the older part of the house was the mine captain's own. A reader writes warmly of the 'exceptionally friendly and helpful' proprietors and staff, whose efforts helped make a stay 'which might otherwise have been marred by miserable weather thoroughly enjoyable'.

◑ *Open all year*

↗ *Once 2 miles beyond Zelah, turn right on to B3284; cross the A3075 and ¾ mile further on turn left signposted Rose-in-Vale. Private car park*

🛏 *2 single, 7 twin, 7 double, 1 four-poster suite, family rooms available; all with bathroom/WC, exc 1 single with shower/WC; TV, room service, hair-dryer, baby-listening in all rooms*

◈ *Dining-room, bar, 2 lounges, games room; conference facilities (max 20 people residential and non-residential); solarium, heated outdoor swimming-pool at hotel (June to Sept), fishing, other sports nearby; babysitting. Wheelchair access to hotel (2 steps), restaurant and 3 ground-floor bedrooms, 1 specially equipped for disabled people*

⊖ *No dogs in public rooms; no smoking in dining-room*

▭ *Access, Amex, Visa*

£ *Single £35 to £36, single occupancy of twin/double £45 to £46, twin/double £69 to £71, four-poster suite £89 to £91, family room from £144; deposit required. Sun L £8; set D £15.50; alc L £5, D £20. Special breaks available*

MOLLINGTON CHESHIRE   MAP 5

Crabwall Manor

PARKGATE ROAD, MOLLINGTON, CHESTER, CHESHIRE CH1 6NE
TEL: CHESTER (0244) 851666   TELEX: 61220 CRAWAL G
FAX: (0244) 851400

Expensive 'town and country' hotel on outskirts of Chester.

The façade of this squat, castellated, brick manor house stretches to either side; wide-angle vision is needed to take in the many extensions and additions that have sprouted from the Tudor core.

Expensive and sleek, the hotel is furnished in regulation issue, upmarket, country-house gear; the public rooms have multi-draped curtains, dried flowers and endless small sofas and scatter cushions. There is a rather impersonal atmosphere, suitable for servicing expense-account business and conference trade. Post-prandial executive games include croquet on the lawn and pot black in the airy, modern snooker room. The luxurious and well-equipped bedrooms are spacious enough to have armchairs, sofas or even a small dining table. One suite, in the old part of the house, has a split-level sitting-room and bedroom. The bathrooms are equally large and lavish, with his 'n' hers washbasins.

There is a large, plush, pillared restaurant that links through into a newer conservatory/dining-room. Chef Michael Truelove cooks in a modern English–French style, and attracts diners from all over the county. Overall, standards and aspirations (and prices) are high, but execution and attention to detail can vary. As well as the à la carte menu, featuring dishes like fillet of John Dory with foie gras and peas and chocolate marquis flavoured with cognac, there is a simpler set-price lunch and dinner menu. The wine list is long and varied, and the house wine is good.

◑ Open all year

⤴ At the end of the M56 follow signs to Queensferry and North Wales (A5117) to the next roundabout. Turn left on to A540 for 2 miles. Crabwall Manor is on the right. Private car park

🛏 42 twin/double, 6 suites (inc 1 four-poster); all with bathroom/WC, TV, room service, hair-dryer, trouser press, baby-listening; no tea/coffee-making facilities in rooms

◈ Restaurant (air-conditioned), bar, 2 lounges, snooker room; air-conditioned conference facilities (max 96 people non-residential, 48 residential); croquet at hotel, other sports nearby; babysitting by arrangement. Wheelchair access to hotel (ramp), restaurant and WC (unisex), 20 ground-floor bedrooms, 1 specially equipped for disabled people

⊖ No dogs

▭ Access, Amex, Diners, Visa

💷 Single occupancy of twin/double £99, twin/double £135, four-poster £200, suite £135 to £170; deposit required. Set L £14.50, D £25.50; alc L, D £40. Special breaks available

---

MORECAMBE LANCASHIRE   **MAP 5**

Midland ☆

MARINE ROAD, MORECAMBE, LANCASHIRE LA6 4BZ
TEL: MORECAMBE (0524) 417180   FAX: (0524) 832827

Legendary art deco seaside hotel that is struggling to keep up appearances.

It is a small miracle that the Midland still stands – but after decades of seaside decline, insensitive refurbishment and neglect, a change of ownership in recent years may have given this once-celebrated hotel fresh hope for the future.

When it was built in 1933, the Midland was a showcase of art deco and one of the leading examples of modernist style and architecture. Designed by Oliver Hill, with interior décor by Eric Gill, it was a striking white ocean liner of a hotel, whose curves echoed those of Morecambe Bay itself.

The circular café was one of the first features to be restored at the beginning of the 1990s by a previous owner. The greatest jewel in the Midland's crown, however, Gill's monumental dining-room relief carved from Portland stone, was hidden away at the time of writing, replaced by a chipboard copy used in a location episode of Agatha Christie's *Poirot* and the subject of legal wrangling between the hotel's current owner, Leslie Whittingham, and the local council.

The structure and a number of original features of the hotel survive, but the interior is now an untidy, dog-eared hotchpotch of styles. Art deco lamps and screens, period cocktail cabinets and Lloyd Loom reproductions have been brought in but they sit uneasily alongside plastic chairs, artificial greenery, smoked glass tubular tables and unsightly '60s brewery redecorations. However, there are things to be grateful for – the Riviera sun lounge, which grandly sweeps around the edge of the hotel, is still the best spot on the coast to sit and enjoy the unbroken vista of bay and beach.

It is probably not worth staying at the hotel unless you have a room facing the sea and are prepared to overlook the threadbare, though adequate, nature of the accommodation. A leap of the imagination is needed to recapture the essence of this faded, fabled pleasure dome. But with vision, a lot of luck and support and a barrelful of money, one day the Midland could be Morecambe's answer to Miami Beach.

◑ Open all year

▰ In the centre of Morecambe. Private car park

🛏 2 single, 25 twin, 21 double, 1 four-poster, 4 family rooms; all with bathroom/WC, TV, room service, trouser press, baby-listening

◈ 3 restaurants, 3 bars, 2 lounges, conservatory; conference facilities (max 100 people non-residential, 50 residential); fishing, golf, tennis, other sports nearby. Wheelchair access to hotel, restaurant and 6 bedrooms specially equipped for disabled people

⊖ None

▭ Access, Amex, Diners, Visa

£ Single £25 to £35, single occupancy of twin/double £25 to £35, twin/double/four-poster £50 to £64, family room £64; deposit required. Set L £9, D £14. Special breaks available

---

MORSTON NORFOLK MAP 7

Morston Hall

 COUNTY HOTEL OF THE YEAR

MORSTON, HOLT, NORFOLK NR25 7AA
TEL: CLEY (0263) 741041 (and fax)

An old house with a fast-growing reputation and a location near beautiful National Trust coastline.

In the mere two years since Tracy and Galton Blackiston opened the new-look Morston Hall with partner Justin Fraser the reputation of both kitchen and accommodation has spread well beyond local hearsay and regulars report they are 'highly impressed with the new team'. Although anxious to play down the association with Miller Howe in Cumbria, the brochure makes it clear that this is where the trio met, and from where many of their ideas originate. Dinner is organised by sittings and a no-choice menu is based on locally grown produce. On a Saturday evening in April, the main course was a roast leg of spring lamb on a rich onion sauce with lamb's gravy. This was preceded by two courses – a roasted red pepper, aubergine and dolcelatte terrine and a fillet of local sea trout in herb sauce – and followed by a choice of four fruit- or chocolate-based desserts. Wines of the month are suggested on the menu or you can browse through the list where they are grouped by grape rather than country: 'This encourages people to try different types, instead of sticking to French,' explains Tracy.

'Rooms remain excellent and spacious,' a reader reports: take Sandringham, which is vast, with a cool, serene atmosphere, or Blickling, which overlooks the three acres of garden. Refurbishment has almost cancelled out the older décor. Within a short walk is the tidal quay of Morston, owned by the National Trust, where you can take sailing lessons in local boats, walk the mud flats or take trips to see the seals.

◐ Open all year, exc early Jan to late Feb

↗ On main A149 coast road, 2 miles west of Blakeney. Car park

🛏 1 twin, 3 double; all with bathroom/WC, TV, room service, hair-dryer

◈ Dining-room, 2 lounges, drying room, conservatory (by end 93); conference facilities (max 20 people non-residential); fishing, golf, other sports nearby.

Wheelchair access to dining-room only

⊖ No children under 10 in dining-room eves; no dogs in public rooms; no smoking in dining-room

▭ Access, Amex, Visa

£ Single occupancy of twin/double £70, twin/double £130 to £140 (rates inc dinner). Sun L £13; set D £21. Special breaks available

MORTEHOE DEVON   **MAP 10**

Watersmeet Hotel ☆

MORTEHOE, WOOLACOMBE, DEVON EX34 7EB
TEL: WOOLACOMBE (0271) 870333   FAX: (0271) 870890

An Edwardian seaside hotel overlooking Morte Bay.

On the outskirts of Woolacombe, well away from any height-of-summer madness, Watersmeet Hotel looks, and is, rather grand. Its lounge runs the entire length of the ground floor, offering spectacular views over the rocky foreshore to the sandy beaches beyond. The elegant restaurant shares the views, and residents' dinner placings rotate past the windows to prevent any suspicions of favouritism. Spacious bedrooms mirror the elegance of the public rooms, the best obviously scooping the sea views. Because Woolacombe attracts lots of elderly visitors the restaurant features a traditional English menu as well as the main 'Bill of Fayre', which changes daily.

Brian and Pat Wheeldon produce a quarterly newsletter with details of bridge, painting and cookery weekends.

◑ *Open all year, exc Dec and Jan*

⤢ *From Barnstaple follow the A361 towards Ilfracombe for 8 miles. Turn left at the roundabout and follow signs to Mortehoe. Private car park*

🛏 *4 single, 9 twin, 9 double, 1 four-poster, 1 suite; all with bathroom/WC, TV, room service; hair-dryer on request; no tea/coffee-making facilities in rooms*

◈ *Restaurant, bar, 3 lounges, drying room, games room; conference facilities (max 30*

people residential and non-residential); tennis, heated swimming-pool at hotel, other sports nearby. Wheelchair access to hotel (1 step), 1 ground-floor bedroom

⊖ *No children under 8 in restaurant; no dogs; no smoking in restaurant*

▭ *Access, Amex, Visa*

£ *Single £47 to £79, twin/double/four-poster/suite £94 to £158 (rates inc dinner); deposit required. Set D £24.50. Special breaks available*

MOSEDALE CUMBRIA   MAP 4

Mosedale House   *𝓛* ❀

MOSEDALE, MUNGRISDALE, CUMBRIA CA11 0XQ
TEL: THRELKELD (07687) 79371

Modern comforts in a Victorian farmhouse on the quiet fringes of Cumbria.

Readers are deeply divided about Mosedale House. One reader found the atmosphere 'extremely unwelcoming' and another complained that main courses were 'thumped down on the table with a take-it-or-leave-it attitude'. A completely different experience was had by a reader from Surrey who found Lesley and Colin Smith to be 'genuinely warm', and by another who pointed out that the Smiths had been particularly good with their baby. Dinners too have provoked contrasting comments from 'everything was excellent' to 'pretty indifferent'.

The hotel is a traditional Victorian stone farmhouse with recently converted barns located at the very foot of Carrock Fell in the unspoilt north-east corner of the Lake District. The public rooms have mostly modern furniture against a more rustic background of bare stone walls. A branding-iron found at the time of the conversion hangs on the wall of the lounge and on the coffee table you may find a photo album chronicling the conversion of the barns. The small dining-room has a tiled fireplace and a beautifully carved bedding chest dating from 1699. A traditional dinner may be carrot soup, pork in cream, bread-and-butter pudding and cheese and biscuits. Mosedale House is unlicensed but there is an extensive list of alternative drinks or you could always bring your own wine.

Some of the bedrooms, all of which have been given animal names, have an understated rustic feel with whitewashed walls and exposed beams and pine furniture, The Owl, a fair-sized double, can be converted into a suite using the Hedgehog next door as a sitting-room. Ewe is a twin room which is suitable for wheelchair access and has a very large adapted bathroom. The Smiths' readiness to provide for people with special needs is refreshing and unusual in the context of a small guesthouse.

◐ *Open all year, exc Xmas*

⤵ *From Penrith take the A66 Keswick road for 9 miles and turn right at the sign for Mungrisdale/Caldbeck. The house is 3½ miles along this road on the left. Private car park*

🛏 *1 single, 2 twin, 2 double, 1 cottage room; all with shower/ WC, cottage room with bathroom/WC; TV, hair-dryer in all rooms*

◇ *Dining-room, lounge, drying room; fishing, golf, other sports nearby. Wheelchair access to hotel, dining-room and WC, 1 ground-floor bedroom specially equipped for disabled people*

⊖ *No smoking*

▭ *None accepted*

£ *Single £19, single occupancy of twin/double £25, twin/double £23 to £46, family room/suite £52 to £63, self-catering cottage £175 to £235 per week; deposit required. Set D £11 (7pm). Special breaks available*

MOTCOMBE WILTSHIRE   **MAP 9**

Coppleridge Inn ☆

MOTCOMBE, SHAFTESBURY, DORSET SP7 9HW
TEL: SHAFTESBURY (0747) 51980   FAX: (0747) 51858

A well-modernised rural inn with restaurant and rooms.

There are not many inns that advertise amongst their facilities a hairdresser and a bottle bank – but, judging by the Saturday lunchtime we visited, the inn was busy enough to make good use of the last amenity. The restored seventeenth-century farmhouse stands on a back road in rural Dorset, in tranquil open countryside looking out towards Shaftesbury and the Blackmoor Vale. Ten new bedrooms facing a central courtyard have been converted from the old dairy; the hairdressing unit and conference and function facilities are part of the old barn. The bedrooms are spacious and freshly decorated. They all have country views (though some may include the country car park). The *en-suite* bathrooms have decent baths, bidets and separate shower cabinets.

The main house has been modernised and lightened with cream walls, new wood and contemporary fabrics, but it still has a traditional, country feel. Various rooms, in which a good range of bar food is served, link through into an à la carte restaurant that looks out on to the beer garden and all-weather tennis courts. There is a wide choice of daily specials such as moules marinière, breast of guinea-fowl stuffed with pâté in madeira sauce, and brill fillet with scallops and Noilly Prat. There is also a good-value three-course bistro menu. Traditional beers are on sale and the wines come from local merchants.

One drawback is that there is no private lounge for residents. The room referred to as the lounge, with high settle seating, flagged floor, open hearth and corner TV, is really the 'snug'. There is, however, lots of space outside for children to play in, and the hotel also offers membership of the local sports centre. Riding and clay pigeon shooting are available nearby, and there are some wonderful walks.

◗ Open all year

⤢ From Shaftesbury take the B3081 towards Gillingham. Take a right turn to Motcombe, 50 yards after the flyover. Go through the village and turn left to Mere. The inn is 200 yards on the left. Private car park

⇌ 4 twin, 4 double, 2 family rooms; all with bathroom/WC, exc 1 double with shower/WC; TV, room service, hair-dryer, mini-bar, baby-listening in all rooms

◇ 2 restaurants, bar, lounge, function room; hairdressing available; conference facilities (max 70 people non-residential, 10 residential); tennis at hotel, fishing, golf, other sports nearby. Wheelchair access to hotel, restaurant and WC (F), 10 ground-floor bedrooms

⊖ No dogs in restaurant or unaccompanied in bedrooms

▭ Access, Amex, Visa

£ Single occupancy of twin/double £38, twin/double £60, family room from £70. Bar meals; set L, D £10; alc L, D £17. Special breaks available

---

MOULSFORD-ON-THAMES OXFORDSHIRE   **MAP 9**

Beetle & Wedge

MOULSFORD-ON-THAMES, OXFORDSHIRE OX10 9JF
TEL: CHOLSEY (0491) 651381   FAX: (0491) 651376

A riverside hotel in a picturesque setting.

At the end of a cul-de-sac beside the River Thames is the Beetle & Wedge, a large Victorian red-brick house with views across the river to surrounding water meadows; the garden has a terrace and lawns that lead down to the river bank, where a barge is moored. Once the home of Jerome K. Jerome, author of *Three Men in a Boat*, the hotel is now well-established and is popular for its food. You can eat either in the formal dining-room or in the more relaxed, busy Boathouse, with its stone-flagged floor and high beamed ceiling, where you'll find a good variety of dishes from pea and ham soup to lemon sole with prawns and a chive sauce and a selection of dishes that are grilled 'from the fire'. In good weather you can eat on the terrace.

The Smiths have reduced the number of bedrooms to ten spacious ones, carpeted in dark blues or turquoise and with pastel-sponged walls enlivened by stencilling, some antiques and pale and floral fabrics. Some of the bathrooms have cast-iron baths.

◑ *Open all year, exc 25 Dec; 1 restaurant closed Sun, Mon eves*

⚡ *On river; Moulsford is 8 miles north-west of Reading. Private car park*

🛏 *4 twin, 4 double, 1 four-poster, 1 suite (some rooms in annexe); all with bathroom/WC, TV, room service, hair-dryer, trouser press, baby-listening*

◈ *2 restaurants, bar, lounge, conservatory; drying facilities; conference facilities (max 50 people non-residential, 10*

residential); fishing, water sports at hotel, other sports nearby; babysitting on request. Wheelchair access to hotel (ramp), restaurant and WC (unisex), 2 ground-floor bedrooms

⊖ *Dogs by arrangement only; no smoking in bedrooms*

▭ *Access, Amex, Diners, Visa*

£ *Twin/double/four-poster £85 to £95, suite £125. Sun L £25; alc L, D £20 to £40. Special breaks available*

MULLION CORNWALL　　　　　　　　　　　　　　**MAP 10**

Polurrian Hotel

MULLION, HELSTON, CORNWALL TR12 7EN
TEL: MULLION (0326) 240421　FAX: (0326) 240083

A beautifully situated family-holiday hotel with extensive leisure facilities.

Perched on a clifftop in a Area of Outstanding Natural Beauty and surrounded by National Trust coastline, Polurrian Hotel turns its Edwardian face away from guests who have to creep up on it from its less exciting rear. What a joy, therefore, to walk into reception and glimpse the amazing sea views straight ahead through the lounge windows. Similarly pleasing views are on offer to diners on the seaward side of the elegant restaurant, although sadly some have to settle for a car park view; table d'hôte menus change daily and feature some unexpectedly un-English dishes like curried eggs on a bed of pilaff rice alongside more standard meat dishes.

Even-numbered bedrooms have the sea views, odd numbers the car park, although all are comfortably fitted out with pleasant modern furnishings; Room 62 has a small four-poster and sunken bath, Room 86 a double bed set at an oblique angle to the door and an adjoining skylit twin for children.

Since the Polurrian is very much a family-holiday hotel it has an excellent leisure club on the other side of the car park. There's also a coffee area, a children's playroom with toys, and a games room.

◑ *Closed Nov to end Mar*

↗ *Follow the A3083 to the Lizard and after 6 miles turn right on to the B3296 to Mullion. Pass through the village and follow signs to Mullion Cove. Pass the cricket field and take the Polurrian road to the right. Private car park*

🛏 *3 single, 17 twin, 10 double, 5 four-poster, 1 suite; all with bathroom/WC, exc 2 singles; TV, room service, baby-listening in all rooms; no tea/coffee-making facilities in rooms*

◈ *Restaurant, bar, 2 lounges, snooker room, drying room; conference facilities (max 80 people non-residential, 40 residential); tennis, sauna/solarium, heated swimming-pool, gym, spa bath, squash, croquet and putting at hotel. Wheelchair access to hotel and restaurant, 9 ground-floor bedrooms*

⊖ *No dogs in public rooms*

▭ *Access, Amex, Diners, Visa*

£ *Single £32 to £76, twin/double £104 to £172, four-poster £96 to £164, family room £104 to £172, suite £116 to £184 (rates inc dinner); deposit required. Bar lunches; set L £13, D £21. Special breaks available*

MUNGRISDALE CUMBRIA   **MAP 4**

Mill Hotel

MUNGRISDALE, NR PENRITH, CUMBRIA CA11 0XR
TEL: THRELKELD (07687) 79659

Hearty dinners and a relaxed atmosphere in an unspoilt part of the Lakes.

The area around Blencathra in the north-eastern part of the Lake District is one of the least touristy and commercialised of the whole region, making it an ideal spot for walkers or those wishing simply to get away from it all – a perfect place, therefore, to come across a hotel like the Mill, with its adjoining whitewashed cottages, which has developed a reputation for its hearty dinners. (Do not confuse it with the similarly named pub next door.)

The inscription over the fireplace in the main lounge dates the original miller's cottage at 1651 and the low ceiling with its exposed beams is a further testament to its antiquity. The furnishings, though, are mostly contemporary with soft pink and green floral pattern sofas and small polished wooden coffee tables, and there is a real log fire for you to toast your toes at in more inclement weather. The paintings on the walls are all originals and Richard and Eleanor Quinlan have invested in the talents of many local artists. The oils and watercolours feature in the bedrooms, too, all of which are furnished in a neat and restrained manner.

Richard is blunt about what he sees as the hotel's paramount attraction: 'People come here for the food.' Eleanor's menu has a narrow choice but there is a vegetarian option. The starter might be tartlet of wild mushrooms with a hint of garlic and for the main course you could choose between casserole of venison with juniper berries and baked avocado with chilli, tomato and cheese. The five desserts on offer may include Grand Marnier parfait with purée of mango. One guest still found room for a spot of tea on returning each afternoon to be greeted with 'two pieces of newly baked gingerbread or other similar goodies'.

◑ Closed Nov to Feb

⤴ From Keswick, the Mill is 2 miles north on the A66. The sign for Mungrisdale is mid-way between Penrith and Keswick. Private car park

🛏 4 twin, 5 double; most with bathroom/WC, 1 with shower/WC; TV, room service, hair-dryer, baby-listening in all rooms

◇ Dining-room, 3 lounges, library, games room, drying room, conservatory; fishing in grounds, other sports nearby; babysitting

⊖ No wheelchair access; no dogs in public rooms; no smoking in dining-room

▭ None accepted

£ Single occupancy of twin/double £30 to £40, twin/double £56 to £70; deposit required. Set D £19.50 (7pm)

MYTHOLMROYD WEST YORKSHIRE　　　　　　　　　　**MAP 5**

Redacre Mill ☆

MYTHOLMROYD, HEBDEN BRIDGE, WEST YORKSHIRE HX7 5DQ
TEL: HALIFAX (0422) 885563

A beautifully restored and converted Victorian warehouse well placed for exploring Calderdale and Brontë Country.

Spending your holiday beside the Rochdale Canal might not seem like the most obvious thing to do with your precious leisure time, but sitting on the waterside terrace with a drink watching mallards and waterhens glide over the water while the sun goes down might change your mind. Redacre Mill, a little way out of the intriguing mill town of Hebden Bridge with its antique shops, steep slopes and characteristic piggy-backed 'flying freehold' houses, is an early-Victorian warehouse built to serve the cotton trade. It has been painstakingly restored by John and Judith Clegg, whose efforts extend to the canalside, with waterside lawns and landscaped gardens, and to the woodland slopes that rise behind, where new broadleaf planting is underway. Enough of the old features have been retained to convince one of the Mill's authenticity; the Winch Room still boasts the hoist that lifted cotton bales from loaded carts, while the Ashton Room has been panelled with wood salvaged from the old mill office. These, like the other comfortable bedrooms, are attractively and individually furnished with good old furniture, often oak or pine – not least in the Pine Room, which, with three windows on two sides, has the best views in the house. Décor is fresh, cottagey and meticulously maintained. All rooms have private facilities.

Guests congregate in the neat combined lounge/dining-room to relax on green leather upholstery, read books and enjoy views over the water. The set menus generally offer two options at each stage, except on Sundays when Yorkshire nationalism dictates that nothing can displace the traditional roast and its famous accompaniment (in fact served as a starter in Yorkshire).

◑ Open all year, exc Xmas and New Year

↗ Take the A646 Halifax to Burnley road. At Mytholmroyd, turn left by the fire station, cross the humpbacked bridge and turn 1st right. Private car park

⊨ 2 twin, 3 double; some with bathroom/WC, most with shower/WC; TV, room service, hair-dryer, baby-listening in all rooms

◈ Dining-room, lounge; fishing, golf, other sports nearby; babysitting

⊖ No wheelchair access; no dogs; no smoking

▭ Access, Visa

£ Single occupancy of twin/double £25 to £35; twin/double £45 to £50; deposit required. Set D £9.50. Special breaks available

---

NEAR SAWREY CUMBRIA   MAP 4

Ees Wyke

NEAR SAWREY, AMBLESIDE, CUMBRIA LA22 0JZ
TEL: HAWKSHEAD (05394) 36393

Top-notch country guesthouse in a superb location and with a gregarious hostess.

'The warm welcome from Margaret and her unfailing charm and humour made our short stay just like a country party. She had all the residents talking to each other – usually about the comfort, the views and, above all, the food.' 'The welcome given by John and Margaret Williams was really something – and as for entertainment, who needed any with Margaret there!' As these enthusiastic reports show, the success of Ees Wyke depends in no small measure on the gregarious Margaret Williams who runs the guesthouse with her husband John.

The large white three-storey house is just on the edge of Near Sawrey village, round the corner from Beatrix Potter's Hill Top Farm; indeed, the Potters used to stay at Ees Wyke when they first holidayed in the Lakes. The views from the house are superb – down sweeping pastures, across Esthwaite Water, and beyond to the Old Man of Coniston. You enter through the porticoed front door and Margaret is quickly on first-name terms as she shows you upstairs to the refreshingly spacious and uncluttered bedrooms. One on the top floor has a window let into the roof, making it very light but not the best room from which to appreciate the views.

Pre-dinner drinks are taken by the open fire in the cosy lounge and things soon warm up as Margaret makes the introductions. The house-party atmosphere continues as you drift next door to the dining-room. Meanwhile, Margaret flits in and out serving the entire dining-room on her own. John turns out a consistently good and varied menu, often with a choice of four main courses, with excellent vegetables and rich sauces. The dining-room comes into its own at breakfast as two of the walls have generous windows, making the most of the views.

- **◑** *Closed Jan and Feb*
- **↗** *1 mile to the west of Far Sawrey between Lake Windermere and Esthwaite Water. Private car park*
- **⇌** *3 twin, 5 double; some with bathroom/WC, most with shower/WC; TV, hair-dryer in all rooms*
- **◈** *Dining-room, 2 lounges, drying room; fishing, golf, other sports nearby. Wheelchair access to hotel (1 step), dining-room and 1 ground-floor bedroom*
- **⊖** *No children under 8; no dogs in public rooms; no smoking in dining-room*
- **▭** *None accepted*
- **£** *Twin/double £68 to £72; deposit required. Set D £12 (7.30pm). Special breaks available*

Pipps Ford

NEEDHAM MARKET, SUFFOLK IP6 8LJ
TEL: CODDENHAM (0449 79) 208 FAX: (0449 79) 561

A welcoming farmhouse in beautiful countryside – ideal for an overnight stop to break a journey or for a longer stay.

At Pipps Ford it's hard to believe that you are only a minute away from the heavy lorries and incessant stream of cars that rumble up the A45. The rambling sixteenth-century farmhouse is hidden in a hollow beside the River Gipping, an Area of Outstanding Natural Beauty; you can walk along the towpath as far as Ipswich or Stowmarket, fish from the banks, canoe or play tennis. Alternatively, you can simply enjoy the environment of a loved family home and calm retreat. Raewyn Hackett-Jones, quietly spoken and with a gentle sense of humour, has been running this guesthouse for over 15 years and has gradually extended the business into outhouses and stable blocks. The patchwork quilt you may find on your bed is her own work and she has designed each room. Named after flowers, the rooms are uniformly comfortable and interesting; for example, Hollyhock is beamed, with a four-poster bed and displays of fans and stencilled bows on the walls, while Morning Glory has a particularly large bathroom.

Dinners are usually communal and served either in a vine-covered conservatory or in a more formal dining-room. Ingredients are always fresh and, with advance warning, Raewyn provides interesting vegetarian dishes as well as main courses such as fillet of beef or roast pheasant. Traditionalists will enjoy the desserts: summer puddings, jam roly-polys and sherry trifles are favourites and home-made ice-creams a speciality. Breakfast is a particular feature: you can choose from farmhouse, health food or continental. Raewyn's ways with eggs include coddled, baked, overturned, ox-eye – and even heart-shaped eggs for honeymooners.

◑ *Closed mid-Dec to mid-Jan; dining-room closed Sun eve*

↗ *Follow private road off roundabout where A140 meets A45. Private car park*

🛏 *3 twin, 2 double, 1 four-poster (some rooms in annexe); all with bathroom/WC, hair-dryer*

◈ *2 dining-rooms, 3 lounges, conservatory; conference facilities (max 25 people non-residential); fishing, tennis,*

swimming-pool at hotel, other sports nearby. Wheelchair access to hotel and 4 ground-floor bedrooms partially equipped for disabled people

⊖ *No children under 5; no dogs; no smoking in bedrooms*

▭ *None accepted*

£ *Single occupancy of twin/double £30 to £38, twin/double/four-poster £56 to £66; deposit required. Set D £17.50 (7.15pm)*

NETHERFIELD EAST SUSSEX   **MAP 8**

Netherfield Place

COUNTY HOTEL OF THE YEAR

BATTLE, EAST SUSSEX TN33 9PP
TEL: BATTLE (0424) 774455

A fine Georgian-style country house boasting superb food and impeccable service.

The most striking feature of this hotel is the feeling of being looked after lavishly from start to finish under the overseeing eye of resident proprietors Michael and Helen Collier. Suitcases are transported from the car park to the red-brick building; mineral water and fresh fruit await in the bedrooms. Colours are tastefully mixed and matched to give each of the 14 rooms a plush individual feel. Courtenay (the rooms are named after knights) is a luxurious double room with its own terrace, sweeping delicate pink curtains and pink velvet Regency-style chairs. Pomeroy has a four-poster bed and murals in the bathroom. Some of the rooms are smaller and less elaborate, but they are comfortable none the less.

The lounge is furnished in dusty pinks and greens, the parquet floor covered with a thick pale green rug. Tasty, delicately prepared morsels are offered with aperitifs while guests reflect over the menu. The soup of wild mushroom and smoked bacon, followed by medallions of Ash-burnham venison in port sauce and then a dessert of apricot cheesecake proved to be a good choice on inspection.

The restaurant, very simple with oak-panelled walls and white table-cloths, has an air of tranquillity and service is attentive. Care is given to detail throughout the meal; a mixture of crudités and dips before the first course, a surprise grapefruit sorbet after the starter. The wine list is fun, with prices from around £5.50 for a half-bottle of house red to £110 for a half-bottle of Château d'Yquem.

◑ *Open all year, exc last week Dec to mid-Jan*

⤴ *Take A2100 northwards from Battle for ¾ mile. Take right-hand turn towards Netherfield; the hotel is 1½ miles on the left. Private car park*

🛏 *4 single, 3 twin, 6 double, 1 four-poster; all with bathroom/ WC, TV, room service, hair-dryer, baby-listening; no tea/ coffee-making facilities in rooms*

◈ *2 restaurants, bar, lounge, drying room, conservatory, sun lounge; conference facilities (max 14*

people residential, 80 non-residential); tennis at hotel, golf, riding, other sports nearby; babysitting. Wheelchair access to restaurant only

⊖ *No young children in restaurant eves; no dogs*

▭ *Access, Amex, Diners, Visa*

£ *Single £56, single occupancy of twin/double £65, twin/double £90 to £95, four-poster £120; deposit required. Set L £15, D £22.50; alc L, D £25. Special breaks available*

NETTLETON WILTSHIRE   MAP 9

Fosse Farmhouse ☆

NETTLETON SHRUB, NETTLETON, NR CHIPPENHAM, WILTSHIRE SN14 7NJ
TEL: CASTLE COMBE (0249) 782286   FAX: (0249) 783066

Immaculately restored country hotel with tea-rooms run by a mother-and-daughter team.

This small and remote Wiltshire farmhouse with a few outlying barns and sheds was a virtual ruin before Caron Cooper bought it and set to work licking it into shape. Ms Cooper used to deal in antiques and the house is full of Victoriana and French country pieces.

Downstairs, the main room is the dining-room. The tables are set with lace cloths and stand in front of an open hearth; plates are stored in the Welsh dresser. The menu offers a range of starters and puddings with one set main course, something like chicken in tarragon or duck with wild mushrooms. 'Good and wholesome,' says one report.

The furniture in the bedrooms in the main house is antique – expect stripped pine, linen sheets, pots of dried flowers and brilliant white walls. One reader was impressed by individual touches such as the china pot designed to hold earrings overnight.

Breakfast and tea are served in the barn across the yard, where tables stand on a cobbled floor. Three more bedrooms on the first floor are generally smaller than the others but are decorated to the same high standard. All our reports emphasise the charming and relaxed atmosphere of this hotel: 'It should appeal to anyone who likes the personal touch in beautiful surroundings.'

◑ Open all year

⤴ From Chippenham take the A420 towards Bristol. After 3 miles turn right on the B4039 for 4 miles. At the Gib take the 1st left, the farmhouse is 1 mile further along. Private car park

🛏 1 single, 1 twin, 3 double, 1 family room; some with bathroom/WC, some with shower/WC; TV, room service, hair-dryer in all rooms

◇ Dining-room, lounge, tea-room;

conference facilities (max 6 people residential); boules at hotel, fishing, golf, other sports nearby

⊖ No wheelchair access; no dogs or smoking in public rooms

▭ Access, Amex, Visa

£ Single £40 to £45, single occupancy of twin/double £55 to £60, twin/double £70 to £95, family room £110 to £120; deposit required. Set L £16, D £21.50. Special breaks available

---

NEW MILTON HAMPSHIRE MAP 9

Chewton Glen

CHRISTCHURCH ROAD, NEW MILTON, HAMPSHIRE BH25 6QS
TEL: NEW MILTON (0425) 275341 TELEX: 41456 CHGLEN G
FAX: (0425) 272310

Seamless luxury at a grand country hotel.

One of Britain's most distinguished hotels, Chewton Glen offers excellent standards of service and just about every kind of facility you could imagine (including a helicopter pad) with a price tag to match. Most of the bedrooms and public rooms overlook the ornamental gardens. You'll find on site a nine-hole golf course, one outdoor and two indoor tennis courts, two swimming-pools and a croquet lawn. As the management can't guarantee the weather, a host of indoor facilities are laid on too: the large, ozone-treated pool brings to mind a lofty Roman bath, with huge pillars outside, classical *trompe-l'oeil* frescoes on the walls and ceilings inside, and a tall window down to water level so that you can look over the glen while you're swimming.

Despite, or perhaps because of, all these demands on their attention, many of the guests seem quite happy to relax in the many spacious lounges, which are bathed in natural light and decorated with rich antiques and beautiful fabrics. The main part of the hotel was built in the early eighteenth century, but the exterior was substantially remodelled in red brick in the first decade of this century. Several sympathetic extensions have since been added, where most of the immaculately luxurious and tasteful bedrooms are now located. All have two washbasins in the bathroom and most have a bath and a separate shower cubicle. Even the least expensive rooms, in the main building, are fairly large and generally have appealing layouts and views.

The Marryat Room Restaurant offers a wide variety of outstanding treats, with generous provision for vegetarians and light eaters and an extensive wine list which is particularly good on clarets.

◑ *Open all year*

⤴ *From the A35 take the turning to Walkford and Highcliffe (ignore signs to New Milton). Go through Walkford, then take the second turning on the left down Chewton Farm Road. The hotel entrance is on the right. Private car park*

⇌ *45 twin/double, 13 suites (1 with four-poster); all with bathroom/ WC, TV, room service, hair-dryer, trouser press; no tea/ coffee-making facilities in rooms; mini-bar on request*

◈ *Restaurant, bar, 3 lounges, 2 conservatories; games room; conference facilities (max 180 people non-residential, 62 residential); golf, tennis, croquet, sauna, solarium, heated indoor and unheated outdoor swimming-pools, gym, treatment rooms, spa, Jacuzzi at hotel, other sports nearby. Wheelchair access to hotel and 12 ground-floor bedrooms*

⊖ *No children under 7; no dogs; no smoking in restaurant*

▭ *Access, Amex, Diners, Visa*

⊞ *Twin/double from £178, four-poster £345, suite from £298; deposit required. Continental B £9, cooked B £14; set L £24.50, D £39; alc L £30, D £45 (prices till Sept 93). Special breaks available*

Headland Hotel ☆

FISTRAL BAY, NEWQUAY, CORNWALL TR7 1EW
TEL: NEWQUAY (0637) 872211   FAX: (0637) 872212

Well-situated hotel with plenty of facilities for family holidays.

This year there seems to have been a concerted spate of letters to ensure a mention for the Headland. After inspection we've decided to include it this year. As you drive through Newquay it is hard to miss the place, a huge red-brick building standing alone on a headland, surrounded by the sea on three sides and with a golf course falling away on the fourth. Inside, the Headland is very much a family holiday hotel, with all the facilities you would expect: indoor and outdoor pools, a snooker room, a children's play area, baby-listening facilities and children's teas. There is even a basement room set aside for teenagers, with a jukebox and pool and table-tennis tables. The hotel offers wheelchair access, lifts, and bathrooms especially adapted for disabled guests.

Bedrooms all offer slightly different décor, although it is rarely very inspiring; most have baths and showers. The restaurant is large enough to accommodate an army, but its size doesn't detract from its elegance or its fine sea views. Daily table d'hôte menus are livened up by highlighting appropriate anniversaries; the dishes offered are more imaginative than might be expected in a resort hotel, and a note indicates that vegetables and sauces can be cooked to individual requirements. A staggering list of 600 wines even features a bottle of 1953 Rothschild for £335. Regulars praise the friendliness of the staff under the family management of John Armstrong.

◖ *Closed mid-Nov to late Dec, Jan to mid-Mar (exc New Year and Feb half-term)*

↗ *On approaching Newquay by the A30, follow signs to Fistral Beach. Private car park*

🛏 *11 single, 15 twin, 21 double, 1 four-poster, 40 family rooms, 16 family suites; most with bathroom/WC, some with shower/WC; TV, room service, baby-listening in all rooms; hair-dryer on request*

◇ *2 restaurants, bar, 5 lounges, TV room, drying room, garden room, games room, children's playroom, coffee shop; conference facilities (max 250 people non-residential); golf, tennis, water sports, sauna/*

solarium, heated swimming-pools (June to Sept), hot-air ballooning, putting, adventure playground and croquet at hotel, other sports nearby; babysitting. Wheelchair access to hotel (ramp), restaurant and WC (unisex), no ground-floor bedrooms but lift

⊖ *No smoking in eating areas*

▭ *Access, Amex, Visa*

£ *Single £33 to £50, single occupancy of twin/double £38 to £65, twin/double £66 to £80, four-poster £76 to £90, family room/family suite from £76 and £80; deposit required. Cooked B £2; snacks from £2; set D £15.50; alc D £17.50. Special breaks available*

NIDD NORTH YORKSHIRE   **MAP 5**

Nidd Hall

NIDD, HARROGATE, NORTH YORKSHIRE HG3 3BN
TEL: HARROGATE (0423) 771598   FAX: (0423) 770931

Sombre-looking company-run Georgian manor with gorgeous public rooms, a stable-block annexe and the inevitable leisure club.

Externally, Nidd Hall is rather forbidding; soaring columns, balustrades and a coat of arms suggest an air of unrelieved pomp. The most striking thing about this large hotel complex set in 45 acres a short drive from Harrogate is the magnificence of its public rooms, and more particularly their superb plaster ceilings in Adam-style colours and patterns. The best of these are to be found in the imposing library, the masculine cocktail bar and bright, portrait-rich restaurant. Colour schemes are cheerful – a vivid canary yellow in the octagonal domed entrance, green in the cocktail bar – and succeed in fending off any tendency towards heaviness in the atmosphere, though the rich red and gold main restaurant and the panelled Oak Room are appropriately dignified.

The menu has a traditional look: perhaps cream of wild mushroom and thyme soup, fillet of venison with pommes purées and an onion jus, and a warm apple and almond tart.

Bedrooms are more predictably the product of the modern country-house look, perfectly comfortable, with co-ordinating décor, good bathrooms and a sprinkling of antiques. Superior rooms in the old house are stuffed with character and fine furniture and are worth the supplement. The single we saw, on the other hand, was rather sad by comparison.

◑ *Open all year*

⤧ *5 miles north of Harrogate, just off the A61 Ripon road. Private car park*

🛏 *3 single, 14 twin, 15 double, 3 four-poster, 3 suites, 21 annexe rooms; all with bathroom/WC, TV, room service, hair-dryer, mini-bar, trouser press, baby-listening*

◈ *Restaurant, bar, lounge, library, games room; conference facilities (max 250 non-residential, 58 residential); fishing, tennis, sauna/solarium, heated swimming-pool, gym,*

squash at hotel; babysitting. Wheelchair access to hotel, restaurant and WC (M, F), no ground-floor bedrooms but lift

⊖ *No dogs; no smoking in restaurant*

▭ *Access, Amex, Diners, JCB, Visa*

£ *Single £95, single occupancy of twin/double £100 to £140, twin/double £120 to £150, four-poster £175 to £200, suite £175 to £230; deposit required. Cooked B £5.50; set L £13/£16, D £20/£25. Special breaks available*

NORTHAMPTON NORTHAMPTONSHIRE   MAP 9

Swallow Hotel

EAGLE DRIVE, NORTHAMPTON, NORTHAMPTONSHIRE NN4 0HW
TEL: NORTHAMPTON (0604) 768700   FAX: (0604) 769011

V. 'l-run, modern, business-orientated hotel with good-sized rooms and refreshingly different décor.

Signs from the motorway direct you to Blackmills Hotel, but don't let this confuse you for Swallow Hotel is one and the same place. Built at the end of 1986 and one of the newest members of the Swallow chain, this hotel is a red-brick low-rise with 122 bedrooms, a complex of conference rooms and a sprawling car park usually full of company cars. Five minutes from the M1, and bordered on two sides by a golf course, it's not surprising the Swallow is popular with business executives; another reason might be the hotel's striking interior. In the lobby, Japanese-style black leather sofas with plain red cushions and tall spindly plants in pebble-filled pots are an unpredictable introduction to décor that turns out to be far from bland. An open-plan lounge with low square sofas in orange and grey continues the high-tech feel, and tall windows opening out on to a terrace make the public rooms light and spacious. Springs Restaurant, with its trellises and greenery, has a café feel and serves food all day; Spires, an octagonal room with glass partitions prettily etched with towers and steeples, is more elegant and formal. A typical choice from the à la carte menu might be avocado and crab mousse, fillet of pork Calvados and a dessert from the trolley. To work this off there is a leisure club with gym and steam room as well as a swimming-pool.

A continuous programme of refurbishment keeps the bedrooms up to scratch, though compared with the public rooms they are quite standard. Light modern fabrics, plenty of space and well-equipped, fully tiled bathrooms are the norm; executive rooms are slightly plusher. Cheerfulness and efficiency are the trademarks of a huge team of staff who keep it all running smoothly.

◑ *Open all year*

⤷ *Leave the M1 at Junction 15 and follow signs for Brackmills; the hotel is 3 miles from the motorway and 1 mile from the centre of Northampton. Private car park*

🛏 *51 single, 40 twin, 23 double, 8 suites; all with bathroom/WC, TV, room service, hair-dryer, mini-bar, trouser press, baby-listening*

◈ *2 restaurants (1 with air-conditioning), bar, lounge; conference facilities (max 220 people non-residential, 120*

residential); sauna/solarium, heated swimming-pool, gym at hotel, other sports nearby; babysitting. Wheelchair access to hotel, restaurant and WC (unisex), 56 ground-floor bedrooms, 4 specially equipped for disabled people

⊖ *No dogs in public rooms*

▭ *Access, Amex, Diners, Visa*

£ *Single £88, single occupancy of twin/double £88, twin/double £99, suite £125. Set L £13.50, D £17.50; alc L, D £20 to £50. Special breaks available*

NORTH BOVEY DEVON   MAP 10

Blackaller Hotel ☆

NORTH BOVEY, NR CHAGFORD, DEVON TQ13 8QY
TEL: CHAGFORD (0647) 40322

A converted woollen mill in a delightful setting beside the River Bovey.

Since taking over seventeenth-century Blackaller 18 months ago, Hazel Phillips and Peter Hunt have refurbished it from top to bottom; the immaculate interior now matches the peerless white exterior, with its picnic tables on the lawn and soaring pine trees. Peter is a keen ornithologist, and everything, from the Dipper Bar to the bedrooms, is named after a bird to be seen in the garden. Pine floorboards take over from the hall flagstones in the small dining-room that faces on to the bar. Beyond a huge stone fireplace the dining-room overlooks the garden; the overall effect is of lots of pink and pine, with rugs piled one on top of another, a big grandfather clock and polished pine tables. Hazel describes her own cooking as 'a bit robust', with main courses drawing heavily on fish, venison, duck and pheasant casseroles; there is always something for vegetarians too. Peter looks after the desserts; if the home-made biscuits are anything to go by, they should be a treat. The pine effect continues in the bedrooms, all with fresh flowers. Only Robin lacks a garden view, but compensates with a particularly large bathroom.

Peek into the sheds when you park your car and you may find four pet Jacob sheep in residence. Blackaller comes highly recommended by readers, a conclusion we heartily endorse.

◑ Open all year, exc Jan

↗ Take the North Bovey road (B3212) from Moreton-hampstead. Private car park

🛏 1 single, 1 twin, 3 double, 1 annexe room; all with bathroom/WC, TV, room service, hair-dryer; baby-listening on request

◈ Dining-room, bar, lounge, drying room; conference facilities (max 20 people non-residential, 6 residential); fishing, riding at hotel, other sports nearby

⊖ No wheelchair access; no dogs in public rooms; no smoking in bedrooms

▭ None accepted

£ Single £23 to £24, single occupancy of double £25 to £30, twin/double £48 to £50, annexe room £48 to £50; deposit required. Set D £13 to £16

NORTH NEWINGTON OXFORDSHIRE　　　　MAP 9

La Madonette ☆　　　　*𝒮𝓛*

NORTH NEWINGTON, BANBURY, OXFORDSHIRE OX15 6AA
TEL: BANBURY (0295) 730212

A rural guesthouse with simple rooms in an old mill house.

Patti Ritter originally started La Madonette as a restaurant and now runs it as a guesthouse offering bed and breakfast only. A couple of miles out of Banbury in the midst of pasture and arable farmland, the old grey stone seventeenth-century house sits snugly in a dip beside a stream with a line of poplars overlooking the garden. Formerly a miller's house, it stands beside the old mill buildings, now converted into three small self-catering apartments. There is a largish garden and an outdoor pool for the use of guests. The predominant colour in the lounge and breakfast room is pink, which, in the former room, contrasts with the deep-blue carpet and two blue sofas.

There are five bedrooms, including two family rooms, and a four-poster room with a corner bath. Décor is a mix of old pine furnishings and simple soft armchairs, a pot plant or two and fresh white duvet covers.

◑ Open all year

↗ Leave the M40 and follow signs to Chipping Norton until Banbury Cross. Turn right on to the B4035 and follow the road for 1½ miles. Turn right for North Newington and the hotel is ½ mile on the left. Private car park

🛏 1 twin, 1 double, 1 four-poster, 2 family rooms, 3 self-catering cottages; four-poster with bathroom/WC, most with shower/WC; TV, room service, hair-dryer, baby-listening in all rooms

◈ Bar, lounge; conference facilities (max 12 people non-residential, 5 residential); unheated swimming-pool at hotel, fishing, golf, other sports nearby; babysitting

⊖ No wheelchair access; no dogs

▭ Access, Visa

£ Single occupancy of twin/double £32, twin/double £42, four-poster £55, family room £45 to £55, cottage £120 to £210 per week; deposit required. Special breaks available

---

NORTON SHROPSHIRE   **MAP 5**

Hundred House Hotel

BRIDGNORTH ROAD, NORTON, NR SHIFNAL, TELFORD, SHROPSHIRE
TF11 9EE
TEL: NORTON (0952 71) 353   FAX: (0952 71) 355

An inn full of character, with romantic bedrooms and a curious garden.

Henry and Sylvia Phillips continue to run Hundred House in inimitable style. In fact, it is a blend of two styles, for Sylvia is one with the passion for patchwork and herbs, while Henry favours waistcoats and *objets trouvés* – his latest find being the pair of doors from a temperance hall which lead out of (but not into) the bar. Hundred House looks, and is, old. The bar is surrounded by a maze of sitting spaces, hung with dried herbs. The restaurant area is separated by a set of altar rails. Upstairs, it is a different world – here, the sweetly romantic reigns. Bedrooms, with flounces of cottagey fabrics, each have their own swing for you to pose on, and are hung with interesting paintings (by Sylvia again) and stocked with curious old pieces of furniture. Around the back, Sylvia's garden features 'constructs' of salvaged stone, pergolas, climbing roses and a pond. The herbs are even further away, as is the donkey which pulls the inn's brewer's dray. This year, son Stuart has joined the enterprise, and will add his own French/Italian style in the kitchen.

◑ Open all year

↗ From the M6 take the M54 north of Birmingham. Exit at Junction 4 and follow signs to Kidderminster (A442). The hotel is in the village of Norton. Private car park

🛏 1 twin, 9 double; all with bathroom/WC, TV, room service, hair-dryer, baby-listening

◈ Restaurant, bar, drying room; conference facilities (max 20 people non-residential, 10 residential)

⊖ No wheelchair access; no dogs in bar and restaurant and by arrangement only in bedrooms

▭ Access, Visa

£ Single occupancy of twin/double £59, twin/double £69 to £88; deposit required. Alc L £15 to £20, D £18 to £25

NOTTINGHAM NOTTINGHAMSHIRE   **MAP 5**

Rutland Square

RUTLAND SQUARE, ST JAMES'S STREET, NOTTINGHAM, NOTTINGHAMSHIRE
NG1 6FJ
TEL: NOTTINGHAM (0602) 411114   FAX: (0602) 410014

A large, slickly run, city-centre hotel close to the castle.

Follow directions for the castle and you'll find Rutland Square Hotel
quite easily, just 50 yards away. This ageless red-brick building with
square Georgian-style windows was once a warehouse, but there is little
evidence of that now. The interior is equally difficult to define, though
muted colours and rich fabrics are the norm throughout, with decorative
plasterwork ceilings, marble floors and plenty of comfortable seating.
The split-level restaurant has a conservatory feel created by its glass
ceiling and trellis mural decorated with birds and butterflies, and the
wide-ranging à la carte menu is chiefly modern English. One reader
wrote to commend the 'good, cheerful and quite informal service'.

Variations in the size of the smartly decorated bedrooms – and of the
beds – are not wholly reflected in the price, so ask for a large one. Lime
oak furniture and flowery padded quilts are standard and rooms are well-
equipped with modern bathrooms. Parking is at the NCP next door, for
which the hotel picks up the tab.

◑ Open all year

⤢ Leave the M1 at Junction 25 and
take the A52 to Nottingham.
Follow signs to Nottingham
Castle. Private car park (limited)

🛏 73 single, 9 twin, 20 double, 1
four-poster, 1 suite; all with
bathroom/WC, TV, room service,
hair-dryer, mini-bar, baby-
listening

◈ 2 restaurants, bar, 2 lounges;
some public areas air-
conditioned; conference facilities
(max 350 people non-residential,
100 residential); golf, tennis,
other sports nearby. Wheelchair
access to hotel, restaurant and
WC (disabled), no ground-floor
bedrooms but lift

⊖ No dogs in restaurant and bar

▭ Access, Amex, Diners, Visa

£ Single £53, twin/double £59,
four-poster £95, suite £120;
deposit required. Continental B,
cooked B £7; set L £5, D
£12.50/£16.50; alc L £11.50
to £12. Special breaks
available

NUNNINGTON NORTH YORKSHIRE   **MAP 3**

Ryedale Lodge

STATION ROAD, NUNNINGTON, NORTH YORKSHIRE YO6 5XB
TEL: NUNNINGTON (04395) 246; changing to (0439) 748246 in early 1994

Mixed reports on this rather isolated converted railway station an easy drive from the tourist honeypot of Helmsley.

There are other hotels in this book that flaunt their previous incarnations more openly, and if you're looking for platform signs, whistles and guards' caps recalling the glory days of the LNER, this is not the place for you. Come instead for the peaceful splendour of the setting amid open countryside and the relaxed atmosphere – though this proved too casual for one visitor, who was aggrieved to find no one to greet him and was eventually checked in by someone in 'trainers and T-shirt, which do not present the image of a well-run establishment'. There were no such lapses when we inspected.

Public rooms display a vigorous modern good taste. The lounge is darker and less cottagey than is usual in country hotels, being enveloped in a blue stippled-effect wallpaper and furnished with lots of sofas in bold modern fabrics; its length and shape betrays its station origins. The main restaurant is rather formal, with crimson wallpaper, polished wood tables and a sideboard laden with silver. Large windows overlook the lounge on one side and, on the other, the Platform Restaurant – a more informal garden-style conservatory where breakfast is served. There is a reasonable choice on the set dinner menu, and one correspondent praised the 'good portions, excellent duck and steak and plenty of vegetables'. Our inspector enjoyed superb Paris brown mushrooms stuffed with chicken mousse in a red wine reduction, cream of tomato soup with orange and basil, and a concoction of layered sole and salmon. Desserts included a delicious chocolate marquise.

Bedrooms divided the correspondents. One judged his 'excellent', while another thought the room 'fairly spartan' for the price. Certainly the décor leans towards the corporate, but the rooms are spacious.

◑ Open all year

↗ One mile west of Nunnington, towards Oswaldkirk. Pass Nunnington Hall on the left, and after 400 yards turn right at the crossroads. Pass a church on your right, and the hotel is 1 mile further on the right. Private car park

🛏 2 twin, 4 double, 1 suite; all with bathroom/WC, TV, room service, hair-dryer, mini-bar, trouser press, baby-listening

◇ Restaurant, lounge, conservatory; conference facilities (max 11 people non-residential, 9 residential); fishing, golf, other sports nearby. Wheelchair access to hotel (no steps), restaurant and WC (unisex), 1 ground-floor bedroom

⊖ No dogs; no smoking in restaurant

▭ Access, Visa

£ Single occupancy of twin/double £49 to £53, twin/double £79 to £83, suite £85 to £91; deposit required. Set D £27. Special breaks available

See our selection of what we consider to be the best hotels in various counties in Hotels of the Year *(page 16).*

Barnsdale Lodge

THE AVENUE, NR EXTON, RUTLAND WATER, NR OAKHAM, LEICESTERSHIRE
LE15 8AH
TEL: OAKHAM (0572) 724678   FAX: (0572) 724961

*A thoughtfully planned business-orientated hotel that
accommodates other guests very well too.*

Photographs in reception show the ruin that Robert Reid took over in
1989 and converted to a slickly run business-orientated hotel. The
limestone farmhouse – about half a mile from the shores of Rutland
Water reservoir – has been extended to accommodate nine bedrooms
based on an Edwardian theme, with antique and reproduction furniture,
rich fabrics, thick quilts, and extra goodies such as a tin of Huntley &
Palmer biscuits. Bathrooms are luxurious and well-equipped. With a
further eight bedrooms in the stable block and conference facilities in the
barn, it's an arrangement that works well.

Four eating areas range from a rustic pub where you have a choice of
seven cheeses for your ploughman's lunch – including Rutland, made
with beer, chives and garlic – through to the formal dining-room with
smart stripy walls and immaculate white tablecloths. The dinner menu
includes Scottish salmon, Dublin Bay prawns, Rutland trout basted in
chestnut butter and a good range of steaks; baked apple and coconut tart
and Edwardian tipsy cake feature among the puddings.

◑ Open all year

🔀 On the A606 Oakham to
Stamford road, 3 miles east of
Oakham. Private car park

🛏 4 single, 6 twin, 4 double, 1
four-poster, 2 family rooms;
most with bathroom/WC, some
with shower/WC; TV, room
service, hair-dryer, baby-listening
in all rooms

◈ 3 restaurants, bar, lounge, drying
room; conference facilities (max
200 people non-residential, 25

residential); golf, water sports,
other sports nearby; babysitting.
Wheelchair access to hotel
(ramp), restaurant and WC
(unisex), 4 ground-floor
bedrooms

⊖ No dogs in some public rooms

▦ Access, Amex, Diners, Visa

£ Single £50, single occupancy of
twin/double £55, twin/double
£70, four-poster/family room
£80. Bar lunches £2 to £9; alc L,
D £20. Special breaks available

The Boultons

4 CATMOSE STREET, OAKHAM, LEICESTERSHIRE LE15 6HW
TEL: OAKHAM (0572) 722844   FAX: (0572) 724473

A town hotel where large, well-equipped rooms cater unusually well for solo travellers.

The Boultons sits on a busy junction on the main road into Oakham, an ancient market town five minutes' drive from Rutland Water. Courting business trade is the name of the game for Emad Saleeb and his staff, and the seventeenth-century coaching-inn was vastly extended in 1990 to accommodate new bedrooms and several conference suites in a red-brick block to the rear. The new rooms are comfortably kitted out with pine furniture and smart modern wallpaper. Half of the rooms in the old part of the inn (where there are low ceilings and beams) are well-equipped singles. The public rooms have the atmosphere of a pub, with a heavily patterned carpet, spindle-back chairs and pew benches.

Le Jardin restaurant is informal and does indeed look out on to a small garden. When it is busy with a function or simply fully booked, staff are friendly and flexible enough to bring you a full-blown restaurant meal in the bar, where you can also obtain bar snacks. The dinner menu, which includes chicken wings, poached fillet of trout, chilli con carne and roast rack of lamb, is pretty standard fare.

◐ *Open all year*

▱ *Centrally located in Oakham; the entrance to the private car park is in South Street*

🛏 *7 single, 4 twin, 12 double, 1 four-poster, 1 family room; most with bathroom/WC, 2 with shower/WC; TV, room service, hair-dryer, trouser press, baby-listening in all rooms*

◈ *Restaurant, bar, lounge, drying room; conference facilities (max 60 people non-residential, 25 residential); water sports, tennis, other sports nearby. Wheelchair access to hotel (1 step) and restaurant, 8 ground-floor bedrooms, 1 specially equipped for disabled people*

⊖ *No dogs in public rooms*

▭ *Access, Amex, Diners, Visa*

£ *Single £40 to £65, twin/double £55 to £70, four-poster £80, family room from £65. Set L £8.50, D £14; alc L, D £20; bar meals*

ODIHAM HAMPSHIRE   **MAP 9**

George Hotel

100 HIGH STREET, ODIHAM, NR BASINGSTOKE, HAMPSHIRE RG25 1LP
TEL: BASINGSTOKE (0256) 702081   FAX: (0256) 704213

A traditional inn which has been extensively refurbished without losing its rustic character.

The cradle of the Royal Veterinary Society, Odiham is set in fertile farming land yet makes an ideal stop-over just a mile from the M3 near Basingstoke. In among the pretty red bricks and tiles of its High Street, the George Hotel offers brisk, helpful service and a well-maintained choice of accommodation.

The façade is Georgian but the inn dates back to 1540 and retains much of its Tudor oak panelling, most notably in Cromwell's restaurant: a huge, beautifully carved fireplace dominates the oak-beamed room, which is hung with horse brasses and pink plates. Run-of-the-mill breakfasts are served here and, in the evening, an interesting menu of olde-English dishes. Food a cut above most pub grub is on offer in the popular back bar, which has a welcoming, lived-in feel: dried flowers, tankards and lethal agricultural implements hang from the oak beams.

Upstairs, winding creaky corridors connect the bedrooms, which have been thoroughly modernised and decorated in fresh colours and reproduction furniture. On a recent visit, our inspector found that the shower above the bath was inefficient and was troubled by structural noise from flues and fans; rooms in the converted stable block at the back may be less noisy, although they do face the hotel car park.

◑ *Open all year (accommodation closed over Xmas); restaurant closed Mon and Sun eves*

↗ *Leave the M3 at Junction 5 and take the Farnham road. Private car park*

🛏 *6 single, 2 twin, 8 double, 2 four-poster; all with bathroom/ WC, TV, room service, hair-dryer*

◈ *Restaurant, bar, lounge; meetings facilities (max 10 people residential and non-residential); golf, riding, other*

sports nearby. Wheelchair access to hotel (2 steps), restaurant and 6 ground-floor bedrooms

⊖ *No dogs in public rooms; 5 bedrooms are non-smoking*

▭ *Access, Amex, Diners, Visa*

£ *Single £62, single occupancy of twin/double £62, twin/double £72, four-poster £85; deposit required. Set L £13, D £13.50; alc D £15.50. Special breaks available*

OLDBURY WEST MIDLANDS   MAP 5

Jonathans' Hotel

COUNTY
HOTEL
OF THE
YEAR

16–24 WOLVERHAMPTON ROAD, OLDBURY, WARLEY, WEST MIDLANDS
B68 0LH
TEL: 021-429 3757   FAX: 021-434 3107

An innovative hotel with luxurious bedrooms and a variety of eating places.

Placed as it is on a busy junction, this hotel doesn't enjoy an ideal location – this doesn't really matter because Jonathans' is essentially an indoor experience. For West Midlanders Jonathans' has long been a venue for a good meal out, then in 1989 the two owners, Jonathans Bedford and Baker, expanded their business into a 30-room hotel, taking over adjoining buildings to do so. What we have now is an innovative collection of cafés, bars and restaurants in re-created Victorian streets where local businesses advertise in mock shopfronts and every square foot is crammed with Victorian paraphernalia. The effect is chaotic and exciting. Local people are enticed in for a £5 lunch from the Sherlock Holmes menu – which includes French onion soup, fish panache with prawn dumplings and chocolate fudge cake – while in the evenings diners come from afar for the more formal surroundings of the restaurant with its heavily patterned walls, and highly polished tables. With one eye on re-creating historical dishes with the emphasis on sauces and relishes, the menu includes chicken terrine with pickled lemons, jugged pheasant, Charles II syllabub and spotted dick.

The bedrooms are also crammed with Victoriana, and though they are crowded there's no skimping on luxury. Rich fabrics, dense flowery patterns, antiques and bric-à-brac exist happily with well-equipped bathrooms.

◑ Open all year; restaurant closed Sun eve

↗ Leave the M5 at Junction 2 or 3. The hotel is at the junction of the A456 and the A4123 towards Birmingham. Private car park

🛏 3 single, 10 double, 2 four-poster, 2 family rooms, 14 suites; all with bathroom/WC, TV, room service, hair-dryer, baby-listening; ironing facilities

◇ 3 restaurants, 4 bars, lounge, library, 2 conservatories, billiards room; conference facilities (max 150 people non-residential, 31 residential); fishing, golf, other sports nearby

⊖ No wheelchair access

▭ Access, Amex, Diners, Visa

£ Single £74, twin/double £89, four-poster/family room/suite £109; deposit required. Set L, £5, D £12.50; alc L, D from £25

OTLEY SUFFOLK   **MAP 8**

Otley House

COUNTY HOTEL OF THE YEAR

HELMINGHAM ROAD, OTLEY, IPSWICH, SUFFOLK IP6 9NR
TEL: HELMINGHAM (0473) 890253   FAX: (0473) 890059

A gorgeous country house run with Scandinavian flair.

Appreciative letters have flooded in about Otley House and its owners, Michael and Lise Hilton. This lovely seventeenth-century house with graceful Georgian additions seems to possess all the right qualities for a happy stay. One couple found their visit 'a wonderful and relaxing experience which we hope to repeat as soon as possible'. Frequently mentioned in letters is the tasteful furniture, and indeed as soon as you enter the wide hall polished antiques, a grandfather clock and large mirrors make an immediate impression. Generous vases of fresh flowers and mature house plants ensure the atmosphere is far from fuddy-duddy. Bedrooms, all different, are just as pleasing (one couple tell us they have so far slept in three out of the four rooms and liked them all). It is hard to single out a favourite: the most striking is the Burgundy Room, which carries off its strong colour because of its size, but if you prefer a more soothing décor try the Blue Room with its huge windows overlooking the garden.

Guests eat together at a long, glossy table in the dining-room, although there is a small Pembroke table if you prefer dinner à deux. Food also comes highly praised and, under Lise's influence, will often include Danish dishes such as marinated fillets of herrings with apples in a curry and apricot sauce as a starter or custard and almond cake as a pudding. After this, you can withdraw to the relaxing drawing-room or opt for a smoke and a game of billiards in the Billiard Room, where leather chesterfields and a log fire give the room the snugness (but not the exclusivity) of a gentleman's club.

◖ Closed 1 Nov to 1 Mar; restaurant closed Sun eve

↗ On the north side of Otley village, on the B1079. Private car park

🛏 2 twin, 1 double, 1 four-poster; all with bathroom/WC, TV, room service, hair-dryer; no tea/coffee-making facilities in rooms

◈ Dining-room, lounge, TV room, billiard room; fishing, golf, riding nearby

⊖ No wheelchair access; no children under 12; no dogs; smoking in billiard room only

▭ None accepted

£ Single occupancy of twin/double £34 to £38, twin/double £46 to £48, four-poster £50. Set D £15.50 (7.30pm)

OUNDLE NORTHAMPTONSHIRE   **MAP 5**

The Talbot

NEW STREET, OUNDLE, PETERBOROUGH, CAMBRIDGESHIRE PE8 4EA
TEL: OUNDLE (0832) 273621   FAX: (0832) 274545

An ancient Forte Heritage inn in a lovely market town – comfortable accommodation if not immaculately kept.

Oundle is a lovely little town of golden limestone buildings with lichen-covered roofs and a high street lined with coffee shops catering for parents of the pupils at the well-known public school. It grew up around a monastery whose inmates, in AD 638, founded a hostelry in the centre of town. Thirteen hundred years on that hostelry has evolved into the Talbot – decorative gables and stone-mullioned windows are seventeenth-century additions. The historical message is driven home by displays of muskets hanging on the wall in the bar, wood-panelling in the restaurant, the odd oil painting, and smoke-stained stone fireplaces throughout. The public bar and lounge have plenty of comfortable seating. Bedrooms are divided between the main building and a court-yard block, with the former having slightly more character if you enjoy crooked walls and low ceilings. All rooms are similarly kitted out with richly patterned quilted bedspreads, plenty of room to move around and modern well-equipped bathrooms. One reader reports that room service was poor and complains of not being shown to her room, and when we visited we found that some areas of the hotel were scruffy and needed attention, but while there's clearly some polishing to be done here the Talbot remains a comfortable hotel. The restaurant is open in the evenings only, with snacks in the bar at lunchtime. A typical 'Heritage' dinner menu includes cream of mushroom soup, braised lambs' liver and topside of English beef.

◐ *Open all year*

⤢ *In the centre of Oundle. Private car park*

🛏 *6 single, 9 twin, 20 double, 3 family rooms, 1 feature room; all with bathroom/WC, TV, room service, hair-dryer, baby-listening, trouser press*

◈ *Restaurant, bar/lounge, games room; conference facilities (max 120 people non-residential, 50*
residential); golf, other sports nearby; babysitting by arrangement

⊖ *No wheelchair access*

▭ *Access, Amex, Diners, Visa*

£ *Single £70, single occupancy of double £70, twin/double £80, feature room £95. Continental B £6, cooked B £8.50; set L £12, D £18; alc D £25. Special breaks available*

OXFORD OXFORDSHIRE   **MAP 9**

Cotswold House

363 BANBURY ROAD, OXFORD, OXFORDSHIRE OX2 7PL
TEL: OXFORD (0865) 310558

A modern guesthouse with good-quality accommodation and friendly hosts.

Jim and Anne O'Kane are enthusiastic hosts and obviously get a kick out of welcoming guests into their home, a modern house with latticed windows on the busy Banbury Road to the north of Oxford. Buses pass by around every 10 minutes and since parking is so difficult in the city centre you would be well advised to leave your car in the small car park at the front of the house if you do visit the dreaming spires. When our inspector visited a new breakfast room with some exposed stone and a varnished wooden floor had just been completed; there is now space for a lounge with large squashy seating to add to guests' comfort. Bedrooms are light and airy, spotless and well-equipped. There are fridges in bedrooms for fresh milk and guests' own drinks (wine glasses are thoughtfully provided). *En-suite* bathrooms have showers and large bottles of shampoo. If you want suggestions of trips out into the surrounding countryside, Jim has lots of ideas and will recommend pubs and restaurants along the way.

◐ *Open all year, exc Xmas and New Year*

⤢ *2 miles north of Oxford city centre on the A4260 Banbury*
Road, inside Oxford ring road. Private car park

🛏 *2 single, 1 twin, 2 double, 2 family rooms; all with shower/*

WC, TV, hair-dryer, fridge

 Breakfast room, lounge

 No wheelchair access; no children under 5; no dogs; no smoking

None accepted

Single £33 to £34, single occupancy of twin/double £40 to £47, twin/double £47 to £50

Old Parsonage

1 BANBURY ROAD, OXFORD, OXFORDSHIRE OX2 6NN
TEL: OXFORD (0865) 310210   FAX: (0865) 311262

A pricey but stylishly refurbished hotel in a historic building near the centre of Oxford.

The Old Parsonage is a mellow stone seventeenth-century building with a varied history. Completely renovated a few years ago under the ownership of Jeremy Mogford (who also owns the popular Browns Restaurant nearby), it has entered that small circle of good hotels in Oxford. The central focus of the hotel is the Parsonage Bar, approached through the stylish open-plan reception. Here cappuccinos, bottles of wine and light bistro-style meals are served by young staff in long green aprons; croustade of duck with green lentils and salad, hummus with ciabatta, lemon tart and treacle pud feature on the menu. The walls are covered with an interesting collection of paintings, prints and drawings, while furnishings are contemporary. A small, quiet lounge has a few boxed games and some photos detailing the history of the house.

Bedrooms have been carefully put together. Fresh modern checks and floral fabrics cover the sofas and beds; Victorian watercolours decorate the walls and pot plants and a few paperbacks in each room are a pleasing touch. Bathrooms are tiled in marble and have hot towel rails, power showers and good lighting.

Open all year

In the centre of Oxford, at the head of St Giles Street, adjacent to the church, where the Banbury and Woodstock roads meet. Private car park

 6 twin, 20 double, 4 suites; all with bathroom/WC, TV, room service, hair-dryer, mini-bar, baby-listening; trouser press and tea/coffee-making facilities on request

Air-conditioned dining-room/bar, lounge; golf, tennis, other sports nearby

No wheelchair access; no dogs in public rooms

Access, Amex, Diners, Visa

Single occupancy of twin/double £105, twin/double £135, suite £190; deposit required. Alc L £12, D £18. Special breaks available

Many hotels offer special rates for stays of a few nights or more. It is worth enquiring when you book.

Randolph Hotel

BEAUMONT STREET, OXFORD, OXFORDSHIRE OXI 2LN
TEL: OXFORD (0865) 247481   FAX: (0865) 791678

A long-time Oxford institution, now thoroughly refurbished.

The neo-Gothic building dating from the 1860s on a busy corner facing the Ashmolean Museum is now a luxurious city-centre hotel, owned by Forte. In mid-afternoon there is a constant bustle as visitors arrive for afternoon tea in the lobby lounge or the impressive vaulted drawing-room. High ceilings and elaborate plasterwork, wood panelling and stone-framed windows are complemented by rich maroon and green colour schemes and good-quality reproduction furniture. The Spires Restaurant in deep purple is adorned with the crests of various colleges and fresh flowers decorate the tables. As well as the dark green cocktail bar there is also a wine bar in the basement which is popular with students; it is open all afternoon and evening selling coffees, light meals and drinks and has its own entrance from the street.

Bedrooms have been decorated in the same rich colours as the public areas and have framed prints on the walls. Single rooms are a good size and smart new bathrooms are a great improvement on the Randolph's pre-refurbishment days.

◑ Open all year

⤢ In the centre of Oxford, opposite the Ashmolean Museum. Private car park

🛏 44 single, 22 twin, 35 double, 8 suites; all with bathroom/WC, TV, room service, hair-dryer, trouser press, baby-listening; mini-bar on request

◈ Restaurant, bar, 2 lounges, wine bar; conference facilities (max 300 people non-residential, 50 residential); golf, tennis, other sports nearby; babysitting. Wheelchair access to hotel (ramp), restaurant and WC (unisex), no ground-floor bedrooms but lift and 1 bedroom specially equipped for disabled people

⊖ No dogs in public rooms

▭ Access, Amex, Diners, Visa

£ Single £115, single occupancy of twin/double £125, twin/double £150, suite from £160. Continental B and cooked B £12.50; set L £15.50/£17.50; D £25; alc L, D £35. Special breaks available

---

Prices are what you can expect to pay in 1994, except where specified to the contrary. Many hoteliers tell us that these prices can be regarded only as approximations.

St Petroc's ☆

4 NEW STREET, PADSTOW, CORNWALL PL28 8EA
TEL: PADSTOW (0841) 532700

*A small, friendly hotel, with brightly coloured abstract paintings
and a tapas bar adding a touch of modernity.*

The tapas bar menu in the street outside offers the first suggestion that
there's more to this reasonably priced seventeenth-century hotel
perched above Padstow's one-way system than you would expect. The
modern mood set by the brilliantly coloured abstract paintings on the
hall's crisp white walls continues in the bar, where tapas are served in a
room full of bright, stripy canvases and stylish colonial chairs. The
Moors Restaurant is equally distinctive, its big black support posts
softened by colourful napkins, mirrors and plants, a piece of coloured
lace draped across the window subtly suggesting a fishing net; diners can
augment the fairly limited à la carte menu with items from the tapas bar,
and there's a delicious choice of ice-cream sundaes, too. Upstairs, the
lounge is more conventional, with comfortable chintzy chairs, a marble
fireplace and two huge mirrors. Smallish bedrooms have beamed ceilings, and several boast views of the Camel Estuary.

◑ Closed late Dec to Mar;
restaurant closed Sun and Wed
eves (exc at holiday times)

⤴ 50 yards from the central square
in Padstow. Car-park nearby
(overnight fee refunded by hotel)

🛏 2 single, 3 twin, 2 double, 2
family rooms, 1 suite; some with
bathroom/WC, some with
shower/WC, 3 public bathrooms;
TV, room service in all rooms;
hair-dryer on request

◈ Restaurant, bar, lounge; drying
facilities on request; conference
facilities (max 12 people
residential and non-residential);
fishing, golf, other sports nearby

⊖ No wheelchair access; no dogs;
no smoking in restaurant

▭ Access, Visa

£ Single £19 to £34, twin/double
£30 to £78, family room rate on
request; deposit required. Alc D
£15

Seafood Restaurant

RIVERSIDE, PADSTOW, CORNWALL PL28 8BY
TEL: PADSTOW (0841) 532485　FAX: (0841) 533344

*Popular harbourside restaurant with comfortable and stylish
rooms.*

Regardless of whether it is lunchtime or dinnertime, the Seafood
Restaurant is likely to be heaving with diners, happily tucking into

mussels and Helford oysters in a picture-packed dining-room that spills over into a conservatory stocked with vigorous greenery. When we inspected, chef Rick Stein was serving the grilled mackerel with a tasty Thai dressing of coriander, dill, lemon grass, lime juice and fish sauce; his fish soup is reputed to be particularly good. It would seem perverse to come here and not sample the seafood, but, just in case, each menu features a token non-fish dish. To wash it all down, there are 192 wines and a 'vintage port of the month' on the wine list.

Upstairs, the spacious bedrooms have stylishly bold but simple colour schemes and big, squashy armchairs to make up for the absence of a lounge. The best open on to balconies with views of the Camel Estuary. Tables for the restaurant's 7.30pm or 9.30pm sittings are automatically booked with room reservations unless you specify otherwise. Parking in Padstow is tricky, although a few bays of the public car park opposite the restaurant are reserved for its clients.

- ◐ Closed Xmas to early Feb; restaurant closed Sun eve
- ↗ On the quayside in Padstow. Car parking opposite
- ⇖ 3 twin, 7 double; all with bathroom/WC, TV, hair-dryer, mini-bar, baby-listening
- ◈ Restaurant, bar, conservatory; fishing, swimming, other sports nearby
- ⊖ No wheelchair access; no dogs in public rooms
- ▭ Access, Amex, Visa
- £ Single occupancy of twin/double £34 to £85, twin/double £56 to £107; deposit required. Set L £20, D £28; alc L £25, D £32. Special breaks available

PAINSWICK GLOUCESTERSHIRE   **MAP 9**

Painswick Hotel

KEMPS LANE, PAINSWICK, GLOUCESTERSHIRE GL6 6YB
TEL: (0452) 812160   TELEX: 43605   FAX: (0452) 814059

A very comfortable hotel on the edge of a steep Cotswold village.

This is a comfortable place – rather an odd shape, though, for the rectors who once inhabited it had the chapel (now the bar) centrally placed – and the sitting-room, with low squashy sofas and a mammoth fire, is eminently relaxing and the bedrooms are well-appointed and spacious. Various oriental ornaments from Chinese vases to Thai bronzes counterpoint the Georgian features of the original rooms. Service is quietly friendly.

The menu lists interesting fish dishes – prawn mousse with red pimientos, for example – and this extends to the breakfast kippers, which are locally smoked. Home-made rolls and good cheese are two more plus points. The food comes promptly to your table in a high-ceilinged, calm and formal dining-room.

◑ Open all year

🔁 Painswick is on the A46 between Stroud and Cheltenham. The hotel is situated behind the church. Private car park

🛏 2 single, 6 twin, 8 double, 2 four-poster, 2 family rooms; all with bathroom/WC, exc 1 single with shower/WC; TV, room service, hair-dryer, baby-listening in all rooms

◈ 3 restaurants, bar, 2 lounges, library; conference facilities (max 40 people non-residential, 16 residential); croquet at hotel, fishing, tennis nearby; babysitting

⊖ No wheelchair access; no dogs in public rooms

▭ Access, Amex, Visa

£ Single £65, single occupancy of twin/double £85, twin/double £95, four-poster/family room £120; deposit required. Set L, D £18.50/£23.50. Special breaks available

---

PARRACOMBE DEVON   **MAP 10**

Heddon's Gate Hotel

HEDDON'S MOUTH, PARRACOMBE, BARNSTAPLE, DEVON EX31 4PZ
TEL: PARRACOMBE (05983) 313

Generously proportioned country-house retreat in wild, isolated countryside on the edge of Exmoor.

Buried in the National Trust's wooded Heddon's Gate estate, Heddon's Gate Hotel is a building that has grown and changed so much that one recent visitor almost failed to recognise it as the youth hostel she had once stayed in. At night the only sound outside is the hooting of owls. Inside it is rather noisier, with a selection of clocks chiming the hours and half-hours and a gong summoning guests to dinner at 8pm. On one side of the hall is a long, thin dining-room, while on the other a lounge bar with photographs of Lynmouth in the 1890s and curious wall-lights on leaf and branch supports opens into a small games room and a second lounge where afternoon tea and after-dinner coffee are served. Upstairs, room names offer clues to their very different décor. Most extraordinary is the Chinese Room, with the bath tucked away behind an arch in a wonderful red-tiled bathroom, but the Master Bedroom is also worth a mention with its impressive half-tester. The views from all rooms are stunning.

One seven-times visitor writes that Robert Deville's food 'just gets better'; afternoon teas with dainty sandwiches, scones with jam and cream and different cakes every day come in for particular praise. When we inspected, a tasty home-made tomato soup was followed by salmon and haddock kedgeree served in a scallop shell, and pungent carbonnade of venison with tiny pastry deer. Cream slightly overwhelmed the delicate raspberry fool, which was followed by coffee and a selection of chocolates.

◑ Closed 1 Nov to Apr (or Easter if earlier)

↗ From the A39 4 miles west of Lynton, take the road signposted 'Martinhoe and Woody Bay'. Take the next left. Carry straight on at next crossroads and down a steep hill. The hotel drive is on the right. Private car park

🛏 1 single, 3 twin, 5 double, 1 four-poster, 1 suite, 3 cottage rooms; all with bathroom/WC, exc 1 double with shower/WC; TV, hair-dryer in all rooms

◈ Dining-room, bar, lounge, library, card room; table tennis at hotel, fishing, riding nearby. Wheelchair access to dining-room, ground-floor bedrooms in cottages

⊖ No children under 10; no dogs or smoking in dining-room

▭ None accepted

£ Single £45 to £52, single occupancy of twin/double £63 to £90, twin/double £85 to £110, four-poster £90 to £105, suite £100 to £120, cottage room £95 to £125 (rates inc dinner). Set D £20 (8pm). Special breaks available

PAULERSPURY NORTHAMPTONSHIRE   MAP 9

Vine House

100 HIGH STREET, PAULERSPURY, NR TOWCESTER, NORTHAMPTONSHIRE
NN12 7NA
TEL: PAULERSPURY (032 733) 267   FAX: (032 733) 309

A well-established restaurant just off the A5, with comfortable rooms and young, enthusiastic hosts.

Though you'd have to look hard to spot the difference, the contemporary paintings on the wall in Marcus and Julie Springett's restaurant are not pricey works by some well-known artist but are by the hand of four-year-old Sam. Marcus does the cooking, and is proud to tell you that everything in his kitchen is home-made, including the bread. A typical evening menu lists a choice of five starters and five main courses which might include deep-fried calf's liver with leeks and wild mushroom sauce, pigeon shepherd's pie with a truffle gravy and fillet of port with black pudding and a confit of apples and sage mustard sauce; coconut ice-cream and ginger mousse feature among the puddings.

The six bedrooms are named after grape varieties, and range from Syrah, a fussy pink room with flowery walls and bedcovers, to Tokay, with a pine four-poster and plain walls. All rooms are *en suite* with modern, well-equipped bathrooms, though none are huge. Downstairs, the small bar and sitting-room are rather crowded with furniture but are comfortable, with sofas and window seats and piles of books to browse through, many of them with a culinary theme.

◑ Open all year; restaurant closed Sun and Mon eves

↗ Just off the A5 in the village of Paulerspury. Private car park

🛏 1 single, 2 twin, 2 double, 1 four-poster; most with shower/WC, exc 1 double with bathroom/WC; TV in all rooms

◈ Dining-room, bar, lounge; conference facilities (max 12 people non-residential); fishing, golf, other sports nearby

⊖ No wheelchair access; no dogs

▢ Visa

£ Single £39, single occupancy of twin/double £39, twin/double/four-poster £62. Alc L £14, D £19.50

PELYNT CORNWALL　　　　　　　　　　　　　**MAP 10**

Jubilee Inn ☆

PELYNT, NR LOOE, CORNWALL PL13 2JZ
TEL: LANREATH (0503) 220312　FAX: (0503) 220920

A welcoming roadside pub-hotel with an attractive restaurant.

The picture of Queen Victoria hanging in front of this sixteenth-century hotel makes it plain which jubilee it took its name from, but should any doubt linger the walls of the public bar are also liberally adorned with portraits of the matriarch, with a few of a youthful Queen Elizabeth II thrown in for good measure. Much of the ground floor is taken up with public bars opening one from another; some, like the Victoria Lounge, are cosier than others. The rest of the ground floor is filled with an attractive dining-room, its wooden tables invitingly laid with flowers and candles; an extensive bill of fare should offer something for every eater, and there is an equally varied bar menu too.

Behind the bars a bright and sunny plant-filled extension houses a spiral staircase leading to the bedrooms and a disappointingly drab lounge. Bedrooms vary considerably in size and furnishings: Room Nine has a big, solid double bed and pretty tiled fireplace; Room Four a lancet window in its bathroom. A two-year-old annexe at the back houses another three rooms including a honeymoon suite with a delicate four-poster bed, beamed ceilings and a spacious bathroom.

◑ Open all year

↵ 4 miles west of Looe, on the Looe/Lostwithiel road. Private car park

⇔ 2 twin, 6 double, 1 four-poster, 3 family rooms, 3 annexe rooms; most with bathroom/WC, some with shower/WC; TV, room service, hair-dryer, baby-listening in all rooms

◈ Restaurant, bar, lounge, drying room, games room; conference facilities (max 20 people non-residential and residential); fishing, golf, other sports nearby. Wheelchair access to restaurant and WC (unisex) only

⊖ None

▢ Access, Visa

£ Single occupancy of twin/double £31 to £33, twin/double £52 to £56, four-poster £60; deposit required. Set L £9.50; alc L, D £15.50. Special breaks available

---

Use the index at the back of the book if you know the name of a hotel but are unsure about its precise location.

North Lakes Hotel

ULLSWATER ROAD, PENRITH, CUMBRIA CA11 8QT
TEL: PENRITH (0768) 68111   FAX: (0768) 68291

Part of a chain of business hotels but with more individuality and style than many of its kind.

Turning into the North Lakes Hotel almost straight from Junction 40 of the M6 you might have to do a double take. With its long, low-rise pebbledash exterior it may seem more like a small council estate than a typical Cumbrian hotel – and the huge car park adds nothing on the aesthetic front. At first glance everything seems to say 'functional' with a capital F but this place merits a closer look. Inside, the huge lobby and its surrounding lounges have been set out in ersatz rusticana with such careful attention to detail that the overall effect is rather convincing: exposed beams, wooden floors with rugs and stone fireplaces with roaring log fires. The snug Stag Bar is busy at lunchtimes when a selection of hot foods is served, but the main dinner is served in the spacious Martindale Restaurant with its rug-covered stone floor and stone fireplace. Garlic mushrooms might be followed by steamed fillet of salmon on fresh hazelnut dressing.

The bedrooms have well co-ordinated fabrics and furnishings and have everything you would expect with a bit more style, though standard doubles feel a little on the small side. Extensive leisure facilities are available and the hotel makes a positive point of welcoming children of all ages.

- ◑ Open all year
- ⤢ 2 minutes from Junction 40 of the M6 on the A66. Private car park
- 🛏 40 twin, 25 double, 4 four-poster, 6 family rooms, 10 suites; all with bathroom/WC, TV, room service, hair-dryer, trouser press, baby-listening
- ◇ Restaurant, 2 bars, 2 lounges, games room, air-conditioned conference facilities (max 200 people non-residential, 85 residential); leisure club, heated swimming-pool, 2 squash courts, gym, Jacuzzi, snooker at hotel, fishing, golf nearby. Wheelchair access to hotel (ramp), restaurant, WC (M, F) and 23 ground-floor bedrooms, 2 specially equipped for disabled people
- ⊖ No dogs in public rooms
- ▭ Access, Amex, Diners, Visa
- £ Single occupancy of twin/double £89, twin/double/family room £89, four-poster £99, suite £109; deposit required. Alc L from £8, D from £18. Special breaks available

See our selection of what we consider to be the best hotels in various counties in Hotels of the Year *(page 16).*

Abbey Hotel

ABBEY STREET, PENZANCE, CORNWALL TR18 4AR
TEL: PENZANCE (0736) 66906   FAX: (0736) 51163

Exquisitely stylish small hotel in a Gothic house overlooking Penzance harbour.

Abbey Hotel, with its turquoise façade and Gothic windows, is unmissable. Inside, every room has been individually designed and furnished with the wonderful one-off pieces of furniture and artefacts Jean and Michael Cox have picked up on their travels, including a statue of the Hindu elephant-god Ganesh which presides over the downstairs dining-room. A big first-floor lounge has three sofas squared off around a log fire; huge windows overlook a small rear garden. However, it's the bedrooms that really set this hotel apart: each is unique, both in its bold colour scheme and its fittings; furniture tends to the gargantuan, and rugs pile up on the carpets. There are lots of quirky details, like the bathroom door of Room Three cunningly concealed behind book spines so it appears to be a bookcase; Room One has a half-tester bed and a vast bathroom complete with ancient weighing machine and shelves of plates. Second-floor rooms are tucked into the eaves and have appropriately contorted shapes. Several have skylights, the one in Room Six being right over the bed.

In such an individual hotel, the three-course dinner menus are bound to throw up some surprises – carrot and cardamom soup perhaps, or ginger and lychee ice-cream.

◑ Open all year, exc Xmas period

↗ On entering Penzance take the sea-front road. After 300 yards, just before the bridge, turn right. After 10 yards turn left and drive up slipway – the hotel is at the top. Private car park

⇌ 2 twin, 3 double, 1 family room, 1 suite; some with bathroom/WC, some with shower/WC; TV; hair-dryer on request; limited room service

◈ Dining-room, lounge; fishing, golf, other sports nearby; babysitting

⊖ No wheelchair access; no dogs in public rooms

▭ Access, Amex, Visa

£ Single £60 to £75, twin/double £80 to £120, family room £85 to £160, suite £120 to £200; deposit required. Set D £21.50. Special breaks available

Peterstow Country House ☆

PETERSTOW, ROSS-ON-WYE, HEREFORD AND WORCESTER HR9 6LB
TEL: ROSS-ON-WYE (0989) 62826   FAX: (0989) 67264

A well-furnished and friendly hotel.

A large, rather plain rectory a few miles outside Ross-on-Wye has been transformed by Mike and Jeanne Denne over the past four years into a high-quality country-house hotel. Original features of the building (notably the stone-flagged floor of the entrance hall) have been set off by pretty and comfortable soft furnishings and fabrics, while the bar has been created from a demolished chemist's shop, the old shelves and drawers now containing alcoholic rather than medicinal tinctures. The large, comfortable drawing-room and formally laid-out dining-room with its polished tables look out over lawns and cedar trees, while the bedrooms – some quite cottagey, others decidedly grand – have plenty of space and excellent bathrooms. Major points in favour of this hotel are the friendliness of the staff and the efforts made to ensure that guests have everything they need – this more than compensates for the slightly frazzled atmosphere when the hotel is very busy. The food is modern English with French overtones – well-presented though perhaps a little underflavoured for some tastes. The house wine is remarkably good value.

It is worth discussing the sort of bedroom you would like when you book – some beds are too short for tall people and distant traffic noise may disturb very light sleepers in some rooms.

◑ Open all year

↗ At Ross-on-Wye take the A49 to Hereford for 3 miles to Peterstow Common. Take the 2nd turning on the right. Private car park

🛏 3 twin, 4 double, 2 half-tester; some with bathroom/WC; remainder with shower/WC; TV, room service in all rooms

◈ Dining-room, bar, lounge, conference room, drying room; conference facilities (max 9 people residential, 40 non-residential); fishing, clay pigeon shooting at hotel, other sports nearby. Wheelchair access to hotel, dining-room and WC (M, F), I ground-floor bedroom

⊖ No children under 7; no dogs; no smoking in dining-room

▭ Access, Amex, Diners, Visa

£ Single occupancy of twin/double £39 to £69, twin/double from £50, half-tester/family room £90; deposit required. Set L £12.50, D £19.50/£22.50. Special breaks available

---

PICKERING NORTH YORKSHIRE   **MAP 3**

White Swan

MARKET PLACE, PICKERING, NORTH YORKSHIRE YO18 7AA
TEL: PICKERING (0751) 72288 changing to (0751) 472288 in late 1993

Everything a traditional inn in a bustling market town should be – friendly, full of character and with tasty food.

Stay at the White Swan and you'll quickly come to the conclusion that proprietor Deirdre Buchanan is the most professional of châtelaines, and not just because the framed certificates in reception testify to her numerous catering industry qualifications. The lady runs a tight ship, with thoughtfulness and respect not just for the needs of her guests, but for the heritage of this lovely old inn.

The traditional bar, crowded at lunchtime, is a highly polished affair, complete with horse brasses, tankards, horseshoes and ginger beer bottles. The next-door snug is popular with parents, whose offspring take great delight in the strange, robotic-looking doorstop. Things move up a notch in the restaurant, with its bentwood and antique-style chairs, crisp white linen and red and green print drapes. It's called the St-Emilion room in deference to its owner's abiding passion – 70 of the wines in the 170-bin list hail from Bordeaux's right bank and wooden wine-case ends with the growers' marques decorate the walls. Food is unapologetically traditional; fillet of smoked trout with creamed apple and horseradish, roast Aylesbury duckling with a prune and orange sauce, and bread-and-butter pudding are typical offerings. In the bar, the fresh Whitby codling and thick-cut chips were memorable.

The small residents' lounge is cosy, with beams, antiques, tied-back curtains, willow pattern plates, games and jigsaws. Bedrooms are frilly and cottagey, many having light bamboo and rattan or pine furniture. Bathrooms have everything you are likely to need.

◑ Open all year

⤴ Pickering is at the junction of the A169 and A170. The White Swan is in the centre of the market place. Private car park

🛏 5 twin, 6 double, 1 family room, 1 suite; all with bathroom/WC, TV, room service, hair-dryer, baby-listening; trouser press in some rooms

◈ Restaurant, bar, lounge, snug; conference facilities (max 12 people residential and non-residential); fishing, golf, other sports nearby. Wheelchair access to public rooms only

⊖ No dogs in bar or restaurant

▭ Access, Visa

£ Single occupancy of twin/double £35 to £55, twin/double £50 to £77, family room from £65 and £90, suite £70 to £99; deposit required. Set L £10.50, D £17.50. Special breaks available

---

PIMPERNE DORSET   **MAP 9**

Fairfield House ☆

CHURCH ROAD, PIMPERNE, BLANDFORD FORUM, DORSET DT11 8UB
TEL: (0258) 456756   FAX: (0258) 480053

Friendly, family-run restaurant-with-rooms where the emphasis is on relaxed country pursuits.

After many years hard labour on Fleet Street, Alan Bromley and his wife Frances have retired to this red-brick and flint Grade-II listed Georgian farmhouse which they run as a restaurant with accommodation. Happily, it still retains the feel of a family home, complete with a pet golden labrador. Throughout the house there are splendid oil portraits and landscapes by Chris Sanders RA, a relative. The furniture in the public rooms and bar is well-worn and comfortable, and there is no perceptible trace of the handiwork of an interior designer. The hallway has an upright piano and walking sticks, and piles of Ordnance Survey maps which guests can use to plan their exploration of this part of Dorset.

Meals are taken in the dining-room, which has light blue walls and pink tablecloths. The menu sticks to trusted favourites, so you might start with mushrooms in garlic, followed by a peppered steak and chocolate mousse. The bedrooms in the main house vary in size and are furnished with a mish-mash of utilitarian pieces; the freshly converted rooms in what used to be the old servants' quarters have pine furniture and pink or green walls. One room on the ground floor has a bathroom designed for use by guests with disabilities.

◐ *Open all year*

↗ *Take the A354 from Blandford Forum for I mile. In Pimperne take the 1st left (Church Road). Private car park*

🛏 *2 twin, 2 double, I family room; twins with bathroom/WC, remainder with shower/WC, I public bathroom; TV, room service, hair-dryer, baby-listening in all rooms*

◇ *Restaurant, bar, lounge, drying room; ironing facilities; conference facilities (max 5*

people residential and non-residential); fishing, golf, other sports nearby. Wheelchair access to hotel (ramp), restaurant and WC (unisex), I ground-floor bedroom specially equipped for disabled people

⊖ *No dogs; smoking in lounge only*

▭ *Access, Amex, Diners, Visa*

£ *Single occupancy of twin/double £38 to £43, twin/double/family room £55 to £58; deposit required. Alc L £9 to £16, D £13 to £18*

POOLE DORSET   **MAP 9**

Mansion House

THAMES STREET, POOLE, DORSET BH15 1JN
TEL: POOLE (0202) 685666   FAX: (0202) 665709

A formally run Georgian-house hotel and dining club set in the quaint backstreets of Poole.

This smart red-brick Georgian house, tucked away in a narrow back-street of the dock district of Poole, used to be the mayor's residence – and something of the formal atmosphere still clings to the house today, from the moment you are welcomed at the front door by a member of staff immaculately turned out in morning dress. The grandest space in the house is the stone-flagged hallway, which leads to a sweeping staircase. Guests make their way up it past nineteenth-century portraits and plaster pillars to the residents' lounge. This room, decorated in Wedgwood blue and gold, has deep sofas and a fireplace.

Meals are taken in the basement dining club – residents automatically become members. It used to be the house's wine cellar, but now has light wood panelling and green and pink upholstered furniture. The menu, with its fair share of seafood, is mainly a solid selection of a dozen or more trusted dishes such as beef with mustard sauce or duckling with apricots. There is also a bar with a low roof and exposed brick walls.

The bedrooms are gentle on the eye, with muted pinks, blues and greens and reproduction Georgian furniture. There is a theme to each room's decoration: for example, Oriental has hand-painted fans on the wall and Indian Summer has prints from the Raj.

◑ *Open all year; restaurant closed Sun eve*

⤴ *In Poole, follow signs for 'Ferries'. Turn left on Poole Quay and first left again by the Customs House. Private car park*

🛏 *9 single, 6 twin, 13 double, family room and suite available; all with bathroom/WC, TV, room service, hair-dryer, trouser press, baby-listening; no tea/coffee-making facilities in rooms*

◇ *Restaurant (air-conditioned), 2 bars (air-conditioned), lounge;*

conference facilities (max 40 people non-residential, 30 residential); fishing, tennis, other sports nearby

⊖ *No wheelchair access; no children under 5 in restaurant eves; dogs by arrangement only*

▭ *Access, Amex, Diners, Visa*

£ *Single £73, single occupancy of twin/double £75, twin/double/ family room £110, suite £130. Set L £13.50, D £15; alc L £16, D £18 to £30. Special breaks available*

Pool Court

POOL BANK, POOL-IN-WHARFEDALE, OTLEY, WEST YORKSHIRE LS21 1EH
TEL: LEEDS (0532) 842288　FAX: (0532) 843115

A foodie temple with comfortable rooms in a well-bred Georgian mansion.

The brochure's adverts for suppliers of Rolex watches and Jaguar motorcars could easily excite the suspicion that in this location you're in expense-account territory with the meter ticking. In fact, despite the splendour of the surroundings and the quality of the food, the cheerful, unstuffy staff are welcoming to families and a 'spoil yourself' weekend tariff knocks a substantial hole in the weekday rate.

Pool Court's chosen designation is 'restaurant-with-rooms', but that shouldn't lead you to conclude that the rooms are in any way an afterthought. Individually decorated and restfully furnished in the country-house style, sprinkled with antiques and liberally dusted with extras like bath robes, cotton buds and bath toys, they are indisputably plush. Bear in mind, however, that the 'small doubles' are well-named, and that the single tucks its loo and shower behind a partition.

The bar and lounge go in for cane-effect chairs and bamboo-framed tables to achieve a vaguely colonial feel. The Alcove Restaurant is graced by classically simple décor and gold-framed architectural drawings, while the Georgian Cellar Restaurant has modern furniture below a vaulted ceiling. The food remains the major draw: perhaps pigeon and hazelnut ravioli with crispy fried vegetables, roast garlic and a honey and soya sauce, followed by char-grilled fillet of beef with wild mushrooms, then a hot raspberry soufflé. 'Healthy eating' dishes are flagged. The cosmopolitan wine list has an admirable selection of half-bottles.

🌓 *Closed 25 Dec for 2 weeks; restaurant usually closed Sun, Mon eves*

🔁 *3 miles north of Leeds/Bradford Airport, on the A658. Private car park*

🛏 *1 single, 2 twin/double, 3 double; all with bathroom/WC, exc single with shower/WC; TV, room service, hair-dryer, mini-bar in all rooms; tea/coffee-making facilities and baby-listening by arrangement*

◇ *Air-conditioned restaurant, bar, lounge, private dining-room; conference facilities (max 30 people non-residential, 6 residential); fishing, golf, other sports nearby. Wheelchair access to public rooms only*

⊖ *No dogs but kennel facilities can be arranged; no cigars, pipes in restaurant*

▭ *Access, Amex, Diners, Visa*

£ *Single £70, single occupancy of twin/double £85 to £95, twin/double £95 to £120; deposit required. Cooked B £8; L by prior arrangement for parties of 10 or more; set D £24.50/£28.50/£32.50; alc D £18. Special breaks available*

PORLOCK SOMERSET   **MAP 10**

The Oaks Hotel ☆

PORLOCK, SOMERSET TA24 8ES
TEL: PORLOCK (0643) 862265 (and fax)

An immaculately decorated family-run hotel with marvellous views out to Porlock Bay.

Although Tim Riley is adamant that he hasn't lost any guests yet, actually getting into the Oaks can be tricky, positioned as it is on a blind bend on a hill. Once into the grounds, however, you relax immediately. The Oaks is a large Edwardian country house and has a dining-room with huge picture windows. Four-course-dinners-with-a-view lean heavily on local produce: main-course Exmoor venison and Devonshire rump steaks rub shoulders with more exotic starters such as Mississippi bake and salmon and avocado roulade. One reader writes that the food was 'far superior to most five-star hotels'.

The ten bedrooms all have slightly different colour schemes but similar pine fittings. Two have big brass bedsteads, one a half-tester bed. Front rooms overlook the sea, side rooms Porlock village and the curious truncated church spire. Deer can sometimes be seen grazing in the fields outside.

◑ *Open all year*

▰ *On the A39, west of Minehead. Private car park*

🛏 *3 twin, 7 double; all with bathroom/WC, TV, room service, hair-dryer*

◈ *Restaurant, bar, 2 lounges;*

fishing, golf, other sports nearby

⊖ *No wheelchair access; no dogs in public rooms; no smoking in some public rooms*

▭ *None accepted*

£ *Single occupancy of twin/double £43, twin/double £75. Set D £19*

PORT ISAAC CORNWALL　　　　　　　　　　　　　　**MAP 10**

Old School Hotel

PORT ISAAC, CORNWALL PL29 3RB
TEL: BODMIN (0208) 880721

A Victorian junior school that's been turned into a small clifftop hotel complete with banqueting hall.

Hard though it is to believe it now, the Old School was virtually derelict when Mike and Lesley Warner took it on 12 years or so ago. Today its least exciting part is the bar lounge, which is much like many other bustling pub interiors. Tucked behind it, however, the old school hall has been turned into a 'medieval' banqueting hall, complete with appropriate mural. A long table, overlooked by a wooden gallery, runs down the middle of the room, while pews from a Methodist chapel have been pressed into service to create alcove seating around the walls. Non-residents can book the banqueting hall, in which case residents may have to eat in the lounge instead. Not surprisingly the menu concentrates on fish, although there are a few standards like lasagne and chicken breasts as well as vegetarian options.

　　All the bedrooms are comfortably furnished and some offer spectacular views of Port Isaac Bay below. The best, perhaps, is Number Eight in what was once the headmaster's house; a half-tester bed, positioned to take advantage of the views through the fine old windows, is surrounded by furniture specially made to blend in with the original wooden beams.

◑ *Open all year*

▰ *From Delabole take the B3314 and B3267 to Port Isaac. Then take the harbour road. Private car park*

🛏 *1 twin, 7 double, 5 family suites, 6 annexe rooms; most with bathroom/WC, some with shower/WC; TV, room service, hair-dryer, baby-listening in all*

rooms; mini-bar, trouser press in suites

◈ *Restaurant, bar, lounge, TV room; conference facilities (max 25 people non-residential and residential); fishing, golf, other sports nearby; babysitting. Wheelchair access to hotel, restaurant and 6 ground-floor bedrooms*

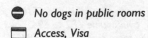 No dogs in public rooms

🖳 Access, Visa

£ Single occupancy of twin/double
£24 to £36, twin/double £40 to

£51, family suites £52 to £74,
annexe room £30 to £40;
deposit required. Alc L from £10,
D from £16. Special breaks
available

Port Gaverne Hotel

PORT GAVERNE, NR PORT ISAAC, CORNWALL PL29 3SQ
TEL: BODMIN (0208) 880244   FAX: (0208) 880151

*A larger-than-it-looks pub-hotel overlooking uncommercialised
Port Gaverne Bay on a strip of Heritage Coast.*

Port Gaverne Hotel overflows into the row of eighteenth-century fish-
sellers' cottages across the road, which means there isn't much of the tiny
village that doesn't form part of the enterprise. From the outside the
hotel looks much like any other pretty, whitewashed pub with slate roof
and rambling roses over the door. Inside, however, it seems to go on for
ever. Much of the ground floor consists of picture-covered public bars,
some of them busy and bustling, others – for example the Wheelhouse
back bar and the Cabin bar with its dioramas of Port Gaverne in days
gone by and an old ship's table – darker and cosier. A rather characterless
dining-room hosts lunchtime buffets during the summer and dinners all
year round. Reports have criticised the dinner system: there are two
sittings, one at 7.30pm, the other at 8.30pm, and in theory guests can
choose which they prefer. One reader wrote to protest at being assigned
to the earlier time without consultation and moved away from the table to
drink coffee elsewhere: 'Brisk service is one thing, mealtimes run like a
Sandhurst cadet course is another.' A la carte dinner menus balance fish
dishes with a selection of alternatives.

Upstairs, an airy sitting-room opens on to a rooftop sun lounge. All the
bedrooms are comfortably, if simply, furnished, although some in
the new annexe have wildly patterned wallpaper that runs amok as far as
the bathrooms. Those rooms in the seventeenth-century part are smaller
but are compensated for with interesting beamed ceilings. The lavora-
tory of Room Six slots into a dormer window with great views; more
unnervingly, users of the private bathroom opposite Room Four must
bathe beneath the unyielding gaze of a stuffed red and green parrot.

If all rooms in the main building are full you may be given one of the
light, airy self-catering suites opposite.

◑ Closed 8 Jan to 19 Feb

↗ Port Gaverne is signposted from
the B3314 south of Delabole via
the B3267. Private car park

🛏 2 single, 3 twin, 7 double, 4

family rooms, 2 annexe rooms;
all with bathroom/WC, exc 1
single; TV, room service, hair-
dryer, baby-listening in all rooms

 Restaurant, 2 bars, lounge, TV

room; fishing, golf, other sports nearby

⊖ No wheelchair access; no dogs or smoking in restaurant

▭ Access, Amex, Diners, Visa

£ Single £41 to £45, single occupancy of twin/double £51 to £55, twin/double £82 to £94, family room from £86 and £94, annexe room £82 to £90; deposit required. Alc D £16.50; buffet lunches

---

Slipway Hotel ☆

HARBOUR FRONT, PORT ISAAC, CORNWALL PL29 3RH
TEL: BODMIN (0208) 880264

A moderately priced seafood restaurant-with-rooms.

Given that the Slipway's reception is on the first floor, approached via a flight of slate steps from outside, it is easy to lose your bearings and imagine that the split-level restaurant is partly in the basement when in fact it straddles the ground and first floors. The hotel is in what was once a group of sixteenth-century cottages and then a ships' chandler's, immediately opposite the lifeboat station and a harbour where fishermen can be seen bringing in the lobster pots; the narrow streets can get very busy with daytrippers in summer. The bar, too, bustles in the high season, but there's a small first-floor TV lounge for residents to escape to. The Bishop brothers, who have recently taken over the Slipway, emphasise the restaurant's seafood credentials and a menu that is particularly strong on lobster dishes. For non-seafood alternatives, daily specials include items such as T-bone steaks and duck breasts; vegetarians are catered for with dishes like falafel supplementing the more usual lasagne. Upstairs, some of the small bedrooms have exposed stone walls, sloping beamed ceilings and harbour views. Room Three features a cupboard made out of driftwood by Napoleonic prisoners of war.

◑ Open all year, exc 31 Oct to 18 Dec and 8 Jan to 1 Apr

⤢ Take the A30 from Exeter and follow signs from Launceston. Private car park

⇌ 2 single, 2 twin, 5 double, 1 family room; half with shower/WC, 2 public bathrooms

◈ Restaurant, bar, lounge, drying room; conference facilities (max 60 people non-residential, 10 residential); fishing, golf, other sports nearby

⊖ No wheelchair access; no dogs

▭ Access, Amex, Visa

£ Single £15 to £19, single occupancy of twin/double £25 to £30, twin/double £30 to £50, family room rate on request; deposit required. Set L £2.50 to £7.50, D £15 to £20. Special breaks available

---

Hotels in our Visitors' Book *towards the end of the* Guide *are additional hotels that may be worth a visit. Reports on these hotels are welcome.*

PORTLOE CORNWALL   **MAP 10**

The Lugger Hotel ☆

PORTLOE, NR TRURO, CORNWALL TR2 5RD
TEL: TRURO (0872) 501322   FAX: (0872) 501691

*A very attractive whitewashed pub-hotel that is perfectly
positioned above Portloe harbour.*

At the very end of the road where Portloe fades into the sea you'll come
across the whitewashed Lugger Hotel, perched high up above the rocky
bay, with terraces outside the main building allowing guests to watch
boats being dragged up on to the beach. Given that the position is
apparently perfect for cornering the catch, it is rather disappointing that
the table d'hôte menus are not more crab- and lobster-orientated.

Not surprisingly, the Lugger's history is full of smuggling stories, and
one of its landlords, Black Dunstan, was actually hanged for smuggling
in the 1890s. Nowadays the Powells prefer to concentrate on running a
hotel which now has 19 rooms, those in the Godolphin Wing being
bigger (and probably quieter) but less full of character than those in the
original seventeenth-century pub, where the dictates of an ancient
building ensure that rooms are rather small; Gardenia only just manages
to squeeze a half-tester bed into a beam-roofed room but has lovely sea
views. Competition for the four sea-facing tables in the low-ceilinged
restaurant is likely to be fierce; should you land one of those at the back
you can console yourself by studying the many smuggling and shipwreck
posters.

◑ Open all year, exc late Nov to
early Feb

⚡ Take the B3287 to Tregony,
then the A3078 St Mawes road.
After 2 miles fork left for Veryan
and Portloe, then turn left at
T-junction for Portloe. Private car
park

🛏 3 single, 7 twin, 7 double, 2
suites; most with bathroom/WC,
some with shower/WC; TV, room
service, hair-dryer, mini-bar

◈ Restaurant (air-conditioned), bar,
2 lounges; sauna/solarium at
hotel, fishing, golf, other sports

nearby. Wheelchair access to
hotel (ramp), restaurant and 5
ground-floor bedrooms

⊖ No children under 12; no dogs;
no smoking in restaurant

▭ Access, Amex, Diners, Visa

£ Single £50 to £64, single
occupancy of twin/double £50 to
£100, twin/double £100 to
£128, suite £100 to £132 (rates
inc dinner); deposit required. Sun
L £10; bar lunches; set D £20;
alc D £20 to £25. Special breaks
available

---

*The text of entries is based on unsolicited reports sent in by readers and
backed up by inspections. The factual details are from questionnaires the
Guide sends to all hotels that feature in the book.*

PORTSCATHO CORNWALL   MAP 10

Roseland House Hotel

ROSEVINE, NR PORTSCATHO, CORNWALL TR2 5EW
TEL: TRURO (0872) 580644   FAX: (0872) 580801

A small hotel offering popular food and spectacular sea views at moderate prices.

Despite a pretty courtyard rock garden, the Roseland House Hotel is not a very exciting building. However, it would be hard to better the sea views from its bedroom windows, some of them framed by gigantic pines, which positively urge you to rush across the daisy-spattered lawn to the cliff and down the path to the private beach (sadly, on inspection, not as clean as it might be). The bedrooms themselves are a little old-fashioned, with candlewick bedspreads, busily patterned carpets and rather functional furniture, though one boasts a small, frilly four-poster bed.

Downstairs, the lounge has comfortable pink and green armchairs and lots of books. The best tables in the dining-room are definitely those by the window, particularly the two that are isolated in a conservatory-style extension; it's over dinner that you'll best appreciate what one reader enthusiastically describes as Anthony and Carolyn Hindley's 'quiet, sincere and warm' hospitality. The five-course meals, which come included in the very reasonable room rates, are obviously as popular with locals as with guests; when we inspected a pleasant leek soup was being served with hefty chunks of bread, the scallops were delicious, the sole bonne femme came with a selection of standard English vegetables and the chocolate mousse was a dream.

◑ Open all year

↗ From St Austell take the A390 road towards Truro. Just beyond Sticker fork left on to the B3287 to Tregony. At the bottom of the hill, turn left on to the A3078 St Mawes Road. After 10 to 15 mins the hotel signs lead down to the left. Private car park

🛏 2 single, 4 twin, 7 double, 1 four-poster, 2 family rooms, 2 suites; all with bathroom/WC, exc 2 rooms with shower/WC; TV, room service, baby-listening in all rooms

◈ Dining-room, bar, 2 lounges, conservatory; fishing, private beach at hotel, other sports nearby. Wheelchair access to hotel (1 step), dining-room and WC (unisex), 5 ground-floor bedrooms

⊖ No dogs; no smoking in bedrooms and restricted in public rooms

▭ Access, Visa

£ Single £36 to £39, single occupancy of twin/double £48 to £52, twin/double/four-poster/suite £78 to £88, family room rate on request (rates inc dinner); deposit required. Sun L £9; set L from £2.50, D £15.50

POSTBRIDGE DEVON   **MAP 10**

Lydgate House

POSTBRIDGE, DEVON PL20 6TJ
TEL: TAVISTOCK (0822) 88209

*A small, quiet hotel attractively positioned above a Dartmoor
valley with a famous clapper bridge.*

Tucked away down a tiny untarmacked side road, Lydgate House avoids
all Postbridge's through traffic, a bonus to add to its plateau site looking
down on a steep-sided valley. This being Dartmoor, there's a bar and a
good stock of books and tapes in case the weather should make walking
too damp a proposition – and if you can't go outside there are always the
fine photographs of moorland scenery for sale on the walls of the dining-
room to look at instead. Despite the hotel's small size, Hilary Townsend
and Judy Gordon-Jones' table d'hôte menus still manage an either/or
choice, with one dish always suitable for vegetarians; puddings such as
chocolate lovers' tart are perfect for rounding off a good day's hiking.
There's a multi-levelled family room on the ground floor; the double bed
is up steps from a screened-off single, and more steps lead up to a sitting
area complete with chaise-longue. Upstairs, rooms are smaller, Room
Six is particularly attractive, with a television and plants slotted into a
niche in the wall, while Room One has a pretty bathroom decorated by
the same artist who painted muddy hiking boots on the boot-room door.

◑ Open all year, exc Jan and Feb

⤴ Leave the A38 at Ashburton and
travel towards Two Bridges. Turn
right on to the B3212 and after
3 miles arrive in Postbridge.
Turn right after hump-back
bridge. Private car park

🛏 1 single, 2 twin, 4 double, 1
family room; most with
bathroom/WC, some with
shower/WC; TV, hair-dryer in all
rooms

◈ Dining-room, bar, lounge, drying
room, conservatory; conference

facilities (max 10 people
residential); fishing, river
swimming, mountain biking at
hotel, golf, tennis, other sports
nearby

⊖ No wheelchair access; no dogs in
public rooms; smoking in lounge
only

▭ Access, Visa

£ Single £28, single occupancy of
twin/double £32 to £38, twin/
double £48 to £56, family room
£84; deposit required. Set D £14
(7.30pm)

POULTON-LE-FYLDE LANCASHIRE   **MAP 5**

River House

SKIPPOOL CREEK, THORNTON-LE-FYLDE, NR BLACKPOOL, LANCASHIRE
FY5 5LF
TEL: POULTON-LE-FYLDE (0253) 883497   FAX: (0253) 892083

An engaging, nonconformist small hotel overlooking the Wyre Estuary. Recommended for connoisseurs of Victorian plumbing.

Go to the River House to be treated as an individual rather than a room number. Like the Victorian baths and the 1941 Golden Nugget gaming machine, this hotel is a collector's item; small wonder that assorted cabinet ministers and one of the world's most famous ballet dancers have struggled down an obscure lane, subject to flooding, to stay here. One well-known politician actually found himself wading ankle-deep in water when his Blackpool taxi driver refused to go any further.

This tiny, charismatic hotel, four rooms only, defies categorisation. The gregarious owner, Bill Scott is uncompromising in his view of the good things of life. Although some guests may feel unequal to the force of the Scott personality, the majority will quickly feel at ease.

Built in 1830 for a gentleman farmer, the house is a mellow, iconoclastic jumble of styles and furnishings, cats and dogs. Rooms at the front have romantic views over the estuary and Bowland Fells, as misty as a Turner painting in the morning light. Two have 1860s hooded baths, priceless Heath Robinson contraptions of pipes, showers and sprays that promise pleasure and palpitations in equal part.

Good food, drink and conversation rate highly in the Scott canon of hospitality. The restaurant has a well-established reputation for genuine, sound cooking with an emphasis on game and fish fresh from Fleetwood, and the wine list is impressive. Breakfasts offer home-made bread, honey from the comb and a leisurely read of the morning papers.

◐ Open all year; restaurant closed Sun eve

⤣ Take the A585 to Fleetwood and follow the road through 3 sets of traffic lights. At the roundabout take the third exit towards Little Thornton. As you leave the roundabout immediately on the left-hand side is Wyre Road leading to Skippool Creek. The house is at the end of this road on the left. Private car park

🛏 1 single, 2 double, 1 half-tester; all with bathroom/WC, exc single with shower/WC; TV, room service, hair-dryer, trouser press in all rooms

◇ Restaurant, bar, lounge, conservatory; conference facilities (max 20 people non-residential); golf, riding, other sports nearby

⊖ No wheelchair access; no dogs in public rooms

▭ Access, Visa

£ Single £65, single occupancy of twin/double £65, twin/double/half-tester £100. Set L, D £18.50; alc L, D £35 to £40

POWBURN NORTHUMBERLAND   **MAP 3**

Breamish House

POWBURN, NR ALNWICK, NORTHUMBERLAND NE66 4LL
TEL: POWBURN (0665) 78266   FAX: (0665) 78500

Pretty bedrooms and good food in an agreeable setting.

The history of the building has been upwardly mobile; the seventeenth-century farmhouse was gentrified into a hunting-lodge during the nineteenth century by the addition of a pedimented Georgian-style entrance. Public rooms are spacious and comfortable without being imposing. Light pours into the residents' drawing-room from windows on two sides, framed by splendid drapes that testify to owner Doreen Johnson's flair for interior design. Pink and green velour chairs mingle among tasteful fabric-covered sofas. The second, darker, sitting-room with blue wallcovering, leather chesterfields and a Lowry print has a more manly feel, while the front-facing dining-room is a traditional spot with plain walls cheered up by floral borders and framed caricatures. The limited-choice set menu served at a single sitting is essentially English, and the home-cooked food is generally praised, perhaps terrine of local rabbit layered with pistachio nuts served with a Cumberland sauce, followed by cream of parsnip soup, poached fillet of salmon served with a fresh dill sauce, and dessert.

Bedrooms, named after trees, are pleasantly furnished and individually decorated in a chintzy style. Sycamore and the recently refurbished Willow are among the most memorable, but all are comfortable and equipped to a very high standard with lots of extras.

The only niggle this year has been over service. One reader, pleased by the friendly reception, good-sized room and plentiful hot water, thought service at dinner was 'appalling'. Things did not improve in the morning, when dilatory service meant 'we had to forget about a cooked breakfast'. He was further discomfited on returning to his room to prepare for departure only to find that it had been made up and all the towels removed.

◐ Open all year, exc Jan and 1st week Feb

↗ 22 miles north of Morpeth on the A697 Coldstream road. There is a sharp right-hand bend as you enter Powburn; the hotel gates are on the left, approached by a long drive. Private car park

🛏 1 single, 3 twin, 6 double, 1 family cottage room; most with bathroom/WC, some with shower/WC; TV, room service (limited), hair-dryer, baby-listening in all rooms

◇ Dining-room, 2 lounges; conference facilities (max 15 people non-residential and residential); fishing, golf, riding nearby. Wheelchair access to restaurant and WC (unisex) only

⊖ Children under 12 by arrangement only; no dogs in public rooms; no smoking in restaurant and discouraged in bedrooms

▭ Access, Visa

£ Single £37 to £49, single occupancy of twin/double £45 to £66, twin/double £50 to £96, cottage room £68 to £97; deposit required. Sun L £13; set D £20; snack lunches from £3.50. Special breaks available

---

See the inside front cover for a brief explanation of how to use the Guide.

Three Horseshoes Inn

POWERSTOCK, BRIDPORT, DORSET DT6 3TF
TEL: POWERSTOCK (0308) 485328

Inexpensive rooms above a country pub possessing a reputation for good food with a bias towards fish and seafood.

The 'Shoes', as it is known locally, is perched high on an Arcadian Dorset hillside, reached through narrow, steep-banked lanes of wild-flower hedgerows. The pub is celebrated for the freshly cooked food served in the bar and restaurant. An extensive, changing menu of full meals and bar snacks is chalked up on boards in the thatched bar; people travel from miles around to dine, and to drink the real ale, draught scrumpy and freshly squeezed citron pressé. 'Small' dishes may include fish soup, scallop gratin or a salad of lightly fried pigeon breasts. Seafood pasta or Roman gnocchi may be amongst the fresh pasta dishes; main courses offer sea bass, grilled Dover sole, roast rack of Dorset lamb or mustard rabbit.

The four simple bedrooms look out on to the road; all are neatly but plainly furnished with old-fashioned dark furniture. As there is no private residents' lounge all activity is centred around the bar, which may be heaven for some but less so for others.

◑ Open all year

↗ Leave Bridport on the A3066 for Beaminster. At Gore Cross turn right, signposted Powerstock, and follow the signs. Private car park

🛏 1 single, 3 double; 2 with bathroom/WC, TV, trouser press

◈ Restaurant, bar, dining-room; fishing, golf, other sports nearby

⊖ No wheelchair access; no dogs in restaurant or dining-room; no smoking in restaurant

▭ Access, Amex, Visa

£ Single £24, double £45; deposit required. Set L £10.50; alc L £16.50, D £22.50. Special breaks available

---

PRESTBURY CHESHIRE   **MAP 5**

White House Manor ☆

COUNTY HOTEL OF THE YEAR

NEW ROAD, THE VILLAGE, PRESTBURY, CHESHIRE SK10 4HP
TEL: PRESTBURY (0625) 829376   FAX: (0625) 828627

Small, smart and stylish. Individual, themed rooms designed to pamper with copious comforts.

Prestbury is a well-kept and well-heeled village, home to local bigwigs and captains of industry. Now there is a small hotel in the village to match the needs of these groups and other fortunate travellers. An offshoot of the well-established White House Restaurant, the Manor provides a level of sybaritic style, designer chic and glossy good ideas that is outstanding given the scale. The atmosphere is luxuriously relaxed and hospitable, and the originality of much of the design so stirred local interest that owner Judith Wakeham found herself regularly conducting guided tours when she first opened.

Each of the nine bedrooms in the house, which dates back to the late 1700s, is completely different, beautifully designed to a theme. What they do have in common are immensely comfortable beds, power showers and body jets, black-out blinds, cut glass, bone china cups and flowering pot plants. One regular lady visitor even insists on having the house cat with her.

The Manor is within walking distance of the restaurant (noted for fashionable modern cooking), but has its own kitchen for breakfasts and room service. Breakfasts are taken in the sunny conservatory or are served in the bedrooms on mahogany trays set with Irish linen, Sheffield silver and pretty china. Freshly squeezed juice, locally smoked bacon and sausages and fresh croissants make a satisfying start to any day.

◑ *Open all year; restaurant closed Sun eve*

🔄 *2 miles from Wilmslow on the A538 Prestbury Road. Drive through the village and the hotel is on the right-hand side on the bend. Private car park*

🛏 *3 single, 1 twin, 4 double, 1 four-poster; some with bathroom/WC, some with shower/WC; TV, room service, hair-dryer, mini-bar, trouser press, baby-listening in all rooms*

◈ *Restaurant, bar, lounge, drying room, conservatory; conference facilities (max 40 people non-residential, 9 residential); fishing, golf, other sports nearby; babysitting. Wheelchair access to hotel, restaurant and WC (M,F), 2 ground-floor bedrooms*

⊖ *No dogs in public rooms*

▭ *Access, Amex, Diners, Visa*

£ *Single £65, single occupancy of twin/double £80, twin/double £90, four-poster £110; deposit required. Continental B £5, cooked B £8.50; set L £12, D £17; alc L, D £22. Special breaks available*

QUORN LEICESTERSHIRE   MAP 5

Quorn Country Hotel

66 LEICESTER ROAD, QUORN, LOUGHBOROUGH, LEICESTERSHIRE LE12 8BB
TEL: QUORN (0509) 415050   FAX: (0509) 415557

A small, well-established hotel with cheerful service.

Quorn's status as a country-house hotel is more secure since the bypass was built, taking much of the Loughborough-to-Leicester traffic away from the centre of the village. Formerly a gentlemen's club, the ruddy-coloured building has a large garden that makes it even more secluded and there is plenty of space to park. As well as floor-to-ceiling windows, the Orangery dining-room has cane chairs and a summery mural on one wall to give it an appealing garden feel. Dinner from the à la carte menu might include Stilton mushrooms, and crispy duck served with plum sauce. Service is friendly. Prettily upholstered sofas and seating arranged in small groups mean that the public areas avoid the impersonal feel large spaces sometimes fall victim to.

The reasonably sized bedrooms are well-decorated with light, mostly floral fabrics. Facilities include well-designed bathrooms, a choice of duvet or blankets and overnight shoe-cleaning – there's a car-cleaning service on offer too.

◑ Open all year, exc 1 Jan

↗ On the old A6 between Leicester and Loughborough. Leave the M1 at Junction 23. Private car park

🛏 11 twin, 5 double, 3 suites (1 a four-poster); all with bathroom/WC, TV, room service, hair-dryer, mini-bar, trouser press, baby-listening, air-conditioning

◈ 2 restaurants, bar, lounge, conservatory (hotel fully air-conditioned); ironing facilities; conference facilities (max 120 people non-residential, 20

residential); fishing at hotel, golf, other sports nearby. Wheelchair access to hotel (ramp) and restaurant, 8 ground-floor bedrooms, 1 specially equipped for disabled people

⊖ No dogs in public rooms

▭ Access, Amex, Diners, Visa

£ Single £80, single occupancy of twin/double £80, twin/double £92, suite £120. Continental B from £4; cooked B £9; Sun L £11.50; set D £18. Special breaks available

---

RAVENSTONEDALE CUMRBIA   MAP 3

Black Swan

RAVENSTONEDALE, KIRKBY STEPHEN, CUMBRIA CA17 4NG
TEL: NEWBIGGIN-ON-LUNE (05396) 23204

Solid Victorian hotel with hospitable hosts in pleasant countryside.

Fresh fruit in your hotel room for most people signifies nothing more than the thoughtfulness of the proprietors but the crisp green apples at the Black Swan also have a symbolic role, as Gordon and Norma Stuart like to think of their retreat, in a sleepy corner of the Vale of Eden, as an overpowering temptation for the jaded palates of hapless city-dwellers. The Victorian building of Lakeland stone stands at the bottom of a tranquil village street across the road from Scandal Beck whose meanderings guests are free to follow. At the end of the day all can choose from one of the six real ales and fifty wines available in the two bars. Residents tend to gather in the cosy first bar. With its deep-red carpet, low ceiling, a photo of a battleship on one wall and a print of a cat on another – it is a long way from the world of the theme pub! The second bar with stone walls hung with lithographs of Lakeland scenes is popular with walkers and has more of the feel of a local.

The bedrooms are all decorated in either deep comforting autumnal hues or smart stripes. Room Seven, which used to be the card room, has been recently converted and is bright and spacious with its own stone fireplace and a bathroom that has a bathtub and a power shower. Room Ten on the top floor is a twin with pine furniture and a bright floral duvet and has probably the best of the views. Dinner is served in simple yet elegant surroundings. Garlic and herb cream cheese pâté with slices of apple may be followed by spring vegetable soup and then oven-baked rainbow trout with toasted almonds and a choice of desserts. A reader sums up nicely the feelings of several others: 'This is a "good" pub/hotel in every sense – service, food and friendliness of staff.'

◑ Open all year

↗ Leave the M6 at Junction 38 and take the A685 towards Brough. Ravenstonedale is less than 10 minutes from the motorway. Private car park

🛏 1 single, 5 twin, 11 double; all with bathroom/WC, exc 2 doubles with shower/WC; TV, hair-dryer, baby-listening in all rooms; room service by arrangement

◇ 2 dining-rooms, 2 bars, 2 lounges, drying room; fishing, tennis at hotel. Wheelchair access to hotel (no steps), restaurant and WC (M, F), 3 ground-floor bedrooms specially equipped for disabled people

⊖ No dogs in public rooms; no smoking in dining-rooms

▭ Access, Amex, Diners, Visa

£ Single £41, single occupancy of twin/double £38 to £41, twin/double £57 to £60; deposit required. Set L £8.50, D £20; alc L from £4.50, D from £8. Special breaks available

Fat Lamb

CROSSBANK, RAVENSTONEDALE, KIRKBY STEPHEN, CUMBRIA CA17 4LL
TEL: NEWBIGGIN-ON-LUNE (05396) 23242

A country inn with a friendly atmosphere in an unspoilt corner of Cumbria.

The aerial photograph of the Fat Lamb which hangs on the wall of the television lounge shows that it is located at the outer reaches of the county's cultivated farmland where the wilder moorland begins. 'Four cars is a traffic jam around here,' jokes Paul Bonsall, who has been in charge for fifteen years. The sense of getting away from it all is enhanced by the inn's own lake and seven-acre nature reserve with hides that enable guests to observe all sorts of birdlife and animals – even a llama. Those content to sit in the garden may find they have to share it with a cluster of rabbits.

The cosy bar area has an old stove and hearth where a log fire burns. The low beams and harness on the wall add a touch of rusticity and the home-made collage dedicated to the llama or 'Cumbrian long-necked sheep' a touch of wry eccentricity. Paul likes to keep a separate coffee lounge for residents only so they can mingle away from the crowded bar area and there is also a television lounge with soft sofas and armchairs in autumnal shades. Almost every spare inch of the dining-room walls is taken up by a vast array of china plates and saucers, otherwise the room is simple and functional. The dinner menu might include hot mulled mushrooms, followed by Russian borscht soup and then baked trout with mustard sauce and a choice of desserts and cheeses. All of the bedrooms have great views and are simply and pleasantly decorated. Room Ten has light oak furniture with floral patterned carpet and duvet.

◑ Open all year

⤢ On the A683 between Kirkby Stephen and Sedburgh at the junction of a minor road running north to Ravenstonedale. Private car park

🛏 1 twin, 7 double, 4 family rooms; all with bathroom/WC, hair-dryer; TV on request

◈ Restaurant, bar, lounge, TV room, drying room; fishing at hotel, tennis, riding nearby. Wheelchair access to hotel, restaurant and WC (M, F), 5 ground-floor bedrooms, 4 specially equipped for disabled people

⊖ No smoking in restaurant or bedrooms

▭ None accepted

£ Single occupancy of twin/double £35 to £36, twin/double £54 to £56, family room rate on request; deposit required. Set L £12, D £16.50. Special breaks available

---

READING BERKSHIRE   MAP 9

Holiday Inn

CAVERSHAM BRIDGE, RICHFIELD AVENUE, READING, BERKSHIRE RG1 8BD
TEL: READING (0734) 391818   FAX: (0734) 391665

A large modern business hotel with a leisure club.

The Holiday Inn belongs to the Queens Moat House chain of hotels and is in a central position beside a busy junction and overlooking the Thames. From the car park you enter into a large, light, high-ceilinged area broken up by partitions of plants and varying colour schemes and styles. Here you will find the reception, the bar, the club-style lounge and the Bridges Restaurant, with its stylish black wrought-iron chairs and tables covered with crisp white tablecloths. Beyond, glass doors lead out on to the terrace. You can also relax in the pub, the Three Men in a Boat, or in the leisure centre, where executives can pump iron or splash up and down the pool.

Some bedrooms are non-smoking and some are designed for female travellers, with extra goodies in the bathrooms, a more feminine style of décor and security spy holes on bedroom doors. All are attractive in pastels with bold co-ordinated fabrics.

◑ Open all year, exc 25 to 30 Dec

↗ Leave the M4 at Junction 10 and follow signs for Caversham. The hotel is next to Caversham Bridge overlooking the river. Private car park

🛏 1 single, 49 twin, 50 double, 1 four-poster, 11 suites; all with bathroom/WC, TV, room service, hair-dryer, mini-bar, trouser press, baby-listening

◇ Restaurant, 2 bars, lounge; air-conditioned conference facilities (max 200 people non-residential, 112 residential); heated swimming-pool at hotel, other sports nearby; babysitting. Wheelchair access to hotel (ramp), restaurant and WC (unisex), no ground-floor bedrooms but large lift and 1 bedroom equipped for disabled people

⊖ None

▭ Access, Amex, Diners, Visa

£ Single and single occupancy of twin/double £102, twin/double £102, four-poster £205, suite £205. Continental B £6.50, cooked B £9; set L £14.50, D £19; alc L from £14.50, D £19

REDMILE LEICESTERSHIRE   **MAP 5**

Peacock Farm

REDMILE, NOTTINGHAMSHIRE NG13 0GQ
TEL: BOTTESFORD (0949) 42475

A well-run, informal country guesthouse with flexible, warm-hearted hosts.

Peacock Farm is a ramshackle collection of outbuildings, converted cow byres and caravans and, in the middle of it all, an eighteenth-century farmhouse. A working farm until the 1960s, the building was once a brick-making factory. Today it's a paradise for kids – there's an adventure playground, an indoor splash pool with plenty of space for parents to sit around it, an assortment of animals, bicycles you can borrow and walks along the banks of the Grantham canal.

The bedrooms are a motley assortment of sizes and styles, some *en suite* and others sharing bathrooms. The converted coach-house where roses grow up the wall is chalet-style, with wood-lined walls and bunk beds; Room Ten has pretty fabrics and french windows out on to the lawn; Room Three, in the main house, is simple and modern, with dormer windows giving views of nearby Belvoir Castle, home to the Duke of Rutland from whose coat of arms Peacock Farm gets its name.

Business people and families mix happily in the small restaurant, with its pine furniture and old farm implements. When we visited, Nicky was looking for a new chef as the old one had moved on, and was doing much of the cooking herself to ensure standards were kept up. A typical dinner from the short menu and 'specials' blackboard might include mushroom salad provençal, gravad lax, trout with Pernod or beef Wellington. One reader applauded the 'great shepherd's pie'.

◖ Open all year

⤴ Follow signs to Belvoir Castle. The farm is ½ mile out of Redmile village. Private car park

🛏 I single, 2 twin, 3 double, 4 family rooms; some with shower/WC, I with bathroom/WC; TV, baby-listening in all rooms

◈ Restaurant, bar, lounge, games room, drying room; conference facilities (max 10 people non-residential); unheated swimming-pool, croquet at hotel, other sports nearby. Wheelchair access to hotel and restaurant, 2 ground-floor bedrooms

⊖ No dogs; no smoking in restaurant

▭ Access, Visa

£ Single £19, single occupancy of twin/double £22 to £29, twin/double £34 to £42. Set D £12; alc D £17; light meals

---

REETH NORTH YORKSHIRE   **MAP 3**

Arkleside Hotel

REETH, RICHMOND, NORTH YORKSHIRE DL11 6SG
TEL: RICHMOND (0748) 84200   FAX: (0748) 84619

A real home-from-home with lovely hosts in a stunning area of Swaledale.

The combination of genuine northern warmth and the stunning views enjoyed from the rear-facing public rooms make this unpretentious hotel a clear winner. Malcolm and Sylvia Darby encourage first-name terms from the word go – 'You're one of the family from the start,' observed one correspondent. Public rooms are comfortable, with lots of chintz, flowers and knick-knacks, from the stone-walled bar with its prints of old Sheffield to the cosy, traditional lounge with its floral-patterned sofa and table loaded with reading matter. The sun-trap dining-room boasts a grandfather clock, wall-mounted plates and an embroidered sampler, as well as superb views of the Dale. Dinner is a traditional five-course affair featuring Yorkshire favourites – home-made soups, roasts and fresh fish, and, of course, cheese. 'Dinner – duck – very good indeed, though vegetables a little disappointing,' read one report. Breakfast is a generous, well-cooked start to the day.

Bedrooms are a reasonable size, neatly decorated in a sweet, frilly, rather feminine country-style with a good mix of old and new furniture and lots of oak and pine. 'All very good-humoured, kindly and excellent value,' concluded one guest.

◖ Closed Jan, Feb

⤴ Turn off the A1 at the Catterick and Richmond sign. Go into Richmond and follow signs to Reeth. Turn right by the war memorial. Private car park

🛏 3 twin, 5 double; all with shower/WC, exc I double with

shower only; TV, room service, hair-dryer in all rooms

◇ Dining-room, bar, lounge, drying facilities; conference facilities (max 20 people non-residential, 12 residential); tennis, golf, fishing, riding nearby

● No wheelchair access; no children under 10; no dogs in public rooms; smoking in bar only

▭ Access, Visa

£ Single occupancy of twin/double £35 to £40, twin/double £52 to £60; deposit required. Set D £15 (8pm). Special breaks available

Burgoyne Hotel

ON THE GREEN, REETH, RICHMOND, NORTH YORKSHIRE DL11 6SN
TEL: RICHMOND (0748) 84200   FAX: (0748) 84619/84691

A smart, handsomely furnished house run with care and attention.

The substantial, mainly nineteenth-century house is a model of elegance and restrained good taste, with a successful mix of antique, modern and reproduction furniture that achieves a relaxing, comfortable style with a traditional slant. The elegant main lounge has rich, deep-blue country-house décor, displays of plates, and a generous endowment of magazines and books. The smaller, non-smoking sitting-room blends an exposed stone wall with a gallery of classical and Venetian prints and a comfortable assembly of green velour and loose-covered chairs. Both dining-rooms have tasteful décor with ribbons adorning the walls. Food is generally traditional: 'The emphasis seems to be on broadly English cooking and demonstrates that this is not always the death knell for eating pleasure,' wrote one visitor, who found it 'one of the main attractions' of his stay. The menu is short but well-judged and affords reasonable choice at each stage – you might opt for salmon and sole pancakes *au gratin*, followed by cream of carrot and swede soup, roasted suprême of chicken and rhubarb and ginger crumble.

Bedrooms are tastefully decorated and attractively furnished with a mixture of antique, Edwardian, good reproduction and modern furniture. Proportions are generous and colour schemes, while predominantly autumnal or green, burst out of the mould in Keld and Grinton with cheerful yellow brightness. Views from most are stunning – at their best in July, when heather cushions the hills like velvet, says co-proprietor Derek Hickson.

◐ Open all year, exc 3 Jan to 1st weekend Feb

↗ From Richmond take the A6108 Richmond to Leyburn road. After 5 miles, take a right fork, the B6270, to Reeth. The hotel overlooks the green. Private car park

⇌ 2 twin, 6 double; all with bathroom/WC, exc 2 doubles with shower/WC; TV, room service, hair-dryer, baby-listening in all rooms

◇ 2 dining-rooms, 2 lounges, drying room; conference facilities (max 10 people non-residential and residential); fishing, riding, other sports nearby; babysitting

⊖ No wheelchair access; no unattended dogs in bedrooms; smoking in lounge only

▭ Access, Visa

£ Single occupancy of twin/double £50 to £60, twin/double £60 to £70. Sun L £12; set D £19.50

RENDCOMB GLOUCESTERSHIRE　　　　　　　　**MAP 9**

Shawswell

RENDCOMB, NR CIRENCESTER, GLOUCESTERSHIRE GL7 7HD
TEL: CIRENCESTER (0285) 831779

A far-away-from-it-all guesthouse on the fringes of the Cotswolds.

After all those country-house hotels the country guesthouse was bound to follow – and it is a welcome concept, for it implies value and friendliness on the one hand and something a little posher than the typical farmhouse bed and breakfast on the other. David and Muriel Gomm's enterprise is a good prototype, for here is an utterly isolated seventeenth-century house, carefully restored and turned into a refuge for country-lovers. The sitting-room is comfortable and relaxing with a wood-burning stove and wing chairs, and the furnishings are generally a high-quality mix of the antique and the new – to be seen to good effect in the Blue Room, where the bathroom gleams in smart modernity while the bedroom is tastefully cottagey with blue and white china. Shawswell's dinners, with a choice at each course, are unlikely to disappoint, either in price or quality. Uncomplicated, well-flavoured dishes prepared with great care are the rule.

◑ Closed Dec and Jan; dining-room closed Wed and Sun eves

↗ From the A435 follow signs to Rendcomb. After passing the post office, follow the 'Shawswell No Through Road' for 1½ miles. Turn left and immediately right at the old stone barn. Private car park

⇌ 1 single, 1 twin, 2 double, 1 four-poster; all with bathroom/WC, exc single with shower/WC; TV in all rooms; hair-dryer on request

◇ Dining-room, lounge; fishing, golf, swimming-pool, gym nearby

⊖ No wheelchair access; no children under 10; no dogs; smoking in lounge only

▭ None accepted

£ Single £30 to £35, single occupancy of twin/double £30 to £35, twin/double £45 to £55, four-poster £50 to £60; deposit required. Set D £16. Special breaks available

---

 This denotes that the hotel is in an exceptionally peaceful situation where you can be assured of a restful stay.

RHYDYCROESAU SHROPSHIRE   **MAP 5**

Pen-y-Dyffryn Hall

RHYDYCROESAU, NR OSWESTRY, SHROPSHIRE SY10 7DT
TEL: OSWESTRY (0691) 653700

Wonderful countryside, and the hotel gets lots of praise too.

A visitor to this isolated old rectory sums up the virtues of the place in useful telegraphese: 'A comfortable hotel in lovely surroundings, with magnificent views. Surprisingly large bed and bathrooms, beautifully furnished. Good friendly service, good home-cooked food, wine a little limited. Very nice couple running it. Very reasonable prices. P.S. Very good strong coffee.' Another visitor reassures canine guests: 'The owners were very tolerant towards my very large boisterous dog.' Miles and Audrey Hunter run Pen-y-Dyffryn in a welcoming and very informal style. It is very much a go-as-you-please hotel, with comfortably battered armchairs, bright floral fabrics in the bedrooms and excellent towels in the bathrooms. The countryside, wild and with only the sheep for company, is close to where Offa built his dyke, and this hotel makes an ideal base for walkers, dog-owners or not.

◑ Open all year

⤷ From Oswestry take the B4580 (Willow Street) out of town. The hotel is 3 miles west of Oswestry on the left. Private car park

🛏 1 single, 2 twin, 2 double, 1 four-poster, 1 family room; all with bathroom/WC, exc single and 1 double with shower/WC; TV, room service, hair-dryer, trouser press, baby-listening in all rooms

◇ 2 restaurants, bar, 2 lounges; conference facilities (max 30 people non-residential, 7 residential); fishing, walks at hotel, other sports nearby. Wheelchair access to restaurants only

⊖ No smoking in restaurant

▭ Access, Amex, Visa

£ Single and single occupancy of twin/double £35 to £40, twin/double £58 to £64, four-poster/family room £69 to £77; deposit required. Set D £13.50; alc D £16 to £20. Special breaks available

---

RICHMOND NORTH YORKSHIRE   **MAP 3**

Howe Villa

WHITCLIFFE MILL, RICHMOND, NORTH YORKSHIRE DL10 4TJ
TEL: RICHMOND (0748) 850055

A small riverside hotel that has cheerful hosts, smashing food and lovely gardens.

'Turn left at the tyre service centre' is hardly the most enticing of directions, but in fact there's nothing prosaic about the place once you get there and come face to face with an immaculate early-nineteenth-century mansion fronted by a tiny fountain, trim lawns and splendid woodland gardens that hug the banks of the River Swale. You won't be disappointed when you enter within, either. Teddy bears on an old settle return your gaze in a hallway which leads upstairs to spacious public rooms, a high-ceilinged drawing-room and a bright dining-room over-looking the river.

A sense of fair play dictates that occupants of the one viewless bedroom are allocated the window table in the dining-room. It's impossible not to be won over by a menu which begins with 'Your favourite drink'. What follows is equally agreeable – an Anglo-French menu with set soup and main courses and a choice of starters and puddings. You might dine on sole and smoked salmon mousseline, followed by carrot and coriander soup, rack of roast lamb with a herb crust and a rosemary and redcurrant sauce, tarte au citron, and Swaledale cheese.

Bedrooms are generously proportioned, and comfortably furnished in a pleasant, tasteful but unfussy way. Bathrooms are spacious. Tom and Anita Berry's friendly warmth has won them an army of regulars, one of whom reported, 'Still as good as ever. A lovely place.'

◑ Closed Dec, Jan, Feb

⤢ Howe Villa is half a mile from the centre of Richmond. Leave Richmond on the A6108 towards Leyburn. Turn left at the tyre service station and keep left, following the signs to Howe Villa. Private car park

🛏 3 twin, 2 double; all with bathroom/WC, TV, room service, hair-dryer

◈ Dining-room, lounge; fishing, golf, riding, other sports nearby

⊖ No wheelchair access; no children under 12; no dogs; no smoking in bedrooms

▭ None accepted

£ Single occupancy of twin/double £56, twin/double £100 to £110 (rates inc dinner); deposit required. Set D £20 (7.30pm)

RINGWOOD HAMPSHIRE   **MAP 9**

Moortown Lodge

244 CHRISTCHURCH ROAD, RINGWOOD, HAMPSHIRE BH24 3AS
TEL: RINGWOOD (0425) 471404

Friendly, well-kept and very handy for the New Forest.

A typical white-painted Georgian house, Moortown Lodge used to be the fishing lodge of the Moortown estate, the home of William Gladstone's family. It's now a compact and homely hotel run by Jilly and Bob Burrows-Jones, who have slowly and carefully refurbished the place over the past seven years.

They've taken inspiration from the style of French *logis*: window shutters and two *tricolores* give the game away on the outside, while the interior is hung with maps and pictures of France. The dinnertime table d'hôte and gourmet menus are good value, offering, where possible, local produce adapted to a French style: typical dishes include fillet of lamb with a sherry and mushroom sauce, and veal with a Stilton cream sauce. The dining-room is adorned with flowers and crisp white tablecloths and has a fresh, relaxing feel, as does the small lounge, which is furnished with dark leather and blue velvet armchairs and an array of books. The six small bedrooms are decorated in bright, largely floral patterns to compensate for the slight shortage of light from the windows. All rooms have secondary glazing – the minor road at the front is busy during the day but quiet at night.

- ◑ Open all year, exc 25 Dec to 14 Jan
- ⤢ 1½ miles south of Ringwood on the B3347. Private car park
- 🛏 1 single, 2 twin, 2 double, 1 four-poster; some with shower/WC, 1 with bathroom/WC, 1 public shower; TV, room service in all rooms; hair-dryer on request
- ◈ Restaurant, bar, lounge; fishing, golf, other sports nearby
- ⊖ No wheelchair access; no dogs; no smoking in restaurant
- ▭ Access, Visa
- £ Single £29 to £31, single occupancy of twin/double £38 and from £40, twin/double £52 and from £56, four-poster £60 to £66; deposit required. Set D £17; alc D £24.50. Special breaks available

Hotel Renouf

BRADLEY WAY, ROCHFORD, ESSEX SS4 1BU
TEL: SOUTHEND-ON-SEA (0702) 541334   FAX: (0702) 549563

A much-acclaimed hotel/restaurant lying a handy distance from Southend Airport.

Praise has poured in for Derek Renouf's hotel-and-restaurant venture in Rochford – which is surprising if you go by first impressions, since the red-brick building next to a pay-and-display car park looks more like an edge-of-town supermarket than 'the finest restaurant in this part of Essex', as one local claims it to be. In fact it is easy to wonder whether you have come to the right place until you are well across the threshold. In this case, though, appearances deceive, and any initial doubts will be vanquished by the service, accommodation and food you encounter within. 'Strangers are treated as friends of the family,' endorses one guest; 'We consider the prices very sensible and pleasing,' says another.

The comfortable bedrooms hold no particular surprises; they are slickly decorated and have lots of facilities. Certificates, photographs, framed diplomas and awards on the walls mean that only the completely unobservant will remain ignorant of Derek Renouf's successes. Duck dishes, mostly prepared for a minimum of two diners, are the speciality of the house: you can enjoy pressed duck framboise, fresh Aylesbury duck or breast of duck cassis. If you prefer to duck out, there are plenty of fish and meat dishes. Pictures of cricket teams and signed bats in the bar suggest that Derek has other interests too and, indeed, the *Renouf Times* lists a bevy of events, both sporting and jazz-orientated, which guests are welcome to attend.

◑ Open all year, exc 26 to 30 Dec

🔁 Close to the railway station in Rochford just off the A127. Private car park

🛏 7 single, 15 twin/double, 1 suite, 1 family room; all with bathroom/WC, TV, room service, hair-dryer, baby-listening; trouser press, mini-bar in some rooms

◈ Restaurant (air-conditioned), bar, lounge, function room; conference facilities (max 40 people residential, 70 non-residential); fishing, golf, other sports nearby. Wheelchair access to hotel (1 step), restaurant and WC (unisex), 7 ground-floor bedrooms, 1 specially equipped for disabled people

⬤ Dogs in public rooms by arrangement only

▭ Access, Amex, Diners, Visa

£ Single £58, single occupancy of twin/double £68, twin/double £78, suite £98, family room £93; deposit required. Set L £12.50, D £19.50; alc L, D £30

ROCKBOURNE HAMPSHIRE   **MAP 9**

Shearings   ℒ 🌿

ROCKBOURNE, FORDINGBRIDGE, HAMPSHIRE SP6 3NA
TEL: ROCKBOURNE (07253) 256 (and fax)

A family welcome at an idyllic country cottage.

Rockbourne feels like a distillation of rural Englishness, with rows of thatched cottages and a stream running along the main street. Situated in a sleepy spot, the village even boasts a Roman villa. Shearings, a sixteenth-century timber-framed red-brick house where even the portico is thatched, is reached by crossing a tiny bridge over the village stream.

Inside, you'll find low oak beams (some nearly 1,000 years old) and an archetypal cottagey feel, with pressed flower pictures and chinzy chairs. The owners, Colin and Rosemary Watts, are former diplomats and like to treat guests as family. If dining, you'll be served pre-prandial drinks in the lounge or on the well-tended lawns at the back of the house, and you'll eat *en famille* in the candlelit dining-room – one reader has called the food 'an absolute indulgence', going on to praise the Watts for being 'gracious and considerate' hosts.

The three bedrooms upstairs run off a long, uneven-floored landing. Though small, they're bright and charmingly decorated, with open beams criss-crossing simple white walls.

◑ Closed mid-Dec to mid-Feb; dining-room closed Sun eves

⬈ From Salisbury take the A354 Blandford road; I mile after Coombe Bisset turn left to Rockbourne. From Fordingbridge take the B3078 towards Damerham; before reaching Damerham turn right to Rockbourne. Private car park

🛏 I single, I twin, I double; I with private bathroom, 2 with shower room; hair-dryer in all rooms

◈ Dining-room, breakfast room, lounge, TV room, games room; croquet at hotel, other sports nearby

⊖ No wheelchair access; no children under 12; no dogs; no smoking in bedrooms

▭ None accepted

£ Single £22, single occupancy of twin/double £29, twin/double £44 to £46; deposit required. Set D £19 (8pm, by arrangement only); packed lunches by arrangement (prices till Apr 94). Special breaks available

---

ROGATE WEST SUSSEX　　　　　　　　　　　　　　　　**MAP 9**

Mizzards Farm

ROGATE, PETERSFIELD, HAMPSHIRE GU3I 5HS
TEL: ROGATE (0730) 821656

Peaceful seclusion in an excellent countryside bed and breakfast.

Down a pot-holed dirt road by the River Rother you'll find this grand stone and brick building which has been turned into a bed and breakfast

MIZZARDS FARM
-ROGATE-

of the highest quality by the Francis family. The farmhouse dates from the sixteenth century, though it has been extended at various times since; it has fine views over acres of lawns, flower-beds and peaceful open country. The centrepiece is a large, baronial-type hall, open to the rafters two floors above and girded by a polished wooden staircase and galleried landing. Here guests take their well-presented breakfasts – complete with home-produced honey and jam – on the flagstone floor in front of the huge fireplace. At the far end of the house is a spacious drawing-room, elegantly furnished with comfortable sofas, open fire and grand piano (and a payphone).

The pop star who once owned the house has left his mark upstairs in an extraordinary bedroom with a pink satin canopy, white pillars and a double bath. The two other rooms – a large twin and a smaller double – are much more what you'd expect: pretty and cottagey, with antique furniture, landscape prints, fresh flowers and books. A correspondent praised Julian and Harriet Francis for their courtesy and competence, adding, 'it is difficult to imagine a more relaxing situation'.

◐ Open all year, exc Xmas

⤵ Travel south from the crossroads in Rogate, over the bridge and take the first road on the right. Private car park

🛏 I twin, I double, I four-poster; all with bathroom/WC, TV, room service, hair-dryer

◈ Breakfast room, lounge, drying room; heated swimming-pool

(Apr to Oct) at hotel, other sports nearby

⊖ No wheelchair access; no children under 7; no dogs; no smoking

▭ None accepted

£ Single occupancy of twin/double £30 to £34, twin/double £44, four-poster £50; deposit required

---

ROMALDKIRK CO DURHAM　　　　　　　　　　　**MAP 3**

Rose and Crown

ROMALDKIRK, BARNARD CASTLE, CO DURHAM DL12 9EB
TEL: TEESDALE (0833) 50213　FAX: (0833) 50828

Mixed reports on this traditional village inn well-placed for exploring Co. Durham, Northumbria and the fringes of Cumbria.

You're well advised to pre-book if you want to eat at this warm stone inn surrounded by rolling hills and bleak moorland on a Saturday or Sunday; locals come in droves, attracted by the reputation of the food. The atmosphere is countrified and uncontrived – hunting photos line the walls, old gin traps, brass plates, horse brasses and a log fire adorn the rustic bars, and the floorboards creak on the stairs to the main-house bedrooms. Things are a touch more refined and formal in the wood-panelled restaurant, though the lively bar with its lengthy supper menu has its own compensations, despite a certain casualness in the service. While restaurant diners are eating hot mousselines of crab with a butter sauce, cauliflower and blue cheese soup, monkfish tails cooked in Noilly Prat with tomatoes, mushrooms, tarragon and chives, the bar supper brigade tuck into venison pâté, pork fillets in cream sauce with pasta and salad, and a wicked walnut and syrup tart. The cosy residents' lounge has modern sofas, heavy beams, antique tables and a gallery of characters including Jester and Don Quixote above the electric fire.

One visitor who stayed in an annexe room was complimentary about the level of comfort: 'One of the best we have ever come across. Both it and the bathroom were spacious and very well equipped.' Another was damning about a main-house room – judging it 'Less than adequate. Would benefit from a refurbish' – and was displeased with the bathroom: 'Defunct shower. No shelves to place toiletries on.' The three bedrooms we inspected were neat, with modern pine or lovely antique furniture, bold modern fabrics and crown canopies.

While our disgruntled correspondent found the welcome 'perfunctory', another advised, 'We have every intention to return. We couldn't have been more comfortable nor had a friendlier welcome.' More reports, please.

◗ Open all year, exc 25, 26 Dec; restaurant closed Sun eve

⤢ Romaldkirk is 6 miles north-west of Barnard Castle on the B6277. Private car park

🛏 5 twin, 3 double, 1 four-poster, 1 family room, 2 suites (some rooms in annexe); most with bathroom/WC, some with shower/WC; TV, baby-listening in all rooms; limited room service

◈ Restaurant, 2 bars, lounge, drying room; conference facilities (max 12 people non-residential and residential); fishing, golf, other sports nearby. Wheelchair access to hotel (no steps) and restaurant, 5 ground-floor bedrooms, 1 specially equipped for disabled people

⊖ No dogs in restaurant or lounge

▭ Access, Visa

£ Single £52, single occupancy of twin/double £52, twin/double £75, four-poster/family room/ suite £88; deposit required. Set L £11.50, D £23. Special breaks available

---

ROSEDALE ABBEY NORTH YORKSHIRE　　　　　　　**MAP 3**

White Horse Farm Hotel

ROSEDALE ABBEY, NR PICKERING, NORTH YORKSHIRE YO18 8SE
TEL: LASTINGHAM (07515) 239

A satisfyingly traditional, comfortable but unpretentious inn deep in the North York Moors National Park.

There are more stylish places to stay in North Yorkshire, but few can match the stupendous views from this rambling converted farmhouse or grant an opportunity to eat in a neo-Gothic restaurant. The lounge is a cosy, homely affair with brown velour sofas, a swirling patterned carpet and a log-effect electric fire, as well as a beamed ceiling, Queen Anne-style chairs and lots of tourist information. Roomy bedrooms have emulsioned woodchip walls and teak furniture, but floral borders and bright fabrics help to cheer them up.

The bar is a rugged affair, popular with hikers and day-trippers. Lamps hang from the beams, and foxes' heads, stuffed birds and a collection of tankards add to the rustic feel, while caricatures and a Singer Sargent print add a hint of sophistication. A good choice of hearty food is chalked up on a blackboard.

Best of all is the Misericord Restaurant, with its wonderfully churchy atmosphere derived from Gothic arches and windows, tapestry wall hangings, and candles flickering in red lamps. Food is as traditionally English as its setting; perhaps mushrooms sautéed in a creamy paprika sauce served with a crispy fried croûton, home-made soup, a chunky venison casserole in a rich game gravy, and home-made fruit cake with Wensleydale cheese.

- ◐ Open all year, exc 24 to 26 Dec
- ↗ Take A170 out of Pickering, turn right at sign for Rosedale, follow signs for 7 miles. Upon entering the village, turn left at sign to hotel. Private car park
- 🛏 3 twin, 11 double, 1 family room, some rooms in annexe; some with bathroom/WC, most with shower/WC; TV, baby-listening in all rooms
- ◇ Restaurant, bar, lounge, drying room; conference facilities (max

15 people residential, 30 non-residential); fishing, golf, riding, other sports nearby
- ⊖ No wheelchair access; no dogs in restaurant
- ▭ Access, Amex, Diners, Visa
- £ Single occupancy of twin/double £32 to £35, twin/double £54 to £60, family room from £64; deposit required. Sun L £7.50; set D from £15; alc L, D £17. Special breaks available

---

ROSS-ON-WYE HEREFORD AND WORCESTER   **MAP 9**

The Chase Hotel ☆

GLOUCESTER ROAD, ROSS-ON-WYE, HEREFORD AND WORCESTER
HR9 5LH
TEL: ROSS-ON-WYE (0989) 763161   FAX: (0989) 768330

A well-kept hotel in an interesting building, ideal for conferences.

The interior of the Chase was much altered around 1890, although the house is older. It stands four-square (except for the modern extension) in a small piece of parkland on the outskirts of Ross-on-Wye, looking very much the gentleman's residence, with portico and Tuscan-arched ground-floor windows. Inside, there are High Gothic features – a row of arches marching down the patterned tiles of the entrance hall and a stylish carved staircase. The public rooms are spacious and given unity by the acres of blue carpet that seems to run throughout the building. The restaurant is split by an arch between the original room of the house and the modern extension; it is a little narrow, but warmly apricot in colour. Bedrooms are good, though not lavish, with modern dark or white wooden furniture and pretty bathrooms. Dinner avoids too much fanciness: maybe chicken stuffed with tomato and mushroom sauce or plaice rolled with a salmon mousse and white wine sauce.

◑ *Open all year*

↗ *Leave the M50 at Junction 4 and take the A40 towards Gloucester. At next roundabout turn right for the town centre. The hotel is 1½ miles along this road on the left-hand side. Private car park*

🛏 *15 twin, 21 double, 2 four-poster, 1 family room; all with bathroom/WC, TV, room service, hair-dryer, trouser press, baby-listening*

◈ *Restaurant, bar, lounge; conference facilities (max 300 people non-residential, 50 residential); fishing, golf, other sports nearby. Wheelchair access to hotel (ramp), restaurant and WC (M, F) only*

⊖ *No dogs*

▭ *Access, Amex, Diners, Visa*

£ *Single occupancy of twin/double £50, twin/double £60, four-poster £100, family room £80; deposit required. Set L £12.50, D £20; alc L, D £25 to £32.50 (prices till Sept 93). Special breaks available*

Upper Pengethley Farm

ROSS-ON-WYE, HEREFORD AND WORCESTER HR9 6LL
TEL: HAREWOOD END (0989 87) 687

Great value in this lovely farmhouse bed and breakfast.

Up a bumpy track a few miles west of Ross-on-Wye, you will find the Partridges' Georgian farmhouse sitting prettily in the middle of the clutter of a mixed farm, with a small lake and a lawn in front. It is an ideal hideaway for country-lovers, made extra good by the quality of Sue Partridge's bedrooms and by the breakfast room in the former kitchen, where a huge pine dresser and a piano dominate the surroundings. Bedrooms are of more than adequate size and are all well-furnished with interesting pieces picked up in local salerooms. There is even a suite – the upstairs double has its own small lounge. Bathrooms, unlike those in so many bed and breakfasts, are all large and well-equipped. Add to these things is the fact that the farmhouse stands in especially attractive countryside, with views dropping towards the Wye.

◑ *Open all year, exc Xmas and New Year*

↗ *The farm is situated on the A49 Hereford to Ross-on-Wye road, 4 miles from Ross-on-Wye. It is next to the Pengethley Hotel and a garden centre. Private car park*

🛏 *1 twin, 1 double, 1 suite; all with bathroom/WC; TV*

◈ *Breakfast room*

⊖ *No wheelchair access; no dogs in public rooms; no smoking*

▭ *None accepted*

£ *Single occupancy of twin/double £17.50, twin/double/suite £35*

ROSTHWAITE CUMBRIA   **MAP 4**

Hazel Bank

ROSTHWAITE, BORROWDALE, KEWSICK, CUMBRIA CA12 5XB
TEL: BORROWDALE (07687) 77248

A genuinely friendly atmosphere in a value-for-money guesthouse.

When businesses are thriving the received wisdom dictates expansion, but at Hazel Bank John and Gwen Nuttall have decided that small is beautiful – in recent years they have been reducing the number of bedrooms down to the present and final six. Each is named after the fell it overlooks: Great Gable is a large and stylish four-poster room, while Bowfell is a slightly smaller twin with bright floral bedcovers and two large pink armchairs. Scafell Pike is similarly bright and spacious, with a striking print of the fell on one wall. All have brand-new bathrooms.

The stone-built Victorian house has an elevated position that enables more sedentary guests to enjoy the splendid panorama without having to get out of their armchairs. The lounge has also been subject to the Nuttalls' rolling refurbishment programme, with a complete redecoration and recarpeting finished in early 1993.

Gwen, a no-nonsense Mancunian who treats guests like members of the family, makes no apologies for providing a dinner aimed at those whose appetites have been sharpened by the great outdoors. 'Food fads and fashions come and go,' she observes, so the table d'hôte menu is traditional British: smoked venison salad may be followed by halibut in fresh watercress sauce with a Bakewell tart among a choice of desserts. Cumbrian cheeses round off the meal.

◐ Closed from end Oct to Apr (exc long weekends Nov and Mar)

⬀ From Keswick follow the B5289 signposted Borrowdale. Just before Rosthwaite village, turn left, crossing the river over the humpbacked bridge. Private car park.

🛏 1 single, 3 twin, 1 double, 1 four-poster; all with bathroom/WC, TV, hair-dryer

◈ Dining-room, lounge, drying room; fishing nearby

⊖ No wheelchair access; no children under 6; no dogs in public rooms and by prior arrangements in bedrooms; no smoking

▭ Access, Visa

£ Single £42, twin/double £84, four-poster £84 (rates inc dinner, 7pm); deposit required. Special breaks available

ROWSLEY DERBYSHIRE   **MAP 5**

Peacock Hotel

ROWSLEY, MATLOCK, DERBYSHIRE DE4 2EB
TEL: MATLOCK (0629) 733518   FAX: (0629) 732671

Well-run, traditional hotel belonging to the Jarvis chain, with uniformed staff and good-sized bedrooms.

Day-trippers seek out the Peacock Hotel for lunches and afternoon teas, and you can see why they come. Its position next to the busy A6 means that the garden suffers some traffic noise, but it's so pretty you don't really mind; uniformed staff glide between rustic benches and tables against a backdrop of hollyhocks, poppies and foxgloves. Inside, you can't miss the peacock theme, for at every turn there is a painting, woodcarving or brass ornament to drive the message home – even the curtains in the restful blue sitting-room have a peacock print. A stuffed brown trout is encased near the entrance and if this inspires you, the hotel has 12 rods along the River Wye. Roast Derbyshire chicken, pan-fried lamb's liver with black pudding and rosemary and poached salmon may be on the menu, with traditional trifle and farmhouse cheeses to follow. The solid oak tables and chairs in the beamed dining-rooms are hand-made.

The bedrooms are similarly equipped with antiques, dried flowers and fresh fruit, and a basket of goodies in the bathroom. Some rooms are smart with striped paper, others pretty with flowery fabrics and plain walls. Those overlooking the garden are best.

◑ Open all year

⤢ In the village of Rowsley, on the A6, 3 miles south of Bakewell, 5 miles north of Matlock. Private car park

🛏 2 single, 5 twin, 6 double, 1 four-poster; most with bathroom/WC, some with shower/WC; TV, room service, baby-listening, trouser press, hair-dryer in all rooms

◇ 3 dining-rooms, bar, lounge; conference facilities (max 18 people non-residential, 8 residential); fishing in grounds, other sports nearby

⊖ No wheelchair access; no dogs in public rooms and in some bedrooms by arrangement only

▭ Access, Amex, Diners, Visa

£ Single £48 to £58, single occupancy of twin/double £58 to £68, twin/double £58 to £78, four-poster £99. Continental B £7, cooked B £9.50; set L £13.50, D £22; alc D £26. Special breaks available

---

RUGBY WARWICKSHIRE   **MAP 5**

Avondale Guest House

16 ELSEE ROAD, RUGBY, WARWICKSHIRE CV21 3BA
TEL: RUGBY (0788) 578639

Good-value accommodation in a simple bed and breakfast in a quiet residential street close to the town centre.

William Webb Ellis put the town on the map when he ran with the ball in his hands during a game of football, and so invented rugby. It's a pleasant enough town today, composed mostly of red-brick buildings and leafy residential streets. Carole Webb, a friendly and charming host, runs a neat bed and breakfast that has no pretensions to be anything more – a formula that works well. The main room downstairs, serving as both sitting- and dining-room, is a riot of patterns and colour, from a collection of willow pattern plates on the walls to flowery tablecloths and cottagey loose-covered sofa and chairs. Along with a standard full English breakfast, Carole provides fruit juice and cereals and is happy to accommodate special requests where she can. The bedrooms are light, well-aired and very well-kept, with modern furnishings that are comfortable rather than stylish.

◐ Open all year, exc Xmas

↗ Off Moultrie road, close to Rugby public school. Private car park

🛏 3 twin, 1 family room; 1 with shower/WC, 2 public bathrooms; TV in all rooms

◈ Dining-room/lounge; fishing, golf, other sports nearby

⊖ No wheelchair access; no dogs; no smoking

▭ None accepted

£ Single occupancy of twin/double £20 to £25, twin/double £34 to £38

RUSHLAKE GREEN EAST SUSSEX   **MAP 8**

Stone House

RUSHLAKE GREEN, HEATHFIELD, EAST SUSSEX TN21 9QJ
TEL: RUSHLAKE GREEN (0435) 830553   FAX: (0435) 830726

'A real haven, magnificent food and wonderful surroundings.'

Warnings to drive slowly up to Stone House should be heeded – the narrow road skirts the large duck pond and it wouldn't take much on a dark night to overstep the mark. The other reason for approaching the huge grey fifteenth-century stone manor house at a slow pace is that you may find the family of six geese ambling across the road.

This aristocratic family home belongs to Peter and Jane Dunn, who have restored and modernised rooms and opened the doors to the public, allowing people to take a peek at their family history. On the right of the entrance hall is the drawing-room, where full-length bay windows overlook the gardens and pond and cabinets containing eighteenth-century china and antiques line the salmon-coloured walls. The library on the other side of the hall is also littered with beautiful antiques and paintings.

Jane does all the cooking and your meal may be smoked salmon pancakes with crème fraîche and dill, followed by fillet of pork with a sauce of cherries, cranberries and port or roast quail stuffed with apricots. Dinner is taken in the intimate, dark, pine-panelled dining-room; a red-brick floor and copper-topped fireplace give the room a glow, and a collection of china dogs peers down from the mantelpiece.

Of the bedrooms, the two four-poster rooms are the most luxurious and have bathrooms big enough to entertain in. The Green Room is very pretty, with even the hot-water bottles covered to match the décor. All are extremely comfortable, with antique furnishings and high beds.

◐ Open all year, exc 23 Dec to 16 Jan

↗ From Heathfield take the B2096 towards Battle and take the 4th turning on the right to Rushlake Green. In the village, take a left turn with the green to the right. Continue to crossroads and the entrance is on the left. Private car park

🛏 2 twin, 4 double, 2 four-poster; all with bathroom/WC, TV, room service; hair-dryer on request

✧ Restaurant, lounge, drying room, library, games room; conference facilities (max 16 people non-residential, 8 residential); snooker, billiards, clay pigeon and game shooting, croquet at hotel, other sports nearby

⊖ No wheelchair access; no children under 9; no dogs in public rooms

▭ None accepted

£ Single £55 to £72, single occupancy of twin/double £55 to £72, twin/double £85 to £95, four-poster £120 to £163. Set D £25

RUSPER WEST SUSSEX   **MAP 9**

Ghyll Manor Hotel

HIGH STREET, RUSPER, NR HORSHAM, WEST SUSSEX RH12 4PX
TEL: CRAWLEY (0293) 871571   FAX: (0293) 871419

A Tudor-style hotel in a rural landscape, convenient for Gatwick.

Ghyll Manor is an attractive white brick and timbered building with a pleasant terrace and extensive grounds. It is reached via a tangle of country lanes that can be confusing. Although Forte-owned (and on the market), the hotel has a friendly ambience compared to some of the more anonymous airport hotels nearby, and rich colours and spacious rooms make it quite plush. Interesting extras like the cherub lamps on the landing give the place character. The restaurant has a low beamed ceiling and is lavishly done out with elaborate gilt wall lamps, rich red screens and grand piano; there are fresh flowers on every table and a sample menu could be something like cauliflower fritters with a blue cheese dip, carpetbag steak or red bean hotpot with braised rice. The lounge is warm and intimate, with a mixture of red and pink sofas and armchairs; it leads through to a small bar with a red-brick floor and bright green cane sofas.

Bedrooms are good-sized and attractively decorated, though the ones in the Stable Mews are slightly less interesting. Pinks is very large and has a Regency air given by its gilt mirror and gold-coloured taps. Beams is aptly named, having a slanting beamed roof as well as lead-latticed windows, a grand four-poster bed and a huge bathroom.

◐ Open all year

↗ In the centre of Rusper, 3½ miles east of the A24. Private car park

🛏 4 single, 2 twin, 10 double, 4 four-poster, 1 family room, 2 suites, 2 cottages; all with bathroom/WC, TV, room service, hair-dryer, trouser press, baby-listening

◈ Restaurant, bar, library; conference facilities (max 100 people non-residential, 25 residential); tennis, croquet at hotel, other sports nearby; babysitting by arrangement. Wheelchair access to hotel and restaurant, 7 ground-floor bedrooms

⊖ No smoking in restaurant

▭ Access, Amex, Diners, Visa

£ Single £70, single occupancy of twin/double £80, twin/double £95, four-poster £95, family room/suite/cottage £100. Continental B £6, cooked B £8.50; set D £17; alc L from £3, D £30. Special breaks available

---

RYE EAST SUSSEX   **MAP 8**

Jeake's House

MERMAID STREET, RYE, EAST SUSSEX TN31 7ET
TEL: RYE (0797) 222828   FAX: (0797) 222623

A delightful, historic bed and breakfast, run with great pride.

Jeake's House stands on what must be one of the prettiest streets in England, a medieval cobbled way of white-painted, red-tiled cottages with names like 'House with two front doors' and 'House with a seat'. Jeake's was built as a wool store and later became a Baptist school: a plaque records the laying of the foundation stone (noon on 13 June 1689), with a horoscope showing the exact aspects of the heavens at that time. A galleried chapel added to the house in the following century now serves as a splendid setting for breakfast – a most civilised affair, served to the sounds of baroque music under the gaze of family portraits.

Bedrooms are a delight: furnished with brass or mahogany beds, balloon-back chairs, linen sheets and lace, they're generally Victorian in style, but with plenty of individuality. There is also a sitting-room area, with a bar made from church pews. In our postbag this year, one reader's praise for Jeake's was 'undiluted', reserving special mention for the decoration, breakfasts and for Francis and Jenny Hadfield's style of management – 'attentive without being in any way intrusive'.

◐ Open all year

↗ Centrally located in old Rye. On-street parking nearby

🛏 1 single, 1 twin, 6 double, 2 family rooms, 1 four-poster, 1 four-poster suite; most with bathroom/WC, some with shower/WC, 2 public bathrooms; TV, room service, hair-dryer, baby-listening in all rooms

◈ Dining-room, bar, 2 lounges;

golf, water sports, other sports nearby

⊖ No wheelchair access; no dogs in public rooms; no smoking in dining-room

▭ Access, Amex, Visa

£ Single £22, single occupancy of twin/double £34 to £50, twin/double £39 to £55, four-poster £55, family room £71, four-poster suite £78; deposit required. Special breaks available

---

Little Orchard House

WEST STREET, RYE, EAST SUSSEX TN31 7ES
TEL: RYE (0797) 223831

Rambling bed and breakfast with an unusual tower for self-caterers, situated in a quiet side-street in central Rye.

This establishment is something of a surprise, for there is far more space than you would credit in the little red-brick house. The lounge is a bright and cheerful maze of fresh floral displays, flowery chairs, books and ducks, all of which seem to have been scattered at random. Upstairs is another sitting-room with more books and an array of teddies. The bedrooms continue the floral theme and are quite striking: Lloyd George is a bright room in yellow and black with a lovely fireplace made from local marble; the Hayloft is on two levels, with a slanting ceiling and a double pine bed with coronet. The Garden Room, the most romantic of the bedrooms, has lots of flowers and lace and a magnificent solid oak bed made out of a local tree. It is the creative work of proprietor Robert Brinkhurst. Sara Brinkhurst painted flowers in the bathrooms where slanting walls wouldn't allow for pictures to be hung. English breakfast is served in the kitchen at the long wooden table and that is also the time to get restaurant recommendations and local information.

The Smuggler's Watchtower, built in 1768, is a three-storey brick tower, a delightful place for self-caterers to stay, with its own living-room, kitchen/diner, pine bathroom and four-poster bedroom.

◑ Open all year

⤢ Centrally located in Rye. Travel through Landgate Arch and take 3rd turning on left. Public parking close to hotel

⇌ I twin, I double, I four-poster, tower room; all with bathroom exc double and tower room with shower/WC; TV, hair-dryer in all rooms

◈ Breakfast room, lounge, library; tennis, other sports nearby

⊖ No wheelchair access; no children under 12; no dogs; no smoking in some bedrooms

▭ Access, Visa

£ Single occupancy of twin/double £35 to £60, twin/double £56 to £76, four-poster £70 to £84, tower room £60 to £90; deposit required. Special breaks available

Old Vicarage

66 CHURCH SQUARE, RYE, EAST SUSSEX TN31 7HF
TEL: RYE (0797) 222119   FAX: (0797) 227466

A flowery bed and breakfast at a good price in a quiet location in the busy town of Rye.

Look for the pale pink house with red and pink roses adorning the garden gate – distinctive features that differentiate it from the many other Old Vicarages that seem to flourish in Rye. It looks like a fairytale house but is in fact a good, solid, bed and breakfast run by Paul and Julia Masters and their friendly staff.

Over 400 years old, the house is a Grade-II listed building of mainly Georgian design. It was a vicarage until 1889 when it became privately owned, later to be the residence of writer Henry James. The bedrooms are bright and cheerful in flowery fabrics; each has its own attraction, whether it be the four-posters in Rooms Five or Six or the coronet bed decoration in Room Four. Another has a slanting beamed roof.

The floor of the lounge resembles a dazzling chess board with a thick rug and a floral, brown and green settee. Hidden just off the lounge is a tiny study. English or continental breakfast can be taken in the small dining-room overlooking the garden.

◑ Open all year, exc Xmas

▨ Go along Cinque Ports Street through Landgate Arch to High Street. Turn third left into West Street. By St Mary's Church. On-street parking (limited)

⇔ 1 twin, 1 double, 2 four-poster, 1 family room 1 suite; 1 with bathroom/WC, most with shower/WC, 1 public bathroom; TV, hair-dryer in all rooms; trouser press in half of rooms

◈ Breakfast room, lounge, library/study; golf, water sports, other sports nearby

⊖ No wheelchair access; no children under 10; no dogs; no smoking in bedrooms

▭ None accepted

£ Single occupancy of twin/double £30 to £48, twin/double £37 to £54, four-poster £52 to £56, family room £65 to £70, suite £52 to £54; deposit required. Special breaks available

ST ALBANS HERTFORDSHIRE   **MAP 9**

Sopwell House

COTTONMILL LANE, SOPWELL, ST ALBANS, HERTFORDSHIRE AL1 2HQ
TEL: WALTHAM CROSS (0727) 864477   FAX: (0727) 844741

A health and conference centre in an extended Georgian house.

The white-painted Georgian building is separated from the road by fields and is relatively unspoilt. Drive into the car park at one side and you'll be faced with the various modern extensions that house a banqueting centre, sports centre and meeting-rooms. Small business meetings may take place in a corner of the library lounge – perhaps one of the more attractive rooms, with deep settees, red armchairs and shelves of books. The menu in the Magnolia Conservatory Restaurant features such dishes as roast venison with a rich chocolate sauce, perhaps followed by strawberry syllabub; alternatively, you can dine in the less formal brasserie.

The spacious bedrooms have good-quality dark wood furnishings and bathrooms with high-pressure showers. The health centre, with its splendid art deco-style pool, saunas, steam room and various beauty treatments, adds to the hotel's attractions.

◑ Open all year

⤢ From the M25 Junction 21A follow St Albans sign to the M10 roundabout and then the A414. Take the first left and follow signs to Sopwell. Private car park

🛏 10 single, 16 twin, 40 double, 18 four-poster, 6 family rooms, 2 suites; all with bathroom/WC, TV, room service, hair-dryer, trouser press, baby-listening; mini-bar in 2 suites

◈ 2 restaurants, 2 bars, lounge, library, games room; conference facilities (max 400 people non-residential, 92 residential); sauna/solarium, heated indoor swimming-pool, gym, beauty treatments rooms, steam and spa baths, snooker at hotel, other sports nearby; babysitting. Wheelchair access to hotel, restaurant and WC (M,F), no ground-floor bedrooms but lift

⊖ None

▭ Access, Amex, Diners, Visa

£ Single £68 to £100, twin/double £83 to £112, four-poster £90 to £120, family room rate on request, suite £100 to £129. Continental B £6, cooked B £8; set L £15, £17, D £19.50, £20.50; alc L £19, D £27. Special breaks available

---

ST AUSTELL CORNWALL　　　　　　　　　　　　　**MAP 10**

Boscundle Manor

TREGREHAN, ST AUSTELL, CORNWALL PL25 3RL
TEL: ST AUSTELL (0726) 813557　FAX: (0726) 814997

A small country-house hotel with excellent food and lively service.

Boscundle Manor is an attractive red-brick Georgian hotel, created out of three houses, one owned by a farmer, one by a tea-seller and one by the captain of *Wheal Eliza*, the remains of which survive in the grounds above the house. The hall opens straight into a long, thin but remarkably comfortable lounge with a big log fire where Andrew Flint orchestrates post-dinner entertainment, revolving around his cats, Leo and Ruth, and hilarious tales of two male peacocks which recently adopted the Flints. The dining-room is similarly long and thin, with low ceilings and panelled walls. Four-course table d'hôte menus offer only limited choice and when we inspected, Mary Flint's salmon mayonnaise was thoroughly satisfying, as were the red mullet on a bed of fennel leaves and the chocolate mousse to follow. Breakfast is served in a conservatory overlooking the garden.

Upstairs, bedrooms reflect the building's age, with sloping and uneven floor levels. All are extremely comfortable with a mixture of modern and antique furniture; bathrooms feature spa baths complete with instructions to prevent you disappearing beneath a sea of bubble bath. Room Five is better stocked with books than your average branch library, with six entire shelves of them.

◑ Closed end Oct to 1 Apr (or Easter if earlier)

⬀ 2 miles east of St Austell off the A390, 150 yards up road signposted Tregrehan. Private car park

🛏 2 single, 3 twin, 2 double, 1 garden room, 2 cottages; all with bathroom/WC, exc singles with shower/WC; TV, room service, hair-dryer, trouser press, mini-bar, baby-listening in all rooms

◈ 2 restaurants, bar, lounge, conservatory, exercise room; golf, heated outdoor swimming-pool (May to early Sept), gym, croquet at hotel, other sports nearby

⊖ No wheelchair access; no dogs in public rooms

▭ Access, Visa

£ Single £60 to £70, single occupancy of twin/double £70 to £80, twin/double/garden room £100 to £120, suite £130 to £150; deposit required. Set D £22.50. Special breaks available

---

ST BLAZEY CORNWALL   **MAP 10**

Nanscawen House

PRIDEAUX ROAD, ST BLAZEY, CORNWALL PL24 2SR
TEL: ST AUSTELL (0726) 814488 (and fax)

A comfortable and welcoming small hotel with huge rooms.

From the outside Nanscawen House is an attractive stone building which does not quite suggest the size of the rooms inside, particularly the vast and comfortable pale green lounge. The only small room is a conservatory full of wicker chairs and plants where meals are served. Janet and Keith Martin provide a warm welcome. Janet keeps menus fairly simple; dinners are nevertheless delicious, with starters such as pan-fried Brie and home-made walnut and onion bread, and main courses like Parma ham-wrapped chicken with vegetables straight from the garden. Upstairs, the Rashleigh Suite must be one of the biggest hotel rooms ever, with no fewer than five windows and a bathroom on a similar scale complete with spa bath; the Treffry and Prideaux Suites only seem small in comparison. Treffry has crown-canopy twin beds and pretty stencilling on the walls and Prideaux, with its four-poster bed, is perhaps a little fussily decorated for some tastes. The grounds feature an outdoor hot tub where on warm nights you can sit and soak beneath a starlit sky.

◐ Open all year, exc 25, 26 Dec; restaurant closed Sun eve and throughout July and Aug

↗ From Plymouth on the A38, turn left at Dobwalls to A390 St Austell. In St Blazey turn right directly after railway crossing, opposite the garage. The house is ¾ mile on the right. Private car park

🛏 1 twin, 1 double, 1 four-poster; all with bathroom/WC, TV, hair-dryer

◈ Dining-room, bar, lounge, conservatory; heated swimming-pool (Apr to Sept), Jacuzzi at hotel, fishing, other sports nearby

⊖ No wheelchair access; no children under 12; no dogs; no smoking

▭ Access, Visa

£ Single occupancy of twin/double £50, twin/double/four-poster £60 to £70; deposit required. Set D £20 (7.15pm). Special breaks available

---

SAINTBURY GLOUCESTERSHIRE   **MAP 9**

Cusack's Glebe

SAINTBURY, NR BROADWAY, HEREFORD AND WORCESTER WR12 7PX
TEL: BROADWAY (0386) 852210

A small, rural bed and breakfast with lots of character.

High above the valley where Broadway lies is Cusack's Glebe, a fourteenth-century farmhouse surrounded by paddocks and garden. As you open the gate noisy dogs rush to meet you, followed by Emile or Juliet Carro. Inside, the place shows its antiquity by its sloping ceilings and steep stairs. There is a small sitting-room for guests, with a ticking clock and small tables for breakfasting. Both the guest bedrooms have character, and are furnished with old pieces of furniture passed down through the generations. The Red Room, with four-poster, suitably red decoration and carved oak chests, boasts a tiny bathroom tucked under the eaves. The second room, also with a four-poster, has only a shower but is big enough for families to use. The garden is well worth wandering around, and there are good views of the rolling countryside.

◐ Open all year, exc Xmas

↗ Saintbury is between Broadway and Chipping Campden; Cusack's Glebe is one mile from Broadway Golf Club, 300 yards off the B4232. Private car park

🛏 1 four-poster, 1 family/four-poster room; both with bathroom/WC, TV, room service, hair-dryer, mini-bar

◈ Lounge; golf, riding nearby

⊖ No wheelchair access; no children under 8; no dogs; no smoking

▭ None accepted

£ Four-poster £55 to £60, family room £65 to £70; deposit required. Special breaks available

ST IVES CORNWALL　　　　　　　　　　　　　　　**MAP 10**

Garrack Hotel ☆

BURTHALLAN LANE, ST IVES, CORNWALL TR26 3AA
TEL: PENZANCE (0736) 796199　FAX: (0736) 798955

Family-holiday hotel in a quiet part of St Ives, with a brand new leisure centre.

The Kilby family has been running the Garrack Hotel since 1965, but there is no resting on laurels here; this year the entire reception area is being redesigned around an atrium, and, after a fire last year, a new leisure centre has just been built, with an indoor pool, sauna, sunbed and weights area. Inside the main part of the hotel there is a succession of small rooms: a curvy bar area opens into a sequence of small lounges, and the dining-room splits into three distinct areas, which are used in rotation according to the time of year. After all this the main lounge has disappointingly old-fashioned furniture, as do many of the rather ordinary bedrooms. The one striking exception is the impressive suite at the back of the new atrium which is probably as high-tech as hotel rooms come – when not needed as a conventional double bedroom, a rollaway bed converts it into a family suite. Alternatively, all the furniture can be moved to make it into a small conference room. Even more impressively, it has been designed to suit disabled guests; the bathroom has an anti-slip tiled floor and there is an emergency call system.

◐ Open all year

⤤ Leave Hayle by-pass by the 2nd exit signed St Ives; take a left at the mini-roundabout on to the B3311. Travel 3 miles to a T-junction; turn right and pass through Halse Town. Join the B3306 and turn left after 200 yards by the petrol station. Follow signs for Porthmeor Beach, car parks and the hotel. Private car park

🛏 2 single, 3 twin, 5 double, 2 four-poster, 3 family rooms, 2 annexe rooms; most with bathroom/WC, some with shower/WC; TV, room service, baby-listening in all rooms; hair-dryer on request

◈ Restaurant, 2 bars, 2 lounges, TV room, drying room; conference facilities (max 35 people non-residential, 20 residential); sauna/solarium, heated swimming-pool, gym, spa at hotel, other sports nearby. Wheelchair access to hotel, restaurant and WC, 11 ground-floor bedrooms, 1 specially equipped for disabled people

⊖ No children under 4 in restaurant eves; no dogs in public rooms and by arrangement only in bedrooms

▭ Access, Amex, Diners, Visa

£ Single and single occupancy of twin/double £45 to £56, twin/double/annexe £72 to £96, four-poster £89 to £111, family room £72 to £96; deposit required. Set D £16.50; alc L, D £16

ST JOHN'S CHAPEL CO DURHAM   **MAP 3**

Pennine Lodge

ST JOHN'S CHAPEL, WEARDALE, CO DURHAM DL13 1QX
TEL: WEARDALE (0388) 537247

A smashing country guesthouse with rustic style and cheerful hosts.

It is hard for a modest guesthouse to look like an inviting place to stay when the weather is miserable but Pennine Lodge manages it, thanks to the warmth of its hosts, an all-pervasive cosiness and a collection of knick-knacks. The proverbial cats and dogs were being hurled from the heavens with a vengeance on the morning our inspector called at the rugged farmhouse, but inside guests were sitting around a lovely polished old table, chatting happily to hosts Mr and Mrs Raine. The room, cheerfully done up with antlers, animal heads and buffalo horns, retains the welcoming informality of a farmhouse kitchen thanks to its dresser and wood-burning fire. The menu offers 'dinner-party English, with lots of fresh veg,' wrote one visitor – and you might find grapefruit and orange cocktail, pheasant casserole, apple, orange and ginger tart and cheese and biscuits, all skilfully cooked and presented.

The beamed residents' lounge upstairs confirms the Raines' mania for collecting. Amid the grandfather clock and country furniture you'll find a carved stand holding a collection of walking sticks. The five bedrooms have chintzy décor and soft furnishings as well as lovely old furniture; a brass-framed, inlaid bed in Room Two, a splendid chest of drawers in Room Four, a fine wardrobe and dressing-table and a (silent) grandfather clock in Room Five.

◑ *Closed Oct to Mar*

↗ *St John's Chapel is half-way between Alston and Stanhope on the A689. Private car park*

🛏 *2 twin, 2 double, 1 four-poster; some with bathroom/WC, some with shower/WC; hair-dryer on request*

◈ *Dining-room, lounge; fishing,* *tennis, riding nearby*

⊖ *No wheelchair access; no children under 8; no dogs in public rooms; no smoking*

▭ *None accepted*

£ *Single occupancy of twin/double £19, twin/double/four-poster £38; deposit required. Set D £10 (7pm). Special breaks available*

If you make a booking using a credit card, and find after cancelling that the full amount has been charged to your card, raise the matter with your credit card company. They will ask the hotelier to confirm whether the room was re-let, and to justify the charge made.

ST JUST CORNWALL   **MAP 10**

Manor Farm

BOTALLACK, ST JUST, NR PENZANCE, CORNWALL TR19 7QG
TEL: PENZANCE (0736) 788525

A homely bed and breakfast near Cape Cornwall offering interesting furnishings and substantial breakfasts.

After 43 years of welcoming guests to the homely seventeenth-century farmhouse featured in the television versions of *Poldark* and *Penmarric*, Joyce Cargeeg is a past master at the art of rustling up breakfasts to keep them going all day. In the breakfast room, a screen from Kalimantan with inlaid mother-of-pearl chickens rubs shoulders with a typically English granite fireplace. Cereals are laid out along antique tables, and Joyce dishes up massive mixed grills to follow. The Khazakhstan bread on the menu? 'People don't come on holiday to get the same as they do at home,' she explains.

Manor Farm is actually very small, its narrow hallway filled up with antique maps and a fine bench with a wooden bear's head at each end. The lounge ceiling is so low that the big desk-cabinet seems to be propping it up. Upstairs, the three bedrooms also feature hefty old furniture, although space has been found for *en-suite* facilities. From Sima's Room there are fine views over the sea and the countryside, while a painting of an old tin mine evokes a Cornish way of life now taken over by the heritage industry.

◗ Open all year

⤴ Follow the B3306 to the north of St Just and fork left towards the coast. Pass the Queen's Arms to the right and Manor Farm is straight ahead at the next junction. Private car park

🛏 1 twin, 1 double, 1 four-poster; all with shower/WC, TV, hair-dryer

◈ Breakfast room, lounge, library/ study; fishing, golf, tennis, other sports nearby

⊖ No wheelchair access; no dogs; no smoking

▭ None accepted

£ Single occupancy of twin/double £18 to £20, twin/double £36 to £40, four-poster £40; deposit required. Special breaks available

ST KEYNE CORNWALL   **MAP 10**

Well House

ST KEYNE, LISKEARD, CORNWALL PL14 4RN
TEL: LISKEARD (0579) 342001

A luxurious country-house hotel in a quiet village.

The Well House takes its name from a springhead right next to its gardens; legend has it that whichever of a newly married couple drank from the well first would wear the trousers in the marriage. Not that there is anything mistily medieval about the Well House itself, where some bedrooms are, if anything, distinctively modern, featuring stylish black, white and grey colour schemes. Less modern is the ground-floor lounge, with comfy chairs and sofas around the log fire; given the diminutive scale of the bar, this is probably the better place to sup your pre-dinner drink while chatting to host Nick Wainford. Alternatively it is worth taking a turn round the gardens, which are full of wild garlic and boast several ponds, a stream and a croquet lawn.

Food is excellent. As dusk falls, elegant pink and green curtains are drawn and candles lit; gentle background music is likely to come courtesy of Enya or Mary Black; service is efficient but unobtrusive. When we inspected a rich quail terrine was being served with caramelised orange, while the turbot came with stuffed tomatoes and broccoli in a hollandaise sauce; an extensive cheeseboard featuring several regional cheeses was accompanied by walnut bread, and the chocolate marquise was exquisitely filling.

◑ *Open all year*

⤴ *From Liskeard take the B3254 to St Keyne. Pass through the village and past the church and take the road to St Keyne Well. The hotel is ½ mile from the church. Private car park*

🛏 *3 twin, 3 double, 1 family room; all with bathroom/WC, TV, room service, hair-dryer, trouser press, baby-listening; no tea/coffee-making facilities in rooms*

◇ *Restaurant, bar, lounge; conference facilities (max 12 people non-residential, 7 residential); tennis, croquet, heated outdoor swimming-pool at hotel, other sports nearby. Wheelchair access to restaurant only*

⊖ *No children under 8 in restaurant eves*

▭ *Access, Visa*

£ *Single occupancy of twin/double £60, twin/double £72 to £105, family room £125 to £140; deposit required. Cooked B £9.50; set L £21, D £19/£25/£30 (prices till end Oct 93). Special breaks available*

ST MARGARETS AT CLIFFE KENT   MAP 8

Wallett's Court

WEST CLIFFE, ST MARGARETS AT CLIFFE, DOVER, KENT CT15 6EW
TEL: DOVER (0304) 852424   FAX: (0304) 853430

Seventeenth-century manor house convenient for Dover Docks.

A hop from the docks, you can smell the sea air as you pull up on the red gravel car park at Wallett's Court. The main house is an attractive whitewashed seventeenth-century manor house with black lattice window frames. The character of the house shows traces of many different periods but an air of the medieval prevails, with beamed ceilings and wooden staircases alongside brass rubbings of serious-looking medieval knights, tapestries and coats of arms.

The dining-room is supported by carved wooden totem-pole pillars, and a warm ambience is provided by the brick fireplace aglow with an interesting array of hanging copper implements. Service is quietly friendly and your meal might consist of potted pheasant served with tangy Cumberland sauce followed by wing of skate sautéed in butter or perhaps fillets of Kentish venison in an orange and cinnamon sauce.

Bedrooms in the main house are a good size, with candlewick bedspreads, floral beige and pink carpets, glass wall hangings and dried flowers. The Queen Eleanor room has an impressive brick fireplace – albeit a little disappointingly filled with an electric fire rather than logs. The rooms in the converted barn are smaller, plainer and cheaper.

◑ *Closed Xmas period; restaurant closed Sun eve*

⤤ *On the B2058 off the A258 Dover to Deal road, 5 minutes from Dover docks. Private car park*

🛏 *2 twin, 4 double, 1 four-poster, 1 family room; some with bathroom/WC, some with shower/WC; TV, room service, hair-dryer, baby-listening in all rooms*

◈ *2 dining-rooms, bar, lounge, games room; tennis at hotel, other sports nearby*

⊖ *No wheelchair access; no dogs; no smoking in dining-room*

▭ *Access, Visa*

£ *Single occupancy of twin/double £35 to £40, twin/double £50 to £60, four-poster £70, family room rate on request; deposit required. Set D £20. Special breaks available*

ST MARTIN'S ISLES OF SCILLY   **MAP 10**

St Martin's

LOWERTOWN, ST MARTINS, ISLES OF SCILLY, TR25 0QW
TEL: SCILLONIA (0720) 22092   FAX: (0720) 22298

Simply the best: a well-run and cosseting hotel in a beautiful position.

Michael Bryant ensures the smooth running of a relaxing and cosseting environment at St Martin's, the only hotel on the island. The low-rise modern building has a prime site overlooking the sandy beaches of Tresco. Inside are beautiful flowers, tiled floors and plenty of picture windows to make the best of views. A bar-lounge, run by Julian the on-the-button barman, is furnished in coral and green with plenty of sofas and coffee-table magazines. The restaurant upstairs has a modern triangular bay window, and lucky guests are seated facing west to see spectacular sunsets. Menus are light and imaginative with game (baked breast of guinea-fowl with an apricot mousse accompanied by red wine gravy) and plenty of fish (including a fish course, such as grilled Round Island Pollock). Don't get too settled though, as guests have to walk to a room at the back to choose their dessert, all beautifully presented but perhaps requiring a touch too much effort. Service is correct but friendly. It's good to see the same high standards shown to children – with youngsters delighted by their bread rolls baked in the shape of a mouse. Breakfasts are extensive: plenty of choice of fruit and cereals from a buffet, plus a served cooked choice.

Bedrooms are light and modern in style, furnished throughout with flowery fabrics; make sure you choose one with a sea view. One of the most popular is Puffin, a large de-luxe room decorated in pink.

◐ *Closed Oct to Mar*

⤢ *There are helicopter/ferry services from Penzance and a Skybus service from Land's End. Direct flights from Plymouth, Heathrow and Exeter airports. There are no cars on the Scillies*

🛏 *14 twin, 2 double, 2 four-poster, 4 family rooms, 2 suites; all with bathroom/WC, TV, room service, hair-dryer, baby-listening; trouser press on request; no tea/coffee-making facilities in rooms*

◈ *Restaurant, bar, 2 lounges, games room, drying room; conference facilities (max 24 people residential, 48 non-residential); fishing, croquet,*

water sports, clay pigeon shooting, indoor heated swimming-pool, riding (by 1994) at hotel, other sports nearby; babysitting

⊖ *No wheelchair access; no dogs in public rooms and in some bedrooms by arrangement only; no smoking in restaurant and 1 lounge*

▭ *Access, Amex, Diners, Visa*

£ *Single occupancy of twin/double £90 to £114, twin/double/four-poster £130 to £178, family room/suite £160 to £208 (rates inc dinner); deposit required. Bar lunches from £2.50; set D £25*

ST MARY'S ISLES OF SCILLY   **MAP 10**

Atlantic Hotel ☆

ST MARY'S, ISLES OF SCILLY TR21 0PL
TEL: SCILLONIA (0720) 22417   FAX: (0720) 23009

A rambling harbour-side inn with fresh bedrooms.

From the street the Atlantic looks like a traditional rambling inn, dark and secretive. Inside however, the decoration is fresh and bright with a comfortable beamed lounge and lovely restaurant that looks right out over the waterfront. As with many hotels on the Scillies, the hotel has a policy of moving guests towards the key window tables as their stay progresses – a nice touch that leaves no one feeling left out.

Readers have particularly praised the staff, 'friendly, helpful and efficient – given a lift to the airport by the manager to catch the helicopter when there was no bus'. Bedrooms are flowery and comfortable and sea views are charged extra. For special occasions there is the Rosevear Room with its four-poster and rosy pink décor.

◑ Closed Nov to Feb

⤢ The bus from the airport stops outside the hotel. There are no cars on the Scillies

🛏 1 single, 6 twin, 12 double, 1 four-poster, 3 family rooms; all with bathroom/WC, exc 3 doubles with shower/WC; TV in all rooms

◇ Restaurant, bar; fishing, golf,

other sports nearby

⊖ No wheelchair access

▭ Access, Visa

£ Single £58 to £61, single occupancy of twin/double £85 to £87, twin/double £97 to £104, four-poster £132 to £138, family room £168 and £172 (rates inc dinner). Set D £16.50

Tregarthen's Hotel

ST MARY'S, ISLES OF SCILLY TR21 0PP
TEL: SCILLONIA (0720) 22540   FAX: (0720) 22089

Traditional hotel with friendly staff.

The white and blue of Tregarthen's is immediately visible as your boat docks at the quay. Its position as the first hotel in the Scillies was assured about 100 years ago by owner Captain Frank Tregarthen, who won the Blue Riband to carry the Royal Mail. It was the custom for the Captain himself to carry the mail from the Post Office to his ship, giving him plenty of time to chat to the passengers and recommend that they stay at his place.

Nowadays the hotel tends to attract an older clientele, many of whom holiday here and meet up each year. It is part of the Best Western Group, with friendly staff throughout: from Phil the porter, through to the extremely efficient receptionist who remembers residents' names and wishes them bon voyage, and the chatty restaurant manager.

The style is comfortable rather than stylish. Bedrooms are pink and flowery, not overly large but spick and span. Guests enter the lounge straight from reception, so it tends to become a bit of a thoroughfare as residents pop out for their after-dinner strolls. The greeting in the restaurant could be better – residents are expected to find their tables from the seating plan – but the menu was very popular on our inspection visits, with guests groaning after the traditional English meals (and traditional English portions) that they wouldn't be able to keep up this eating for long.

◑ Closed from last week Oct to mid-Mar

⤢ Guests are met at the quay or airport. The hotel is a 1-mile bus journey from the airport. There are no cars on the Scillies

🛏 5 single, 12 twin, 6 double, 5 family rooms, 1 suite; all with bathroom/WC, TV, room service, hair-dryer, trouser press, baby-listening

◇ Restaurant, bar, lounge, drying

room; conference facilities (max 30 people residential and non-residential); fishing, golf, other sports nearby; babysitting

⊖ No wheelchair access; no children under 5; no dogs in bedrooms

▭ Access, Amex, Diners, Visa

£ Single £52 to £68, single occupancy of twin/double £76 to £85, twin/double £92 to £120, suite £118 to £136, family room rate from £104 and £136 (rates inc dinner); deposit required. Set D £18.50; bar lunches from £7 (meal prices till Oct 93). Special breaks available

---

ST MAWES CORNWALL   MAP 10

Hotel Tresanton

27 LOWER CASTLE ROAD, ST MAWES, TRURO, CORNWALL TR2 5DR
TEL: ST MAWES (0326) 270544   FAX: (0326) 270002

A small, split-level hotel with comfortable rooms.

Pretty white and blue Tresanton is sensibly situated away from the bustle of St Mawes harbour, although the street in front is so narrow that parking is a problem; stop to drop off your bags and let the management work out what to do with your car. Reception is at street level, while the lounge, bar and bedrooms are all up a flight of steps in a newer building overlooking a small pond and a terrace facing the Fal Estuary. The restaurant has more fine estuary views and an unexpected oriental ambience; don't miss two fine panels of 1830s Chinese wallpaper framed on the walls. The à la carte menus have an oriental tinge, too; alongside the more predictable fish dishes, one hot appetiser consists of a selection of Asian fancies, including samosas, spring roll and crispy wun-tun; two of the most popular main courses are Thai curries. More traditionally, afternoon cream teas are included in the room rates.

Bedroom names are teasers until you realise that each is named after a person or place appearing in a picture on the back of its door. First-floor rooms are bigger than those on the second, but most have spectacular estuary views; even better, some have private terraces too. Colour schemes are mainly soothing and modern, although beware lurid purple tiles fading to mauve in the bathroom of Room 21.

◑ Closed 1 Nov to 23 Dec and 3 Jan to 1 Mar

⇱ From St Austell take the B3287 from Sticker to Tregony, then the A3078 from Tregony to St Mawes. Private car park

⇖ 4 single, 9 twin, 4 double, 4 suites; all with bathroom/WC, exc 1 suite with shower/WC; TV, room service, hair-dryer in all rooms; no tea/coffee-making facilities in rooms

◈ Restaurant, bar, lounge; fishing, tennis, water sports nearby

⊖ No wheelchair access; no children under 10; no dogs in public rooms

▭ Access, Amex, Diners, Visa

£ Single £63, twin/double £90 to £154, suite £184 (rates inc dinner); deposit required. Alc L from £3, D £19. Special breaks available

Idle Rocks

HARBOURSIDE, I TREDENHAM ROAD, ST MAWES, CORNWALL TR2 5AN
TEL: TRURO (0326) 270771   FAX: (0326) 270062

A comfortable and welcoming harbour-facing hotel.

St Mawes' narrow streets mean that guests at the Idle Rocks must use a public car park (cheap) across the road. That minor problem and the building's undramatic exterior aside, though, this is a wonderful hotel, looking out, as its name suggests, on the 'idle rocks' of a popular resort. From the welcoming reception desk you can already glimpse the views, and the lounges, bar and restaurant are all positioned to make the most of them. Both lounges have big, squashy, enticing armchairs, while the bar and dining-room capitalise on the village's maritime traditions, with pictures and models of ships on their walls. Three-course table d'hôte menus take a basically cautious approach, but with twists in the tail: chicken liver pâté served in a filo basket, grilled sirloin steak on a green peppercorn and herb cream.

Upstairs, bedrooms are named after birds, and pictures of the appropriate species hang on their walls. Furnishings are a comfortable mix of old and new. Lapwing has a pretty pink crown-canopy bed, lots of dried flowers and toiletries, and estuary views from both bedroom and bathroom. Swan lacks the views but is very comfortable, with gold bedcovers and cosy armchairs.

◑ Open all year

⤴ By the harbour in St Mawes. On-street parking and public car park nearby

🛏 2 single, 2 twin, 13 double, 7 annexe rooms (4 self-catering cottages); most with bathroom/WC, some with shower/WC; TV, room service, hair-dryer, baby-listening in all rooms

◈ Restaurant, bar, 2 lounges; conference facilities (max 50 people non-residential, 21 residential – winter only); fishing, tennis, riding, water sports nearby. Wheelchair access to hotel, restaurant and WCs, I ground-floor bedroom

⊖ No smoking in I lounge

▭ Access, Visa

£ Single £44 to £80, twin/double/family room £102 to £160, annexe room £88 to £116 (rates inc dinner); deposit required. Bar lunches; set D £16.50; alc D £19 to £25. Special breaks available

SALCOMBE DEVON   **MAP 10**

Soar Mill Cove Hotel

SALCOMBE, DEVON TQ7 3DS
TEL: SALCOMBE (0548) 561566   FAX: (0548) 561223

A luxurious country-house hotel above an isolated bay.

The grounds of Soar Mill Cove Hotel blend seamlessly into the surrounding countryside and coastline, much of it owned by the National Trust. The building itself, while modern, is only one storey high. Inside, the bar and lounge are comfortable rather than exciting, while the elegant restaurant looks out over a swimming-pool, the best tables lined up to take advantage of the views. The importance the Makepeaces attach to eating is suggested by the daily menus, which give information about the provenance of the ingredients; a typical snippet might read: 'After last night's bass provençale, David has brought us a beautiful 9½ lb hake. Stuffed with a fine vegetable mousseline and gently poached in court-bouillon with bay and thyme, served with a rosé wine sauce.'

Not surprisingly the best feature of the bedrooms (all of them sizeable) is their superb views – Room 16, for example, has windows facing on to the sea as well as the moor – and several have patio doors. Crown-canopy beds have bright and varied fabrics and there is usually space for big armchairs or even a two-piece suite; the tiled bathrooms, however, are all much of a muchness.

◑ Closed Nov to end Jan

⤵ From the A381 at Malborough turn right through village and then left (signposted Soar) after the church. Follow this road for 2 miles towards the sea. Private car park

🛏 2 single, 5 twin, 4 double, 4 family rooms, I suite; all with bathroom/WC, TV, room service, hair-dryer, trouser press, baby-listening

◈ 2 restaurants, bar, 2 lounges, drying room, games room; fishing, tennis, water sports, 2 swimming-pools at hotel, other sports nearby. Wheelchair access to hotel (no steps), restaurant and 16 ground-floor bedrooms

⊖ No children under 4 in restaurants eves; no dogs in public rooms; no smoking in restaurants

▭ Access, Visa

£ Single £58 to £90, single occupancy of twin/double £70 to £130, twin/double £110 to £160, suite £160 to £320, family room rate on request (rates inc dinner); deposit required. Alc L £12; set D £29. Special breaks available

Tides Reach

SOUTH SANDS, SALCOMBE, DEVON TQ8 8LJ
TEL: SALCOMBE (0548) 843466   FAX: (0548) 843954

A sizeable holiday hotel overlooking a sandy bay, with a small, duck-filled garden.

The first thing to be said about Tides Reach is that to reach it you must negotiate a series of wild hairpin bends down from Salcombe. The second is that an artist appears to have run wild inside it, spraying vivid colours everywhere; bright blue in the front lounge, startling green in the back dining-room, more blues and greens in some of the bedrooms. That aside, if you like natural greenery you'll love Tides Reach, where reception is approached via a plant-filled conservatory complete with small pond. Look out, too, for the aquarium in the bar. There is also a garden with a duck-dotted stream running through it; sunbeds are lined around it, although from them the hotel looks rather like a faceless Costa effort.

In the best rooms the colour schemes are toned down, and there are crown-canopy beds in peach, gold and yellow and lots of armchairs. Back rooms with views of the hills rather than the estuary are cheapest. Should the weather turn nasty Tides Reach has a wealth of facilities in its games area: a squash court, sauna, solarium, gym, snooker table, table tennis and, best of all, a huge indoor pool surrounded by foliage.

◐ *Closed Nov to Feb*

🔁 *Follow the A381 from Kingsbridge through Malborough to Salcombe. Turn right in Salcombe at seafront and follow signs to South Sands. Private car park*

🛏 *18 twin, 17 double, 3 family rooms; all with bathroom/WC, TV, room service, hair-dryer*

◈ *Restaurant, 2 bars, 3 lounges, games room, conservatory, drying room; sauna, solarium, heated swimming-pool,*

gym, squash at hotel, other sports nearby. Wheelchair access to restaurant only

⊖ *No children under 8; no dogs in public rooms; no smoking in restaurant and 1 lounge*

▭ *Access, Amex, Diners, Visa*

£ *Single occupancy of twin/double £64 to £82, twin/double £120 to £144, family room (4 people) £194 to £252 (rates inc dinner); deposit required. Set D £24.50; alc D £28.50; bar meals from £2.50*

SALTFORD AVON   **MAP 9**

Brunel's Tunnel House

HIGH STREET, SALTFORD, BRISTOL, AVON BS18 3BQ
TEL: BATH (0225) 873873   FAX: (0225) 874875

Georgian house with an unusual history and welcoming hosts.

Isambard Kingdom Brunel bought this three-storied Georgian house which stands above a tunnel on the London to Bristol rail link because the owners thought the passing trains would disturb the peace. They were wrong – if you do hear a faint rumble, it will be the heavy freight trains, not the super-fast Intercity passenger trains passing beneath.

Today the house is run as a guesthouse by Sarah Leighton and her mother Muriel Mitchell, who are polite and welcoming hosts. Dinner is served at 7pm sharp and comes from a fixed menu. So you might sit down to something like grapefruit to start, followed by lamb chops in a mint, orange and redcurrant sauce, with a slice of kiwi-fruit tart to finish. The dining-room is decorated with interesting glass and pottery pieces that stand on shelves on either side of the fireplace. After-dinner coffee is served in the extremely snug bar.

The stairs are lined with photos of Brunel and his work and lead to the bedrooms, which are of a good size and are decorated in pink or magnolia and furnished with a mix of pine and modern pieces.

◐ Open all year, exc 24, 25, 26 Dec; restaurant closed Sun eves

🔁 Saltford is mid-way between Bath and Bristol on the A4. In the centre of the village turn off the A4 by the side of Saltford Motor Services into Beech Road. The hotel faces the bottom of this road. Private car park

🛏 1 twin, 6 double; most with shower/WC, 1 double with bathroom/WC; TV, room service, baby-listening in all rooms; hair-

dryer, ironing facilities on request

◇ Dining-room, bar/lounge; conference facilities (max 14 people non-residential, 8 residential); fishing, golf, other sports nearby

⊖ No wheelchair access; no dogs; no smoking in dining-room

▭ Access, Amex, Visa

£ Single occupancy of twin/double £40 to £46, twin/double £48 to £56; deposit required. Set D £14 (7pm). Special breaks available

---

SANDIWAY CHESHIRE   **MAP 5**

Nunsmere Hall ☆

TARPORLEY ROAD, SANDIWAY, CHESHIRE CW8 2ES
TEL: NORTHWICH (0606) 889100   FAX: (0606) 889055

Luxury weekend and conference hotel with noted cuisine in tranquil lakeside setting.

Since Malcolm and Julie McHardy took over Nunsmere Hall, the turn-of-the-century home of a local shipping magnate, they have worked assiduously to turn it into an exclusive bolt-hole. 1993 saw the completion of ground-floor refurbishment, with the transformation of the drawing-room from cerise wedding cake to swish mix of moiré silk, soft colours and striped sofas. Nunsmere's trade is mostly top-of-the-range corporate, with an increasing number of weekend conference packages. It tends to attract tanned executive types with red Ferraris, but there are also jovial northern 'suits', gourmandising weekenders and, on Sundays, it is booked solid with family groups enjoying brunch.

The up-market restaurant is very much the centrepiece of the hotel. Chef Paul Kitching was trained at Gidleigh Park and produces a frequently changing carte, where the price of the main dish includes choice of starter, dessert and coffee. Typical dishes may be baked Cornish baby seabass with a lightly poached farmhouse egg and a tomato and basil butter, roast loin of Scottish lamb or grilled fillet of beef with a garlic cream sauce. There is also a menu 'dégustation' and cheaper set lunches. The wine list highlights classic Bordeaux and Burgundy and has useful tasting notes.

The McHardys have practically doubled the place in size, adding well-equipped boardrooms, conference facilities and extra bedrooms. All the rooms are individually and expensively furnished; the new bedrooms are especially spacious. The immense Orchid is styled on an oriental theme, with lacquered furniture, Chinese vases and screens. Chestnut is an appealing dormer room with decorative beams – a sort of de-luxe garret.

◑ *Open all year*

↗ *Take the A530 from Middlewich and turn left at 1st roundabout on to the A556. Continue through Sandiway till the 2nd set of traffic lights, turn left on to A49 Whitchurch road. The hall is 1 mile further along. Private car park*

🛏 *7 twin, 19 double, 3 four-poster, 3 suites; all with bathroom/WC, TV, room service, hair-dryer, trouser press*

◇ *Restaurant, bar, lounge, library, games room; conservatory; conference facilities (max 48 people non-residential and residential); snooker at hotel, fishing, golf, other sports nearby. Wheelchair access to hotel, restaurant and WC (unisex), 2 ground-floor rooms specially equipped for disabled people*

⊖ *No dogs; no smoking in restaurant and some bedrooms*

▭ *Access, Amex, Diners, JCB, Visa*

£ *Single occupancy of twin/double £95, twin/double £120, four-poster from £175, suite from £170. Set L £12.50/£15.50; alc D £22.50/£28.50. Special breaks available*

SANDRINGHAM NORFOLK   **MAP 7**

Park House

SANDRINGHAM, KING'S LYNN, NORFOLK PE35 6EH
TEL: DERSINGHAM (0485) 543000

A large country house that is comprehensively equipped for disabled guests.

Lying within the boundaries of the Queen's Sandringham estate, Park House is specifically kitted out to cater for the needs of disabled people. The large Victorian house was presented to the Leonard Cheshire Foundation in the 1980s by the Queen, and has rooms for carers, relatives and friends who wish to accompany people with disabilities. It claims to provide for everyone – specially adapted buses are used to take groups on outings in the area and the swimming-pool has a hoist system for easier access. Not surprisingly, it is booked well ahead so it is essential to book many months in advance if you want to be sure of a room. The spacious bedrooms are traditionally decorated in low-key colours, and many have views over the local cricket pitch. Some have bed and bath hoists.

There are plenty of places to relax: a broad courtyard conservatory, a library, music room, games room and drawing-room. Tennis, snooker, bowls and plenty of other games are available. Lunch is buffet-style; a three-course meal is served in the evening, and although the dining-room is designed with maximum convenience in mind, the smart Scandinavian furniture and crisp tablecloths make it easy on the eye too.

◑ Open all year, exc 1 week in mid-Dec

↗ Turn right off the A149, 3 miles north of Knight's Hill roundabout, and follow hotel signs. Private car park

🛏 8 single, 8 twin; twins with bathroom/WC, singles with shower/WC; TV in all rooms

◈ Dining-room, bar, 2 lounges, games room, conservatory; heated outdoor swimming-pool

(May to Sept). Hotel designed specifically for use by disabled people, all bedrooms are specially equipped

⊖ Guide dogs only; smoking in 1 lounge and conservatory only

▭ Access, Visa

£ Single £51 to £69, single occupancy of twin £62 to £98, twin £84 to £120 (rates inc dinner). Set L £12, D from £6.50

SCOLE NORFOLK   **MAP 7**

Scole Inn

NORWICH ROAD, SCOLE, NR DISS, NORFOLK IP21 4DR
TEL: DISS (0379) 740481   FAX: (0379) 740762

A chunky old inn with plenty of period fittings and character.

It may appear strange to be recommending a hotel which lies directly on the thundering A-road linking Norwich and Ipswich, but step inside this historic coaching-inn and the reasons will become clear. The seventeenth-century inn is listed as a Grade-I building and both exterior and interior are largely unchanged and unspoilt.

It is a good idea to request a room at the back of the building, because even though they are double-glazed the front rooms still suffer from noise. Those in the main body of the inn are the nicest as they combine smart fittings with plenty of character. The others, in a converted stable block beyond the car park, are disappointing. With slatted wooden walls and ugly pictures, they are only good for those who want to come and go as they please without having to trek through the main house.

There is a choice between bar food, served in low-lit, smoky bars aglow with huge log fires, or a more formal restaurant with invitingly crisp pink tablecloths and sparkling glassware. Traditional fare such as steak and kidney pies and game is a speciality.

◑ Open all year

↗ On the A140 between Ipswich and Norwich. Private car park

🛏 3 twin, 14 double, 5 four-poster/

half-tester, 1 family room; all with bathroom/WC, TV, hair-dryer, trouser press

◈ Restaurant (air-conditioned), 2 bars; conference facilities (max

23 people residential); golf,
heated swimming-pool.
Wheelchair access to restaurant
and WC, 7 ground-floor
bedrooms

⊖ No dogs in public rooms

▭ Access, Amex, Diners, Visa

£ Single occupancy of twin/double
£55, twin/double £65, four-
poster £85, family room from
£65. Set L £10, D £15 (prices till
end 93). Special breaks available

SEATOLLER CUMBRIA   **MAP 4**

Seatoller House

SEATOLLER, BORROWDALE, KESWICK, CUMBRIA CA12 5XN
TEL: BORROWDALE (07687) 77218

Informal, venerable guesthouse at the foot of the Honister Pass.

'It is a heavenly place,' says one reader of Seatoller. Located at the head
of the Borrowdale Valley it is an ideal spot for walkers and climbers. It is
not surprising to discover that it has been a guesthouse since the 1860s,
though the building actually dates back to the early seventeenth century.
It was at Seatoller House that the historian G. M. Trevelyan along with
some friends started the 'Manhunt' – a large-scale version of a childhood
game in which three 'hares' make full use of the surrounding wooded
hills to escape the 20 or so 'hounds' in hot pursuit. It is still played to this
day, as the photos of the 'Masters of the Hunt' will testify, and host David
Pepper has been known to join in on occasion. David is a friendly and
unobtrusive host who understands his guests' needs, providing a drying-
room for the walking gear and a small tea-room where they can help
themselves to a refreshing post-ramble brew. The two comfortable
sitting-rooms, both with views of Borrowdale Fell, combine the modern
with the Victorian under low ceilings with exposed beams. The dining-
room has a slate floor part-covered by rugs and two specially commissioned large oak tables. The no-choice menu is all good traditional stuff:
leek and potato soup followed by Cumberland lamb and rounded off with
a chocolate cheesecake. 'English cooking at its best,' in the opinion of
one reader.

The bedrooms, individualised by slate etchings of animals over the
doors, are comfortable; some of the older bedroom furniture has recently
been replaced with new pine.

◑ Closed mid-Nov to mid-Mar;
restaurant closed Tues eve

⤢ 8 miles south of Keswick on the
B5289. Private car park

🛏 2 twin, 1 double, 6 family rooms,
1 annexe room; all with
bathroom/WC

◈ Dining-room, lounge, library,
drying room; fishing nearby

⊖ No wheelchair access; no
children under 5; no dogs in
public rooms; no smoking in
bedrooms or some public
rooms

▭ None accepted

£ Single occupancy of twin/double
£24, twin/double/annexe £45;
deposit required. Set D £9 (7pm)

SEAVIEW ISLE OF WIGHT   **MAP 9**

Seaview Hotel

HIGH STREET, SEAVIEW, ISLE OF WIGHT PO34 5EX
TEL: ISLE OF WIGHT (0983) 612711   FAX: (0983) 613729

A spruce seaside hotel with bold decoration and a fine restaurant.

Just a stone's throw from the water's edge, the Seaview presents itself in a thoroughly shipshape and Bristol fashion after 12 years of careful and courteous management by Nick and Nicola Hayward. A smart front patio overhung with nautical flags looks down the street to the harbour. The seafaring theme continues inside, but it is well-coordinated with the beautiful décor. Gently ticking ships' clocks lend a relaxing tempo to the restaurant, where deep-green walls are set off by immaculate table settings of silver and flowers on starched linen cloths. The Haywards pride themselves on their use of fresh local produce: kippers on the bone at breakfast, sophisticated dishes of fish and shellfish for dinner, set off by asparagus, garlic, fresh herbs and wine from the island.

The Isle of Wight's marine history really comes to the fore in the hotel's two bars, which are hung with pictures of Solent ships, lifebelts and ropes. Residents have a choice of comfortable drawing-rooms – a warm, tasteful space with a first-floor bay window for non-smokers and a less attractive retreat for smokers on the ground floor. Bedrooms are done out in strong, elegant colours, with antique furniture and plenty of light. The rich floral bathrooms have smart, traditional fittings.

◐ Open all year; restaurant closed Sun eve

↗ Take the B3330 from Ryde and follow signs to Seaview. The hotel is 25 yards from the sea front. Private car park

🛏 10 twin, 5 double, 1 suite; all with bathroom/WC, TV, room service, baby-listening; no tea/coffee-making facilities in rooms

◇ Restaurant, 2 bars, 2 lounges, drying room; conference facilities

(max 25 people non-residential, 14 residential); water sports, other sports nearby. Wheelchair access to public areas only

⊖ Smoking discouraged in restaurant

▭ Access, Amex, Diners, Visa

£ Single occupancy of twin/double from £40, twin/double from £60, suite from £80; deposit required. Set L £11; alc L £18, D from £18. Special breaks available

---

SEAVINGTON ST MARY SOMERSET   **MAP 10**

The Pheasant

WATER STREET, SEAVINGTON ST MARY, NR ILMINSTER, SOMERSET
TA19 0QH
TEL: SOUTH PETHERTON (0460) 40502   FAX: (0460) 42388

Pub-hotel in a quiet village, with attractively decorated modern rooms.

Thatch pheasants running along the ridge of a roof tell you that you have reached the Pheasant, a sturdy seventeenth-century ex-farmhouse at the heart of an Ilminster dormitory village. Here you'll find a very English mix of bar and restaurant making the most of their oak beams and fireplaces, and bedrooms where everything is spanking new, if often tinged with nostalgia. Three-course table d'hôte menus offer plenty of choice: items like Thai butterfly prawns come as a pleasant surprise.

Bedrooms in the Pheasant are immaculately, indeed luxuriously, decorated. Most make a feature of big beds and all have lots of character, with sloping ceilings and brightly coloured curtains. Across a courtyard decorated with hanging flower-baskets is a barn with extra rooms, some with big brass bedsteads.

◑ Closed 26 Dec to 4 Jan; restaurant closed Sun eve

🔁 I mile from the South Petherton beginning of the A303 Ilminster bypass; follow signs for 'Ilminster local services' and Seavington St Michael. Private car park

🛏 4 twin, 3 double, I four-poster; all with bathroom/WC, TV, room service, hair-dryer, trouser press

◈ Restaurant, bar, lounge; golf, tennis, riding nearby. Wheelchair access to hotel, restaurant and WC, 4 ground-floor bedrooms

⊖ No dogs

▭ Access, Amex, Diners, Visa

£ Single occupancy of twin/double £50, twin/double/four-poster £70; deposit required; 10% service charge added to bill. Alc D £16

SEDBUSK NORTH YORKSHIRE · MAP 3

Stone House

SEDBUSK, NR HAWES, WENSLEYDALE, NORTH YORKSHIRE DL8 3PT
TEL: WENSLEYDALE (0969) 667571   FAX: (0969) 667720

A restful, popular country hotel with cheerful, friendly service.

'A really enjoyable experience. Ten out of ten for warmth of welcome and comfort – really like staying as a guest in a country house,' wrote one reader. Our inspector agreed. The Taplin family's mellow stone house in the heart of Wensleydale has beamed ceilings, horse brasses, copperware and eccentric collections. Visiting Americans must think they're in heaven.

The restaurant, subtly lit by candles and deco-style lamps, is so full of interesting bits and pieces that it's difficult to stifle the urge to go walkabout and peer over other diners' shoulders to admire display cases of Dinky cars and thimbles, various woodcarvings and framed prints of svelte ladies in couture that recall Cecil Beaton's designs for *My Fair Lady*. Food from the short set menu is straightforward: perhaps Dale country pâté and wholemeal toast, chicken in an orange sauce, fresh fruit salad and a cheeseboard. 'Food not inspiring but ample and served by cheerful and helpful waitresses,' noted one visitor.

The wood-panelled, cottagey lounge has plenty of wood-framed chairs, a wood-burning stove, bundles of *Yorkshire Life* to browse through and collections of pipes, toby jugs and Doulton figurines. Most of the bedrooms have chintzy décor and varnished pine or oak furniture. Three of the ground-floor rooms have conservatory areas. 'Highly recommended,' concluded a correspondent.

◑ Closed Jan and weekdays mid-Nov to Xmas

↗ Take Muker Road from Hawes, at T-junction, turn right (signposted Askrigg); hotel is 500 yards on left. Private car park

🛏 1 single, 7 twin, 7 double, 3 four-poster (some rooms in annexe); most with bathroom/WC, some with shower/WC; TV, baby-listening in all rooms; hair-dryer on request

◇ Dining-room, bar, lounge, billiard room/library, drying room; conference facilities (max 50 people non-residential, 18 residential); tennis at hotel, fishing nearby. Wheelchair access to hotel (3 steps), restaurant, 5 ground-floor bedrooms

⊖ No smoking or dogs in dining-room

▭ Access, Visa

£ Single £30, single occupancy of twin/double £33 and from £42, twin/double £47 to £60, four-poster £72 (£6 for each child staying in a family room); deposit required. Set D £15. Special breaks available

---

SEDGEFORD NORFOLK **MAP 7**

Sedgeford Hall ☆

SEDGEFORD, NR HUNSTANTON, NORFOLK PE36 5LT
TEL: HEACHAM (0485) 70902

A taste of grand country living on a private estate in a verdant corner of Norfolk.

Next door to the Queen's estate at Sandringham, Sedgeford Hall commands its own impressive 1,200 acres of pastures and woodland – a corner of north-west Norfolk which has been designated an Area of Outstanding Natural Beauty. Tall iron gates open on to a gravel drive which sweeps to a halt by the hall, a Queen Anne building with a pillared front door and long, elegant façade. The Campbells have been running the hall as a guesthouse for around seven years and most of their rooms are in an adjacent cottage which they converted. The bedrooms are generally large: one of the nicest, Room One, has red striped walls, canopied bed and sofa. Rooms Two and Three have their own front door, so that guests can come and go as they please.

Dinner is served in a gracious, marble-tiled dining-room with ruched curtains, portraits and large mirrors. All the guests gather around one table to indulge in the no-choice menu. By contrast, breakfast is taken in a fresh conservatory extension in blues and yellows – a room guaranteed to wake you up.

◑ Open all year

▸ From King's Lynn take the A149 north towards Hunstanton. At Heacham Lavender Farm turn right, signposted Docking (B1454). Fork right in Sedgeford, signposted Fring, and the hotel is ²/₃rds mile on the right. Private car park

⇤ 1 twin, 2 double; all with bathroom/WC, TV, hair-dryer, baby-listening

◈ Dining-room, lounge, library,

conservatory; heated indoor swimming-pool at hotel, fishing, golf, other sports nearby. Wheelchair access to hotel, restaurant and WC (unisex), 1 ground-floor bedroom

⊖ No dogs in public rooms and some bedrooms

▭ None accepted

£ Single occupancy of twin/double £40, twin/double £68; deposit required. Set D £21

SHEFFIELD SOUTH YORKSHIRE   **MAP 5**

Whitley Hall ☆

ELLIOTT LANE, GRENOSIDE, SHEFFIELD, SOUTH YORKSHIRE S30 3NR
TEL: SHEFFIELD (0742) 454444   FAX: (0742) 455414

A carefully run country-house hotel with a business slant in a neo-suburban location.

To those unfamiliar with the area, the speed with which urban decay gives way to leafy suburbia and then to countryside surprises. Whitley Hall, a sooty crow-stepped sandstone building of sixteenth-century ancestry, has the advantage of being set amid 30 acres of garden although it is just half a mile from the A61 and an easy drive from Sheffield city centre.

Public areas blend the genuinely old with the nostalgic look of the modern country-house school. The latter prevails in the sitting-room, with its wooden mantelpiece, floral wallpaper, display case of Crown Derby and velvet curtains, while the restaurant, where the date 1584 is inscribed, revels in its antiquity with stone walls, hangings and leaded windows. Diners can choose between an à la carte selection and a set menu which changes monthly and offers five courses; perhaps salad Alexander, followed by soup, Scottish salmon, home-made pastries and a cheeseboard.

Bedroom corridors in pink woodchip are rather scruffy but the rooms themselves are spacious and attractive, with modern light wood furniture, modish bold fabrics, fan-style lamps and good, modern bathrooms. Move up a notch and you can have the panelled Peacock Room, with its four-poster and red and green décor.

◐ Open all year, exc 25, 26 Dec and Bank Hol Mons

↗ Leave the M1 at Junction 35 and follow signs for A629. Proceed down the hill and turn left into Nether Lane. Turn right at traffic lights, then left opposite Arundel pub. Turn right into Whitley Lane. Private car park

🛏 2 single, 10 twin, 2 double, 1 four-poster; all with bathroom/WC, exc 1 single with shower/WC; TV, room service, hair-dryer, trouser press, baby-listening in all rooms

◈ Restaurant, 2 bars, lounge, 4 private dining/conference rooms; conference facilities (max 120 people non-residential, 28 residential); fishing, golf, other sports nearby

⊖ No wheelchair access; no dogs in public rooms

▭ Access, Amex, Diners, Visa

£ Single £40 to £54, single occupancy of twin/double £54, twin/double £50 to £68, four-poster £85; deposit required. Set L £12.50, D £18; alc L, D £20

SHENINGTON OXFORDSHIRE   **MAP 9**

Sugarswell Farm

SHENINGTON, BANBURY, OXFORDSHIRE OX15 6HW
TEL: BANBURY (0295) 680512

Isolated bed-and-breakfast in a modern farmhouse.

This comfortable modern farmhouse is in a peaceful isolated position, in the midst of flat farmland. Rosemary Nunneley offers a comfortable base from which to explore the surrounding countryside. Guests dine together in the deep red dining-room on good home cooking which guests have commended highly. Rooms are scattered with antiques and collections of china; in the lounge, guests can gather around the brick fireplace to plan their next day's sightseeing.

Bedrooms are spacious, with floral fabrics for the beds and curtains, pinks and greens being the predominant colours.

◐ Open all year

↗ From Banbury take the A422 Stratford-upon-Avon road. After 8 miles turn off left to Shenington and drive through the village. At the T-junction turn right, and right again at the crossroads. The farm is ¼ mile along this road. Private car park

🛏 2 twin, 1 double; all with bathroom/WC, hair-dryer

◈ Dining-room, lounge; conference facilities (max 12 people non-residential, 6 residential); fishing, golf, riding nearby

⊖ No wheelchair access; no children under 15; no dogs; no smoking

▭ None accepted

£ Single occupancy of twin/double £30 to £35, twin/double £40 to £50; deposit required. Set L (by arrangement) £12, D £17

Please let us know if an establishment has changed hands.

SHEPTON MALLET SOMERSET   **MAP 9**

Bowlish House

WELLS ROAD, SHEPTON MALLET, SOMERSET BA4 5JD
TEL: SHEPTON MALLET (0749) 342022

An elegant Georgian town house which looks much bigger than it actually is.

'We are always being asked to do wedding parties and having to turn them down,' says hotelier Bob Morley. With so few bedrooms you can see his point, but you can also see why people might be confused. From the outside, Bowlish House, with its pedimented Palladian windows and mounting-block, certainly looks as if it should be able to accommodate the hordes. To one side of the flagstone-floored hall there is a bar with an impressive cast-iron fireplace, to the other a sitting-room adorned with oil paintings of forgotten worthies; more of them gaze down on the dining-room and its conservatory extension, full of plants and big wicker chairs. Three-course dinner menus are described by one reader as 'excellent and imaginative'; perhaps slices of chicken suprême, or the more unusual, like fillet of brill, grilled and served with a warm olive oil, herb and coriander seed dressing.

There are comfortable bedrooms, albeit with slightly old-fashioned decoration; the double-access bathroom, letting you go in one door and out of another to confuse your partner, is certainly fun.

- ◑ Open all year, exc 1 week in autumn and spring
- ⊅ On the A371 Wells road, on the outskirts of Shepton Mallet. Private car park
- 🛏 1 twin, 2 double, family room available; all with bathroom/WC, TV; hair-dryer and room service on request
- ◈ Dining-room, bar, lounge, conservatory; conference

- facilities (max 24 people non-residential); fishing, golf, other sports nearby
- ⊖ No wheelchair access; no dogs in public rooms
- ▭ Access, Visa
- £ Single occupancy of twin/double £48, twin/double £48, family room £53. Cooked B £3.50; set D £22.50

SHERBOURNE WARWICKSHIRE   **MAP 9**

Old Rectory

VICARAGE LANE, SHERBOURNE, NR WARWICK, WARWICKSHIRE CV35 8AB
TEL: BARFORD (0926) 624562 (and fax)

A characterful former rectory with comfortable rooms and friendly hosts, convenient for the M40, NEC and Stratford.

The Old Rectory is a Georgian country house that finds itself no longer quite in the country – only half a mile from the M40 motorway, on the busy A46. Originally the White Horse Inn, and later the home of the Canon of Warwickshire, the Old Rectory has a chequered history and is rumoured to have a ghost. The building has two bedrooms in the old garages, six more in cottages at the bottom of the walled garden, and a family-sized annexe a few yards from the house. All are good-sized and well-co-ordinated, with brass and iron beds in most rooms, quality fabrics and a fair smattering of antiques. Number Four in the main house, with its brass double bed, patchwork quilt, wicker chairs and antique washstand in the enormous *en-suite* bathroom, gets our vote for the most appealing. Clive Wale, co-manager with wife Joanne, is keen to point out that this is a guesthouse, not a hotel: 'That way I can put my feet up in the afternoon if I feel like it and watch the racing.' The dining-room positively gleams with its solid antique table and chairs, immaculate mustard-coloured rug on the wooden floor and fine porcelain on the imposing dark wood dresser. Guests have breakfast together here; and a light supper, which might include beef lasagne with baked potato, honey roast ham platter or oak-smoked Scotch salmon, is served either here or in your room if you prefer.

◖ Open all year, exc 24, 25, 26 Dec

↗ On the A46, 3 miles south-west of Warwick. The hotel is at the junction of the A46 (heading towards Stratford) and Vicarage Lane. Private car park

🛏 4 single, 2 twin, 5 double, 3 family rooms; most with bathroom/WC, remainder with shower/WC; TV in all rooms

◈ Dining-room, bar/lounge; conference facilities (max 10 people residential); golf, tennis, other sports nearby. Wheelchair access to hotel and dining-room, 8 ground-floor bedrooms

⊖ No dogs or smoking in public rooms

▭ Access, Amex, Visa

£ Single £30, single occupancy of twin/double £30 to £37, twin/double £39 to £45, family room £50 to £65; deposit required. Light evening meals only. Special breaks available

---

SHERIFF HUTTON NORTH YORKSHIRE   **MAP 5**

Rangers House

SHERIFF HUTTON PARK, SHERIFF HUTTON, NORTH YORKSHIRE YO6 1RH
TEL: SHERIFF HUTTON (0347) 878397   FAX: (0347) 878666

A historic house in the country with friendly owners who invite you to treat it as a home.

If you've had enough of Victorian piles whose owners demand that you treat their monuments with a reverence more properly exhibited in cathedrals, Rangers House could be the place for you. It was built in 1639 as a brewhouse and stable for the Royal hunting lodge when

Charles I was on the throne. It's a place with a lived-in air where you feel able to kick off your shoes and relax.

The main hall is dominated by a huge fireplace and a staircase that sweeps up to a galleried landing. Floorboards, rugs and a stag's head accentuate the period flavour, while the blazing fire, knick-knacks and lots of family photos soften it. The bar/conservatory is a sort of adult playroom, with a treasure-trove-cum-junkyard feel. Farming implements hang on the walls alongside a Confederate flag; an aircraft propeller announces Sid Butler's aviation interests, and the front of a post-office counter acts as the bar. The dining-room is more traditional, with a parquet floor, antique chairs and well-spaced tables. The set dinners offer two options at each stage and are heartily traditional; perhaps cream of winter vegetable soup, followed by Scotch salmon poached with wine and herbs, steamed syrup sponge and cheese and biscuits.

Bedrooms are comfortable, with good old furniture and antiques. There is woodchip on the walls, but fresh paint, cottagey duvets, bedspreads and drapes – and teddies – make them cheerful.

◑ *Open all year*

▧ *Turn off the A64 at Flaxton, pass through Flaxton and Lilling and a sharp right into Sheriff Hutton Park. Follow this road for 1 mile. Private car park*

⇌ *1 single, 1 twin, 3 double, 1 family room; some with bathroom/WC, 1 with shower/ WC, 1 public shower room, 1 public bathroom; room service, hair-dryer in all rooms*

◈ *Dining-room, lounge, conservatory, library, drying room, games room; drying facilities; fishing, golf, riding, tennis nearby*

⊖ *No wheelchair access; no dogs*

▭ *None accepted*

£ *Single £32, single occupancy of twin/double £45 to £48, twin/ double £60 to £64, family room £80; deposit required. Set D £20. Special breaks available*

SHIPDHAM NORFOLK   **MAP 7**

Shipdham Place

CHURCH CLOSE, SHIPDHAM, THETFORD, NORFOLK IP25 7LX
TEL: DEREHAM (0362) 820303

No-nonsense Georgian house with the emphasis on home cooking.

'No bar, no piped music and no hall porter to tip,' states the brochure firmly, for Shipdham Place prides itself on being a straightforward, relaxing country restaurant-with-rooms. The old rectory has a plain fawn façade, supportive pillars on either side of the porch and solid white shutters. Similarly, the garden has a verdant, overgrown and unfussy look to it. Inside, the chesterfield sofas and fresh flowers of the morning-room compete with the Panel Room (a cosy lounge with log fires, stripped pine panelling and quarry tiles) for comfort and space. Small individual tables in the old rectory dining-room seat around 30, and low-hanging lamps create an intimate atmosphere. Tina Poulton does the cooking and her set menu usually includes a good choice. A warm salad of bacon and feta cheese or melon with Cointreau may be among the starters; lamb or pork cutlets, fish or poultry feature among the main courses and there are home-made puddings or ice-creams to finish, plus a cheeseboard.

Despite the emphasis on the restaurant, the bedrooms are of a high standard. Numbers One and Two are spacious and have pine or wicker furniture.

◐ *Open all year*

▨ *Midway between East Dereham and Watton on the A1075. Opposite the church in Shipdham. Private car park*

🛏 *3 twin, 3 double, 2 four-poster; all with bathroom/WC, exc 1 double; TV, room service, hair-dryer in all rooms; no tea/coffee-making facilities in rooms*

◇ *2 restaurants, bar, 2 lounges; conference facilities (max 25 people non-residential, 8 residential); golf, tennis, other sports nearby*

⊖ *No wheelchair access; no dogs in public rooms; no smoking in restaurants*

▢ *Access, Amex, Visa*

💷 *Single £30 to £50, single occupancy of twin/double £30 to £50, twin/double £40 to £65, four-poster £65. Set L £9 (by arrangement only), D £19*

SHIPHAM SOMERSET   **MAP 10**

Daneswood House

CUCK HILL, SHIPHAM, NR WINSCOMBE, SOMERSET BS25 1RD
TEL: WINSCOMBE (0934) 843145   FAX: (0934) 843824

A small, welcoming country-house hotel with spectacular views of the Mendips.

Externally the architecture of this 1904 house can't hope to compete with the spectacular views of the Mendips and Wales over which it presides. Big, quiet bedrooms in the main building boast individual colour schemes and lavish fabrics, but furnishings are slightly old-fashioned; the honeymoon suite features a seven-foot bed, a sunken bath and ancient gramophone. Rooms have views of a wood or hills. Six years ago hotelier David Hodges added a wing of two-storied suites to the house. Not surprisingly, rooms in this extension are more modern.

The dark and elegant dining-room has William Morris-style wall-paper. On one side linenfold-panel doors open on to a cosy lounge, while on the other a pair of eighteenth-century church doors, lovingly restored, lead into a light, airy breakfast room. There's a strong Italian flavour to the dinner menus, which change daily and feature a mix of familiar sirloins and roasts alongside more exotic fare.

◑ Open all year

➐ South of Bristol, 1½ miles off the A38 towards Cheddar. Private car park

🛏 6 double, 3 family rooms, 3 suites; most with bathroom/WC, some with shower/WC; TV, room service, hair-dryer, trouser press, baby-listening in all rooms

◈ 2 restaurants, bar, lounge, conservatory; drying facilities; conference facilities (max 20 people non-residential and residential); fishing, dry ski slope, other sports nearby. Wheelchair access to hotel (ramp), restaurant and WC (M, F), 3 ground-floor bedrooms

⊖ No dogs in public rooms and by arrangement only in bedrooms

▭ Access, Amex, Diners, Visa

£ Single occupancy of double £68, twin/double £80, family room/ suite £113; deposit required. Set L £15/£22, D £22. Special breaks available

---

SHIPTON GORGE DORSET   MAP 10

Innsacre Country Restaurant

SHIPTON GORGE, BRIDPORT, DORSET DT6 4LJ
TEL: BRIDPORT (0308) 56137

Friendly restaurant and functional bedrooms.

This seventeenth-century farmhouse built of local stone is tucked neatly into a steep-sided valley in one of Dorset's seemingly endless supply of sleepy hamlets. Although it's no longer a working farm, you can still expect to see some pet pigs and goats.

The dividing walls of the original building's interior have been knocked down, and on stepping through the front door you are at once in a large open-plan room. Walls are of roughly hewn stone and are decorated with a few plates. Immediately in front is the bar, and to the right, separated by a curtain, are the well-spaced tables. Wherever possible local produce is used, so expect New Forest venison and Abbotsbury oysters (delicious!). There is also ample opportunity to be adventurous. Why not try pigeon with chocolate linguini and coffee sauce? The atmosphere cultivated by the Davieses is relaxed and informal. The bedrooms eschew the flowery cottage look in favour of a sparer style with white walls, blue and white linen and dark carved furniture.

◑ Open all year, exc 2 weeks in Nov, 25 and 26 Dec; restaurant closed Sun and Mon eves (though suppers provided on request)

➐ 2 miles east of Bridport. Just south of the A35 Bridport to Dorchester road, take the turning signposted Shipton Gorge and Burton Bradstock. Innsacre is signposted from here. Private car park

🛏 1 twin, 4 double, 1 family room; all with bathroom/WC, TV, hair-dryer, baby-listening

◈ Restaurant, bar, lounge, drying room, residents' lounge; conference facilities (max 12

people non-residential, 6
residential); golf, riding, other
sports nearby. Wheelchair access
to restaurant only

● No dogs in restaurant; smoking
in bar and lounge only

▭ Access, Visa

£ Single occupancy of twin/double
£30 to £45, twin/double £50 to
£66, family room £70 to £99;
deposit required. Set L for parties
(by arrangement), D £20.
Special breaks available

SHIPTON-UNDER-WYCHWOOD OXFORDSHIRE   MAP 9

Shaven Crown

SHIPTON-UNDER-WYCHWOOD, CHIPPING NORTON, OXFORDSHIRE
OX7 6BA
TEL: SHIPTON-UNDER-WYCHWOOD (0993) 830330

A small family-run hotel in a fourteenth-century hospice.

Originally a hospice in the fourteenth century, the Shaven Crown is now
run by the Brookes family as a small hotel whose attractive stone
buildings surround a central courtyard. The reception is in the corner of
the Great Hall, which has a splendid double-collared brace roof; this
also functions as the lounge, where guests are served coffee in front of
the open fire after dinner. An open twin staircase leads up to bedroom
floors on either side of the hall. The rooms are simple, with a slightly
monastic feel; one twin with plain white walls and flowery curtains has an
old-fashioned bathroom separated from the bedroom by an open arch.
The wooden-floored restaurant is a pleasant room, simply furnished
with solid elm tables and chairs. You can eat here or in the public bar
across the courtyard, a snug room with wooden-framed partitions
between the tables and an open fire, above which there is a blackboard
listing reasonably priced bar meals.

◐ Open all year

⤢ Four miles north of Burford on
the A361, opposite the church
and on the village green. Private
car park

⇋ 1 single, 3 twin, 4 double, 1
four-poster/family room; most
with bathroom/WC, some with
shower/WC; TV in all rooms;
hair-dryer on request

◇ Restaurant, bar, lounge; limited
conference facilities (max 12
people residential and non-
residential); bowls at hotel, golf,
fishing, other sports nearby.

Wheelchair access to hotel,
restaurant and 1 ground-floor
bedroom

● No children under 5 in
restaurant eves; no dogs in
bedrooms

▭ Access, Visa

£ Single £33, single occupancy of
twin/double £53, twin/double
£66 to £75, four-poster/family
room £82; deposit required. Bar
meals; Sun L £14.50; set D
£18.50 (prices till Apr 94).
Special breaks available

SHREWLEY WARWICKSHIRE   **MAP 9**

Shrewley House

HOCKLEY ROAD, SHREWLEY, NR WARWICK, WARWICKSHIRE CV35 7AT
TEL: CLAVERDON (0926 84) 2549   FAX: (0926 84) 2216

Beautifully kept bedrooms in an informal bed and breakfast.

Since the Greens opened their home to guests in 1989 they have gone
from strength to strength. Benefiting from a fortuitous location – rural,
yet with easy access to the NEC and all the Midlands tourist sights – and
the Greens' good business sense, this is an enterprise that deserves its
success. The newest part of this rambling red-brick former farmhouse
dates from around 1786. The shire horses once bred here are no longer
around – their stalls have been converted into two-bedroomed self-
catering cottages. The four main bedrooms are in the house and three
still bear the children's names, though they have been refurbished to an
exceptionally high standard. Joanne's Room has flowery wallpaper and a
pine four-poster bed draped in white cotton and lace; Samantha's Room
is similarly pretty, while Robert's Room is a smaller double, slightly more
masculine with stripy fabrics. All have good-sized modern bathrooms.
Less grand is the sitting-room, which is full of comfy chairs, lots of
books, CD player and piano; the dining-room is pretty, with views of the
garden.

◑ *Open all year; evening meals by
arrangement only*

⤷ *5 miles north-west of Warwick
on the B4439, which runs
between the A41 Warwick road
and the A34 Stratford road.
Private car park*

🛏 *1 double, 2 four-poster, 1 suite,
3 cottages; all with bathroom/
WC, TV, room service, hair-
dryer, mini-bar, baby-listening;
trouser press on request*

◈ *Dining-room, 2 lounges, drying
room; conference facilities (max*

*8 people residential); fishing,
golf, other sports nearby;
babysitting*

⊖ *No wheelchair access; no dogs or
smoking in public rooms*

▭ *Access, Visa*

💷 *Single occupancy of double £30
to £40, double £45 to £50, four-
poster £52, suite £37 to £82,
cottage room £35 to £50;
deposit required. Set D from £14
(by arrangement); suppers from
£7.50*

SHREWSBURY SHROPSHIRE   **MAP 5**

Albright Hussey ☆

ELLESMERE ROAD, SHREWSBURY, SHROPSHIRE SY4 3AF
TEL: BOMERE HEATH (0939) 290571/290523   FAX: (0939) 291143

A fascinating sixteenth-century moated grange, now a solid, family-run hotel.

Seen in the distance from the main road, the building looks an extraordinary mixture of a decorated black and white half-timbered cottage with a brick and stone extension a whole storey higher. It is more harmonious in close-up, given interest if not beauty by the antiquity of the Tudor architecture and the black swans in the moat. The Subbiani family has turned Albright Hussey into a comfortable country hotel of the medium-posh variety without losing any of the building's character. The drawing-room is a little dark, while the restaurant is a forest of dark panelling and heavy beams, with a little lovers' alcove by the massive fireplace. The à la carte dinner menu is firmly Italian, the lunch menu resolutely English.

The bedrooms are much brighter and quite big enough to spend time in. Hussey has great views and a triumph of a bathroom, where problems involving the sacred nature of the ancient timbers have been resolved by putting the bath into the centre of the room and making it into a kind of four-poster.

◑ Open all year

⤴ 2½ miles from Shrewsbury on the A528 Ellesmere road. Private car park

🛏 4 double, 1 four-poster; all with bathroom/WC, TV, room service, hair-dryer, trouser press, baby-listening

◈ 2 dining-rooms, bar, lounge, drying room; conference facilities (max 40 people non-residential);

golf, riding nearby; babysitting. Wheelchair access to dining-rooms only

⊖ No children under 5; dogs by arrangement only

▭ Access, Amex, Diners, Visa

£ Single occupancy of double from £65, double from £85, four-poster £100; deposit required. Set L £10, D £17; alc L, D from £18. Special breaks available

The Manse ☆

16 SWAN HILL, SHREWSBURY, SHROPSHIRE SY1 1NL
TEL: SHREWSBURY (0743) 242659

A very pretty town house bed and breakfast, and good value too.

Maureen Cox's house lies at the bottom of a steep and narrow Shrewsbury street close to the river and only a few minutes' walk from the centre of town. It is a three-storey Georgian building, nicely proportioned from the outside and with a comfortable, indeed plush, interior. Guests have the use of a lavish first-floor drawing-room which runs the length of the house and contains several sofas to tempt you into relaxation. Downstairs, the breakfast room is equally calm and full of light, with a large single table and a dresser.

There are only two bedrooms: the best is the twin upstairs which has lots of space but a bathroom shared with the family. The double is smaller, with separate shower, but equally comfortable.

- ◑ Open all year, exc Xmas period
- ↗ In Shrewsbury, turn into Swan Hill opposite Kingsland Bridge. The Manse is 1st on the left. Private car park and on-street parking
- ⇌ 1 twin, 1 double; 1 with shower/ WC, 1 with washbasin; TV, hair-dryer in both rooms
- ◈ Dining-room, lounge
- ⊖ No wheelchair access; no children under 10; no dogs; no smoking in bedrooms
- ▭ None accepted
- £ Single occupancy of twin/double £20 to £30, twin £30 to £32, double £35 to £36

Sandford House

ST JULIAN'S FRIARS, SHREWSBURY, SHROPSHIRE SY1 1XL
TEL: SHREWSBURY (0743) 343829

A friendly welcome and simple bedrooms close to the town centre.

This honest, well-proportioned house in a cul-de-sac not far from the centre of Shrewsbury was once, according to local legend, an institution for fallen women. What they made of the elaborate plasterwork in what is now the dining-room and lounge is unrecorded, but the ceilings and walls of these rooms with their elaborate mouldings are certainly among the most attractive aspects of Sandford House. Otherwise, this is a simple, good-value guesthouse with 'everything scrupulously clean – the crockery really shone'. Bedrooms are on the small and sparsely furnished side, so ask for Room Six, which is by far the best – a large and comfortable double room with a pretty ceiling. Number Four is the next best. A reader writes to tell us that parking is not easy, and once your car is in the tiny yard it is as well to leave it there.

- ◑ Open all year
- ↗ Cross over English Bridge towards town centre; St Julian's Friars is first on left. Private car park
- ⇌ 2 single, 3 twin, 4 double, 1 family room; 1 with bathroom/ WC, some with shower/WC, 2 public bathrooms; TV, room service, hair-dryer, baby-listening in all rooms
- ◈ Dining-room, bar, lounge; tennis, riding, other sports nearby
- ⊖ No wheelchair access; no dogs in public rooms
- ▭ Access, Visa
- £ Single £23 to £29, single occupancy of twin/double £25 to £31, twin/double £38 to £44, family room from £49; deposit preferred. Special breaks available

---

The Guide *office can quickly spot when a hotelier is encouraging customers to write a letter recommending inclusion – and sadly, several hotels have been doing this in 1993. Such reports do not further a hotel's cause.*

SHURDINGTON GLOUCESTERSHIRE   **MAP 9**

The Greenway

SHURDINGTON, CHELTENHAM, GLOUCESTERSHIRE GL51 5UG
TEL: CHELTENHAM (0242) 862352   FAX: (0242) 862780

A carefully managed country-house hotel close to Cheltenham.

The Greenway, a sixteenth-century Cotswold manor house, makes a plush base for those with business or racing interests in Cheltenham. The view from the conservatory section of the dining-room looks across a sunken garden to the fields and the rising slopes of the Cotswolds.

This is a comfortable and elegant hotel, given class by its large drawing-room and hall and its magnificent fireplaces. The style is set by the lavish flower arrangements and the prints of horses which decorate the bar. Bedrooms are spacious, with a good range of facilities. Those in the converted coach-house inevitably have less character than the rooms in the main building. Since our last edition there has been a change of chef: Chris Colmer has introduced a menu of modern British cooking, with some 'revivals' such as braised pig's trotters and venison pie included on the carte.

◗ Open all year, exc 1 week from New Year's weekend; restaurant closed Sat lunch and Bank Hol Mons

🡕 2½ miles south of Cheltenham town centre, off the A46. Private car park

🛏 2 single, 8 twin, 9 double; all with bathroom/WC, TV, room service, hair-dryer; tea/coffee-making facilities on request

◈ Restaurant, bar, 2 lounges; conference facilities (max 18 people residential and non-residential); croquet at hotel, other sports nearby. Wheelchair access to hotel (ramp), restaurant and WC (M,F), 4 ground-floor bedrooms

⊖ No children under 7; no dogs

▭ Access, Amex, Diners, Visa

£ Single £85 to £94, single occupancy of twin/double £85 to £94, twin/double £120 to £192; deposit required. Set L £15, D £25; alc D £33. Special breaks available

---

SIDMOUTH DEVON   **MAP 10**

Hotel Riviera ☆

THE ESPLANADE, SIDMOUTH, DEVON EX10 8AY
TEL: SIDMOUTH (0395) 515201   TELEX: 42551 EXONIA G
FAX: (0395) 577775

A large Regency sea-front hotel which has just undergone major refurbishment.

The Hotel Riviera's curvy grey façade will look familiar to viewers of television's recent dramatisation of the Wodehouse Jeeves books, for which it provided a glamorous backdrop. In a resort that attracts more than its fair share of elderly visitors the Riviera is popular with a slightly wider age band. In summer the potted palms and sun umbrellas on the patio look very jolly, but indoors things are rather grander, with the cushions in the lounge so plump the chairs look more like thrones. The startlingly red piano bar at the rear is very popular at lunchtimes, even out of season. As you would expect, set menus in the dining-room are solidly English, and look sustaining enough to satisfy the hungriest diner; there's also a more imaginative à la carte menu.

A lift gives access to the second- and third-floor bedrooms, which have identically elegant peachy decorations. The best inevitably monopolise the sea views, with armchairs in their bay windows. Redecoration of all the bedrooms should be completed by the end of 1993.

◑ Open all year

▨ On the esplanade in Sidmouth. Private car park

🛏 8 single, 13 twin, 6 double, 2 suites; all with bathroom/WC, TV, room service, hair-dryer, baby-listening; trouser press in de-luxe rooms only

◈ Restaurant (air-conditioned), 2 bars (1 air-conditioned), lounge, ballroom, drying room, conservatory; conference facilities (max 90 people non-residential, 50 residential);

fishing, water sports, other sports nearby; babysitting. Wheelchair access to hotel (1 step), restaurant and WC (disabled), 2 bedrooms specially equipped for disabled people

⊖ No dogs in public rooms

▭ Access, Amex, Diners, Visa

£ Single from £51 and £61, twin/double from £92 and £112, suite £124 to £144; deposit required. Set L £11.50, D £7 (£18.50 for non-residents); alc L, D from £16.50. Special breaks available

SIMONSBATH SOMERSET   MAP 10

Simonsbath House

SIMONSBATH, EXMOOR, SOMERSET TA24 7SH
TEL: EXFORD (064 383) 259

A grand country-house hotel in a remote part of Exmoor, popular with walkers.

Simonsbath itself is a blink-and-you'll-miss-it clutch of houses and a pottery, so the scale of its hotel, once a seventeenth-century hunting lodge, comes as a surprise. Turn round in the porch and you'll be gazing out on nothing but barren moorland, the only sounds being the jackdaws and the river. Inside, much of the ground floor is taken up by a sunken lounge where coats of arms are lined up authoritatively on the chimney breast and chairs are clumped together in cosy groups. Beyond, there's a small library-cum-bar. Under the stairs is an original inglenook fireplace, now full of dried flowers. Past that, the dining-room's cool sea-green and white walls are in striking contrast to the dark panelling of the lounge. The four-course dinner menus change daily; desserts look most imaginative. Lunch can be taken in the Boevey Restaurant, set apart from the hotel at the bottom of the drive.

After the grandeur of the public rooms the staircarpet and corridor decoration look a little faded. The bedrooms make up for it, though, with their varied colour schemes.

◗ Closed Dec, Jan

⤴ In Simonsbath village, on the B3223. Private car park

🛏 3 twin, 4 four-poster; all with bathroom/WC, TV, room service, hair-dryer; no tea/coffee-making facilities in rooms

◈ Dining-room, bar, lounge, library, drying room; fishing, riding nearby

⊖ No wheelchair access; no children under 10; no dogs; no smoking in dining-room

▭ Access, Amex, Diners, Visa

£ Single occupancy of twin/double £44 to £60, twin/double/four-poster £78 to £90; deposit required. Set D £20.50

SINGLETON LANCASHIRE   **MAP 5**

Singleton Lodge

LODGE LANE, SINGLETON, NR BLACKPOOL, LANCASHIRE FY6 8LT
TEL: POULTON-LE-FYLDE (0253) 883854   FAX: (0253) 894432

Unassuming small hotel in a country setting, yet still within easy reach of the Golden Mile.

You can just about spot Blackpool Tower from the drive of this old Fylde vicarage. That is about the only intrusion of candy-floss culture into this peaceful spot, with its patch of parkland, ha-ha, sheep, pheasants and resident pair of horses (Jessie and Jasper). The pleasant rural aspect is only marred by what seems to be a home for retired caravans next door.

It is an unaffected and friendly little hotel, where the focus tends to be around the bar and bar lounge. There may be standard issue furniture but there are also open fires, brasses and old photos of the house and village, plus more recent ones of local anglers and the Wyre salmon that didn't get away.

The bedrooms have co-ordinated but simple floral prints. There are lace and satin decorative cushions, pine or Victorian furniture, fresh fruit and magazines. Draped curtains and sprays of dried flowers raise the dining-room a notch above the run-of-the-mill. The food is plain and homely, with generous portions; a typical dinner menu might include potted shrimps, asparagus soup, roast duck and Bakewell sponge.

◗ Open all year, exc 25 to 26 Dec, 1 Jan; restaurant closed Sun eve

⤴ Leave the M55 at Junction 3 and take the A585 Fleetwood road.

Continue on this road for 3 miles to a set of traffic lights. Turn left, then left into Lodge Lane. The house is the third entrance on the left. Private car park

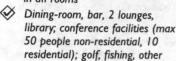

I single, I twin, 5 double, I four-poster, 2 family rooms; all with bathroom/WC, exc I room with shower/WC; TV, room service, hair-dryer, trouser press in all rooms

 Dining-room, bar, 2 lounges, library; conference facilities (max 50 people non-residential, 10 residential); golf, fishing, other sports nearby. Wheelchair access

to restaurant and WC (unisex) only

 Dogs by arrangement only

 Access, Amex, Visa

 Single and single occupancy of twin/double £48, twin/double/four-poster £60, family room £70; deposit required. Sun L £10; alc D £14 (prices till end Mar 94)

SLAIDBURN LANCASHIRE   **MAP 5**

Parrock Head Hotel

WOODHOUSE LANE, SLAIDBURN, NR CLITHEROE, LANCASHIRE BB7 3AH
TEL: CLITHEROE (0200) 446614/446313

Well-converted, whitewashed farmhouse tucked into beautiful Lancashire fellside. Good for walkers and weekend retreats.

The seventeenth-century 'long' farmhouse offers both civilised comforts and a relaxing, informal atmosphere.

The (very) low-beamed restaurant has built up a reputation for good cooking, and the daily-changing menu is simple but tempting. Home-made soup or hot mushrooms in Stilton and white wine sauce might be followed by roast loin of Bowland lamb stuffed with apricots and pine nuts. Puddings might include French apple tart or raspberry mousse. Breakfasts, appropriately, offer Lancashire black pudding, as well as Cumberland sausage and Aberdeen kippers.

En-suite bedrooms are split between the farmhouse and two adjacent cottages; farmhouse rooms have the most character, but all are pleasantly furnished with low-key, soft florals. The Swedish House is virtually self-contained, and its two rooms would be a good choice for extended family groups. The 'best' bedroom is Room One, leading off the lounge. Sunny and spacious with cream and gilt furniture and co-ordinated prints. The residents' lounge and library are up an open flight of stairs leading from the bar/reception area. The latter has cottage-style furniture and lots of local maps and literature. In the comfortable lounge you can sit by the open hearth as the outsize, eighteenth-century Parliament clock ticks reassuringly away.

 Open all year

 I mile north-west of village. Private car park

 4 twin, 5 double; all with bathroom/WC, TV, room service, baby-listening; hair-dryer on request

 Restaurant, bar, 2 lounges, library, drying room; conference facilities (max 20 people non-residential, 9 residential); fishing, golf nearby. Wheelchair access to hotel (1 step), restaurant and WC (M,F), 7 ground-floor bedrooms

⊖ No dogs in public rooms and bedrooms in house; no smoking in restaurant

▭ Access, Amex, Visa

£ Single occupancy of twin/double from £40, twin/double from £59; deposit required. Sun L £11.50; alc D £13.50 to £17.50. Special breaks available

---

SMARDEN KENT   **MAP 8**

The Bell   ℒ

BELL LANE, SMARDEN, KENT TN27 8PW
TEL: SMARDEN (0233) 770283

A friendly inn set a little off the beaten track.

The Bell is first and foremost a good pub, with the added attraction of having reasonably priced rooms above the bar. It is a red and white low-slung building with a red tiled roof. Inside, three main bars with a mixture of oak beams, dark wooden tables, candles and inglenook fireplaces form the public areas. Each draws a mixed clientele of old and young, from smart-suited professionals to local farmers; the atmosphere is generally warm and sociable. Tucked out of the way around a corner is a small bar, a popular place for those eating the good hearty pub grub.

Bedrooms are reached via a narrow metal spiral staircase (which requires some agility). On the whole they are pretty average in size and décor, with simple pastel colours and views over open countryside.

Breakfast, of the serve-yourself-from-the-fridge variety, consists of cereals, bread, tea and coffee.

◑ Open all year, exc 25 Dec

🔁 In the village of Smarden off the B2077 between Charing and Biddenden. Private car park

🛏 3 twin, 1 double; 2 public shower rooms; all with TV

◈ 3 bars; fishing, golf, riding nearby

⊖ No wheelchair access

▭ Access, Visa

£ Single occupancy of twin/double £20, twin/double £32; deposit required. Alc L, D from £2.50 to £12

SOMERTON SOMERSET   **MAP 10**

The Lynch

4 BEHIND BERRY, SOMERTON, SOMERSET TA11 7PD
TEL: SOMERTON (0458) 272316

A stylishly elegant Georgian house in attractive grounds, offering bed and breakfast only.

Although Roy Copeland has stopped offering evening meals at the Lynch, guests can still smile at the Cruikshank cartoons adorning the walls over breakfast – when they are not looking out of the window at the antics of the black swans, Bahama pintails and other exotic waterfowl on a large pond in the garden, that is. The Lynch is a solid, elegant Georgian town house topped off with a glass lantern and with the odd blocked-up window serving as a reminder that other unpopular taxes predated the poll tax. The five bedrooms, named after places where a previous owner had lived, are extremely comfortable, boasting great swathes of colourful fabrics and striking wallpaper. The best is probably Goldington, which has a Georgian four-poster bed and large bathroom, but Alderley and Kendal, squeezed in under skylit sloping ceilings, perhaps have more character. The Lynch lacks a real lounge, although there is a small sitting area at the back of the breakfast room. Instead you can climb up into the lantern for fine views over the grounds, an adjacent trout farm and two self-catering cottages created out of the old stables and a shed.

◑ Open all year, exc 25, 26 Dec

⤢ On the north edge of Somerton, ¼ mile off the B3151 Yeovil to Street road. Private car park

🛏 2 twin, 2 double, 1 four-poster; all with bathroom/WC, TV, room service, hair-dryer

◈ Breakfast room, sitting-room;

golf, riding, other sports nearby

⊖ No wheelchair access; no dogs or smoking in public rooms

▭ Access, Visa

£ Single occupancy of twin/double £35 to £40, twin/double £45 to £55, four-poster £65; deposit required

---

SOURTON DEVON   **MAP 10**

Collaven Manor Hotel

SOURTON, NR OKEHAMPTON, DEVON EX20 4HH
TEL: BRIDESTOWE (083 786) 522/217   FAX: (083 786) 570

A small country-house hotel retaining many of its fifteenth-century features.

Collaven Manor Hotel is so densely coated in creeper you can hardly make out the fifteenth-century building with its Victorian add-ons. Its architectural history is rather puzzling; from the presence of not one but four bread ovens set into its fine stone fireplaces, hotelier Kati Chapple thinks it must have started life as four separate cottages, later knocked into one. As you stand on the stairs and look back at the long, narrow hallway with its raftered ceiling, you could almost be gazing down a very old church nave. Downstairs, the lounge, bar and overflow dining-room all boast low beamed ceilings, although the main dining-room opens up a bit, offering fine country views through its french windows. Five-course table d'hôte menus offer plentiful choice and a sensible balance between the traditional (rabbit braised in cider) and more unusual dishes like tart of spiced courgettes and caramelised onions.

Upstairs, the bedrooms in the older part of the house are as quaint as the public rooms, several having exposed stone walls and beamed ceilings. In general, light modern colour schemes rub shoulders with antique furnishings.

◐ Open all year

↗ On the A386 Tavistock to Okehampton road, 10 miles north of Tavistock, 4 miles south-west of Okehampton. Private car park

🛏 2 single, 2 twin, 2 double, 1 four-poster; most with bathroom/WC, some with shower/WC; TV, hair-dryer, baby-listening in all rooms; limited room service

◇ 2 restaurants, bar, lounge; conference facilities (max 25 people non-residential, 9 residential); croquet, pitch and putt at hotel, golf, riding, other sports nearby

⊖ No wheelchair access; no children under 7 at dinner; no dogs in public rooms; no smoking in restaurant

▭ Access, Visa

£ Single £51, single occupancy of twin/double £67, twin/double £79 to £85, four-poster £95. Sun L £12; set L £11, D from £16.50 (prices till Mar 94). Special breaks available

---

SOUTH MOLTON DEVON   **MAP 10**

Park House ☆

SOUTH MOLTON, DEVON, EX36 3ED
TEL: SOUTH MOLTON (0769) 572610   FAX: (0769) 573261

A comfortable country-house hotel with award-winning gardens.

A pair of wrought-iron gates apparently leading nowhere act as a signpost for Park House, a large 1840s merchant's house in a lovely walled garden, which offers shooting and fishing over 80 acres of land. Much of the ground floor is taken up with a pair of lounges, the first is full of chintzy chairs, the second, through a pair of glass doors, evokes the feel of a traditional English pub until you start to notice the odd pieces of African memorabilia, a spear here, a headrest there, relics of Michael Gornall's years in the British Army in Kenya. Across the spacious hall, the dining-room feels cosy, an impression heightened by the naïve painting of an outsize pig on the wall. Anne Gornall describes her three-course dinners as 'unsophisticated', with lots of roasts and steaks.

A Regency stairway sweeps up to a grand galleried landing supported by marble columns, beyond which the eight bedrooms are nothing like as grand; Rooms Five and Six are probably largest. Since the hotel doesn't accept children under 12, the connecting single adjoining Room Two is usually used as a dressing room.

◐ Closed 10 Jan to 10 Mar

↗ Leave the M5 at Junction 27 and follow the A361 towards Barnstaple for approx 28 miles. After the 2nd roundabout take the next left (signed Pathfields). Hotel is 300 yards on the left. Private car park

2 twin, 6 double; most with bathroom/WC, some with shower/WC; TV, room service, hair-dryer in all rooms

 Dining-room, bar, 2 lounges, TV room, drying room; conference facilities (max 16 people non-residential, 8 residential); fishing at hotel, golf, tennis, other sports nearby

No wheelchair access; no children under 12; dogs restricted to 1 room only

Access, Amex, Visa

Single occupancy of twin/double £44, twin/double from £70; deposit required. Set D £16; alc L from £5 (prices till Sept 93). Special breaks available

Whitechapel Manor

SOUTH MOLTON, DEVON EX36 3EG
TEL: SOUTH MOLTON (0769) 573377   FAX: (0769) 573797

Supreme tranquillity in an isolated Elizabethan stone manor house with terraced garden.

Whitechapel Manor, a two-storied stone manor house, is a place to indulge fantasies that you're Anne Boleyn trysting with Henry VIII. Actually, the building is newer than that but not much, having come into being in the reign of Anne's daughter Elizabeth I. From the minute you pull up in the car park below the terraced garden, you're swept up in a world of quiet, unostentatious luxury; don't even dream of carrying your own suitcase if you want to avoid a barrage of tut-tutting. Once through the small stone porch you're straight into what would be an even larger lounge but for the Jacobean panelled screen used to slice off a reception area. Beyond it the lounge, with its low plaster-panelled ceiling, looks irresistibly inviting.

The best bedroom has a vast four-poster and an original painted panel over the fireplace, although you need to be tall to appreciate the view from the window. The naturally lit bathroom is equally enormous. The stairs to the left wing were apparently laid by someone who had imbibed too much wine the night before; floors, too, lurch off in all directions.

A small lounge bar with huge fireplace provides the perfect setting for pre-dinner drinks. What's to say about the three- and four-course dinners, beyond the fact that they're a dream? On inspection the pheasant sausage with wild rice was deliciously soft, the pork tenderloin melted in the mouth, and the dessert barely left room for the petits fours to follow. Service, too, is perfect, discreet and yet attentive, and it says much for hotelier John Shapland's conversational skills that he makes everyone feel at home in what could be dauntingly grand surroundings.

Open all year

Leave the M5 at Junction 27 and follow signs to Barnstaple. At the second roundabout turn right. The hotel is a further 1 mile down an unmarked track. Private car park

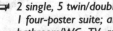 2 single, 5 twin/double, 2 double, 1 four-poster suite; all with bathroom/WC, TV, room service,

hair-dryer, baby-listening; no tea/
coffee-making facilities in rooms

◇ Restaurant, bar, 2 lounges;
conference facilities (max 15
people residential, 42 non-
residential); croquet at hotel,
other sports nearby

● No wheelchair access; no dogs;

no smoking in restaurant

▭ Access, Amex, Diners, JCB, Visa

£ Single £65 to £80, single
occupancy of twin/double £83 to
£145, twin/double £98 to £160,
four-poster suite £160; deposit
required. Set L from £16, D from
£26. Special breaks available

SOUTH PETHERTON SOMERSET   **MAP 10**

Oaklands House

8 PALMER STREET, SOUTH PETHERTON, SOMERSET TA13 5DB
TEL: (0460) 40272/41998

Graceful Georgian hotel-cum-restaurant with a French flavour.

Huge Ionic columns grace the porch of Oaklands House, a solid, honey-
coloured building with restaurant at the front and wine bar/bistro at the
rear. The restaurant, Le Tire Bouchon, is well-established but South
Petherton folk are taking longer to cotton on to the wine bar, part of
which is in what was once a flagstone-floored scullery with hand pump
intact. Since the Merlozzis, who own the hotel, are Corsican it comes as
no surprise to discover a French menu featuring dishes like *parfait de foies
de canard et sa brioche*, and *filet de chevreuil aux cinq poivres*. After dinner
guests can relax in comfortable cream armchairs in a large front-facing
lounge or in a back drawing-room; the latter is a shrine to Napoleon,
kitted out with more mementoes of François Merlozzi's hero than you
would think possible.

The Napoleonic theme continues upstairs, where the five bedrooms
are named after characters associated with the great man. The rooms are
large, although some bathrooms are cramped and windowless. Decoration and furnishings are elegant.

◑ Open all year, exc Xmas to mid-
Jan

◪ In South Petherton near the post
office. Private car park

⇔ 2 twin, 3 double; some with
bathroom/WC, some with
shower/WC; room service in all
rooms; TV, hair-dryer on request

◇ Restaurant, 3 lounges;
conference facilities (max 12
people non-residential,

5 residential); heated outdoor
swimming-pool at hotel, fishing,
golf, other sports nearby

● No wheelchair access; dogs in
bedrooms by arrangement only

▭ Access, Visa

£ Single occupancy of twin/double
£50, twin/double £60 to £70;
deposit required. Sun L £8.50;
set D £21. Special breaks
available

---

*Dog lovers: some hotels not only welcome dogs, but provide gourmet meals for
them. Ask.*

SOUTHWOLD SUFFOLK   **MAP 7**

The Crown

HIGH STREET, SOUTHWOLD, SUFFOLK IP18 6DP
TEL: SOUTHWOLD (0502) 722275   FAX: (0502) 724805

A high-street pub offering decent rooms in this engaging town.

A Cinderella to the larger Swan Hotel up the road (see next entry), the Crown offers good basic accommodation. Both hotels are owned by Adnams, the local brewers, but the Crown is the one to choose if you prefer a simpler room, a less formal restaurant and a lower bill at the end of your stay. 'This is an inn, not a grand hotel,' states the information sheet left in guests' bedrooms. For all its modesty, the hospitality is sincere and friendly. On arrival, you are asked what time you'd like a hot drink delivered to your room in the morning and which complimentary newspaper you'd like. After that you are left to relax in your room, which is likely to be solidly furnished with wooden furniture and flowery wallpaper.

Dinner, served in the bar, is just as unfussy. A congenial atmosphere prevails in the sunny yellow room equipped with scrubbed wooden tables, chairs and settles. From the L-shaped bar, you can order tasty dishes such as dressed local crab with salad and rye bread, which will be efficiently served at your table by waiting staff. A light breakfast comprising freshly squeezed orange or local apple juice, cereals and croissant or toast is included in the room price, but if the sea air has made you hungry, you can pay a few pounds extra for bacon and eggs, a 'Crown' kipper or buckwheat pancakes and maple syrup.

◑ Open all year, exc 1 week in Jan

↗ In the centre of Southwold. Private car park

🛏 2 single, 4 twin, 5 double, 1 family room; all with bathroom/WC, exc 1 twin with shower/WC; TV, hair-dryer in all rooms; limited room service; baby-listening on request; no tea/coffee-making facilities in rooms

◈ Restaurant (air-conditioned), 2 bars, lounge; conference facilities

(max 25 people non-residential, 12 residential); fishing, golf, tennis nearby; babysitting by arrangement

⊖ No wheelchair access; no dogs; no smoking in restaurant

▭ Access, Amex, Visa

£ Single £37, single occupancy of twin/double £47, twin/double £57, family room £60 to £80. Cooked B £4; set L £13/£15, D £17.50/£19.50

The Swan

MARKET PLACE, SOUTHWOLD, SUFFOLK IP18 6EG
TEL: SOUTHWOLD (0502) 722186   FAX: (0502) 724800

This dignified old hotel has many regulars.

The Swan Hotel is something of an institution in Southwold – on a Sunday afternoon it is *the* place to splash out on a devilish cream tea with freshly baked scones and luscious strawberry jam, or a traditional English tea of smoked salmon and cucumber sandwiches accompanied by moist fruit cake.

The standard of bedrooms matches the teas. You aren't likely to get a room with a good view of the sea – although from those at the front of the hotel, for example, Room 19, a smart suite, you can see a stretch of water. An additional 18 garden rooms have been added at the back of the hotel around a former bowling green, now a sheltered grassy area. These rooms, although lacking the character and individuality of those in the main nineteenth-century building, allow guests to come and go more independently.

Fixed-price menus are offered in the formal dining-room. The cheapest may start off modestly with mushroom soup, fresh mackerel pâté or chicken terrine, continue, perhaps, with poached fillet of lemon sole and finish with glazed lemon tart.

◑ *Open all year*

⤢ *Centrally situated in Southwold's market square. Private car park*

🛏 *6 single, 19 twin, 18 double, 1 four-poster suite, 1 suite; all with bathroom/WC, exc 2 singles with shower/WC; TV, room service, hair-dryer, baby-listening*

in all rooms; trouser press on request; no tea/coffee-making facilities in rooms

◈ *Dining-room, bar, lounge, study; conference facilities (max 40 people residential and non-residential); golf, tennis, other sports nearby; babysitting by*

THE SWAN
-SOUTHWOLD-

arrangement. Wheelchair access to hotel, restaurant and WC (unisex), 18 ground-floor bedrooms

 No children under 5 in dining-room after 7pm; dogs in garden bedrooms only; no smoking in dining-room.

 Access, Amex, Diner, Visa

£ Single £46 to £65, single occupancy of twin/double £74, twin/double £79 to £112, four-poster £135, suite £125 to £135; deposit required. Set L £11.50/£16.50, D £17.50/£29.50 (prices till Easter 94). Special breaks available

---

SOWERBY NORTH YORKSHIRE　　　　　　　　　　**MAP 3**

Sheppard's

FRONT STREET, SOWERBY, THIRSK YO7 1JF
TEL: THIRSK (0845) 523655　FAX: (0845) 524720

Mixed reports on this bustling restaurant-with-rooms in a prosperous race-going area.

This imaginative amalgam of an old creeper-clad stable block, a granary and a recent extension housing a bistro and more bedrooms is certainly an enterprising concern. The general feel is rustic and rural, with a dash of urban chic in the garden bistro. Here rough brick and plastered white walls are illuminated by light pouring through a glass atrium; the trendy feel is carried over into the large adjacent bar, where there are plenty of sofas to sit on while you consider the menu and the extra dishes chalked up on the blackboard. The connecting restaurant in the old stable block is darker, more formal and more traditional, with beams, a gallery section and crisp white table linen. The older bedrooms are homely, while those in the extension are more feminine. All are bright and clean, with mostly modish fabrics and lots of old pine. One guest thought both his superior double room and the 'beautifully laundered bath towel' were a little small. Readers' reports, backed up by an inspection, indicate that the food is consistently reliable. Daily specials include a lot of fresh fish. A bistro meal might include Wensleydale mushrooms with bacon and onions, grilled rainbow trout glazed with honey and almonds and butterscotch cheesecake. 'Delicious,' reported one guest. 'Excellent: among the best tasted in the north,' said another, before adding a sting in the tail: 'We were told on the phone we did not need to book a table; when we arrived the restaurant was full so we had to eat in the bistro. Fortunately this was fine, but we were cross about the misinformation.'

The news is certainly not all good. Our inspector shared one reader's view that the initial greeting was 'perfunctory', but thereafter found service prompt, friendly and obliging. Our correspondent, while praising 'helpful serving staff who cheerfully helped us to identify herbs used in the dishes,' felt the owner was 'practically downright rude' and seemed as if he could barely wait for his guests to leave. More reports, please.

◑ *Open all year, exc first week Jan*

⬀ *½ mile from Thirsk Market Square, take Sowerby Road from Castle Gate, Thirsk. Private car park*

🛏 *1 family twin, 6 double, 1 four-poster, 3 annexe rooms; most with bathroom/WC; TV, room service, hair-dryer in all rooms*

◈ *3 restaurants, bar, 2 lounges, conservatory; conference facilities (max 50 people non-residential); fishing, golf, gliding,*

other sports nearby

⊖ *No wheelchair access; no children under 10; no dogs; some bedrooms non-smoking*

▭ *Access, Visa*

⊞ *Single occupancy of twin/double £50 to £55, twin/double £40 to £74, four-poster £84, family room £60 to £80; deposit required. Sun L £9.50; alc L £15 (bistro), D £15 (bistro), £24 (restaurant). Special breaks available*

SPARK BRIDGE CUMBRIA   **MAP 4**

Bridgefield House ☆

LOWICK BRIDGE, SPARK BRIDGE, NR ULVERSTON, CUMBRIA LA12 8DA
TEL: LOWICK BRIDGE (0229) 885239   FAX: (0229) 885379

Victorian house in a tranquil Lakeland valley with a reputation for good food.

The sturdy, Victorian house built of Lakeland slate is tucked away on a wooded hillside and enjoys unbroken views down the valley to the River Crake. The house has an air of unpretentious hospitality; neat and sensible, it has a practical comfort that needs no dressing-up. The rooms are plainly furnished but the welcome by Rosemary and David Glister is warm and natural. Unlike many hoteliers, they are in favour of babies and children and cater particularly well for them. Simple high teas are provided at no extra cost.

The best bedrooms face south over the valley but all are roomy, with high ceilings and modernised bathrooms. Chenille bedspreads and neutral colours give a rather dated look. Rosemary has been described as one of the top five women chefs in the country, and the size of the dining-room reflects the importance that meals assume at Bridgefield. She cooks a daily-changing six-course menu, with a choice of starters and dessert, with care and imagination. Typical dishes might include duck liver pâté with damson sauce, warm prawn and wild mushroom salad, pea, pear and applemint soup, sautéed strips of fillet steak in mustard and cream sauce and boned breast of pheasant in dry cider and garlic with red cabbage, plus exciting vegetables, lush puddings and a single cheese or savoury. Breakfasts are described quite simply by one reader as 'superb'.

◑ Open all year

⤢ 500 yards from Lowick Bridge on the back road to Spark Bridge. Private car park

🛏 3 twin, 2 double; all with bathroom/WC, room service, hair-dryer, baby-listening; tea/coffee-making facilities on request

◈ Dining-room, bar, lounge, drying room; conference facilities (max

5 people residential); fishing, golf nearby; babysitting

⊖ No wheelchair access; no dogs in public rooms; no smoking in dining-room

▭ Access, Visa

£ Single occupancy of twin/double £30, twin/double £60; deposit required. Set D £20 (8pm). Special breaks available

---

Lowick House

**LOWICK GREEN, SPARK BRIDGE, NR ULVERSTON, CUMBRIA LA12 8DX
TEL: LOWICK BRIDGE (0229) 885227**

Gracious family home set in attractive landscaped gardens.

Tucked in on the right-hand side at the beginning of the A5084 to Coniston, Lowick House can be easily missed. That there is nothing to proclaim the presence of accommodation here is hardly surprising as the house is one of Britain's 215 Wolsey Lodges and thus is essentially a family home and not a hotel. The concept is based on the tradition of the eponymous cardinal, a renowned *bon viveur*, who accepted (and expected) lavish hospitality at country houses throughout the kingdom. Nowadays, the spirit of country hospitality is kept alive by people like Dorothy Sutcliffe, an engaging hostess.

The low, whitewashed house dates back to 1730 and stands in two acres of landscaped gardens through which a trout stream flows. Inside, there is an atmosphere of elegance and family tradition: the lounge has a light oak wall at one end with a fine carved mantelpiece, the walls have many family photos. The television lounge has a low, beamed ceiling and a wooden floor with a large rug. The dining-room has one long table at which a communal meal, cooked by Dorothy, is served. The six-course dinner includes a traditional main course, maybe beef, grouse, pheasant or lamb, as well as a soup and a fish course. The bedrooms feature antique furniture and rich fabrics, such as the original silks which are draped over the Victorian half-tester. All have appropriately grand bathrooms and relaxing views across verdant gardens.

◑ Open all year, exc Xmas and New Year

⤢ Leave the M6 at Junction 36 and take the A590 towards Barrow. At Greenodd turn right on to the A5092. Pass the Farmers Arms pub on the right, then fork on to the A5084 (signposted

Coniston). Lowick House is 100 yards on the right. Private car park

🛏 1 twin, 1 double, 1 half-tester; all with bathroom/WC; no tea/coffee-making facilities in rooms

◈ Dining-room, lounge, TV room;

drying room; golf, riding, other
sports nearby

● No wheelchair access; no
children; no dogs; no smoking

▭ None accepted

£ Single occupancy of twin/double
£40, twin/double/half-tester £60;
deposit required. Set D £18

SPREYTON DEVON   **MAP 10**

Downhayes

SPREYTON, CREDITON, DEVON EX17 5AR
TEL: BOW (0363) 82378

*Small, intimate Wolsey Lodge in a farmhouse just north of
Dartmoor.*

Downhayes, when you find it, is a long, low farmhouse where your nights
are unlikely to be disturbed by anything noisier than an owl. There are
only three bedrooms, one of them opening on to the garden and
adjoining the guests' lounge, a snug room with big log fire, choice of
magazines and books. Bedrooms are simply but attractively furnished
and brightened with fresh flowers. The Hines are attentive hosts, careful
to check that guests are warm enough and have a newspaper to read, but
they don't necessarily eat with them as is the case in some Wolsey
Lodges.

In the dining-room deep salmon-coloured walls frame views of the
countryside. Meals feature good home cooking and although there's no
choice, guests' likes and dislikes are checked when they book. Space
permits only two polished elm dining tables, so the Hines only accept a
full quota of six guests if four of them know each other and can be seated
together. Aware that intimacy can all too easily become overwhelming,
they will redirect the two unattached guests to their own sitting-room
with its stunning picture window if the four friends seem to be mono-
polising the lounge.

◑ Open all year, exc 20 to 29
Dec

⤢ Leave the A30 Exeter to
Okehampton road at Whiddon
Down ('Merrymeet' roundabout),
16 miles west of Exeter. Follow
signs to Spreyton. Downhayes is
on the left, 1½ miles north of
Spreyton on the road to Bow.
Private car park

🛏 2 twin, 1 double; 2 with
bathroom/WC, 1 public
bathroom

◈ Dining-room, lounge (with TV),
games room; fishing, golf, other
sports nearby

● No wheelchair access; no
children under 12; no dogs; no
smoking in bedrooms

▭ Visa

£ Single occupancy of twin/double
£28 to £35, twin/double £40 to
£50; deposit required. Set L £8
(by arrangement only), D £15.
Special breaks available

The George of Stamford

71 ST MARTINS, STAMFORD, LINCOLNSHIRE PE9 2LB
TEL: STAMFORD (0780) 55171   FAX: (0780) 57070/66104

A well-established and bustling old coaching-inn in a lovely medieval town; stylish rooms and good food.

The first sign of the George Inn is a gallows sign which spans the narrow street. In the era of stagecoach travel the sign was supposed to warn off highwaymen – though it can't have worked, because many of them, disguised in pilfered finery, used to stay here when 'resting between jobs'. On any day of the week the conservatory-style Garden Lounge is busy with people chatting over a light lunch, while the more formal oak-panelled restaurant hosts meetings of local groups and the lounge, with its huge sofas, exposed stone walls and log fire, is popular with people popping in for tea.

The bedrooms are stylishly kitted out with rich fabrics in strong colours and a mix of reproduction and antique furniture. Rooms over-looking the pretty inner courtyard are the most peaceful. Our favourite is Room 42, a large standard double in the attic with its own staircase, yellow décor, dark beams and a huge light bathroom.

Every room has a copy of the hotel's wine list, which is just as well as you need time to take it all in. Italian wines are particularly well represented. Dinner is on the whole traditionally British and might include Scottish salmon, pan-fried pigeon breast and roast rack of lamb with orange, garlic and rosemary.

◑ Open all year

↗ Exit from A1 marked Stamford; hotel is one mile from here to town centre. Private car park

🛏 12 single, 10 twin, 17 double, 4 four-poster, 3 family rooms, 1 suite; all with bathroom/WC, TV, room service, hair-dryer, trouser press, baby-listening; no tea/coffee-making facilities in rooms

◈ 2 restaurants, 2 bars, 2 lounges; conference facilities (max 47 people residential, 50 non-residential); giant chess set, croquet at hotel, other sports nearby; babysitting. Wheelchair access to restaurant (unisex) only

⊖ None

▭ Access, Amex, Diners, Visa

£ Single £75, single occupancy of twin/double £81, twin/double £100, four-poster £154, suite £118, family room £154; deposit required. Set L £15.50; alc L, D £25. Special breaks available

---

STANTON WICK AVON　　　　　　　　　　　　　　**MAP 9**

Carpenters Arms

STANTON WICK, PENSFORD, BRISTOL, AVON BS18 4BX
TEL: MENDIP (0761) 490202　FAX: (0761) 490763

A popular pub with both bar and restaurant food and good rooms.

This country inn stands on the edge of the village and has fine views from its hilltop location. Originally a row of miners' cottages dating from the seventeenth century, it is built from dark stone and flint and is covered with ivy. The emphasis here is on food; diners can choose from a selection of pub favourites, such as grills, scampi and ploughman's, which are served in the main bar area known as Coopers Parlour. This has a low, beamed ceiling and log fires. The staff are young and efficient and last year's complaint about the less-than-enthusiastic welcome given to guests seems to have been ironed out. If you fancy eating in a more formal setting, the restaurant serves hearty dishes such as steak stuffed with Stilton cheese, or roast rack of lamb.

The bedrooms are decorated with spriggy wallpaper and flowery curtains; nine in a new extension have cottagey, floral wallpapers.

◗ *Open all year; restaurant closed Sun eve*

↗ *Turn off the A37 Wells to Bristol road at Pensford; alternatively turn off the A368 Bath to Weston-super-Mare road. Private car park*

🛏 *3 twin, 9 double; all with bathroom/WC, TV, hair-dryer, trouser press*

◈ *2 restaurants, bar, lounge; conference facilities (max 40*

people non-residential, 12 residential); fishing, golf, tennis, riding nearby

⊖ *Wheelchair access to pub and restaurant only; no dogs; no smoking in bedrooms*

▭ *Access, Visa*

£ *Single occupancy of twin/double £46, twin/double £53; deposit required. Bar meals; alc D £20. Special breaks available*

STAPLEFORD LEICESTERSHIRE　　　　　　　　　　**MAP 5**

Stapleford Park　

STAPLEFORD, NR MELTON MOWBRAY, LEICESTERSHIRE LE14 2EF
TEL: WYMONDHAM (057 284) 522　FAX: (057 284) 651

A stately home with a grand interior, pricey good-sized rooms and unstuffy owners with an idiosyncratic style.

Situated in flat Leicestershire countryside, Stapleford Park is a grand Jacobean manor house totally obscured from view by mature trees. The beautiful parkland, with grazing sheep beyond the ha-ha and waterfowl on the lake, was laid out by Capability Brown. American owners Bob and

Wendy Payton run a quirky household with a mixed bag of styles, from the breakfast room, a converted fifteenth-century kitchen with vaulted ceiling and rope matting floor, to Tiffany, a 1920s bedroom with embroidered art-deco bedspread. Other bedrooms take designers as their theme – the David Hicks room, for example, with its bed in the centre of the room and *trompe-l'oeil* barrel ceiling.

Downstairs rooms are grand in size and accommodate a mish-mash of furnishings from the comfortable mix of new and antique sofas in the drawing-room to the clubby atmosphere of the library. Dinner in the mustard-coloured restaurant – a lovely room with ornately carved wooden panels – may include salmon with couscous or lamb carpaccio. The Paytons' genuine attempt at hospitality works well, and there's undoubtedly good humour in Rufus the giant schnauzer's tartan neckerchief and the Peter Rabbit breakfast crockery.

◐ *Open all year*

↗ *Leave the A1 at the Colsterworth roundabout and turn on to the B676 towards Melton Mowbray. The turn for Stapleford is 1 mile past the village of Saxby, on the left. Private car park*

🛏 *32 twin/double, 1 four-poster, 2 suites; all with bathroom/WC, TV, room service, hair-dryer, trouser press, baby-listening; no tea/coffee-making facilities in rooms*

◈ *3 dining-rooms, bar, 4 lounges, drying room; conference facilities (max 200 people non-residential,*
35 residential); fishing, tennis, clay shooting, miniature golf, basketball, croquet at hotel, other sports nearby. Wheelchair access to hotel (ramps), restaurant, WC (disabled), no ground-floor bedrooms but lift

⊖ *No smoking in dining-rooms*

▭ *Access, Amex, Diners, Visa*

£ *Single occupancy of twin/double from £125, twin/double from £125, four-poster £195, suite from £200; deposit required. Cooked B £8.50; alc L from £4.50, D from £30. Special breaks available*

STOKE-BY-NAYLAND SUFFOLK   MAP 8

Angel Inn

POLSTEAD ROAD, STOKE-BY-NAYLAND, NR COLCHESTER, ESSEX CO6 4SA
TEL: NAYLAND (0206) 263245   FAX: (0206) 37324

A good base for exploring Constable country.

The Angel Inn was opened in 1536 to meet a need for accommodation previously provided by monastic orders but severely limited when Henry VIII decided to commence the dissolution of the monasteries. The speciality in the bedrooms is arresting wallpaper – bold flowers, birds and other fearless designs have been chosen by someone with nerves of steel. Despite the chance of waking up in the morning and imagining yourself giftwrapped, they seem to work, and give the rooms a degree of individuality which their size and shape don't confer. Room Six would suit limbo dancers: a low beam is slung across the room.

Lunches and dinners are served either in a pine-furnished bar or in the old brew house, now beautifully converted into a more formal restaurant and possessing high, raftered ceilings, brick walls, a crooked chimney breast, a deep well and an inspired décor of greens and reds. Substantial menus including steaks, fish dishes and vegetarian options are available.

◑ Open all year, exc 25, 26 Dec and 1 Jan

↗ 1 mile off the A134, halfway between Colchester and Sudbury. Private car park

🛏 1 twin, 5 double; all with bathroom/WC, TV, room service, hair-dryer

◈ 2 restaurants, 2 bars, lounge; fishing, golf, other sports nearby. Wheelchair access to restaurant and WC only

⊖ No children under 10; no dogs

▭ Access, Amex, Diners, Visa

£ Single occupancy of twin/double £42, twin/double £55. Alc L £11, D £14 (prices till end 93)

STOKESLEY NORTH YORKSHIRE   **MAP 3**

Chapters ☆

27 HIGH STREET, STOKESLEY, MIDDLESBROUGH, CLEVELAND TS9 5AD
TEL: MIDDLESBROUGH (0642) 711888 (and fax)

A tastefully converted town house with outstanding food.

Go-ahead young restaurateurs Alan and Catherine Thompson have converted this eighteenth-century coaching-inn with skill and style. Chapters is perhaps best-known for its food, an established restaurant having been supplemented by a 50-cover bistro last year. The former has beams, shuttered windows overlooking the courtyard, white basketweave chairs, a tiled floor scattered with rugs, pink and green table linen and lots of plants. Fish is imaginatively presented; perhaps a seafood salad of salmon teriyaki, smoked salmon parcel, followed by breast of chicken filled with a chicken mousseline on a lime sauce with a wild rice pilau, then a citron tart with lime mousse and orange sauce. The cheerful bistro has white rendered walls, lots of fresh flowers and a tiled floor; there's a large bar in the centre, and menus and paintings on the walls. Dishes chalked up on the blackboard when we inspected included tagliatelle tossed with fresh salmon, smoked salmon and pesto.

Bedrooms vary in size and are individually decorated in a country-house style with flowery décor or more masculine stripes, good reproduction furniture and lots of lamps and prints.

◑ Open all year

↗ 10 miles east of the A19, 5 miles south of Middlesbrough. On-street parking

🛏 3 single, 5 twin, 4 double, 1 suite; all with bathroom/WC, exc 2 singles with shower/WC; TV, room service, hair-dryer, baby-listening in all rooms

◈ 2 restaurants, bar, lounge; conference facilities (max 30 people non-residential, 13

residential); fishing, golf, tennis,
other sports nearby

⊖ No wheelchair access; no dogs in
public rooms; smoking limited in
public rooms

▭ Access, Amex, Diners, Visa

£ Single £44, single occupancy of
twin/double £48, twin/double
£59, suite £66. Set D £18; alc D
from £18. Special breaks
available

STOKE UPON TERN SHROPSHIRE   **MAP 5**

Stoke Manor

STOKE UPON TERN, MARKET DRAYTON, SHROPSHIRE TF9 2DU
TEL: HODNET (0630) 84222   FAX: (0630) 84666

A bed and breakfast on a farm with good bedrooms and a bar.

It is not easy to find this farmhouse among the lanes and cottages which
compose the rambling village of Stoke upon Tern, but you will know you
have arrived when you find a farm with a row of antique tractors in one of
the outbuildings. There are further agricultural relics to provide talking
points in Mike and Julia Thomas's farmhouse, especially if you have
gathered with other guests in the cellar bar.

   The bedrooms are the strong point here (although the farm kitchen is
lovely and many guests choose to sneak in to sit there rather than in the
rather less lovely residents' lounge). The three rooms are massive, well-
furnished and have views across open fields. The nicest is the Blue
Room, with its walk-in cupboard where jam was once stored.

◑ Closed Dec

🔼 Between the A41 and A53 in
village of Stoke upon Tern.
Private car park

🛏 1 twin, 1 double, 1 family room;
all with bathroom/WC, TV,
room-service, hair-dryer, baby-
listening

◈ Dining-room, bar, lounge; fishing,
shooting at hotel, golf nearby

⊖ No wheelchair access; no
children under 5; no dogs;
smoking in bar and lounge
only

▭ None accepted

£ Single occupancy of twin/double
£25, twin/double £40 to £44,
family room £60 to £66; deposit
required

STON EASTON SOMERSET   **MAP 9**

Ston Easton Park

STON EASTON, BATH, SOMERSET BA3 4DF
TEL: MENDIP (0761) 241631   FAX: (0761) 241377

A wonderful Palladian mansion in Humphrey Repton gardens, with unforgettable cuisine.

Ston Easton is everything you've ever dreamed a Georgian stately home would be, huge and rambling yet light and graceful at the same time. In the massive lounge, chairs are arranged in clusters to break it into more manageable dimensions and a roaring log fire draws the eye down from the fantastic plasterwork and chandeliers. It's here that you get your first taste of the cuisine for which Ston Easton is famed, with a selection of canapés each lovingly described by waiters who manage to remember what you ate last night.

The dining-room is probably the least impressive room in the house, but then people don't come here to stare at the walls; they come to tuck in with relish to unforgettable food. On inspection, it was hard to believe anything could better the galantine of maize-fed chicken stuffed with pistachio and truffle and served on a tomato chutney, or the chef's special red mullet with langoustine tails. However, the poached pear filled with chocolate baked in filo pastry and set on a red sabayon did just that. It would have been nice to comment on the home-made sweets served with Colombian coffee in the homely library, but our inspector was beyond tasting another thing.

The master bedroom, as large as most people's houses and with a stupendous Chippendale four-poster is one to go for. However, even the smallest rooms are enormous, and you'd have to be something of a grouch to find anything to complain about.

◑ *Open all year*

↗ *From Bath follow signs for Bristol (A4). At the roundabout by the Globe Inn take the 2nd exit to Corston (A39). Follow road through Marksbury, Farmborough and Hallatrow. Turn left at junction with A37 and follow signs to Ston Easton Park. Private car park*

🛏 *13 twin/double, 2 four-poster, 4 suites, 2 cottages; all with bathroom/WC, TV, room service, hair-dryer; no tea/coffee-making facilities in rooms*

◈ *Restaurant, 3 lounges, billiard room, library, drying room; conference facilities (max 40 people residential and non-residential); tennis, croquet, clay and game shooting at hotel, other sports nearby*

⊖ *No wheelchair access; no children under 7, exc babies; no dogs in hotel (but free kennelling in grounds); no smoking in restaurant*

▭ *Access, Amex, Diners, Visa*

£ *Single occupancy of twin/double from £85, twin/double from £135, four-poster from £195, suite £245 to £325, cottage suite £265. Cooked B £8.50; set L £26, D £38.50. Special breaks available*

The Guide *is totally independent, accepts no free hospitality, and survives on the number of copies sold each year.*

Stonor Arms

STONOR, NR HENLEY-ON-THAMES, OXFORDSHIRE RG9 6HE
TEL: HENLEY-ON-THAMES (0491) 638345 FAX: (0491) 638863

A smart country hotel with a popular brasserie and restaurant.

In a valley of the Chiltern Hills and handy for Henley-in-Arden, this establishment terms itself 'a fine country house and restaurant'. The public areas are quite extensive, with interesting and attractive touches that include some good paintings. The flagstoned bar fills up with diners who have come to eat in either the brasserie-style conservatory restaurant, where dishes such as chicken with a yogurt and lime dressing are served, or in the more traditional Stonor Restaurant, with its fine paintings and polished wood. Breakfast is delicious, with lots of fresh fruit, yogurt, croissants and brioche if a cooked breakfast doesn't appeal.

The bedroom block to the rear has rooms overlooking the wooded hillside of Stonor Park or the walled garden. Room 14 is a very large twin with a fresh blue and white colour scheme, a scattering of antique furnishings and a smart marble-tiled bathroom.

◐ Open all year; retaurant closed Sun eve

🔀 From Henley take the A423 to Oxford. I mile from Henley take the right turning to Stonor. The Stonor Arms is in the centre of the village. Private car park

🛏 8 twin/double, I suite; all with bathroom/WC, TV, room service, hair-dryer

◇ 2 restaurants, bar, lounge, conservatory; conference facilities (max 12 people non-residential, 9 residential); golf, riding nearby. Wheelchair access to hotel, restaurant and WC (unisex), 6 ground-floor bedrooms, I specially equipped for disabled people

⊖ No children in restaurants eves; no dogs

▭ Access, Amex, Visa

£ Single occupancy of twin/double £83, twin/double £93, suite £138; deposit required. Set D £27.50; alc L from £3.50 to £11

Wyck Hill House

BURFORD ROAD, STOW-ON-THE-WOLD, GLOUCESTERSHIRE GL54 IHY
TEL: COTSWOLD (0451) 831936 FAX: (0451) 832243

A comfortable, clubby, Cotswold country house.

The eighteenth-century flair for placing country houses to take best advantage of the landscape can be seen to spectacular effect at Wyck Hill House, for the views over the Windrush Valley are one of the best reasons for staying here. There are other reasons too, for this is an amiable country hotel, suitably wood-smoky and panelled, with tinges of Gothic Revival to be found in the pillared hall and the imposing staircase. The library is a lovely room to sit in, but if it is already fully occupied there is a second lounge. The original dining-room is resplendently formal, with a touch of the exotic East given by the ogee curves of the pelmets round the windows. The à la carte dinner served here is well thought of and fairly traditional, with such dishes as roasted ballotine of pork or loin of lamb, followed by a hot chocolate fondant. The conservatory, which leads off the dining-room, is less sumptuous, and more suitable for the light lunches which the hotel now serves. Bedrooms are large – some very large – and well furnished in traditional country-house style, with expensive and heavy fabrics.

◑ *Open all year*

↗ *Wyck Hill is on the west side of the A424, 2 miles south-east of Stow. Private car park*

🛏 *25 twin/double, I four-poster, 3 family rooms, I suite; all with bathroom/WC, TV, room service, hair-dryer, trouser press, baby-listening*

◇ *2 restaurants (one air-conditioned), bar, 3 lounges, library; conference facilities (max 20 people residential and non-*

residential); croquet at hotel, other sports nearby; babysitting by arrangement

⊖ *No wheelchair access; no dogs in public rooms; no smoking in restaurants*

▭ *Access, Amex, Diners, Visa*

£ *Single occupancy of twin/double £65, twin/double £90, four-poster £170, family room £130, suite £180. Set L £12, D £27.50; alc D £30 to £35. Special breaks available*

STRATFORD-UPON-AVON WARWICKSHIRE   **MAP 9**

Caterham House
COUNTY HOTEL OF THE YEAR

58/59 ROTHER STREET, STRATFORD-UPON-AVON, WARWICKSHIRE
CV37 6LT
TEL: STRATFORD-UPON-AVON (0789) 267309

A small, stylish hotel with an informal atmosphere and a good French restaurant.

'As a base for the RSC, Caterham House is well-nigh perfect,' reports one contented reader. We agree. This red-brick Georgian house was a small bed and breakfast until mid-1992 when it expanded next door, had a restaurant added, and so became a small hotel. It is a fair indication of the Maurys' hospitality that, loyal to regular guests, they have kept two rooms in the attic at the old prices. Each room is individual, with quality fabrics and antiques; all have plenty of space.

Downstairs is no less stylish. The sitting-room, with its antique Dutch sideboard, Greek murals on washed yellow walls and comfortable leather sofas, acts as bar and anteroom for the restaurant too. Dominique Maury keeps a chatty, informal atmosphere going as he hands around drinks and takes your dinner order. The Bonaparte Restaurant is French with an exclusively French wine list. It is worth lingering over an à la carte meal, which might include king prawns served with apple purée flamed with Calvados, medallions of monkfish with grapefruit and mint sauce, or potted goose with red beans, white haricot beans and flageolets.

◑ *Open all year; restaurant closed Sun and Mon eves*

⤢ *In the centre of Stratford, opposite the police station. Private car park*

🛏 *5 twin, 6 double, 2 family rooms; 1 room with bathroom/WC, some with shower/WC, 2 public bathrooms; room service in all rooms; hair-dryer, baby-listening on request; no tea/coffee-making facilities in rooms*

◈ *Restaurant, bar, lounge, drying room; conference facilities (max*

30 people non-residential, 13 residential); fishing, golf, other sports nearby; babysitting. Wheelchair access to restaurant and WC (disabled) only

⊖ *No dogs in public rooms and by arrangement only in bedrooms*

▭ *Access, Visa*

£ *Single occupancy of twin/double £35 to £52, twin/double £36 to £56, family room £55; deposit required. Set L £10 to £13.50, D £13.50; alc D £20 to £25*

Victoria Spa Lodge

BISHOPTON LANE, STRATFORD-UPON-AVON, WARWICKSHIRE CV37 9QY
TEL: STRATFORD-UPON-AVON (0789) 267985　FAX: (0789) 204728

A well-run bed and breakfast in a beautiful Victorian house.

Victoria Spa Lodge occupies a peaceful spot away from the tourist traffic of the town centre. Built in 1837 as a hotel for gentlefolk coming here to take the water, the house has actually spent most of its history as a family home. Now Paul and Dreen Tozer combine both functions in cheerful surroundings with immaculate rooms. They are proud to tell you that Princess Vicky, Queen Victoria's eldest daughter, was one of the first guests to stay here. The clematis-covered sandstone house has beautiful Victorian features such as tall hexagonal chimneys, geometric patterned windows and elegant fireplaces which the Tozers complement with delicate light fittings, lace and lots of bric-à-brac. The large dining/ sitting-room with its polished floorboards, dusky pink walls and collection of plates and red glass is particularly light and pretty.

The seven bedrooms are similarly light, though they vary in size and décor. Flowery wallpaper and modern furniture are the norm, along with a generous supply of goodies. Two characterful family rooms in the attic have been newly decorated in bold colours. Breakfast is buffet-style, with full English breakfast and vegetarian options.

◑ *Open all year*

⤢ *1½ miles north of Stratford at the junction of the A3400 and*

A46. Private car park

🛏 *1 twin, 3 double, 3 family rooms; all with shower/WC, exc 1 with* bathroom/WC; TV, hair-dryer in all rooms

◇ Dining-room (air-conditioned), lounge; fishing, golf, other sports nearby

⬤ No wheelchair access; no dogs; no smoking in public rooms

▭ Access, Visa

£ Single occupancy of twin/double £30 to £35, twin/double £39 to £45; deposit required. Special breaks available

---

STRETTON LEICESTERSHIRE　　　　　　　　　　**MAP 5**

Ram Jam Inn

GREAT NORTH ROAD, STRETTON, OAKHAM, LEICESTERSHIRE LE15 7QX
TEL: STAMFORD (0780) 410776　FAX: (0780) 410361

An exceptionally well-run motel-style inn on the A1.

The Ram Jam Inn knocks chain motels into a cocked hat. Don't be put off by its unattractive position on a busy stretch of road that even its own brochure describes as 'featureless'. Once you're inside the inn is everything a watering hole should be, with cheerful staff serving good food at all times and high standard, reasonably priced bedrooms. A history of the inn admits that many of the stories dreamed up about it are bunkum, but everyone seems to agree that the name Ram Jam comes from the landlord's special brew in the eighteenth century. The main café/snack bar is fast-paced, with young enthusiastic staff in stripy shirts serving food all day; among the good-value light meals are carrot and coriander soup, stir-fried duck with oriental vegetables, pasta dishes and salads. If you want to be more relaxed there is a slightly more formal restaurant leading off the lounge where the 'real-meal' menu has a choice of half-a-dozen starters and main courses with an international bent, including Algerian char-grilled chicken, Egyptian falafel and a Mediterranean platter of stuffed vine leaves and hummus (though there are steaks, too).

The eight bedrooms are all large, and all but one face away from the road and overlook the orchard. With limed pine furniture, bright modern fabrics, good lighting and spacious white bathrooms with plenty of goodies, they are comfortable and well-equipped.

◐ Open all year, exc 25 Dec

⤵ On the A1, 9 miles north of Stamford. Travelling north, turn off through the Texaco service station just past the B668 turn off; travelling south, leave by the B668 exit. Private car park

🛏 5 twin, 1 double, 1 family room; all with bathroom/WC, TV

◇ Restaurant, bar, lounge, 2 snack areas; conference facilities (max 40 people non-residential, 7 residential); riding, golf nearby. Wheelchair access to restaurant and WC (M,F) only

⬤ No dogs in public rooms

▭ Access, Amex, Visa

£ Single occupancy of twin/double £39, twin/double £49, family room £62; deposit required. Cooked B £4; alc L, D from £8; bar snacks available

STURMINSTER NEWTON DORSET   **MAP 9**

Plumber Manor

STURMINSTER NEWTON, DORSET DT10 2AF
TEL: STURMINSTER NEWTON (0258) 472507   FAX: (0258) 473370

Enjoy the country life at this loved and lived-in family home and restaurant.

When the Prideaux Brune ancestors decided to build a family home back in the seventeenth century, they bagged a prime spot for themselves. The drowsy Dorset countryside surrounding the low, stone Jacobean manor has changed little over the years. Inside, however, a small social revolution has taken place. *Noblesse oblige* these days means the landed gentry rolling up their sleeves to cook for and look after their guests.

Richard (co-owner, hunting squire, waiter and barman) describes Plumber as a restaurant-with-bedrooms; others call it a country-house hotel. Bedrooms and grounds are spacious but there are fewer lounges and less obvious formal service than in more conventional, full-blown country-house hotels. One guest described Berty and Humphrey, the two family dogs who take guests for a walk, as 'the perfect hosts'.

Not surprisingly, the house bears the imprint of generations of Prideaux Brunes; their imposing portraits line the walls. The main focus is on the restaurant – three elegant rooms that run along one side of the house. One of the smaller rooms used to be the wine cellar, and has arboreal murals. Brian Prideaux Brune is in charge of the kitchen. Two fixed-price menus may include hot crab tartlets with ginger, smoked salmon paupiettes with avocado fromage, fillet of venison with apple and orange sauces, and medallions of beef with grainy mustard, brandy and cream. Bedrooms in the main house are comfortable, with spriggy florals and old furniture. The newer courtyard rooms are large and smartly turned out.

◑ Closed Feb

↗ 2 miles south-west of Sturminster Newton, on the road to Hazelbury Bryan. Plumber Manor is 1¼ miles from the A357. Private car park

🛏 2 single, 14 twin/double; all with bathroom/WC, TV, hair-dryer, trouser press

◈ 3 restaurants, bar/lounge, lounge; conference facilities (max 20 people non-residential, 12 residential); tennis at hotel, other sports nearby. Wheelchair access to hotel, restaurant and WC (unisex), 10 ground-floor bedrooms, 2 specially equipped for disabled people

⊖ Children under 10 by prior arrangement only; dogs in 2 bedrooms only; no smoking in 2 bedrooms

▭ Access, Amex, Diners, Visa

£ Single £60, single occupancy of twin/double £60 to £80, twin/double £80 to £120. Sun L £17.50; set D £20 to £25. Special breaks available

SUTTON COLDFIELD WEST MIDLANDS   **MAP 5**

New Hall

WALMLEY ROAD, WALMLEY, SUTTON COLDFIELD, WEST MIDLANDS
B76 8QX
TEL: 021-378 2442   TELEX: 333580 NEWHAL G   FAX: 021-378 4637

A moated manor house just outside Birmingham with beautiful grounds and extremely luxurious bedrooms.

Ian and Caroline Parkes have made a superb job of turning this 800-year-old manor house, with its pink stone castellated roofline and a lily-filled moat, into a smoothly run luxury hotel. With a wealth of historical features as a backdrop, the Parkes have created stylish and comfortable rooms. The drawing-room, with pretty green and salmon pink furnishings, huge flower arrangements and doors out on to a flagstoned terrace also has Scrabble and Monopoly to entertain you. The dining-room is particularly beautiful – perhaps especially so in the daylight, when the sun shines through the colourful Flemish stained-glass windows. Dinner is served by uniformed staff, and though the menu describes itself as 'unmistakably English', trendy European ingredients are used too, so that you'll find cannelloni and Italian vegetable broth alongside grilled Dover sole and roast quail on savoy cabbage with truffle jus.

Bedrooms in the original part of the house are named after different varieties of lilies in the moat, and, with their creaking floorboards and curiously shaped bathrooms, are slightly more characterful than those in the newer wings. All are large and stylishly furnished with rich fabrics, antiques and designer wallpaper.

◑ *Open all year*

↱ *Leave M6 at Junction 5 and follow A452 signposted Sutton Coldfield. At the 3rd roundabout turn right, continue on B4148 through Walmley village; after 1 mile turn left to New Hall. Private car park*

🛏 *4 single, 16 twin, 31 double, 3 four-poster, 6 suites; all with bathroom/WC, TV, room service, hair-dryer, trouser press, baby-listening*

◈ *Restaurant, bar, 2 lounges; conference facilities (max 40 people non-residential, 25 residential), helipad, golf driving net, croquet, putting at hotel. Wheelchair access to hotel, restaurant and WC (unisex), 21 ground-floor bedrooms, 1 specially equipped for disabled people*

⊖ *No children under 8; no dogs; no smoking in restaurant*

▭ *Access, Amex, Diners, Visa*

£ *Single from £93, single occupancy of twin/double from £93, twin/double from £110, four-poster from £160, suite from £145; deposit required. Cooked B £10, continental B £8; set L from £5, D £27; alc D from £35. Special breaks available*

We mention those hotels that don't accept dogs; guide dogs, however, are almost always an exception. Telephone ahead to make sure.

SWAFFHAM NORFOLK   **MAP 7**

Stratton House

ASH CLOSE, SWAFFHAM, NORFOLK PE37 7NH
TEL: SWAFFHAM (0760) 723845   FAX: (0760) 720458

A real retreat, with friendly hosts who show meticulous attention to detail.

If you like lots of bits and bobs in your bathroom, Strattons will suit you – there are conditioners, shampoos, massage oils, bath salts, rubber ducks and moisturisers, as well as shells and starfish for decoration. Les and Vanessa Scott have successfully achieved a lavish, pampered atmosphere which is in keeping with the original use of this eighteenth-century Palladian house, once a retreat from the summer heat for London dilettanti. The 'bedchambers' are all decadently furnished with a plethora of folds and flounces. The Venetian Room has peacock blue walls, extravagant curtains, lacy drapes and a beautiful walnut bed covered with snowy white quilt and pillows. Readers' verdicts on décor and the Scotts' hospitality are overwhelmingly positive: 'comfortable and well-furnished', 'the welcome is very warm'.

Evening meals and breakfasts are served in the small Rustic Restaurant, which, although dark, is enlivened by a garden perspective painted on one wall. Dinner is very much up to you – Les asks what you want to eat, suggests this and that, and you come to an agreement. Whatever you choose it is likely to be interesting. English cheeses are a speciality, too. You can take coffee in the lounge, a homely jumble of china cats and dogs, dried flowers, books and photographs, where Bertie the Siamese will come and curl up on your lap.

◐ Open all year, exc 25 and 26 Dec

↗ At north end of market place, behind shop fronts. The entrance to Ash Close is between estate agents William Brown and Express Cleaners. Private car park

🛏 I single, I twin, 4 double, I family room; all with shower/WC, exc I double with bathroom/WC; TV, room service, hair-dryer, baby-listening in all rooms

◇ Restaurant, bar, drawing-room, lounge, drying room; conference facilities (max 7 people residential, 20 non-residential); golf, fishing, other sports nearby; babysitting

⊖ No wheelchair access; smoking in lounge only

▭ Access, Amex, Visa

£ Single £52, single occupancy of twin/double £53, twin/double £70, family room £80; deposit required. Lunches by arrangement; set D £20; alc D £22.50 (prices till Jan 94). Special breaks available

Where we know an establishment accepts credit cards, we list them. There may be a surcharge if you pay by credit card. It is always best to check whether the card you want to use is acceptable when booking.

SWINHOPE LINCOLNSHIRE   **MAP 5**

Hoe Hill

SWINHOPE, NR BINBROOK, LINCOLNSHIRE LN3 6HX
TEL: BINBROOK (0472) 398206

An exceptionally good-value bed and breakfast with superb evening meals by arrangement, large rooms and a tireless host.

Erica Curd describes the landscape around her eighteenth-century converted farmhouse cottages as 'windswept, with rotten soil'. Two hundred years ago this made growing crops difficult in the Lincolnshire Wolds, and farming wild rabbits was common. Hoe Hill, with its walled garden and paddock, was at that time occupied by the 'warren bailiff' – a fancy name for the rabbit catcher. Today Erica's superb evening meals, served at 7.30pm, are more likely to include fish than rabbit, as Grimsby is only 11 miles away. Alternatively, you might be offered asparagus soup, medallions of lamb, crème caramel, then chocolates and coffee. Everything is home-made, including the bread, and the meals are unbelievably good-value, particularly as sherry and wine are complimentary. After dinner, head for the sitting-room with its log fire, deep-pink walls and functional but comfortable furnishings, and you will probably be joined by Arthur the cat.

Each of the three bedrooms is large and immaculately kept. Erica has prettified the rooms with embroidered pillowcases, patterned fabrics and frills. The huge shared bathroom is amusingly decorated with penguin wallpaper and clouds on the sloping ceiling. Breakfast includes everything from healthy yogurt and dried fruit to traditional fry-ups.

- Open all year, exc owners' holidays
- On the B1203 Market Rasen to Grimsby road, 1 mile from Binbrook, heading north towards Grimsby. Private car park
- 2 twin, 1 double; 2 public bathrooms; hair-dryer, trouser press, baby-listening in all rooms
- Dining-room, lounge, drying room, study; fishing, golf nearby
- No wheelchair access; no children under 5; no dogs; no smoking in bedrooms
- None accepted
- Single occupancy of twin/double £15, twin/double £30; deposit required. Set D £10 (7.30pm, by arrangement only). Special breaks available

TALLAND CORNWALL   **MAP 10**

Talland Bay

NR LOOE, CORNWALL PL13 2JB
TEL: POLPERRO (0503) 72667   FAX: (0503) 72940

A luxurious country-house hotel with a lovely garden and spectacular sea views.

Talland Bay Hotel is an unexceptional white building which looks much more appealing from the garden, from where you can appreciate its black shutters and lichen-splattered slate roof. The garden is a glorious suntrap with spectacular, unmarred views of the bay beyond. Inside, this is a comfortable and elegant hotel, likely to change owners imminently as Major Hayman retires. As well as a small non-smoking lounge it boasts a bigger one with log fire, a flower-filled sun lounge for enjoying the views and a bar opening on to the terrace beyond. Part of the dining-room has pleasant panelled walls, the rear extension overlooks the garden. Four-course table d'hôte menus are fairly conservative, but feature dishes like spinach and sultana ramekin with a cream cheese salad for vegetarians. In keeping with the immaculate décor of the public areas, the bedrooms are all smart and come with all sorts of extras. They vary considerably in size; Room One has plenty of space for a four-poster bed and a window seat, but in Room Three a size-expanding mirror in the wardrobe door cannot quite conceal the fact that the crown-canopy bed virtually fills the room.

◑ *Closed Jan*

🡒 *From Looe take the A387 and turn left at hotel sign. Follow this lane for 1 mile. The hotel is on the left. Private car park*

🛏 *4 single, 11 twin, 2 double, 2 four-poster, 2 family rooms, 1 suite, 1 annexe room, 1 cottage suite; all with bathroom/WC, TV, room service, hair-dryer, baby-listening; trouser press in some rooms*

◇ *Restaurant, bar, 2 lounges, games room; conference facilities (max 50 people non-residential, 24 residential); sauna, solarium, heated outdoor swimming-pool (May to Sept) at hotel, other sports nearby. Wheelchair access to hotel (2 steps) and restaurant, 2 ground-floor bedrooms*

⊖ *No children under 5 in restaurant eves; no dogs in public rooms and by arrangement only in bedrooms; no smoking in restaurant and 1 lounge*

▭ *Access, Amex, Diners, Visa*

£ *Single £50 to £76, single occupancy of twin/double £60, twin/double £102 to £153, four-poster £115 to £171, family room £162 to £223 (4 people), suite £102 to £146, annexe room £102 to £127, cottage suite £102 to £136 (rates inc dinner); deposit required. Set L £10, D £24; alc D £35. Special breaks available*

TARPORLEY CHESHIRE   **MAP 5**

Willington Hall

TARPORLEY, CHESHIRE CW6 0NB
TEL: KELSALL (0829) 52321   FAX: (0829) 52596

Designer-free zone in Victorian country house of faded charm.

Willington Hall evokes a very English, between-the-wars feel. Like an old country squire in a darned tweed jacket, it has a down-at-heel gravitas, frayed but still dignified. The plain, understated, slightly shabby décor is part of the nostalgic attraction.

Bar meals overlooking the garden and rolling Cheshire Plain are a big draw. The restaurant is also popular, especially for shooting-party dinners. The hotel is still co-owned by a descendant of the original owner and there is an assortment of family furniture and portraits in the rooms, all of which have enough space for old-fashioned, low-slung chairs and sofas. The *en-suite* bathrooms are simple and functional.

Although one disappointed lady did complain about service being a bit chaotic, judging by the number of repeat bookings, many guests seem happy with the idiosyncratic atmosphere.

◐ Open all year, exc 25 Dec; dining-room closed Sun eve

⤴ Tarporley is off the A51 mid-way between Nantwich and Chester. Turn right at the Bull's Head in Clotton. Private car park

⤟ 2 single, 5 twin, 3 double, family room available; all with bathroom/WC, TV, room service, hair-dryer

◈ 3 dining-rooms, 2 bars, lounge, drying room; conference facilities

(max 20 people non-residential, 10 residential); tennis at hotel, other sports nearby. Wheelchair access to hotel (2 steps), restaurant and WC only

⊖ No dogs in public rooms

▭ Access, Diners, Visa

£ Single £38, single occupancy of twin/double £48, twin/double £65 to £68, family room £78. Cooked B £6, continental B £4; alc L, D £15 to £20; bar meals

---

TAUNTON SOMERSET   **MAP 10**

Castle Hotel

CASTLE GREEN, TAUNTON, SOMERSET TA1 1NF
TEL: TAUNTON (0823) 272671   FAX: (0823) 336066

A grand town-centre hotel next door to Taunton Castle Museum.

The huge Castle Hotel, on a site which once formed part of Taunton Castle, has been hosting guests for over 300 years. The building is at its best in late spring, when its grey stonework and Gothic windows vanish behind a violet cloak of flowering wistaria. Once through the doors, however, you escape into a partially medieval world of grand stairways and reproduction French tapestries. During the day the lounge bar is surprisingly quiet; at night it's another story as it fills up with a mixture of businessfolk and locals bent on an upmarket night out. An overspill lounge behind the stairs looks cosier but is apparently plagued by noise from the next-door pub.

Bedrooms are vast and have been refurbished to provide huge beds, comfy sofas and armchairs and luxurious bathrooms. The dining-room is light and pretty, with potted ferns, swathes of fabric and cane chairs. One reader writes of 'first-class food and wine', and certainly this is a great place to come for traditional three-course Sunday lunches in stylish surroundings. Another reader comments on the excellent service: 'Our room was cool and a phone call to reception produced, immediately, a fan heater and a young man to plug it in and set it up.'

◑ Open all year

⤢ From Taunton town centre follow signs for the Castle. Private car park

🛏 11 single, 20 twin/double, 3 four-poster, 1 suite; all with bathroom/WC, TV, room service, baby-listening; hair-dryer on request; no tea/coffee-making facilities in rooms

◈ Restaurant, bar, lounge; conference facilities (max 100 people non-residential, 35 residential); fishing, golf, other sports nearby; babysitting by arrangement. Wheelchair access to hotel (1 step), restaurant and WC, no ground-floor bedrooms but lift

⊖ No dogs in public rooms

▭ Access, Amex, Diners, Visa

£ Single £60, single occupancy of twin/double £70, twin/double/four-poster £90, suite £135 to £180; deposit required. Set L £14/£15/£26/£30, D £18/£22/£30 (prices till end 93). Special breaks available

---

TAVISTOCK DEVON   **MAP 10**

Horn of Plenty

GULWORTHY, TAVISTOCK, DEVON PL19 8JD
TEL: TAVISTOCK (0822) 832528 (and fax)

A Georgian restaurant-with-rooms offering first-class food.

The imposing Georgian house is used for the serious business of eating, with all but one of the bedrooms relegated to the converted coach-house at the back. Not that relegation is any bad thing here, for the coach-house rooms (really suites) are enormous and full of character, with beamed ceilings, huge beds and french windows opening on to the garden; only the bathrooms are disappointing, with rather flimsy baths, though Elaine Gatehouse – who took on the Horn two years ago – already has replacements in hand.

The lounge, where dinner orders are taken, is especially comfortable, with lots of big red armchairs and several settees. The restaurant is mainly a long, thin verandah room with a log fire and views of the Devon countryside. When we inspected, the local goats' cheese topped with sun-dried tomatoes baked in a leaf of crisp pastry was perhaps a little bland, as indeed were the pan-fried medallions of pork served with wild mushrooms and a sherry sauce. The vanilla bavarois with a passion-fruit coulis was, however, delicious.

Service both at dinner and again in the morning at breakfast was unobtrusively attentive. One small quibble: the table d'hôte menu has so many supplements, even for desserts, that it might be better to make it à la carte.

◑ Open all year, exc 25, 26 Dec

⤢ Take the A390 from Tavistock towards Liskeard. When 3 miles from Tavistock turn right at Gulworthy Cross. After ½ mile turn left – the hotel is 500 yards on the right. Private car park

🛏 7 twin/double (most in annexe); most with bathroom/WC, some with shower/WC; TV, room service, hair-dryer, mini-bar, baby-listening in all rooms

◈ 2 restaurants, bar, lounge; conference facilities (max 18 people non-residential, 7 residential); fishing, golf, other sports nearby. Wheelchair access to hotel (ramp), restaurant and 4 ground-floor bedrooms

⊖ No children under 13 in restaurant eves; no smoking in some bedrooms

▭ Access, Amex, Visa

£ Single occupancy of twin/double £58 to £70, twin/double £78 to £90. Cooked B £5; set L £14.50, D £25.50. Special breaks available

---

TEFFONT EVIAS WILTSHIRE   **MAP 9**

Howard's House

TEFFONT EVIAS, SALISBURY, WILTSHIRE SP3 5RJ
TEL: SALISBURY (0722) 716392   FAX: (0722) 716820

A renovated dower house providing a comfortable base.

Teffont Evias is one of those pretty villages that form the backbone of England, with sheep in the fields and horses in a stud farm at one end and a stream running past a parish church at the other. Howard's House has been transformed from a derelict Tudor farmhouse into a hotel. Colours throughout are light and bright – predominantly yellow and green in the public rooms, with flowers to match. Bedrooms are a good size and are furnished with beige carpets and lots of modern flowery chintz. One of the attractions of the house is the very relaxed feel to it – there are no rules, children and dogs are welcome and there are no dress codes. The food fully justifies a stay on its own account; the set-price menu might include warm smoked salmon with a chervil butter sauce and a poached egg tartlet, then sliced rosettes of lamb on steamed spinach with an infusion of rosemary and redcurrants as a main course. On inspection the raspberry and chocolate roulade was luscious – but, surprisingly, the cheese had run out on a Saturday evening.

◑ Open all year; restaurant closed Sun eve

⤢ On the A303 heading west, pass by the turning to Wylye and take the turning signposted Teffont Magna on the left. Turn left at the Black Horse pub. Private car park

🛏 9 double; all with bathroom/WC, TV, room service; no tea/coffee-making facilities in rooms

◈ Dining-room, lounge; fishing, golf

nearby; babysitting. Wheelchair access to restaurant and WC (M) only

● No dogs in public rooms; smoking discouraged in dining-room

▭ Access, Amex, Diners, Visa

£ Single occupancy of twin/double £70, twin/double £90; deposit required. Sun L £17.50; Set D £25.50/£27.50 (prices till Sept 93). Special breaks available

---

TEIGNMOUTH DEVON   **MAP 10**

Thomas Luny House

TEIGN STREET, TEIGNMOUTH, DEVON TQ14 8EG
TEL: TEIGNMOUTH (0626) 772976

A small Georgian Wolsey Lodge five minutes' walk from the sea.

Thomas Luny, whose house this originally was, was an eighteenth-century maritime artist. When Alison and John Allan bought the house it was in a state of disrepair, which they have since rectified by carefully restoring it to something resembling its Luny heyday.

There are four individually decorated bedrooms, all of them spacious; best is probably the Chinese Room, with a model Japanese travelling theatre astride a chest of drawers, but the Luny Room, with its big sea chest and ancient weighing machine, is also rather fun. Sadly the garden is very small, so the views are not inspiring. In the big double lounge you'll meet the rest of the pleasant and relaxed Allan family and their pets, Sam the dog and William the cat. Here, too, you'll learn what's for dinner, which is served to all the guests at a single sitting. When we inspected, the avocado in redcurrant vinaigrette sauce was pleasingly different and preceded salmon in lemon-butter sauce with broccoli, leeks and potatoes, leaving little room for a filling slab of grape meringue pie.

◐ Open all year, exc mid-Dec to mid-Jan

↗ In Teignmouth follow signs for the quay, then for Teign Street. Private car park

⇌ 2 twin, 1 double, 1 four-poster; all with bathroom/WC; TV, room service; hair-dryer on request; no tea/coffee-making facilities in rooms

◈ Dining-room, 2 lounges; fishing, golf, other sports nearby

● No wheelchair access; no children under 12; no dogs; no smoking in dining-room

▭ None accepted

£ Single occupancy of twin/double £30, twin/double/four-poster £60. Set D £14.50 (8pm, residents only). Special breaks available

---

Hotels in our Visitors' Book *towards the end of the* Guide *are additional hotels that may be worth a visit. Reports on these hotels are welcome.*

TENTERDEN KENT   **MAP 8**

Little Silver Country Hotel ☆

ST MICHAELS, TENTERDEN, KENT TN30 6SP
TEL: HIGH MALDEN (0233) 850321   FAX: (0233) 850647

A small, peaceful country hotel with attentive hosts.

Rosemary Frith and Dorothy Lawson dreamed of running an old country-house hotel. Turning their backs on their careers as nursery nurse and teacher, they made their dream a reality and they are more than happy to whisk out the photo album and tell the stories of the hotel's transformation from dilapidated barn to the impressive double-chimneyed, Tudor-style house and homely hotel it has become. Rooms are a good size, with thick beige carpets, floral bedspreads and matching curtains in pastel shades of pink and green. Room Ten is their pride – a four-poster bed dominates the room and a small Jacuzzi is tucked away in the bathroom.

Service is enthusiastic and in the small and intimate dining-room there is a little lamp and china ornamental basket of strawberries on each table. You can choose from a simple menu of home cooking, such as a starter of melon boats served with a glass of emerald Midori liqueur, followed by rainbow trout and fresh vegetables or a lasagne. Settle yourself in a huge old leather armchair in front of the open log fire in the lounge, while discovering Rosemary and Dorothy's passion for plates and ducks. A full English breakfast is taken in the Victorian-style conservatory overlooking the well-manicured gardens.

◗ Open all year

↗ 9 miles south-west of Ashford on the A28, ¾ mile north of Tenterden. Private car park

⇌ 3 twin, 3 double, 1 four-poster, 3 family rooms; half with bathroom/WC, half with shower/WC; TV, room service, hair-dryer, trouser press, baby-listening

◇ Restaurant, bar, lounge, conservatory, games room; conference facilities (max 175 non-residential, 10 residential); fishing, golf, other sports nearby.

Wheelchair access to hotel (1 ramp, 1 step), restaurant and WC (M,F), 4 ground-floor bedrooms, 3 specially equipped for disabled people

⊖ Dogs by prior arrangement only; no smoking in eating areas

▭ Access, Amex, Visa

£ Single occupancy of twin/double £55, twin/double £70, four-poster £98, family room £85 to £90; deposit required. Alc L £12 to £14, D from £14. Special breaks available

This denotes that the hotel is in an exceptionally peaceful situation where you can be assured of a restful stay.

TETBURY GLOUCESTERSHIRE   **MAP 9**

Calcot Manor

TETBURY, GLOUCESTERSHIRE GL8 8YJ
TEL: TETBURY (0666) 890391   FAX: (0666) 890394

A classy Cotswold hotel with changes in the air.

Richard Ball recently took over the running of this long-established hotel from his parents and has plans to make modest changes – notably in converting some of the cottage bedrooms into suites. Even so, Calcot is unlikely to turn into a cheap hotel overnight, for this is a place of some luxury, although one with a welcome lack of airs and graces. The big sandstone grange sprawls over the high ground outside Tetbury, and there is a colourful and peaceful garden. Inside, the atmosphere is friendly and warm, partly created by the soft pastel colours and the simple furnishings of the large open-plan bar and sitting-room. A further sitting-room beyond is a sunny combination of yellows, blues and cream. Bedrooms are far from small, while top-of-the-range Norfolk has plenty of room to prowl among the soft blue/green furnishings before plunging into the pale blue whirlpool bath.

Chef Ben Davies' food is described as 'slightly more Mediterranean than of old'. If the shellfish soup finished with deep-fried leeks, followed by lamb with marinated red cabbage, spinach and sweetbreads is too rich, there is a lighter three-course option.

◑ Open all year

↗ 4 miles west of Tetbury on the A4135, just before the intersection with the A46. Private car park

🛏 6 twin/double, 1 four-poster, 7 cottage rooms; all with bathroom/WC, TV, room service, hair-dryer; no tea/coffee-making facilities in rooms

◈ Restaurant, bar, lounge, drying facilities; conference facilities (max 20 people non-residential, 15 residential); croquet, heated outdoor swimming-pool (May to Sept) at hotel, other sports nearby. Wheelchair access to hotel, restaurant and WC (unisex), 6 ground-floor bedrooms

⊖ No children under 8; no dogs

▭ Access, Amex, Diners, Visa

£ Single occupancy of twin/double £75 to £100, twin/double/cottage £87 to £125, four-poster £135, family room rate on request; deposit required. Set L £17, D £18; alc D £26. Special breaks available

THAKEHAM WEST SUSSEX   **MAP 9**

Abingworth Hall

THAKEHAM ROAD, STORRINGTON, WEST SUSSEX RH20 3EF
TEL: WEST CHILTINGTON (0798) 813636   FAX: (0798) 813914

A quiet country hotel with romantic gardens.

One of the pleasures to be enjoyed at Abingworth Manor is taking a seat on the terrace on a summer's evening and admiring the smart gardens, while you deliberate over the menu. A salad of smoked bacon with Roquefort followed by grilled sliced breast of duck with peppercorn and port wine sauce turned out to be a good choice for our inspector. The restaurant is formal, with pale lemon walls and designer peach and grey drapes; the service is quietly efficient. As you move through to the oak-panelled drawing-room for coffee accompanied by fine little chocolates, the atmosphere relaxes somewhat and the level of noise increases. Next door is a rather grand, predominantly pink cocktail lounge with a grand piano and a small bar; just off the lounge is the conservatory, with cane chairs overlooking the gardens and terrace.

Philip and Pauline Bulman are the proprietors and they have succeeded in recapturing the style of the Hall from its inter-war years. Bedrooms are, on the whole, stylish and colour co-ordinated, the ones in the main house overlooking the front gardens being the most popular. One of the best is Number Nine, plush with a lemon and blue coronet and a very spacious bathroom. One guest complained that her room overlooking the back garden was overpriced for its size – and its view of the dustbins!

◗ Open all year, exc first 2 weeks Jan

⤢ 2 miles north of Storrington on the B2139. Private car park

🛏 3 single, 4 twin, 12 double, 1 suite; all with bathroom/WC, exc 1 double with shower/WC; TV, room service, hair-dryer in all rooms; trouser press in some rooms; no tea/coffee-making facilities in rooms

◈ Restaurant, bar, lounge, conservatory; conference

facilities (max 45 people non-residential, 20 residential); fishing, tennis, putting at hotel, golf, riding nearby

⊜ No wheelchair access; no dogs

▭ Access, Visa

£ Single £70, single occupancy of twin/double £70, twin/double £80 to £96, suite £164; deposit required. Set L £12.50, D £19.50; alc D £30. Special breaks available

---

THORNBURY AVON   **MAP 9**

Thornbury Castle

CASTLE STREET, THORNBURY, NR BRISTOL, AVON BS12 1HH
TEL: THORNBURY (0454) 281182   FAX: (0454) 416188

A castle that makes for an unusual but pricey treat.

Thornbury has everything that a good castle should: suits of armour, heraldic designs, tapestries and candlelit rooms. It also has everything that a luxury hotel needs: interesting bedrooms, fine food and efficient service. The castle's exterior looks the part, with creeper-clad walls topped with crenellations and turrets and a surrounding of immaculate lawns and gardens. The wood-panelled lounge is decorated with portraits and crests, lit by candles and warmed by a huge fire. The bedrooms in the main building come in a variety of shapes and sizes, but all have patterned wallpaper and matching floral bedspreads. Consider going for one of the turret rooms across the courtyard, such as Howard. This room is the size of a squash court, with exposed grey stone walls decorated with heavy tapestries. A four-poster stands in the centre of the room, and even the wardrobe dates back to 1708.

Meals are taken in a red octagonal dining-room. The menu has classic dishes that are well-executed and attractively presented; you could have breast of pigeon with cheese followed by lamb in madeira sauce and finally an individual treacle tart. The staff are courteous. A special mention goes to Pepe, who wears the hats of bellboy, cocktail waiter and maître d'hôtel with equal charm and efficiency.

◐ Open all year, exc 3 days in Jan

⤴ Leave the M4 or M5 motorway and take the A38 towards Thornbury. Turn off this road on to the B4061 and continue to the monumental water pump. Bear left and continue for 300 yards – the entrance to the castle is to the left of the parish church in Thornbury. Private car park

🛏 2 single, 4 twin, 3 double, 8 four-poster, 1 suite; all with bathroom/WC, TV, room service, hair-dryer, trouser press; tea/coffee-making facilities on request

◈ 3 dining-rooms, 2 lounges, library; conference facilities (max 28 people non-residential, 20 residential); croquet at hotel, other sports nearby

⊖ No wheelchair access; no children under 12; no dogs; no smoking in dining-rooms

▭ Access, Amex, Diners, Visa

£ Single £75 to £85, twin/double £95 to £195, four-poster £150 to £200, suite £170 to £195. Cooked B £7.50; set L £18, D £31. Special breaks available

---

THORNHAM NORFOLK   **MAP 7**

Lifeboat Inn ✩

SHIP LANE, THORNHAM, NORFOLK PE36 6LT
TEL: THORNHAM (0485) 26236   FAX: (0485) 26323

Log fires and snug rooms make this traditional old pub a welcome retreat from the elements.

The long, whitewashed façade of this old inn is exposed to the full brunt of the wind, giving it a bleak, desolate look which belies the cosiness inside. Since smuggling times it has been a refuge from wind and sea and, although first built as a beer house for sailors, it now serves delicious food too. Crackling log fires warm the sixteenth-century bar area where beams are hung with lanterns, buoys, tankards and horseshoes. Intimate tables and long wooden settles are arranged for those who just want to down a pint or to choose from the bar menu which, far from bog-standard chicken-in-a-basket meals, may include ragoût of fresh vegetables and wild mushrooms or mouthwatering fish pies. Alternatively, you can choose to sit in the soft pinks of the restaurant where there is an imaginative set dinner menu (how about suprême of chicken filled with banana, then wrapped in bacon on curry sauce as a main course?).

Upstairs, most bedrooms face the sea; there are a couple in the original part of the inn and eleven in a clever extension, which blends into the old. Décor is similar throughout – white walls and pine furniture.

◑ *Open all year*

↗ *Thornham is on the A149, 4 miles from Hunstanton. The Lifeboat Inn, is signposted left off this main road. Private car park*

🛏 *13 twin/double; all with bathroom/WC, TV, room service, hair-dryer, baby-listening*

◇ *Restaurant, 3 bars, conservatory; conference facilities (max 50 people non-residential, 13 residential); fishing, golf, other*

sports nearby; babysitting. Wheelchair access to hotel, restaurant and 1 ground-floor room

⊖ *No dogs in restaurant*

▭ *Access, Diners, Visa*

£ *Single occupancy of twin/double £38, twin/double £65; deposit required. Bar meals from £2.50; set D £17.50; alc L £10.50, D £25. Special breaks available*

THORNTON CLEVELEYS LANCASHIRE   MAP 5

Victorian House

TRUNNAH ROAD, THORNTON CLEVELEYS, LANCASHIRE FY5 4HF
TEL: BLACKPOOL (0253) 860619   FAX: (0253) 865350

French restaurant-with-rooms provides a small oasis of stylish Victoriana in an unprepossessing area.

Up until about ten years ago, this Victorian house used to be a convent. It is now in the indulgence rather than the mortification business. The surrounding area of industrial and housing estates does not prepare you for the atmospheric, stagey interior. This is a highly effective re-creation complete with stuffed chairs, lace cloths, dark patterned wallpaper and heavy velvet curtains. There is lots of bric-à-brac scattered around, including some interesting pieces such as the 1920s Blackpool photo and the old French wall clock in the parlour. Only the new conservatory adds an intrusive note – but it does make for a most agreeable spot in which to have breakfast.

The three comfortable bedrooms keep to the theme, even down to the brass kettles. The Blue Room is a particularly good-sized twin, with a roomy bathroom and small dressing-room attached. The furniture is solid and dark.

The French food in the Upstairs Downstairs dining-room is excellent value. Typical dishes might include Roquefort and hazelnut salad, creamy crab and broccoli chowder, escalope of salmon with sorrel sauce or loin of lamb.

◑ Open all year, exc last 2 weeks Jan; dining-room closed Sun eve

▰ Leave the M55 at Junction 3, take A585 towards Fleetwood. Follow B5268 towards Thornton and turn left at the church on the Fleetwood Road. Private car park

🛏 1 twin, 1 double, 1 four-poster; all with bathroom/WC, TV, room service, hair-dryer, trouser press

◈ Dining-room, bar, lounge, conservatory; golf, riding, other sports nearby

⊖ No wheelchair access; no children under 6; no dogs in public rooms

▭ Access, Visa

£ Single occupancy of twin/double £47, twin/double/four-poster £70. Set D £19; alc L £10

THUNDRIDGE HERTFORDSHIRE　　　　　　　**MAP 9**

Hanbury Manor　　

THUNDRIDGE, NR WARE, HERTFORDSHIRE SG12 0SD
TEL: WARE (0920) 487722   FAX: (0920) 487692

An extended mansion with lots of facilities – good for an indulgent but pricey weekend break.

The imposing red-brick building with masses of tall candy-twist chimneys was converted from a convent school and opened as a luxury hotel in 1990. A great deal of money has been invested into the complex, which includes an 18-hole championship golf course designed by Jack Nicklaus II.

The old part of the hotel has some splendid rooms. The Oak Hall, with its carved panelling, tapestries, stone fireplace and minstrels' gallery, is the main lounge; there is also a library with shelves of leather-bound books and bright soft furnishings, and a cocktail bar. The Zodiac Room is the main restaurant, with planetary signs moulded onto the ceiling. One reader complains that the necessity of reserving a table for the evening when checking in in mid-afternoon was not made clear and consequently he was unable to sample the menu constructed under the 'inspired guidance' of Albert Roux. Sunday lunch received mixed comments, with 'roast beef not as rare or as tender as we hoped' although it was followed by 'exceptionally good summer pudding with clotted cream'. Breakfast is taken in the conservatory.

Suites overlooking the golf course have large alcove windows and are much larger than standard doubles. All are decorated to a high standard, if slightly anonymous in style.

◑ Open all year

▰ On the A10. Leave the M25 at Junction 25. Private car park

🛏 11 single, 47 twin, 32 double, 3 four-poster, 10 suites (some rooms in annexe); all with bathroom/WC, TV, room service, hair-dryer, trouser press, mini-bar; tea/coffee-making facilities in a third of rooms

3 restaurants, 2 bars, 2 lounges, snooker room, library, conservatory; air-conditioned conference facilities (max 112 people non-residential and residential); crèche; golf, tennis, sauna, solarium, heated swimming-pool, health spa, gym, dance studio, squash at hotel, other sports nearby; babysitting. Wheelchair access to hotel (2 steps), restaurant and WC

(unisex), 3 ground-floor bedrooms specially equipped for disabled people

No dogs in public rooms

Access, Amex, Diners, JCB, Visa

Single from £98, single occupancy of twin/double from £98, twin/double from £110/£190/£220, four-poster £275, suite £350; deposit required. Set L from £19.50, D from £25; alc L, D from £15. Special breaks available

---

TINTAGEL CORNWALL   **MAP 10**

Trebrea Lodge

TRENALE, TINTAGEL, CORNWALL PL34 0HR
TEL: CAMELFORD (0840) 770410

An imposing Georgian hotel in a quiet rural setting away from the bustle of Tintagel.

Once you have done the rounds of Tintagel's Arthurian sites you may well want to make a swift escape, in which case Trebrea Lodge, a striking three-storied Georgian town house in Cornish stone, makes a perfect, if rather unexpected, haven. With a sundial and fountain in its front courtyard and huge portraits gracing the hall and stairwell, the hotel has, as chef-hotelier Sean Devlin puts it, 'delusions of grandeur', although his friendly welcome quickly brings it back down to earth. A flagstone-floored hall leads to a dining-room which, with its oak panelling and carved chimney breast, looks more Jacobean than Georgian. Four-course dinner menus change daily, and favour sea trout and wild Tamar salmon. Across the hall the non-smoking lounge with log fire is smaller and cosier than the upstairs one for smokers, which is decorated with deep-mustard walls and furnished with big, comfortable chairs, two striking sofas and three screens.

Beamed corridors lead to the bedrooms, where antique-dealer and joint hotelier Fergus Cochrane has created a good mix of antique and modern fittings.

Open all year

Leave Tintagel on the Boscastle road and turn right at the RC church. Take a right turning at top of lane. Private car park

2 twin, 3 double, 1 four-poster, 1 family room; some with bathroom/WC, some with shower/WC; TV, hair-dryer in all rooms; baby-listening on request

◈ Dining-room, 2 lounges, drying room; fishing, golf, other sports nearby. Wheelchair access to dining-room only

● No children under 5; smoking in 1 lounge only

▭ Access, Amex, Visa

£ Single occupancy of twin/double £40 to £48, twin/double £58 to £68, four-poster £68, family room rate on request; deposit required. Set D £15 (8pm). Special breaks available

---

TITCHWELL NORFOLK   **MAP 7**

Titchwell Manor

TITCHWELL, NR BRANCASTER, KING'S LYNN, NORFOLK PE31 8BB
TEL: BRANCASTER (0485) 210221   FAX: (0485) 210104

This friendly hotel makes a good base for exploring the area.

With a coastline of reed beds, sand dunes and marshes, Titchwell is a paradise for birdwatchers and walkers. Margaret and Ian Snaithe provide their guests with maps of local footpaths and Norfolk bird reserves on booking.

The long, sweeping views from the front rooms make up for the occasional car purring by. If you arrive on a cold day, the first impression you will get is of blazing log fires which warm the bar and lounge areas, and friendly staff who will be happy to make you a cup of tea. Birdwatching magazines lie on coffee tables and soft sofas welcome weary walkers. There is a choice of either bar snacks in a pine-furnished room at one end of the house or the more formal Garden Restaurant with high-backed chairs and pink tablecloths at the other. Here, there is a set menu with four or five choices per course, plus an à la carte. Outbuildings have been converted into bedrooms to add to those in the main house. Some could be considered over-flowery but all are comfortable.

◐ Open all year

↗ On the A149 between Thornham and Brancaster. Private car park

🛏 3 single, 6 twin, 5 double, 1 family room; most with bathroom/WC, some with shower/WC; TV, room service, hair-dryer, trouser press, baby-listening in all rooms

◈ Restaurant, bar, lounge; conference facilities (max 15 people residential); fishing, golf, other sports nearby. Wheelchair access to hotel and restaurant, 4 ground-floor bedrooms

● No dogs in public rooms; no smoking in restaurant

▭ Access, Amex, Diners, Visa

£ Single £35 to £39, twin/double/family room £70 to £78; deposit required. Set L £10, D £17.50; alc D £28. Special breaks available

---

Many hotels put up their tariffs in the spring. You are advised to confirm prices when you book.

TORQUAY DEVON **MAP 10**

Mulberry House ☆

1 SCARBOROUGH ROAD, TORQUAY, DEVON TQ2 5UJ
TEL: TORQUAY (0803) 213639

A hidden-away restaurant with excellent food and three very pretty rooms.

You will need careful directions to find gleaming white Mulberry House, easily overlooked on the corner of a street of Identikit suburban guest-houses. A marvellous tea-shop with two tiled Victorian fireplaces and lots of round wooden tables fills the ground floor; the walls are thick with interesting pictures, and a clock with its workings on display tolls the hours. Owner Lesley Cooper has recently redecorated three very pretty bedrooms upstairs. One has a private bathroom, attractively done out with fish pictures, mirrors and plants. Furnishings are mainly in antique pine, and the old fireplaces are filled with books or pine cones.

On Friday and Saturday nights guests eat in the company of non-residents; simpler dinners are available Sunday to Thursday. Mulberry House is too small to warrant a lounge or bar, but there is a table and chairs grouped on the landing where guests can drink tea.

- *Open all year*
- *From the centre of Torquay sea front, turn up Belgrave Road. Scarborough Road is the 1st right. On-street parking*
- *1 twin, 2 double; 1 double with bathroom/WC, the remainder with shower/WC; TV, room service, hair-dryer in all rooms; no tea/coffee-making facilities in rooms*
- *Restaurant*
- *No wheelchair access; no dogs; no smoking in restaurant*
- *None accepted*
- *Single occupancy of twin/double £25, twin/double £37; deposit required. Set L £7.50/£9, D £16.50; alc L £9 to £11.50, D £9.50 to £17.50. Special breaks available*

Denotes somewhere you can rely on a good meal – either the hotel features in the 1994 edition of our sister publication, The Good Food Guide, *or our inspectors thought the cooking impressive, whether particularly competent home cooking or more lavish cuisine.*

TOWERSEY OXFORDSHIRE   **MAP 9**

Upper Green Farm

COUNTY
HOTEL
OF THE
YEAR

SL

MANOR ROAD, TOWERSEY, OXFORDSHIRE OX9 3QR
TEL: THAME (0844) 212496   FAX: (0844) 260399

A picture-book B&B in a delightful cottage and barn conversion.

Set back from the road amidst green fields with neat white fencing is a
cottage and black timber barn beside a small lake with resident ducks and
a small boat moored up amongst the reeds. This charming rural scene
seems almost too good to be true – but it isn't. The warm welcome from
Euan and Marjorie Aitken creates a sense of well-being, as does your
bedroom, either in the carefully converted barn or in the cottage. The
rooms are fresh and pretty with white walls, a mix of antiques and pine
furnishings, crisp white sheets and duvet covers and a scattering of
interesting objects. All are provided with good bathrooms. The barn
rooms radiate off a sitting-room with high rafters and a stone-flagged
floor; guests staying in the two rooms in the cottage have a separate
sitting-room, though everyone starts the day in the neat breakfast room,
where a hay manger filled with dried flowers is a feature.

◐ Open all year

⤢ From the Thame ring-road take
the Towersey road. The farm is
just past Towersey Manor on the
left. Private car park

🛏 1 single, 2 twin, 5 double; most
with bathroom/WC, rest with
shower/WC; TV, hair-dryer in all
rooms

◇ Dining-room, 2 lounges;
conference facilities (max 10

people residential and non-
residential); tennis, riding, other
sports nearby. Wheelchair access
to farm, restaurant and 2
ground-floor bedrooms

⊖ No children under 13; no dogs;
no smoking

▭ None accepted

£ Single £28, single occupancy of
twin/double £28 to £37, twin/
double £38 to £50

---

*If you have a small appetite, or just aren't feeling hungry, check if you can be
given a reduction if you don't want the full menu. At some hotels you could
easily end up paying £30 for one course and a coffee.*

---

*Where we know an establishment accepts credit cards, we list them. There
may be a surcharge if you pay by credit card. It is always best to check
whether the card you want to use is acceptable when booking.*

Island Hotel ☆

TRESCO, ISLES OF SCILLY TR24 0PU
TEL: SCILLONIA (0720) 22883   FAX: (0720) 23008

Beautifully situated old favourite in lovely gardens.

The Island Hotel is one of those institutions that attracts praise and criticism in equal measure. All readers agree that the site is wonderful, looking out to St Martin's and the Eastern Isles with its own private beach alongside. Inside, extensions a few years ago have created a large and airy bar and lounge area, furnished with large pink striped sofas and white rattan. Ivan Curtis, the manager, is an affable host. The restaurant relies on its picture windows for its appeal, though there is rather institutional furniture.

Food attracts mixed reports: some rave about the Sunday evening cold buffet – 'a masterpiece' – while others rate it 'a shadow of past delights'.

Bedrooms in the older part of the hotel are a fair size but rather old-fashioned and unremarkable in beige and browns. Far better are rooms in the new wing: large with a sitting area and balcony and decorated in bright pinks and greens. Some guests, however, bemoan the lack of fresh flowers in the bedrooms, and the fact that beds are not turned down unless specifically requested.

◐ *Closed Nov to Mar*

🔁 *The Island Hotel is a 20-minute helicopter flight from Penzance. There are no cars on the Scillies*

🛏 *5 single, 34 twin/double, 1 suite; all with bathroom/WC, TV, room service, baby-listening; hair-dryer, mini-bar in some rooms*

◇ *Restaurant, bar, lounge, drying room, library, games room; tennis, swimming-pool at hotel,* *other sports nearby; babysitting*

⊖ *No wheelchair access; no dogs; no smoking in restaurant*

▭ *Access, Amex, Visa*

£ *Single £80 to £95, single occupancy of twin/double £120 to £144, twin/double £140 to £220, suite £190 to £240 (rates inc dinner); deposit required. Set D £24. Special breaks available*

The text of entries is based on unsolicited reports sent in by readers and backed up by inspections. The factual details are from questionnaires the Guide *sends to all hotels that feature in the book.*

Report forms are at the back of the Guide; *write a letter if you prefer.*

TRING HERTFORDSHIRE MAP 9

Pendley Manor

COW LANE, TRING, HERTFORDSHIRE HP23 5QY
TEL: TRING (0442) 891891   FAX: (0442) 890687

A heavily extended manor house with good conference facilities in a tranquil setting.

In 1987 Pendley Manor began a major refurbishment programme, which included the building of a new conference wing in a style sympathetic to the original Victorian Tudor-style mansion. Mid-week you may find the hotel full with conference guests, and weddings keep the hotel busy at weekends. The old house retains a traditional elegance, with fine plasterwork on ceilings, marble and carved fireplaces and swathes of material framing large windows. Morning coffee is served on crested china in the calm of the drawing-room, dinner (such as lamb with a saffron couscous and a coriander sauce) in the restrained surroundings of the restaurant. The central carved staircase and stained-glass window are an impressive sight, much used as a backdrop for wedding photos.

Bedrooms in the old house have much more character than those in the new wing, though the furnishings are equally modern and good quality in both.

◖ Open all year

🔁 Take the A41 from Tring towards Hemel Hempstead. Cow Lane is 1 mile on the left-hand side. Private car park

🛏 4 single, 4 twin, 57 double, 4 executive rooms, 2 suites; all with bathroom/WC, TV, room service, hair-dryer, trouser press; no tea/coffee-making facilities in rooms

◈ 2 restaurants, bar, lounge, conservatory; conference facilities (max 200 people non-residential, 70 residential); tennis at hotel, other sports nearby; babysitting. Wheelchair access to hotel (ramp), restaurant and WC (unisex), 17 ground-floor bedrooms, 1 specially equipped for disabled people

⊖ None

▭ Access, Amex, Visa

💷 Single £85, single occupancy of twin/double £85, twin/double £95, executive room £125, suite £125. Set L £16, D £22.50. Special breaks available

TRISPEN CORNWALL MAP 10

Laniley House

OFF NEWQUAY ROAD, NR TRISPEN, TRURO, CORNWALL TR4 9AU
TEL: TRURO (0872) 75201

A secluded, family-run bed and breakfast.

The long tarmacked drive to Laniley House leads you past a field of goats, an old red telephone box and an assortment of cars awaiting repair. This is a chunky Victorian building where Jackie Gartner offers bed and breakfast in three bedrooms, named after their colour schemes – Blue, Pink and Yellow. Inside, the house offers as many surprises as do the grounds, from the elephant's head in the hallway to the trellising on the bright pink breakfast room walls. Here a single table beneath a chandelier seats all six guests, who can therefore expect to get to know each other quickly. In the lounge a big black marble fireplace is piled high with fir cones. Upstairs, the bedrooms are tamer than the rooms below, although in the Yellow Room the yellow extends to the *en-suite* bath and toilet. The Pink Room features a combination of beds for 'the short and stubby' and 'the long and thin', as Mr Gartner senior succinctly puts it; the Blue is a more conventional (and quite sizeable) double.

◐ Open all year, exc Xmas and New Year

▨ 3 miles north of Truro on the A3076 Newquay road. Turn off right at the Frogmore/Trehane turning. Private car park

🛏 1 twin, 2 double; 1 double with bathroom/WC; 1 public

bathroom; TV in all rooms

◈ Breakfast room, lounge

⊖ No wheelchair access; no children under 13; no dogs; no smoking

▭ None accepted

£ Twin/double £34 to £36

Mortal Man Hotel

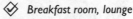

TROUTBECK, WINDERMERE, CUMBRIA LA23 1PL
TEL: AMBLESIDE (05394) 33193   FAX: (05394) 31261

A country inn with comfortable rooms in an ideal location.

When considering a suitable location for exploring the Lake District, would-be visitors are usually on the lookout for somewhere that's close to the action, a good touring base and yet away from the crowds. The Mortal Man, in the sleepy hamlet of Troutbeck, is all of these and more, with a genuine country pub ambience and, in the words of one reader, 'a hotelier who cares about his visitors'. Christopher Poulsom, who runs the hotel with his wife Annette, is certainly that.

The most welcoming part of the hotel is the residents' bar, with its exposed beams, horse brasses and dark wooden panelling. The lounge and the dining-room ('now no smoking – hoorah,' reports one reader) are plain and homely, with the emphasis on comfort rather than elegance; both have stone fireplaces and fell views. Bedrooms are also simply furnished and have plain white walls and rather small bathrooms.

Dinner is a five-course affair with a choice of four main courses that may include fillet of red bream stuffed with diced vegetables and herbs and then baked in a cheese sauce. 'Breakfast could be earlier than 9am,' suggested one reader, who has reported back, joyously, that it has now been shifted to 8.30am – 'that's what listening to your guests is all about.'

◑ Closed mid-Nov to mid-Feb

↗ Troutbeck is on the A592, 3 miles north of Windermere. Private car park

🛏 2 single, 6 twin, 4 double; all with bathroom/WC, TV, hairdryer, trouser press; room service by arrangement

◈ Dining-room, bar, lounge, drying room; fishing, golf, other sports nearby. Wheelchair access to dining-room only

⊖ No children under 5; no smoking in dining-room

▭ None accepted

£ Single £45 to £55, twin/double £90 to £110 (rates inc dinner). Sun L £12; set D £19

TROWBRIDGE WILTSHIRE   MAP 9

Old Manor ☆

TROWLE, TROWBRIDGE, WILTSHIRE BA14 9BL
TEL: TROWBRIDGE (0225) 777393   FAX: (0225) 765443

An extended manor house with a choice of smoking and non-smoking rooms.

The Old Manor is situated on a Domesday Book site just outside Trowbridge. In the intervening years a main road has appeared nearby and a housing estate has sprung up across the meadow, but it is none the less a useful place for stopovers and business trips. The delightful main house is a mixture of architectural styles – principally Queen Anne, though parts date back to medieval times. A restaurant and new bedrooms have been created from barn and stables respectively.

Apart from the more spacious, rustic-style restaurant that serves home-cooked meals to residents and their guests only, the size of most of the rooms can best be described as compact. However, the three linked sitting-rooms in the old house are extremely attractive and well furnished with antiques, old pictures, easy chairs and open fires.

Bedrooms are divided into smoking and non-smoking rooms. All are agreeable and some have four-posters and half-testers.

◑ Open all year, exc Xmas period; dining-room closed Sun eve

↗ On the A363 between Bradford-on-Avon and Trowbridge. Private car park

🛏 2 single, 2 double, 3 four-poster, 8 annexe rooms; all with bathroom/WC, TV, room service, hair-dryer; baby-listening on request

◈ Restaurant, 2 lounges, library; fishing, golf, other sports nearby. Wheelchair access to hotel, restaurant and 9 ground-floor bedrooms

⊖ No children under 12 in lounges; no dogs; smoking in 1 lounge and some bedrooms

▭ Access, Amex, Diners, JCB, Visa

£ Single £45, single occupancy of double £45, double £60, four-poster £70, annexe room £64; deposit required. Alc D £20

TRURO CORNWALL   **MAP 10**

Alverton Manor

TREGOLLS ROAD, TRURO, CORNWALL TR1 1XQ
TEL: TRURO (0872) 76633   FAX: (0872) 222989

*A luxurious hotel in a nineteenth-century ex-convent on the
outskirts of Truro.*

Walking into Gothic Alverton Manor feels a bit like walking into a
church – which is hardly surprising, for it was home to the Bishop of
Truro in the 1880s and then to the Sisters of the Epiphany; what was
their chapel is now a large conference hall with an intriguing lighting
system. As soon as you reach reception, however, the austere ecclesiastical past gives way to the much more luxurious present of a hotel suitable
for business travellers as well as holidaymakers. All the public rooms are
big and light and the bar is almost lost at the far end of the ground-floor
lounge, where lots of comfortable chairs are arranged round not one but
two marble fireplaces; there is also a separate library to sit in. The
elegantly decorated Terrace Restaurant has à la carte and three-course
table d'hôte menus; familiar dishes come with imaginative twists, such as
saddle of mature venison on a nest of wholewheat noodles, and fillet of
finest beef on a glazed Stilton and beer sauce.

All the bedrooms are boldly and distinctly decorated, with huge beds
and lots of vividly covered fabrics for curtains and covers. A few rooms
are squeezed up in the roof and several are on the ground floor – Room
Five is best for disabled guests, with wide doors and lights on long
switches.

◑ *Open all year*

⤢ *On the A39 (Tregolls Road) from
St Austell leading into Truro.
Private car park*

🛏 *4 single, 4 twin, 12 double, 5
suites; all with bathroom/WC, exc
3 singles with shower/WC; TV,
room service, hair-dryer, trouser
press in all rooms; no tea/coffee-
making facilities in rooms*

◇ *Restaurant, 2 bars, lounge,
snooker room, library,
conservatory, drying room;
conference facilities (max 200
people non-residential, 25*

*residential); snooker at hotel,
golf, water sports, other sports
nearby. Wheelchair access to
hotel (1 step), restaurant and
WC (M,F), 3 ground-floor
bedrooms, 1 specially equipped
for disabled people*

⊖ *No dogs or smoking in
restaurant*

▭ *Access, Amex, Diners, Visa*

£ *Single £45 to £55, twin/double
£55 to £70, suite £80 to £90;
deposit required. Set D £16.50;
alc L, D £19 to £25. Special
breaks available*

*Use the index at the back of the book if you know the name of a hotel but are
unsure about its precise location.*

TUTBURY STAFFORDSHIRE   **MAP 5**

Mill House

CORNMILL LANE, TUTBURY, NR BURTON-ON-TRENT, STAFFORDSHIRE
DE13 9HA
TEL: BURTON-ON-TRENT (0283) 813300/813634

*Immaculate bed-and-breakfast accommodation in a peaceful
Georgian house surrounded by fields and next to the River Dove.*

If you are visiting the Potteries or looking for peace and quiet in this very
green part of Staffordshire, Mill House makes a good base. The
Chapmans' neat red-brick Georgian house is bordered on one side by
the mill stream, crowded with lilies and rushes, and on another by a
motley set of outbuildings that make up David's sheepskin business.
Elizabeth puts most of her energy into the associated shop and so doesn't
provide evening meals; she runs a smooth bed-and-breakfast operation
and the local pub is only half a mile away. The three bedrooms are well
co-ordinated with rich fabrics and appealing colours, and are given
pretty touches like patchwork cushions and silk flower arrangements.
Guests eat breakfast all together around one table in the breakfast room,
where you can also stretch out in front of a log and coal fire in the
evenings.

◑ Open all year, exc 25, 26 Dec

↗ 3½ miles off the A38, mid-way
between the villages of Rolleston
and Tutbury. Private car park

🛏 3 twin; 1 with bathroom/WC, 2
with shower/WC; TV in all
rooms; hair-dryer on request

◈ Breakfast room; fishing at hotel,

golf, other sports nearby

⊖ No wheelchair access; no
children under 8; no dogs; no
smoking

▭ None accepted

£ Single occupancy of twin £35 to
£40, twin £48 to £58

TWO BRIDGES DEVON   **MAP 10**

Prince Hall Hotel ☆

TWO BRIDGES, NR YELVERTON, DEVON PL20 6SA
TEL: PRINCETOWN (0822) 890403

A comfortable family-run hotel in the middle of Dartmoor.

It would be hard to imagine a hotel more remote than Prince Hall Hotel,
or one with more wonderful surroundings; no matter which window you
look out of there'll be a panorama of moorland tors, hump-backed stone
bridges, tiny streams and endless lines of sheep. For relaxing indoors, the
lounge and bar are comfortably if not excitingly decorated, with a log
fire and wood-burning stove respectively. In the dining-room beyond

another fireplace has been pressed into service for storing wine racks and the fine selection of French labels quickly makes sense when you discover that the proprietor Jean-Claude Denat is himself French. Menus, too, have a French twist while still making the most of local ingredients, particularly fish.

Upstairs, the bedrooms, named after local tors, are mostly spacious (Houndtor in particular) and comfortable, with very different colour schemes and mainly old furniture; Haytor, Crockern Tor and Top Tor are perhaps the prettiest.

◑ *Closed for 2 months during winter*

↗ *Follow signs from Ashburton (on the A38) for Two Bridges and Princetown. The hotel is situated on the left-hand side of the B3357, 1 mile from Two Bridges. Private car park*

🛏 *1 single, 3 twin, 2 double, 2 four-poster; most with bathroom/ WC, some with shower/WC; TV, room service in all rooms; hair-dryer on request*

◈ *Dining-room, bar, lounge, drying*

room; fishing (Apr to Sept) at hotel, clay pigeon shooting, golf, other sports nearby

⊖ *No wheelchair access; children discouraged; no dogs in dining-room and bar; no smoking in dining-room*

▭ *Access, Amex, Diners, Visa*

£ *Single from £43, single occupancy of twin/double from £51, twin/double from £85, four-poster £95 (rates inc dinner); deposit required. Set D £20. Special breaks available*

UCKFIELD EAST SUSSEX   MAP 8

Hooke Hall

250 HIGH STREET, UCKFIELD, EAST SUSSEX TN22 1EN
TEL: UCKFIELD (0825) 761578   FAX: (0825) 768025

A town house with a mixture of elegant and interesting bedrooms.

Hooke Hall is a smart hotel with quirky character – the plants in the pram and the huge, weird, carved wooden bird in the hall soon let you know you're in for something a little different. Juliet Percy gives a wicked grin when asked about the names of the bedrooms on the first floor, for they are all called after famous lovers. She is responsible for the individual and sometimes flamboyant décor of the rooms. Mme de Pompadour is a spacious mini-suite with red and white floral décor; the pink chaise-longue, rocking horse and rocking chair add to the feel of luxury bestowed by the four-poster bed. Lady Hamilton is also lavishly deco-rated, this time in blue and green, but suffers from a little road noise. It is interesting to note that the 'ladies' are all quite large and grand, whereas Casanova is distinctly small in comparison!

Rooms on the second floor are smaller than those on the first, but have beamed ceilings and good-sized bathrooms. The public rooms are more subtle than the bedrooms; the comfortable drawing-room has a plump green sofa and a couple of armchairs, while the dining-room is quite small but stylish, with designer curtains and handsome antique furniture.

◐ *Open all year, exc 24 to 31 Dec; restaurant closed Sun and Mon eves*

⬀ *At the northern end of the High Street in the centre of Uckfield. Private car park*

🛏 *8 twin/double, 1 four-poster; all with bathroom/WC, exc 1 twin/ double with shower/WC; TV, hair-dryer, mini-bar, trouser press, baby-listening in all rooms*

◈ *Dining-room, lounge, library/ study; conference facilities (max 20 people non-residential, 9 residential); golf, tennis, other*

sports nearby; babysitting. Wheelchair access to dining-room only

⊖ *No children under 12; no dogs; no smoking in dining-room*

▭ *Access, Visa*

£ *Single occupancy of twin/double £40 to £43, twin/double £50 to £70, four-poster £90 to £110; deposit required for overseas bookings. Continental B £5, cooked B £7; set D £25; alc L £15 (service charge added to meal bills). Special breaks available*

Horsted Place

LITTLE HORSTED, NR UCKFIELD, EAST SUSSEX TN22 5TS
TEL: ISFIELD (0825) 750581　FAX: (0825) 750459

More of a stately home than a hotel, concentrating on suites rather than just bedrooms.

A winding drive leads to a golf course and an imposing red-brick country house with turrets and towers to give it an air of majesty. A tripwire at the entrance to the car park lets the staff know that someone has arrived and brings them out to meet, greet and carry the bags – a useful ploy, as there is no obvious reception. Pre-dinner drinks can be taken in the salmon-coloured drawing-room with its reddish-brown floorboards, thick rugs and two grey marble fireplaces flanking the main entrance. The library, further down the corridor, was set for a conference dinner when our inspector visited, and there was great surprise as the food was brought in via a secret passage, camouflaged to blend in with the bookshelves. In the dining hall, salmon-coloured walls are adorned by heavy gilt-framed pictures; large round tables overlook the car park and part of the golf course.

Suites are the order of the day here and although we feel they are a bit on the expensive side, all the rooms we inspected were elegant, light and airy.

◐ *Open all year*

⬀ *2 miles south of Uckfield on the A26 Lewes road at the junction with the A22. Private car park*

🛏 *6 twin, 3 double, 8 suites; all with bathroom/WC, TV, room service, hair-dryer, baby-listening*

◈ *Restaurant, 2 lounges, library,*

private dining-room, drying room; conference facilities (max 100 people non-residential, 17 residential); fishing, golf, tennis, heated swimming-pool, croquet at hotel, riding nearby; babysitting. Wheelchair access to hotel (ramp), restaurant and WC (M, F), 2 ground-floor bedrooms

⊖ No dogs; no smoking in restaurant

▭ Access, Amex, Diners, Visa

£ Single occupancy of twin/double £115 to £140, twin/double £140 to £160, suite £185 to £245; deposit required. Continental B £8.50, cooked B £10.50; set L £15, D £28.50. Special breaks available

UFFINGTON OXFORDSHIRE   MAP 9

The Craven

FERNHAM ROAD, UFFINGTON, OXFORDSHIRE SN7 7RD
TEL: UFFINGTON (0367) 820449

A pretty cottage bed and breakfast in a sleepy village.

Follow tourist signs for the Vale of the White Horse and you'll pass the Craven, a small seventeenth-century thatched cottage just outside the small village of Uffington. Carol Wadsworth's home is full of interesting odds and ends and antiques. Though it is not large, its layout is at first confusing; a narrow staircase leads to a twisting corridor, off which are low-ceilinged rooms decorated with collections of china and interesting pictures. The four-poster bedroom has flowery fabrics and a bathroom with some old weighing scales that might appal you, as no pounds or ounces are included on the scale – just stones.

Evening meals, ordered in advance, are taken in an easy-going atmosphere around a pine table in the kitchen. Good home cooking is on offer – perhaps carrot soup followed by shepherd's pie, a choice of fresh vegetables and a plum crumble with cream or custard. There is an open fireplace in the lounge, a restful room in pale greens where you can relax after your meal.

◑ Open all year; no meals Sat eve

➔ Take the A420 from Oxford to Swindon, and after 15 miles turn left to Fernham. At Fernham turn left. Drive through the village and take the first right on leaving the village. The hotel is 1½ miles down the hill on the right. Private car park

🛏 2 single, 1 twin, 2 double, 1 four-poster, 1 family room; some with bathroom/WC; room service, hair-dryer, baby-listening in all rooms; no tea/coffee-making facilities in rooms

◈ Lounge, TV room, drying room; golf, tennis, other sports nearby; babysitting. Wheelchair access to house and WC, 2 ground-floor bedrooms, 1 specially equipped for disabled people

⊖ No dogs; no smoking in bedrooms

▭ None accepted

£ Single £27 to £33, single

occupancy of twin/double £27 to £33, twin/double £20 to £52, four-poster £54, family room (3 people) £47 to £63. Set L from £5, D £12.50. Special breaks available

ULLINGSWICK HEREFORD AND WORCESTER   MAP 9

The Steppes ☆

ULLINGSWICK, NR HEREFORD, HEREFORD AND WORCESTER HR1 3JG
TEL: HEREFORD (0432) 820424

A country hotel where good-natured hosts ensure a jolly atmosphere.

Nowadays teddy bears on your bed are two a penny in hotels, but when you return to your room to find a teddy propped up reading your book through your reading glasses you are inclined to wonder if the furry brutes are going to take over the universe. This sort of gentle humour infects the Steppes, and it stems from Henry Howland's determination to make his guests feel both looked after and at ease.

The Steppes is an old, slate-roofed, black and white farmhouse, with barns and cottage round a courtyard behind. These outbuildings now contain the bedrooms – all constructed by Henry – and very comfortable and well-appointed they are, with large amounts of storage space and a rustic look given by bunches of dried flowers and the old roof beams. The dining-room is a low, dark room, at its best of an evening, and the food comes in substantial portions; the breakfast menu is particularly good. This peaceful hotel is distinguished from others of its kind by the quality of care.

◑ Open all year, exc 2 weeks prior to Xmas and 2 weeks after New Year

⬈ Just off the main A417 Gloucester to Leominster road. Private car park

🛏 6 doubles; all with bathroom/WC, TV, room service, hairdryer, mini-bar

◈ Dining-room, bar, lounge, drying room; fishing, golf, tennis, riding nearby

⊖ No wheelchair access; no children under 10; dogs in some bedrooms only; smoking in lounge and some bedrooms only

▭ Access, Visa

£ Single occupancy of double £35, double £70; deposit required. Set D £20 (7.30pm). Special breaks available

ULLSWATER CUMBRIA   MAP 4

Sharrow Bay

LAKE ULLSWATER, PENRITH, CUMBRIA CA10 2LZ
TEL: POOLEY BRIDGE (07684) 86301   FAX: (07684) 86349

Often emulated but never bettered, Sharrow Bay is the epitome of the country-house hotel.

Francis Coulson and Brian Sack, who founded their country-house hotel here over 40 years ago, like to think of it as a refuge from the quotidian stresses and strains. Situated on the eastern shore of Ullswater, the hotel has views that are simply unrivalled; added to this are the exceptional cuisine and comfort.

Within the grounds of the main building there is the garden cottage and, at the entrance, the Edwardian lodge gatehouse. Bank House, a converted Elizabethan farmhouse, which features a superb stone fireplace from Warwick Castle, is about a mile down the road and Thwaite Cottage is a little further afield. All have luxuriously furnished bedrooms with antique furniture, porcelain and richly coloured coronets above elaborate headboards, but the effect is always one of grand comfort rather than opulence.

The lounges are spacious areas where Victorian antiques co-exist alongside big, soft, inviting sofas against the backdrop of a décor where autumnal hues often predominate. The dining-room is divided into two areas, one with a canopied ceiling and the other with great views of the lake. Lunch and dinner menus are based on traditional British tastes. Dinner may begin with terrine of duck, venison, pigeon and grouse served with Cumberland sauce, spicy oranges and toasted brioche, followed by fillet of brill with red wine sauce, then fresh orange sorbet; the main course may be tournedos of Scottish fillet steak, served on a bed of peperonata with béarnaise sauce tartlet and glazed button onions. The afternoon teas have become almost as celebrated, with visitors flooding in from far and wide – be sure to book.

◑ Closed Dec, Jan and most of Feb

↗ Leave the M6 at Junction 40 and follow the signs for Ullswater. At Pooley Bridge take a right-hand turn to Howtown. Follow this road for 2 miles to the lakeside. Private car park

⇔ 4 single, 9 twin/king-size, 10 double, 5 suites (some rooms in cottages); most with bathroom/WC; TV, room service, hairdryer, trouser press in all rooms; mini-bar in some rooms; no tea/coffee-making facilities in rooms

◈ 2 dining-rooms, 4 lounges, conservatory, drying room; conference facilities (max 12 people residential); riding, water sports, other sports nearby

⊖ No children under 13; no dogs

▭ None accepted

£ Single £85 to £120, twin/double £170 to £300, suite/cottage room £280 to £300 (rates inc dinner). Set L £29.50, D £39.50

ULVERSTON CUMBRIA   **MAP 4**

Trinity House

PRINCES STREET, ULVERSTON, CUMBRIA LA12 7NB
TEL: BARROW-IN-FURNESS (0229) 587639 (and fax)

Inauspiciously located but stylish Georgian town house.

Don't be fooled by the rather sombre grey pebble-dashed exterior of this two-storey Georgian town house. Inside you will find boldness and imagination everywhere. Vigorous colour schemes, unusual fabrics and a flair for contemporary design techniques give Trinity House a distinctly exuberant feel. 'It's one of our favourite places,' says one satisfied reader. The hard-backed chairs and chaise-longue in the lounge are meant to be functional as much as decorative but they can't live with the competition from the two huge pink armchairs. Bright green ragged-effect walls provide a vivid backdrop for the modern prints depicting scenes from Lakeland life. The spacious dining-room employs similar paint effects but this time in bright pink with almost brash primary-coloured floral curtains.

Stephanie Thomson and Keith Sutton manage the hotel with an agreeable lightness of touch. You can doze in till eleven and still come down to a breakfast of bacon, free-range eggs and Waberthwaite sausages. The dinner menu, which includes a choice of at least two vegetarian dishes, emphasises the fresh and local: mushrooms sautéed in butter and garlic followed by rack of Cumbrian lamb with an apple and mint-flavoured gravy and then sticky toffee pudding for dessert.

Bedrooms are reasonably sized, individually decorated and have antique brass and wooden beds and marble fireplaces.

○ Open all year

↗ Approaching Ulverston on the A590, the hotel is on the left of the main road after the second set of traffic lights. Private car park

🛏 1 single, 2 twin, 3 double, 1 family room; most with bathroom/WC, some with shower/WC; TV, room service in all rooms

◇ Dining-room, bar/lounge; golf, riding, other sports nearby.

Wheelchair access to hotel (ramp), restaurant and WC (F), 1 ground-floor bedroom specially equipped for disabled people

⊖ None

▭ Access, Amex, JCB, Visa

£ Single £40, single occupancy of twin/double £42, twin/double £50 to £60, family room £60; deposit required. Set D £12; alc D £14 to £16. Special breaks available

UPPINGHAM LEICESTERSHIRE   **MAP 5**

Lake Isle

16 HIGH STREET EAST, UPPINGHAM, LEICESTERSHIRE LE15 9PZ
TEL: UPPINGHAM (0572) 822951 (and fax)

A cheerful hotel with the emphasis on the informal restaurant.

From the street the Lake Isle appears to be a three-storey, solidly built terraced house, but in fact it stretches much further back than you would expect and has ten bedrooms as well as two cottage annexes – all very efficiently run by David and Claire Whitfield. The bedrooms in the main house are named after wine regions of France; those on the first floor are made light by large casement windows, while those on the second floor are smaller and darker. All are comfortably furnished with good-quality fabrics and cheerful colours. Dom Pérignon is perhaps the largest and possesses a whirlpool bath. There is also an elegant sitting-room on the first floor, with deep coral walls, ruched curtains, window seats and comfortable sofas.

However, the mainstay of the business is the restaurant. With an informal farmhouse feel created by stripped pine tables, wooden walls painted deep green and red, candles and fresh flowers on each table, it is a lovely room and the food has a good reputation. When we visited, the table d'hôte dinner menu included carrot and orange soup, steamed baby brill with white wine, grapes and button mushrooms, and duck with French cherry and kirsch sauce.

◐ *Open all year*

↗ *In Uppingham's High Street, reached via Reeves Yard. Take 1st right turn after hotel into Queen Street, then 2 right turns to the rear of the hotel. Private car park*

⇌ *1 single, 2 twin, 7 double, 2 cottage suites; all with bathroom/WC, TV, room service, hair-dryer, trouser press*

◇ *Restaurant, bar, lounge; conference facilities (max 10 people residential and non-residential)*

⊖ *No wheelchair access; no dogs or smoking in public rooms*

▭ *Access, Amex, Diners, Visa*

£ *Single £45, twin/double £66, suite £75; deposit required. Set L £12.50, D £19.50. Special breaks available*

Rutland House

61 HIGH STREET EAST, UPPINGHAM, LEICESTERSHIRE LE15 9PY
TEL: UPPINGHAM (0572) 822497 (and fax)

A comfortable, no-frills bed and breakfast near the town centre with airy modern rooms and large bathrooms.

Uppingham is a quiet market town of narrow alleys and a higgledy-piggledy collection of buildings that spans several centuries. Rutland House is an ironstone Victorian terrace house offering good-value rooms with no frills. Jenny Hitchen provides bed and breakfast only, but as there are nine restaurants and pubs with food within a few minutes' walk this isn't a problem.

The four bedrooms are large and light, with ordinary modern furnishings and flowery curtains. Rooms at the front are double-glazed – more for warmth than to keep out street noise, which is negligible.

◐ *Open all year*

↗ *Centrally located in Uppingham.*

High Street East is approached via the market square. Rutland

House is just past the art gallery. Private car park

🛏 1 single, 1 twin, 2 double; all with bathroom/WC, TV, trouser press

�🗸 Breakfast room; fishing, golf, other sports nearby. Wheelchair access to hotel and breakfast

room, 1 ground-floor bedroom

⊖ No dogs or smoking in public rooms

▭ Visa

£ Single £28, single occupancy of twin/double £28, twin/double £38, family room £46; deposit required

---

VELLOW SOMERSET   **MAP 10**

Curdon Mill

VELLOW, WILLITON, SOMERSET TA4 4LS
TEL: STOGUMBER (0984) 56522   FAX: (0984) 56197

A welcoming family-run hotel in a converted watermill with lovely gardens.

You need to creep up on the Curdon Mill from the rear to see it to its best advantage, with lilies and primroses decorating the banks of a small stream. Here, too, is the 100-year-old water-wheel which can still be turned on request. The building itself is tall and thin (six-footers will have to watch their heads on the top-floor beams) but skylights cut into the roof let light flood in so it never feels cramped. The six bedrooms are named after their very different colour schemes and fittings: the Walnut Room has walnut fittings, while the Candy Room is all feminine frills and flounces. None is particularly large but all are very comfortable. Chintzy chairs in the first-floor sitting-room are arranged to encourage chatting.

The mill shaft cuts across a flower-filled dining-room whose wooden furnishings include a fine Victorian settle with primitive carvings and a huge Welsh dresser. Daphne Criddle, once a domestic science teacher, prepares wholesome, countryish food. A typical menu might feature hot mushroom and prawn creams, followed by roast Gressingham duck in orange sauce.

◐ Open all year

🡖 Leave Taunton on the A358 towards Williton. Just before Williton take the left turning for Vellow – the mill is 1 mile on the left. Private car park

🛏 3 twin, 3 double; all with shower/WC, exc 1 twin with bathroom/WC; TV, room service, hair-dryer in all rooms

�🗸 Restaurant, bar, lounge, drying room; conference facilities (max 40 people non-residential);

fishing, tennis, heated outdoor swimming-pool (Apr to Sept), other sports nearby

⊖ No wheelchair access; no children under 8; no dogs; smoking in lounge only

▭ Visa

£ Single occupancy of twin/double £28, twin/double £40 to £60; deposit required. Alc D £16.50/£19.50; Sun L £11.50. Special breaks available

Hillside

151 MITCHELL AVENUE, VENTNOR, ISLE OF WIGHT PO38 1DR
TEL: ISLE OF WIGHT (0983) 852271

A warm and traditional family hotel in attractive grounds.

The Hillside has a satisfyingly lofty outlook over the town's grey rooftops and the Channel beyond. The hotel's best feature is a long, attractive conservatory, filled with plants and comfortable wooden furniture. The building itself was constructed as an inn out of sturdy grey stone in 1801, but later fell into the hands of the poet John Sterling. Faced with the need to accommodate six children, Sterling added a third storey and topped it off with a quirky thatched roof, which the present owners, Brenda and Peter Hart, maintain with care.

The Harts have opened up 11 comfortable rooms, which vary greatly in décor. Some are rather plain, but the best, such as Room Four, are done out in rich flowery patterns, with smart bathrooms, basket chairs and large windows with sea views. Downstairs, the bar and lounge are more homely than stylish, while the dining-room, decorated in lemony colours with bamboo furniture, has more of a seaside air. Service is chatty and relaxed. Dinners, which are ordered over English breakfast, are inexpensive and varied, offering a particularly good line in vegetable main dishes.

- ◑ Open all year
- ⤢ A few minutes' drive from the centre of Ventnor on the B3327 to Newport. Private car park
- 🛏 1 single, 2 twin, 7 double, 1 family room; some with bathroom/WC, most with shower/WC; TV, hair-dryer in all rooms
- ◈ Dining-room, bar, lounge, library, conservatory, drying room;

laundry facilities
- ⊖ No wheelchair access; no children under 5; no dogs in some public rooms; no smoking in public rooms
- ▭ Access, Amex, Visa
- £ Single £19 to £21, single occupancy of twin/double £36 to £38, twin/double £37 to £41, family room £51 to £57; deposit required. Alc D £8.50

Nare Hotel

CARNE BEACH, VERYAN, NR TRURO, CORNWALL TR2 5PF
TEL: TRURO (0872) 501279   FAX: (0872) 501856

A large and luxurious hotel overlooking a sandy beach.

Nare Hotel's long, low, cream building gives little clue to its charms – which, of course, lie in the wonderful sea views. The Nare offers a much wider choice of food than many hotels, the four-course table d'hôte menu always including vegetarian dishes as well as a selection of hot and cold meat and fish dishes. Between noon and 2pm guests can lunch in white bamboo-style chairs in the light, airy Gwendra Room where yet another mouth-watering menu features dishes such as mugs of prawns, fresh local crab sandwiches and croûte bretonne.

In the five years since the Grays took over the Nare the bedrooms have been upgraded to a high standard and now feature vivid colour schemes, comfortable modern furnishings, and lots of the extras. The best rooms have sea views; Room Ten has both sea and garden views, and french windows on to a patio. A pretty geranium-filled conservatory with spiral staircase leads to a wing of brand-new rooms which are particularly spacious and elegant.

Behind the car park pet donkeys Carlie and Nelly await in eternal hope of being fed some of the carrots kept at reception for just this purpose.

◑ Open all year, exc for 6 weeks from 6 Jan

⤢ 1 mile west of Veryan, on Carne Beach. Private car park

🛏 4 single, 13 twin, 13 double, 3 family rooms, 2 suites; all with bathroom/WC, TV, room service, hair-dryer; baby-listening in most rooms

◈ Restaurant, 2 bars, 4 lounges, 2 games rooms, drying room, conservatory, luncheon room; conference facilities (max 50 people non-residential, 35 residential); tennis, billiards, sauna, solarium, outdoor heated swimming-pool (Easter to Oct), water sports, gym, tennis and boating at hotel, other sports nearby; babysitting (small fee). Wheelchair access to hotel, restaurant and WC (M,F), 5 ground-floor bedrooms, 2 specially equipped for the disabled

⊖ No children under 7 at dinner; no dogs in public rooms

▭ Access, Visa

£ Single £44 to £103, twin/double £88 to £176, family room £110 to £220, suite £220 to £260; deposit required. Sun L £13; set L £11.50, D £25; alc L, D £30

VOWCHURCH HEREFORD AND WORCESTER   **MAP 9**

Croft Country House

VOWCHURCH, HEREFORD AND WORCESTER HR2 0QE
TEL: GOLDEN VALLEY (0981) 550226

Cheerful and friendly base on the Welsh border.

On the Welsh border, deep in that isolated stretch of pastoral landscape called the Golden Valley, the Croft makes a good refuge from urban life. 'Croft' is more apposite to this establishment than 'Country House' for it is neither huge nor massively smart. It is run in a cheerful, friendly fashion by the Molinary family, who go out of their way to please. Bedrooms are varied. In the main house, the best is the Croft Room, with a large cream double bed and an airy bathroom. Coach house rooms are smaller but have character, and there is also a separate sitting-room.

The Croft boasts a dining-room and a breakfast room, both very pleasantly arranged, and a large garden. There are views of the Welsh hills in the distance, from which your evening meal, in the shape of Welsh lamb, may come. Starters and pudding range from further afield – perhaps gravad lax and then jam roly-poly pudding and custard.

◗ Open all year

⬈ From Hereford take the A465 Abergavenny road for 4 miles, turn right at petrol station and follow road through to Vowchurch. Private car park

🛏 I single, I twin, 4 double, I four-poster, I family room; all with bathroom/WC, exc single with shower/WC; TV, room service, hair-dryer in all rooms

◈ Restaurant, dining-room, bar, lounge, TV room, conservatory; tennis, croquet at hotel, golf, riding, tennis nearby

⊖ No wheelchair access; no children under 14; no dogs; no smoking

▭ Access, Visa

£ Single £22, single occupancy of twin/double £34, twin/double £44, four-poster suite £54, suite £76, family room £66. Sun L £10/£12 (and on request), D £12.50/£14.50. Special breaks available

---

WALKINGTON HUMBERSIDE   **MAP 5**

Manor House

NORTHLANDS, WALKINGTON, NR BEVERLEY, HUMBERSIDE HU17 8RT
TEL: HULL (0482) 881645   FAX: (0482) 866501

A mock-Tudor manor with glamorous bedrooms.

Once inside the Baughs' greying yellow-brick nineteenth-century house there's no getting away from the equestrian connection, with a riding crop on the hall table, rosettes gained from sporting triumphs on display and gracious pictures of sleek steeds for all to admire. The large, airy bedrooms with their king-sized beds are named after horse trials, but these are most definitely silk dressing gown rather than hacking jacket territory, with flowery drapes, dainty china and the sort of storage space in which most people could hang their entire wardrobe. The bathrooms, with Hollywood lights around the mirrors, corner baths and gold taps, are distinctly glitzy.

The bright lounge is elegantly furnished in country-house style with chandeliers and heavily pleated curtains; a bar stands at one end. The core of the house, however, is the restaurant, divided between an extravagantly cultivated conservatory section and a smaller, more formal room. Cooking is nouvellish.

◗ Open all year, exc 25, 26, Dec; restaurant closed Sun

⬈ Leave the M62 at Junction 38.

The hotel is signposted in Walkington. Private car park

🛏 7 double; all with bathroom/WC,

TV, room service, hair-dryer, mini-bar; baby-listening in most rooms

 Dining-room, lounge/bar, conservatory; conference facilities (max 20 people non-residential, 7 residential); golf, riding nearby

● No wheelchair access; no dogs in public rooms

▭ Access, Visa

£ Single occupancy of double £70, double £80 to £100; deposit required. Set L, D £15; alc D £27.50. Special breaks available

WAREHAM DORSET   MAP 9

Priory

CHURCH GREEN, WAREHAM, DORSET BH20 4ND
TEL: WAREHAM (0929) 551666   FAX: (0929) 554519

Sixteenth-century priory turned into small luxury hotel.

Good reports continue to come in about the Priory; one says, 'We were captivated by the place and like it more each time we visit.' The Priory stands in the shadow of Wareham's village church under the gargoyles' watchful eyes. The sixteenth-century sandstone building is covered in creepers and moss.

The corridors and main hallway show the building's monastic origins, with exposed stone walls and stone-flagged floors covered with blood-red carpets. The dining-room is in the wine cellar. Cooking is solid rather than outstanding. You might have something like parsnip and apple soup followed by beef with prunes, with a selection from the sweets trolley or a tray of English cheeses to finish.

The lounge has beautiful oak floorboards, easy chairs and antique pieces. A baby grand stands in the corner.

Bedrooms are decorated in soothing pinks and magnolias and the bathrooms have brilliant white tiles. The converted boathouse suites are also recommended by our readers.

◑ Open all year

↴ Leave the A351 along the North Causeway and enter North Street. Turn left past the Town Hall, right into Church Street. Private car park

⇥ 3 single, 12 twin/double, 2 four-poster, 2 suites; all with bathroom/WC, exc 2 doubles with shower/WC; TV, room service, hair-dryer, mini-bar; trouser press, tea/coffee-making facilities on request

◈ 2 dining-rooms, bar, 2 lounges, TV room; conference facilities

(max 20 people residential and non-residential); fishing, croquet at hotel, other sports nearby. Wheelchair access to hotel, restaurant and WC (unisex), 4 ground-floor bedrooms

● No dogs

▭ Access, Amex, Diners, Visa

£ Single £70, single occupancy of twin/double £80 to £105, twin/double £80 to £120, four-poster £150, suite £175. Sun L £17; set L £12/£14; D from £22.50; alc D £31. Special breaks available

WARKWORTH NORTHUMBERLAND **MAP 3**

Warkworth House ☆

16 BRIDGE STREET, WARKWORTH, NORTHUMBERLAND NE65 0XB
TEL: ALNWICK (0665) 711276   FAX: (0665) 713323

A fine old house with an emphasis on comfort and good facilities.

Warkworth House is a neat sandstone house built in the eighteenth century and reconstructed in 1830, when it acquired its most glorious treasure – the ornate staircase recovered from the demolished Branden-burg House in London. If you have ever dreamt of sweeping regally down a staircase, this is your chance.

The hotel has recently been refurbished in a neat, rather bland modern style, but some fine plasterwork, stained glass and panelling remain. Duncan Oliver is a friendly chap who chats happily to customers from his perch behind the pumps in the cosy bar. The residents' lounge has traditional wallpaper, claret leather chesterfields and a very untraditional small waterfall arrangement. The traditional food – perhaps deep-fried whitebait followed by leek and potato soup, whole rainbow trout in lemon butter, and pudding – is served in a narrow restaurant with a heavily patterned carpet, traditional chairs and wall-lamps.

Bedrooms are modishly decorated with crown canopies, pastel or chintzy décor and a mix of good old and new furniture. Ground-floor rooms have been specially designed with disabled guests in mind.

◑ Open all year

⤴ From the A1 north of Morpeth, take the B6345 towards Warkworth Castle. Private car park

🛏 1 single, 4 twin, 5 double, 1 four-poster, 2 family rooms, 1 suite; all with bathroom/WC, TV, room service, hair-dryer; trouser press in some rooms

◈ Restaurant, bar, lounge, drying room; fishing, golf, other sports

nearby. Wheelchair access to hotel, restaurant and 2 ground-floor bedrooms specially equipped for disabled people

⊖ No smoking in restaurant

▭ Access, Amex, Diners, Visa

£ Single £45 to £49, single occupancy of twin/double £45 to £49, twin/double/four-poster £60 to £65, family room £75 to £80, suite £65; deposit required. Sun L £7.50; bar meals; set D £14

WARMINSTER WILTSHIRE **MAP 9**

Bishopstrow House

WARMINSTER, WILTSHIRE BA12 9HH
TEL: WARMINSTER (0985) 212312   FAX: (0985) 216769

A competitively priced country-house hotel with private fishing.

Bishopstrow changed hands a few years ago, since when there has been an on-going, gradual programme of refurbishment; by the end of 1993 most of the bedrooms will have had a facelift and the brown tiled '70s bathrooms will have been replaced. Bedrooms in the Stable Block and Garden Wing are more recent additions. Most of these rooms are of a similar standard, spacious and furnished with well-chosen, harmonious fabrics. Bathrooms feature marble tops and fittings.

In the main house, the Oval Room, the original master bedroom, is the one to go for; it is a complete oval shape, with curved windows and walls and a beautifully crafted curved door. The public rooms have an easy elegance. Delicious afternoon teas with home-made scones and jams are served to guests relaxing on the ivory damask sofas amongst the lovely flower arrangements.

The dining-room is simply furnished. The menu tries to be bold and inventive but sometimes misses the mark; dishes can be cooked more plainly on request. Hotel service is professional but pleasant, and David Dowden, the young manager, is on the ball and charming.

◑ Open all year

🔁 Approaching Warminster on the B3414, after a sharp left-hand bend, take a right turn into the hotel's drive. Private car park

🛏 1 single, 25 twin/double, 1 four-poster, 3 family rooms, 2 suites; all with bathroom/WC, TV, room service, hair-dryer, baby-listening; trouser press in some rooms; no tea/coffee-making facilities in rooms

◈ 2 dining-rooms, bar, 2 lounges, library, conservatory; conference facilities (max 60 people non-residential, 35 residential); fishing, tennis, sauna, indoor and outdoor heated swimming-pools at hotel, other sports nearby

⊖ No wheelchair access; no dogs in public rooms

▭ Access, Amex, Diners, Visa

£ Single £98, single occupancy of twin/double £98, twin/double £123, four-poster £175, family room £130, suite £256; deposit required. Set L £10.50, D £31; alc L £25, D £31 (prices till end 93). Special breaks available

---

WASDALE HEAD CUMBRIA   **MAP 4**

Wasdale Head Inn

WASDALE HEAD, NR GOSFORTH, CUMBRIA CA20 1EX
TEL: WASDALE (09467) 26229   FAX: (09467) 26334

A remote and long-established inn ideal for serious fell walkers.

The three-storey inn has been a refuge from treacherous terrain since the Norman Conquest but wasn't granted a licence until 1856, after which time it developed into a centre for rock climbers and mountaineers. The ground floor retains much of the atmosphere of a nineteenth-century inn – particularly in the snug residents' bar, with its heavy dark oak panelling, crooked tables and benches and open fire. A variety of real ales is served through a small hatch, for the main bar, often crowded with walkers, is on the other side. The long, low-ceilinged dining-room is in a similar style with solid, dark wood furniture – a pleasant place in which to enjoy a hearty but not particularly imaginative five-course menu. Food is served in the bar, too, and there is a lounge with comfy sofas where you can go to relax. Upstairs, the atmosphere is much more modern; bedrooms, updated with pine panelling, are reasonably large though not especially comfortable.

◑ *Closed mid-Nov to 28 Dec and mid-Jan to mid-Feb*

⤢ *Follow signs for Wasdale Head from Gosforth or Holmrook off the A595. Private car park*

🛏 *1 single, 3 twin, 1 double, 1 family room; all with bathroom/ WC, hair-dryer, trouser press, baby-listening*

◈ *Restaurant, bar, lounge, drying*

room; fishing, riding nearby

⊖ *No wheelchair access; no children under 8 in restaurant eves; no dogs in public rooms*

▭ *Access, Visa*

£ *Single £25, single occupancy of twin/double £30, twin/double £50, family room rate on request; deposit required. Alc D £16; bar lunches*

WATERHOUSES STAFFORDSHIRE　　　　　　MAP 5

Old Beams

LEEK ROAD, WATERHOUSES, STAFFORDSHIRE ST10 3HW
TEL: LEEK (0538) 308254　FAX: (0538) 308157

Stylish bedrooms and highly recommended food in an immaculately kept restaurant-with-rooms.

Once inside Old Beams you can forget the traffic thundering by and enjoy the surroundings and a fine meal. The conservatory, with coral-coloured chairs, a grand piano and a mural of a masked ball in progress, makes a lovely room for a party and serves as overspill for the more formal restaurant, which has low ceilings and beams, white tablecloths and spindle-back chairs. In keeping with the age of this part of the house, a 250-year-old former inn, Ann Wallis has had heavy hessian curtains embroidered with wool. Nigel Wallis is the head chef and produces fine meals which might include a warm salad of grilled goats' cheese, roast fillet of lamb with baby vegetables and luxury dishes such as lobster, wood pigeon and foie gras.

　Five of the six rooms are in an annexe across the road, furnished to a very high standard and quieter than you would expect, thanks to double-glazing. Each stylish room is named after a local pottery. In Wedgwood, cornflower blue, of course, even the alarm clock is colour co-ordinated. Our favourites are Royal Doulton and Stafford.

◑ *Open all year, exc 2 to 3 weeks in Jan; restaurant closed Sun and Mon eves*

⤢ *From Ashbourne take the A52 and continue on this road to Leek. On passing through*

Waterhouses the hotel is on the right (A523). Private car park

I twin, 4 double, I four-poster; all with bathroom/WC, TV, room service, hair-dryer, baby listening; no tea/coffee-making facilities in rooms

Restaurant, bar, lounge, conservatory; limited meetings facilities; fishing in grounds, other sports nearby. Wheelchair access to hotel (ramp),

restaurant and WC (unisex), 3 ground-floor bedrooms, I specially equipped for disabled people

No dogs; no smoking in restaurant and discouraged in bedrooms

Access, Amex, Diners, Visa

Single occupancy of twin/double £55, double £72 to £95, four-poster £95; deposit required. Set L £17.50, D £18.50 to £32

WATERMILLOCK CUMBRIA   **MAP 4**

Old Church

WATERMILLOCK, ULLSWATER, PENRITH, CUMBRIA CA11 0JN
TEL: POOLEY BRIDGE (07684) 86204   FAX: (07684) 86368

A lakeside country-house hotel with some striking interior designs.

Old Church is run by Kevin and Maureen Whitemore, who are just as concerned with the aesthetics inside the hotel as the scenery outside – the hand of Maureen, who runs soft furnishing courses at the hotel, is much in evidence. The public areas contain a diversity of styles. The entrance hall has burgundy walls and a red patterned carpet with a couple of sofas beside a real fire; the small bar area with its leather buttonback sofas is light, with its blue floral wallpaper and pink carpet. It is the main lounge, however, that really catches the eye. Two pink bookcases stand in the corners under a pink ceiling; the walls and curtains are of a matching design in greens, pinks and pale blues, and two large lamps stand by the pink and lime-coloured sofas.

After all this the dining-room can seem almost bare in comparison. The five-course dinner may include smoked salmon salad with paw-paw and lime dressing, broccoli soup, roast leg of Lakeland lamb followed by sticky toffee pudding and cheeses. The bedrooms are suitably stylish and well-co-ordinated. Green Woodpecker and Heron are large doubles with dark wood furnishings and bright décor.

Closed Nov to Mar

3 miles south of Pooley Bridge just off the A592, 15 minutes from Junction 40 of the M6. Private car park

3 twin, 7 double; all with bathroom/WC, TV, room service, hair-dryer, baby-listening; tea/coffee-making facilities on request

Dining-room, bar, lounge; conference facilities (max 12 people non-residential, 10 residential); fishing, water sports, sailing, rowing boat at hotel, other sports nearby

No wheelchair access; no children in restaurant eves; no dogs; no smoking in dining-room

Access, Visa

Single occupancy of twin/double
£45 to £75, twin/double £90 to   £150. Set D £23.50

Rampsbeck

WATERMILLOCK, ULLSWATER, PENRITH, CUMBRIA CA11 0LP
TEL: POOLEY BRIDGE (07684) 86442/86688   FAX: (07684) 86442

A traditional country-house hotel in spacious lakeside grounds.

The immaculate grey and white building stands in 18 acres of parkland and gardens on the north-west shore of Ullswater. The small croquet lawn at the front of the hotel hints at the way that Tom and Marion Gibb and Marion's mother Mrs McDowell have sought to maintain an air of tradition at Rampsbeck. This is backed up by a high level of service from proprietors and staff alike.

The elegant main lounge area has a high ceiling, and french windows leading into the garden. There is an ornate white fireplace and a mixture of furniture styles, from soft sofas to a burgundy chaise-longue. The entrance hall boasts another attractive fireplace, this time in stone with a carved wooden mantelpiece, and there is a good-sized bar area with church pew-style seating.

The table d'hôte menu that may include salmon marinated with fresh herbs and served with sweet mustard sauce or mussel chowder; dessert may be poached peach coated with white wine, served with a tuile basket of maple syrup and walnut ice-cream, farmhouse cheeses follow.

Silver Crag, a large double bedroom with a small balcony and lake views, has a half-tester bed with white covers and a small pale-green three-piece suite and a large bathroom.

◑ Open all year, exc 4 Jan to early Feb

↗ Leave the M6 at Junction 40 and follow signs for the A592 and Ullswater. Turn left at the T-junction at the lake's edge. The hotel is on the left after 1¼ miles. Private car park

🛏 2 single, 3 twin, 13 double, 1 four-poster, 1 suite; all with bathroom/WC, exc 2 rooms with shower/WC; TV, limited room service, hair-dryer in all rooms; tea/coffee-making facilities on request

◈ Restaurant, bar, 2 lounges, drying room; conference facilities

(max 25 people residential and non-residential); fishing, water sports at hotel, other sports nearby

⊖ No wheelchair access; no children under 5; no dogs in public rooms and by arrangement only in bedrooms; no smoking in restaurant and some bedrooms

▭ Access, Visa

£ Single £50, single occupancy of twin/double £65, twin/double £75, four-poster £110, suite £140; deposit required. Set L £20/£25, D £24 to £32.50. Special breaks available

Hurstone Country Hotel

WATERROW, WIVELISCOMBE, TAUNTON, SOMERSET TA4 2AT
TEL: WIVELISCOMBE (0984) 23441

A small and homely Edwardian hotel with lovely views.

The unspectacular, creeper-clad 1920s façade is misleading; the building dates back in part to 1327. Inside what owner John Bone calls 'a hotel in a house in the country' rather than a country-house hotel, it's a surprise to find the lounge all wooden beams and big fireplace, the walls and surfaces providing a home for his collection of old prints and photographs; there's a lovely one of an old man in a smoking cap on the landing.

The five recently redecorated bedrooms are comfortable and have very different, if not especially imaginative, colour schemes brightened up with lots of dried flower arrangements. There are more dried flowers, prints of animals and birds and a piano in the long, narrow dining-room. Menus feature a choice of Somerset fare such as deep-fried Hurstone cheese with redcurrant sauce and medallions of pork with cider and apple.

- ◗ Open all year
- ⤤ ¼ mile off the B3227 at Waterrow (the hotel is well signposted). Private car park
- 🛏 1 twin, 3 double, 1 suite; all with bathroom/WC; TV, room service, hair-dryer, mini-bar, baby-listening
- ◇ Restaurant, bar, 2 lounges; fishing nearby
- ⊜ No wheelchair access; no dogs in public rooms; no smoking in restaurant, 1 lounge and 2 bedrooms
- ▭ Access, Amex, Diners, Visa
- ⊞ Single occupancy of twin/double £30 to £35, twin/double £60 to £70, suite price on application; deposit required. Sun L £9.50; set D from £16.50. Special breaks available

Water Yeat

WATER YEAT, NR ULVERSTON, CUMBRIA LA12 8DJ
TEL: LOWICK BRIDGE (0229) 885306

A seventeenth-century farmhouse whose simplicity is enlivened by the eclectic tastes of the Labats.

The chances are that before you have had time to take your car key from the ignition either Jill or Pierre Labat will already be at your side with a big smile to welcome you to Water Yeat. From then until the moment you leave, this multilingual and widely travelled Anglo-French couple will make sure you are relaxed, comfortable and well-fed.

Their double act transforms dinner into a memorable occasion. While Jill is preparing, perhaps, the salad of locally smoked fish with orange and grapefruit in a sherry vinegar and walnut oil dressing or a main course such as pot-roast guinea-fowl with cucumber and rosé wine, Pierre is describing the evening's selections with such relish that the guest is left in a state of heightened anticipation. After a dessert of nutty chocolate fudge pie or apple, lemon and passion fruit pudding, coffee is taken in the lounge with big floral sofas.

The walls of the 1660s farmhouse are hung with Peruvian tapestries and the mantelpiece above the stone fireplace is adorned with a fungus from Alaska. The bedrooms are simply furnished with bright patterned duvets and matching curtains.

◑ Closed mid-Dec to mid-Feb; dining-room closed Sun eve

↗ On the A5084, 7 miles south of Coniston, 7 miles north of Ulverston, on the western side of Coniston Water. Private car park

🛏 2 single, 2 twin, 2 double, 1 family room; 1 with bathroom/WC, 2 with shower/WC, 2 public bathrooms

◈ Dining-room, lounge, drying room; fishing, tennis, other sports nearby

⊖ No wheelchair access; no children under 4; no dogs; no smoking in bedrooms

▭ None accepted

£ Single £18 to £20, single occupancy of twin/double £22 to £37, twin/double £35 to £53, family room £56 to £60; deposit required. Set D £15.50. Special breaks available

---

WATH NORTH YORKSHIRE   **MAP 3**

Sportsman's Arms

WATH-IN-NIDDERDALE, PATELEY BRIDGE, HARROGATE, NORTH YORKSHIRE HG3 5PP
TEL: HARROGATE (0423) 711306

Accomplished but unstuffy restaurant-with-rooms in a scenic area.

This low-slung, mellow stone seventeenth-century coaching-inn is an ideal base for exploring the local countryside. The restaurant and accommodation side are the focus of Ray Carter's business, although there's still a cheery bar complete with a blazing fire, a blackboard menu of bar food and a large photo of Basil Fawlty. The general air is relaxed and unpretentious. The main residents' lounge is large, having a real fire, beams studded with pewter tankards, traditional sofas and a collection of (empty) champagne bottles.

The restaurant is light and airy, with high-backed chairs, crystal candleholders, lots of plants and framed modern art posters. The menu relies heavily on local produce, and the cooking is assured; you might dine on warm chicken livers with apple chutney, fillet of Whitby haddock in a cheese and mushroom sauce, and a good selection of local cheeses. One correspondent, while endorsing our previous reports on the warmth of the welcome and the friendliness of the staff, commented that, 'Guests should be aware that there is no choice for Sunday dinner, although the quality of cooking is still high.'

Bedrooms are generously proportioned and pleasantly furnished, with attractive lamps and Impressionist prints.

◐ Open all year, exc 25 Dec

↗ From the A59 Harrogate to Skipton road take the B6165 to Pateley Bridge. At Pateley Bridge follow signs for Ramsgill but turn off at Wath after 1½ miles. Private car park

🛏 2 twin, 5 double; 2 rooms with shower/WC, 2 public bathrooms; TV, room service in all rooms

◈ Restaurant, bar, 2 lounges; fishing at hotel, tennis, riding nearby. Wheelchair access to restaurant only

⊖ No dogs or smoking in bedrooms

▭ Access, Visa

£ Single occupancy of twin/double £22 to £30, twin/double £35 to £50. Set L £13, D £19; alc L £8 to £15, D £12 to £22

WEEDON NORTHAMPTONSHIRE　　　　　　　　　　　**MAP 9**

Crossroads

HIGH STREET, WEEDON, NORTHAMPTONSHIRE NN7 4PX
TEL: DAVENTRY (0327) 40354　FAX: (0327) 40849

Well-equipped rooms in a motel-style chain hotel.

More a hotel to break a journey at than a luxury retreat, the Crossroads at Weedon is a few minutes' drive from the M1. Weekend prices are inexpensive and bedrooms are well-equipped and comfortable. A modern motel-style red-brick building, the hotel has a children's playground at the front and a separate bedroom block overlooking fields. The décor offers few surprises: bedrooms are large with pink-stained wooden furniture co-ordinating with blue and pink light modern fabrics. Bathrooms too are a good size. Some rooms were still to be refurbished to this standard when we visited. There is a choice of places to eat, including a pub-style restaurant with help-yourself hot plates and dishes that are less exciting than they sound. Uniformed staff are informal and friendly.

◐ Open all year

↗ 4 miles south-east of Daventry, at the junction of the A5 and A45, 3 miles from Junction 16 of the M1. Private car park

🛏 10 single, 15 twin, 16 double, 3 four-poster, 4 family rooms; all

with bathroom/WC, TV, room service, hair-dryer, trouser press, baby-listening

◈ 2 restaurants, bar, lounge, coffee parlour, drying room; conference facilities (max 70 people residential); tennis, at hotel, golf,

fishing, other sports nearby.
Wheelchair access to hotel,
restaurant and 12 ground-floor
bedrooms, 2 specially equipped
for disabled people

⊖ No dogs in public rooms and by
arrangement only in bedrooms

▭ Access, Amex, Diners, Visa

£ Single £30 to £47, twin/double
£38 to £52, four-poster £52,
family room from £57. Set L
from £7, D £15 to £17. Special
breaks available

WELLAND HEREFORD AND WORCESTER   **MAP 9**

Holdfast Cottage

WELLAND, NR MALVERN, HEREFORD AND WORCESTER WR13 6NA
TEL: HANLEY SWAN (0684) 310288

Enthusiastic new owners at this pretty little hotel.

Stephen and Jane Knowles took over Holdfast Cottage in the spring of
1993, shortly before our inspection. It is too soon for us to be sure of their
success, but if their enthusiasm for their task is anything to go by they will
do well and we are giving them a full entry with some confidence.
Holdfast Cottage is well-placed for lovers of the Malvern Hills. It is a
low, white building, wistaria-clad, and with a canopied terrace running
along the front, making it look a little like a railway station. The sitting-
room, where severe fiddle-back chairs contrast with battered leather
clubland sofas, is a room purpose-built for Bertie Wooster to entertain
his aunts in. There is a small bar in crushed red velvet and a plain,
spacious dining-room. Bedrooms are light, bright, floral and comfortable. Managing somehow to cope with her small children at the same
time, Jane produces home-cooked dinners with three or four choices at
each course: onion, tomato and red wine soup and Italian baked fish
perhaps.

◑ Open all year

➡ On the A4104 halfway between
Little Malvern and Welland.
Private car park

🛏 1 single, 2 twin, 5 double; all
with bathroom/WC, exc single
with shower/WC; TV, room
service, hair-dryer in all rooms

◈ Dining-room, bar, lounge,
conservatory; conference
facilities (max 10 people

residential, 14 non-residential);
fishing, golf, other sports nearby

⊖ No wheelchair access; no dogs in
public rooms; smoking in bar and
lounge only

▭ Access, Visa

£ Single £35, single occupancy of
twin/double £44 to £48, twin/
double £66 to £72; deposit
required. Set D £15. Special
breaks available

---

*We mention those hotels that don't accept dogs; guide dogs, however, are
almost always an exception. Telephone ahead to make sure.*

WELLS SOMERSET   **MAP 9**

Swan Hotel ☆

11 SADLER STREET, WELLS, SOMERSET BA5 2RX
TEL: WELLS (0749) 678877   FAX: (0749) 677647

A rambling city-centre hotel overlooking Wells Cathedral.

The Swan boasts an uninterrupted view of the spectacular, newly restored thirteenth-century west front of Wells Cathedral. Its pebble-dashed exterior cannot claim to be the most attractive hotel frontage in town. However, the olde-worlde interior which befits its fifteenth-century origins is more inviting, with wood panelling in the lounge and dining-room, old-fashioned fire buckets in the hall, and corridors so rambling they might have defeated Theseus. Hidden amongst more run-of-the-mill rooms is a real gem: Room 40 boasts a four-poster bed looking straight on to the cathedral. The five brand-new doubles cosily converted out of an adjacent cottage, contrast with the darker, panelled rooms of the old building.

Service is brisk and efficient. Dinner menus change nightly and, although not imaginative, regularly remember vegetarians. Diners eat surrounded by the hotel owner's collection of costumes worn by Henry Irving.

◑ Open all year

⤴ In the centre of town, opposite the cathedral. On the right-hand side of the one-way system. Private car park

🛏 9 single, 10 twin, 10 double, 9 four-poster, family rooms available; all with bathroom/WC, exc 5 single with shower/WC; TV, room service, baby-listening in all rooms; trouser press in singles; hair-dryer on request

◈ Restaurant, bar, lounge, drying room, study; conference facilities (max 30 people residential, 60 non-residential); squash at hotel, fishing, golf, other sports nearby; babysitting. Wheelchair access to hotel (1 ramp), restaurant and 2 ground-floor bedrooms

⊖ No dogs in restaurant

▭ Access, Amex, Diners, Visa

£ Single £63, single occupancy of twin/double £67, twin/double £84, four-poster £91, family room £95; deposit required. Set L £11.50, D £15.50. Special breaks available

WELWYN GARDEN CITY HERTFORDSHIRE   **MAP 9**

Tewin Bury Farmhouse

TEWIN, NR WELWYN GARDEN CITY, HERTFORDSHIRE AL6 0JB
TEL: TEWIN (0438) 717793   FAX: (0438) 840440

A relaxed farmyard setting for a popular lunchtime restaurant.

When you arrive at the end of the drive up to Tewin Bury farmhouse, it becomes apparent that the Williamses have lots to keep them busy on their 400-acre arable farm. The old farmyard is surrounded on three sides by the Tewin Bury Pie Restaurant, the farm shop, the red-brick farmhouse where Vaughan and Angela Williams started their bed-and-breakfast business and the barns that were converted into bedrooms in 1989.

The 13 bedrooms in the barns are attractively done out with pine furniture, light floral fabrics, Lloyd Loom chairs and exposed beams and stonework. Some overlook the old barns that are now used for summer barbecues and weddings.

The black-beamed, white-walled restaurant is a bustling lunchtime spot popular with the locals. Cheese and prawn salads, sandwiches in home-made bread and baked potatoes typify the lunchtime menu; in the evenings, rack of lamb with rosemary and garlic, steak and mushroom pie and salmon en croûte all feature, followed by home-made sweets from the trolley.

◑ *Open all year, exc 25 Dec to 1 Jan*

⤴ *Leave the A1 at Junction 6 and follow signs for the B1000. After 2½ miles take the left turning to Tewin. The farmhouse is opposite Panshanger golf course. Private car park*

🛏 *3 four-poster, 6 family rooms; all with bathroom/WC, TV, room service, hair-dryer, trouser press, baby-listening*

◈ *Restaurant, bar, lounge;*

conference facilities (max 12 people residential); fishing at hotel, other sports nearby; babysitting. Wheelchair access to hotel, restaurant and 3 ground-floor bedrooms

⊖ *No dogs in public rooms*

▭ *Access, Amex, Visa*

£ *Single occupancy £40 to £59, four-poster/family room £55 to £65; deposit required. Alc L £7.50; set D £13.50, £15*

WEM SHROPSHIRE   **MAP 5**

Soulton Hall ☆

WEM, SHROPSHIRE SY4 5RS
TEL: WEM (0939) 232786 (and fax)

An Elizabethan country house unaffected by 1980s' fashion.

This distinctly spooky-looking red-brick mansion hidden among the fields of rural Shropshire may not be everyone's cup of tea. It has avoided being refurbished by some large hotel group and filled with imported antiques. Consequently, the furnishing of the public rooms is plain, as is the dinner menu (though there is a good choice and a well-balanced, good-value wine list). If you can live with this, you will be compensated by the spacious bedrooms, the friendly family atmosphere and the interest of staying in an ancient house. The panelled double bedroom is the most attractive, but the others are well-appointed and have more than adequate bathrooms. There is a rough but pleasing garden for sunny days and a working farm next door. All in all, an inexpensive country hideaway.

◐ Open all year

⤢ Wem is on the B5476, 5 miles south of Whitchurch. Soulton Hall is 2 miles down the B5065, just over a hump-backed bridge. Private car park

🛏 2 single, 2 twin, 2 double, family room available; all with bathroom/WC; TV, room service, hair-dryer

◇ Dining-room, bar, lounge, drying room; conference facilities (max 20 people non-residential, 6 residential); fishing, riding at hotel, golf, swimming-pool

nearby; babysitting by arrangement

⊖ No wheelchair access; no children in dining-room eves; no dogs in public rooms and discouraged in bedrooms; smoking in bar only

▭ Visa

£ Single £22 to £33, single occupancy of twin/double £28 to £33, twin/double £43 to £54, family room rate on request; deposit required. Set D £15. Special breaks available

---

WEST BEXINGTON DORSET — MAP 9

The Manor

BEACH ROAD, WEST BEXINGTON, NR DORCHESTER, DORSET DT2 9DF
TEL: BURTON BRADSTOCK (0308) 897616   FAX: (0308) 897035

Relaxed family hotel with sea views, large garden and cosy bar.

The manor house, built of light stone and with a large conservatory, overlooks Chesil Beach. The hallway is rather dark, with carved wood panelling and a stone floor, so guests are best advised to follow the pleasing hubbub that rises up from the cellar bar, where an aromatic wood fire burns in the hearth. At lunchtime diners choose selections from the blackboard menu. Meals are also served in the dining-room. Here the menu is weighted towards fish – with steak, venison or duck as alternatives. On the ground floor are the two residents' lounges, with well-worn, comfortable easy chairs clustered around a brick fireplace. The walls are decorated with pictures of racehorses.

Some of the cottagey bedrooms, brightly decorated in blues, apricots and yellows, are on the small side, though you may have a fine sea view. There are many good things here, so it's a shame to report that for the second year running we have had otherwise favourable readers' reports which mention a lack of friendliness from the staff.

◐ Open all year

⤢ 5 miles south-east of Bridport on the B3157. Private car park

🛏 1 single, 3 twin, 8 double, 1 family room; all with bathroom/WC, exc 4 doubles with shower/

WC; TV, room service, hair-dryer, trouser-press, baby-listening in all rooms

◇ Restaurant, bar, 2 lounges, conservatory; conference

facilities (max 60 people non-residential); golf, riding nearby

 Single £43 to £46, single occupancy of twin/double £43 to £46, twin/double/family room £72 to £76; deposit required. Set L £14.50, D £19. Special breaks available

⊖ No wheelchair access; no dogs in public rooms

▭ Access, Amex, Diners, Visa

WESTDEAN EAST SUSSEX   **MAP 8**

Old Parsonage

WESTDEAN, ALFRISTON, NR SEAFORD, EAST SUSSEX BN25 4AL
TEL: ALFRISTON (0323) 870432

An exceptional medieval house with modern comforts.

Set in the quiet hamlet of Westdean and surrounded by Friston Forest, the Old Parsonage is reputed to be the oldest small medieval house in the country, having been built by the monks from Wilmington Priory in 1280. It is the abode of Raymond and Angela Woodhams, who are clearly proud of its beautifully decorated and preserved medieval interior.

The Woodhams derive pleasure, too, from providing a personal service for their guests – one visitor describes how on going out for a walk every morning he would find handwritten notes on the mat suggesting, with careful directions, a new walk that he might care to try. The Hall, reached by a stone spiral staircase, is the most expensive bedroom and has a handsome four-poster bed, a fine high timbered ceiling and striking views over the churchyard to the Norman belltower. The Solar and Hidden rooms are equally comfortable. Breakfasts only are served and one reader remarked, 'These were so splendid that I was sad not to be able to try lunch or dinner there as well.'

◖ Closed Xmas and New Year

⤤ Off the A259 Brighton to Hastings coast road, east of Seaford. Private car park

🛏 1 twin, 1 double, 1 four-poster; all with bathroom/WC, hair-dryer

◈ Lounge, library/study; fishing, golf, other sports nearby

⊖ No wheelchair access; no children under 12; no dogs; no smoking in bedrooms

▭ None accepted

 Single occupancy of twin/double £30 to £40, twin/double £45 to £55, four-poster £60

WEST DOWN DEVON   **MAP 10**

Long House

THE SQUARE, WEST DOWN, NR ILFRACOMBE, DEVON EX34 8NF
TEL: ILFRACOMBE (0271) 863242

A welcoming tea-shop with rooms in the centre of a small village.

You can hardly miss the Long House, which stands at the convergence of all roads to West Down, opposite the Crown pub. A black and white half-timbered building with a small garden, it used to accommodate the village smithy and then the post office-cum-shop; the cottagey tea-shop, which doubles as the hotel dining-room, retains hooks in the ceiling once used for hanging up produce. With only four bedrooms the Long House is bound to feel intimate. However, the rooms, including the downstairs lounge with big log fire, are surprisingly large; even the plant-filled bathrooms are big enough to swing a horse in. Furnishings are an attractive mix of old and new. One reader complained of being cold, and in March the bedrooms (although not the bathrooms) were certainly cool.

On inspection the no-choice dinner of stuffed mushrooms, roast duck on a bed of rice and apple charlotte was very enjoyable. Classical music accompanies mealtimes, prompting one guest to write that it was 'like the "Last Night of the Proms"' in a visitors' book. Pauline and Rob Hart are enormously welcoming; many returnees are spoken of warmly as friends.

◑ Closed early Nov to early Mar

⤴ Situated ½ mile off the A361 Barnstaple to Ilfracombe road, 4 miles from Woolacombe Bay. On-street parking

🛏 1 twin, 3 double; all with bathroom/WC, exc 1 double with shower/WC; TV, room service, baby-listening in all rooms; hair-dryer on request

◈ Dining-room, bar/lounge, lounge, drying room; fishing, golf, other sports nearby

⊖ No wheelchair access; no dogs; no smoking in dining-room and discouraged elsewhere

▭ Access, Visa

£ Single occupancy of twin/double £29, twin/double £50; deposit required. Set D £13.50; alc L £6.50. Special breaks available

---

WEST MERSEA ESSEX   **MAP 8**

Blackwater Hotel

20–22 CHURCH ROAD, WEST MERSEA, COLCHESTER, ESSEX CO5 8QH
TEL: COLCHESTER (0206) 383338/383038

A popular hotel which adheres to the French formula of good food and simple rooms.

The Champenois Restaurant, the culinary side of Eddie and Monique Chapleos' business, has put this quiet island backwater on the map. It is the sort of place that Francophiles will instantly recognise – a family-run small hotel with simple rooms and an emphasis on food. The dishes served in the dining-room are strongly influenced by their Gallic origins – French onion soup, moules marinière or half-a-dozen snails to start with; skate wing au beurre noir, chicken supreme provençale or sirloin steak au poivre among the main courses. Champagne, of course, features large among the wines provided. Breakfast blends in more with English than French traditions – full cooked meals and fresh croissants appear too.

Rooms are on the compact side, with candlewick bedspreads, separate bathrooms and thinnish walls.

◑ *Closed 1st 3 weeks Jan; restaurant closed Sun eve*

⤢ *West Mersea is at the west end of Mersea Island. Drive through the village until you reach the church on your left and the White Hart pub on your right; turn right into Church Road. Private car park*

⇌ *3 twin, 4 double; most rooms with bathroom/WC, 1 with shower/WC, 2 public bathrooms; TV in all rooms; hair-dryer on request*

✧ *2 restaurants, bar, lounge; golf, riding, other sports nearby*

⊖ *No wheelchair access; dogs in bedrooms only by arrangement*

▭ *Access, Amex, Visa*

£ *Single £31 to £40, single occupancy of twin/double £31 to £40, twin/double £40 to £68; deposit required. Sun L £13 to £15; alc L, D £21. Special breaks available*

WESTON-UNDER-REDCASTLE SHROPSHIRE　　MAP 5

Citadel

WESTON-UNDER-REDCASTLE, NR SHREWSBURY, SHROPSHIRE SY4 5JY
TEL: HODNET (063 084) 204; changing to (0630) 685204 in 1994

A rather fine mock castle on a Shropshire hilltop.

This strange place was built as a dower house in the 1820s and might come straight from a Gothic romance of the time. Huge red sandstone towers pierced by arched windows and decorative arrow slits are linked by pretend curtain walls with suitable battlements. The building is fronted by a kind of esplanade where guests park their cars. Inside, the mock-medieval atmosphere continues, helped by tapestries, a roaring fire and the coffered ceiling in the dining-room. It is also comfortable – elegant, too, with plenty of fresh flowers, a grand piano and a full-sized billiard table. The most interesting bedroom is the tower room; furnishings are a little old-fashioned, but suit the castle well. Guests eat together round the long dining-room table. Bring your own wine.

◑ *Closed Nov to Mar, exc for parties of 4 to 6 people staying 2 nights min; restaurant closed Sun eve*

⤢ *On the A49, 12 miles north of Shrewsbury, 8 miles south of Whitchurch; follow signs to Weston/Hawkstone Park. The hotel is ¼ mile out of the village of Weston, on Hodnet road. Private car park*

⇌ *2 twin, 1 double; 2 private bathrooms; TV, room service, hair-dryer in all rooms; tea/coffee-making facilities on request*

✧ *Dining-room, lounge, drying room, games room; conference facilities (max 12 people non-residential, 6 residential); fishing, riding at hotel, golf nearby*

● No wheelchair access; no children in dining-room eves; no dogs; no smoking in bedrooms

▭ None accepted

£▭ Single occupancy of twin/double £35 to £40, twin/double £50 to £60; deposit required. Set D £16.50 (7.30pm). Special breaks available

WEST WITTON NORTH YORKSHIRE   **MAP 3**

Wensleydale Heifer

WEST WITTON, WENSLEYDALE, NORTH YORKSHIRE DL8 4LS
TEL: WENSLEYDALE (0969) 22322   FAX: (0969) 24183

An attractive roadside inn with comfortable rooms.

Step inside the Wensleydale Heifer and your eye alights on beams, wall-mounted plates, a warming pan and a grandfather clock – the seventeenth-century inn is as it should be. The dark wood bar is likely to be busy, with locals and visitors perched on lovely old bench-style seating, but there are nooks and crannies where you can plonk yourself away for a quieter time, as well as a lounge with chintzy armchairs in which to sup your pint of Old Peculier.

There are more beams and rough walls in the large restaurant, where the four-course set menu finds room for both traditional and fancier fare, such as goats' cheese in filo pastry served on hot salad leaves with walnut vinaigrette, followed by a fish dish or an intriguing-sounding venison with bubble and squeak. Alternatively there's a sweet little bistro enlivened by a fishmonger's advert and photos of pre-war Yorkshire cricket teams. Standard bistro-fare – garlic mushrooms, pasta and hot orange liqueur pancakes – is on offer.

Bedrooms are comfortably furnished in a variety of styles, from smart four-posters with modish autumnal décor and reproduction mahogany furniture to humbler rooms kitted out in a more homely way.

◑ Open all year

↗ West of the village of West Witton, on the A684 Leyburn to Hawes road. Private car park

🛏 3 twin, 2 double, 3 four-poster, 1 family room, 1 suite, 9 annexe rooms; most with bathroom/WC, some with shower/WC; TV, room service, hair-dryer, baby-listening in all rooms

◇ Restaurant, bistro, bar, lounge, drying room; conference facilities

(max 12 people residential and non-residential); fishing, golf, riding nearby

● No wheelchair access

▭ Access, Amex, Diners, Visa

£▭ Single occupancy of twin/double £45, twin/double £70, four-poster/family room £75, suite £85; deposit required. Set L £11.50, D £22.50. Special breaks available

 This denotes that you can get a twin or double room for £50 or less per night inclusive of breakfast.

WHAPLODE LINCOLNSHIRE   **MAP 5**

Guy Wells

EASTGATE, WHAPLODE, SPALDING, LINCOLNSHIRE PE12 6TZ
TEL: HOLBEACH (0406) 22239

*A Queen Anne farmhouse near the sea with inexpensive,
comfortable rooms and exceptionally hospitable hosts.*

Anne and Richard Thompson's smart Queen Anne farmhouse is surrounded by mature trees and a wild garden. They run an arable farm with acres of flowers such as daffodils, lilies and tulips, and Richard will happily show you around; in fact both he and Anne are expert hosts, offering you tea on arrival and striking just the right balance between chatting and leaving you to your privacy. The three bedrooms, with their plain walls and cottagey fabrics, have old-fashioned furnishings, views over the garden and loads of space. The biggest, a double, has been newly decorated in candyfloss pink and, with its corner position and large casement windows, is a light, pretty room.

A wood-burning stove, comfortable sofas and a large amount of books and magazines make the sitting-room a hospitable place to relax before dinner, which Anne cooks every evening on request except Wednesdays. A typical meal in summer might include apple, melon and orange in mint and olive oil dressing, gammon casserole with sweet and sour sauce, and queen's pudding or ice-cream. Bring your own wine.

◗ *Open all year, exc Xmas*

🄑 *2 miles west of Holbeach on the A151, the farm is the first house on the left down Eastgate. Private car park*

🛏 *1 twin, 1 double, 1 half-tester; double with shower/WC, 1 public bathroom; TV on request*

◈ *Dining-room, lounge; fishing, golf, other sports nearby*

⊖ *No wheelchair access; no children under 12; no dogs; no smoking*

▭ *None accepted*

£ *Single occupancy of twin/double £25 to £29, twin/double £34 to £37, half-tester £34; deposit required. Set D £11.50 (by arrangement only). Special breaks available*

WHEDDON CROSS SOMERSET   **MAP 10**

Raleigh Manor

Small, family-run country-house hotel with wonderful views.

Raleigh Manor is an isolated, tile-hung Victorian house overlooking the Brendon Hills. Inside, it has the elegant lines of a Georgian house, with a

WHEDDON CROSS, NR DUNSTER, SOMERSET TA24 7BB
TEL: TIMBERSCOMBE (0643) 841484

curving staircase sweeping up to a landing which boasts graceful arches and wooden balustrades. Chris and Jenny Piper took over in June 1992 and already they have refurbished the dining-room, giving it honeysuckle-coloured walls and lovely swagged curtains. Here Chris discreetly serves Jenny's cooking; the sticky toffee pudding with hot butterscotch sauce was going down a treat when we inspected. Their next project is to inject more character into the perfectly comfortable back lounge. Rather perversely, the brown and cream front library, which looks like a smoking room, is actually for non-smokers. A pleasant conservatory has wicker chairs.

Most of the upstairs bedrooms are fairly small with uninspiring fittings, although several boast attractive fireplaces. Best is the Squire's Bedroom, with huge half-tester bed and walnut furnishings.

◑ *Closed Xmas to mid-Mar*

🔁 *Turn left 200 yards north of Wheddon Cross down a private road. Raleigh Manor is 800 yards past Watercombe farm, across the fields. Private car park*

🛏 *1 single, 2 twin, 3 double, 1 four-poster; all with bathroom/WC, exc 1 twin with shower/WC; TV in all rooms; hair-dryer, baby-listening on request*

◈ *Dining-room, lounge, library,*

conservatory; fishing, riding, water sports nearby

⊖ *No wheelchair access; no dogs in public rooms; no smoking in library and dining-room*

▭ *Access, Visa*

£ *Single £29, single occupancy of twin/double £29, twin/double £58, four-poster £72; deposit required. Set D £17; alc L from £3.50, D to £22*

WHIMPLE DEVON   **MAP 10**

Woodhayes

WHIMPLE, NR EXETER, DEVON EX5 2TD
TEL: WHIMPLE (0404) 822237

Elegant Georgian hotel which offers a particularly warm welcome.

A curving drive sweeps round to Woodhayes, a trip-wire activating a bell so Katherine Rendle will know you're coming and be ready to greet you. Woodhayes is an immaculately maintained Georgian ex-vicarage where plants have colonised every corner and the scent of peachy pot-pourri fills the hall. One reader commented that the 'quality and quantity of culinary delights' served in the graceful dining-room amazed him, which is perhaps less surprising when you learn that both Katherine and husband Frank are trained chefs. A typical evening might produce avocado, apple and smoked salmon salad, to be followed by pan-fried fillet of beef on a purée of potatoes with a mustard sauce, and home-made ice-cream.

Peaches, pinks and lemons are the preferred colours for hall, lounges and bedrooms, and everywhere feels spacious and airy. The most unexpected room is the snug rear bar in what was the original kitchen, where drinks are served across an old shop-counter.

◐ Open all year

⏏ 8 miles east of Exeter off the A30 Exeter to Honiton road. Take the turning for Whimple and the hotel is just before the village. Private car park

🛏 2 twin, 4 double; all with bathroom/WC, TV, room service, hair-dryer; no tea/coffee-making facilities in rooms

◈ Restaurant, bar, 2 lounges; tennis, croquet at hotel

⊖ No wheelchair access; no children under 12; no dogs

▭ Access, Amex, Diners, Visa

£ Single occupancy of twin/double £70, twin/double £90. Set L £15 (by arrangement), D £25. Special breaks available

---

WHITEWELL LANCASHIRE

MAP 5

Inn at Whitewell

WHITEWELL, FOREST OF BOWLAND, NR CLITHEROE, LANCASHIRE BB7 3AT
TEL: DUNSOP BRIDGE (0200) 448222

Relaxed, riverside fishing inn that mixes wit and classic style.

The Inn at Whitewell is a surprising place, for there are not many country inns that have their own *en-suite* art gallery, wine merchant and high-class gents' outfitters, plus eight miles of private trout and salmon fishing. The end of 1993 should see the completion of bedroom refurbishment and the installation of a new kitchen and reception area. Meanwhile, there is a slight blight over the current state of the dining-room that looks out over the Hodder. One trusts, however, that the corridor along to the art gallery will remain untouched; the quirky collection of old sporting paraphernalia (including a stuffed fox playing cricket) is one of the best surprises.

The snug and bar, with open fires, comfortable settles and the occasional comatose terrier, has long been known for high-quality real ale and excellent bar food. This includes Cumberland sausage, gravad lax, steak and kidney pie, cheeses and the Inn's own blend of coffee. Dinners might include regional specialities such as black pudding and best end of Bowland lamb.

The bedrooms reflect the individuality of owner Richard Bowman. Each of the remodelled rooms has been hung with paintings and prints from the gallery or family collection. Several rooms have peat-burning fires, some have wonderful antique Victorian baths. There are comfortable armchairs and sofas, old-fashioned telephones and high-tech cassette and CD decks.

◐ Open all year

⏏ Whitewell is 6 miles north-west of Clitheroe. Private car park

🛏 7 twin/double, 1 four-poster, 1 suite, family rooms available; all with bathroom/WC, TV (exc

1), room service, hair-dryer; trouser press, baby-listening on request; no tea/coffee-making facilities in rooms

 2 dining-rooms, bar, games room, drying room; conference facilities (max 150 people non-residential, 9 residential); fishing at hotel, other sports nearby; babysitting. Wheelchair access to restaurant and WC only

 None

Access, Amex, Diners, Visa

Single occupancy of twin/double £38 to £47, twin/double/four-poster £49 to £63, family room rate from £72, suite £90; deposit preferred. Alc L £7.50, D £16

WICKHAM HAMPSHIRE   **MAP 9**

Old House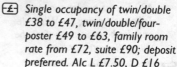

THE SQUARE, WICKHAM, HAMPSHIRE PO17 5JG
TEL: WICKHAM (0329) 833049   FAX: (0329) 833672

Elegant Georgian hotel with a strong French flavour and an excellent restaurant.

Dating from about 1715, the Old House shows its age in the best possible way: it is a typical town house of the period with three elegant storeys of white windows and red brick, clad in creepers and bright flowers. In the lounges you will find a huge fireplace, painted wood panelling and wooden floors and window seats, as well as bright, comfortable sofas and armchairs, prints and antique furniture.

The French origins of Annie Skipwith, who runs the hotel with husband Richard, are shown in the small bar, which has a typical provincial Gallic atmosphere, with red floor tiles and a heavy carved wooden counter. The neat, austere restaurant beyond used to be the outhouse and stables, and the Skipwiths have left the walls exposed to complement the high, sloping roof with low tie-beams beneath. The cooking is French. You might be offered a slice of lamb leg with fresh mint and a wine sauce after you have sampled a refreshing terrine of full-flavoured skate with asparagus on a bed of crème fraîche. Service is polite and helpful, though a little stiff.

Most of the bedrooms are large (although bathrooms can be small) and some have attractive fireplaces. One of the best is Room Six, a split-level double at the back, with pretty wallpaper, oak beams and a sloping ceiling.

Closed week Xmas and New Year, Easter weekend, 2 weeks Aug; restaurant closed Sun eve

3 miles north of Fareham in the village square, at the junction of the B2177 and A32. Private car park

3 single, 3 twin, 5 double, 1 family room (some rooms in annexe); all with bathroom/WC, TV, room service, hair-dryer, trouser press, baby-listening; tea/coffee-making facilities on request

◇ Restaurant, bar, 2 lounges; conference facilities (max 14 people residential); fishing, golf, other sports nearby. Wheelchair access to restaurant only

● No dogs

▭ Access, Amex, Diners, Visa

£ Single and single occupancy of twin/double from £65, twin/double from £75, family room from £85, annexe room from £80; deposit required. Alc L £19 (not available Sat to Mon), D £23. Special breaks available

WIDEGATES CORNWALL   **MAP 10**

Coombe Farm

WIDEGATES, NR LOOE, CORNWALL PL13 1QN
TEL: WIDEGATES (05034) 223

A small, family-run hotel in attractive countryside.

As Sally Low shows you round Coombe Farm you can hardly miss what she calls its 'talking points' – eye-catching bits and bobs decorating walls and mantelpieces and massing in the stairwell. The house itself, a double-eaved 1920s ivy-clad edifice, stands well back from the road in ten acres of grounds. It is a friendly place, where dogs rush to greet new arrivals. Both lounge and dining-room have spectacular views, and dinners offer four set courses which, unusually for Cornwall, rarely include fish. Most of the rooms are big enough to accommodate an extra single or bunk bed as well as the usual double or twin beds; one of the most popular is Number Seven. Across the car park from the house, three old cottages contain another three big, slate-floored family rooms which are particularly attractive; in Number Nine blue and white Spanish bathroom tiles evoke a Mediterranean feel.

◐ Closed Nov to end Feb

↗ On the B3253, 3½ miles east of Looe and 1 mile west of Hessenford. Private car park

⮞ 2 twin, 2 double, 3 family rooms, 3 in cottage annexe; all with shower/WC, TV, hair-dryer

◇ Dining-room, lounge, games room; outdoor heated swimming-pool (summer), croquet, snooker, table tennis at hotel, other sports nearby. Wheelchair access to hotel (1 step), restaurant and 5 ground-floor bedrooms

● No children under 5; no dogs; no smoking

▭ None accepted

£ Single occupancy of twin/double £17 to £23, twin/double £33 to £45, family room/annexe room rates on request; deposit required. Set D £10.50 (7pm); packed lunches. Special breaks available

---

All entries in the Guide *are rewritten every year, not least because standards fluctuate. Don't trust an out-of-date* Guide.

WILLESLEY WILTSHIRE　　　　　　　　　　　　　　**MAP 9**

Tavern House ☆

WILLESLEY, NR TETBURY, GLOUCESTERSHIRE GL8 8QU
TEL: TETBURY (0666) 880444

A smart bed and breakfast close to the home of Prince Charles.

Tim and Janet Tremellen's converted coaching-inn lies close to the gates of the renowned Westonbirt Arboretum. This is a smart, no-corners-cut bed and breakfast, with bedrooms done up with deep carpets and good furniture and fully modernised bathrooms. Janet even hand-wraps the soap. There is a small breakfast room and a larger residents' lounge formally arranged with old gold chairs and antimacassars. There is also a large and peaceful garden. Traffic noise may be a problem in some bedrooms.

◑ Open all year

▸ Leave the M4 at Junction 18 and follow the A46 Cirencester road for 3 miles. Then follow signs to Tetbury on the A433. Tavern House is 1 mile before Westonbirt Arboretum. Private car park

▭ 1 twin, 3 double; all with bathroom/WC, TV, hair-dryer, trouser press; room service by arrangement

◈ Dining-room, lounge, drying room; golf, tennis, riding nearby

⊖ No wheelchair access; no children under 10; no dogs; smoking in lounge only

▭ Access, Visa

£ Single occupancy of twin/double £35 to £55, twin/double £53 to £57; deposit required. Special breaks available

---

WILMCOTE WARWICKSHIRE　　　　　　　　　　　　　**MAP 9**

Pear Tree Cottage　　　　　

CHURCH ROAD, WILMCOTE, STRATFORD-UPON-AVON, WARWICKSHIRE CV37 9UX
TEL: STRATFORD-UPON-AVON (0789) 205889　FAX: (0789) 262862

A smartly furnished, good-value bed and breakfast.

Pear Tree Cottage is a half-timbered, Elizabethan listed building, with mullioned windows, and surrounded by a beautifully kept English country garden. Inside you'll find low ceilings, flagstone floors, polished oak furniture, and, in the racing-green hall and stairwell, framed pieces of lovely antique embroidery. All the bedrooms are a cut-above-average in style and comfort, with light colours, pretty floral-print duvets and well-equipped modern bathrooms; some have modern pine furniture, while others have solid brass bedsteads. Arden is perhaps the most atmospheric with its black beams, white iron bedstead and antique chairs. Ted and Margaret Mander provide breakfast, with plenty of fresh fruit, but no dinner. Two stone cottages next to the house are available on a self-catering basis.

◑ Open all year, exc Xmas to New Year	for guests' use; golf, riding, other sports nearby
⤧ 3½ miles north-west of Stratford off the A3400. Private car park	⊖ No wheelchair access; no children under 2; no dogs in public rooms
⇌ 2 twin, 4 double, 1 family room (also 2 self-catering cottages); some with bathroom/WC, most with shower/WC; TV, hair-dryer in all rooms	▭ None accepted
	£ Single occupancy of twin/double £28 to £32, twin/double £38 to £42, family room £38 to £45. Special breaks available
◈ Lounge, TV room, mini kitchens	

WIMBORNE MINSTER DORSET   MAP 9

Beechleas ☆

17 POOLE ROAD, WIMBORNE MINSTER, DORSET BH21 1QA
TEL: BOURNEMOUTH (0202) 841684

Smartly decorated bedrooms in a small town-house hotel.

Beechleas is a small Georgian house that has been thoroughly renovated by Josephine McQuillan and her builder husband. They have made effective use of the available space. Décor throughout is in light, airy shades of cream and apricot, from the neat little drawing-room to the fresh-looking and well-equipped bedrooms with their co-ordinated fabrics and either pine or cane furniture. First-floor rooms are the most spacious, while those on the second floor have a cosier, under-the-eaves atmosphere. Two identical coach-houses have contemporary mews-type rooms.

The large conservatory extension gives the space that the tiny original dining-room could never have provided. The latter, however, adds a dash of atmosphere with its marble fireplace and open fire in winter. Meals are freshly prepared: maybe home-made asparagus soup, suprême of chicken with ginger and whisky sauce and citrus cheesecake.

◑ Open all year, exc 24 Dec to last week Jan	facilities in rooms
⤧ Take the A31 and the B3073 to Wimborne Minster, then the A349 towards Poole. Beechleas is on the right-hand side. Private car park	◈ Restaurant, lounge, conservatory
	⊖ No wheelchair access; no dogs; smoking in lounge only
	▭ Access, Amex, Visa
⇌ 2 twin, 3 double, 4 cottages; all with bathroom/WC, TV, room service, hair-dryer, baby-listening; no tea/coffee-making	£ Single occupancy of twin/double £53 to £73, twin/double £63 to £83, cottage room £63 to £73. Continental B £5, cooked B £8.50; alc D £16.50

Wykeham Arms

75 KINGSGATE STREET, WINCHESTER, HAMPSHIRE SO23 9PE
TEL: WINCHESTER (0962) 853834   FAX: (0962) 854411

A well-run, welcoming inn with good bedrooms and food.

The Wykeham Arms carries a wealth of history. It was opened in 1755 as the Fleur-de-Lys (a name which was killed off by the Napoleonic Wars) and has since expanded to take the coach-house and a watchmaker's shop into its red-brick mishmash. As well as watchmaking paraphernalia and old-fashioned college desks, the various rooms of the pub are furnished with a wild assortment of military, sporting and drinking memorabilia. However, publican Graeme Jameson has not allowed musty nostalgia to smother the place, as the airy bar is smartly decorated with a rich blue carpet and plenty of fresh pine. Food is adventurous and appealing.

Up the creaking stairs and along the higgledy-piggledy corridors, the low-ceilinged comfortable bedrooms continue the rustic mood. Each contains a selection of books, flowers and toiletries. There's a sauna in the attic (mind your head!) and a bright, welcoming breakfast room on the first floor with pine, prints and flowers.

◖ Open all year; restaurant closed Sun eve

▨ Immediately south of the cathedral by Kingsgate at the junction of Canon Street and Kingsgate Road. Private car park

⇌ 2 twin, 5 double; all with bathroom/WC, TV, hair-dryer, mini-bar

◈ 3 dining-rooms, 2 bars, drying room; conference facilities (max 10 people non-residential); sauna at hotel

⊖ No wheelchair access; no children under 14; restrictions on smoking

▭ Access, Amex, Visa

£ Single occupancy of twin/double £63 to £65, twin/double £73 to £75. Alc L £10, D £15

Archway

13 COLLEGE ROAD, WINDERMERE, CUMBRIA LA23 1BU
TEL: WINDERMERE (05394) 45613

Great value in a small and friendly guesthouse in a quiet street at the hub of the Lake District.

A stream of positive reports fully justifies the Archway's inclusion in this year's Guide. 'The Greenhalghs' attention to detail and unfailing cheerfulness are amazing,' is just one typical comment. 'The standard of accommodation and cuisine has never slipped from the highest level,' enthuses a regular visitor. The rooms are comfortable, with a combination of pine furniture, patchwork quilts and modern prints, though they are on the small side.

Dinners are healthy and wholesome, but it is Aurea Greenhalgh's breakfasts that really linger in the memory: 'exemplary' was one verdict. The full English breakfast includes dry-cured bacon, spicy Cumberland sausages and black pudding; alternatively, you could sample the boiled duck eggs or the delicious American pancakes. Early morning is an ideal time to while away an hour in the relaxing atmosphere of the lounge. One reader who made a return visit was impressed: 'They remembered our likes and dislikes.'

◐ Open all year; restaurant closed Sun eve

⊿ Leave A591 Ambleside/Kendal road at Windermere and take left from the main street into College Road. Private car park and on-street parking

🛏 1 single, 2 twin, 2 double; all with shower/WC, TV, room service; hair-dryer on request

◈ Dining-room, lounge

⊖ No wheelchair access; no children under 10; no dogs; no smoking

▭ Access, Visa

£ Single £20 to £25, single occupancy of twin/double £30 to £36, twin/double £40 to £50; deposit required. Set D £10.50 (6.45pm)

Holbeck Ghyll

HOLBECK LANE, WINDERMERE, CUMBRIA LA23 1LU
TEL: AMBLESIDE (05394) 32375   FAX: (05394) 34743

Impressive country house in a quiet spot.

The dry stone exterior has probably changed little since it was built by a Lancashire industrialist in the early nineteenth century, but inside it is the legacy of Lord Lonsdale, who used Holbeck Ghyll as a hunting-lodge, that catches the eye. David and Patricia Nicholson seem to relish the connection with the colourful Lord Lonsdale and suggest that the small carved hearts that crop up in the stone and woodwork throughout the building may have been secretly dedicated to his mistress.

Integrating more modern furnishings into an environment of stained glass and inglenook halls can be a daunting task but it has been done seamlessly. Added to this is the chatty and likeable nature of the Nicholsons and the efforts of their youthful and professional staff. Dinner maintains an air of tradition both in the oak-panelled surroundings and in the menu, where the main course may be liver baked in a melting butter pastry parcel or a vegetarian dish, such as a bake of grated potato and leeks.

Bedrooms vary considerably in both size and décor and although they are all well co-ordinated some of the larger rooms, for example, Rooms Six and Seven, have more luxurious furnishings.

◑ *Open all year*

▨ *3 miles north of Windermere on the Ambleside road. Turn right to Troutbeck after Brockhole Visitors' Centre. The hotel is ½ mile on the left. Private car park*

⊯ *6 twin, 6 double, 1 four-poster, 1 family room; all with bathroom/ WC, exc 1 double with shower/ WC; TV, hair-dryer, room service, baby-listening in all rooms; no tea/coffee-making facilities in rooms*

◈ *Restaurant, bar, 2 lounges, snooker room; conference facilities (max 14 people*

residential, 30 non-residential); putting green, snooker at hotel, fishing, golf, other sports nearby; babysitting by arrangement

⊖ *No wheelchair access; no children under 8 in restaurant eves; no dogs in public rooms; no smoking in restaurant*

▭ *Access, Amex, Visa*

£ *Single occupancy of twin/double £55 to £75, twin/double £100 to £190, four-poster £120 and £190, family room £120 and £150 (rates inc dinner); deposit required. Set D £27.50/£31. Special breaks available*

Miller Howe

RAYRIGG ROAD, WINDERMERE, CUMBRIA LA23 1EY
TEL: WINDERMERE (05394) 42536   FAX: (05394) 45664

Charming service, celebrated cuisine and an idyllic setting.

Over the last 25 years or so John Tovey has made his hotel a Lakeland institution. Dinners are occasions: satisfied diners talk of the atmosphere of a first night, meals unfolding with the drama of a five-act play. Tovey's culinary instincts are towards the exuberant and the challenging. One summer evening's menu began with the curiously pudding-like fanned charentais melon with raspberry purée egg flip sauce. The tomato, apple and celery soup that followed was transformed by garlic croûtons and shallow-fried apple. Salmon cubes marinated in soy, ginger and orange provided an oriental flavour before the main course of roast loin of pork on coffee cream sauce with madeira gravy. Vegetables are imaginative: buttered spinach with nutmeg, carrots with Pernod and swede with mustard. The wine list has an increasing number of New World wines which stand up well against such strong flavours.

The hotel itself is a relaxing and friendly place where the elegance is always a little understated. Fine antiques blend with huge bunches of freshly arranged flowers, while cherubs (John Tovey's passion) frolic freely. There are three small lounges with rather sober colour schemes, leather chesterfields and large oil paintings. The spacious conservatory is brighter, with white plastic seating and a number of plants and hanging baskets. The bedrooms are spacious and the emphasis is on providing a relaxing environment.

◑ Closed after Xmas to mid-Mar

⤢ On the A592 between Windermere and Bowness. Private car park

🛏 9 twin, 4 double; most with bathroom/WC, 2 with shower/WC; TV, room service, hairdryer, trouser press in all rooms; no tea/coffee-making facilities in rooms

◇ 2 dining-rooms, 3 lounges, conservatory, drying room; limited conference facilities (max 20 people residential); fishing, water sports, other sports nearby

⊖ No wheelchair access; no children under 12; no dogs in public rooms; no smoking in dining-rooms

▭ Access, Amex, Diners, Visa

£ Single occupancy rate on application, twin/double £140 to £250 (rates inc dinner); 12½% service charge added to bills. Set L £12.50, D £32. Special breaks available

---

WINSTER DERBYSHIRE   **MAP 5**

Dower House

MAIN STREET, WINSTER, DERBYSHIRE DE4 2DH
TEL: WINSTER (0629) 650213   FAX: (0629) 650894

Excellent bed and breakfast in a sixteenth-century stone house.

There are no signs, so you need to know that Helen Bastin and Geoff Dalton's Dower House is the square three-storey stone house behind walls at the end of the main street. An immaculate garden with a neat lawn and tidy borders is an indication of what you can expect inside. The sunny yellow sitting-room has beams, a stone and parquet floor and a comfortable mix of modern and antique furniture. Helen's dried-flower arrangements decorate the bedrooms, which are large and bright, with characterful features such as beams and fireplaces. Breakfast around one solid oak table in the cool pink dining-room includes a healthy combination of fresh fruit and yogurt, and jams are all home-made.

◑ Closed 1 Nov to 28 Feb

⤢ Turn off the A6 Matlock to Bakewell road on to the B5057 to Winster. The hotel is at the end of the main street. Private car park

🛏 2 twin, 1 double, 2 with bathroom/WC, 1 with shower/WC; TV, hair-dryer in all rooms; ironing facilities on request

◇ Dining-room, lounge, drying room; fishing, golf, other sports nearby

⊖ No wheelchair access; no children under 10; no dogs in public rooms; smoking in lounge only

▭ None accepted

£ Single occupancy of twin/double £30 to £35; twin/double £45 to £55; deposit required

---

Use the index at the back of the book if you know the name of a hotel but are unsure about its precise location.

WINTERINGHAM HUMBERSIDE　　　　　　　　　**MAP 5**

Winteringham Fields

WINTERINGHAM, SOUTH HUMBERSIDE DN15 9PF
TEL: SCUNTHORPE (0724) 733096　FAX: (0724) 733898

Glorious food, immaculate service and stunning décor.

Germain and Annie Schwab, hosts at this converted and expanded 400-year-old farmhouse in a small, otherwise unremarkable village, obviously enjoy their work. Annie oversaw the conversion, chose and superintended the exquisite interior decoration, and tracked down the wonderful antiques that now make the house such a memorable temple of (mainly) Victoriana.

You can peruse the menu in the panelled, elegant bar with its heavy drapes, paisley walls and statuettes. The main restaurant is a light and airy affair with deco figures, striped walls and lots of dried floral arrangements. Swiss-born Germain's culinary skills are finely honed and the adventurous à la carte menu is partnered by the set 'Menu Epicurien', which may feature a bed of sautéed spinach with a mousse of chicken and smoked bacon, followed by a salad of hake, mignonettes of veal served with noodles, and feuilleté of apples and pears.

The bedrooms, two of which are in the courtyard, are furnished and designed with painstaking care and vibrant originality. Bathrooms are equally impressive.

◑ *Closed 2 weeks at Xmas and first week Aug; restaurant closed Sun eves*

⤢ *Winteringham is on the south bank of the Humber estuary, 6 miles west of the Humber Bridge, off the A1077. Hotel is at crossroads in centre of village. Private car park*

⇝ *3 twin, 2 double, 1 four-poster, 1 suite; most with bathroom/WC, some with shower/WC; TV, room service, hair-dryer in all rooms; no tea/coffee-making facilities in rooms*

◈ *2 restaurants, bar, lounge, library/study, conservatory; fishing, golf, riding nearby*

⊖ *No wheelchair access; no children under 5; no dogs; no smoking in bedrooms*

▭ *Access*

£ *Single occupancy of twin/double £65, twin/double £80 to £90, four-poster/suite £95. Cooked B £6; set L £15, D £33; alc L, D £35*

WITHERSLACK CUMBRIA　　　　　　　　　**MAP 4**

Old Vicarage

CHURCH ROAD, WITHERSLACK, GRANGE-OVER-SANDS, CUMBRIA LA11 6RS
TEL: WITHERSLACK (05395) 52381　FAX: (05395) 52373

Thoughtfully developed, small country-house hotel with good food.

'Witherslack is everything I like about a hotel: delightful décor, friendly staff, interesting but not precious cooking,' writes one reader. Inside the 1803 vicarage distinctive wall-coverings dictate the mood of the rooms – autumnal colours in the intimate and rather sombre dining-rooms, bright blue in the breakfast room that looks out over the gardens. The sitting-rooms are also on the garden side of the house, and there's also a terrace. Both rooms are quite small but they are neatly furnished with cane or round-back chairs.

The bedrooms in the main house are traditional, with floral drapes, pine or brass bedsteads and cane armchairs (although Room Five is a little disconcerting – the bath is actually in the bedroom).

There's a full five-course menu, and a cheaper three-course option. Dinner might include Loch Fyne oysters or vermicelli with rosemary followed by steak, a roast or a tasty vegetarian option. Breakfasts are particularly impressive, with freshly squeezed orange juice, a choice of grills and Cumberland porridge with its dash of whisky.

◑ Open all year

⤲ Leave the M6 at Junction 36, following the signs to Barrow-in-Furness. Turn off the A590 into Witherslack and 50 yards past the telephone box, turn left. The hotel is ¾ mile along this lane on the left. Private car park

🛏 1 single, 3 twin, 4 double, 1 four-poster, 1 family room, 5 annexe rooms; most with bathroom/WC, some with shower/WC; TV, room service, hair-dryer in all rooms; mini-bar in some rooms

◇ 2 dining-rooms, 2 lounges; conference facilities (max 12 people residential, 18 non-residential); tennis at hotel, other sports nearby; babysitting by arrangement. Wheelchair access to hotel (3 steps) and 5 ground-floor bedrooms

⊖ No dogs in public rooms

▭ Access, Amex, Diners, Visa

£ Single £40, single occupancy of twin/double from £58, twin/double from £98, four-poster from £158, family room/annexe £138. Sun L £15; set D £19.50 (8pm). Special breaks available

---

WITHYPOOL SOMERSET　　　　　　　　　　　**MAP 10**

Royal Oak Inn

WITHYPOOL, SOMERSET TA24 7QP
TEL: EXFORD (064 383) 506/7　FAX: (064 383) 659

A sixteenth-century inn full of hunting trophies and cartoons and with fine, if meaty, menus.

Withypool is not much more than a dot on the map, but the Royal Oak, where R. D. Blackmore stayed while writing *Lorna Doone*, is very much its heart. An unextraordinary exterior opens on to a reception area which is little more than a below-stairs cubby-hole; there you can admire some of the antlers and mounted fish adorning the walls, before moving into the Rod Room and residents' bar where stags' heads compete with hunting cartoons for attention. Wooden beams, log fires and horse brasses make for a dark, if traditionally English, atmosphere. In contrast, the hotel dining-room, with its flouncy curtains, flowers and graceful antique sideboards, seems to have strayed from another building. To make the most of the Royal Oak's gourmet reputation it pays to be a carnivore; menus tend to the meaty, with lots of farmhouse sausages, Gressingham duck and juicy steaks. Bar lunches are reputedly excellent.

Upstairs, there are bedrooms to suit a multitude of tastes, some cottagey with pine furniture and floral fabrics, others more elegant with French-style white and gilt fittings.

◑ *Open all year, exc 25 and 26 Dec*

🡕 *Take North Devon Link Road towards Barnstaple. Take turning to North Molton and then on towards Withypool. Private car park*

🛏 *1 twin, 5 double, 1 four-poster, 1 family room; some with bathroom/WC, some with shower/WC, public bathrooms; TV, room service, hair-dryer, baby-listening in all rooms*

◈ *Dining-room, 2 bars, lounge, drying room; fishing, riding, clay pigeon shooting nearby*

⊖ *No wheelchair access; no children under 10*

▭ *Access, Amex, Diners, Visa*

£ *Single occupancy of twin/double £32 to £46, twin/double £56 to £70, four-poster £70, family room £88; deposit required. Set D £19.50; alc D £23; bar lunches. Special breaks available*

Westerclose Country House ☆

WITHYPOOL, SOMERSET TA24 7QR
TEL: EXFORD (064 383) 302

A comfortable and welcoming family-run country-house hotel.

Once a hunting lodge for the Nicholson (of Nicholson gin) family, Westerclose is a light, airy building. The reception lurks in the corner of a wooden-floored lounge where a log-burner throws out welcoming warmth. An archway leads through a library complete with children's books and games to a conservatory bar full of flourishing plants interspersed with colonial-style cane furniture. Clever use of mirrors makes the Barle Restaurant, already large, appear even bigger. Tinker Foster's daughter Jo is in charge of the cooking; four-course dinners feature items such as spicy bean casserole, skate with black butter and capers, and chocolate oblivion truffle torte. A typical lunch menu features terrine of four cheeses with cucumber pickle.

A pinewood staircase twists up from the lounge to the ten bedrooms where structural oddities have been turned into novel features; in Room

11, what looks like an extraordinary four-poster is actually a bed incorporating a ceiling-support beam. Children will no doubt love the donkeys in the paddock outside.

◑ *Closed Jan and Feb*

⤴ *Enter Withypool village, turn right at the inn and follow hotel signs. Private car park*

🛏 *2 single, 4 twin, 3 double, 1 four-poster, family room available; all with bathroom/WC, exc 1 single with shower/WC; TV in all rooms; baby-listening on request*

◈ *Restaurant, bar, 2 lounges, drying room, conservatory;*

fishing, riding nearby, stabling at hotel; babysitting on request. Wheelchair access to restaurant only

⊖ *No smoking in restaurant*

▭ *Access, Amex, Visa*

£ *Single £28, single occupancy of twin/double £42 to £47, twin/double £56 to £62, family room rate £95 to £100; deposit required. Set D £19; alc L, D £15. Special breaks available*

WOODSTOCK OXFORDSHIRE   MAP 9

Feathers

MARKET STREET, WOODSTOCK, OXFORDSHIRE OX20 1SX
TEL: WOODSTOCK (0993) 812291   FAX: (0993) 813158

A smart town-house hotel with a fine restaurant.

Four seventeenth-century honey-coloured stone houses in the centre of Woodstock have been knocked together to create a stylish town-house hotel. The bar is a popular place for lunch and when our inspector visited there were people waiting for a seat in the bar or in the small, deep-red study with its marble fireplace and richly coloured furnishings; in summer the overflow can be seated in the gravelled courtyard garden amidst abundant shrubbery. The restaurant is a lovely room, with wood panelling and yellow and blue padded seating. The food is praised, though one diner complains about the 'breakneck speed' with which he was served: 'I was in and out in 35 minutes in spite of my protestations that we were not in a hurry.'

Bedrooms are all individually decorated to a high standard with fine fabrics, some antiques and original paintings. However, Room 26 overlooks the fire escape and one guest said of Room 27, 'It was above the kitchen exhaust fan, and I was awoken by odours in the morning.'

◐ *Open all year*

⤴ *Centrally located in Woodstock. If you come from the south, Market Street is the second turning on the left after Blenheim Palace gates. On-street parking*

🛏 *1 single, 6 twin, 7 double, 3*

suites; suites with bathroom/WC, rest with shower/WC, exc 1 double; TV, room service, hair-dryer, baby-listening in all rooms; tea/coffee-making facilities on request

◈ *Restaurant (air-conditioned), bar, 2 lounges; conference facilities* (max 17 people residential, 25 non-residential); golf, tennis, other sports nearby. Wheelchair access to restaurant and WC (M) only

⊖ None

🖵 Access, Amex, Diners, Visa

💷 Single £75, single occupancy of twin/double £75 to £95, twin/double £98 to £138, suite £138; deposit required. Cooked B £6.50; set L £15.50/£18.50; alc L, D £25 to £30

WOODY BAY DEVON   **MAP 10**

Woody Bay ☆

WOODY BAY, DEVON EX31 4QX
TEL: PARRACOMBE (05983) 264

A well-maintained, family-run Victorian country-house hotel.

Built in the 1890s, Woody Bay Hotel was part of a solicitor's overly ambitious scheme to develop the bay as a rival to Lynton with a cliff railway, roads and a pier. In the restaurant and bar you'll find photographs of the pier before it blew down in 1902. In the bar, too, you'll probably bump into pub-lunchers still recovering from the steep 40-minute hike back up from the bay. Since Collette and Martin Petch took over two years ago, the dining-room has been completely refurbished.

Bedrooms all have different colour schemes, some, like the bright blue and yellow in Number One, rather startling. Rooms Nine and Ten interlock to form a family suite. One of the singles, although long and thin, has marvellous views.

◑ Closed weekdays Nov to Jan (exc Xmas and New Year)

🡥 Take the A361 towards Barnstaple, then the A399 towards Blackmoor Gate. Then right on the A39. After 5 miles Woody Bay is signposted. Private car park

🛏 1 single, 3 twin, 5 double, 2 four-poster, 1 family room; most with bathroom/WC, some with shower/WC, 4 public bathrooms; TV on request

◇ Restaurant, bar, lounge, drying room; conference facilities (max

30 people non-residential, 13 residential); fishing, golf, other sports nearby.

⊖ No wheelchair access; no dogs in restaurant and lounge; no smoking in restaurant

🖵 Access, Visa

💷 Single £43 to £48, single occupancy of twin/double £43 to £48, twin/double £86 to £96, family room from £86 and £96, four-poster £94 to £104; deposit required. Set D £16; alc D £20. Special breaks available

---

Being witness to father and son bickering furiously about how to face recessionary problems in the panelled hall of the grand family room one feared the worst. It was like playing Inspector Morse.

WOOLACOMBE DEVON   **MAP 10**

Little Beach

THE ESPLANADE, WOOLACOMBE, DEVON EX34 7DJ
TEL: WOOLACOMBE (0271) 870398

A small Edwardian sea-front hotel with contemporary fittings.

Steps wind up to the Little Beach and a sun-trap terrace overlooking the sea; on colder days a small front sun lounge offers the same views from warmer surroundings. Brian Welling came from the antiques trade, so the hall, lounge and dining-room boast many period fittings and there's even a small antiques shop, specialising in inlaid boxes, tucked at the back of the hotel. His wife Nola looks after the food, served in a narrow dining-room where cabinets display yet more of Brian's trophies. Menus incorporate English staples such as steak and kidney pudding and Devonshire apple sponge. For the more adventurous, starters sometimes include chicken satay with peanut sauce or crab and sweetcorn soup. The best of the ten upstairs bedrooms have sea views and balconies.

◐ *Closed Nov to early Mar*

↗ *From Barnstaple take the A361 to Ilfracombe. After 10 miles turn left at Mullacott Cross roundabout, signposted Woolacombe 3 miles. Private car park*

🛏 *2 single, 1 twin, 7 double; some with bathroom/WC, some with shower/WC, 1 public bathroom; TV, hair-dryer in all rooms; trouser press on request*

◇ *Dining-room, bar, 2 lounges,*

drying room; golf, water sports, other sports nearby

⊖ *No wheelchair access; no children under 7; no dogs in public rooms; smoking in bedroom and bar only*

▭ *Access, Visa*

£ *Single £28 to £31, single occupancy of twin/double £28 to £31, twin/double £48 to £73; deposit required. Set D £14. Special breaks available*

WOOLSTASTON SHROPSHIRE   **MAP 5**

Rectory Farm

WOOLSTASTON, CHURCH STRETTON, SHROPSHIRE SY6 6NN
TEL: CHURCH STRETTON (0694) 751306

A wonderfully positioned bed and breakfast in an old farmhouse with lots of character.

Rectory Farm is a low, typically black and white half-timbered Shropshire farmhouse, positioned to get the very best of the superb views. It is a seventeenth-century building, suitably creaky and cottagey, with fine panelling in the lounge. Mrs Davis, a warm and ebullient hostess, keeps the place spotless – even the copper pipework in the bathrooms gleams. The residents' lounge is laid out quite formally, with a central fireplace and lots of shining brasswork. The bedrooms have the best of the views; a helmeted warrior peers at you in one of them. There is plenty of space, although very fussy guests might think the bathrooms a little small. Breakfast is served in the converted stable block.

◐ *Closed 20 Dec to 31 Jan*

🔋 *Leave the A49 Shrewsbury to Hereford road at Leebotwood. Continue for 1¾ miles to Woolstaston. The farm is to the right of the village green. Private car park*

🛏 *2 twin, 1 double; all with bathroom/WC*

◈ *Lounge, TV room*

⊖ *No wheelchair access; no children under 12; no dogs; no smoking in bedrooms*

▭ *None accepted*

£ *Single occupancy of twin/double £36, twin/double £36*

WOOLSTONE GLOUCESTERSHIRE   MAP 9

Old Rectory ☆

WOOLSTONE, NR CHELTENHAM, GLOUCESTERSHIRE GL52 4RG
TEL: CHELTENHAM (0242) 673766

Bed and breakfast in a grand nineteenth-century rectory.

No expense was spared when this huge rectory was built in 1891; it dwarfs the church in this tiny village. A Canadian heiress had married the rector, and their new home was endowed with Canadian pine doorways, ornate fireplaces, and fine proportions. Now it belongs to the Taylor family, who use the magnificent dining-room to host wedding receptions and also take guests for bed and breakfast. Of the three rooms, the double and twin on the first floor are much better than the little room tucked under the lavish stairway – not least because they get the best of the views. Furnishings are not spectacular, but there are good facilities.

◐ *Closed Nov to Mar*

🔋 *From Cheltenham take the A435 towards Evesham. 2 miles north of Bishop's Cleeve, turn right to Woolstone. The Old Rectory is down the 1st drive on the left after the church. Private car park*

🛏 *2 twin, 1 double, 6 cottages; all with bathroom/WC, exc double with shower/WC; TV; hair-dryer in all rooms*

◈ *Dining-room, bar, TV room,*

drying room; conference facilities (max 50 people non-residential, 26 residential); fishing, golf, other sports nearby; babysitting by arrangement

⊖ *No wheelchair access; no dogs; no smoking*

▭ *None accepted*

£ *Single occupancy of twin/double, twin/double £38, cottages £38 per room; deposit required*

All reports are welcome on any hotel, whether or not it is in the Guide.

WOOLTON HILL HAMPSHIRE   **MAP 9**

Hollington House ☆

WOOLTON HILL, NR NEWBURY, BERKSHIRE RG15 9XR
TEL: HIGHCLERE (0635) 255100   FAX: (0635) 255075

An unstuffy country house with good food in fine surroundings.

John Guy and his wife Penny opened this large Edwardian country house in 1992 after restoration and refurbishment. They have created a luxurious country-house hotel where, as the forthright owner says, 'We don't bow and scrape, but treat people like normal happy human beings.'

On cool days, a fire burns in the wood-panelled entrance hall and in the light sitting-room with its plush blue, pink and yellow upholstery. The Oak Room Restaurant is wood-panelled and has an elaborate plasterwork ceiling. Chef Richard Lovett produces an English menu with a French influence; you might have carrot and ginger soup with coriander rolls to start, with roasted saddle of lamb on a minted pea purée as a main course. One reader describes dessert – a passion-fruit tart – as 'out of this world'.

Bedrooms are extremely comfortable and individually decorated with antiques and fine fabrics. Bathrooms are special, some having double showers fitted with oversize 'deluge' shower heads and maybe a sunken bath.

◑ Open all year

🔁 From Newbury take the A343 towards Andover, then follow signs to Hollington Herb Garden. Private car park

🛏 1 single, 4 twin, 14 double, 1 suite; all with bathroom/WC, TV, room service, hair-dryer, trouser-press, baby-listening

◈ 2 restaurants, 3 lounges, drying room, library/study; conference facilities (max 22 people residential and non-residential); tennis, heated swimming-pool, mini-golf, bicycles at hotel, other sports nearby; babysitting. Wheelchair access to hotel (ramp), restaurant and WC (M, F), no ground-floor bedrooms but lift

⊖ No dogs; no pipes or cigars in the restaurant

▭ Access, Amex, Visa

£ Single £90, single occupancy of twin/double £90, twin/double £105 to £250, suite £195; deposit required. Set L £15, D £20; alc L £24/£28, D £35/£40. Special breaks available

---

WORFIELD SHROPSHIRE   **MAP 5**

Old Vicarage Hotel

WORFIELD, BRIDGNORTH, SHROPSHIRE WV15 5JZ
TEL: WORFIELD (074 64) 497   FAX: (074 64) 552

A place for people who like precision in their lives.

Everything at the Old Vicarage has been chosen and organised with the utmost good taste; there is no clutter. The house is a huge Edwardian red-brick structure with gables and chimneys everywhere, built well away from the church it once served. You can sit in either the chintzy bar lounge or the conservatory, which is modern but cleverly disguised to look in-period. The bedrooms are splendid; those in the old coach-house have been well converted, with old beams left where possible. The furniture is a mixture of the antique and the modern. Carefully chosen prints and watercolours abound.

The dinner menu augurs well – terrine of chicken and herb mousse, followed by red mullet on leeks with saffron and tomato cream sauce, perhaps – and our inspector was presented with an excellent fennel and prawn soup for lunch at extremely short notice.

◐ Open all year

⤢ I mile from the A454 and 2 miles from the A442, to the east of Bridgnorth. Near the cricket ground in Worfield, not the church. Private car park

🛏 4 twin, 8 double, I four-poster, I suite; most with bathroom/ WC, some with shower/WC; TV, room service, hair-dryer, trouser press, mini-bar, baby-listening

◈ Restaurant, bar, lounge, conservatory; conference facilities (max 24 people non-residential, 14 residential); golf, tennis, other sports nearby. Wheelchair access to hotel (2 steps or ramp), restaurant and WC, 2 ground-floor bedrooms, I specially equipped for disabled people

⊖ No children under 8 in restaurant eves; no dogs in public rooms; no smoking in public rooms and some bedrooms

▭ Access, Amex, Diners, Visa

£ Single occupancy of twin/double £50 to £64, twin/double £80 to £85, four-poster/suite £95 to £100; deposit required. Set L £11.50/£14.50, D £19.50 to £27.50. Special breaks available

WORLESTON CHESHIRE   **MAP 5**

Rookery Hall

WORLESTON, NR NANTWICH, CHESHIRE CW5 6DQ
TEL: CREWE (0270) 610016   FAX: (0270) 626027

Victorian country-house hotel extended into a luxury conference centre.

The rooks are still in evidence in the grounds of this Regency pile that has sprouted a rash of new extensions. The Coach House, converted from the old Georgian stables, is an up-to-the-minute self-contained conference centre. All the reception rooms are stylish and luxurious, if a touch anonymous. The most handsome room is the panelled dining-room, darkly polished, gleaming with silver and cut glass. Avoid staying in Room Six in the new wing if you are a light-sensitive sleeper. Spacious and luxurious it may be, as are all the rooms, but it is on the ground floor and immediately outside the window is a powerful halogen floodlight. There were also housekeeping niggles on our inspection; missing protective cover on the shower hand spray, loose toilet handle, no shampoo in the goodies basket. More importantly, the bath was singularly high to get in and out of – tricky for the elderly, arthritic or short of stature. The beds, however, were very comfortable.

Rookery Hall has been noted in the past for fine food. There has, however, been a change of head chef since the Guide was last published and, on the basis of an inspection meal, standards (but not prices) have fallen considerably. Breakfasts are a better bet – local sausages and black pudding. Loch Fyne kippers, scrambled eggs and smoked salmon.

◐ Open all year

⤢ Off the B5074 at Worleston. Private car park

🛏 2 single, 39 twin/double, 1 four-poster, 3 suites; all with bathroom/WC, TV, room service, hair-dryer, trouser-press

◈ Restaurant, bar, 2 lounges; conference facilities (max 100 people non-residential, 45 residential); tennis at hotel, other sports nearby; babysitting by arrangement. Wheelchair access to hotel (1 step), restaurant, WC, 6 ground-floor bedrooms, 1 specially equipped for disabled people

⊖ No dogs

▭ Access, Amex, Diners, Visa

£ Single £95, single occupancy of twin/double £95, twin/double £115, four-poster £215, suite £215; deposit required. Set L £16.50, D £28; alc D £28.50. Special breaks available

---

YATTENDON BERKSHIRE   **MAP 9**

Royal Oak

THE SQUARE, YATTENDON, NR NEWBURY, BERKSHIRE RG16 0UF
TEL: HERMITAGE (0635) 201325   FAX: (0635) 201926

A pretty pub with rooms and a popular restaurant.

This pretty red-brick pub and hotel covered in creepers is at the heart of the small village of Yattendon. The bar retains a smidgen of olde-worlde atmosphere with its low beamed ceilings, large open fireplaces and uneven tiled floor; tables are laid ready for visitors who come to enjoy bar food that includes half-a-dozen oysters or a ragoût of salmon, monkfish, Dover sole and seafood in a saffron sauce. On summer weekends the bar overflows into the pretty gardens or to the tables at the front of the hotel. The restaurant is a small, light, elegant room with well-spaced tables where you can sample the varied two-course menus produced by the new chef, Paul Collins. You can retire to the lounge afterwards for coffee.

Refurbishment was planned as we went to press – the aim is to freshen up public rooms without changing their character and to update the bedrooms. These are comfortable and of a reasonable size, with a few antiques and dark wood furnishings.

◑ Open all year; restaurant closed Sun eve

↗ In centre of Yattendon village. Leave the M4 at Junction 12 and take the A4 towards Newbury for 1 mile. At 2nd roundabout take 3rd exit towards Pangbourne, then left towards Yattendon. Private car park

⇔ 2 twin, 3 double; all with bathroom/WC, TV, room service, hair-dryer; tea/coffee-making facilities on request

◈ Restaurant, bar, lounge; conference facilities (max 25 people non-residential); golf, tennis, riding, other sports nearby. Wheelchair access to restaurant only

⊖ None

▭ Amex, Diners, Visa

£ Single occupancy of twin/double £60 to £70, twin/double £70 to £80. Set L £12.50, D £17; alc L, D £27.50. Special breaks available

YORK NORTH YORKSHIRE   MAP 5

Holmwood House Hotel

114 HOLGATE ROAD, YORK, NORTH YORKSHIRE YO2 4BB
TEL: YORK (0904) 626183   FAX: (0904) 670899

Enthusiastic endorsements for this immaculate town-house bed and breakfast and for its charming hosts.

'The next time we go back to York this will be our place,' concluded one recent visitor to Roberto and Christina Gramellini's bed and breakfast in a residential area close to the centre of York – a view echoed by a number of correspondents. The Victorian terrace is unremarkable, but Holmwood House stands out from its neighbours on account of its bright white paintwork and the flower boxes and baskets that adorn the outside.

Inside it's the same story. A tasteful, uncluttered high-ceilinged lounge with a mixture of antique tables, good pine furniture and restful green décor. Roberto is a chatty, ebullient chap, and his advice on local restaurants has been praised by several correspondents. Breakfast – 'lovely orange eggs and super sausages' – is served in a neat basement room with an old range and cheerful pink décor.

Bedrooms are light and attractive, with a good mix of pine, cane and antique furniture, and well-kept cottagey décor. One guest enthused about his 'lovely four-poster bedroom'. Guests have been equally fulsome in their tributes to the Gramellinis themselves. 'Splendid people,' said one; 'perfect hosts,' reported another.

◑ Open all year

↯ Just outside the city walls on the A59 York to Harrogate road. Private car park

⇔ 2 twin, 6 double, 2 four-poster, 1 family room, 1 king-size; most with bathroom/WC, some with shower/WC; TV, room service, hair-dryer in all rooms

2 dining-rooms, lounge; fishing, golf, other sports nearby. Wheelchair access to hotel (3 steps), restaurant and WC (unisex), 4 ground-floor bedrooms

No children under 8; no dogs in public rooms and by arrangement only in bedrooms; smoking in lounge only

Access, Amex, Visa

Single occupancy of twin/double £40 to £50, twin/double £50 to £55, four-poster £54 to £60, family room £69 to £75, king-size £58 to £65; deposit required. Set D (by arrangement only)

Middlethorpe Hall

BISHOPTHORPE ROAD, YORK, NORTH YORKSHIRE YO2 1QB
TEL: YORK (0904) 641241   FAX: (0904) 620176

A thoroughbred country-house hotel with a business pedigree.

The owners, Historic House Hotels, have carefully selected décor, antiques and paintings that are contemporary with the style of the house – to take afternoon tea in the library or in the front hall surrounded by antique screens, portraits, and rugs on a classically tiled floor is to be catapulted back in time to a leisured, more elegant England.

The drawing-room has a magnificently restored pre-Adam plaster ceiling, Regency sofas and chairs and a surfeit of antiques, rugs, chandeliers and portraits. Both restaurants are elegant and formal, worthy venues for accomplished cuisine; the menus may include warm salad of marinated chicken and chicken livers, followed by roast fillet of sea bass with a fennel and saffron sauce, then mille-feuille of chocolate with minted strawberries.

Bedrooms are individually decorated, with splendid antiques, bold, bright, modern fabrics and a rather derivative country-house style. That said, you will be admirably comfortable whether in the more traditional rooms of the old house or in the courtyard rooms.

Open all year

The Hall is 1½ miles south of York, beside York racecourse. Private car park

4 single, 10 twin, 8 double, 1 four-poster, 6 suites, 3 cottage suites; all with bathroom/WC, TV, room service, hair-dryer, trouser press; tea/coffee-making facilities in cottage suites

Restaurant, grill, 2 dispense bars, 2 lounges, library; conference facilities (max 63 people non-residential, 30 residential);

croquet at hotel, other sports nearby

No wheelchair access; no children under 8; no dogs

Access, Amex, Diners, Visa

Single £83, single occupancy of twin/double £99, twin/double £115 to £129, four-poster £159, suite £189, cottage suite £165; deposit required. Continental B £7, cooked B £10; set L £15 to £17, D £30; alc L, D £42.50 (prices till Sept 93). Special breaks available

SCOTLAND

ABERFELDY TAYSIDE **MAP I**

Farleyer House

ABERFELDY, PERTHSHIRE PH15 2JE
TEL: ABERFELDY (0887) 820332   FAX: (0887) 829430

An elegant country house in the southern Highlands.

The big white harled complex shimmers in the sunlight above sweeping lawns and surrounding woods. Most of the building is given over to the grand country-house style. A stag's head and watercolours of grouse and deer hang in the hall; the panelled green dining-room plays host to understated classical cooking. Upstairs, the beautiful, light, parquet-floored drawing-room and underplayed library bar, its fireplace engraved with Scots warriors and coats of arms, are very habitable. In contrast is the relatively recent Scottish Bistro, where background music comes courtesy of Abba and the Beatles. Wine and food are chalked up on blackboards. As we went to press we heard that the chef, Frances Atkins, was due to move on, so there may be more changes here.

Large, co-ordinated bedrooms are faultlessly comfortable, but verging on the empty and impersonal.

◑ *Open all year*

🔁 *From Aberfeldy take the B846 to Kinloch Rannoch through Weem – the hotel is 1 mile on the right. Private car park*

🛏 *1 single, 3 twin, 5 double, 1 family room, 1 suite; all with bathroom/WC, TV, hair-dryer, room service; no tea/coffee-making facilities in rooms*

◈ *2 restaurants, lounge, TV room, library, drying room, bistro; conference facilities (max 15 people residential); golf at hotel, other sports nearby; babysitting. Wheelchair access to restaurant and WC (unisex) only*

⊖ *No dogs (kennelling available)*

▭ *Access, Amex, Diners, Visa*

£ *Single £50 to £70, single occupancy of twin/double £70 to £90, twin/double £70 to £90, family room/suite £90 to £120 (rates inc dinner); deposit required. Set D £26; alc L, D £5 to £20.*

Guinach House ☆

BY THE BIRKS, ABERFELDY, PERTHSHIRE PH15 2ET
TEL: ABERFELDY (0887) 820251

Unostentatious guesthouse run by a trained chef and his wife.

Guinach House is a welcoming place on the edge of town in a garden of crocuses and a gnomed rockery. Albert MacKay describes his dining-room as 'intimate, but not silver, not over-the-top'. Menus vary remarkably for a small establishment, offering the sophisticated, such as steamed scallops served on a Noilly Prat cream sauce with asparagus tips, and the traditional, such as profiteroles in chocolate sauce. Drinks and coffee are served in a homely lounge furnished with gold buttonbacks.

Bedrooms are generally old-fashioned, perhaps with a candlewick bedspread. They have pleasant valley views.

◑ *Open all year*

⤴ *From Aberfeldy take the road to Crieff and pass the church of Scotland. Private car park*

⇌ *1 single, 2 twin, 4 double (family rooms available); some with bathroom/WC, most with shower/WC; TV, hair-dryer in all rooms*

◈ *Dining-room, lounge, drying room; fishing, golf, other sports nearby. Wheelchair access to hotel (1 step), restaurant and WC (M,F), 1 ground-floor bedroom*

⊖ *No dogs in public rooms; no smoking in dining-room*

▭ *Access, Visa*

£ *Single £20 to £35, single occupancy of twin/double £28 to £49, twin/double £40 to £70, family room rate on request; deposit required. Set L £12.50, D £18.50. Special breaks available*

ACHILTIBUIE HIGHLAND   **MAP 1**

Summer Isles

ACHILTIBUIE, BY ULLAPOOL, ROSS-SHIRE IV26 2YG
TEL: ACHILTIBUIE (085 482) 282   FAX: (085 482) 251

A classy little hotel in a bewitchingly lovely retreat.

Mark and Geraldine Irvine and their refreshingly forthright staff have created a convivial but unpushy atmosphere at their first-rate white-washed hotel. At 8pm guests troop off for the substantial set dinner. Inventively presented vegetables accompany fresh local meat and fish. Leave room for later courses: the desserts trolley may be devastating, and some would die for a day left alone with the cheeseboard. One recipient of a packed lunch that included lobster, prawn and mayonnaise sand-wiches comments that it was 'so large that my wife and I ate half of it the following day'.

The bedrooms are very fetching without being luxurious, the most popular being in converted cottages with great island views.

◑ *Closed mid-Oct to Easter*

⤴ *10 miles north of Ullapool on the A835 turn left on to a single-track road to Achiltibuie. The village is 15 miles along this road, and the hotel 1 mile further on the left. Private car park*

⇌ *1 single, 5 twin, 5 double, 1 suite; all with bathroom/WC, exc 1 single; hair-dryer in all rooms; no tea/coffee-making facilities in rooms*

◈ *Dining-room, restaurant, 2 bars, 2 lounges, TV room, drying room, study; fishing nearby*

⊖ *No wheelchair access; no children under 8; no dogs in public rooms*

▭ *None accepted*

£ *Single £41, single occupancy of twin/double £58, twin/double*

£85, suite £112; deposit
required. Set D £31 (8pm)

*(prices till Oct 93). Special
breaks available*

ALLOA CENTRAL   MAP 2

Gean House ☆

GEAN PARK, TULLIBODY ROAD, ALLOA, CLACKMANNANSHIRE FK10 2AS
TEL: ALLOA (0259) 219275   FAX: (0259) 213827

One of the most sumptuously furnished country houses imaginable.

This Edwardian mansion is the creation of John Taylor and Antony
Misfud, previously restaurateurs and interior designers in Stratford-
upon-Avon. As well as being the chef – the food, particularly the
regularly featured bread-and-butter pudding, has received commenda-
tions – Antony is a dried-flower arranger. The title can only belittle his
works of art: miniature trees of conkers, garlands of shells and even teddy
bears of moss enliven every part of the house. Hints of modernity such as
blue glass candelabra complement fine period furnishings in a superbly
restored classic country house with stuccoed ceilings, walnut panelling
and a galleried great hall.

Every bedroom is irreproachably stylish. Indulgences include a pot of
mints, a tin of biscuits, a glass decanter of bubble bath and loo paper
ribboned in tartan. It's worth going for the extra space and comfort of one
of the three de-luxe rooms.

◐ Open all year

🔁 The park entrance is off the
B9096. Private car park

🛏 4 twin, 4 double, 2 family rooms;
all with bathroom/WC, TV, room
service, hair-dryer, baby-
listening; no tea/coffee-making
facilities in rooms

◇ 2 dining-rooms, 2 lounges,
library/study; conference facilities
(max 50 people non-residential,
10 residential); fishing, golf,

other sports nearby; babysitting.
Wheelchair access to hotel
(ramp), dining-room and WC, 1
ground-floor bedroom

⊖ No dogs; no smoking in dining-
rooms

▭ Access, Amex, Diners, Visa

£ Single occupancy of twin/double
£70, twin/double £120 to £140,
family room rate on request;
deposit required. Cooked B
£9.50; set L £16.50, D £29

ARDRISHAIG STRATHCLYDE   MAP 2

Fascadale House

TARBERT ROAD, ARDRISHAIG, BY LOCHGILPHEAD, ARGYLL PA30 8EP
TEL: LOCHGILPHEAD (0546) 603845

A first-rate bed and breakfast of country-house standards.

Friendly Michael and Monica Farka's stone Victorian villa lies in an attractive garden on the edge of Ardrishaig. Their very spacious and elegant home offers top-end-of-the-scale bed-and-breakfast accommodation. High ceilings, ornate cornicing and a fine carved staircase characterise the house. The large sitting-room, its bay windows looking out over Loch Fyne, comfortably doubles as a breakfast room. There is no stinting on your morning meal: as well as grapefruit and porridge you could have hash browns, black pudding and fried bread. Upstairs, the three bedrooms are big, attractive and different. The largest is notable for the fact that its bathroom's handbasin is a 1928 replica of those made for the Savoy.

◑ Closed Nov to Feb inclusive

▨ From Glasgow take A82 Loch Lomond road to Tarbet, then A83 signposted Campbeltown. Continue towards Lochgilphead and Ardrishaig on the A83; Fascadale House is 1 mile from south of Ardrishaig. Private car park

🛏 1 single, 1 twin, 1 family room, 3 cottages; all with bathroom/WC, exc single; 1 public bathroom; hair-dryer on request

◈ Breakfast room/lounge, drying room; fishing, golf, other sports nearby

⊖ No wheelchair access; no dogs; no smoking

▭ None accepted

£ Single £20, single occupancy of twin/double £22, twin/double £44, family room £46, cottage from £90 per week; deposit required

---

ARDUAINE STRATHCLYDE   MAP 2

Loch Melfort Hotel

ARDUAINE, BY OBAN, ARGYLL PA34 4XG
TEL: KILMELFORD (085 22) 233   FAX: (085 22) 214

Energetically run, freshly furnished hotel with splendid views.

Loch Melfort's claim to have the finest location on the west coast is not to be disregarded – from the house's position at the head of the loch, virtually every room looks across to sleepy inlets and the hazy outlines of mountains. Rosalind Lewis is on hand to greet you and show you to your room. The chalet-style Cedar Wing gains no prizes for architectural merit, but its bedrooms, in co-ordinated light colours and unfancy fittings, have either balconies or patios reached through sliding glass doors. Bedrooms in the main part of the cream-coloured Edwardian building are more individual.

The sitting-room is spruce in bright-patterned fabrics. Service in the dining-room where the view dominates the décor is, if anything, over-attentive, with encouragements to enjoy the food accompanying the arrival of every course. Philip Lewis's menus appeal to those with greater and lesser appetites: you're asked how much soup you want; the pudding trolley's range extends from rhubarb fudge crumble to lime mousse and fruit salad. The main emphasis of the cuisine lies with seafood, with a special buffet on Sunday and oysters, scallops and lobster as daily supplements. A blackboard shows an upmarket lunchtime menu in the Chartroom Bar.

◐ *Open all year, exc 4 Jan to end Feb*

↗ *19 miles south of Oban on the A816 to Lochgilphead. Private car park*

⇌ *1 single, 15 twin, 9 double; all with bathroom/WC, exc single with shower/WC; TV, room service, hair-dryer, baby-listening in all rooms*

◇ *Restaurant, 2 bars, 2 lounges, library, drying room; conference*

facilities (max 20 people residential and non-residential); fishing, riding, water sports nearby. Wheelchair access to hotel (3 steps), restaurant and WC, 10 ground-floor bedrooms

⊖ *No dogs in public rooms; no smoking in restaurant*

▭ *Access, Visa*

£ *Single and single occupancy of twin/double £57, twin/double £94. Set D £24; bar meals*

ARISAIG HIGHLAND   **MAP 1**

Arisaig House

BEASDALE, BY ARISAIG, INVERNESS-SHIRE PH39 4NR
TEL: ARISAIG (068 75) 622   FAX: (068 75) 626

A smart, conventional country house with lovely gardens.

Though Arisaig House is Victorian the rear courtyard has something of a Gallic château about it, its three sides studded with a mass of dormer and peephole windows. At the rear of the house, lawns lead to lovely wooded gardens. Light floods through long windows into reception rooms furnished in smart, unfussy, country-house style. The drawing-room is particularly pleasant, with a white Italian vaulted ceiling, while the high-ceilinged, part-panelled dining-room is imposing. A new chef has arrived since last year: his menus might offer leek, aubergine and artichoke feuilleté, quail with a raisin and grape quenelle finished off with fresh figs poached with port.

Bedroom prices vary according to size and aspect; those that look out on sea and gardens are most popular. Sympathetic colour schemes and a few antiques make them all pleasant.

◐ *Closed Nov to Mar*

↗ *2 miles north of Fort William, take the A830, signposted Mallaig. Arisaig House is 32 miles on, just after Beasdale railway station, 3 miles before village of Arisaig. Private car park*

⇌ *6 twin, 5 double, 2 suites; all with bathroom/WC, TV, room service, hair-dryer, trouser press; no tea/coffee-making facilities in rooms*

◇ *Restaurant, bar, 3 lounges, billiard room, drying room;*

limited conference facilities (max
12 people residential and non-
residential); fishing, water sports
nearby. Wheelchair access to
restaurant only

● No children under 10; no dogs;
no smoking in restaurant

▭ Access, Visa

£ Single occupancy of twin/double
from £75, twin/double/suite from
£137; deposit required. Set D
£32, alc D £38. Special breaks
available

AUCHENCAIRN DUMFRIES & GALLOWAY   MAP 2

Balcary Bay Hotel

SHORE ROAD, AUCHENCAIRN, BY CASTLE DOUGLAS,
KIRKCUDBRIGHTSHIRE DG7 1QZ
TEL: AUCHENCAIRN (055 664) 217/311   FAX: (055 664) 272

*Unstuffy hotel with a smuggling history in a lovely waterside
position.*

A framed letter explains that Balcary was built by a company of smugglers 'for the purpose of carrying on their illicit trade with the Isle of
Man'. The seventeenth-century building is now a friendly hotel run by
the attentive and easy-going Lamb family.

A correspondent describes its protected, waterside spot as 'a superb
setting with outstanding views. Its gardens, where we could take tea in
the afternoon, are a picture.' Day-trippers come for bar lunches –
sandwiches, platters of food and tempting puddings – served in the bar
and sitting-room. Residents can hide away in their own light sea-facing
lounge. Four-course limited-choice dinners in the airy, spacious dining-
room have been deemed 'excellent, very substantial and well-presented'.
As for breakfasts: 'Super, with large menu including haggis, kippers.'

Bedrooms can be a little on the small side, but are pleasantly furnished
in bold floral wallpaper.

◑ Closed mid-Nov till early Mar

⤢ Off the A711 Dumfries to
Kirkcudbright road, 2 miles out
of Auchencairn on the shore
road. Private car park

🛏 3 single, 7 twin, 5 double, 1
four-poster, 1 family room; all
with bathroom/WC, exc 1 single
with shower/WC; TV, room
service, hair-dryer, baby-listening
in all rooms; trouser press on
request

◇ Dining-room, bar, 2 lounges,
snooker room, drying room;

fishing, golf, other sports nearby;
babysitting by arrangement.
Wheelchair access to dining-
room and bar only

● No dogs in public rooms

▭ Access, Visa

£ Single £47, single occupancy of
twin/double from £70, twin/
double from £76, four-poster/
family room £94; deposit
required. Set D £18; alc L from
£10, D £20 (prices till end Nov
93). Special breaks available

Collin House

AUCHENCAIRN, CASTLE DOUGLAS, KIRKCUDBRIGHTSHIRE DG7 1QN
TEL: AUCHENCAIRN (0556 64) 292

Comfortable home in a commanding rural position.

Collin House opened in June 1991. The view from it is lovely, over fields that slope down to the Solway Firth. Stables at the back and horses in the paddock, as well as equine photos throughout the house and a fascinating tapestry detailing a 100 years of Grand National winners in the hall, betray Pam Wood's former career as horse trainer. John's four-course dinners offer choices at all except the soup stage; you might, perhaps, choose a salad of lobster with raspberry vinaigrette, tomato and tarragon sauce, wild salmon with a sorrel sauce, and avocado ice-cream.

The house is decorated elegantly but not over-formally: its dining-room with shiny polished tables, the sitting-room a natural mix of comfy chairs and a log fire when needed. In most bedrooms expect a traditional country-house style with attractive antiques and smart, spacious bathrooms.

◑ *Closed 4 Jan to 12 Mar*

🔁 *Turn right ¼ mile east of Auchencairn off the A711 where signposted. Private car park*

🛏 *3 twin, 3 double; all with bathroom/WC, TV, room service, hair-dryer*

◈ *Dining-room, lounge, drying room, library; fishing, golf, other sports nearby*

⊖ *No wheelchair access; dogs in bedrooms only (by arrangement); no smoking in dining-room*

▭ *Access, Visa*

£ *Single occupancy of twin/double £48 to £52, twin/double £66 to £74; deposit required. Set L £7.50, D £26. Special breaks available*

AUCHTERARDER TAYSIDE   **MAP 2**

Auchterarder House

AUCHTERARDER, PERTHSHIRE PH3 1DZ
TEL: AUCHTERARDER (0764) 663646   FAX: (0764) 662939

A superlatively furnished, exclusive country house.

They don't come much more imposing than this massive, ruddy stone Victorian pile, with a turret, crow-stepped gables and an outsize portico. It used to be the country residence of James Reid, one of Scotland's most successful industrialists. In the Second World War it became a girls' school and lockers still line the upstairs hallway. In 1983 the Brown family turned the property into a hotel.

The interior is quite simply stunning: there are chandeliers, candelabra, stuccoed ceilings, a grand piano. The most unusual room is the conservatory, with marble pillars, a plethora of pot plants and a fountain. On the day of our inspector's visit there were only two sets of diners, so for more intimacy tables had been arranged in the library – a nice touch. There are two types of bedroom: those in the turret, converted from servants' quarters, are much cheaper and more modern; those in the main wing are superb, with original built-in furniture.

◑ Open all year

⤴ On the B8062, 1½ miles north-west of Auchterarder. Private car park

🛏 10 twin, 2 double, 3 suites; all with bathroom/WC, TV, room service, hair-dryer, trouser press; no tea/coffee-making facilities in rooms

◈ Restaurant, lounge, drying room, library, conservatory; conference facilities (max 50 people non-residential, 15 residential);

croquet, putting at hotel, fishing, golf, other sports nearby; babysitting by arrangement.

⊖ No wheelchair access; no children under 10; no dogs in public rooms; no smoking in restaurant

▭ Access, Amex, Diners, Visa

£ Single occupancy of twin/double £70 to £110, twin/double £110 to £195, suite £125 to £145; deposit required. Set L £18.50, D £37.50. Special breaks available

---

Gleneagles

AUCHTERARDER, PERTHSHIRE PH3 1NF
TEL: AUCHTERARDER (0764) 662231   FAX: (0764) 662134

Traditional Edwardian railway hotel in a vast estate.

Of course Gleneagles is expensive, but if you're hyperactive, the fixed daily fee for the use of the cornucopia of facilities might be value for money. You could try to fit in visits to the Mark Phillips Equestrian Centre, the Jackie Stewart Shooting School, or one of the three golf courses.

As the sporting centres are scattered round the estate away from the main building, the inactive don't feel hounded. Of an afternoon, blue-rinsed ladies browse in the hotel's own Harvey Nicks and Burberrys on the shopping mall; the yet-to-be-coiffeured head off to the beauty salon; and families settle down in tartan armchairs in the pillared drawing-room to a big tea. Despite its size, it's not an anonymous hotel. All staff, from shop assistants to waitresses, pass the time of day with guests.

Bedrooms vary enormously in style and price. Some colour schemes might be a bit bold for some tastes; others are gentler and more feminine.

◑ Open all year

⤴ On the A823, just off the A9 mid-way between Stirling and Perth. Private car park

🛏 29 single, 59 twin, 121 double, 9 four-poster, 18 suites; all with

bathroom/WC, TV, room service, hair-dryer, mini-bar, trouser press; no tea/coffee-making facilities in rooms

◈ 3 restaurants, 4 bars, lounge, drawing-room, conservatory, games room; air-conditioned conference facilities (max 400 people); golf, tennis, riding, heated swimming-pool, gym, health spa, shooting school, water sports, falconry at hotel; babysitting. Wheelchair access to hotel (ramp), restaurant and WC (M, F), 13 ground-floor bedrooms, 2 specially equipped for disabled people

⊖ None

▭ Access, Amex, Diners, JCB, Visa

£ Single £115 to £145, single occupancy of twin/double £135, twin/double/four-poster £165 to £225, suite £245 to £880; deposit required. Set L £25, D £38.50; alc £50 (prices till Mar 94). Special breaks available

---

AUCHTERHOUSE TAYSIDE   **MAP 1**

Old Mansion House

AUCHTERHOUSE, BY DUNDEE, ANGUS DD3 0QN
TEL: AUCHTERHOUSE (082 626) 366   FAX: (082 626) 400

Professionally run and friendly hotel in a fascinating old building.

The chunky, whitewashed mansion with high dormer windows looks impressively austere, and you fear there may be draughty recesses inside. Not a bit of it. Everything is cosy and snug among some extraordinary architectural embellishments, such as a Jacobean fireplace in the old drawing-room emblazoned with a coat of arms and a fantastic dining-room ceiling dripping with plaster pendants. Dinner, a cut-glass and candlelit affair, is à la carte. Stone stairs lead to a book-lined bar, with a beautiful arch over the bar itself; at the rear of the building is a more workaday beamed drinking hole which offers a substantial lunch and a one-dish evening menu. Room Four used to be a nursery, its ceiling decorated with a representation of the pregnant Lady Buchan and four children. A reader says: 'Full marks to Mr and Mrs Bell in *every* respect of their operation. It is pretty faultless and I will certainly return.'

◑ Open all year, exc Xmas and New Year

↗ Take the A923 Coupar Angus road out of Dundee, cross the Kingsway and fork right at Muirhead on the A954. The hotel is on the left 2 miles on. Private car park

⇌ 3 twin, 2 four-poster, 1 family room; all with bathroom/WC, TV, room service, hair-dryer, mini-bar, baby-listening

◈ Restaurant, 2 bars, drawing-room; tennis, croquet, swimming-pool at hotel

⊖ No wheelchair access; no children in restaurant eves; no dogs in public rooms; no smoking in restaurant

▭ Access, Amex, Diners, Visa

£ Single occupancy of twin £70, twin £80 to £100, four-poster/family room £110. Set L £15; alc L, D £25

All rooms have tea/coffee-making facilities unless we specify to the contrary.

BALLACHULISH HIGHLAND **MAP I**

Ballachulish House

BALLACHULISH, ARGYLL PA39 4JX
TEL: BALLACHULISH (085 52) 266 (and fax)

*The only unwelcoming greeting you might receive at this
eighteenth-century home is from one of its resident ghosts.*

John and Liz Grey's lovely blue and white home is part of the Wolsey
Lodge chain, but is not of the kind where you have to eat *en famille* or
suffer excessive jovial hospitality. Family antiques, ornaments and paintings fill the L-shaped sitting-room. A little chandelier, a pillared fireplace and polished tables adorn the roomy dining-room. Liz's five-
course meals have been praised. 'No concessions to nouvelle cuisine,'
says the brochure. When the hotel is busy, expect a choice at most
courses; dishes may include scallops pan-fried with herbs or a cheese
and garlic tart to start, sole or duck as a main course and blackberry and
apple meringue or lemon syllabub for pudding.

Antiques furnish comely, personalised bedrooms; the two at the front
of the house are large, the two at the back cottagey.

◑ *Open all year, exc Xmas*

▞ *From Crianlarich take the A82 to
Ballachulish, at the roundabout
before Balluchulish Bridge take
the A828 towards Oban. The
hotel is 200 yards on left. Private
car park*

⊨ *2 twin, I double I family room;
all with bathroom/WC, hair-
dryer; TV on request*

◈ *Dining-room, drawing-room,
drying room; fishing, riding,*

water sports nearby

⊖ *No wheelchair access; no
children under 10 in dining-room
eves; no dogs in public rooms
and by arrangement only in
bedrooms; smoking in drawing-
room only*

▭ *Access, Visa*

£ *Single occupancy of twin/double
£37 to £48, twin/double £50 to
£76; deposit required. Set D
£19.50 (7.30 pm)*

BALLATER GRAMPIAN **MAP I**

Craigendarroch Hotel

BRAEMAR ROAD, BALLATER, DEESIDE AB35 5XA
TEL: BALLATER (03397) 55858   FAX: (03397) 55447

A busy complex, popular with families and sporty types.

This is a vast, efficiently run holiday complex. As well as a dry ski slope
and a curling lake (when iced over), 90-plus well-equipped lodges stud
the 29-acre estate. As well as the lodges, a first-rate leisure centre keeps
Craigendarroch busy all year round. You can relax in sofas or the smart
café while others exert themselves in the pools and squash courts.

The core of the enterprise is a ruddy old building where you can dine stylishly and expensively in the excellent Oaks Restaurant. There is a second, less exclusive restaurant, which also serves a vast assortment of breakfasts. Bedrooms are distinctively good: well-equipped, modern and cheerful, with large windows.

◑ Open all year

🔁 ½ mile outside Ballater on the A93 Braemar road. Private car park

🛏 24 twin, 18 double, 1 four-poster, 6 family rooms, 1 suite; all with bathroom/WC, TV, room service, hair-dryer, trouser press, baby-listening

◈ 3 restaurants, 2 bars, snooker room, study; conference facilities (max 50 people residential, 250 non-residential); tennis, sauna/solarium, heated swimming-pool, gym, health and beauty salon, spa bath at hotel, other sports nearby; crèche, adventure playground for children. Wheelchair access to hotel (ramp), 2 restaurants and WC (unisex), no ground-floor bedrooms but a lift, 1 bedroom specially equipped for disabled people

⊝ No dogs; no smoking in 1 restaurant

▭ Access, Amex, Diners, Visa

£ Single occupancy of twin/double £99, twin/double £125, four-poster £160, suite £175, family room £140 to £155; deposit required. Set D £10; alc L, D from £6

Tullich Lodge

BY BALLATER, ABERDEENSHIRE AB35 5SB
TEL: BALLATER (03397) 55406   FAX: (03397) 55397

A Victorian experience at this Scottish baronial mansion.

There are not many country houses in which a period style has been so thoroughly matched to the building as in Hector Macdonald and Neil Bannister's crenellated, turreted late-nineteenth-century lodge. Period antiques and heavy curtains carefully and stylishly carry the Victorian feel throughout the house.

First-time guests may feel a bit overawed by the regulars in the bar, where your outgoing hosts may encourage you to mix, but there are quieter places to escape to if you wish. The four-course dinner menu offers no choices, but if you don't fancy a particular dish just say so. Jacket and tie is the appropriate form of dress in the mahogany-panelled dining-room. An April menu offered smoked eel, tomato soup with pesto and roast rib of beef, with vanilla ice-cream in a basket with bramble purée, or cheeses, to finish.

◑ Closed Dec to end Mar

🔁 1½ miles east of Ballater on the A93 Aberdeen to Braemar road. Private car park

🛏 3 single, 4 twin, 3 double; most with bathroom/WC, some with shower/WC; room service, hair-dryer, baby-listening in all rooms;

trouser press in some rooms; no tea/coffee-making facilities in rooms

Dining-room, bar, 2 lounges, drying room. Wheelchair access to dining-room and bar only

● No dogs in public rooms; no smoking in dining-room

▭ Access, Amex, Diners, Visa

£ Single £95, single occupancy of twin/double £132, twin/double £190 (rates inc dinner). Light lunches £7; set D £23. Special breaks available

---

BALLINDALLOCH GRAMPIAN   **MAP 1**

Delnashaugh Inn

BALLINDALLOCH, BANFFSHIRE AB37 9AS
TEL: BALLINDALLOCH (0807) 500255   FAX: (0807) 500389

An inn in name only: a spruce Speyside hotel.

The old drovers' inn is immaculate both inside and out. Whitewashed walls and woodwork picked out in turquoise colour the long roadside building. The low-ceilinged modern-style interior is thoroughly smart; collections of monochrome armchairs are placed around coffee tables in the bar and sitting-room. Striking blue fish pictures bring to life a spick-and-span, intimate, candlelit dining-room. Service under David Ogden and his staff is polite and proper. Marion Ogden prepares delicious, unfancy four-course meals. As well as soup of the day and a selection of puddings or cheeses, you might choose home-made chicken liver pâté to start and lamb in mint sauce as a main course. Bedrooms, all in light modern furniture and with little buttonback armchairs, continue the trim, fresh, colourful décor.

◑ Closed Dec to mid-Feb

⬀ On the A95, 15 miles north-east of Grantown-on-Spey. Car park

⭤ 1 single, 8 twin; all with bathroom/WC, TV, room service, hair-dryer, baby-listening

Dining-room, bar, lounge; rod room, drying room; fishing, shooting at hotel. Wheelchair access to hotel (ramp), dining-room, WC (unisex) and 5 ground-floor bedrooms

● No dogs

▭ Access, Visa

£ Single £50, twin £130 (rates inc dinner). Set D £19.50

BALQUHIDDER CENTRAL   **MAP 2**

Monachyle Mhor ☆

BALQUHIDDER, LOCHEARNHEAD, PERTHSHIRE FK19 8PQ
TEL: STRATHYRE (08774) 622   FAX: (08774) 305

An off-the-beaten-track farmhouse run with bags of joie de vivre.

A delightful single-track lane takes you miles along the edge of Loch Voil to a farmhouse that stands above not one but two lochs. The sheep-farming Lewises own all the surrounding land. Jean evidently relishes playing host, confiding that the house often still buzzes after midnight.

The little bar in the heart of the building hums with noise and life. Old family pieces – an oak refectory table, Windsor chairs – furnish the original dining-room, but equally attractive is the pine conservatory across the front of the house that makes the best of the lovely views. Jean (helped by her sous-chef son) cooks well-complemented food.

For a bit of peace and quiet, head for the very homely sitting-room, with family antiques such as an old trunk here and an old writing desk there, or to the bedrooms upstairs. Don't expect great luxury and you won't be disappointed. The best is Room Four, a large double with a rocking chair by the window.

- ◑ *Open all year*
- ↗ *10 miles north of Callander on the A84. Turn right to Kingshouse and Balquhidder and continue for 2 miles to village; then proceed another 4 miles along lochside road. Private car park*
- 🛏 *1 twin, 4 double; most with bathroom/WC, some with shower/WC; room service, hair-dryer in all rooms*

- ◈ *Dining-room, bar, lounge, drying room, conservatory; conference facilities (max 20 people non-residential); fishing, stalking at hotel*
- ⊖ *No wheelchair access; no children under 10; no dogs; no smoking in bedrooms*
- 💳 *Access, Visa*
- £ *Twin/double £46; deposit required. Set L £13, D £15 to £18*

BANCHORY GRAMPIAN   **MAP 1**

Banchory Lodge

BANCHORY, KINCARDINE & DEESIDE AB31 3HS
TEL: BANCHORY (03302) 82625   FAX: (03302) 5019

An unstarchy comfortable riverside country-house hotel.

Regulars evidently feel they can really relax here – Banchory Lodge's atmosphere seems to cultivate such indolence. Of course there are others who will want to try their skill at landing salmon. The Georgian building, owned by the Jaffrays since 1966, has an uncultivated, well-established feel, from a slight fraying of a stair carpet to an excellent gents complete with brushes, hand cream and flannels. Pictures depicting country pursuits hang on the walls and fires glow in the bar and drawing-room. Hearty four-course dinners with a large assortment of traditional puddings are served in the Victorian dining-room, and the buffet in the breakfast room will fortify anglers for the day.

Bedrooms are big on comfort, with thoughtful additions like bathroom armchairs. The best are the de luxe river-facing rooms in the original building.

- Open all year, exc end Dec to end Jan
- 18 miles inland from Aberdeen on the A93, 2 minutes from centre of Banchory. Private car park
- 3 twin, 6 double, 2 four-poster, 9 family rooms, 2 suites; all with bathroom/WC; TV, room service, hair-dryer, baby-listening
- Dining-room, bar, lounge, drying room, study, games room; conference facilities (max 20 people residential); fishing (Feb to Sept), sauna at hotel, other sports nearby
- No wheelchair access
- Access, Amex, Diners, Visa
- Single occupancy of twin/double £65, twin/double £90, four-poster/family room £100, suite £110; deposit required. Set L £10, D £24.50. Special breaks available

---

Raemoir House Hotel ☆

BANCHORY, KINCARDINE & DEESIDE AB31 3HS
TEL: BANCHORY (03302) 4884   FAX: (03302) 2171

Magnificently dated, much-loved family-run country house.

The Sabin family began renting Raemoir House during the Second World War and soon opened it as a hotel. To refurbish or not to refurbish is the question. The main bone of contention is the 100-year-old tapestry wallpaper that covers much of the house. A long hallway connects the massive public rooms, filled with well-worn antiques; an elaborately carved Tudor four-poster supports the bar. The pine-panelled morning room has deep sofas and ceiling-length windows draped in gold. In the less stylish white and pink dining-room the menus offer largely traditional country-house fare, with a lengthy vegetarian selection.

Many bedrooms are named after countries to indicate their style of furnishing – French has gilt mirrors, Italian has inlaid period pieces and Old English an ancient four-poster.

- Open all year, exc 1st 2 weeks in Jan
- Take the A93 Aberdeen to Braemar road and at Banchory take the A980 (Torphins) road. Private car park
- 5 single, 7 twin, 7 double, 1 four-poster, 20 cottage/apartment rooms; most with bathroom/WC, some with shower/WC; TV, room service, hair-dryer, trouser press, baby-listening in all rooms
- Dining-room, bar, 2 lounges, TV room, ballroom, drying room; conference facilities (max 60 people non-residential, 30 residential); fishing, golf, tennis, sauna/solarium, gym, helipad, croquet at hotel, other sports nearby. Wheelchair access to hotel and apartments, restaurant and WC (M,F), 7 ground-floor bedrooms
- No children under 10 at dinner; no dogs or smoking in dining-room
- Access, Amex, Diners, Visa
- Single from £53, single occupancy of twin/double £68,

twin/double £115, four-poster £125, self-catering cottage rate on request; deposit required. Bar

lunches from £2; Sun L £14.50; set D £24.50; alc D £15. Special breaks available

BLAIRGOWRIE TAYSIDE   MAP 1

Kinloch House

BY BLAIRGOWRIE, PERTHSHIRE PH10 6SG
TEL: BLAIRGOWRIE (0250) 884237   FAX: (0250) 884333

A study in how to run a country-house hotel.

The moment you step into the oak-panelled hall of this Edwardian-styled country-house hotel an attendant greets you, and a roaring fire adds to the welcoming atmosphere. As your bags are whisked upstairs, you take in the stained-glass skylight and the portraits on the galleried landing. The only house rule is jacket and tie at dinner. Lots of thought has gone into your room: there are guidebooks, novels and magazines. Furniture mixes antique and pine, and the rooms in the new wing have particularly stylish bathrooms.

Choose a seat from the period buttonbacks in the bar or from the Lloyd Loom furniture in the sweet-smelling conservatory. Owner David Shentall comes to take your order from the four-course table d'hôte menu. Through to the dining-room, simply but smartly done in greens. The food is delicious, tending to the traditional in style and content, with old-fashioned numbers on the dessert trolley. A difficult diner who sends back a steak twice and ends up demanding duck is dealt with impeccably.

The following morning, breakfast is top notch: you can choose from scrambled eggs and smoked salmon, Arbroath smokie, smoked haddock, calves' liver.

◖ Open all year, exc 2 weeks at Xmas

On the A923, 3 miles west of Blairgowrie. Private car park

4 single, 6 twin, 3 double, 5 four-poster, 1 family room, 2 suites; all with bathroom/WC; TV, room service, hair-dryer, trouser press, baby-listening

◈ Dining-room, bar, lounge, TV room, drying room, conservatory; fishing, golf, other sports nearby. Wheelchair access to hotel (ramp), restaurant and

WC, 4 ground-floor bedrooms especially equipped for disabled people

⊝ No children under 7 in dining-room; dogs in certain bedrooms only; no smoking in dining-room

▭ Access, Amex, Diners, Visa

£ Single £73, single occupancy of twin/double £95, twin/double/four-poster £145, suite £178, family room rate on request (rates inc dinner). Set L £14, D £23

BRAE SHETLAND ISLANDS   **MAP 1**

Busta House

BRAE, SHETLAND ZE2 9QN
TEL: BRAE (080 622) 506   TELEX: 9312100218
FAX: (080 622) 588

An eighteenth-century laird's house on the loch shore.

This white, slightly austere, country house has an intriguing history.
Built in 1714 for the Gifford family it is reputedly the oldest continuously
inhabited house in the Shetland Isles. Among the spooky tales that Peter
and Judith Jones's staff will tell you is the story of a young woman who
married the Gifford heir and only revealed her existence to the family
after all the male heirs were drowned in a boating accident. The family
took her son as their own but sent the woman into exile, and now a
restless spirit roams the house looking for her lost child. Despite this,
Busta is a friendly place, with a popular bar. The dining-room is formal
and the food is fresh, home-cooked, with the emphasis inevitably on fish.
A typical à la carte meal might include tuna and smoked salmon crêpes,
Shetland double lamb cutlets with a red wine and mushroom sauce, and
home-made honey and walnut ice-cream. Bar meals tend to be slightly
simpler.

Bedrooms are surprisingly modern and are well-equipped. They vary
in size, but all are comfortable.

○ Closed 21 Dec to 6 Jan

⤴ From Lerwick take the A970 north to Brae. Bear left and take the left turn for Busta. Private car park

🛏 2 single, 8 twin, 9 double, 1 four-poster; most with bathroom/ WC, some with shower/WC; TV, room service, hair-dryer, trouser press, baby-listening in all rooms

◈ Restaurant, bar, 2 lounges, library, drying room; conference facilities (max 25 people residential); hotel fishing boat. Wheelchair access to restaurant only

⊖ No dogs in public rooms; no smoking in restaurant or library

▭ Access, Amex, Diners, Visa

£ Single £59, single occupancy of twin/double £69, twin/double £77, four-poster £83. Set D £20.50; bar meals. Special breaks available

BUNESSAN STRATHCLYDE   **MAP 2**

Ardfenaig House ☆

BY BUNESSAN, ISLE OF MULL, ARGYLL PA67 6DX
TEL: FIONNPHORT (06817) 210 (and fax)

A civilised home in a secluded lochside spot on Mull.

Malcolm and Jane Davidson have only been here since March 1991 after seeing an ad in the *Financial Times*. Their home has a white-shuttered grey stone Victorian front masking a much older building. It stands perfectly situated at the top of little Loch Caol under rock-sprinkled hills, its lawns running down to the water's edge.

The house is unostentatiously smart and comfortable. The front rooms, lighter and with loch views, are more appealing than the back rooms. Hence the sitting-room, with requisite log fire, sofas and personal paintings and china, makes more of an impression than the pine-furnished dining-room at the rear of the house. Likewise, choose one of the three loch-facing bedrooms. All the rooms are spacious, decorated in pine, floral fabrics and wicker chairs.

Jane's dinners comprise a hot or cold starter – perhaps avocado with raspberry vinaigrette or smoked venison – a set main course such as chicken in a white wine and mushroom sauce, and a hot or cold pudding.

◐ *Closed Nov to Mar*

⬈ *2 miles west of Bunessan on the A849. Turn right on the private road signposted 'Ardfenaig House, ½ mile'. Private car park*

🛏 *1 single, 2 twin, 2 double; 5 bathrooms; room service, hair-dryer in all rooms*

◈ *Dining-room, bar, lounge, TV room, drying room; fishing, water sports nearby. Wheelchair access to dining-room only*

⊖ *No children under 12; no dogs; no smoking in bedrooms and at guests' approval in public rooms*

▭ *Access, Visa*

£ *Single £70 to £85, twin/double £140 to £170 (rates inc dinner); deposit required. Set D £23.50*

CALLANDER CENTRAL   **MAP 2**

Roman Camp

CALLANDER, PERTHSHIRE FK17 8BG
TEL: CALLANDER (0877) 30003; changes to (0877) 330003 in 1994
FAX: (0877) 31533; changes to (0877) 331533 in 1994

A professionally run hotel with pretty rooms in a lovely, secluded old building.

Scottish TV has recently picked out Roman Camp, run by Eric and Marion Brown, as the country's most romantic hotel, and indeed its hideaway position off the high street of touristy Callander, its walled and riverside gardens and charming old building make it a fair choice. The seventeenth-century manor house that was used as a shooting-lodge by the Earls of Moray feels inn-like, with low ceilings, beams and creaky floors. This style prevails in the cosy bar and long dining-room, although in the latter the modern seating unfortunately detracts from the ceiling and timbers painted in period style. The tempting but pricey four-course set dinner comes with canapés and coffee and petits fours. Bedrooms in the original building are very pretty, with stencilled furniture, but they can be small: Lady Esher is the largest, with a magnificent fireplace sporting a clock and cherubs; those in the Victorian wing of the house are generally bigger but less attractive.

◗ Open all year

🔁 Head north on A84 from Stirling to Oban, turn left off Callander main street down 200-yard driveway to hotel. Private car park

🛏 4 twin, 6 double, 1 four-poster, 3 suites, family room available; all with bathroom/WC, TV, room service, hair-dryer, baby-listening

◈ Dining-room, bar, drawing-room, library, conservatory, drying room; conference facilities (max 40 people non-residential, 14 residential); fishing at hotel, other sports nearby; babysitting. Wheelchair access to hotel, restaurant and WC (M,F), 7 ground-floor bedrooms, 1 specially equipped for disabled people

⊖ No children under 2 in dining-room eves; no dogs in public rooms; no smoking in dining-room

▭ Access, Amex, Diners, Visa

£ Single occupancy of twin/double £50 to £70, twin/double £70 to £120, four-poster £70 to £90, suite £110 to £145, family room £120 to £155; deposit required. Set L £12.50 to £17, D £30; alc L to £38, D to £40. Special breaks available

---

CANONBIE DUMFRIES & GALLOWAY   **MAP 2**

Riverside Inn

CANONBIE, DUMFRIESSHIRE DG14 0UX
TEL: CANONBIE (03873) 71512/71295

A seventeenth-century whitewashed inn that's likely to please.

The welcome is warm and proprietors/chefs Robert and Susan Phillips wander around in the course of the evening talking to regulars and strangers alike, while Fluffy the cat ambles into the bar. Windsor chairs and flowers on slatted-topped tables make it smart and attractive, and equally relaxing is the sitting-room – with leather chesterfields – that encloses a plain dining-room.

Bar food, chalked on a blackboard, is of excellent quality and value. Main courses consist largely of the likes of steak or sole with salad and chips; soups and puddings are more exciting. The restaurant's five-course table d'hôte menu relies on unfussy presentation and first-rate Scottish ingredients: fish of the day, unpasteurised north-country cheese, Cumberland sausage, haggis, for example.

Our inspector's bedroom was large, with wing-chairs, chunky pieces of furniture and a spacious bathroom with pleasing prints.

◗ Closed 25 and 26 Dec, 1 and 2 Jan, all Feb and 2 weeks in Nov; restaurant closed Sun eve (but suppers available)

🔁 Leave the M6 at Junction 44 and take the A7 Edinburgh road for 10 miles, then follow signs to Canonbie. Private car park

🛏 3 twin, 2 double, 1 four-poster; all with bathroom/WC, exc

doubles with shower/WC, 2
public bathrooms; TV, room
service, hair-dryer in all rooms

◈ Dining-room, bar, lounge; fishing,
golf, other sports nearby.
Wheelchair access to hotel (1
step), restaurant and 1 ground-
floor bedroom

⊖ No children under 5; no dogs; no
smoking in public rooms

▭ Access, Visa

£ Single occupancy of twin/double
£55, twin/double £72, four-
poster £84; deposit required. Set
D £21; alc L £5 to £15. Special
breaks available

CRINAN STRATHCLYDE   MAP 2

Crinan Hotel

CRINAN, ARGYLL PA31 8SR
TEL: CRINAN (054 683) 261   FAX: (054 683) 292

*Yachtspeople, seafoodies, art-lovers and West Coast scenery-lovers
– all may develop a soft spot for this hotel.*

Seafood aficionados dining in the Lock 16 Restaurant, perched atop the
hotel, will be eating a proportion of the catch less than four hours after it
has been landed. The restaurant is only open May to September and
when the boats return with a catch to sell. At 8pm prompt you embark on
a menu which may include Loch Craignish mussels marinière, wild
smoked salmon and Sound of Jura lobster.

Nick Ryan has evolved an informal atmosphere over his twenty-odd
years here, assisted by a mix of professional staff and local fishermen's
wives. His wife, well-known Scottish artist Frances Macdonald, has
made the hotel devastatingly attractive in places. Adding to the maritime
bric-à-brac of sea chests and charts, her art – once of local landscapes,
now of interiors – fills the lockside bar, pink and blue sitting-room and
traditional brown and cream Westward Restaurant. (A steak might make
an appearance on the dinner menu here, but fish still predominates.)

All bedrooms, unelaborate but pretty in light florals and pine, have a
sea or lock view.

◑ Open all year, exc Xmas period

↗ Crinan village is at the north end
of the Crinan Canal – follow the
B841 from Cairnbaan. Private
car park

🛏 2 single, 12 twin, 6 double, 1
family room, 1 suite; all with
bathroom/WC, TV, room service;
tea/coffee-making facilities, hair-
dryer, trouser press on request

◈ 2 restaurants, 3 bars, 2 lounges,
drying room; conference facilities
(max 60 people non-residential,

22 residential); fishing, other
sports nearby. Wheelchair access
to hotel, restaurant and WC, no
ground-floor bedrooms but a lift
and 2 bedrooms specially
equipped for disabled people

⊖ No dogs in restaurants

▭ Access, Amex, Visa

£ Single £75, single occupancy of
twin/double £100, twin/double
£100 to £120, family room
£100, suite £240; deposit
required. Set D £25 to £37.50

CROMARTY HIGHLAND
MAP 1

Royal Hotel

MARINE TERRACE, CROMARTY, ROSS-SHIRE IV11 8YN
TEL: CROMARTY (03817) 217 (and fax)

A cosy waterfront inn with a hospitable Scottish landlord.

Stewart Morrison exactly fits the image of the archetypal hospitable Scottish landlord, spruce in a kilt day in, day out – 'Shifting kegs creases trousers,' he explains. The four eighteenth-century coastguards' cottages were converted into the Admiral Napier Hotel in 1830, to be renamed later when the sailor fell from favour. Behind a pine and wicker-furnished conservatory lies a lovely blue sitting-room with a coal fire. Sounds of raucous laughter may emanate from the bar next door, likely to be more convivial than the dining-room. The bar menu and daily specials come recommended, particularly the various savoury pancakes and fish dishes like crab soup, a mussel and onion stew or a trout tantaliser.

Bedrooms are large and simply done – with good-quality furniture and the requisite mod cons.

◐ Open all year; dining-room closed Sun eve

🔁 From the A9 turn right 1 mile north of Inverness on to the A832. Private car park

🛏 2 single, 2 twin, 4 double, 2 family rooms; all with bathroom/ WC, exc 1 family room with shower/WC; TV, hair-dryer, baby-listening in all rooms

◈ Dining-room, 2 bars, 2 lounges; conference facilities (max 12 people residential, 25 non-residential); shooting, bird-watching, other sports nearby; babysitting. Wheelchair access to dining-room only

⊖ No dogs in public rooms; no smoking in some public rooms

▭ Access, Amex, Visa

£ Single £30, single occupancy of twin/double £35, twin/double/ family room £50. Set L £11, D £16.50. Special breaks available

DERVAIG STRATHCLYDE
MAP 1

Druimnacroish

DRUIMNACROISH, DERVAIG, ISLE OF MULL, ARGYLL PA75 6QW
TEL: DERVAIG (06884) 274   FAX: (06884) 311

A charming, inspiring couple have created an oasis from next to nothing.

When the McLeans bought the old watermill in 1974 it was roofless. It is now hard to believe, looking at the much-extended smart stone building; the McLeans are justifiably proud of their achievements.

The house is supremely relaxing. Sitting-rooms are usually forsaken for the splendid outsize conservatory, where you can relax in peacock wicker chairs and garden loungers and study the abundant fruit on the vines and fig and orange trees. Wendy's dinners, served in the old-fashioned dining-room with studded leather seating, often begin with a fishy starter such as smoked salmon or avocado and prawns, followed by a roast or perhaps salmon, then a selection of puddings – always a fresh fruit bowl, something with and something without chocolate.

Bedrooms, though faultlessly comfortable, feel dated, with stripy wallpaper, reproduction buttonbacks and bright patterned carpets.

◑ Closed Nov to mid-Apr

⬀ From the Craignure ferry landing take the A849 Tobermory road. North of Salen fork left towards Dervaig for 8 miles. Private car park

🛏 4 twin, 2 double; all with bathroom/WC, TV, room service, hair-dryer

◈ Dining-room, bar, 3 lounges, conservatory; fishing, golf, riding, water sports nearby.

Wheelchair access to hotel, restaurant and WC, 2 ground-floor bedrooms

⊖ No children under 12; no dogs in public rooms; smoking in 1 lounge only

▢ Access, Amex, Diners, Visa

£ Single occupancy of twin/double £55, twin/double £110; deposit required. Set D £25 (8pm). Special breaks available

---

DRUMNADROCHIT HIGHLAND   **MAP 1**

Polmaily House

DRUMNADROCHIT, INVERNESS-SHIRE IV3 6XT
TEL: DRUMNADROCHIT (0456) 450343 FAX: (0456) 450813

Ambivalent impressions of this restful country house in a peaceful valley away from the ballyhoo of Loch Ness monster-spotters.

The guide has received mixed reports on Polmaily: one questioned its welcome for children, another felt it was run for the owners' convenience rather than that of the guests, whereas a third described it as 'first-rate in all respects'. Our inspector reckoned he had stayed in more comfortable and welcoming country houses but none the less had an enjoyable stay.

All our correspondents agree, however, on the excellence of the food. The two-part dining-room in the eighteenth-century part of the house acts as a setting for Alison Parsons' creative dishes, such as asparagus with creamed leeks and smoked ham, or traditional fare, such as bread-and-butter pudding. The breakfast selection of black, white or fruit pudding and various fish – kippers, kedgeree, haddock, Arbroath smokies, home-made fish cakes – suggests it is best to reserve a space in the tummy for the morning.

Nick Parsons officiates courteously outside the kitchens. The house, firmly Edwardian in feel if not everywhere in date, achieves a good balance of country home and hotel: family portraits hang in the hall.

Guests can enjoy the old furniture, fire, landscapes and books of the drawing-room, and there's a further games, books and TV room upstairs.

The four main rooms overlook the acres of mature gardens; Number Eight, at the back, is the quietest.

◐ Open all year

🔃 2 miles west of Drumnadrochit on the A831 Cannich road. Private car park

🛏 2 single, 2 twin, 3 double, 1 four-poster, 1 family room; all with bathroom/WC, exc singles, 3 public bathrooms

◇ Restaurant, bar, lounge, TV room; tennis, unheated swimming-pool at hotel, other sports nearby.

Wheelchair access to restaurant and WC (unisex) only

⊖ No dogs; no smoking in restaurant

▭ Access, Visa

£ Single £45, twin/double/four-poster/family room £50 to £100; deposit required. Set D £23 (prices till end 93). Special breaks available

---

DUNKELD TAYSIDE   **MAP 1**

Kinnaird

KINNAIRD ESTATE, BY DUNKELD, PERTHSHIRE PH8 0LB
TEL: PITLOCHRY (0796) 482440   FAX: (0796) 482289

A seriously luxurious small country-house hotel.

This is the kind of establishment where the gents is better equipped than most hotel bedrooms. Kinnaird was renovated by Mrs Constance Ward, who began taking paying guests in 1990. Bedrooms are voluptuous, with exuberant fabrics and armchairs in front of gas log fires. The hotel's sole whimsy is a Kinnaird teddy on each bed: 'They sell better than the rooms themselves,' quips manager Douglas Jack.

Overall, the subdued efficiency of the management style and the elegance of the eighteenth-century public rooms can give the house a rarified atmosphere. Fine paintings abound; tables stand yards apart in the dining-room, painted in nineteenth-century Italianate frescoes. The Edwardian wing, where a cedar-panelled drawing-room oozes warmth and comfort and opens on to a fine billiard room, is more relaxing.

John Webber offers very accomplished and beautifully presented nouvelle cuisine. Amuse-gueules and petits fours receive as much praise as the dishes on the three- or four-course dinner menu.

◐ Closed Feb

🔃 After passing Dunkeld village on your right, turn left on to the B898 signposted Dalguise and Balnaguard. After 4½ miles

Kinnaird's main gates are on the right. Private car park

🛏 1 twin, 7 double, 1 suite; all with bathroom/WC, TV, room service, hair-dryer; no tea/coffee-making facilities in rooms

2 dining-rooms, lounge, billiard room, drying room, study; conference facilities (max 25 people non-residential, 9 residential); fishing, tennis, shooting, croquet at hotel, golf, other sports nearby. Wheelchair access to hotel (ramps), dining-rooms and WC (unisex), 1 ground-floor bedroom specially equipped for disabled people, and lift

⊖ No children under 12; no dogs (kennel facilities available); no smoking in dining-rooms

▭ Access, Amex, Visa

£ Single occupancy of twin/double £95 to £135, twin/double £155 to £195, suite £230. Set L £19.50/£24, D £34/£38 (prices till Apr 94). Special breaks available

---

DUNVEGAN HIGHLAND   **MAP 1**

Harlosh House ☆

BY DUNVEGAN, ISLE OF SKYE, HIGHLAND IV55 8ZG
TEL: DUNVEGAN (047 022) 367   FAX: (047 022) 413

Magnificent views, isolation and sophisticated food.

The eighteenth-century whitewashed house has been a farmhouse, a school, even a butcher's. As a hotel it epitomises cosiness. Pine pieces decorate cottagey white bedrooms. Downstairs, a bar hatch opens on to the little, dowdy sitting-room; a coal fire burns and a telescope is trained on the mountains. The heavy wood tables in the equally small panelled and beamed dining-room stand too close together to offer much privacy. The menu, ambitiously long for such a small place, is exciting: a meal of avocado and smoked sprat salad, skate in black butter, home-made ice-cream, cafetière coffee and *petits fours* was deliciously created by chef Peter Elford. Lindsey Elford provides a cheery welcome.

◑ Closed mid-Oct to Easter

↗ Follow signs for Dunvegan. Once south of Dunvegan on the A863 follow signs for Harlosh. Follow this minor road for 2 miles. Private car park

🛏 4 twin, 2 double, family rooms available; most with bathroom/WC, some with shower/WC; room service, hair-dryer in all rooms

 Dining-room, bar/lounge, drying room; ironing facilities; fishing, riding nearby. Wheelchair access to restaurant only

⊖ No dogs; smoking in lounge only

▭ Access, Visa

£ Single occupancy of twin/double £66, twin/double £64 to £88, family room £106; deposit required. Alc D £20 to £25

Use the maps at the back of the Guide *to pinpoint hotels in a particular area.*

Castleton House

GLAMIS, BY FORFAR, ANGUS DD8 1SJ
TEL: GLAMIS (0307) 840340   FAX: (0307) 840506

Small, smart Edwardian country house.

The Edwardian house's finest feature is a large skylight over a balustraded gallery with an elegant staircase. Public rooms, though plush, lack an element of individuality. As well as a formal dining-room with drapes and gleaming wood you can eat in the large conservatory, the house's most enterprising room with its tartan curtains and lime green tables. Chef patron William Little offers a good-value set menu for the dining-room as well as an à la carte.

With just six bedrooms, the sleeping side of the operation is on a smaller scale. The furnishings are of high quality.

◗ Open all year

⤣ On the A94 between Coupar Angus and Forfar. Private car park

🛏 5 twin, 1 double; all with bathroom/WC, TV, room service, hair-dryer

◈ 2 restaurants, bar, lounge, drying room, conservatory; fishing, golf nearby. Wheelchair access to restaurant and WC (unisex) only

⛔ No dogs

▭ Access, Amex, Visa

£ Single occupancy of twin/double £65, twin/double £95. Set L £12.50, D £21.50; alc D £23

The Albany

39–43 ALBANY STREET, EDINBURGH EH1 3QY
TEL: 031-556 0397   FAX: 031-557 6633

A traditional hotel in a Georgian town house.

This fine set of terrace houses dating from 1812 has scrolled plaster and rosework on its façade. It has its architectural merits inside too, such as an impressive central stairway topped by a circular skylight. The sitting-room is a little formal for serious use, but downstairs PMs, a clubby basement bar, gets its share of local office types having a drink among the leather wall seats and bookshelves. You can get something like a burger, steak sandwich or pork chop here. The PMs restaurant is small and softly-lit. Its mixed grill or a dish of pork, beef and lamb fillets is likely to satisfy any appetite; a more interesting choice might be a mousse of lemon sole filled with lobster.

Guests with conservative tastes will approve of the unadorned bedrooms, which to date have escaped the clutches of interior designers but may need sprucing up a little in places. They are generally of a good size and are quiet – particularly so at the back.

◑ Open all year, exc 25, 26 Dec and 1, 2 Jan

↗ Albany Street runs parallel to Princes Street, near the bus station and St Andrew's Square. On-street parking and public car park nearby

🛏 5 single, 14 twin, 1 double, 2 family rooms; some with bathroom/WC, some with shower/WC; TV, room service, hair-dryer, baby-listening in all rooms

◇ Restaurant, bar, 2 lounges;

conference facilities (max 20 people residential and non-residential); golf, tennis, other sports nearby

⊖ No wheelchair access; no dogs in public rooms

▭ Access, Visa

£ Single £49 to £68, single occupancy of twin/double £55 to £75, twin/double £59 to £89; children under 12 free; deposit required. Cooked B not inc in room price. Set L £7, D £16.50; alc L, D £26.50

Channings ☆

12–16 SOUTH LEARMONTH GARDENS, EDINBURGH EH4 1EZ
TEL: 031-315 2226   FAX: 031-332 9631

Swanky business hotel with all the frills.

Five Edwardian bay-windowed houses in an Edinburgh brown stone terrace have been knocked together to form a luxurious base. The result is a series of small lounges and seating areas on the ground floor, all formally decked out in heavy drapes and soft sofas, and co-ordinated papers and borders in pastel blues and pinks. Bedrooms are 'individually designed': those at the front are usually spacious, but one reader complained that her double (Room 25) was 'only marginally bigger than the double bed', with a bathroom to match.

The basement brasserie suffers the perennial problem of lack of light, but soft yellow opaque uplighting gives a feeling of warmth; the tables are rather too close together. The menu draws inspiration from both sides of the Channel: bouillabaisse and cassoulet are up there along with roast venison and sirloin steak. The three-course table d'hôte menu has been described as 'good dinner-party fare without any pretensions apart from its ubiquitous coulis' and is deemed good value at £15.

◑ Open all year, exc Xmas period

↗ To the north of the city, just off the Queensferry Road. 10 minutes' walk from the west end of Princes Street. On-street parking

🛏 7 single, 17 twin, 24 double, family room available; most with bathroom/WC, some with shower/WC; TV, room service, hair-dryer, trouser press, baby-listening in all rooms

◇ Restaurant, bar, lounge, library;

conference facilities (max 35 people non-residential, 20 residential); golf, riding, other sports nearby

● No wheelchair access; no dogs; restricted smoking in restaurant

▭ Access, Amex, Diners, Visa

£ Single £73 to £83, single occupancy of twin/double £79 to £93, twin/double £95 to £115, family room rate on request; deposit required. Set L £6, D £15. Special breaks available

Drummond House ☆

17 DRUMMOND PLACE, EDINBURGH EH3 6PL
TEL: 031-557 9189 (and fax)

Accommodation in a stylishly restored Georgian house.

'I have never experienced the warmth and hospitality offered to me at Drummond House. The elegant surroundings, gourmet food and wine were a wonderful surprise. I felt like a valued friend staying in their home rather than a paying guest. What more could one want?'

Josephine and Alan Dougall started taking guests in August 1992. The terraced Georgian house, on a square in the New Town, used to be a students' rooming-house, but has since undergone a costly conversion to turn it into one home. The Dougalls in fact make a living out of restoring lovely old Edinburgh buildings – the most acceptable of property developers.

First impressions are of pillars, rugged stone floors and tapestries hanging over the staircase. The pine-floored bedrooms with strikingly simple furniture are less daunting. One has a high Victorian bed; another has a matching set of art deco walnut furniture.

Socialising with your hosts is the form. Josephine's dinners – usually comprising Scottish ingredients such as game, venison or lamb – are served *en famille* in the formal dining-room, preceded by drinks.

◑ Open all year

↗ Drummon Place is just north of St Andrew Square and Waverley Station. At the east end of Great King Street. On-street parking

⏃ 1 twin, 2 double; all with bathroom/WC, hair-dryer, TV on request; no tea/coffee-making facilities in rooms

◈ Dining-room, lounge; fishing, golf, other sports nearby

● No wheelchair access; no children under 12; no dogs; no smoking

▭ Access, Visa

£ Single occupancy of twin/double £50, twin/double £70; deposit required. Set D £25 (7.30pm)

Scandic Crown

80 HIGH STREET, THE ROYAL MILE, EDINBURGH EH1 1TH
TEL: 031-557 9797   FAX: 031-557 9789

A business hotel in the heart of the old town.

The new look Scandic Crown offers a shiny black and white marble foyer and a lounge in the Advocate's Library, furnished with leather chester-fields and providing 'butler' service, power breakfasts and a day-long menu of oysters, lobster and brioche filled with pâté de foie gras. The old bistro has been revamped too, and its replacement, Carrubbers, takes up an interior courtyard of jasminc-fillcd window boxes and colourful murals. An à la carte menu complements the smorgasbord buffet.

Staff are as professional and friendly as ever; a snug basement bar stays open into the small hours; a compact, stylish leisure complex provides exercise; the car park in Edinburgh's congested centre is a great bonus. The many bedrooms pamper to the modern traveller's every imagined and unimagined need. If you don't sleep well you're offered a free night's accommodation.

◑ *Open all year*

🡵 *From Waverley Station, cross North Bridge to the first set of traffic lights. The hotel is on the left on the Royal Mile. Private car park*

🛏 *26 single, 122 twin, 72 double, 8 family rooms, 10 suites; all with bathroom/WC, TV, room service, hair-dryer, mini-bar, trouser press*

◇ *Restaurant, bar, lounge, library; conference facilities (max 220 people residential and non-residential); sauna, solarium, heated swimming-pool, gym at hotel, other sports nearby; babysitting by arrangement. Wheelchair access to hotel, restaurant and WC, 3 bedrooms specially equipped for disabled people*

⊖ *Dogs by arrangement*

▭ *Access, Amex, Diners, Visa*

£ *Single £94, single occupancy of twin/double £114, twin/double £135, suite £240, family room rate on request (prices till end Mar 94). Cooked B £10; alc L, D from £15*

Sibbet House

26 NORTHUMBERLAND STREET, EDINBURGH EH3 6LS
TEL: 031-556 1078   FAX: 031-557 9445

A small, enthusiastically run luxury guesthouse.

Sibbet House has beautiful period features such as a cupola over the high stairwell. Its owners, Jim Sibbet and his exuberant French wife Aurore, dabble in antiques, so it's sumptuously furnished: decorative plates cover the walls, chandeliers hang from ceilings and chunky Victorian side-boards line the dining-room. The Sibbets may socialise with you in the evening in the grand guests' drawing-room on the first floor, where there's a little bar.

Attention to colour and detail make the three bedrooms – named Blue, Yellow and Green – delightful. The coronet-draped Blue room is the best, enlivened by such details as mini-chandeliers for bedside lights and an exercise bike in the bathroom. A concise report summarises: 'Comfortable, clean, excellent-value guesthouse in a very convenient central location.'

◑ Open all year

🔀 Northumberland Street runs parallel to Princes Street, four streets north. Private car park and on-street parking

🛏 1 double, 2 family rooms; double with bathroom/WC, family rooms with shower/WC; TV, hair-dryer, trouser press in all rooms

◈ Dining-room, drawing-room, library; golf, tennis, other sports nearby

⊖ No wheelchair access; no dogs; no smoking

▭ Access, Visa

£ Single occupancy of double £35 to £50, double £45 to £60, family room £60; deposit required. Set D £18.50

---

28 Northumberland Street

28 NORTHUMBERLAND STREET, EDINBURGH, LOTHIAN EH3 6LS
TEL: 031-557 8036   FAX: 031-558 3453

A top-of-the-range bed and breakfast in the Georgian New Town.

A report lavishes praise: 'Warmth, elegance, total comfort, relaxed atmosphere and discreet attention make staying at the home of Ian and Eirlys Smith a real delight. We cannot recommend them highly enough.' The house's basement has been converted into guest bedrooms. The feminine single has a tented ceiling and a massive bathroom next door; the two twins, one in blue and the other in red, have coronet beds and quality period furniture; the Blue Room has french windows.

Breakfast, taken on a large dining-table in an impressively proportioned room, is beautifully done and served on lovely china. As well as a full Scottish breakfast, there may also be a fresh fruit salad.

◑ Open all year

🔀 Northumberland Street runs parallel to Princes Street, 4 streets to the North. On-street parking

🛏 1 single, 2 twin; single with bathroom/WC, twins with shower/WC; TV, hair-dryer, trouser press in all rooms

◈ Dining-room/residents' lounge; tennis, swimming, other sports nearby

⊖ No wheelchair access; no dogs; no smoking

▭ Access, Visa

£ Single £25 to £35, single occupancy of twin/double £45 to £55, twin/double £50 to £70; deposit required

---

Prices are what you can expect to pay in 1994, except where specified to the contrary. Many hoteliers tell us that these prices can be regarded only as approximations.

ELGIN GRAMPIAN MAP 1

Mansion House Hotel

THE HAUGH, ELGIN, MORAYSHIRE IV30 1AW
TEL: ELGIN (0343) 548811 FAX: (0343) 547916

A Victorian country house with plush bedrooms.

Mansion House feels pretty countrified Inside, the dark stone Victorian building is staple country-house fare, with elegant furnishings in the piano lounge and restaurant and a fine selection of malts in the still room.

The layout of the house is a little odd, with the billiard room in the centre of the building and a smart leisure complex at the rear. Soon all the bedrooms are to have four-posters. All have bright designs, good-quality furniture and a host of extras, though some are a little cramped and one guest complained about housekeeping standards. There is an extensive bar menu (from soup to steak via haggis and black pudding) and an à la carte restaurant menu. Portuguese owner Fernando Oliveira makes a point of chatting to guests.

◐ Open all year

⤢ Behind Ladyhill in the town centre. Private car park

🛏 2 single, 4 twin, 14 four-poster; all with bathroom/WC, TV, room service, hair-dryer, mini-bar, trouser press, baby-listening

◈ Dining-room, bar, lounge, library/ study, games room; conference facilities (max 100 people non-residential, 20 residential);

sauna/solarium, heated swimming-pool, gym at hotel, other sports nearby

⊖ No wheelchair access; no dogs

▭ Access, Amex, Diners, Visa

£ Single £75, single occupancy of twin/double £90, twin/double £110, four-poster £140; deposit required. Alc L, D £25; bar lunches. Special breaks available

---

ERISKA STRATHCLYDE MAP 1

Isle of Eriska

LEDAIG, BY OBAN, ARGYLL PA37 1SD
TEL: LEDAIG (0631 72) 371 FAX: (0631 72) 531

Everything you could want from a first-rate country-house hotel.

'As a rule we never return to the same hotel but we returned to Eriska and were not disappointed,' declares a satisfied customer. The late-Victorian baronial mansion, all towers and chimneys, commands its lilliputian territory. Swathes of lawn for croquet, putting or sun-lounging keep the wilder parts of the domain at bay. 'The Buchanan-Smith family are marvellous hosts,' writes one happy guest. Over 20 years they have created a grand but very relaxing and habitable country house. A crackling fire, a ticking grandfather clock and a rustle of newspapers in the oak-panelled hall set the scene. Surrounding rooms, all light with long windows, fine plasterwork ceilings and carved fireplaces, offer acres of space. They vie for loveliness: the drawing-room has fine furniture and a grand piano; the L-shaped dining-room and its wheatsheaf chairs is suitably formal; but the leather-seated library/bar is the most popular. Bedrooms, with interesting fabrics and furniture, are very individual. Corner rooms such as Lismore and Kerrera are particularly popular.

Impressive six-course dinners often have a roast carved at the table as their centrepiece. At earlier stages there might be roast monkfish on a bed of home-made black pasta or chilled white fish terrine with lemon yogurt.

◑ *Closed Dec to Mar*

↗ *Take the A85 Crianlarich road over Connel Bridge. Isle of Eriska is signposted from Benderloch. Private car park*

🛏 *2 single, 4 twin, 9 double, 1 family room, 1 suite; all with bathroom/WC, TV, room service, hair-dryer, trouser press, baby-listening*

◈ *Dining-room, 2 lounges, library; conference facilities (max 17 people residential); tennis, riding, croquet, putting green, clay pigeon shooting, fishing, water sports at hotel, golf, gliding*

nearby; babysitting by arrangement. Wheelchair access to hotel (ramp) and dining-room, 2 ground-floor bedrooms specially equipped for disabled people

⊖ *No children under 10 in dining-room eves; no dogs in public rooms*

▭ *Access, Visa*

£ *Single £125, twin/double/family room £135 to £170, suite £315; deposit required. Set D £35 (prices till end 93). Special breaks available*

ETTRICKBRIDGE BORDERS   **MAP 2**

Ettrickshaws

ETTRICKBRIDGE, BY SELKIRK, SELKIRKSHIRE TD7 5HW
TEL: ETTRICKBRIDGE (0750) 52229

The position of this small country-house hotel is its best asset.

The late-Victorian pebbledash building retains original features such as panelling, ornate fireplaces and an internal bell system (no longer working). The furnishings may strike you as somewhat lurid in places – a bright purple carpet in the hall, an oriental-style metallic wallpaper in the dining-room – but in public rooms and bedrooms alike there is plenty of space and enough comfort.

David and Barbara White, here since 1988, do pretty much everything themselves. David does the cooking. Starters include a soup and perhaps haggis, main courses a fish or meat dish such as beef Stroganoff, and desserts ice-creams or something substantial like bread-and-butter pudding.

◑ Closed Dec and Jan

⤢ 1½ miles west of Ettrickbridge on the B7009. Private car park

🛏 3 twin, 3 double (family room available); all with bathroom/WC, exc 1 twin with shower/WC; TV in all rooms; room service, hair-dryer on request

◈ Restaurant, bar, lounge, drying room; fishing at hotel, golf, riding nearby

⊖ No wheelchair access; no children under 9; no dogs in public rooms; no smoking in some public rooms

▭ Access, Diners, Visa

£ Single occupancy of twin/double £45 to £55, twin/double £64 to £72, family room £80 to £90; deposit required. Bar lunches; set D £13.50; alc D £18. Special breaks available

---

FETTERCAIRN GRAMPIAN   **MAP 1**

Ramsay Arms

FETTERCAIRN, KINCARDINESHIRE AB30 1XX
TEL: FETTERCAIRN (0561) 340334   FAX: (0561) 340500

A simple Victorian coaching-inn below the Grampians.

Queen Victoria stayed here incognito (a nineteenth-century hotel inspector?). An extract from her diary reads: 'We reached the small, quiet town, or rather village, of Fettercairn . . . and we got out at the quiet little inn, "Ramsay Arms", quite unobserved, and went at once upstairs.'

Jeff and Kate Evans cheerfully run an unelaborate sort of place, partly because of financial dictates, partly because that's the way locals like it. One side of the bar is spit 'n' sawdust with darts, pool and TV, the other side, a little more salubrious, is used for lunch and supper bar food: offerings include steaks, home-made soups and pies. Grander dining – with lots of game – takes place in the panelled Gladstone Room. There are three smart refurbished bedrooms; the rest are resolutely old-fashioned, with woodchip wallpaper, old armchairs and solid oak furniture.

◑ Open all year

⤢ Take the B974 from the A94 Forfar to Aberdeen road. Private car park

🛏 3 single, 5 twin, 2 double, 1 four-poster, 1 family room; all with bathroom/WC, TV, room service, hair-dryer

◈ Dining-room, 2 bars, lounge, drying room; conference facilities (max 40 people non-residential, 12 residential); sauna, Jacuzzi at hotel, other sports nearby; babysitting

⊖ No wheelchair access

▭ Access, Diners, Visa

£ Single £33, single occupancy of twin/double £33, twin/double £50, four-poster £55, family room from £56; deposit required. Bar meals £7.50; alc D £15

Are you aware of your rights as a consumer when you book into a hotel? Check them out on page 837.

Factor's House

TORLUNDY, FORT WILLIAM, INVERNESS-SHIRE PH33 6SN
TEL: FORT WILLIAM (0397) 705767   FAX: (0397) 702953

Effective, modern accommodation in a home run with informality.

The Factor's House was built at Inverlochy Castle's driveway entrance for the estate manager at the turn of this century; it underwent a major overhaul in its conversion into a hotel in the 1980s, so it feels more modern than Edwardian. Bedrooms, some of which are on the small side, have a spartan design of bamboo and two-tone walls. A handsome extension with a high wooden ceiling contains the dining-room. The cooking is homely and straightforward; a blackboard announces a choice of dishes such as smoked salmon or prawn bisque, steak, sole or chicken, and profiteroles or apple pie.

Informality is the lynchpin to this small hotel. Peter Hobbs and his wife join you for coffee in the casual sitting-room after dinner.

◑ *Closed Nov to Mar; dining-room closed Sun, Mon eves*

↗ *3 miles north of Fort William, just off the A82 Inverness road. Private car park*

🛏 *2 twin, 4 double; all with bathroom/WC, TV, room service; hair-dryer on request; no tea/coffee-making facilities in rooms*

◈ *Dining-room, lounge, TV room,*

drying room; tennis at hotel, fishing, golf, other sports nearby

⊖ *No wheelchair access; no children under 6 in dining-room, no dogs in public rooms and by arrangement only in bedrooms*

▭ *Access, Amex, Visa*

£ *Single occupancy of twin/double £47 to £65, twin/double £65 to £83; deposit required. Set D £20*

Inverlochy Castle

TORLUNDY, FORT WILLIAM, INVERNESS-SHIRE PH33 6SN
TEL: FORT WILLIAM (0397) 702177   FAX: (0397) 702953

Scotland's grandest, most famous country-house hotel.

A rather blinkered inspector thought nothing of the motorcade of Daimlers and police motorcycles when he visited. He had blundered in on a state visit: the President of Portugal was just finishing his lunch. There can be few hotels where an inspector is still welcomed in such circumstances, but managing director Michael Leonard found time to chat and offer coffee. It is this level of service that makes Inverlochy particularly memorable. One guest found it to be impeccable – 'Courteous, attentive and yet not cloying.'

The great hall would probably win a competition for the UK's most awesome hotel room: an extraordinarily ornate chandelier hangs from a painted ceiling of celestial cherubs. Gilt mirrors and ormolu furniture furnish the less showy though equally sumptuous drawing-room. Up-stairs, a splendid array of stags' heads peer down from the green and white striped walls of the billiard room. The quality and freshness of bedrooms was 'of the highest possible standard', continued the above report.

In the dauntingly formal restaurant our correspondent found that though the standard of cuisine was not equivalent to that of top-flight London restaurants (though prices are), the cooking over a three-night stay achieved a uniformly high standard.

◐ *Closed Dec to 1 Mar*

↗ *On the A82 Glasgow to Inverness road, 3 miles north of Fort William, just past the golf club. Private car park*

🛏 *1 single, 14 twin/double, 1 suite; all with bathroom/WC, TV, room service, hair-dryer, trouser press, baby-listening; no tea/coffee-making facilities in rooms*

◈ *2 dining-rooms, 2 lounges, billiard room, library, drying room; conference facilities (max 30 people non-residential, 16*

residential); fishing, tennis, billiards at hotel, golf, other sports nearby; babysitting

⊖ *No wheelchair access; no children under 12 in dining-rooms eves; no dogs*

▭ *Access, Amex, Visa*

£ *Single £135 to £145, twin/double £220 to £275, suite £280 to £285; deposit required. Set L £24 to £27, D £40; alc L £28 (prices till end 93). Special breaks available*

GALASHIELS BORDERS   **MAP 2**

Woodlands Country House

WINDYKNOWE ROAD, GALASHIELS, SELKIRKSHIRE TD1 1RQ
TEL: GALASHIELS (0896) 4722 (and fax)

An imposing building but relaxed atmosphere.

This Gothic mansion, with requisite gargoyles and crenellations, was built in 1860 for a local mill owner; it became a hospital during the Second World War, before converting to a children's home. The present owners, Kevin and Nicki Winsland, have been here since 1989, and run a friendly, relaxed hotel.

The interior has some fine features, such as high ceilings and wood panelling. A stone archway with carved capitals leads to a lush dining-room in pinks and burgundies, with chandelier and marble fireplace. Cuisine is themed by ports around the world (from soused herrings – Bremen – to steak in a light teriyaki sauce – Tokyo). The comfortable but less stylish bar has an extensive bistro menu, and a new venture was about to open when our inspector visited – the Sanderson Steak House. Bedrooms and bathrooms, furnished in reproduction furniture, are generally spacious and unfancy.

◑ Open all year

⤤ Off the A7 from Edinburgh or Carlisle, through Galashiels. The hotel is on the back road towards Peebles. Travel up Hall Street and take the 2nd right. Private car park

🛏 2 single, 2 twin, 4 double, 1 half-tester (family rooms available); all with bathroom/WC, exc 1 single with shower/WC; TV, room service, hair-dryer, trouser press, baby-listening in all rooms

◈ 2 restaurants, bar, lounge, drying room, conservatory; golf, tennis, other sports nearby

⊖ No wheelchair access; no dogs in public rooms

▭ Access, Visa

£ Single £40, single occupancy of twin/double £47, twin/double/half-tester £68, family room £88. Set L £13, D £18.50; alc L £4 to £10, D £5 to £13. Special breaks available

---

GARVE HIGHLAND   **MAP 1**

Inchbae Lodge ☆

BY GARVE, ROSS-SHIRE IV23 2PH
TEL: AULTGUISH (09975) 269

Isolated Victorian hunting-lodge in the northern Highlands.

The countryside all around is spectacular, but the facing hillside, recently denuded of trees, looks rather wounded. There are chalet rooms, used only in summer and good for people with dogs: 'A bit tired, but warm, clean and spacious with a verandah,' comments a report. Main-house rooms are considerably better, light and with pine furniture. Locals drop in at the Victorian building's cosy little bar, with wheelbacks and wall seats and tables sliced from tree trunks, for a drink and a natter. For residents there's a comfortable if a little characterless sitting-room.

Leslie and Charlotte Mitchell pride themselves on their food, and a guest describes the four-course dinner as 'excellent'. It might feature game such as partridge or grouse. There's also an interesting good-value bar menu, offering anything from mussels to 'casserole dish of the day'.

◑ Open all year, exc 25, 26 Dec (chalet bedrooms closed in winter)

⤤ 6 miles west of Garve on the A835 Inverness to Ullapool Road. Private car park

🛏 4 twin, 5 double, 3 family rooms; some with bathroom/WC, most with shower/WC; room service to all rooms

◈ Dining-room, bar, 2 lounges, drying room; fishing, clay pigeon shooting, stalking at hotel; baby-listening on request

⊖ No wheelchair access; no dogs in public rooms; no smoking in dining-room

▭ None accepted

£ Single occupancy of twin/double £33, twin/double £56, family room from £56; deposit required. Bar meals from £5; set D £21. Special breaks available

GIFFORD LOTHIAN
MAP 2

Forbes Lodge

GIFFORD, EAST LOTHIAN EH41 4JE
TEL: GIFFORD (062 081) 212

A fascinating, spiritedly run private home of Wolsey Lodge ilk.

'Nothing changes here from year to year,' assures the admirable Lady Marioth Hay, 'except a bit of wallpaper peeling.' The handsome brown stone Georgian building lies within the pretty estate village of Gifford amidst a lovely garden that holds sweet-smelling rare plants.

Family heirlooms overload the house – life-size family portraits and the like which were once in better proportion in the palatial rooms of nearby Yester House. Lady Marioth joins guests for a drink in the drawing-room before serving dinner round a single dining-table in a room decorated in a pillar motif. A couple wanting English cooking were offered smoked salmon mousse, pheasant and rhubarb tart. Vegetables and fruit are home-grown. 'Sumptuous dinner and excellent cooked breakfast,' judges a reader.

Bedroom shutters are closed during the day to stop the sunlight fading watercolours. Beautiful ornaments and fine writing cabinets can also be found in all four. 'Exceptionally comfortable beds, flowers, fresh milk for tea, a great selection of bath essences in a very large bathroom,' enthuses a guest.

- ◐ Open all year; dining-room open by arrangement only
- ↗ Take the road to Haddington and follow the signs to Gifford. Turn towards Edinburgh and Forbes Lodge is the first house on the right, beyond the bridge over the stream
- 🛏 2 single (1 four-poster room), 2 twin; some with bathroom/WC
- ◈ Dining-room, drawing-room, drying room, library; golf nearby
- ⊖ No wheelchair access; no children under 12; no dogs; no smoking in bedrooms
- ▭ None accepted
- £ Single £40, single occupancy of twin/double £40, twin/double £80; deposit required. Set D £18 (by arrangement, 8pm)

GLASGOW STRATHCLYDE
MAP 2

Babbity Bowster

16–18 BLACKFRIARS STREET, GLASGOW G1 1PE
TEL: 041-552 5055

Simple bedrooms in a venue serving a variety of purposes.

Babbity Bowster is a Robert Adam building in a side-street in the Merchant City area of Glasgow. It opened in 1986 after a complete restoration from 'an advanced state of dereliction'. In the bar, its understated décor of grey bench seats and tables offset by striking photos of Glasgow characters, there are all sorts: a boisterous group of blokes; an artist supping a glass of wine, his leather portfolio case propped against the bar; a young woman reading the newspaper over a sandwich. Bar staff have dexterous social skills, equally at ease with all, and strangers are made to feel as welcome as regulars.

The bar food offers something for everyone: sandwiches, chillies, haggis, neeps and tatties, Loch Fyne mussels and much more. The restaurant upstairs is informal, the kitchen opening on to a lovely pine-furnished dining-room. As you reach the top of the building, the poster-covered stairs become bare to reveal a little oasis of six compact, no-frills, modern bedrooms in blues and greys.

- ◑ *Open all year, restaurant closed Sun eve*
- ↗ *In the city centre. Private car park*
- ⭗ *1 single, 4 twin, 1 double; all with shower/WC*
- ◈ *Restaurant, café/bar*
- ⊖ *No wheelchair access; no dogs*
- ▭ *Access, Amex, Visa*
- £ *Single £36, single occupancy of twin/double £40, twin/double £56. Continental B £2, cooked B £4; set L £5 to £8, D £11.50/ £14.50; alc D £10 to £15*

One Devonshire Gardens

1 DEVONSHIRE GARDENS, GLASGOW G12 0UX
TEL: 041-339 2001   FAX: 041-337 1663

The place to stay in Glasgow: a highly individual hotel.

'Please ring for personal attention,' it says on each of the three doorways of its section of the Victorian terrace. A white-pinafored factotum greets you as you step into this haven of peace. The drawing-room is equipped with the plushest of sofas, trunks and sets of miniature portraits, and the cosy Club Bar with tartan chairs and elephant stools. Diners congregate in another splendid, opulently furnished sitting-room before proceeding to the dining-room, an extravagant affair arranged round a silk-leafed tree and theatrically spotlit at night. The cuisine offered by the fixed-price four-course menu is classy and assured.

The beautifully designed bedrooms are all vastly different, but all have the most luxurious fabrics and exceptional marble bathrooms. Perhaps the boldest is a room where the fabrics and the bathroom are black. Staff are chirpy yet singularly professional.

- ◑ *Open all year*
- ↗ *From the M8 take the A82 Dumbarton/Kelvinside turn-off. Turn right into Great Western Road. At the ninth set of traffic lights turn left into Hyndland Road, then first right to Devonshire Gardens. Private car park*
- ⭗ *3 twin, 13 double, 9 four-poster, 2 suites; most with bathroom/ WC, some with shower/WC; TV, room service, hair-dryer, mini-bar, baby-listening in all rooms;*

no tea/coffee-making facilities in rooms

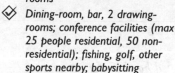 Dining-room, bar, 2 drawing-rooms; conference facilities (max 25 people residential, 50 non-residential); fishing, golf, other sports nearby; babysitting

● No wheelchair access; no dogs in bedrooms; no smoking

▭ Access, Amex, Diners, Visa

£ Single occupancy of twin/double £110 to £115, twin/double/four-poster £100 to £145, suite £180; deposit required. Continental B £7.50, cooked B £10; set L £19, D £35 (prices till end 93)

The Town House

4 HUGHENDEN TERRACE, GLASGOW G12 9XR
TEL: 041-357 0862   FAX: 041-339 9605

Guesthouse accommodation in a lovely building.

Bill and Charlotte Thow's Town House offers a radically different conversion of a fine Victorian building. First impressions of carefully exposed cornice work, carved lintels over pine-stripped doors and a grand skylit stairway suggest that this is not the inexpensive guesthouse you thought it was. Other aspects of the establishment are less elaborate, however. Bedrooms share the spaciousness of the rest of the building but are undecorative and kitted out with simple furniture. Neither of the bright, high-ceilinged front rooms is fancily furnished, but prints by a local artist enliven the dining-room and books and brown leather sofas make the sitting-room welcoming. Breakfast can be full Scottish of the porridge and kippers variety; the straightforward dinner menu may include staples such as salmon or sirloin steaks.

◑ Open all year

↗ From the A82 Great Western Road, turn right at the Hyndland signpost and then first right into Hughenden Road; right at the mini-roundabout. On-street parking

🛏 1 twin, 7 double, 2 family rooms; all with shower/WC, TV, baby-listening; hair-dryer on request; limited room service

◈ Dining-room, lounge; conference facilities (max 10 people residential, 20 non-residential); golf, tennis, swimming-pool nearby

● No wheelchair access; no dogs; no smoking in dining-room

▭ Access, Visa

£ Single occupancy of twin/double £44 to £48, twin/double £59 to £60, family room from £60; deposit required. Alc D £20

It is always worth enquiring about the availability of special breaks or weekend prices. The prices we quote are the standard rates for one night – most hotels offer reduced rates for longer stays.

Town House

54 WEST GEORGE STREET, GLASGOW G2 1NG
TEL: 041-332 3320   FAX: 041-332 9756

Out-of-the-ordinary business-oriented hotel in the city centre.

The splendid red sandstone early Edwardian building has great lions guarding its portals. It was once the Liberal Club, and also formed part of the Royal Scottish Academy of Music and Drama. The most impressive room is the old recital room, now a colossal dining-room, with ceiling-length windows, minstrels' gallery, grand piano, fountain and stucco work; the spacious cocktail bar can't compete, but is nevertheless elegant. A little street noise is audible in the high-quality, quite masculine, well-designed bedrooms. Standard rooms are large; superior rooms are even bigger, with sofas. The key card system for bedroom entry is fallible, reports a guest. The cuisine, described as 'modern British', makes good use of local ingredients, offering complicated concoctions such as breast of guinea-fowl wrapped in a lattice of pastry.

A critical letter focuses on housekeeping problems, at the same time praising staff for being friendly and helpful.

◑ Open all year

⤢ At the George Square end of West George Street, in the city centre. Parking difficult; limited on-street parking

🛏 3 single, 11 twin, 16 double, 2 four-poster, 2 suites; all with bathroom/WC, TV, room service, hair-dryer, trouser press, mini-bar, baby-listening

◈ Restaurant, bar, lounge; conference facilities (max 150 people non-residential, 34 residential); golf, tennis, other sports nearby

⊖ No wheelchair access; no dogs in public rooms

▭ Access, Amex, Diners, Visa

£ Single £80, single occupancy of twin/double £80, twin/double £91, four-poster £97, suite £133, family room rate on request. Continental B £6.50, cooked B £9; set L £12, D £19; alc L, D £30

GLENBORRODALE HIGHLAND   **MAP 1**

Glenborrodale Castle

GLENBORRODALE, ACHARACLE, ARGYLL PH36 4JP
TEL: GLENBORRODALE (09724) 266   FAX: (09724) 224

The position, architecture and interior of this Victorian Gothic castle make it Scotland's most visually seductive hotel.

Glenborrodale's red sandstone towers thrust out of luxuriant vegetation in the most protected of spots on the shores of Loch Sunart. On the loch, the sails of yachts slowly appear and disappear round little islands to a backdrop of mountainous coastline. One guest accurately sums up the hotel's main drawback by focusing on its lack of a welcoming family, something for which the professionalism of the staff, led by manager Charles Carroll, cannot make up.

Inside, arches and vaulted corridors lead to breathtakingly sumptuous reception rooms, the beauty and richness of the rugs, antiques and soft furnishings concomitant with the fine panelling and marble. Pastoral scenes on tapestry-style paintings enliven a less exuberant dining-room. A reader reckons you can expect to eat well but unmemorably from inventive but not over-refined cuisine.

Bedrooms are supremely attractive and of course comfortable, as are the lovely bathrooms, many with freestanding Victorian baths. Criticism about an inexcusable lack of hot water was a one-off, we suppose.

◑ *Closed from 31 Oct to Easter*

⤷ *Take the Corran ferry to Ardgour and take the road to Salen. At Salen turn left by the Salen hotel to Glenborrodale. The castle is on the far side of the village, on the right-hand side. Private car park*

🛏 *4 twin, 7 double, 5 four-poster; all with bathroom/WC, TV, hairdryer, room service*

◈ *Dining-room, bar, 2 lounges, TV room, games room, drying room, conservatory; conference*

facilities (max 10 people nonresidential and residential); fishing, tennis, gym, sauna/solarium at hotel; babysitting

⊖ *No wheelchair access; no dogs in public rooms; no smoking in dining-room*

▭ *Access, Amex, Visa*

£ *Single occupancy of twin/double £105, twin/double £160, fourposter £220, suite £260; deposit required. Cooked B £6.50; set L £19.50, D £32.50. Special breaks available*

GLENCRIPESDALE HIGHLAND   MAP 1

Glencripesdale House

LOCH SUNART, ACHARACLE, ARGYLL PH36 4JH
TEL: SALEN (0967 85) 263

A safari-style journey to a remote converted farmhouse.

A photo of a 2CV and a Ferrari accompanies directions to Glencripesdale to provide proof that anything can make it along the eight-mile pot-holed track through the forest of the Laudale estate. 'The journey took us 1½ hours,' reports one adventurer (make of car not given). It's Little Red Riding Hood stuff: you might have passed owner Bill Hemmings out in the forest chopping wood. After such a journey, you can rely on Sue Hemmings giving you the warmest of welcomes. The farmhouse was derelict when the Hemmings bought it in 1982 but now the atmosphere is delightful and guests are given the run of the very cosy, tasteful home that the couple have created. A stove warms the library-cum-sittingroom where carefully prepared files on history, wildlife, and so forth fill you in on local life. Enterprising decorations like wicker lobsters and paper rocking horses brighten the little dining-room. The food has been judged 'superb'. A dinner might comprise hummus and taramasalata with home-made bread, a Highland casserole of beef and venison, a raspberry sponge or fruit salad, and Scottish cheeses to finish.

Colourful patchwork quilts and a homely assortment of stuffed toys, books and mobiles make for winning bedrooms, all with a loch view.

◑ *Closed Nov to Feb, exc Xmas and New Year*

⬈ *Archaracle is the postal address only; the hotel is 35 miles away on the south side of Loch Sunart. Take the A861 from the Corran ferry towards Strontian and fork left on to the A884. Follow signs for 'Laudale 2' – the hotel is 8 miles along on a forestry track through the Laudale Estate. Hosts will supply detailed directions. Private car park*

⛏ *2 twin, 2 double; all with bathroom/WC; hair dryer on*

request; no tea/coffee-making facilities in rooms

◈ *Dining-room, library/lounge, games room, drying room, conservatory; water sports at hotel, fishing nearby*

⊖ *No wheelchair access; no dogs; no smoking in dining-room*

▭ *None accepted*

£ *£55 to £63 per person (rates inc dinner, packed lunch and afternoon tea); deposit required. Set D £17.50 (7pm)*

GRANTOWN-ON-SPEY HIGHLAND   MAP 1

Culdearn House ☆

WOODLANDS TERRACE, GRANTOWN-ON-SPEY, MORAY PM26 3JU
TEL: GRANTOWN-ON-SPEY (0479) 2106; changes to (0479) 872106 mid-Nov 1993
FAX: (0479) 3641; changes to (0479) 873641 mid-Nov 1993

Full marks for the passion with which this small venture is run.

Once in a while you come across a seemingly ordinary little hotel which has been elevated from the commonplace solely by dint of the enthusiasm, confidence and ambition of the hotelier. Such is Culdearn House. In the winter of 92/93, the refurbishment of bedrooms took place – mod cons, smart modern wood furniture and big bold prints.

Kilted Alasdair Little introduces diners in the comfortable rather than stylish sitting-room. With typical confidence – he states: 'This is the best place to eat in town.' Expect uncomplicated cuisine from Isobel Little: melon or pâté laced with brandy, a beef casserole, traditional home-made puddings. After dinner, any excuse for a celebration may result in a knees-up. A local pipe major and a Highland dancing girl may entertain, doubtless lubricated by Alasdair's wide and personally described selection of malts.

◑ *Closed Nov to end Feb*

⬈ *Enter Grantown-on-Spey on the*

A95 from the south and turn left at the 30mph sign. Private car park

- 1 single, 3 twin, 5 double, 2 with bathroom/WC, the remainder with shower/WC; TV, hair-dryer in all rooms

- Dining-room, lounge, drying room; fishing, golf, tennis, riding nearby. Wheelchair access to hotel, dining-room and 1 ground-floor bedroom

- No children under 5; no dogs; smoking in lounge only

- Access, Visa

- Single £30, twin/double £60; deposit required. Set D £15. Special breaks available

---

GULLANE LOTHIAN   **MAP 2**

Greywalls

GREYWALLS, MUIRFIELD, GULLANE, EAST LOTHIAN EH31 2EG
TEL: GULLANE (0620) 842144   FAX: (0620) 842241

Lutyens' only Scottish creation: a beautiful hotel adjacent to championship golf courses.

It's a crime that a hotel with the most sublime of façades should have such a dreary name. Lutyens designed the gorgeous symmetrical curve that greets you on arrival, while Gertrude Jekyll created the lovely walled gardens brimming with roses. The house has been in the same family for three generations and was converted into a hotel after the last war. Lutyens' houses are notable for their homely scale, so it's understandable that the Weaver family have had to add rooms – a dining-room, a second sitting-room, more bedrooms. The most original parts are naturally the most enjoyable. Delicate architectural features – a little arch, a marble fireplace, a wonderful library of light panelling and original shelving – are a delight.

All bedrooms have either garden or golf-course views. Those in the ground-floor extension are modern in style and decorated, perhaps, in yellow or in peach. Rooms in the original part of the building are more distinctive.

Feedback would be appreciated on Paul Baron's modern and not over-complicated four-course dinners that offer an even spread of meat, fish and game, done with varying degrees of elaboration.

- Closed Nov to Mar

- From the A1 take the North Berwick turn-off and the A198 to Gullane. From Edinburgh take the A198 to Gullane. Private car park

- 3 single, 18 twin/double, 1 four-poster; all with bathroom/WC, TV, room service, hair-dryer; baby-listening by arrangement;

no tea/coffee-making facilities in rooms

- 2 dining-rooms, bar, lounge, drying room, library, sun room; conference facilities (max 20 people residential and non-residential); tennis, croquet at hotel, fishing, golf, riding nearby; babysitting by arrangement. Wheelchair access to hotel, dining-room and WC (M,F), 3 ground-floor bedrooms

⊖ No dogs in public rooms

▭ Access, Amex, Diners, Visa

£ Single £90, single occupancy of

twin/double £130, twin/double/four-poster £150; deposit required. Alc L £17; set D £33 (prices till Nov 93). Special breaks available

---

HAWKCRAIG FIFE ··· MAP 2

Hawkcraig House ☆

HAWKCRAIG POINT, ABERDOUR, FIFE KY3 0TZ
TEL: ABERDOUR (0383) 860335

A simple waterside guesthouse run with pride.

Amidst the tiny ramshackle development of a couple of decaying wooden jetties, a small hotel and a stony strand, Hawkcraig House, with stripped joists for a porch, fits unobtrusively. But Hawkcraig's interior is beautifully kept. A butter churn and plates on pine door lintels decorate the hall, and ferns and china cabinets the landing. The house's layout is upside down: the two simple, smallish bedrooms are downstairs. Across the hall is the breakfast room/sitting-room, offering games, books, hi-fi and TV. Upstairs, you'll be served pre-dinner drinks in the comfortable main sitting-room. In the small dining-room, chatty Elma Barrie serves highly regarded set meals which might consist of cream of chicken and leek soup, sole in saffron sauce, leg of lamb and a choice of puddings.

◑ Closed Nov to Feb

↗ Turn off A921 in Easter Aberdour and follow Hawkcraig road to a large car park (don't pay!). Drive through and down a very steep access road. Private car park

⊨ 1 twin, 1 double; double with bathroom/WC, twin with shower/WC; TV in both rooms

◇ Dining-room, lounge, breakfast room, conservatory; fishing, golf, other sports nearby

⊖ No wheelchair access; no children under 10; no dogs; no smoking

▭ None accepted

£ Single occupancy of twin/double £23 to £25, twin/double £36 to £40. Set D £17 (by arrangement only)

INNERLEITHEN BORDERS ··· MAP 2

The Ley

INNERLEITHEN, PEEBLESSHIRE EH44 6NL
TEL: INNERLEITHEN (0896) 830240 (and fax)

Secluded, beautifully furnished guesthouse off the Tweed Valley.

The Ley offers what is best about the Wolsey Lodge consortium –

namely that you're staying in someone's home as a very personal guest – but shuns the often-abhorred practice of enforced communal dining. In early spring snowdrops coat the floor of the 30 acres of pathed woodland that envelop the white-harled Victorian house, its lawns and beautifully tended kitchen garden. On long summer evenings, deer come up to the house at dinnertime.

The McVicars came here in 1985 and they have created a homely yet sophisticated place. Delicate chandeliers and interesting paintings complement comfortable soft furnishings and a rugged parquet floor in interconnecting sitting-rooms. In the more formal dining-room, Willie serves Doreen's delicious four-course dinners (no choice until pudding). Inventive soups and salmon feature regularly.

Upstairs, bedrooms are substantial and have lovely furniture – a rosewood cabinet or a chaise-longue perhaps. Larch, a round room occupying a wide-girthed tower at one end of the building, is the best.

◑ Closed mid-Oct to mid-Feb

↗ Take the A72 from Galashiels to Innerleithen, turn right on to the B709 for Heriot, continue for 2 miles through the golf course, then turn left across a white bridge for the Ley. Private car park

🛏 1 single, 2 twin, 1 double; half with bathroom/WC, half with shower/WC; hair-dryer, trouser press in all rooms; TV on request

◈ Dining-room, lounge, TV room, drying room; fishing, golf, other sports nearby

⊖ No wheelchair access; no children under 12; no dogs; no smoking in bedrooms

▭ None accepted

£ Single £30, single occupancy of twin/double £38 to £41, twin/double £66 to £72. Set D £18.50 (8pm)

INVERNESS HIGHLAND   **MAP 1**

Dunain Park

NR INVERNESS, INVERNESS-SHIRE IV3 6JN
TEL: INVERNESS (0463) 230512   FAX: (0463) 224532

A classic country-house hotel of the unstuffy kind.

The early Victorian campanile is more imposing than the Georgian part of Dunain Park, set in six acres of woodland and lawns. A couple of comfortable, elegant sitting-rooms lie off long hallway, and there are three adjoining dining-rooms with cut glass and flowers on the tables. Ann Nicoll's food is excellent, the short, imaginative menu offering Scottish food with a French influence. 'Very satisfying breakfasts,' reported one reader. 'It's nice to enjoy real tea with a strainer.'

The six smart bedrooms of the new wing, each with separate sitting area and fancy bathroom, are the highest priced. The cottage accommodation is extremely spacious, and there are even kitchens. However, the rooms in the old part of the main house have most character.

◑ Open all year, exc 3 weeks in Jan or Feb

⤢ 1 mile from Inverness town boundary, just off A82 Fort William road. Private car park

🛏 1 single, 2 twin, 2 double, 1 four-poster, 6 suites, 2 cottages; all with bathroom/WC, TV, room service, hair-dryer, trouser press; tea/coffee-making facilities on request

◈ Dining-room, 2 lounges; sauna, heated indoor swimming-pool at hotel, other sports nearby. Wheelchair access to hotel and restaurant, 3 ground-floor bedrooms, 1 specially equipped for disabled people

● No dogs in public rooms

▭ Access, Amex, Diners, Visa

£ Single occupancy of twin/double £60 to £80, twin/double £80 to £120, four-poster £90 to £130, suite £90 to £140, cottage £80 to £120; deposit required. Alc D £25. Special breaks available

IONA STRATHCLYDE　　　　　　　　　　　　MAP 1

Argyll House

ISLE OF IONA, ARGYLL PA76 6SJ
TEL: IONA (068 17) 334 (and fax)

An evening stroll from this cosy waterside hotel is idyllic.

Our inspector was the only guest at the Argyll one April night: a convention of druids had cancelled. As Iona is a Christian centre *par excellence*, many visitors come for reasons of religion. The Argyll is a nineteenth-century inn with sharply V-shaped dormers. A local cook, a housekeeper and owner Fiona Menzies oversee the infectiously cheerful international brigade of young staff who are generally capable and friendly. A gong summons guests to dinner at 7pm in the pillared dining-room. There is always a vegetarian main-course choice in the safe set meal – you might opt for a creamy soup, lemon sole, chocolate mousse set with prunes, then cheese and biscuits.

There are pot plants and Lloyd Loom furniture in the sea-facing sun lounge, the surfeit of reading matter can help you while away an evening. Bedrooms are too small to want to spend much time in, though they are universally pretty in pine and reproduction wood.

◑ Closed mid-Oct to Easter

⤢ 200 yards from the ferry jetty on Iona. Cars parked (free of charge) at Fionnphort, Isle of Mull

🛏 10 single, 4 twin, 3 double, 2 family rooms; most with bathroom/WC, 4 public bathrooms; hair-dryer, baby-listening on request

◈ Dining-room, 2 lounges, conservatory, drying room; fishing, golf nearby

● No wheelchair access; no dogs in dining-room and lounges; no smoking in dining-room and 1 lounge

▭ Access, Visa

£ Single £29 to £37, single occupancy of twin/double £46 to £60, twin/double £54 to £70, family room £78 to £87; deposit required. Set D £16.50 (7pm); alc L £7.50. Special breaks available

ISLE ORNSAY HIGHLAND   **MAP 1**

Eilean Iarmain ☆

SLEAT, ISLE OF SKYE, IV43 8QR
TEL: ISLE ORNSAY (04713) 332   FAX: (04713) 275

An inviting nineteenth-century inn in an idyllic spot.

Part of Sir Iain and Lady Noble's estate, Eilean Iarmain stands among old, well-kept, whitewashed houses at the waterside of the narrow Sound of Sleat. A golden weathercock tops a little tower that leads to the locals' bar, but you will be more taken with the hotel proper. Enticingly cosy little front rooms have big bay extensions; the sitting-room is warm with antiques, decorative plates and brasses, while the smartly laid out dining-room has orange fabric walls. On a limited-choice four-course dinner menu you might be offered oysters from the estate's own beds, or scallops landed at the little jetty just yards away.

Half the bedrooms lie in the main house, half in the old Garden House. Antiques predominate in all; some have brass beds, while Number Two has a lovely old half-tester.

◑ *Open all year*

⤴ *From the ferry crossing follow the A851 towards Isle Ornsay. Private car park*

🛏 *4 twin, 6 double, 1 four-poster, 1 family room; all with bathroom/ WC, exc double with shower/ WC; room service, baby-listening in all rooms; TV, trouser press in 1 room; hair-dryer on request*

◈ *Restaurant, bar, lounge; conference facilities (max 100 non-residential, 12 residential); shooting at hotel, fishing, riding, other sports nearby*

⊖ *No wheelchair access*

▭ *Access, Amex, Visa*

£ *Single occupancy of twin/double £46, twin/double £72, four-poster £72, family room rate on request; deposit required. Set L £9.50, D £19.50. Special breaks available*

JEDBURGH BORDERS   **MAP 2**

Hundalee House

JEDBURGH, ROXBURGHSHIRE TD8 6PA
TEL: JEDBURGH (0835) 863011

A rural B&B in a somewhat grand eighteenth-century residence.

Hundalee stands in a lovely position, at the end of a long lane in farmland. Topiaried hedges give way to lawns at the back and to a flower meadow. The rooms downstairs are impressive: substantial breakfasts are taken round a large polished table in the Georgian dining-room with chandelier and gilt mirror, while the under-used lounge has ceiling-to-floor curtains, ferns and a piano. Bedrooms are well-equipped and pleasantly furnished, the most spacious being in the main wing of the house. Further bedrooms are in the old servants' wing: the reproduction four-poster room is the most expensive room but is in fact the most cramped. Mrs Whittaker welcomes guests enthusiastically.

◑ Closed Nov to Mar

↗ 1 mile south of Jedburgh off the A68. Private car park

🛏 2 twin, 2 double, 1 four-poster; some with shower/WC; 1 public bathroom; TV in all rooms

◈ Breakfast room, lounge; fishing, golf, other sports nearby

⊖ No wheelchair access, no dogs; no smoking

▭ None accepted

£ Single occupancy of twin/double £20 to £30, twin/double £30 to £40, four-poster £40; deposit required

Spinney

LANGLEE, JEDBURGH, ROXBURGHSHIRE TD8 6PB
TEL: JEDBURGH (0835) 863525 (and fax)

A modern B&B with a caring, outgoing hostess.

This natty little B&B makes an inexpensive place to stay if you want to explore Jedburgh. Sandra Fry's L-shaped, slate-hung home suggests order and smartness, from the rock garden to the spacious sitting-room with leather chesterfields and dining-room made fresh with flowers. Two of the immaculately kept cottagey bedrooms have *en-suite* shower rooms. Double-glazing excludes most of the traffic noise.

◑ Closed mid-Nov to mid-Mar

↗ 2 miles south of Jedburgh on the A68. Private car park

🛏 1 twin, 2 double; 2 with shower/WC, 1 double with no en-suite facilities

◈ Breakfast room, lounge

⊖ No wheelchair access; no children under 5; no dogs; no smoking in bedrooms

▭ None accepted

£ Twin/double £34 to £36; deposit required

KELSO BORDERS　　　　　　　　　　　　　　**MAP 2**

Ednam House

BRIDGE STREET, KELSO, ROXBURGHSHIRE TD5 7HT
TEL: KELSO (0573) 224168　FAX: (0573) 226319

A stay at this Georgian mansion is a walk back in time.

The brown stone Georgian mansion exudes an air of preserved decay, the designed interiors and food of so many of today's country-house hotels passing it by. The house has been in the Brooks family for four generations; the very thickness of the signing-in book tells of how long it's been a hotel. Dated furnishings such as loose-covered armchairs and a circular ottoman furnish stately sitting-rooms, one adorned with stuccoed cherubs and a chariot. Old photos – 'Fall of Pretoria; celebrations in Kelso; June 1900' – hang on the walls of the locals' bar. Waitresses in black pinafores serve in the restaurant, its décor and cuisine that of a dowdy club; unmatching candlesticks, daffodils and paper napkins dress the tables. The food is plentiful and wholesome but unenterprising: juices and avocado for starters, a soup course, roasts, substantial puddings, Welsh rarebit. Some bedrooms are a bit frayed, others positively cramped.

◑ Closed 24 Dec to 9 Jan

⤢ 100 yards from the town square in Kelso – the main gate is on the right of Bridge Street. Private car park

🛏 11 single, 16 twin, 3 double, 2 family rooms; most with bathroom/WC, some with shower/WC; TV, room service, hair-dryer, trouser press, baby-listening in all rooms

⬦ Dining-room, 2 bars, 3 lounges, drying room; fishing, golf, other sports nearby

⊖ No wheelchair access

▭ Access, Visa

£ Single £43, twin/double £87; deposit required. Bar lunches from £1.50; Sun L £11; set D £17.50. Special breaks available

---

Sunlaws House Hotel ☆

KELSO, ROXBURGHSHIRE TD5 8JZ
TEL: KELSO (0573) 450331   FAX: (0573) 450611

Massive and luxurious Georgian and Victorian pile.

Sunlaws has a splendid history which stretches over 500 years: in 1745 Bonnie Prince Charlie is said to have spent a night here. The Duke of Roxburghe is the present owner and his family seat, Floors Castle, is just up the road.

The house is eye-catchingly grand: outsize portraits hang on the stairs; fireplaces, one an elegant Adam, another an over-elaborate Gothic, vie with high-quality furnishings for attention. Beautiful bookcases holding some priceless tomes from Floors line the particularly fine bar, the setting for good-sounding lunches at give-away prices. Evening meals may include Scotch broth, Border lamb, fish pie and wild salmon.

The large four-poster bedrooms, with antiques and lots of light (particularly corner rooms), offer better value than standard doubles. The five stable-block rooms have a more modern style.

◑ Open all year

⤢ 3 miles south of Kelso on the A698. Private car park

🛏 1 single, 10 twin, 8 double, 2 four-poster, 1 suite; all with bathroom/WC; TV, room service, hair-dryer, baby-listening; mini-bar on request; trouser press in some rooms

Restaurant, bar/library, lounge, drawing-room, drying room, conservatory; conference facilities (max 40 people non-residential, 22 residential); fishing, tennis, riding, clay pigeon shooting at hotel, other sports nearby

● No dogs or smoking in restaurant

▢ Access, Amex, Diners, Visa

£ Single £85 to £90, single occupancy of twin/double £85 to £90, twin/double £128 to £130, four-poster £135 to £140, suite £155 to £160, family room rate £160 to £170; deposit required. Set L £10/£14, D £26. Special breaks available

KENTALLEN HIGHLAND   MAP 1

Ardsheal House

KENTALLEN, APPIN, ARGYLL PA38 4BX
TEL: DUROR (063 174) 227   FAX: (063 174) 342

American owners have turned this distinguished house into an interesting country-house hotel.

This fascinating building dates from 1760, with Victorian and Edwardian additions, and stands on the site of an older manor that was totally destroyed during the 1745 Uprisings. Various rooms exude age: a tiny panelled bar was once the butler's pantry; under the creaking oak staircase in the hall lies a barrel window; a magnificent brass lamp hangs over the table in the lovely pine-panelled snooker room.

The genial and articulate owners, Robert and Jane Taylor, came here in the Seventies from city jobs in Manhattan. Bedrooms offer interesting transatlantic pieces; Number Two has a sleigh bed that was designed by the creator of Lincoln's bed in the White House. The draught-conscious Victorians designed the house with only four bedrooms looking seawards. One of these, Number 11, is the best and most expensive.

Lunches and dinners are served in a traditional dining-room, much extended into the garden by a large conservatory. When the cuisine is good it is very good, but inconsistencies have been noted. The five-course table d'hôte dinner menu features fish and game and offers a two-choice option at each stage with salad before pudding.

◑ Open all year, exc 3 weeks in Jan

⤧ On the A828, 4 miles south of the Ballachulish Bridge. Private car park

⇌ 1 single, 11 twin/double, 1 family room; some with bathroom/WC, some with shower/WC; room service (limited), hair-dryer, baby-listening in all rooms; no tea/coffee-making facilities in rooms

◈ Dining-room/conservatory, bar, 3 lounges, TV room, games room, library/study; conference facilities (max 12 people residential, 20 non-residential); tennis at hotel, riding, water sports nearby; babysitting

● No wheelchair access; no dogs or smoking in dining-room

▢ Access, Amex, Visa

£ Single £85, single occupancy of

twin/double from £100, twin/double £128 to £180, family room rate on request (rates inc

dinner); deposit required. Set L £17.50, D £32.50 (8.30pm)

KILDRUMMY GRAMPIAN   **MAP 1**

Kildrummy Castle

KILDRUMMY, BY ALFORD, ABERDEENSHIRE AB33 8RA
TEL: KILDRUMMY (09755) 71288   FAX: (09755) 71345

Baronial-style hotel in a lovely spot, alongside separately owned gardens and castle ruins.

The extensive remains of the original thirteenth-century Kildrummy Castle are some of the best around, and come with requisite turbulent history. A certain Colonel Ogston bought the site in 1898 and added alpine and Japanese water gardens and the present hotel. The exterior, topped with battlements, tall chimneys and urns, complements the palatial interior. The grand, panelled hall has carved lions at the foot of the stairs, and matching sets of furniture adorn the sizeable and comfortable drawing-room, library and bar. The dining-room is elegant Victorian, its table d'hôte menu typically offering game, lamb and salmon. Bedrooms mix Victorian and reproduction furniture. Attic rooms have less of a period style.

◑ Open all year, exc Jan

↗ Off the A97 Huntly to Ballater road, 35 miles west of Aberdeen. Private car park

🛏 1 single, 5 twin, 5 double, 2 four-poster, 2 family rooms, 1 suite; all with bathroom/WC, exc 1 twin with shower/WC; TV, room service, hair-dryer, trouser press, baby-listening in all rooms

◈ Dining-room, bar, lounge, billiard room, drying room, library; conference facilities (max 20 people non-residential, 16 residential); fishing, golf, riding nearby; babysitting

⊖ No wheelchair access; no dogs in public rooms; no smoking in dining-room

▭ Access, Amex, JCB, Visa

💷 Single £70, twin/double £110 to £130, four-poster/suite £130, family room rate on request. Set L £13.50, D £25; alc L £29, D £33. Special breaks available

---

KILLIECRANKIE TAYSIDE   **MAP 1**

Killiecrankie Hotel

PASS OF KILLIECRANKIE, BY PITLOCHRY, PERTHSHIRE PH16 5LG
TEL: PITLOCHRY (0796) 473220   FAX: (0796) 472451

Well-run hotel offering reductions for out-of-season breaks.

Colin and Carole Anderson are professional hoteliers, attentive and friendly; their establishment may strike you as like a homely yet smart inn. Two conservatories flank the porch, one with pine tables the other enlarging a more formal dining-room. High-quality food comes either as a four-course dinner – perhaps a spicy prawn soup, baked salmon filled with a fresh oyster in a ginger and lemon grass butter sauce, fresh strawberry pavlova, French and Scottish cheeses – or as a wide-ranging à la carte selection.

The less spruce upstairs sitting-room is due to be made into a bedroom and an extension will be added for a new sitting-room. Pine-furnished cottagey bedrooms squeeze into the space that the sloping roofs of the building allow.

◑ Open all year, exc Jan and Feb

↗ Midway between Pitlochry and Blair Atholl. Private car park

🛏 3 single, 2 twin, 6 doubl, family room available; all with bathroom/WC, exc 2 singles with shower/WC; TV, room service, hair-dryer, baby-listening in all rooms

◈ Dining-room, bar, lounge; fishing, golf, other sports nearby. Wheelchair access to hotel (1 step) and restaurant, 4 ground-floor bedrooms

⊖ No children under 5 in dining-room eves; no dogs in public rooms; no smoking in dining-room

▭ Access, Visa

£ Single £39 to £48, single occupancy of twin/double £49 to £68, twin/double £78 to £90; deposit required. Set D £25. Special breaks available

---

KILMORE STRATHCLYDE   **MAP 2**

Glenfeochan House

KILMORE, BY OBAN, ARGYLL PA34 4QR
TEL: KILMORE (0631 77) 273   FAX: (0631 77) 624

A graceful baronial mansion in beautiful gardens.

The turreted baronial sandstone building stands perfectly poised among the greens and russets of surrounding woods and meadows. Ornate plasterwork, a carved American pine staircase and understated, elegant furnishings in the drawing-room impress. Dinner comes amid decanters and silver at a long refectory table. Charming Patricia Baber cooks set meals tailored to guests' tastes; one such when inspected was wild home-smoked salmon, chicken in a tarragon and cream sauce, and strawberry sorbet in a brandy-snap basket.

The spacious bedrooms are colourful yet restrained. The Garden Room has both loch and garden views; the Tulip Room has beautiful inlaid furniture, and a circular tower bathroom.

◑ Closed 1 Nov to 1 Mar

↗ 5 miles south of Oban off the A816. Private car park

🛏 1 twin, 2 double; all with bathroom/WC, TV, hair-dryer

◈ Dining-room, drawing-room, drying room; fishing, croquet,

clay pigeon shooting at hotel,
other sports nearby

⊖ No wheelchair access; no
children under 10; no dogs;
smoking in drawing-room only

▭ None accepted

£ Single occupancy of twin/double
£93, twin/double £124; deposit
required. Set D £30 (8pm);
packed lunches £6. Special
breaks available

KINGUSSIE HIGHLAND   MAP 1

Homewood Lodge

NEWTONMORE ROAD, KINGUSSIE, INVERNESS-SHIRE PH21 1HD
TEL: KINGUSSIE (0540) 661507

A fun guesthouse on the outskirts of Kingussie.

A plea in the bedroom literature reads: 'This is a new venture for both of us and if we make mistakes we ask you to kindly bear with us.' Bill and Shirley Murchie bought Homewood Lodge at the end of 1992. Boyish enthusiasm and jollity infects their approach to their new way of life – even the headache of trying to start up a guesthouse business in the face of adjacent building work is coolly dismissed.

Though they had been open only a month when our inspector visited, the hall was already heaving under a mass of brochures and a map marked up with all the local places to visit. The front-facing sitting- and dining-rooms are plain and fresh. Shirley's chicken dish is a favourite (she won't say what the sauce is) and it might be preceded by broad bean soup and followed by rhubarb crumble.

Spriggy duvets, smart little shower rooms, simple pine furniture and size, space and light characterise the bedrooms.

◑ Open all year, exc Xmas and
New Year

↗ On the A86 Newtonmore road to
the west of Kingussie. Private car
park

🛏 1 double, 3 family rooms; all
with shower/WC

◈ Dining-room, lounge, drying
room; fishing, golf, tennis, other
sports nearby

⊖ No wheelchair access; no
children under 7; no dogs; no
smoking

▭ None accepted

£ Single occupancy of double £20,
double/family room £39; deposit
required. Set D £9.50 (7pm).
Special breaks available

KINLOCH RANNOCH TAYSIDE   MAP 1

Cuilmore Cottage ☆

KINLOCH RANNOCH, PERTHSHIRE PH16 5QB
TEL: KINLOCH RANNOCH (0882) 632218

A simple lochside croft that makes a feature of its food.

This eighteenth-century whitewashed cottage lies on the outskirts of remote Kinloch Rannoch, 100 yards from the loch. The rural scene is inviting: geese waddle by the road; smoke billows from the chimney; vines envelop the porch.

Jens and Anita Steffen's home is a tiny place to take guests – there are just a few small rooms downstairs, including a simple sitting-room with a fire and a dining-room with an old range. Guests enjoy four-course dinners round the one pine table. Anita's broad repertoire of dishes covers plenty of game and fish, cooked both traditionally and inventively.

Upstairs, a single bedroom has recently disappeared to make way for a bathroom for the two remaining bedrooms. The rooms have lots of personality, and are full of books and ornaments.

◑ Closed Nov, Dec, Jan	◈ Dining-room, lounge; fishing at hotel, rafting, ski-ing, other sports nearby
⤢ Take the B846 from Aberfeldy to Kinloch Rannoch. The cottage is 100 yards from the eastern corner of the loch. Private car park	⊖ No wheelchair access; no smoking in bedrooms
	▭ None accepted
⇌ 1 twin, 1 double; both with private facilities, hair-dryer	£ Twin/double £40. Set D £22

Gladstone House ☆

48 HIGH STREET, KIRKCUDBRIGHT DG6 4JX
TEL: KIRKCUDBRIGHT (0557) 31734

Not the cheapest of bed and breakfasts, but high quality in a fine Georgian house.

Kirkcudbright is the south-west's most alluring town, with old streets and a picturesque port. Gladstone House is a lovely brown stone Georgian building in a quiet corner of the old town. Keen-to-please Sue and Jim Westbrook started taking guests in the spring of 1991. Bedrooms have sloping ceilings and, through massive dormer windows protruding from the slate roof, views over the rooftops; they are cosy, smart and cottagey, with untreated pine furniture and tartan bedspreads. Guests have their own comfortable sitting-room on the first floor, full of books and records. Breakfast is served downstairs in a small, smart, green and white breakfast room.

◑ Open all year	tennis nearby
⤢ A short walk from the harbour and castle in Kirkcudbright. On-street parking	⊖ No wheelchair access; no children under 12; no dogs; no smoking
⇌ 3 double; 2 with bathroom/WC, 1 with shower/WC; TV in all rooms	▭ Access, Visa
◈ Breakfast room, lounge; golf,	£ Single occupancy of double £30 to £35, double £48 to £54; deposit required

KIRKWALL ORKNEY ISLANDS   **MAP I**

Foveran Hotel

ST OLA, KIRKWALL, ORKNEY KW15 ISF
TEL: KIRKWALL (0856) 872389   FAX: (0856) 876430

Good food, excellent service and attractive public rooms.

One of the most striking things about this small, unremarkable-looking
but comfortable hotel is the owl motif that runs through it. You'll see
them first of all in reception and then in the corridors. The building was
extensively refurbished a couple of years ago, and public rooms are
attractive. The small residents' lounge is a quiet corner in which to watch
TV. The cosy larger lounge, shared with non-resident diners, is a
pleasant spot. The pine-ceilinged restaurant has a light, airy feel, with
racing green carpets and white walls adorned with wrought iron, rattan
or bamboo owls. Our inspection meal of Peedie pots (ramekins of baked
Orkney cheese and onion) with garlic bread, local salmon steak and
pudding was excellent, and efficiently served by friendly staff. Breakfast
is equally good, and there are binoculars beside the window tables to let
you watch the birds over Scapa Flow.

Bedrooms have a simple Scandinavian feel, with lots of pine and bright
modern fabrics to contrast with the stark white walls.

◐ Open all year

⤴ From Kirkwall take the A964 to
Orphir for 2 miles. Take the left
turning signposted for the hotel.
Private car park

🛏 3 single, 3 twin, 2 double, I
family room; some with
bathroom/WC, most with
shower/WC; TV, room service,
hair-dryer, baby-listening in all
rooms

◈ Restaurant, lounge, TV room,

drying room, conservatory;
fishing, golf, other sports nearby;
babysitting. Wheelchair access to
hotel (ramp), restaurant and WC
(M,F), 9 ground-floor bedrooms

⊖ No dogs in public rooms

▭ Access, Visa

£ Single £42 to £50, single
occupancy of twin/double £47 to
£55, twin/double/family room
£68 to £75; deposit required. Alc
D £15

KIRN STRATHCLYDE   **MAP 2**

Enmore Hotel

MARINE PARADE, KIRN, DUNOON, ARGYLL PA23 8HH
TEL: DUNOON (0369) 2230   FAX: (0369) 2148

Positive reports on food and comfort for this most welcoming hotel.

The Enmore, just along the coast from the half-hourly ferry to Gourock,
overlooks the water. Angela and David Wilson came here in 1979 ('the
flowers were out and we decided to stay') and have since established a

free-and-easy place with a certain amount of panache. The most relaxing room is the large, light sitting-room, which has a little bar off it. The dining-room is more formal: on David's imaginative five-course set menus (a choice for starter and main course only) diners get welcomed by name.

Bedrooms are in a pleasant mishmash of styles, one with net drapes on a four-poster, another with a waterbed, a third a family room with a large leather sofa.

◑ Open all year

⤴ On the seafront at Kirn, 1 mile north of Dunoon on the A815. Private car park

🛏 3 single, 2 twin, 2 double, 3 four-poster, 1 family room, 1 suite; most with bathroom/WC, some with shower/WC; TV, room service, hair-dryer, baby-listening in all rooms; tea/coffee-making facilities on request

◈ Dining-room, bar, 2 lounges, drying room; conference facilities (max 25 people non-residential,

12 residential); squash at hotel, other sports nearby

⊖ No wheelchair access; no children under 7 in dining-room eves; no dogs or smoking in dining-room

▭ Access, Visa

£ Single £30 to £35, single occupancy of twin/double £45, twin/double £50, family room £70, four-poster/suite £120; deposit required. Set L £10, D £25; alc L £5 to £10, D £5 to £20. Special breaks available

---

LAIRG HIGHLAND   **MAP 1**

Achany House

BY LAIRG, SUTHERLAND IV27 4EE
TEL: LAIRG (0549) 2172   FAX: (0549) 2433

A fine turreted mansion – more private house than hotel.

This deliciously romantic mansion, its twin towers making its façade appear perfectly proportioned, stands proud over the surrounding land. Once the seat of the Clan of Munro before the Mathesons came by, it's now owned by Erika Havers-Strong, who, with the help of cook and housekeeper Margaret Bain, invites guests into her private home. Erika manages to create an unforced house-party atmosphere that is relaxed and informal. In her five years at the house she has imbued it with a level of civilised comfort; bedrooms are roomy and attractive and you dine (five traditional Scottish courses) off a magnificent mahogany table.

◑ Closed early Nov to Apr

⤴ From Inverness take the A9 to Bonar Bridge and turn north on to the A836. North of Invershin, turn on to the A837 and follow signs to 'Falls of Shin' on the B864. The house is 2 miles north of 'Falls of Shin'. Private car park

🛏 2 single, 1 twin, 1 double; 4 private bathrooms; hair-dryer in all rooms; room service on request

◈ Dining-room, drawing-room, TV room, drying room, study/ breakfast room; fishing, riding nearby

⊖ No wheelchair access; no children under 14; dogs by arrangement only; smoking in TV room only

▭ Access, Visa

💷 Single £35, single occupancy of twin/double £35, twin/double £70. Packed L £6.50, set D £25

LARGS STRATHCLYDE

MAP 2

Brisbane House

---

14 GREENOCK ROAD, ESPLANADE, LARGS, AYRSHIRE KA30 8NF
TEL: LARGS (0475) 687200   FAX: (0475) 676295

A smart modern hotel in a converted Georgian building.

Brisbane House is owned by two partners, one of whom is half-Italian, the other half-Swiss. A shiny marble foyer and bathrooms as well as entries such as 'fondue bourguignonne fribourg' and 'tournedos à la Suisse' on the menu reflect their different nationalities. Scotland is represented in the concept of high tea, while morc serious diners can choose from a seafood table d'hôte and extensive à la carte.

The hotel's décor is confident and modern throughout, from the chandeliers and bright patterned carpets in the formal dining-room and the large bar to the extraordinary glinting brown wall material (Japanese, apparently) in the smart bedrooms. All except singles have a sea view. Staff are capable and efficient.

◑ Open all year

🔁 On the Clyde Estuary on the A78. Private car park

🛏 6 single, 5 twin, 8 double, 4 family rooms; all with bathroom/WC, exc singles with shower/WC; TV, room service, hair-dryer, trouser press, baby-listening in all rooms

◈ Restaurant, bar/lounge; conference facilities (max 100 people non-residential, 40 residential); laundry facilities; fishing, golf, other sports nearby; babysitting on request. Wheelchair access to public rooms only

⊖ No dogs

▭ Access, Amex, Diners, Visa

💷 Single £50, single occupancy of twin/double £65, twin/double £80, suite/family room £90; deposit required. Set D £20; alc L from £4, D from £10. Special breaks available

---

LESLIE GRAMPIAN

MAP 1

Leslie Castle

REGIONAL HOTEL OF THE YEAR

LESLIE, BY INSCH, ABERDEENSHIRE AB52 6NX
TEL: INSCH (0464) 20869   FAX: (0464) 21076

Lonesome fortified guesthouse, superbly restored.

The Leslie clan has been here on and off since 1070 when there was a wooden fort on the site. The present owners undertook a ten-year task of renovating the decaying roofless ruin. Their achievement has won a Scottish regeneration design award. The place now looks quite superb, a fairy-tale castle standing proud in the open, fertile valley.

Inside, twentieth-century style has been moulded on to the idea of an ancestral home, with new dark oak pieces furnishing the rooms. The lower parts of the building have flagged floors. In the dining-room, chairs are engraved with the Leslie crest and there are portraits of the baron and his wife. The latter does the cooking: expect four-course dinners with a choice at each stage, perhaps smoked salmon or soup, fillet steak in a whisky sauce or duck, a mousse or flan for pudding, and cheese to finish. The next-door 'withdrawing-room' is very much a lived-in family room, with leather sofas and a big fire. The brown wood and white walls of the large bedrooms are appropriately simple for a castle, but at the same time very comfortable. Three have their own little walk-in turrets, with a miniature window and a gap from which to pour the boiling oil.

◑ Open all year

🔁 From Aberdeen/Inverness A96 road, 7 miles north of Inverurie, take B9002 signposted Insch. After 2 miles turn left to Auchleven/Clatt. At Auchleven crossroads, go straight over and follow signposts to Leslie for 2 miles. The castle is on the right, just before hamlet of Leslie. Private car park

🛏 1 twin, 1 double, 2 four-poster, family rooms available; all with bathroom/WC, TV, room service (limited), hair-dryer, trouser press, baby-listening

◈ 2 dining-rooms, lounge; drying facilities; limited meetings facilities; golf, fishing, other sports nearby; babysitting

⊖ No wheelchair access; no dogs; smoking discouraged

▭ Access, Amex, Visa

💷 Single occupancy of twin/double £80 to £85, twin/double £110 to £120, four-poster £120 to £132; deposit required. L by arrangement; set D £27.50 (8pm)

LICKISTO WESTERN ISLES   **MAP 1**

Two Waters

LICKISTO, ISLE OF HARRIS, WESTERN ISLES PA85 3EL
TEL: MANISH (0859 83) 246

Enter into a captivating way of life by staying in this pally Anglicised home on Harris.

Guests at Two Waters soon become absorbed into the Barbers' distinctive way of life. Landlubbers venture out to sea with John for some serious fishing: photo albums show prize catches of skate weighing over 100 lb. Over after-dinner coffee in the comfy sitting-room city dwellers chat enthusiastically about weather reports and listen hushed to tall stories about the ferociousness of Harris winters. At breakfast everyone tries John's home-smoked fish – on one sitting kippers, Arbroath smokies and haddock.

The guesthouse has a free-and-easy atmosphere. Jill's excellent dinners, served round one large table, might start with a fish terrine, followed by beef in wine and Guinness, then individual bread-and-butter puddings.

The four pretty, roomy bedrooms show care and bathrooms are well-maintained. 'Your classification of good meal, good value and exceptionally peaceful location was well justified,' concludes one reader.

◑ *Closed Oct to end Apr*

↗ *From Tarbert ferry point travel south on the A859 towards Rodel for 5 miles. Turn left on the C79 (Rodel via east) for 2 miles. Two Waters is on the left-hand side past the second bridge. Private car park*

🛏 *2 twin, 2 double; 1 with bathroom/WC, 3 with shower/*

WC; hair-dryer in all rooms

◈ *Dining-room, lounge, drying room; fishing, golf nearby, boat available*

⊖ *No wheelchair access; no children under 12*

▭ *None accepted*

£ *Twin/double £48. Set D £12 (7pm)*

LOCHINVER HIGHLAND   **MAP 1**

Inver Lodge Hotel

LOCHINVER, SUTHERLAND IV27 4LU
TEL: LOCHINVER (05714) 496   FAX: (05714) 395

A thoroughly comfortable and well-designed modern hotel.

Readers have been enthusiastic about the sheer quality of this hotel. Bedrooms, with first-class modern furnishings and fabrics, have all the mod cons that you would expect in a city-centre business hotel. The two most expensive and luxurious rooms are on a corner of the building with both a mountain and sea aspect.

An open-plan arrangement connects the lofty reception hall with the bar, both with smart sets of modern furnishings. The range of dishes on the six-course dinner table d'hôte menu varies from the plain – gravad lax, steak – to complicated, such as a pork fillet, chicken liver and mushroom mousse in filo pastry glazed with a cider sauce. Service is correct but pleasant, with manager Nicholas Gorton jovial and helpful.

◑ *Closed from 16 Oct to 1 Apr*

↗ *Take the A837 to Lochinver. In the village, take the first left after the village hall. Private car park*

🛏 *11 twin, 9 double; all with bathroom/WC, TV, room service,*

hair-dryer, trouser press, mini-bar

◈ *Dining-room, bar, lounge, billiard room, drying room; sauna at hotel, fishing nearby. Wheelchair access to hotel (ramp), restaurant and WC*

(unisex), 11 ground-floor
bedrooms

⊖ No children under 7 in dining-
room eves; no dogs in public
rooms

▭ Access, Amex, Diners, JCB, Visa

£ Single occupancy of twin/double
£56 to £65, twin/double £100 to
£112; deposit required. Set L
£14, D £27; alc D £16

MARKINCH FIFE   MAP 2

Balbirnie House ☆

BALBIRNIE PARK, MARKINCH, BY GLENROTHES, FIFE KY7 6NE
TEL: KIRKCALDY (0592) 610066   FAX: (0592) 610529

A large, lavish country house in a landscaped park.

A more impressive hotel building than Balbirnie House, once the family
home of the Balfours, would be hard to find. A massive Greek revival
mansion in a large park enveloped by a golf course, it contains an array of
stately, sumptuous rooms, resplendent with the finest furniture and the
plushest soft furnishings. The most stunning room is the 70-foot-long
gallery, lit by a number of lunette windows. You can eat very well and in
style in the formal dining-rooms, and very affordably at lunchtime in the
Gamekeeper's Inn, inventively decorated with dried flowers hanging
from meat hooks. All the bedrooms are beautifully and individually
furnished, sprinkled with antiques and paintings. Service is correct but
serious.

◑ Open all year

↗ Leave the M90 at Junction 3,
follow the A92 to Glenrothes,
then 1st right on to B9130.
Private car park

🛏 2 single, 18 twin, 7 double, 1
four-poster, 2 suites; all with
bathroom/WC, TV, room service,
hair-dryer, trouser press

◇ 3 restaurants, 2 bars, lounge,
drying room, library, games
room; conference facilities (max
120 non-residential, 30
residential); golf, riding at hotel,
fishing, swimming, other sports
nearby; babysitting.

Wheelchair access to hotel
(ramp), restaurant and WC
(unisex), 7 ground-floor
bedrooms, 1 specially equipped
for disabled people

⊖ No dogs in public rooms

▭ Access, Amex, Diners, Visa

£ Single £85, single occupancy of
twin/double £95, twin/double
£125, four-poster/family room
£180, suite £225; deposit
preferred. Set L from £7, D
£22.50; alc L £20 to £30, D
from £25 (prices till end Mar
94). Special breaks available

Hoteliers do not pay for entries in The Which? Hotel Guide, *and the
Editor and her inspectors accept no free hospitality. Consumers' Association
does not permit hoteliers to mention their inclusion in* The Which? Hotel
Guide *in any advertising material.*

MARNOCH GRAMPIAN **MAP I**

Old Manse of Marnoch ☆

BRIDGE OF MARNOCH, BY HUNTLY, ABERDEENSHIRE AB54 5RS
TEL: ABERCHIRDER (0466) 780873

A smart guesthouse in a remote corner of the north-east.

The Old Manse is a lovely stone Georgian building that nestles in a valley. Patrick and Keren Carter came here in 1986, refugees from the oil industry in the Middle East and Aberdeen. Their family home is delightfully fresh-smelling, stylish and comfortable. Interesting objects catch the eye: a Rob Roy figurehead by the front door, oriental drawings, a ship in a bottle, a teddy bear on a chaise-longue. Dining has recently changed from communal to separate tables. A positive report draws attention to the huge choice on the breakfast menu (three types of sausage, devilled ham, herring in oatmeal, kedgeree, kippers, smoked haddock, Scotch woodcock and much more besides!), but notes that there is none on the dinner menu.

Bedrooms are beautifully furnished, one with a walnut bed and wardrobe, another with a marble-topped dressing-table.

◐ Open all year, exc 2 weeks in Nov and a few winter days

⬈ On the B9117, less than a mile from the A97 Huntly/Banff route. Private car park

🛏 2 twin, 3 double; all with bathroom/WC, exc 1 twin with shower/WC; TV, hair-dryer in all rooms; room service on request

◈ Dining-room, lounge, TV room/study, drying room; fishing, golf, other sports nearby

⊖ No wheelchair access; no children under 12; no dogs in public rooms; no smoking in 1 lounge

▭ None accepted

£ Single occupancy of twin/double £45 to £60, twin/double £60 to £80; deposit required. Set L £10, D £17.50 (8pm). Special breaks available

MARYCULTER GRAMPIAN **MAP I**

Maryculter House Hotel

SOUTH DEESIDE ROAD, MARYCULTER, ABERDEENSHIRE AB1 0BB
TEL: ABERDEEN (0224) 732124   FAX: (0224) 733510

An impressively managed, business-oriented hotel.

The ancient origins of Maryculter House, in the thirteenth century the site for a college of the Knights Templar, have become subsumed in latterday building. When our inspector visited in early 1993 it was still a bit raw in places, with fresh-smelling paint in a pictureless new wing and a garden in need of some landscaping. Some bedrooms, though, are right on top of the river. Rooms in the older building are furnished with pine fittings, while those in the new wing are slightly smaller with smart modern furnishings.

The good range of public rooms includes the vaulted stone-walled cocktail bar, the cosy Priory Restaurant and the Poachers' Pocket Bar, a popular place for above-average bar food.

◑ *Open all year; dining-room closed Sun eve*

↗ *On the B9077, beside the River Dee in Maryculter. Private car park*

⇌ *1 single, 14 twin, 7 double, 1 family room; all with bathroom/ WC, TV, room service, hair-dryer, trouser press, baby-listening*

◈ *2 dining-rooms, 2 bars, lounge; conference facilities (max 46 people residential, 200 non-residential); fishing, golf,*

tennis, other sports nearby; babysitting by arrangement. Wheelchair access to hotel, dining-rooms and WC (unisex), 7 ground-floor bedrooms, 1 specially equipped for disabled people

⊖ *None*

▭ *Access, Amex, Diners, Visa*

£ *Single £51 to £103, twin/double £51 to £108, family room rate on request. Continental B £6.50, cooked B £7.50; set L from £9, D £26.50*

MOFFAT DUMFRIES & GALLOWAY   **MAP 2**

Beechwood

HARTHOPE PLACE, MOFFAT, DUMFRIESSHIRE DG10 9RS
TEL: MOFFAT (0683) 20210   FAX: (0683) 20889

Caring hosts and good food in an unostentatious Victorian house.

Beechwood gazes over the town's suburbs and is backed by acres of its own woods. Reports have been good on balance. Lynda and Jeffrey Rogers are 'friendly and efficient,' says one; another praises them for 'working very hard to ensure that their guests enjoy their stay'. The public rooms are attractive and spacious: a peach-coloured dining-room, an exuberantly decorated sitting-room, its walls covered with drapes, books and plates, and a bar with a small, plain conservatory for lunches. The restaurant has a good reputation. A five-course dinner was reckoned 'first-rate: beautifully cooked, carefully presented and excellent value for money' by one diner. Breakfasts get the thumbs-up for such delights as fresh orange juice and scrambled eggs with 'fresh chanterelle mushrooms gathered in our own woods'.

Bedrooms lack the style of the public rooms and a complaint about their size ('they should be fine for midgets') is justified, particularly for the doubles. However, much effort has gone into making them welcoming.

◑ *Closed 2 Jan to 16 Feb*

↗ *At the north end of Moffat. Turn*

off the main road into Harthope Place and follow the road round to the left for 200 yards. Private car park

🛏 3 twin, 3 double, 1 family room; all with bathroom/WC, exc 1 double with shower/WC; TV, room service, hair-dryer, baby-listening in all rooms

◈ Restaurant, bar, lounge, library, conservatory, drying room; conference facilities (max 14 people non-residential, 7

residential); fishing, golf, other sports nearby. Wheelchair access to restaurant only

⊖ No dogs or smoking in restaurant

▭ Access, Amex, Visa

£ Single occupancy of twin/double £47, twin/double £68, family room £83. Set L £11.50, D £19. Special breaks available

Well View Hotel ☆

BALLPLAY ROAD, MOFFAT, DUMFRIESSHIRE DG10 9JU
TEL: MOFFAT (0683) 20184

Quality food, wine and hospitality hidden in an ordinary-looking little hotel.

The position of this solid Victorian villa, in the suburbs of Moffat looking out over a modern housing estate, is inauspicious; inside, save for a bit of decorative plasterwork and cornicing, it's visually unexciting. All of which only goes to show that there's more to a good hotel than its looks.

Janet and John Schuckardt, ex-teachers from Carlisle, exude a passion for hotelkeeping and fizz with energy. Janet's in charge in the kitchen. Canapés precede highly praised table d'hôte five-course dinners that offer startling variety, from a seafood casserole to a grape, cheese and apple salad or spiced beef kofta as a starter.

A thoroughly positive report draws attention to other good points. The owners ('correct but friendly') ask whether guests want a non-smoking bedroom when booking. A bedroom, 'though on the small side, was beautifully equipped: baby decanter of amontillado, towelling bathrobes, fluffy towels, lots of toiletries'.

◑ Open all year, exc 1st week Jan

⤢ Take the A708 out of Moffat towards Selkirk and pass the fire station on the left-hand side. Ballplay Road is 1st left. Private car park

🛏 2 twin, 2 double, 1 four-poster, 1 suite; half with bathroom/WC, half with shower/WC; TV, hair-dryer in all rooms

◈ 2 restaurants, lounge; fishing,

golf, other sports nearby

⊖ No wheelchair access; no dogs; no smoking in restaurant and some bedrooms

▭ Access, Visa

£ Single occupancy of twin/double £30 to £40, twin/double £46 to £66, four-poster/suite £56 to £76; deposit required. Set L £10, D £21

MUIR OF ORD HIGHLAND　　　　　　　　　**MAP 1**

Dower House ☆

HIGHFIELD, MUIR OF ORD, ROSS-SHIRE IV6 7XN
TEL: MUIR OF ORD (0463) 870090 (and fax)

An imaginatively furnished bungalow in three acres of pleasant gardens.

Tired of staying in Scottish baronial piles? The Dower House offers luxury equal to many of Scotland's grander hotels, but on a severely reduced scale. This nineteenth-century, deep-pitched slate-roofed bungalow is laid out in an H shape in a style called cottage orné. It's very cosy inside, somewhat like a dolls' house; inhabitants can seem to dwarf the rooms. Off the entrance to one side is a small sitting-room, with sofas, bookshelves, fire and honesty bar. Across the way is a narrow, low-lit dining-room with gleaming wooden tables; a further oddly placed seating area with a piano lies at the far end.

Interesting corridors, with paintings, displays of cigarette cards and stained glass, lead to lovely bedrooms. Victorian pieces like a half-tester or a brass bed furnish some, others have pine pieces such as a rocking chair; there's even an old organ in one.

Robyn and Mena Aitchison came here in 1988. Robyn cooks, serving high-quality, inventive four-course dinners with a choice at each stage except the soup course. Thus one dinner comprised Mediterranean fish tart or marinated quail, cream of Jerusalem artichoke soup, venison with wildberry sauce or scallops with ginger butter sauce, and crème brûlée or pear crêpes with sabayon sauce.

◑ Open all year

⤢ 1 mile north of Muir of Ord on the A862 Dingwall road. Private car park

🛏 3 twin, 2 double; all with bathroom/WC, exc 1 twin with shower/WC; TV, room service, hair-dryer in all rooms; no tea/coffee-making facilities in rooms

◈ Dining-room, lounge, drying room; conference facilities (max 5 people residential and non-residential); fishing, golf, other sports nearby; babysitting. Wheelchair access to hotel, restaurant and 5 ground-floor bedrooms

⊖ No smoking in dining-room

▭ Access, Visa

£ Single occupancy of twin/double £35 to £70, twin/double £140 to £180 (rates inc dinner); deposit required. Set L £15 (by arrangement), D £25. Special breaks available

---

If you make a booking using a credit card, and find after cancelling that the full amount has been charged to your card, raise the matter with your credit card company. They will ask the hotelier to confirm whether the room was re-let, and to justify the charge made.

NAIRN HIGHLAND   **MAP 1**

Clifton House

VIEWFIELD STREET, NAIRN, NAIRNSHIRE IV12 4HW
TEL: NAIRN (0667) 53119   FAX: (0667) 52836

This nonconformist hotel has a theatrical bent and devotees.

The dress rehearsal of Noël Coward's *Nude with Violin* was taking place the night our inspector visited. J. Gordon Macintyre welcomes guests, as he has done since 1952. A guided tour of the hotel – as good a performance as anything on show later – is in many ways fruitless, the impresario at every turn exclaiming 'That's not usually here,' in reference to make-up boxes on the stairs, bedrooms given over to dressing-rooms and the dining-room converted into a stage.

'What's really important,' confides J. Gordon Macintyre with a vice-like grip on your biceps, 'is colour, books, curtains, that you can get your laundry back the same day, that there are 18 kinds of tea at breakfast, which, by the way, you can take any time up to lunch.' Every room in the rambling house is a decadent Aladdin's cave of colour: antiques and knick-knacks, of yellows, purples and oranges, of exuberant drapes, beautiful mahogany pieces, of busts, plates, paintings. Four bedrooms have disappeared since last year ('a bit poky'). *Objets d'art*, books and delightful oddities such as screened bathrooms have found their way into the remainder.

The food is excellent: perhaps oysters, foie gras, coquilles St Jacques to start, salmon au beurre blanc for a main course and crème brûlée for pudding.

◗ Closed Dec and Jan

🔀 Enter Nairn on the A96, turn west at the only roundabout in the town, down Marine Road. The hotel is ½ mile on the left. Private car park

🛏 4 single (inc 1 four-poster), 3 twin, 3 double, 2 four-poster; all with bathroom/WC, room service, hair-dryer; no tea/coffee-making facilities in rooms

◈ 2 dining-rooms, drawing-room, sitting-room, TV room, drying room; golf, tennis, other sports nearby

⊖ No wheelchair access; no dogs in public rooms

▭ Access, Amex, Diners, Visa

£ Single £54, twin/double £90 to £96, four-poster £96 to £100; deposit preferred. Alc L, D £25 (prices till end 93). Special breaks available

---

Scottish hoteliers blessed with beautiful soft, peaty water continue to be incensed by guests who complain there must be something wrong with the plumbing because the water's brown. Our advice: if it's good enough for the whisky, it should be OK for your bath.

NEWTONMORE HIGHLAND　　　　　　　　　　**MAP 1**

Ard-na-Coille

KINGUSSIE ROAD, NEWTONMORE, INVERNESS-SHIRE PH20 1AY
TEL: NEWTONMORE (0540) 673214　FAX: (0540) 673453

*First-rate food and warm service in an undemonstrative small
hotel in sight of the Cairngorms.*

Barry Cottam and Nancy Ferrier attribute some of the inspiration of
their cooking to friend David Wilson of Peat Inn fame. Food is simply
done but with flair. A set no-choice meal might comprise char-grilled
Loch Linnhe scallops, a creamy carrot and ginger soup, beautifully
tender medallions of mallard, a powerful selection of Scottish cheeses
and home-made pistachio and ginger ice-cream.

　　The harled Edwardian house with Hockney-blue windows was once a
shooting-lodge. It feels homely inside, with plates, prints and pictures on
the walls and stairs. The dark panelling and stag's head makes the
dining-room a little austere, but it's small enough to be intimate. If you
get the small single bedroom you've been hard done by: other rooms have
lovely views, and lots of light and space.

● Open all year, exc mid-Nov to
late Dec and 1 week Apr, 1
week Sept

◿ On the A86 Newtonmore to
Kingussie road at the north-east
end of Newtonmore. Private car
park

🛏 1 single, 2 twin, 3 double, 1
family room; most with
bathroom/WC, some with
shower/WC; hair-dryer, baby-
listening in all rooms; no tea/
coffee-making facilities in rooms

◈ 2 dining-rooms, lounge, TV room,
drying room; fishing, golf, other
sports nearby

● No wheelchair access; no dogs in
public rooms and in 2 bedrooms
only; no smoking in dining-rooms

▭ Access, Visa

£ Single £63, single occupancy of
twin/double £85, twin/double/
family room £126 (rates inc
dinner); deposit required. Set D
£28.50 (7.45pm). Special breaks
available

OBAN STRATHCLYDE　　　　　　　　　　**MAP 2**

Knipoch Hotel

KILNINVER, BY OBAN, ARGYLL PA34 4QT
TEL: KILNINVER (085 26) 251　FAX: (085 26) 249

A hotel with first-rate food, wine and welcome.

The position of the Craig family's elongated yellow-fronted hotel is a
good one. The building offers considerable interest if you seek out the
original structures in the framework of the hotel's more modern parts:
old stone walls in one of the dining-rooms reveal a sixteenth-century

core; a fine set of fireplaces include a medieval construction from Ypres Cathedral. Works by local artists and a set of Russell Flints offset the slight frigidity of fawn leather seating. Bedrooms, in a wing a decade old, let the side down a bit: they are modern, on the small side, possibly a bit garish.

However, all of this has minimal importance for visiting epicureans, for the cooking has a high reputation. The kitchen repertoire has no truck with adventurism but features well-established dishes. Fish-smoking, bread-baking and coffee-roasting are all done in-house. Guests can choose from a three-course as well as a five-course no-choice menu. A spring menu included scallops with fresh ginger and spring onion, followed by breast of duck with madeira sauce. Expect Mr Craig to be enthusiastic and welcoming, and staff friendly and professional.

◑ Closed mid-Nov to mid-Feb

⤧ 6 miles south of Oban on the A816. Private car park

🛏 4 twin, 11 double, 2 family rooms; all with bathroom/WC, TV, room service, hair-dryer, baby-listening; tea/coffee-making facilities on request

◈ 3 dining-rooms, bar, lounge; fishing, golf, other sports nearby

⊖ No wheelchair access; no dogs

▭ Access, Amex, Diners, Visa

£ Single occupancy of twin/double £59, twin/double £118, family room £133. Set L £18.50 (by arrangement), D £27.50/£37.50

PEAT INN FIFE   **MAP 2**

Peat Inn

PEAT INN, BY CUPAR, FIFE KY15 5LH
TEL: PEAT INN (0334 84) 206   FAX: (0334 84) 530

Superb modern cuisine and luxurious bedrooms in a quiet spot.

It's not just in the food – some of the finest you can eat in Scotland – that you find the Wilsons' daring, confident touches. They also appear in the bedrooms, added in 1987 by the creation of a purpose-built stone block. These are not mere rooms – rather, they are split-level suites, and your breakfast is laid out in the morning in the sitting area upstairs. Bathrooms are marble; patterns have bold designs.

Across the gravel yard is the white, pink-lintelled inn itself, heart of the operation. As you proceed into the inner sanctum everything becomes understated, ensuring that nothing detracts from the food: the three cosy beamed dining areas have stone or white walls and plain linen cloths. The food is delicately presented, direct in taste. A particular feature is the six-course tasting menu: on a winter's night there was a ragoût of seafood in a spiced butter sauce, roast monkfish on a bed of potato and onion in a meat sauce, julienne of pigeon with pulses in a beef broth, and medallions of venison in a red wine sauce with port – not to mention cheese and pudding.

◑ Closed Sun, Mon

↗ At the junction of the B940 and B941, 6 miles south-west of St Andrews. Private car park

🛏 8 suites; all with bathroom/WC, TV, room service, hair-dryer; no tea/coffee-making facilities in rooms

◈ Dining-room, lounge; small meetings facilities; fishing, golf, riding nearby. Wheelchair access to hotel, dining-room and WC (unisex), 1 bedroom specially equipped for disabled people

⊖ No dogs or smoking in public rooms

▭ Access, Amex, Diners, Visa

£ Single occupancy of suite £95, suite £130 to £140; deposit required. Set L £18.50, D £30; alc D £35

PEEBLES BORDERS　　　　　　　　　　　　　　**MAP 2**

Cringletie House

PEEBLES, PEEBLESSHIRE EH45 8PL
TEL: PEEBLES (0721) 730233　FAX: (0721) 730244

A traditional, family-run country-house hotel in fine grounds.

The slate-roofed towers and lofty chimneys on Stanley Maguire's large Victorian sandstone house lord it over a fine setting of banks of daffodils, extensive lawns and Border valley views. Inside there are plenty of architectural attractions: carved doorways, plastered walls, elegant alcoves and marble fireplaces, of which the panelled and frescoed first-floor drawing-room holds the finest. The bar feels a bit like an airport lounge, the dining-rooms are a bit cramped. Undemonstrative bedrooms are comfortable and all priced the same, despite great variety in size. Pine furniture decorates the cosy, cottagey rooms on the top floor; the high-ceilinged lower floor rooms, which tend to be more spacious, have dark wood reproduction furniture.

Guests on a three-night stay found the food 'not as good as previous years'. Expect a four-course dinner with four options at each stage except for the soup. Traditional dishes are often given a stylish twist: vegetarian haggis with whisky cream, lamb fillet with coriander yogurt. However, these same guests, who have been coming regularly for the last half-dozen years, reckoned overall that the hotel is as good as always, and the value-for-money quotient remains high.

◑ Closed 2 Jan to Mar

↗ 2 miles north of Peebles on the A703. Private car park

🛏 1 single, 8 twin, 4 double; all with bathroom/WC, TV, room service, hair-dryer, trouser press, baby-listening; no tea/coffee-making facilities in rooms

◈ 2 dining-rooms, bar, 2 lounges, drying room; tennis, croquet at hotel, other sports nearby. Wheelchair access to hotel and 2 ground-floor bedrooms

⊖ No dogs in public rooms; no smoking in dining-rooms and 1 lounge

▭ Access, Visa

£ Single £48, single occupancy of twin/double £60, twin/double £86; deposit preferred. Sun L £14, set D £23.50. Special breaks available

PLOCKTON HIGHLAND   **MAP 1**

Haven Hotel

PLOCKTON, ROSS-SHIRE IV52 8TW
TEL: PLOCKTON (0599 84) 223

A no-frills hotel that offers excellent value for money.

There is something dogmatically unadorned about this much-extended
Victorian merchant's house. Though it is smart and neat, modern soft
furnishings rather than period pieces deck out the sitting-rooms, while
the only distraction from food and fellow guests in the cream and brown
dining-room is a bizarrely placed organ. However, on a full Bank
Holiday evening none of the mixed bunch of happy guests – from young,
casually dressed couples to more formal types in full Scottish regalia –
seemed to mind. Good-value four-course dinners were being tucked
away with relish (how about a whole quail, soup, scallops and scampi,
summer pudding and coffee?). Tired vegetables let down an otherwise
very enjoyable meal. Staff are involved, friendly and attentive; courteous
proprietors Marjorie Nichols and John Graham oversee the proceed-
ings.

The inspector's comfortably furnished but plainly decorated bedroom
was well-equipped with mod cons. Situated in the rear extension, it
suffered from the noise of fellow guests through its thin walls.

◗ Open all year, exc 18 Dec to 10 Feb

🡕 Take the A82 to Glengarry, then the A87 to Kyle of Lochalsh. A local road to Plockton is signposted. Private car park

🛏 2 single, 5 twin, 6 double; all with bathroom/WC, TV, room service, hair-dryer, trouser press

◈ Restaurant, bar, 2 lounges, drying room, conservatory; fishing, golf, water sports, swimming nearby

⊖ No wheelchair access; no children under 7; no dogs in public rooms; no smoking in restaurant and 2 lounges

▭ Access, Visa

£ Single £32 to £35, single occupancy of twin/double £32 to £35, twin/double £64 to £70; deposit required. Set D £20; alc L (residents only). Special breaks available

PORT APPIN STRATHCLYDE   **MAP 1**

Airds Hotel

PORT APPIN, APPIN, ARGYLL PA38 4DF
TEL: APPIN (063 173) 236   FAX: (063 173) 535

This top-notch, urbane hotel has one of Scotland's best restaurants.

The simplicity of the white 300-year-old ferry inn with grey lattice shutters deceives, for this hotel verges on the luxurious. The appealingly co-ordinated country-house style bedrooms come in varying sizes and are priced accordingly, but all are kitted out with fluffy bathrobes and towels. A striking tiled conservatory hides superlative sitting-rooms, one white-panelled, one in red, with top-quality soft furnishings and lovely paintings.

It can be depressing arriving at Airds if you're not staying to eat, for delicious smells emanate from the kitchens. Betty Allen's superb food is not over-elaborate. Her four-course dinners, with choices at each stage except for soup, are tied to the seasons: from an April menu you might have a salad of Loch Linnhe prawns with a herb mayonnaise, cream of carrot and coriander soup, roast saddle of roe deer and poached pear shortcake. Staff are very correct, while kilted Eric Allen manages to be both warm and appropriately formal.

◐ Closed 7 Jan to 7 Mar

↗ 2½ miles off the A828, mid-way between Ballachulish and Connel. Private car park

🛏 1 single, 5 twin, 5 double, 1 suite; all with bathroom/WC, TV, room service, hair-dryer, baby-listening; no tea/coffee-making facilities in rooms

◇ Dining-room, bar, 2 lounges, drying room, conservatory; riding, water sports nearby

⊖ No wheelchair access; no dogs

▭ Access, Amex, Visa

£ Single £64 to £90, single occupancy of twin/double £80 to £160, twin/double £130 to £170, suite £170 to £190; deposit required. Set L £10, D £35

PORTPATRICK DUMFRIES & GALLOWAY   **MAP 2**

Crown Hotel

NORTH CRESCENT, PORTPATRICK, WIGTOWNSHIRE DG9 8SX
TEL: PORTPATRICK (0776) 810261   FAX: (0776) 810551

An attractive harbourside inn with pretty views.

The Crown sits right on the harbourside. At the front of the hotel is a collection of traditional little bar rooms furnished with wooden-topped converted sewing tables; at the back is a surprisingly large, fresh, modern restaurant, extending into a flower-filled conservatory. The various parts of the bars and dining-room happily accommodate young locals, elderly residents and boisterous parties of golfers. Our inspector's bedroom was eye-catching, in a modern cottagey style with a pine floor and light floral fabrics.

You can eat in one of the bars or in the restaurant. On inspection a table d'hôte meal was very affordable but disappointing: a tepid soup, an over-sauced fish, a plastic-tasting lemon meringue pie. Straightforward à la carte dishes such as steaks and seafood platters (including surf on the turf – steak and half a lobster) appeared more promising. Service varied from jovial to unceremonious.

◐ Open all year

⤢ Follow the A77 from Stranraer and turn right at the sea-front. On-street parking

🛏 3 twin, 7 double, 2 family rooms; all with bathroom/WC, TV, baby-listening

◇ Restaurant, 3 bars, lounge, conservatory, drying room; conference facilities (max 12 people residential); fishing, golf, tennis, other sports nearby. Wheelchair access to restaurant and WC (M,F) only

⊖ None

▭ Access, Visa

£ Single occupancy of twin/double £35, twin/double £66. Set D £9.50; alc L £5 to £15, D £7 to £20. Special breaks available

---

Knockinaam Lodge

PORTPATRICK, WIGTOWNSHIRE DG9 9AD
TEL: PORTPATRICK (0776) 810471   FAX: (0776) 810435

First-rate country-house comfort and cuisine in an isolated spot.

The country house is impeccably smart, and Marcel Frichot provides suave service with the assistance of professional staff. Antiques and quality soft furnishings covered in puffed cushions fill the two sitting-rooms. A fascinating collection of clocks is spread throughout the house, the most peculiar being a cantilevered one operated by a ball bearing. The dinners – jacket-and-tie affairs in the intimate dining-room – are highly thought of; they are modern Gallic in style from a short set menu in French with a choice at each course.

Master bedrooms are larger and have better views than standard rooms. All are traditionally styled with period furnishings. One room is called Churchill, in memory of the secret wartime confab between the PM and Eisenhower that took place here.

◐ Closed 4 Jan to 15 Mar

⤢ 3 miles before Portpatrick on the A77 from Stranraer is a turning on the left (well signposted to Knockinaam Lodge). Follow the hotel signs for 3 miles. Private car park

🛏 1 single, 4 twin, 5 double; all with bathroom/WC, TV, room service, hair-dryer; baby-listening on request; no tea/coffee-making facilities in rooms

◇ Dining-room, bar, 2 lounges; conference facilities (max 10 people residential); croquet at hotel, fishing, golf, other sports nearby. Wheelchair access to dining-room only

⊖ No dogs in public rooms; no smoking in dining-room

▭ Access, Amex, Diners, Visa

£ Single £68, twin/double £100 to £136; deposit required. Set L £22.50, D £30. Special breaks available

---

Dog lovers: some hotels not only welcome dogs, but provide gourmet meals for them. Ask.

Viewfield House

PORTREE, ISLE OF SKYE IV51 9EU
TEL: PORTREE (0478) 612217   FAX: (0478) 613517

A fine family home, little changed by the years: one for the sociable.

Few Scottish country-house hotels can offer such consistent lineage: it has been in the Macdonald family for over 200 years. The hall in the Victorian half of the creeper-clad mansion contains what may be the finest collection of taxidermy in a UK hotel: a tiger's head from India, antelope trophies from Africa, numerous birds of prey and game from Scotland. Personal family effects also fill the lovely parquet-floored drawing-room, its old bound books, tiered fireplace and brass-handled long windows exuding the Victorian era. Soft-spoken Hugh Macdonald carefully fosters a house-party atmosphere. A no-choice five-course dinner from the kitchen Aga offers elaborate home cooking.

A batch of new *en-suite* bathrooms in 1992 has radically changed the level of comfort. Most rooms are in the Georgian wing of the house; they can be small, though they have a nice antique piece here and there. The best rooms (costing no extra) are One and Three, in the Victorian part of the house; both are massive, with original wallpaper and chunky period pieces.

◑ Closed mid-Oct to mid-Apr	sports nearby
⬈ On the southern edge of Portree, just off the A850. Driveway is just before the BP filling station. Private car park	⊖ No wheelchair access; no dogs in public rooms; smoking discouraged in dining-room
🛏 2 single, 4 twin, 5 double; most with bathroom/WC, 2 public bathrooms; hair-dryer on request	▭ Access, Visa
◇ Dining-room, lounge, TV room, drying room; fishing, golf, other	£ Single £25 to £40, twin/double £60 to £80, family room rate on request; deposit required. Set D £15 (7.30pm). Special breaks available

Shieldhill Hotel ☆

QUOTHQUAN, BIGGAR, LANARKSHIRE ML12 6NA
TEL: BIGGAR (0899) 20035   FAX: (0899) 21092

An isolated American-run mansion — atmospheric outside, comfortable and elegant but somewhat impersonal within.

'Some think it's more Scottish than a Scot-run home,' claims professionally charming Jack Greenwald, Californian owner of Shieldhill. It certainly looks and feels authentically Scottish, a lumbering pile of grey stone among back lanes and open fields. Shieldhill's unique selling proposition is its age – its old tower, the core of the building, dates back to 1199. The Shieldhill coat of arms above an original doorway is fifteenth century. The rest of the austere three-storey mansion was added in the seventeenth and nineteenth centuries.

Inside, warm-coloured fabrics go some way to offset a certain amount of stiffness and a little lack of individuality in some rooms. In winter, fires blaze in the best rooms – the panelled drawing-room and the generously spaced dining-room. The ambitious food consisting of the likes of baked filo moneybag of chicken and smoked Lochaber cheese, followed, perhaps, by green and yellow courgette soup and honey-glazed breast of Gressingham duck in a soft pink and green peppercorn sauce is said to be generally successful. Bedrooms are well furnished, some having window seats and wing chairs.

◑ Open all year

⤴ From Biggar take the B7016 in the direction of Carnwath for 2 miles. Turn right on to Shieldhill Road for 1½ miles. Private car park

🛏 2 single, 3 twin, 6 double, four-posters and suites available; all with bathroom/WC, TV, room service, hair-dryer; trouser press, baby-listening on request

◈ Restaurant, bar, 2 lounges, library; conference facilities (max 28 people non-residential, 11 residential); fishing, golf, tennis nearby. Wheelchair access to restaurant only

⊖ No children under 11; no dogs; no smoking in bedrooms

▭ Access, Amex, Diners, Visa

£ Single £88, twin/double £98, four-poster £111 to £130, suite £155; deposit required. Alc L £5 to £15; set D £24.50/£28.50. Special breaks available

---

RUM HIGHLAND   **MAP 1**

Kinloch Castle

ISLE OF RUM, INVERNESS-SHIRE PH43 4RR
TEL: MALLAIG (0687) 2037

This monument to Edwardian extravagance is an extraordinary experience.

This folly of a magnitude that defies any logic was built at the turn of the century by textile industry magnate Sir George Bullough. In 1957 his widow passed the castle along with the island on to the Nature Conservancy Council. The castle has changed little since its pre-eminent Edwardian days. Palatial reception rooms, for example, the galleried Great Hall or the smoking room with its full-size billiard table, retain the furniture and decoration collected by Sir George – stags' heads, period antiques, a Steinway piano. Public bathrooms still have their original seven-control fittings over baths, while the massive bedrooms contain ancient beds and fine inlaid furniture.

Kinloch Castle is personally managed by Ian and Kathleen Mac-Arthur. Dining takes place round one large polished table. A game terrine might be followed by tomato and fennel soup, then fillet of beef wrapped in bacon and topped with pâté in a Café de Paris butter and wine sauce, with brandy-snap baskets with iced ginger sorbet to finish.

Much more modest are the bistro and hostel bedrooms. Readers, arriving unannounced by yacht at 4.30 pm, were relegated for their meal to the former – 'neither the food, the welcome, the service nor the ambience were of an acceptable standard'.

◑ Closed Oct to early Mar

🔁 The island is reached by ferry from Mallaig on the mainland. Parking at Mallaig

🛏 2 single, 1 twin, 2 double, 4 four-poster, 6 public bathrooms

◈ 2 restaurants, 3 lounges, billiard room, library, drying room, ballroom, gunroom; fishing nearby

⊖ No wheelchair access; no children under 7; no dogs; smoking in smoking room only

▭ None accepted

£ Single £80, twin/double/four-poster £160 (rates inc dinner); deposit required. Set D £25 (7.30pm); packed lunches £4

ST ANDREWS FIFE   MAP 2

Rufflets

STRATHKINNESS LOW ROAD, ST ANDREWS, FIFE KY16 9TX
TEL: ST ANDREWS (0334) 72594   FAX: (0334) 78703

Long-established, relaxed Edwardian country house.

Rufflets has been a hotel under two generations of Russells since it was bought in 1952. Two squat turrets give shape to the harled mansion's lovely creeper-covered rear façade, which overlooks an immaculate garden of box hedges. Both the green and pink dining-room and elegant burgundy drawing-room back on to the garden. A large collection of Russell Flint watercolours distinguish the drawing-room and the newly decorated bar.

The best bedrooms are those in the turrets; standard rooms are smaller and might be over the kitchen. When our inspector visited, more bedrooms were being built as a top floor to the new wing. If they match the existing rooms in the wing, they will lack the character of those in the original building but will offer a good standard of comfort.

The cuisine features many Scottish ingredients: perhaps Orkney oatcakes with a salmon and horseradish mousse, East Coast sole, Perthshire lamb, Rannoch venison.

◐ Open all year

⤢ On the B939 Ceres/Kirkcaldy road, 1½ miles west of St Andrews. Private car park

🛏 5 single, 9 twin, 1 four-poster, 7 family rooms, 4 cottages; all with bathroom/WC, TV, room service, hair-dryer, trouser press, baby-listening

◇ Restaurant, bar, lounge, drying room; conference facilities (max 50 people non-residential, 45 residential); putting at hotel, fishing, golf, other sports nearby;

babysitting. Wheelchair access to restaurant only

⊖ No dogs; no smoking in some public rooms and bedrooms

▭ Access, Amex, Diners, Visa

£ Single £40 to £75, twin/double £80 to £150, four-poster £80 to £150, family room £80 and £200, cottage £80 to £130; deposit required. Set L £14.50, D £23.50; bar meals from £6; alc D from £15. Special breaks available

---

St Andrews Old Course Hotel

ST ANDREWS, FIFE KY16 9SP
TEL: ST ANDREWS (0334) 74371   FAX: (0334) 77668

Giant luxury hotel by the world's oldest and arguably most famous golf course.

Some might say the hotel spoils the scene. Like a liner on an empty ocean, its immensity on nothing but a sea of green demands attention from afar. Again like a liner, its elegance fades on approach, revealing it to be modern – it was built in 1968. Close up, the adjacent Victorian Jigger Inn comes into view, a tug to the ship. Inside, downstairs corridors seem as decks or walkways, long enough to provide an ample stroll, and offering golf-course views. Such is the scale of the vessel that were it suddenly to set sail for the Antipodes, you know that all you'd be denied in the forthcoming months would be a round of golf.

All sorts of people use the hotel. On a February afternoon guests read the papers in swimming trunks by the health centre's modish pool. Arran-jumpered students from the university canoodle over drinks in the bar. Those in diamond-patterned sweaters corner the pro in the golf shop or study the names and portraits of Open winners in the Hall of Fame.

Stencilling, friezes and *trompe-l'oeil* inventively mix with period styles. In the lobby and along its walkways marble and pillars give a classical air. In the ground-floor library, the fourth-floor parquet-floored bar with leather chesterfields and or the light-panelled grill room, Edwardiana takes over. Bedrooms are impressively comfortable though you pay extra for Old Course views.

◐ Open all year

⤢ Take the A91 to St Andrews. The hotel is adjacent to the '17th

Road Hole' of the Old Course. Private car park

🛏 108 twin/double, 17 suites; all with bathroom/WC, TV, room

service, hair-dryer, mini-bar; no
tea/coffee-making facilities in
rooms; baby-listening on request

◈ Restaurant, bar, 2 lounges,
library, conservatory (all air-
conditioned); conference facilities
(max 300 people non-residential,
125 residential); golf, sauna/
solarium, gym, heated
swimming-pool at hotel, other
sports nearby; babysitting on
request. Wheelchair access to

hotel, restaurant and WC (M,F),
lift to bedrooms, 2 specially
equipped for disabled people

● Dogs by arrangement

▭ Access, Amex, Diners, Visa

£ Single occupancy of twin/double
£150 to £205, twin/double £200
to £235, suite £275 to £425;
deposit required. Set L £2.50 to
£12.50, D £32.50. Special
breaks available

ST FILLANS TAYSIDE　　　　　　　　　MAP 2

Four Seasons Hotel

ST FILLANS, PERTHSHIRE PH6 2NF
TEL: ST FILLANS (0764) 685333 (and fax)

First-rate lochside location for this unassuming family-run hotel.

The main public rooms of this roadside hotel all face the loch: a fresh
dining-room with white walls and tablecloths, an ante-room off it with a
log fire, and a little bar with wall seats. At the far end of the building, with
a separate entrance, is a plain, slate-floored bar for passing trade and bar
food. Bedrooms are old-fashioned with plain bedspreads and simple
wooden furniture. More romantic are the six pine lodges up a steep track
above the hotel.

Alan and Barbara Scott, the delightfully welcoming owners, have been
hotel-keeping for nearly 30 years. Since we last inspected they have
installed torches in the lodges for the walk back from dinner, and for
peace and quiet they have created a tiny lair of a library upstairs. The
enjoyable food is prepared by their son. For breakfast, orange juice
comes freshly squeezed and scrambled egg is accompanied by smoked
salmon. Bar supper and dinner menus offer steaks, fish and game.

◐ Closed Jan and Feb

⤢ On the main A85, 12 miles west
of Crieff, at the east end of Loch
Earn. Private car park

⇌ 7 twin, 1 double, 3 four-poster, 7
family rooms (6 chalets); all with
bathroom/WC, exc double with
shower/WC; TV, room service,
hair-dryer, baby-listening in all
rooms

◈ 2 restaurants, 2 bars, 2 lounges,
drying room, library; conference
facilities (max 60 people non-

residential, 20 residential);
fishing at hotel, golf, tennis
nearby; babysitting. Wheelchair
access to hotel and restaurant, 3
ground-floor bedrooms

● No dogs in public rooms; no
smoking in restaurants

▭ Access, Amex, Visa

£ Single occupancy of twin/double
£35 to £42, twin/double £66 to
£78, family room £66 to £80,
annexe/chalet £50 to £66. Set L
£12.50, D £20; alc L from £9

SCARISTA WESTERN ISLES   **MAP 1**

Scarista House

ISLE OF HARRIS, WESTERN ISLES PA85 3HX
TEL: SCARISTA (0859) 550238; changing to (085 985) 238 mid-Nov   FAX: (0859)
550277; changing to (085 985) 277 mid-Nov

The most civilised place to stay on Harris or Lewis.

Jane and Ian Callaghan appear to be rightly proud of their tasteful, well-bred little country house. Jane studied at the Courtauld Institute and worked in the antiques business: works of art and fine pieces of furniture fill the house, while fires and loose-covered armchairs make for an air of relaxation in the sitting-rooms. In some bedrooms pleasing antiques and cotton damask curtains complement the white walls; others, equally comfortable, have yet to be elegantly moulded.

Candles and silverware dress the two-part dining-room. Jane creates carefully composed and ambitious five-course set dinners that feature seafood as much as possible, and specialities such as nettle soup. Oatcakes, scones, bread and jams are home-made. Breakfasts receive equal attention, the orange juice freshly squeezed, the eggs from home hens, the teas various.

◑ *Closed mid-Oct to Easter*

⤢ *15 miles south-west of Tarbert on the A859. Private car park*

🛏 *3 twin, 5 double; all with bathroom/WC, room service, hair-dryer*

◈ *2 dining-rooms, lounge, drying room, library; golf, fishing, other sports nearby. Wheelchair access to hotel (2 steps) and dining-rooms, 5 ground-floor bedrooms*

⊖ *No children under 8; no dogs in dining-rooms; no smoking in bedrooms in main house*

▭ *None accepted*

£ *Single occupancy of twin/double £53 to £62, twin/double £86 to £94; deposit required. Set L £8, D £25 (8.15pm)*

SCONE TAYSIDE   **MAP 2**

Murrayshall

SCONE, PERTHSHIRE PH2 7PH
TEL: PERTH (0738) 51171   FAX: (0738) 52595

Comfortable country house with its own beautifully landscaped golf course.

If you're a golfer, ask about special breaks: with the clubhouse next to the Victorian building and the eighteenth green just yards from the porch, this may be your idea of heaven. Public rooms are furnished in an unexciting but plush style. The big bar has a log fire in winter, and a range of reading matter from guidebooks to the complete works of

Robert Burns. Mirrors and pillars make the dining-room more out of the ordinary. Most of the bedrooms, in classic modern country-house style mode, have stripy designs. Rooms in the new wing are not as characterful or spacious as those in the original building. The restaurant now offers less ornate, more traditional cuisine.

◐ Open all year, exc 23 to 28 Dec

⤢ From Perth, take the A94 Coupar Angus road. After 4 miles turn right at the Murrayshall signpost just before New Scone. Private car park

⇌ 12 twin, 4 double, 3 suites; all with bathroom/WC, TV, room service, hair-dryer, trouser press, baby-listening; no tea/coffee-making facilities in rooms

◇ Restaurant, 2 bars, lounge; conference facilities (max 75 people non-residential, 19

residential); golf, tennis, croquet, bowls at hotel, other sports nearby. Wheelchair access to hotel, restaurant and WC (unisex) only

⊖ No dogs

▭ Access, Amex, Diners, Visa

£ Single occupancy of twin/double £60 to £75, twin/double £105 to £125; suite £105 to £185; deposit required. Alc L £4.50 to £12, D £16 to £25. Special breaks available

SCOURIE HIGHLAND

MAP 1

Scourie Hotel

SCOURIE, BY LAIRG, SUTHERLAND IV27 4SX
TEL: SCOURIE (0971) 502396   FAX: (0971) 502423

A well-known traditional fishing hotel.

'Guests wishing to fish hotel waters must be in lounges at 9pm. The allocation of beats for the next day's fishing is done by the boardmaster at that time.' Fishing would seem to be the prime reason for staying at the wood-boarded coaching-inn. Otherwise, treat it as a useful pitstop if you're heading round the north coast of Scotland, rather than as a base. Only a few bedrooms on the end of the building have views of Scourie Bay (ask for 2, 10 or 14) and one reader was disappointed with his grim outlook having booked months ahead; some have more old-fashioned furnishings than others. Yet tartan carpets, strong-coloured armchairs, a nice old sideboard here, a grandfather clock there mean the lounges are spruce. Staff are sprightly and Mr Ian Hay, owner for 30 years, is charming.

On inspection the set dinner, served in a cramped dining-room, was plentiful and good value, but stodgy and uninspiring. A pet hate – breakfast was laid for the following morning before guests had finished eating.

◐ Closed mid-Oct to mid-Mar

⤢ On the A894 on the edge of Scourie Bay. Private car park

⇌ 5 single, 6 twin, 7 double, 2 family rooms; most with bathroom/WC, 1 public bathroom; hair-dryer in most rooms

✦ Dining-room, 2 bars (air-conditioned public bar), 2 lounges, drying room; fishing nearby

⊖ No wheelchair access; no dogs in public rooms

▭ Access, Amex, Diners, Visa

£ Single £29 to £39, single occupancy of twin/double £44 to £54, twin/double £52 to £68. Set D £12.50; alc L £10.50. Special breaks available

---

SELKIRK BORDERS   **MAP 2**

Philipburn House

SELKIRK, SELKIRKSHIRE TD7 5LS
TEL: SELKIRK (0750) 20747   FAX: (0750) 21690

A part family-oriented, family-run hotel.

Philipburn markets itself as an unsnobby, cosy country-house hotel. Walking is the most keenly promoted activity, with offers of a local guide and a corner of the house devoted to maps and plenty of local literature.

The unassuming eighteenth-century building contains a succession of cheery rooms: a chintzy sitting-room, a snug pine bar and candlelit coffee-room and, the cornerstone of the hotel, a busy but intimate restaurant. There's a refreshingly wide choice of food: nut provençale and the like on the vegetarian menu, soup and croque-monsieur on the Light Bite menu and ambitious concoctions such as steak on a bed of haggis in a whisky and onion sauce on the table d'hôte.

Pine fittings predominate in pleasant bedrooms. Garden suites, with high ceilings and balconies overlooking the pool, are popular.

◑ Open all year

▰ On the A707 Peebles road, I mile from Selkirk – the hotel is well signposted. Private car park

🛏 4 twin, 4 double, I four-poster, 6 family rooms, 2 suites, I cottage; all with bathroom/WC, TV, room service, hair-dryer, trouser press, baby-listening

✦ Restaurant, bar, lounge, games room, conservatory, drying room; conference facilities (max 30 people non-residential and residential); heated outdoor swimming-pool at hotel, other

sports nearby; babysitting. Wheelchair access to hotel, restaurant and WC (M,F), 3 ground-floor bedrooms, 2 specially equipped for disabled people

⊖ Dogs by arrangement only; smoking discouraged

▭ Access, Visa

£ Single occupancy of twin/double £45, twin/double/four-poster/family room/cottage room £90, suite £99; deposit required. Set L £7.50, D £22.50; alc L, D £10 to £20. Special breaks available.

The Guide *is totally independent, accepts no free hospitality, and survives on the number of copies sold each year.*

SHIELDAIG HIGHLAND **MAP 1**

Tigh an Eilean

SHIELDAIG, BY STRATHCARRON, ROSS-SHIRE IV54 8XN
TEL: SHIELDAIG (05205) 251   FAX: (05205) 321

Carefully nurtured hotel in a remote Highland fishing village.

'Altogether a splendid place to stay.' 'Absolutely wonderful: we were sorry that we were there only for two nights – will go back for a longer stay.' More satisfied customers enthuse about the Stewarts' 'simple but immaculate' hotel. A neatness and freshness imbues every room, the absence of stags' heads and heavy Victorian furniture making a welcome change from the prototype Scottish hotel. The strong colours of cosmopolitan art gallery prints kit out the swish, light dining-room. The cooking is reckoned to be 'plain, simple but good' by one, 'tasty and competent' by another, who particularly liked the use of local produce and the precision of the menu: 'We never had venison, it was either roe deer or red deer.'

Laid-back and charming chef/proprietor Callum Stewart is disarmingly honest about the smallness of some rooms: 'There's nothing we can do about it; guests have been known to take the matter into their own hands and put chairs out in the corridors.' It's just as important to get a room with a sea view as to get a decent-sized one: Number 14 fits both bills. All are most attractive, in light florals or stripes.

◑ Closed end Oct to Easter

⤢ In Shieldaig village off the A896. On-street parking

🛏 3 single, 4 twin, 3 double, 1 family room; all with bathroom/WC, exc 1 single with shower/WC; hair-dryer on request

◈ Dining-room, bar, lounge, TV room, drying room; fishing nearby

⊖ No wheelchair access; no dogs in public rooms

▭ Access, Visa

£ Single £38, twin/double £84; children under 8 free; deposit required. Set D £19

STAFFIN HIGHLAND **MAP 1**

Flodigarry Country House ☆

STAFFIN, PORTREE, ISLE OF SKYE IV51 9HZ
TEL: DUNTULM (0470) 52203   FAX: (0470) 52301

Flora MacDonald once lived in the cottage in the grounds.

Trippers drop in to Flodigarry to see the cottage behind the hotel where Flora MacDonald lived for eight years; it was in fact a descendant of hers who built the country house. Others come for a drink or a bite to eat in the rough-and-ready castellated folly of a bar. The hotel proper has more refinement, with a seductive sitting-room with a mix of upholstered and Lloyd Loom furniture, a grand piano and games and books. More burgundy wicker furnishes an equally inviting iron-pillared conservatory.

Good things have been said of the Scottish home cooking and the fresh ingredients used. The bar menu offers Rambler's Breakfasts, haggis and mashed neeps, lots of fish. For dinner, in a perhaps somewhat cramped dining-room, the breadth of choice of main courses on the table d'hôte menu is such that you can effectively have whatever you could want. Bedrooms have been kept intentionally basic (bathrooms are more decent), and all have worn wooden furniture and are without mod cons.

◑ Open all year

▨ Off the A855, 20 miles north of Portree and 4 miles north of Staffin. Private car park

🛏 4 single, 3 twin, 6 double, I family room, 2 suites, 8 cottage rooms; most with bathroom/WC, some with shower/WC, some with neither, I public bathroom; hair-dryer in all rooms; room service on request

◈ Restaurant, bar, lounge, conservatory; conference facilities (max 40 people residential and non-residential); fishing, riding, water sports nearby; babysitting. Wheelchair access to hotel, restaurant and 5 ground-floor bedrooms, I specially equipped for disabled people

⊖ Dogs in public rooms by arrangement only; no smoking in restaurant

▭ Access, Visa

£ Single £30 to £36, single occupancy of twin/double from £35 and £41, twin/double £50 to £76, family room £50 to £76, suite £90, cottage room £76; deposit required. Sun L £14 (weekdays by arrangement only); bar lunches; set D £18.50. Special breaks available

---

STEWARTON STRATHCLYDE　　　　　　　　　　　**MAP 2**

Chapeltoun House　　

IRVINE ROAD, STEWARTON, AYRSHIRE KA3 3ED
TEL: STEWARTON (0560) 482696　FAX: (0560) 485100

A substantial Edwardian country house in 20 acres of grounds.

Owners and brothers Colin and Graeme McKenzie have been immersed in the hotel business since childhood. They have created a traditional country-house hotel without overweening airs and graces. The building has all the features you would expect of an Edwardian mansion: stuccoed ceilings, oak panelling, big bay windows, elaborate fireplaces. Furnishings such as buttonback armchairs and sofas in the drawing-room and flocked wallpaper and bare wood tables in the dining-room complement the architecture. Bedrooms are named after malts. All are a good size and furnished with antiques, for example a Victorian bed and dressing-table. More expensive rooms may be massive.

Noisettes of wild boar in a port wine, woodland mushroom and fennel sauce might be on the menu.

◑ *Open all year*

⤴ *2 miles from Stewarton on the B769 road towards Irvine. Private car park*

🛏 *3 twin, 4 double, 1 four-poster; all with bathroom/WC, exc 1 double with shower/WC; TV, room service, hair-dryer, trouser press in all rooms; no tea/coffee-making facilities in rooms*

◇ *2 dining-rooms, bar, lounge; conference facilities (max 50 people non-residential, 8 residential); fishing at hotel, golf, riding nearby. Wheelchair access to restaurant only*

⊖ *No children under 12; dogs by arrangement only; no smoking in dining-rooms*

▭ *Access, Amex, Visa*

£ *Single occupancy of twin/double £65 to £74, twin/double £90, four-poster £99 to £129. Set L £16.50, D £25*

STIRLING CENTRAL   **MAP 2**

Heritage

16 ALLAN PARK, STIRLING FK8 2QG
TEL: STIRLING (0786) 473660   FAX: (0786) 451291

A long-established Gallic restaurant-with-rooms.

The Heritage is in a quiet side-street of fine detached Victorian residences. The fascinating craggy grey castle is just a steep walk away. Frenchman Georges Marquetty, chef and owner here for over 20 years – long enough to have a Scottish twang to his English – once worked in Nice. His wife, a Scot, is praised for her French style. The large bar has an intriguing *fin de siècle* air, with tasselled draped curtains, grand portraits, cane-backed armchairs and velvet cushions. In the best French tradition of allowing all attention to focus on the food, the windowless basement restaurant is much simpler, minimally decorated with flower pictures. The à la carte mixes French and Scottish, from escargots, foie gras and bouillabaisse to smoked salmon, game soup and lamb. The food is beautifully cooked and presented.

High-quality fabrics and some antiques furnish spacious, co-ordinated bedrooms that are equipped with attractive modern bathrooms.

◑ *Open all year, exc Xmas and New Year*

⤴ *In Stirling town centre, around the corner from the cinema. Private car park*

🛏 *2 twin, 2 double; all with bathroom/WC, TV, room service, hair-dryer*

◇ *Dining-room, bar, lounge, TV room, drying room; golf, tennis, other sports nearby*

● No wheelchair access; dogs by arrangement only; no smoking in public rooms and discouraged in bedrooms

▭ Access, Visa

£ Single occupancy of twin/double £45 to £50, twin/double £55 to £60; deposit preferred. Set L £11, D £17; alc L, D £15 to £20. Special breaks available

---

STRACHUR STRATHCLYDE   MAP 2

Creggans Inn

STRACHUR, ARGYLL PA27 8BX
TEL: STRACHUR (036 986) 279   FAX: (036 986) 637

An inn on the shores of Loch Fyne.

The roadside inn makes the most of the location: plenty of bedrooms face the loch, as do the purposefully big windows of the dining-room and upstairs sitting-room. Creggans is owned by adventurer and writer Sir Fitzroy Maclean and Lady Maclean.

Certain aspects of our inspector's stay were fine: a decent welcome, a plain, comfortable bedroom with an old-fashioned bathroom, a bar cheery with locals and a fire, a quiet and chintzy residents' sitting-room. But dinner, in the Victorian-style, violently red dining-room, was disappointing; house specialities such as local oysters and mussels or haggis Creggans may be more rewarding. Furthermore, the bedroom was unheated on arrival – and a complaint that the room's telephone was not working proved fruitless.

◑ Open all year

⤴ From Glasgow take the A82 north along Loch Lomond to Arrochar. Turn on to the A83, then the A815 – the Inn is on the left in Strachur. Private car park

🛏 4 single, 11 twin, 6 double; most with bathroom/WC, 3 singles with no private facilities; TV, room service, baby-listening in all rooms; hair-dryer on request; no tea/coffee-making facilities in rooms

◇ Dining-room, 2 bars, lounge, conference room, drying room, games room; conference facilities (max 70 people non-residential, 21 residential); fishing at hotel, tennis nearby. Wheelchair access to hotel (2 steps), restaurant and WC (M,F), 2 ground-floor bedrooms, 1 specially equipped for disabled people

● None

▭ Access, Amex, Diners, Visa

£ Single £30 to £49, single occupancy of twin/double £30 to £59; twin/double £60 to £98; deposit required. Alc L £8 to £12, D £20 (prices till Oct 93). Special breaks available

---

The Guide *office can quickly spot when a hotelier is encouraging customers to write a letter recommending inclusion – and sadly, several hotels have been doing this in 1993. Such reports do not further a hotel's cause.*

STRONTIAN HIGHLAND   **MAP I**

Kilcamb Lodge Hotel

STRONTIAN, ARGYLL PH36 4HY
TEL: STRONTIAN (0967) 2257   FAX: (0967) 2041

A keenly run, unpretentious hotel on Loch Sunart.

The Blakeways, new to Kilcamb at the end of 1991, come across as a diligent and enterprising family. Last winter the sitting-room was refurbished and son Peter went off to learn more about cooking in famous hotels around the country. You enter the Victorian-fronted establishment into a smart, unfussy bar and the spruced-up, cosy sitting-room, now with top-quality upholstery and fleur-de-lys wallpaper. Its alcoves contain books and a collection of love brooches, and a fire crackles in a floral-tiled Victorian fireplace. A second sitting-room offers complete peace and quiet. Save for flowers on the wooden tables the dining-room is unembellished, leaving the scenery through its many windows as the major point of interest. Dishes such as open ravioli of wild mushrooms and iced coffee soufflé with hazelnut praline from a four-course dinner menu cooked by mother and son promise much. Pleasantly furnished bedrooms all have a loch view but their décor appears less carefully considered than that of public rooms.

◑ Closed Nov to end Mar

▣ On the A861 on the shores of Loch Sunart. Turn sharp left after Strontian river bridge. Private car park

🛏 2 single, 4 twin, 4 double; half with bathroom/WC, half with shower/WC; room service, hairdryer, baby-listening in all rooms

◈ Dining-room, bar, lounge, TV room, drying room; fishing, water sports, bicycling nearby

⊖ No wheelchair access; dogs in 2 bedrooms only; smoking in bar only

▭ Access, Visa

£ Single £40, twin/double £80; deposit required. Set D £24

TALLADALE HIGHLAND   **MAP I**

Loch Maree Hotel

TALLADALE, BY ACHNASHEEN, WESTER ROSS IV22 2HL
TEL: KINLOCHEWE (044 584) 288   FAX: (044 584) 241

A swishly furnished hotel that has welcomed fishermen since Victorian times.

About half the guests who come to this long-established fishing hotel are anglers; the loch beside which the Victorian building stands is said to have produced the largest sea trout found in Britain. Boats leave from the hotel's own pier, and ghillies, rod storage and so forth are all laid on. Such is the hotel's spruceness that even those who are only accustomed to dealing with cooked fish on a plate may find it a useful stopover. In the last few years it has been refurbished to a very high standard, with the bold stripes and patterns of the modern country-house style in evidence. Quality dark wood furnishing and stylish modern fabrics make the bedrooms very smart; it's worth paying a little more for a loch view.

There's a wide-ranging bar menu. The even more extensive à la carte dinner menu has a dozen main-course fish dishes which are unelaborate and served in generous portions.

◖ Open all year

⊡ On the south-west shore of Loch Maree, between Kinlochewe and Gairloch. Private car park

🛏 6 single, 14 twin, 7 double, 1 family room; most with bathroom/WC, some with shower/WC; TV, room service, baby-listening in all rooms; hair-dryer on request

◈ Restaurant, 2 bars, lounge, drying room; conference facilities (max 50 people non-residential,

28 residential); fishing at hotel, golf, tennis, other sports nearby; babysitting. Wheelchair access to hotel, restaurant and 12 ground-floor bedrooms, one specially equipped for disabled people

⊖ No dogs in public rooms

▭ Access, Visa

£ Single £20 to £40, twin/double £40 to £90, family rooms £60 to £82, deposit required. No prices for alc meals provided. Special breaks available

---

THURSO HIGHLAND   **MAP 1**

Forss House

FORSS, BY THURSO, CAITHNESS KW14 7XY
TEL: FORSS (0847) 86201

An oasis of comfort in an early nineteenth-century mansion.

A crop of eye-catching chimneys top the expansive mansion. Light from long windows makes the rooms more welcoming than the austere exterior might suggest. Rooms have been adapted for ease and comfort, so the reception hall, with loose-covered sofas and standard lamps, is used as the sitting-room; there is more seating in a traditional but smart bar, and a conservatory of pot plants and cane-backed chairs provides the venue for breakfast. Pink cloths and candles and an Adam fireplace make the dining-room more elegant. A four-course dinner offers such delights as smoked Forss salmon, pâté with Orkney oatcakes and Caithness lamb. Most bedrooms in the main house, furnished with antiques and quality reproduction pieces, are particularly large (Tulloch is the only excep-tion), as are their bathrooms.

Experienced hoteliers Betty and Ian MacGregor runs Forss House correctly and fussily (in the best possible sense).

◖ Open all year

⊡ On the A836, 6 miles west of Thurso. Private car park

🛏 7 twin, 2 cottage rooms; all with bathroom/WC, exc 1 twin with shower/WC; TV, room service,

hair-dryer in all rooms

 Restaurant, 2 bars, lounge, conservatory, drying room; conference facilities (max 30 people non-residential); fishing in grounds, other sports nearby

No wheelchair access; dogs by arrangement only

Access, Amex, Visa

Single occupancy of twin £45, twin/cottage room £80. Set D £17.50 (by arrangement only); alc L £7

TIRORAN STRATHCLYDE   **MAP 2**

Tiroran House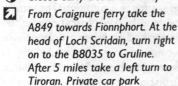

TIRORAN, ISLE OF MULL, ARGYLL PA69 6ES
TEL: TIRORAN (068 15) 232 (and fax)

Mull's most classy country-house hotel.

The interior of Tiroran impresses. Mini chandeliers, top-notch shiny antiques and endless silver knick-knacks fill the two sitting-rooms. A gold-laced Mandarin cloak hangs in the parquet-floored dining-room, off which a tiled, vine-covered conservatory offers meals with a view. Despite such a profusion of fine things, the small scale of the rooms and the ubiquitous stamp of the owners' personality makes the house relaxing. Boldly designed bedrooms have flair: Principal has oriental patterns on fabric and furniture.

Robin Blockey used to be in the air force; some might say his manner still seems idiosyncratically regimental. He runs Tiroran on house-party lines, introducing guests to each other unless they stress a desire for privacy. Sue Blockey's food is highly praised; dinner (at 7.45pm) will include local ingredients. A more traditional set main course follows a choice of imaginative starters, then come puddings that cover old favourites like blackcurrant fool and crème caramel, with Scottish cheeses finish.

Closed early Oct to mid-May

From Craignure ferry take the A849 towards Fionnphort. At the head of Loch Scridain, turn right on to the B8035 to Gruline. After 5 miles take a left turn to Tiroran. Private car park

1 single, 4 twin, 4 double; all with bathroom/WC, hair-dryer; limited room service

Dining-room, 2 lounges, drying room, conservatory, games room; croquet at hotel, fishing nearby

No wheelchair access; no children under 10; dogs in annexe bedrooms only; smoking in 1 lounge and bedrooms

None accepted

Single £125, twin/double from £190 (rates inc dinner). Packed lunches; set L £12.50, D £28.50

TUMMEL BRIDGE TAYSIDE   **MAP 1**

Kynachan Lodge

TUMMEL BRIDGE, BY PITLOCHRY, PERTHSHIRE PH16 5SB
TEL: TUMMEL BRIDGE (0882) 634214   FAX: (0882) 634316

A small welcoming country house with interesting furnishings.

Draw back the curtains in the morning and you'll probably see roe deer grazing in the birch wood yards away. A guest stresses the warmth of the reception and the friendly atmosphere. Val Hampson even comes out in the pouring rain to greet you (her husband Peter, unlike the local wildlife, is more elusive: 'My wife is the one who is good with people'). Those who know their Mings from their Tangs will get particular pleasure from the Hampsons' home, for the smart, traditional country-house rooms warmed by wood fires and comfortable armchairs contain a startling collection of oriental art and sculpture: painted screens, samurai swords. Help yourself to a drink from the honesty bar in the parquet-floored sitting-room and settle down to read a catalogue detailing the pieces and their prices.

Peter's no-choice dinners, served in the small-scale dining-room, offer delicate interesting dishes ('exceptionally good', reckons one guest): asparagus in filo pastry, beef in cream and Drambuie and a delicious chocolate mousse one evening in spring. Black marks, though, for having to order breakfast at dinner (can anyone really gauge how hungry they'll be in 12 hours' time?).

Far-eastern ornaments and antiques inhabit bedrooms. Our inspector's corner room was light, spacious and comfortable, with a pair of wing chairs.

◖ *Closed Nov to Easter*

⤷ *From Pitlochry take the B8019 to Tummel Bridge. Turn left over the Tummel Bridge towards Aberfeldy for ½ mile. The hotel signs are visible on the left. Private car park*

🛏 *3 twin, 2 double, 1 family room, all with bathroom/WC, exc 1 double with shower/WC; TV, hair-dryer in all rooms*

◈ *Dining-room, lounge, drawing-room, drying room, library; fishing at hotel, golf, riding nearby*

⊖ *No wheelchair access; no children under 10; no dogs*

▭ *Access, Visa*

£ *Single occupancy of twin/double £28, twin/double £55. Set D £17.50 (7.30pm)*

The 1995 Guide *will be published in the autumn of 1994. Reports on hotels are welcome at any time of the year, but are extremely valuable in the spring. Send them to* The Which? Hotel Guide, FREEPOST, 2 Marylebone Road, London NW1 1YN. *No stamp is needed if reports are posted in the UK.*

TURNBERRY STRATHCLYDE   MAP 2

Turnberry Hotel

TURNBERRY, AYRSHIRE KA26 9LT
TEL: TURNBERRY (0655) 31000   FAX: (0655) 31706

A superb position, faultless quality, breathtaking facilities, experienced staff: Turnberry is one of Scotland's finest hotels.

Serious golfers can warm up on the putting green and pitch and putt in front of the enormous Edwardian building before pitting their wits against the hotel's famous Ailsa Course. Health freaks come to use the spa facilities. The spa even has its own attractive Mediterranean-style restaurant with menus offering diet-conscious dishes like strawberry and yogurt soup and caraway carrot cake served with cottage cheese.

The inactive are equally well served, though the hotel's endless panelled corridors (it's a sixth of a mile from main restaurant to spa restaurant) may provide unwanted exercise. A succession of dazzling public rooms line the hotel's seaside aspect, each with marbled pillars, crystal chandeliers, stuccoed ceilings and top-quality soft furnishings. All bedrooms, in tasteful, subdued designs, are furnished with antiques.

◗ Open all year

⤵ Travel south from Ayr on the A77 until signs for Turnberry. Turn right for ½ mile to the hotel. Private car park

🛏 99 twin, 21 double, 2 four-poster, 10 suites; all with bathroom/WC, TV, room service, hair-dryer, baby-listening; valet service on request; no tea/coffee-making facilities in rooms

◈ 3 restaurants (1 air-conditioned), 3 bars, 2 lounges, billiard room, drying room, conservatory, library, air-conditioned conference; conference facilities (max 250 people non-residential and residential); golf, tennis, sauna/solarium, gym, squash, spa treatment rooms, indoor swimming-pool, putting at hotel, other sports nearby; babysitting. Wheelchair access to hotel (ramp), restaurant and WC (M,F), 17 ground-floor bedrooms, 1 specially equipped for disabled people

⊖ No dogs in public rooms

▭ Access, Amex, Diners, JCB, Visa

£ Single occupancy of twin/double £140 to £205, twin/double £145 to £250, four-poster £175 to £250, suite £250 to £450; deposit required. Set L £19, D £35; alc L £20, D £45 (meal prices till Oct 93). Special breaks available

UIG WESTERN ISLES   MAP 1

Baile-na-Cille

TIMSGARRY, UIG, ISLE OF LEWIS PA86 9JD
TEL: TIMSGARRY (085 175) 242   FAX: (085 175) 241

A fabulous place for all the family in a fantastic, remote setting.

The Gollins have been here long enough to be onto their second set of dogs, cats and sheep (the sheep tame enough to come and knock their horns against the dining-room windows). Richard used to be a teacher in London: you can tell that from the 'Silly' Reservation Form that looks just like a cheery classroom worksheet, and from the plethora of books and noticeboards throughout the house. There are three sitting-rooms, one 'never smart' with games, a TV and video for kids, another a quiet room with classical CDs, and the main room 'primarily for grown-ups' with lovely views and chintzy sofas. White walls, colourful bedspreads and lovely enlarged photos distinguish modest bedrooms, some in the main house, some in the converted stables, and others in the old cowshed.

Normally, guests sit communally and eat what they're given in the lovely converted byre of a dining-room, but if you want a separate table or have food fads just say. There's nothing so formal as a menu. Joanna's food is first-rate: you might be offered cheese puffs in a curried lentil sauce, salmon in dill hollandaise, rice cake, cheeses. Kids can have an earlier Jolly the Joke King's supper if they want.

◑ Closed 15 Oct to 1 Mar

⤵ Take the B8011 to Timsgarry. At Timsgarry follow the road to the shore. Private car park

🛏 2 single, 3 twin, 4 double, 2 family rooms, 2 annexe rooms, 4 cottages; most with bathroom/WC, 5 public bathrooms; room service, hair-dryer, baby-listening in all rooms

◈ Dining-room, lounge, TV room,

library/study, drying room; conference facilities (max 20 people residential); fishing nearby

⊖ No wheelchair access; some public rooms and bedrooms are non-smoking

▭ Access, Visa

£ From £19 to £26 per person; deposit required. Set D £20 (7.30pm)

ULLAPOOL HIGHLAND   **MAP 1**

Altnaharrie Inn

ULLAPOOL, ROSS-SHIRE IV26 2SS
TEL: DUNDONNELL (085 483) 230

A visit to this unique hotel offers a romantic, aesthetic and culinary experience par excellence.

How many superlatives can one muster to sum up Gunn Eriksen and Fred Brown's *tour de force*? First there's the unmatchable romance of its location. The private *Mother Goose* launch picks you up in Ullapool harbour and takes you on a 10-minute ride across Loch Broom to the creeper-covered drover's inn. You're then transported into a beautiful, highly stylised world. Every curtain or object seems placed for effect.

The use of light, texture and colour feels Mediterranean: white stone walls and clever artificial lighting embolden monochrome fabrics. Bedrooms are equally arresting and thoughtfully conceived, a masterful combination of choice antiques among exposed wood and white walls.

Lastly there's Gunn and her wonderful dinners – very sophisticated, very elaborate and beautifully presented affairs. One of her trademarks is the use of wild ingredients – nettles, sorrel, raspberries – to enhance meat and fish.

Bedrooms are more beautiful than comfortable according to some; dinner is at a fixed time and socialising is a likely part of the experience.

◑ *Closed early Nov to Easter*

↗ *From Inverness take the A835 to Ullapool, then phone hotel for directions where to meet ferry. Advance booking essential. Private car park in Ullapool*

🛏 *2 twin, 6 double; all with bathroom/WC, exc 1 twin with shower/WC; room service, hairdryer in all rooms; no tea/coffee-making facilities in rooms*

◈ *Dining-room, 2 lounges, drying*

facilities; fishing, tennis, riding, water sports nearby

⊖ *No wheelchair access; no children under 8; dogs by arrangement only; no smoking*

▭ *None accepted*

💷 *Single occupancy of twin/double £100 to £175, twin/double £200 to £270 (rates inc dinner); deposit required. Set D £50 (8pm, must book)*

Ceilidh Place   ℒℒ

14 WEST ARGYLE STREET, ULLAPOOL, ROSS-SHIRE IV26 2TY
TEL: ULLAPOOL (0854) 612103   FAX: (0854) 612886

An arty Ullapool institution, imaginatively constructed around a better than decent hotel.

It manages to be all things to all types, and readers – though finding faults – reckon they'll go back. The main action takes place in three converted cottages and an old boatshed. Here at tea-time in the super, sophisticated coffee-shop-cum-bar locals are having a cuppa or just reading the paper. Someone else is having a beer, perhaps. A young couple are tucking into smoked haddock salad and an Italian mushroom casserole, accompanied by a bottle of wine. Others help themselves to tea – anything from Ceylon to apricot – in the adjacent kitchen, where you can also take a drink from the honesty bar and fridge. At the reception, browsers leaf through anything and everything Scottish in the fine bookshop. In the evening, as you dine in the exhibition gallery or the conservatory extension, live folk, classical or jazz music may entertain you. The menu offers lots of fish, plus a meat dish and vegetarian choices. Correspondents have delivered mixed reports on the food and particularly on the service – 'too casual' one evening to 'terrible' another. Our inspector, however, found staff forthcoming and helpful.

Bedrooms are soberly and sensitively decorated in soft oranges and browns and heavy wooden furniture; some have views across the town of Loch Broom. The concerts that take place in the clubhouse across the way are more appealing than the uninviting, run-down bedrooms there.

◑ *Open all year, exc 2 weeks in Jan*

↗ *In Ullapool, West Argyle Street is the 2nd street up from the shore and past the post office. Private car park*

🛏 *2 single, 5 twin, 6 double, 11 annexe rooms with bunk-beds; some rooms with bathroom/WC; hair-dryer, TV, tea/coffee-making facilities on request*

◈ *Restaurant, 2 bars, lounge, coffee-shop; conference facilities*

(max 60 people non-residential, 50 residential); fishing, tennis, other sports nearby. Wheelchair access to restaurant, coffee-shop, bar and WC (M, F) only

⊖ *No dogs in public rooms; no smoking in restaurant*

▭ *Access, Amex, Diners, Visa*

£ *Single £30 to £50, twin/double £30 to £50, annexe room £19 (per person); deposit required. Alc L £4 to £8, D £27*

WALKERBURN BORDERS   MAP 2

Tweed Valley Hotel

WALKERBURN, PEEBLESSHIRE EH43 6AA
TEL: WALKERBURN (089 687) 636   FAX: (089 687) 639

Unpretentious, welcoming country house above the Tweed.

This stern, angular Edwardian brick building has been in the Miller family for some 20 years and you can expect an enthusiastic welcome. Decorative, offbeat collections personalise the hotel, here hats, there antique purses, upstairs a set of '20s and '30s nursery pictures. The building itself has a few architectural treats, such as finely carved posts on the staircase and an impressive dining-room. The two-part bar, with copper-topped tables, is more ordinary. Bedrooms are cheerful and generally in co-ordinated style, some with bed drapes.

Dinner features plenty of local ingredients such as cock-a-leekie soup and lamb stuffed with haggis. Smoked salmon and trout regularly appear on the menu, supplied by the hotel's own smokehouse.

◑ *Open all year*

↗ *On the A72 on the eastern outskirts of Walkerburn. Private car park*

🛏 *4 single, 5 twin, 5 double, 1 four-poster, 1 family room; most with bathroom/WC, some with shower/WC; TV, room service, hair-dryer, baby-listening in all rooms*

◈ *Restaurant, bar, lounge, drying room; conference facilities (max 30 people residential); fishing, sauna, solarium, gym at hotel, other sports nearby. Wheelchair access to restaurant and WC(M) only*

⊖ *No smoking in restaurant*

▭ *Access, Visa*

Single £40 to £52, single occupancy of twin/double £40 to £52, twin/double £80, four-poster £92, family room £80 to £92; deposit required. Set L £8.50/£10.50, D £23; alc L £4.50 to £12, D £25 to £29; bar meals. Special breaks available

WALLS SHETLAND ISLANDS　　　　　　　　　　　　　MAP 1

Burrastow House ☆

WALLS, SHETLAND ISLANDS ZE2 9PB
TEL: WALLS (059 571) 307

A welcome return for this remote eighteenth-century house with comfortable rooms and the best food in Shetland.

Bo Simmons had to put the accommodation side of things on hold for a while before and after the birth of her second child, but we're pleased to report that she's back in business and that standards are as high as ever. The sitting-room is a comfortable, elegant room with green walls shimmering in subdued lighting and the glow of a peat fire. There's a claret chesterfield and comfy floral-patterned sofa and chairs. The dining-room is oak-panelled, lit by candles and the flickering of the fire. Our inspection meal was excellent: salmon, orange and walnut pâté, followed by a filo pastry chicken pie, peach ice-cream and a cheeseboard with home-baked oatcakes.

Our inspector's spacious room was classically tasteful in a minimalist way: rugs on bare boards, simple light blue décor, two basketweave chairs and a good old wardrobe and dressing table.

◑ Closed mid-Oct to mid-Mar

↗ Continue through Walls on Dale Road. Cross a cattle grid and follow signs to Burrastow for 2½ miles. Private car park

🛏 1 double, 1 family room; both with bathroom/WC; TV, room service, hair-dryer on request, baby-listening in family room

◇ Dining-room, lounge, library; fishing at hotel, riding nearby

⊖ No wheelchair access; no dogs or smoking in dining-room

▭ None accepted

£ Single occupancy of double £67, double £112, family room from £112 (rates inc dinner). Set L from £4, D from £22.50. Special breaks available

---

If you have a small appetite, or just aren't feeling hungry, check if you can be given a reduction if you don't want the full menu. At some hotels you could easily end up paying £30 for one course and a coffee.

WHITE BRIDGE HIGHLAND   **MAP I**

Knockie Lodge

WHITE BRIDGE, INVERNESS-SHIRE IVI 2UP
TEL: GORTHLECK (0456) 486276   FAX: (0456) 486389

A finely furnished former sporting-lodge in a magnificent position.

Knockie Lodge lies at the tip of a dead-end road through an estate of sheep, birch woods and moorland. Sculpted classical reliefs of cherubs in green florals enliven the U-shaped whitewashed building. The core is eighteenth century, but its most memorable parts are later additions. Fine Edwardian woodwork embellishes doors and fireplaces in the extremely inviting parquet-floored drawing-room, and the dining-room, classically dressed in shiny antique tables, has dressers heaving with silverware. The most expensive bedrooms, such as Lovat and Grant, have sofas and the best loch views from bay windows.

In May a five-course dinner, choiceless until pudding, offered ham and walnut terrine, cock-a-leekie soup, salmon stuffed sole fillets, bread-and-butter pudding or damson ice-cream, plus a cheeseboard. The service under the hands-on owners, the Milwards, is professional.

◐ *Closed end Oct to end Apr*

↗ *Take the A82 north to Fort Augustus, then the B862 for 8 miles. Turn left at the hotel sign down a narrow road for 2 miles to the hotel. Private car park*

🛏 *2 single, 4 twin, 4 double; all with bathroom/WC; tea/coffee-making facilities and hair-dryer on request*

◇ *Dining-room, 2 lounges, billiard room, drying room, conservatory; conference facilities (max 10 people residential, 12 non-residential); fishing at hotel, golf, riding nearby*

⊖ *No wheelchair access; no children under 10; dogs by arrangement only; no smoking in dining-room*

▭ *Access, Amex, Diners, Visa*

£ *Single £75, single occupancy of twin/double £95 to £142, twin/double £125 to £190 (rates inc dinner); deposit required. Set D £28*

WICK HIGHLAND   **MAP I**

Bilbster House ☆

BY WICK, CAITHNESS KWI 5TB
TEL: WATTEN (095582) 212

A simple bed and breakfast with intriguing touches.

Jeanne and Archie Stewart have been doing bed and breakfasts here for a decade – they used to work in the theatre: in the lounge stands a photo of the Queen's Theatre in Blackpool, which Archie used to manage.

The three bedrooms, Pink, Gold and Green, are distinctive. The best is the Pink Room: its superb full-set of Victorian walnut furniture – dressing table, bed, bedside tables, wardrobe – was Archie's grand-parents' wedding suite. A tea-cosy and the crockery on each breakfast table also relates to your respective bedroom's hue. If you are staying more than a night you will be given a different cooked meal each morning, perhaps a gammon steak one day, a Georgie Best (*B*acon, *E*gg, *S*ausage, *T*omato) the next.

◑ *Open 1 May to 30 Sept*

🡕 *Leave Wick on the A882. After 5½ miles there are signs for Bilbster House. Take a right turn. Private car park*

🛏 *1 twin, 2 double; 2 public bathrooms; hair-dryer on request*

◈ *Dining-room, lounge; fishing, golf, riding, heated swimming-*

pool (Spring 94) nearby

⊖ *No wheelchair access; no dogs in public rooms; no smoking in dining-room*

▭ *None accepted*

£ *Single occupancy of twin/double £13, twin/double £26; deposit required*

WALES

ABERDOVEY GWYNEDD   **MAP 6**

Penhelig Arms

ABERDOVEY, GWYNEDD LL35 0LT
TEL: ABERDOVEY (0654) 767215   FAX: (0654) 767690

Enjoyable food and good estuary views at this old waterside inn.

This nineteenth-century shipbuilders' inn has been in the hands of
Robert and Sally Hughes for four years now, and the verdict remains
steady as she goes. The neat black and white façade, with occasional
panes of bottle glass, is separated from the Dovey estuary and limited
parking spaces by the main coastal road. Inside, the cooking's the draw:
Sally's team of three chefs offers a varied and tasty menu, with dishes
such as smoked chicken roulade and fillet of bream steamed with fresh
lime and spring onion served with red pepper cream sauce. There is even
more choice on Friday and Saturday nights. The restaurant, divided into
two, has panelled walls hung with plates and framed watercolours, a
fireplace stacked with family photos, and an original blacked range. If
you prefer a lighter bar snack, there is a separate Fisherman's Bar. The
residents' bar is rather small, with limited seating clustered round the
window seats, but there is a separate lounge on the first floor, done out in
yellow marbled wallpaper.

  Room Three, graded as superior, has a large slate fireplace and a loo
with a view; standard doubles are quite small.

◑ Open all year, exc 25, 26 Dec

↗ From Machynlleth head into
Aberdovey, go underneath
railway bridge, first hotel on the
right. Private car park

🛏 1 single, 4 twin, 5 double; most
with bathroom/WC, some with
shower/WC; TV, hair-dryer, room
service, baby-listening in all
rooms

◇ Restaurant, 2 bars, lounge,
drying room; meetings facilities

(max 12 people residential);
golf, fishing, other sports nearby

⊖ No wheelchair access; no dogs in
public rooms; smoking
discouraged

▭ Access, Visa

£ Single £34, single occupancy of
twin/double £34, twin/double
£68, superior room £82; deposit
required. Bar lunches from £2;
Sun L £11.50; set D £17.50.
Special breaks available

ABERSOCH GWYNEDD   **MAP 6**

Porth Tocyn Hotel

ABERSOCH, GWYNEDD LL53 7BU
TEL: ABERSOCH (0758) 713303   FAX: (0758) 713538

An uncontrived, welcoming hotel that caters for all ages.

Nick Fletcher-Brewer wrote to us this year to chide us for last year's description of 'plain wooden furniture' in the bedrooms: 'Every single chest of drawers and even the bedside tables are antiques.' This isn't the sort of contrived country house with swags on every pelmet: the emphasis is on good food and friendly concern for guests' needs, at whatever age. So there is a children's room complete with toybox, TV and video, and a children's high tea is served. Dinner is regarded as an adult treat, and, at five courses plus coffee, deservedly so. A starter of crab, asparagus and noodle balls with sweet chilli sauce might be followed by celery, apple and Stilton soup, then grilled mullet topped with prawns and flaked almonds, chocolate terrine, and cheese and fruit.

There is a pretty lounge with blue and pink chintzy armchairs and a slate fireplace.

◑ *Closed mid-Nov to week before Easter*

↗ *The hotel is 2½ miles beyond Abersoch, through the hamlets of Sarn Bach and Bwlchtocyn. On the outskirts of Abersoch on the Sarn Bach road is the first of 3 bilingual signs marked 'Gwesty/ Hotel'. Follow these to Porth Tocyn. Private car park*

🛏 *3 single, 3 twin, 10 double (most with extra bed), 1 family room; all with bathroom/WC, TV, room service, hair-dryer; tea/coffee-making facilities, baby-listening on request*

◇ *Restaurant, bar, 6 lounges, TV room, games room; tennis and heated outdoor pool (May to Sept) at hotel, other sports nearby. Wheelchair access to hotel (1 step), restaurant and WC (unisex), 3 ground-floor bedrooms*

⊖ *No children under 7 in restaurant eves; no dogs in public rooms*

▭ *Access*

£ *Single £57, single occupancy of twin/double £86, twin/double from £94, family room rate on request; deposit required. Set D £17.50/£23; Sun L £14 (prices till end 93). Special breaks available*

ABERYSTWYTH DYFED   MAP 6

Conrah Country House ☆

CHANCERY, NR ABERYSTWYTH, DYFED SY23 4DF
TEL: ABERYSTWYTH (0970) 617941   FAX: (0970) 624546

Comfortable hotel with adventurous cooking; stick to bedrooms in the main house.

The Georgian building was mostly destroyed by fire in 1911 and its replacement is solidly representative of its time, with stained glass, high ceilings and large windows through which you can look upon grazing ponies and donkeys. The lounges offer a mix of chintzy and leather sofas, country magazines and fresh flower arrangements, while the bar feels more modern with its neutral beige and pink scheme and wicker chairs.

Bedrooms in the main building are a reasonable size, with a mixture of modern and antique furniture. The courtyard motel rooms are smaller, neatly decked in blue and white. Food is adventurous, with combinations such as smoked chicken, lettuce, croûtons and banana yogurt for a starter. On inspection the vegetables with the main course of turbot could have done with more cooking. The cheeseboard (all Welsh) is good.

Service is friendly enough, though our inspector felt that more help could have been offered when she struggled into reception with her bags in the pouring rain only to be told to get back into the car to drive round the corner to her motel room.

◑ Open all year, exc 22 to 31 Dec

⤵ 3½ miles south of Aberystwyth on the A487 coast road. Private car park

🛏 2 single, 7 twin, 10 double, 1 family room (some rooms in annexe); most with bathroom/WC, some with shower/WC; TV, room service in all rooms; hairdryer on request

◈ Restaurant, bar, 2 lounges, library, function room; drying facilities; conference facilities (max 40 people non-residential, 20 residential); sauna, heated swimming-pool), croquet at hotel, fishing, golf, other sports nearby. Wheelchair access to hotel (2 steps), restaurant and 9 ground-floor bedrooms

⊖ No children under 5; no dogs; no smoking in restaurant

▭ Access, Amex, Diners, Visa

£ Single £56, single occupancy of twin/double £56 to £89, twin/double £79 to £99, family room £119; deposit required. Set L £15, D £22.50; alc L £14 to £21.50, D £15 to £30. Special breaks available

---

BEAUMARIS GWYNEDD   **MAP 6**

Ye Olde Bulls Head

CASTLE STREET, BEAUMARIS, ANGLESEY, GWYNEDD LL58 8AP
TEL: BEAUMARIS (0248) 810329   FAX: (0248) 811294

Efficiently run old inn with classy bedrooms and a popular bar.

Ye Olde Bulls Head, with its cream and blue Georgian frontage, is an elegant inn. The façade is deceptive – the original posting house dates back to 1472, though most of the place was rebuilt in 1617. Dickens stayed here in 1859, and consequently the bedrooms are named after characters in his books. All are well equipped with items such as brass beds and Victorian baths, and the soft furnishings are a cut above your average pub décor.

Downstairs, the bar is a popular place, creating a jolly atmosphere among the copper and brass-festooned beams and antique cutlasses adorning the walls. The residents' lounge is more sedate, with chintzy sofas and chairs, a large plate collection and varied arrangements of dried and silk flowers.

The dining-room, unusually, is upstairs beneath the sloping beams and rafters; its menu features a fair amount of locally caught fish, such as monkfish in red wine and cream or grilled brill. The no-choice table d'hôte may offer smoked ham salad, sautéed beef with oyster mushrooms, cream and Dijon mustard, and passion-fruit délice. Service from a young receptionist on an inspection visit was briskly efficient.

◑ Open all year, exc 25, 26 Dec and 1 Jan

↗ The inn is in the centre of Beaumaris, on the main street. Private car park

🛏 1 single, 5 twin, 4 double, 1 annexe room; all with bathroom/WC, TV, limited room service, hair-dryer, baby-listening

◈ Dining-room, bar, lounge, drying room; meetings facilities from Spring 94 (max 30 people non-residential, 15 residential); golf, riding, other sports nearby

⊖ No wheelchair access; no children under 7 in dining-room eves; dogs in bar only (not at lunchtimes); no smoking in dining-rooms

▭ Visa

£ Single £42, single occupancy of twin/double £48, twin/double/annexe £72. Sun L £15; set D £19; alc D £25; bar lunches. Special breaks available

BEDDGELERT GWYNEDD   MAP 6

Sygun Fawr ☆

BEDDGELERT, GWYNEDD LL55 4NE
TEL: BEDDGELERT (076 686) 258

A homely, family-run hotel that makes a good base for those climbing Snowdon.

The setting is superb, reached by a single-track road just across the valley from Snowdon. The building has a varied history: once a farm, with the animals living on the windowless ground floor and the owners living above in a sort of watchtower. The oldest, seventeenth-century segment is apparent in the dining-room's bulky stone walls and low beams. Here, around polished communal tables, Christine Crick serves a simple dinner – soup or fruit juice, followed perhaps by lamb-burger, chips and peas, plus dessert, cheese and coffee. Alternative main courses such as chilli con carne or chicken Balinese can be had for a supplement. The small, snug bar records the family's naval connections, with a row of bosun heads and naval shields. The lounge in the nineteenth-century part at the front is more spacious, with comfy chairs and a slate mantelpiece.

Bedrooms are fairly simple, with occasional flourishes (a brass bed and coronet drape in Room Four).

◑ Open all year, exc Jan

↗ The hotel is off the A498 on the Capel Curig side of the village. The hotel is signposted from the bridge. Private car park

🛏 2 twin, 4 double, 1 family room; some with bathroom/WC, most with shower/WC; hair-dryer in all rooms

◈ Dining-room, bar, lounge; sauna

at hotel, fishing, golf, riding, nearby

⊖ No wheelchair access

▭ None accepted

£ Single occupancy of twin/double £29, twin/double £48, family room rate on request; deposit required. Set D £12; alc D £14. Special breaks available

BENLLECH GWYNEDD   MAP 6

Bryn Meirion ☆

AMLWCH ROAD, BENLLECH, ANGLESEY, GWYNEDD LL74 8SR
TEL: TYNYGONGL (0248) 853118

A small guesthouse where guests, both disabled and able-bodied, are catered for with warmth and wit.

Tim and Chris Holland used to work at a residential school for disabled children, he as an engineer, she as a teacher. When they left they decided to set up a guesthouse, and set about adapting a run-down dormer bungalow with the needs of disabled people in mind. However, it's not only for disabled guests, as Christine is anxious to point out – they welcome able-bodied and 'the walking wounded' as well. Thus rooms in the main house have no special adaptations, only simple pine beds and furniture and flowery quilts. In the extension, however, the rooms have been specially adapted, with plenty of rails in the bathrooms, a gantry for lowering you into the bed or bath, drive-in showers, and electric beds which can be adjusted in height. Tim's engineering experience has also come in useful in the dining-room; he has designed tables that wheel-chairs can fit under, and bar stools with extra support. But this is small fry compared with the garden, where his imagination and sense of humour come to the fore – visit ye olde castle, a ramped and turreted construction with views of the sea. Tim's especially proud of his petrol-driven wheelchair with tank-like rollers that can cope with sandy beaches, unlike most ordinary wheelchairs. Christine does the cooking – usually something simple like a roast.

◑ Open all year

⤴ After crossing the Menai Bridge, follow the A5025 Benllech road. The guesthouse is on the right, on the far side of Benllech. Private car park

⇌ 1 single, 4 twin, 4 family rooms; some with bathroom/WC, most with shower/WC, 2 public bathrooms; room service in all rooms; TV in some rooms; hair-dryer on request; laundry facilities

◈ Dining-room, lounge, conservatory; fishing, tennis nearby; babysitting. Wheelchair access to guesthouse (ramp), dining-room and WC (unisex), 7 ground-floor bedrooms, 5 specially equipped for disabled people

⊖ Dogs in public rooms by arrangement; no smoking in lounge or bedrooms

▭ None accepted

£ Single £34 to £36, twin £68 to £72, family room from £68 and 72; deposit required. Set L from £3, D £10

BERRIEW POWYS   **MAP 6**

Lion Hotel ☆

BERRIEW, NR WELSHPOOL, POWYS SY21 8PQ
TEL: BERRIEW (0686) 640452   FAX: (0686) 640844

Luxurious bedrooms and adventurous food in a pretty village site.

Brian and Jean Thomas took over the Lion 10 years ago; five years later, business was so good that they added more bedrooms. Look very carefully, and you may be able to see the join: the black and white half-timbering is just a little too regular in places, because it has been painted instead. The lounge bar has half-timbered walls and a whitewashed ceiling, shiny copper-topped tables, horse brasses, plates and a hunting bugle. There is a small adjoining residents' lounge, complete with stag's head and brown buttonback sofas, plus a hardier local bar. The dining-room, done out in modern light wood tables and peachy medallion-backed chairs, strives for more sophistication and is slightly at odds with the rest of the public rooms. The food, too, is more adventurous than your average country pub fare: Japanese prawns with cajun dip, venison fillet with blackcurrant liqueur sauce, and perhaps halibut steak creole.

   Bedrooms continue the upmarket touch, with coronet drapes and rich chintzes.

◐ Open all year

⤢ 5 miles south of Welshpool on the A483 to Newtown. The Lion is 1 mile from the A483 signposted Berriew. Private car park

🛏 1 single, 1 twin, 4 double, 1 four-poster, family room available; most with bathroom/WC, some with shower/WC; TV, baby-listening in all rooms; trouser press in 1 room; hair-dryer on request

◈ Restaurant, bar, lounge;

conference facilities (max 20 people non-residential, 8 residential); fishing, golf, tennis, other sports nearby

⊖ No wheelchair access; no dogs; no smoking in bedrooms

▭ Access, Amex, Visa

£ Single £43, single occupancy of twin/double £45, twin/double £75 to £80, four-poster £85, family room £90; deposit required. Bar meals £5; set D £15; alc D £18. Special breaks available

BRECHFA DYFED   **MAP 6**

Tŷ Mawr Country Hotel

BRECHFA, NR CARMARTHEN, DYFED SA32 7RA
TEL: CARMARTHEN (0267) 202332   FAX: (0267) 202437

Warm Welsh hospitality and good food in a pretty family-run hotel.

In the four years they've been here Dick and Beryl Tudhope have created a welcoming, restful retreat. Dick's background is in marketing (he can tell you the exact percentage of customers who are repeat business) and he runs the front of house with solicitous assurance. Beryl was formerly head of a primary school; these days she expends her energies in the kitchen, producing dishes such as lamb faggots with spiced lentils and brochettes of swordfish with spicy creole sauce. She's also a great baker, producing home-made croissants and crumpets and passing her skills on in bread-making courses. The building itself is 400 years old, and was at one time converted into three separate cottages. Now the reunited whole is an atmospheric mix of rough unplastered walls, old beams and large stone fireplaces. The five bedrooms, named after Welsh rivers, are quite simple but comfortable, with pine louvred wardrobes, woven Welsh bedcovers and supplies of mineral water and toiletries.

◑ Open all year, exc last week Nov to Xmas and last 2 weeks Jan; restaurant closed Sun and Tues eves

▶ 6½ miles from junction of A40 and B4310 at Nantgaredig. Private car park

🛏 1 twin, 3 double, 1 family room; all with bathroom/WC, room service, hair-dryer, trouser press, baby-listening

◈ Restaurant, bar, lounge, drying room; conference facilities (max 5 people residential); riding, fishing, golf, other sports nearby

⊖ No wheelchair access; no dogs in public rooms; no smoking in bedrooms

▭ Access, Amex, Visa

£ Single occupancy of twin/double £40 to £44, twin/double £64 to £68, family room £80 to £84; deposit required. Set L £12.50, D £18.50. Special breaks available

BROAD HAVEN DYFED   **MAP 6**

Druidstone

BROAD HAVEN, HAVERFORDWEST, PEMBROKESHIRE SA62 3NE
TEL: BROAD HAVEN (0437) 781221

An informal, club-like family holiday centre in a lovely location.

The Druidstone has a track record of hosting unusual activities, from Polish theatre groups singing in caves at midnight to rainforest road-shows and lots of music and drama events. Rod and Jane Bell's unflagging enthusiasm has extended this year to setting aside two weeks to allow children from difficult environments to have a holiday. The sandy beach of Druidston Haven spreads invitingly at the foot of the cliff, the wellies and shrimping nets line up in the porch, and children's T-shirts and painted stones are on display in the hall. The free and easy atmosphere and the lack of rules will appeal to anyone, of whatever age, who wants to be a getaway from city life. Bedrooms are bright and basic – pink panelling and shared bathrooms.

In keeping with the principle of no restrictions, there's no set menu; all dishes are priced individually and you can have as many or as few courses as you wish. Jane usually offers a choice of eight main courses, including two fish and two vegetarian dishes. Alternatively, the snug slate-floored bar downstairs has a board of daily specials such as spinach and tofu quiche, stuffed mushrooms and leek and lentil soup. The young staff are friendly and casual.

◐ *Closed Mon to Wed 6 Nov to 15 Dec and 6 Jan to 12 Feb; dining-room closed Sun eve*

↗ *Take the B4341 westwards towards Broad Haven from Haverfordwest. At the sea in Broad Haven, turn northwards for 2 miles, then turn left to Druidstone Haven. Private car park*

🛏 *2 single, 7 family rooms, 11 cottage rooms; 7 public bathrooms; no tea/coffee-making facilities in rooms*

◇ *Dining-room, bar, lounge; drying facilities; limited conference facilities (max 20 people residential and non-residential); fishing, water sports, riding nearby. Wheelchair access to 2 cottages (4 rooms), dining-room and WC (unisex)*

⊖ *No dogs in dining-room*

▭ *Access, Visa*

£ *Single £25 to £30, single occupancy of family room £35 to £40, family room £50 to £60, cottage £200 to £400; deposit required. Alc L £8, D £14*

CAPEL COCH GWYNEDD   **MAP 6**

Tre-Ysgawen Hall

CAPEL COCH, NR LLANGEFNI, ANGLESEY, GWYNEDD LL77 7UR
TEL: LLANGEFNI (0248) 750750   FAX: (0248) 750035

A fine Victorian country house on a massive scale.

The plain, rather austere brown Victorian building is large enough. Inside, though, the walls seem to stretch up to eternity, and the huge doors make you feel lilliputian. The spacious lounges give plenty of space for privacy – indeed, the sense of emptiness is compounded if there are only a few people staying. The polygonal restaurant – which, with its sloping green ceiling, feels rather like a marquee with windows – is the setting for accurately judged cooking from Steven Morris. The table d'hôte menu has a couple of choices at each course – perhaps salad of pan-fried venison with raspberry and apple dressing followed by roast monkfish on a bed of spaghetti cucumber on a herb mustard sauce, finishing with iced tea parfait with raspberry coulis.

Bedrooms range from master (four-poster bed, overlooking gardens) to de luxe (heavy drapes above bed) and superior (plain headboard, simpler flowery style). Service is willing.

◐ *Open all year*

↗ *From Llangefni follow B5111 road for Amlwch and Llanerchymedd, through village of Rhos-meirch to a house with monkey puzzle trees outside.*

Turn right, follow road for 1 mile, drive is on left. Private car park

🛏 1 single, 7 twin, 9 double, 2 four-poster, 1 suite; all with bathroom/WC, TV, room service, hair-dryer, trouser press, baby-listening; no tea/coffee-making facilities in rooms

◈ Restaurant, bar, lounge, drying room, study, conservatory; conference facilities (max 150 people non-residential, 20 residential); fishing, golf, other sports nearby. Wheelchair access to hotel, restaurant and WC (unisex), 4 ground-floor bedrooms, 2 specially equipped for disabled people

⊖ No dogs in public rooms

▭ Access, Amex, Diners, Visa

£ Single £72, single occupancy of twin/double £72, twin/double £94, four-poster £138, suite £148; deposit required. Continental B £4, cooked B £8; set L £14, D £20; alc D £25. Special breaks available

CAPEL GARMON GWYNEDD   MAP 6

Tan-y-Foel ☆

CAPEL GARMON, NR BETWS-Y-COED, GWYNEDD LL26 0RE
TEL: BETWS-Y-COED (0690) 710507   FAX: (0690) 710681

Splendid tranquillity in some style on the edge of Snowdonia.

The Conwy Valley spreads in a green blanket below; closer to hand are 8 ½ acres of woods and mature gardens, ablaze with rhododendrons in late spring. Renovation and refurbishment by Peter and Janet Pitman continue apace. The alpine-style shutters on some of the bedrooms are to be added to the rest, with fabric-wrapped curtain poles used to frame the views rather than obscure them. The two bedrooms reached from separate entrances outside the house are probably the most stylish, one with Scandinavian-style bleached wood and geometric blue quilt covers, the other with red and green drapes above the bed and oriental-looking tables and lamps. In fact, there are quite a few oriental touches throughout the house – a ceramic leopard and a Buddha sculpture among them.

The two lounges are more conventionally comfortable, with plenty of armchairs and special paint-effect wallpaper. Alternatively there is a small but sunny conservatory extension to the dining-room, with wicker chairs and the bar to hand. Dinner, cooked by Janet, is served at around 7pm, and offers two choices at each stage. On an evening in May you might have had baked duck egg topped with salmon, cream and fennel, followed by grilled sea bream with herb vinaigrette, and bananas in rum.

◑ Open all year

↗ Take the A5 to the junction with the A470 and travel for 2 miles along the A470 until a turning marked Capel Garmon/Nebo. Follow this road for 1 mile and then signs for the hotel. Private car park

🛏 7 twin/double, 2 four-poster; most with shower/WC, some with bathroom/WC; TV, room service, hair-dryer in all rooms

◇ Restaurant, bar, 2 lounges,
conservatory; heated outdoor
swimming-pool (June to Sept) at
hotel, other sports nearby

● No wheelchair access; no
children under 9; no dogs; no
smoking

▭ Access, Amex, Visa

£ Single occupancy of twin/double
£48 to £70, twin/double/four-
poster £76 to £99; deposit
required. Set D £19.50 to £22.
Special breaks available

CARDIFF SOUTH GLAMORGAN   **MAP 6**

Cardiff International

MARY ANN STREET, CARDIFF, SOUTH GLAMORGAN CF1 2EQ
TEL: CARDIFF (0222) 341441   FAX: (0222) 223742

A business hotel that has made an effort to be individual.

Outside, the hotel is a child of its time – all red brick and mirror cladding.
Inside, the lobby is done up to look like a Victorian arcade, with green-
painted wrought iron and shops selling newspapers and other neces-
sities. The bench of stuffed dummies has been the inspiration for several
practical jokes. The Sportsman's Bar is suitably decked out with rugby
shirts and other memorabilia. Hunters Restaurant is a little more
restrained and offers an excellent-value Sunday lunch. Bedrooms offer
all the mod cons and comforts you'd expect in a hotel of this ilk.

◑ Open all year

⤢ Follow signs to city centre, 500
yards from Cardiff Central
Station, opposite the Cardiff
World Trade Centre. Private car
park

🛏 70 twin, 62 double, 8 family
rooms, 3 suites; all with
bathroom/WC, TV, room service,
hair-dryer, trouser press, mini-
bar, baby-listening; air-
conditioning in some bedrooms

◇ Restaurant, bar, lounge, 2
conservatories (all air-
conditioned); conference facilities
(max 40 people residential and

non-residential); tennis, water
sports, other sports nearby.
Wheelchair access to hotel (1
step), restaurant and WC
(unisex), 8 bedrooms specially
equipped for disabled people

● No dogs

▭ Access, Amex, Diners, Visa

£ Single occupancy of twin/double
£70, twin/double £70, family
room £70, suite £130; deposit
required. Cooked B £8.50,
continental B £5.50; set D £15;
alc L, D £22.50. Special breaks
available

---

*Where we know an establishment accepts credit cards, we list them. There
may be a surcharge if you pay by credit card. It is always best to check
whether the card you want to use is acceptable when booking.*

CHIRK CLWYD · MAP 6

Starlings Castle

BRONYGARTH, NR CHIRK, OSWESTRY, SHROPSHIRE SY10 7NU
TEL: GLYN CEIRIOG (0691) 718464 (and fax)

An excellent restaurant-with-rooms in the middle of nowhere.

'Castle' is misleading, for Antony and Jools Pitt's hideaway is really an eighteenth-century sandstone farmhouse. Although in Clwyd, the Pitts use a Shropshire address and postcode 'because the post gets here three days quicker'. Antony's creative streak shows in the food, which has a strong Mediterranean bias, with dishes like provençal fish casserole and tomato and basil salad. On an inspection meal the best end of lamb was meltingly tender, and came with an aubergine and feta tian and tomato sauce. Service can be a little slow – one couple hung around for 10 minutes before Jools appeared to ask them to be seated.

The restaurant itself is laden with plates and pots; a large wooden dresser stacked with glasses and cups splits the long, low room. The L-shaped lounge continues the arty theme, with a case of art books and a display cabinet of interesting coffee sets and shells. The bar is cosier, its walls topped with an art nouveau border and hung with masks. Bedrooms are simple, with a scattering of antique furniture and wicker chairs; our inspector found a single room rather cramped.

◑ Open all year

⤴ From the A5 north of Oswestry take the exit from the roundabout signed Weston Rhyn. Drive 2 miles to Selattyn, turn right, and drive through the village for 2½ miles. Turn right at the top of the hill and follow signs to Starlings Castle. Private car park

🛏 2 single, 2 twin, 4 double; 2 public bathrooms; TV, hair-dryer, baby-listening in all rooms

◈ 2 restaurants, bar, lounge, drying room, conservatory; conference facilities (max 40 people non-residential, 14 residential); fishing, golf, other sports nearby; babysitting. Wheelchair access to restaurant only

⊖ No dogs in public rooms; no smoking in bedrooms

▭ Access, Amex, Diners, Visa

£ Single £20, single occupancy of twin/double £30, twin/double £40. Cooked B £3; alc L, D £20

CRICCIETH GWYNEDD · MAP 6

Mynydd Ednyfed ☆

CAERNARFON ROAD, CRICCIETH, GWYNEDD LL52 0PH
TEL: PORTHMADOG (0766) 523269

Peaceful family-run house with plenty of home comforts.

This hotel comes to us on the back of an enthusiastic reader's report:

'We'll almost certainly make this an annual event: everything was so right.' The solid Welsh country house is owned by Ian and Maureen Edwards, he an ex-footballer who now concentrates on tending the seven acres of land, she a home economist. Décor is unfussy, in neutral pale colours; the newly added conservatory has more zing, with pink-cushioned wicker chairs looking out over the lawns. Bedrooms are a touch above the ordinary, with good pine furniture, firm mattresses and smart florals.

Maureen holds sway in the kitchen, with a young chef to assist her. The menu has several choices at each stage. Starters might include mussels in ginger, garlic, wine and tomato sauce or salmon and spinach pancake with white wine sauce; main courses feature dishes like oriental chicken or breast of guinea-fowl.

◑ *Open all year, exc 25 Dec*

↗ *From Criccieth take the B4411 for ¾ mile, then turn right and follow driveway for ½ mile. Private car park*

🛏 *1 single, 2 twin, 2 double; 2 four-poster, 2 family rooms; most with bathroom/WC, rest with shower/wc; TV, baby-listening in all rooms; room service, hair-dryer on request*

◈ *2 restaurants, bar, lounge, drying room, conservatory; conference facilities (max 12 people residential); tennis, sauna/solarium, gym at hotel, fishing, golf, other sports nearby. Wheelchair access to restaurants only*

⊖ *No dogs in public rooms; no smoking in bedrooms*

▭ *Access, Amex, Visa*

£ *Single £33, twin/double £54, four-poster £60, family room £65; deposit required. Alc D £16. Special breaks available*

CRICKHOWELL POWYS   **MAP 6**

Gliffaes Country Hotel

CRICKHOWELL, POWYS NP8 1RH
TEL: BWLCH (0874) 730371   FAX: (0874) 730463

Very informal, occasionally shabby country house.

One reader took us to task this year for last year's entry concerning cold bedrooms with self-detaching bedheads and the small TV room: 'Any such criticisms should be muted so as not to deter your readers from visiting a quite excellent hotel. The public and private rooms are spacious, comfortable and homely; the food matches this standard; the setting is beautiful. But above all Mr Brabner and all the staff that we met had that rare combination of efficiency and friendly informality; infor-mation and creature comforts were always available when – and only when – wanted.' Another reader, however, complained about two single beds pushed together to make a double with two single quilts, a noisy, unsoundproofed room, curtains not meeting, and an unhelpful attitude to her complaint: 'All our doubles are like that.' Well, there are no quibbles about the beauty of the location, set high above the Usk, in beautifully tended gardens with pools and fountains. Neither have we had any complaints about the public rooms, with their fine plasterwork and panelling, or the conservatory with its views over the Usk. Some of the shabbiness is being addressed – the bar is being refurbished.

◑ *Closed 6 Jan to 25 Feb*

↗ *1 mile off A40, 2½ miles west of Crickhowell. Private car park*

🛏 *5 single, 14 twin/double, 3 lodge rooms; most with bathroom/WC, some with shower/WC; TV, room service, baby-listening in all rooms*

◇ *Dining-room, bar, 2 lounges, TV room, drying room, billiard room, conservatory; conference facilities (max 15 people residential and non-residential);*

tennis, croquet, putting at hotel, fishing nearby

⊖ *No wheelchair access; no children under 10 in dining-room eves; dogs in lodge only; no smoking in dining-room*

▭ *Access, Amex, Diners, Visa*

£ *Single £33 to £41, single occupancy of twin/double £49, twin/double from £65 to £82, family room rate on request. Cooked B £8.50; set L £11, D £18.50; alc D £26.50. Special breaks available*

CWMYSTWYTH DYFED   **MAP 6**

Hafod Lodge ☆

CWMYSTWYTH, ABERYSTWYTH, DYFED SY23 4AD
TEL: PONTRHYDYGROES (0974) 282247

An excellent small guesthouse serving cosmopolitan food.

'We don't consider ourselves to be a hotel – more of a guesthouse,' says Jenny Beard. Some might even consider it to be more like staying with friends, for Jenny and her husband Colin are excellent hosts, taking afternoon teas with you on the small terrace. Formerly the gatehouse to the Hafod estate, the lodge was extended in 1830 when it became the local school – the campanile chimney, minus bell, still stands. The cosier of the two lounges is stuffed with books; the other has a TV.

The small dining-room, with attractive muted carpet and brick fireplace, is the venue for cosmopolitan meals – such as cannelloni of smoked salmon filled with crab mousse, grilled medallions of fillet steak with balsamic sauce, and pineapple and amaretti salad.

The three bedrooms may be furnished with family antique furniture or newer pine.

◑ *Open all year*

↗ *Take the A44 from Rhayader to Ponterwyd, then the A4120 towards Devil's Bridge and the B4574 to Cwmystwyth through the Ystwyth-Myherin forest. Private car park*

🛏 *3 double; 1 with bathroom/WC, 1 with shower/WC, 1 with private facilities; room service in all rooms; hair-dryer and baby-listening on request; no tea/*

coffee-making facilities in
rooms

◇ Dining-room, lounge, TV room,
drying room; fishing, riding
nearby

● No wheelchair access; dogs and
smoking by arrangement only

▭ None accepted

£ Single occupancy of double £25,
double £50. Set D £23. Special
breaks available

EGLWYSFACH DYFED   **MAP 6**

Ynyshir Hall

EGLWYSFACH, MACHYNLLETH, POWYS SY20 8TA
TEL: GLANDYFI (0654) 781209   FAX: (0654) 781366

Artistic, stylish country house set in beautiful landscaped gardens.

Rob Reen is an artist by training, and it shows – although he modestly
claims that it's his wife Joan who runs the show, it's Rob's paintings that
crowd the walls. The white Georgian house sits among 12 acres of
landscaped gardens; inside, the strong colour schemes in apricot, turquoise and lilac provide a complementary background to the collection of
paintings and Clarice Cliff pottery. The lounge has a comfortable mix of
chairs and sofas and a collection of pretty jugs. The drawing-room feels
more formal; oriental rugs are scattered on the floor, and large windows
overlook the garden. Bedrooms, named after famous artists, are highly
individual: the Renoir Suite has 1920s French beds and a bathroom
painted with fluffy white clouds.

The food has been highly praised, chef David Dressler mixing
ingredients and flavours. Past dishes, for example, include roulade of
fresh crab, smoked salmon, cream cheese and chives with caper sauce,
and pan-fried venison with plum sauce served with a lettuce parcel of
rabbit, bacon and mushrooms.

◐ Open all year

↗ 6 miles south-west of
Machynlleth, 11 miles north-east
of Aberystwyth, off the A487.
Private car park

🛏 2 twin, 2 double, 1 four-poster, 3
suites; all with bathroom/WC,
TV, room service, hair-dryer; no
tea/coffee-making facilities in
rooms

◇ Restaurant, breakfast room, bar,
lounge; conference facilities
(max 20 people non-residential,
12 residential); fishing, riding,

other sports nearby

● No wheelchair access; no
children under 9; no dogs in
public rooms and in some
bedrooms only; smoking in bar
only

▭ Access, Amex, Visa

£ Single occupancy of twin/double
£65 to £85, twin/double £70 to
£120, four-poster £100 to £125,
suites £100 to £135; deposit
required. Set L £15/£16, D £23
to £25. Special breaks available

FISHGUARD DYFED   **MAP 6**

Manor House Hotel

MAIN STREET, FISHGUARD, DYFED SA65 9HG
TEL: FISHGUARD (0348) 873260

A small and pleasant family-run hotel in the centre of town.

This small Georgian town-house hotel is very much a hands-on affair run by Ralph Davies and his wife Beatrix. Past the antiques shop on the ground floor, steps lead down to the well-kept garden at the back, with views of the harbour. The dark green lounge is supplied with a piano, books and board games. The basement restaurant has fresh flower arrangements to add colour and the menu and wine list are good value. Beatrix does most of the cooking, including dishes such as New Zealand mussels with garlic crumbs and turkey fillet with an apple, cider, onion and cream purée. Ralph's speciality, Goan pork, is also very popular. Bedrooms are all a good size, with a pleasantly old-fashioned mixture of colours, styles and fabrics.

- ◑ Open all year, exc 24 to 28 Dec and 1 to 2 weeks in Feb
- ⬈ 200 yards from central roundabout in Fishguard square on left-hand side of Cardigan Road towards the Lower Town harbour. On-street parking
- 🛏 2 single, 2 twin, 3 double; 1 with bathroom/WC, 2 with shower/WC; hair-dryer in all rooms; TV in some rooms
- ◈ Restaurant, lounge; fishing, golf, other sports nearby
- ⊖ No wheelchair access; no dogs in public rooms
- ▭ Access, Visa
- £ Single £16, single occupancy of twin/double £22 to £28, twin/double £32 to £42; deposit preferred. Set D £12.50. Special breaks available

Plâs Glyn-y-Mêl

LOWER TOWN, FISHGUARD, PEMBROKESHIRE SA65 9LY
TEL: FISHGUARD (0348) 872296

Small, relaxing country house – good for families.

A flight of steps leads up to the Georgian porch and large entrance hall, but the grandeur is offset by the feeling that this is very much a family home. In the lounge, with garlanded fireplace and huge mirror, a corner display cabinet contains a family collection of Georgian taper sticks. The breakfast room is graced by a large window, and is decked out in dark green with the coving and elegant shell alcove picked out in white. If you prefer to do your own thing, two suites, each with two bedrooms, lounge and private kitchen, have come on stream this year. The other six bedrooms have the use of a shared kitchen. Bedrooms are more simply furnished than the public rooms but there are still sprinklings of family furniture.

◑ Open all year

⬀ Take the A487 out of the centre of Fishguard towards Cardigan. Private car park

🛏 2 single, 2 twin, 4 double, 2 family suites; all with bathroom/WC, TV

◇ Dining-room, lounge, drying room; heated indoor swimming-pool, fishing at hotel

⊖ No wheelchair access; no dogs or smoking in public rooms

▭ None accepted

£ Single and single occupancy of twin/double £40, twin/double £70, family room/suite £80; deposit required

---

Three Main Street

3 MAIN STREET, FISHGUARD, DYFED SA65 9HG
TEL: FISHGUARD (0348) 874275

A friendly, informal restaurant-with-rooms.

Marion Evans used to teach, Inez Ford is an ex-social worker. Together they set up in business about three years ago in this fine Georgian building on the main Fishguard to Cardigan road. They started as a restaurant and coffee-shop; the bedrooms followed later. Public rooms make the most of fashionable original features: bare boards, fireplaces, sophisticated colours such as deep green and burgundy. The small bar, scattered with colourful cushions and wooden sculptures, is particularly pleasant, while the coffee shop, with tablecloths in floral vinyl, is also used as the residents' breakfast room. Bread and pastries, including croissants, are home-made. Food is good and often colourful – perhaps beetroot and hazelnut salad with yogurt and horseradish, or local scallops with dry vermouth, cream and fresh basil.

Bedrooms are plainer than the downstairs rooms but are a good size, as are the bathrooms.

◑ Open all year, exc Feb

⬀ From Fishguard town square take the Newport/Cardigan road. Three Main Street is the second building on the left. Private car park

🛏 1 twin, 2 double; all with shower/WC; TV on request

◇ Restaurant, dining-room, bar; small meetings facilities; fishing, golf, other sports nearby. Wheelchair access to restaurant only

⊖ No dogs; smoking in bar only

▭ None accepted

£ Single occupancy of twin/double £30, twin/double £45; deposit required. Alc L £13.50, D £22.50

Hotels in our Visitors' Book *towards the end of the* Guide *are additional hotels that may be worth a visit. Reports on these hotels are welcome.*

FORDEN POWYS   **MAP 6**

Edderton Hall ☆

FORDEN, NR WELSHPOOL, POWYS SY21 8RZ
TEL: WELSHPOOL (0938) 580339   FAX: (0938) 580452

A slightly ramshackle country house serving good food.

On an inspection visit the hotel was in a certain amount of chaos, recovering from a large barbecue that had been held on the front lawns the previous weekend, but as business is just beginning to pick up after some hard times it should not be judged too harshly. This is no swanky country-house hotel but more of a lived-in, slightly dishevelled country home – and prices reflect this. Evelyn Hawksley says that as business improves she will be able to spend money on, for example, re-covering the battered chairs and sofas in the bar. Husband Warren is a sitting MP. There are Parliamentary pictures above the fireplace in the split-level bar, with its painted coving and woodsmoke aroma. Bedrooms are all very different in size and outlook: the most expensive, overlooking the front, has a four-poster bed and whirlpool bath.

A summer menu featured salmon, 'smoked in two ways', with ginger mayonnaise, avocado, cucumber and samphire; chicken quenelles with green curry sauce and timbale of wild rice; fillet steak with anchovy butter sauce; and chargrilled salmon with asparagus and lime vinaigrette.

◑ Open all year

⤴ From the A483 Welshpool to Newtown road take the Church Stoke/Montgomery A490 road. About 2 miles from Welshpool, turn into the drive opposite Edderton Riding Centre. Private car park

🛏 3 single, 1 twin, 1 double; 2 four-poster, 1 family room; all with bathroom/WC, exc 2 singles with shower/WC; TV, room service in all rooms; hair-dryer on request

◈ 2 dining-rooms, bar, lounge, ballroom; conference facilities (max 40 people non-residential, 8 residential); fishing, golf, other sports nearby

⊖ No wheelchair access

▭ Access, Amex, Diners, Visa

£ Single £25 to £35, single occupancy of twin/double £40, twin/double £55, four-poster £70 and £85, family rooms £55. Set L £11, D £19. Special breaks available

GLYNARTHEN DYFED   **MAP 6**

Penbontbren Farm

GLYNARTHEN, NR CARDIGAN, DYFED SA44 6PE
TEL: ABERPORTH (0239) 810248   FAX: (0239) 811129

True Welsh hospitality in a farm conversion.

Barrie and Nan Humphreys are quietly proud of their Welsh roots, and everything, including the brochure and menu, is printed in both Welsh and English.

The conversion from farm buildings to hotel took Barrie and Nan 15 months and has been done with an eye for comfort and style. The dining-room, which used to be the milking shed, now has a large Welsh dresser with plates and a 120-year-old harp. Nan employs local produce but experiments with foreign dishes such as Javanese chicken. The bar used to be the feed store, and an extra lounge was added about two years ago. Lots of stone walls and pine keep the rustic feeling.

Bedrooms in the former barns and stables feature pine, corn dollies and dried flowers; some have bathrooms lit by skylights.

◑ *Open all year; restaurant open most eves*

⚡ *Travelling south from Aberystwyth on the A487 take first left after Sarnau (signposted Penbontbren). Travelling north on A487 from Cardigan take second right 1 mile after Tan-y-groes (signposted Penbontbren). Private car park*

🛏 *3 twin, 1 double, 6 family rooms; all with bathroom/WC, TV, baby-listening*

◇ *Dining-room, bar, 2 lounges, games room; conference facilities (max 30 people non-residential, 13 residential); fishing, golf, riding, water sports nearby. Wheelchair access to hotel (ramp) and restaurant, 6 ground-floor bedrooms, 2 specially equipped for disabled people*

⊖ *No dogs in public rooms or unaccompanied in bedrooms; no smoking in dining-room*

▭ *Access, Visa*

£ *Single occupancy of twin/double £33 to £38, twin/double/family room £58 to £64; deposit required. Alc D £12. Special breaks available*

GOVILON GWENT   **MAP 6**

Llanwenarth House

GOVILON, ABERGAVENNY, GWENT NP7 9SF
TEL: GILWERN (0873) 830289   FAX: (0873) 832199

A beautifully restored Wolsey Lodge with a long history.

Llanwenarth House has an illustrious history: it was the ancestral home of buccaneer Henry Morgan as well as being used as a Royalist armoury during the Civil War. Bruce and Amanda Weatherill have lived here for 15 years: 'We've spent most of that time renovating,' says Amanda. The *pièce de résistance* is the Georgian atrium, painstakingly restored by Bruce, with the family coats of arms added. Furniture is mostly antique, well polished and cared for. There is an animal theme in the bedrooms, where military chests are stencilled with racing dogs and sheepskin rugs warm the feet. One room has unusual batik-print curtains; most have coronet drapes above the beds.

Amanda's tasty cooking often features home-produced lamb, with starters such as smoked trout and desserts of home-made ice-cream.

◑ Closed mid-Jan to end Feb; restaurant closed some eves

⤦ 2 miles west of Abergavenny. From the junction of the A40 from Monmouth, the A465 from Hereford and the A4042 from Newport, east of Abergavenny, follow the A465 towards Merthyr Tydfil for 3½ miles to next roundabout. Take first exit to Govilon; the ½-mile drive is 150 yards on the right-hand side. Private car park

🛏 2 twin, 2 double family rooms available; half with bathroom/WC, half with shower/WC; TV in

all rooms; hair-dryer on request

◈ Dining-room, drawing-room, drying facilities; croquet at hotel, other sports nearby. Wheelchair access to hotel (1 step) and dining-room, 1 ground-floor bedroom

⊖ No children under 10; no dogs in public rooms; no smoking in dining-room and discouraged in bedrooms

▭ None accepted

£ Single occupancy of twin/double £58, twin/double £70; deposit required. Set D £21 (7.45pm). Special breaks available

---

HAY-ON-WYE POWYS   MAP 6

Old Black Lion

LION STREET, HAY-ON-WYE, HEREFORD HR3 5AD
TEL: HAY-ON-WYE (0497) 820841

An old favourite in the booklovers' nirvana continues to draw plaudits for its warm welcome, good value and interesting food.

'May Hay-on-Wye and the Old Black Lion continue to offer their characteristic charms,' writes a fan who, returning after three years, found the welcome 'as warm and friendly as ever'. The Collinses have been here for six years. 'We want people to feel it's like putting on a pair of carpet slippers – at home and comfortable.'

The pub sits on one of the oldest roads in Hay and is mostly seventeenth-century, though John Collins claims that the cellars are Norman. Acquisitions like the mahogany bar and an old farmhouse settle enhance the character given by the low black beams and sloping floors, and candles are lit in the evenings. Bedrooms, split between the main building and the annexe, have every comfort.

The restaurant is quite small, but people are welcome to eat in the main bar if they wish. 'The sweets are superlative, the main courses are almost over-generous in their content and most imaginative,' notes one reader. The bar menu includes Mediterranean specialities such as stuffed vine leaves as well as more traditional steaks, cobblers and ploughman's.

◑ Open all year

⤦ In the centre of Hay-on-Wye, 2 minutes' walk from the castle. Private car park

🛏 1 single, 4 twin, 4 double, 1 family room; some with bathroom/WC, most with shower/WC; TV in all rooms; hair-dryer on request

Restaurant, bar, lounge; fishing, golf, riding nearby. Wheelchair access to hotel (I step), restaurant and WC, I ground-floor bedroom

No children under 5; no dogs in restaurant

Access, Amex, Visa

Single £19, single occupancy of twin/double £27, twin/double £40, family room from £52; deposit required. Alc L £5 to £10, D £10 to £15 (prices till Easter 94). Special breaks available

---

JEFFRESTON DYFED   MAP 6

Jeffreston Farmhouse ☆

JEFFRESTON, NR KILGETTY, SOUTH PEMBROKESHIRE SA68 0RE
TEL: CAREW (0646) 651291 (and fax)

A friendly farmhouse in a handy location.

Norman and June Williams moved to this seventeenth-century farm-house five years ago after running a restaurant in the Midlands, and June's culinary skills have extended to include local specialities such as Glamorgan sausage (cheese, leeks and breadcrumbs) and laverbread with bacon and oatmeal. The restaurant is everything you would expect in a building of this age: a large stone fireplace takes up one end of the room, with an impressive collection of toby jugs on the shelves above. China cups and jugs hang from hooks on the low beams. The traditional farmhouse feel is continued in the lounges, with their tasselled lampshades, low ceilings and family photos.

The bedrooms are named after islands off the Pembrokeshire coast, and are light and airy, in pinks and whites.

Open all year; restaurant closed Sun and Mon eves

Take the A40 from Carmarthen to St Clears, then the A477 towards Pembroke. At Broadmoor turn right on to the B4586 to Jeffreston. The farmhouse is opposite the church. Private car park

2 twin, 2 double; half with bathroom/WC, half with shower/WC; TV, hair-dryer in all rooms

Dining-room, bar, 2 lounges; fishing, golf, other sports nearby

No wheelchair access; no dogs in public rooms; smoking in lounges only and discouraged in bedrooms

Access, Visa

Single occupancy of twin/double £23, twin/double £44. Set D from £12.50. Special breaks available

---

The Guide *is totally independent, accepts no free hospitality, and survives on the number of copies sold each year.*

LAMPETER DYFED   **MAP 6**

Falcondale ☆

LAMPETER, DYFED SA48 7RX
TEL: LAMPETER (0570) 422910   FAX: (0570) 423559

Comfortable bedrooms in a peaceful base.

The Smiths took Falcondale over in 1977, converting it from a home for the elderly to a hotel. The bedrooms are individually decked out, with fabrics and wallpapers ranging from William Morris-style to more sober browns and greens. Superior rooms have space for a double and single bed, but even the standard rooms are a good size. Those at the front of the house probably have the best views. Bathrooms are slightly on the gloomy side.

The main lounge is comfortable but feels a little institutional – perhaps it's something to do with the sameness of the Louis XIV-style chairs and sofas. The public bar, with its gridwork ceiling and mix of curved leather chairs and chesterfields, works better. There's also a very pleasant lounge on the first floor, lit by a large skylight. The conservatory, used mainly for bar lunches, could do with refurbishing, particularly the curling lino. The table d'hôte menu is short and traditional, offering three choices at each stage – perhaps cream of leek soup or avocado with prawns, followed by roast turkey with chestnut stuffing.

- ◐ Closed 2nd and 3rd week Jan
- ◪ 600 yards west of Lampeter off the A475 or 1½ miles north, off the A482. Private car park
- 🛏 2 twin, 7 double, 2 four-poster, 8 family rooms; all with bathroom/WC, TV, room service, hairdryer, baby-listening
- ◈ Restaurant, 2 bars, 2 lounges, conservatory; conference facilities (max 60 non-residential, 30 residential); fishing, tennis at hotel, golf, riding nearby
- ⊖ No wheelchair access; dogs by arrangement only; smoking in bar only
- ▭ Access, Visa
- £ Single occupancy of twin/double £42 to £50, twin/double £60 to £72, four-poster £90, family room from £98; deposit required. Set L £10, D16; alc D £12 to £18. Special breaks available

LLANARMON DYFFRYN CEIRIOG CLWYD   **MAP 6**

West Arms

LLANARMON DYFFRYN CEIRIOG, NR LLANGOLLEN, CLWYD LL20 7LD
TEL: LLANARMON DYFFRYN CEIRIOG (0691 76) 665   FAX: (0691 76) 622

A characterful old hotel with comfortable bedrooms.

The West Arms Hotel is a converted seventeenth-century farmhouse. Inside, it is awash with inglenook fireplaces, wooden beams and timbers, brass and copper implements. The restaurant is made cosier by the dark-green walls; the bar lounge is lighter, and has some interesting carved wooden seats. Bedrooms in the main building have similar character – exposed beams and timbers shooting out at every angle, rough un-plastered walls, simple white bedspreads. Some have brass beds and antiques. The Willow Suite has a separate sitting area with TV. Rooms in the extension are less appealing.

The restaurant menu is written in Welsh and English, and might include deep-fried Pencarreg cheese with blackcurrant jelly, roast rack of Welsh lamb with a ginger and apricot jelly, and sticky toffee pudding. 'Most enjoyable, very comfortable, excellent food and friendly staff,' sums up one reader.

◑ *Open all year*

🔁 *Turn off the A5 trunk road at Chirk and follow the B4500 along Ceiriog Valley for 13 miles. Private car park*

🛏 *7 twin, 4 double, 2 suites; all with bathroom/WC, room service, baby-listening; hair-dryer on request; TV in suites only; tea/coffee-making facilities on request*

◇ *2 dining-rooms, 2 bars, 3 lounges, TV room, drying room; ironing facilities; conference facilities (max 40 people non-residential, 18 residential); fishing at hotel, golf, riding, other sports nearby. Wheelchair access to hotel (1 step), restaurant and WC, 3 ground-floor bedrooms, 1 specially equipped for disabled people*

⊖ *No dogs or smoking in some bedrooms and public rooms*

▭ *Access, Amex, Diners, Visa*

£ *Single occupancy of twin/double £50, twin/double £78 to £88, suite £99. Set L £12.50, D £21.50.*

LLANDDEINIOLEN GWYNEDD

MAP 6

Ty'n Rhos

COUNTY HOTEL OF THE YEAR

SEION, LLANDDEINIOLEN, CAERNARFON, GWYNEDD LL55 3AE
TEL: PORT DINORWIC (0248) 670489   FAX: (0248) 670079

Excellent farmhouse hotel serving good home-produced food.

The low, slate-hung farmhouse has 11 bedrooms. Nigel Kettle runs the front of house with a long stride and easy humour, greeting guests, showing them to their rooms, serving dinner with a relaxed banter. Lynda's excellent dinners are worth paying attention to. Her no-choice, four-course menu is put up in the late afternoon, and if there's anything you don't like, say so before 7pm and she'll provide an alternative. Mind you, our inspector, who thought she didn't like lemon meringue pie, was completely won over by Lynda's featherlight creation. It was preceded by fresh asparagus served on a large croûton with shavings of Parmesan cheese, then loin of pork stuffed with herbs, accompanied by apple sauce, roast potatoes, broccoli and runner beans. The lounge has a variety of chairs to suit all tastes, plus a selection of games.

Bedrooms have good pine furniture and nicely co-ordinated furnishings. Breakfast is ordered the night before from a list placed on your dinner table.

- ◑ *Closed 20 Dec to 15 Jan, 1 week in Spring and 2 weeks in Nov*
- ⤧ *In hamlet of Seion off the B4366, 4 miles from Caernarfon. Private car park*
- 🛏 *2 single, 3 twin, 6 double; all with bathroom/WC, exc 1 twin with shower/WC; TV in all rooms; hair-dryer on request*
- ◈ *Dining-room, bar, lounge, drying room; fishing, golf nearby.*
- *Wheelchair access to farm (1 step) and dining-room, 3 ground-floor bedrooms*
- ⊖ *No children under 5; no dogs; no smoking in public rooms*
- 💳 *Access, Visa*
- £ *Single £30 to £35, single occupancy of twin/double £45 to £52, twin/double £50 to £70; deposit required. Set D £16.50. Special breaks available*

LLANDEGLA CLWYD   MAP 6

Bodidris Hall

LLANDEGLA, WREXHAM, CLWYD LL11 3AL
TEL: LLANDEGLA (097 888) 434/479   FAX: (097 888) 335

A historic country house slightly let down by service.

Built as a hunting-lodge for Lord Robert Dudley, favourite of Elizabeth I, Bodidris Hall sits at the end of a long country lane. Mullioned creeper-clad windows overlook an artificial stone pond and a small lake. The hotel plays up its royal connections by naming its honeymoon suite, rather ironically, after the Virgin Queen: it has a king-sized four-poster bed and a spa bath. Other bedrooms vary in size and furnishings.

The whole place is strewn with bric-à-brac, historic and otherwise: a suit of armour in the passage to the dining-room, an old rocking horse on the landing, various stags' heads mounted on the walls, a stuffed owl glaring down from the beams in the dining-room. The sixteenth-century duelling staircase, with uneven treads, is more treacherous coming down than going up, so beware. On a damp, chilly evening in June the public rooms seemed a little cheerless. Best was the bar, where red walls added a touch of cosiness.

The spring menu offered five or six choices at each stage. Melon with ham could have done with less of the former, more of the latter; monkfish tail came with a fairly stingy portion of vegetables. Service is willing enough, but slow. We have also heard from a reader who complained about 'unbusinesslike' behaviour when it took ten telephone calls and four weeks for his deposit to be returned after the hotel had cancelled his booking because of electrical work.

- ◑ *Open all year*
- ⤧ *On the A5104, 1 mile east of Llandegla. Private car park*
- 🛏 *1 single, 2 double, 3 four-poster, 2 family rooms; all with bathroom/WC, exc single; TV,*

room service, hair-dryer, baby-listening in all rooms

⬦ Restaurant, bar, 2 lounges; conference facilities (max 50 people non-residential, 14 residential); fishing at hotel, other sports nearby. Wheelchair access to restaurant only

⬤ Dogs by arrangement only; no smoking in bedrooms

▭ Access, Diners, Visa

⊞ Single £25, single occupancy of twin/double £30, twin/double £50 to £70, four-poster £80 to £95, cottage £130; deposit required. Set L £12.50, D £18.50. Special breaks available

---

LLANDEGLEY POWYS   **MAP 6**

Ffaldau Country House

LLANDEGLEY, LLANDRINDOD WELLS, POWYS LD1 5UD
TEL: PENYBONT (0597) 851421

A small but friendly guesthouse, run with enthusiasm.

The cream-washed, sixteenth-century farmhouse has been a staging-post and a Quaker meeting-house in its time. It retains the characteristics of the period – large fireplaces, small, cottagey rooms with low beams – overlaid with personal family mementoes such as a hand-carved wooden train and wedding photos. Upstairs, a sitting-room is well supplied with books and games. The dining-room has a mixture of straight-backed leather chairs and ordinary dining chairs, lacy table-cloths, a piano and brass ornaments. Sylvia Knott's 'gourmet menus' are served up here in the evenings – perhaps plum and tomato soup, followed by rack of lamb with vermouth and mint. Vegetables are home-grown. The desserts are daughter Sara's creations, with choices such as layered blackberry and apple crumb dessert with whipped cream. Bedrooms follow a floral theme, with appropriate fabrics and flower arrangements.

◑ Open all year; Sun, Mon eves light suppers only

↗ Set back from the A44 in Llandegley, 2 miles south-east of Penybont. Private car park

🛏 2 twin, 2 double; 2 with bathroom/WC, 2 with shower/WC; hair-dryer in all rooms; TV in 1 double and 1 twin

⬦ Restaurant, bar/lounge, drying room, TV room; fishing, golf, other sports nearby

⬤ No wheelchair access; no children under 10; no dogs; no smoking in dining-room and bedrooms

▭ Visa

⊞ Single occupancy of twin/double £22, twin/double £36 to £45; deposit required. Set L (by prior arrangement), D £15 to £18; light supper £10. Special breaks available

LLANDRILLO CLWYD　　　　　　　　　　　　**MAP 6**

Tyddyn Llan

LLANDRILLO, NR CORWEN, CLWYD LL21 0ST
TEL: LLANDRILLO (049 084) 264 (and fax)

A sympathetically restored and extended country house.

Peter and Bridget Kindred have lived in this Georgian stone house for ten years now. When they decided to move up from bed and breakfast to more of a fully fledged hotel they added a new dining-room. The original sitting-room, in pink, features Ionic pilasters and a square pillar as well as a gracious marble mantelpiece. The cream-panelled breakfast room, with carved wooden brackets supporting jugs, and the new dining-room, lit by french windows on three sides, are stylish. There's also a small terrace outside, ideal for afternoon tea when the weather's sunny. Bedrooms are a good size and may have brass or wooden beds. One reader, however, noted 'no toilet-roll holder (most inconvenient), towel rail broken on wall and very leaky shower head'.

Meals are 'very well presented and cooked and well balanced', though readers on longer stays noticed some dishes and soups repeated three nights in a row. A June menu offered dishes such as aubergine, pesto and goats' cheese sandwich with salad leaves, cream of broccoli, courgette and almond soup, escalopes of monkfish on a bed of marsh samphire with lemon beurre blanc and citrus fruits, and orange mousse with candied kumquats and mango coulis.

◑ *Open all year, exc 1st week Feb*

↗ *From the A5 at Corwen take the B4401 through Cynwyd to Llandrillo. The house is on the right-hand side as you leave the village. Private car park*

🛏 *4 twin, 6 double; all with bathroom/WC, exc 2 doubles with shower/WC; room service, hair-dryer, baby-listening in all rooms; TV on request; no tea-coffee-making facilities in rooms*

◇ *Restaurant, breakfast room, bar, lounge, TV room, drying room; conference facilities (max 10 people residential, 50 non-residential); croquet, fishing at hotel, riding, swimming-pool nearby. Wheelchair access to restaurant only*

⊖ *No dogs in public rooms*

▭ *Access, Visa*

£ *Single occupancy of twin/double £54 to £58, twin/double £44 to £92; deposit required. Snack lunches; set L £11.50, D £21.50. Special breaks available*

Many hotels offer special rates for stays of a few nights or more. It is worth enquiring when you book.

LLANDUDNO GWYNEDD   **MAP 6**

Bodysgallen Hall

LLANDUDNO, GWYNEDD LL30 1RS
TEL: LLANDUDNO (0492) 584466   FAX: (0492) 582519

A country-house hotel with beautiful gardens.

Bodysgallen Hall dates from the thirteenth century but most of it is
seventeenth century, and the mullioned windows, dark oak panelling and
shouldered chimney breast inscribed with the family motto of the owners
of the time are complemented by Persian rugs strewn over coir matting,
polished clawfoot chairs, portraits in oils and plump sofas. The entrance
hall, library and first-floor drawing-room provide a choice of places to
relax. Bedrooms are equally comfortable and well-appointed, with racks
of old books as well as the usual mod cons. There are also nine cottage
suites, slightly simpler but equally comfortable, with small kitchenettes.

The restaurant is split into a peach-coloured morning-room, used for
breakfast, and a dining-room in yellow. Dinner menus give plenty of
choice: a menu in June included dishes such as warm crab and laverbread flan set on a tomato butter, roast turbot with samphire and saffron
cream, and iced apricot and hazelnut parfait. Lunch is considerably
cheaper.

◗ Open all year

🔀 Take the A55 to its intersection
with the A470, then follow the
A470 towards Llandudno. The
hotel is one mile on the right.
Private car park

🛏 3 single, 15 twin/double, 1 four-
poster, 9 cottage suites; all with
bathroom/WC, exc 1 cottage
with shower/WC; TV, hair-dryer,
limited room service, trouser
press in all rooms; tea/coffee-
making facilities in cottages only

◈ Restaurant, bar, lounge, library;
conference facilities (max 50
people non-residential, 28

residential); tennis, croquet at
hotel, other sports nearby.
Wheelchair access to hotel and
1 ground-floor bedroom only

⊖ No children under 8; dogs in
cottages only

▭ Access, Amex, Diners, Visa

💷 Single from £82, single
occupancy of twin/double from
£90, twin/double from £135,
four-poster from £155, cottage
suites from £170; deposit
required. Continental B £6.50,
cooked B £10; set L from £14, D
from £27.50. Special breaks
available

St Tudno Hotel

PROMENADE, LLANDUDNO, GWYNEDD LL30 2LP
TEL: LLANDUDNO (0492) 874411   FAX: (0492) 860407

A well-run seaside hotel with lots of frills and good cooking.

From the outside the Victorian bay-windowed house looks little different to others in the terrace; inside it's more like stepping back into a Victorian parlour. Lacy blinds, flowery drapes, potted palms and slightly fussy flowery wallpaper characterise the lounge and the bar. There's also a set of *Alice in Wonderland* prints, reminders of the fact that Alice Liddell, model for Lewis Carroll's heroine, came here for family holidays. The Garden Room Restaurant, reached via the coffee lounge, has a fresher feel, decorated with wallpaper patterned with green trellises and climbing plants. Food is 'excellent': smoked trout with horseradish and tarragon might be followed by kiwi-fruit sorbet, breast of Barbary duckling with lentils, wild mushrooms and madeira sauce, chocolate parfait with fresh vanilla sauce. One reader thought it odd that 'coffee after dinner was unlimited but if you wanted tea instead the cost was £1 extra'.

Bedrooms are priced according to size and position; those at the front have great views of the beach and promenade. Frilly pelmets, chintzy swags and coronet drapes are *de rigueur*.

◑ Open all year

⤢ On Llandudno's promenade, opposite the pier entrance and ornamental garden. Small private car park, garaging and on-street parking

🛏 2 single, 7 twin, 8 double, 1 four-poster, 3 family rooms; all with bathroom/WC, exc 2 doubles with shower/WC; TV, room service, hair-dryer, baby-listening, fridge in all rooms; trouser press on request

◈ Air-conditioned restaurant, bar, 2 lounges, drying room; conference facilities (max 25 people residential, 12 non-residential);

heated indoor swimming-pool at hotel, other sports nearby; babysitting

⊖ No wheelchair access; no children under 4 in restaurant eves; no dogs in public rooms and unaccompanied in bedrooms; no smoking in restaurant and 1 lounge

▭ Access, Amex, Visa

£ Single £55 to £60, single occupancy of twin/double £60 to £89, twin/double £70 to £120, four-poster £120, family room from £83; deposit required. Set L £13.50, D £25; bar snacks. Special breaks available

---

LLANFACHRETH GWYNEDD   **MAP 6**

Tŷ Isaf ☆

LLANFACHRETH, NR DOLGELLAU, GWYNEDD LL40 2EA
TEL: DOLGELLAU (0341) 423261

A converted farmhouse with hospitable hosts in a peaceful spot.

Tŷ Isaf is no longer a working farm, though a collection of goats, kept for breeding and milk, will crowd nosily round the gate as you arrive. There is also an ancient butter churner in one of the lounges, Brewis, where beer was once brewed, and the three bedrooms are named after their former functions – Stable (downstairs), Straw Store and Hayloft. All are on the small side but prettily furnished in simple florals and stripped pine beds.

Diana and Graham Silverton's aim is to create a house-party atmosphere, so guests are invited into their private inglenook lounge before dinner for a complimentary drink and chat before being seated round the communal dark polished table in the dining-room. Diana's evening meals offer three choices of starter and main courses – perhaps tomato and rosemary soup followed by home-made steak and kidney pie or chicken paupiettes. There is also a hot pudding as well as old favourites like cheesecake and trifle. Graham takes over the breakfast shift, offering English, American or continental versions as well as smoked haddock or kippers. Fresh goats' milk is available.

◑ *Closed mid-Oct to mid-Nov*

↗ *From Dolgellau go over the town bridge and turn right on to the Bala road. Take a left turn to Llanfachreth and follow the road for 3 miles. Tŷ Isaf is opposite the church. Private car park*

⇌ *1 twin, 2 double; twin with bathroom/WC, doubles with shower/WC; hair-dryer in all rooms.*

◈ *Dining-room, 3 lounges; fishing, golf, other sports nearby*

⊖ *No wheelchair access; no children under 13; dogs in public rooms by arrangement only; no smoking in bedrooms*

▭ *None accepted*

£ *Single occupancy of twin/double £23 to £30, twin/double £46; deposit required. Set D £10 (7.30pm)*

LLANFAIR WATERDINE POWYS   MAP 6

Monaughty Poeth ☆   COUNTY HOTEL OF THE YEAR

LLANFAIR WATERDINE, KNIGHTON, POWYS LD7 1TT
TEL: KNIGHTON (0547) 528348

Wonderfully welcoming farmhouse on the Welsh borders.

The only part of the twelfth-century monastery that remains is the chimney stack, seen to best effect from the smaller of the two bedrooms. The rest of the farmhouse is unmistakably Victorian, in red brick with white facings and a small neat garden. Jocelyn Williams used to teach at a village school 'over the hill' till it closed down. Husband Jim takes care of the 450-acre farm, with its cattle and sheep. Guests have their own lounge and breakfast room, comfortable and homely, with Victorian fireplace, flower arrangements and chintzy chairs. Upstairs, the larger of the two rooms has a lovely view over the Teme valley. A row of children's books is a clue that this was once their daughter's room. Breakfasts, however, are 'excellent and match the warmth of the welcome'.

◑ *Closed Dec and Jan*

↗ *Take the A4355 out of Knighton towards Newtown. Monaughty Poeth is 3 miles from Knighton. Private car park*

⇌ *2 twin/double; 1 public bathroom; TV in both rooms*

◈ *Breakfast room, lounge; fishing by arrangement*

⊜ No wheelchair access; no children under 7; no smoking in bedrooms

▭ None accepted

£ Single occupancy of twin/double £16 to £17, twin/double £31 to £34

LLANGAMMARCH WELLS POWYS   MAP 6

Lake Hotel

LLANGAMMARCH WELLS, POWYS LD4 4BS
TEL: LLANGAMMARCH WELLS (05912) 202   FAX: (05912) 457

Relaxing, unsnooty country house with excellent service.

Lake Country House used to be a spa hotel, but is now investing in water of a different sort: a new lake, dug out in 1993, was still a little rough round the edges when we inspected. The house is Edwardian, partly half-timbered, with long, narrow windows overlooking the grounds. The public rooms are wonderfully spacious, the quality of antique furniture and fabrics impressive. The bar, green and a little drab, is to be turned into another lounge. Bedrooms are smartly furnished with coronet drapes and co-ordinated borders and fabrics; some of the bathrooms are due for renovation.

Food is fancy, and usually includes a soup, such as cream of carrot and lentil, and a starter – perhaps a salad of honeyroast pigeon breast with quails' eggs, pine kernels and crispy bacon. Main courses have included a trio of lamb, beef and pork fillets with wild mushrooms. Service is enthusiastic, obliging, and friendly.

◑ Open all year

⤢ Leave Junction 24 on M4, follow A449 to Raglan, then the A40 to Abergavenny, go through Brecon, turning left on to B4519 and left to Llangammarch Wells. Drive across Mount Eppynt (6 miles), at the foot of the hill turn left at the crossroads. Hotel is 1 mile along road. Private car park

⇋ 16 twin/double/suites, 2 four-poster, 1 family room; all with bathroom/WC, TV, room service, hair-dryer; trouser press in some rooms; no tea/coffee-making facilities in rooms

◇ Dining-room, bar, 2 lounges, games room, drying room; conference facilities (max 60 people non-residential, 20 residential); tennis, fishing, clay pigeon shooting at hotel, other sports nearby. Wheelchair access to hotel, dining-room and WC (M, F), 2 ground-floor bedrooms, specially equipped for disabled people

⊜ No children in dining-room eves; no dogs in public rooms; no smoking in dining-room and some bedrooms

▭ Access, Amex, Visa

£ Single occupancy of twin/double £75, twin/double/four-poster £98, suite/family room from £120; deposit required. Set L £15.50, D £24.50

LLANGOLLEN CLWYD   **MAP 6**

Gales

18 BRIDGE STREET, LLANGOLLEN, CLWYD LL20 8PF
TEL: LLANGOLLEN (0978) 860089   FAX: (0978) 861313

A popular wine bar with well-furnished bedrooms.

The good-value, wide-ranging wine list combined with a no-nonsense approach to food continue to draw both locals and tourists alike. Smoked meats from a local smokehouse seem popular – both chicken and pheasant were chalked up when we visited, together with burgundy lamb casserole. There is no separate residents' lounge: you sit at one of the wooden tables in the busy, sociable wine bar and soak up the atmosphere. Breakfast is usually taken in a small raised section of the bar looking out on to the street.

Bedrooms are quite classy, with antique carved and brass beds. Richard Gale was busy converting the next-door building into another six rooms and two suites when we inspected.

◐ Open all year, exc 25 Dec to 2 Jan; restaurant closed Sun

↗ 9 miles south-west of Wrexham. Coming from the south on the A5, turn right at the traffic lights in Llangollen and right again before the bridge. The hotel is 50 yards on the right. Private car park

🛏 2 twin, 5 double, 1 family room; some with bathroom/WC, most with shower/WC; TV, hair-dryer, baby-listening in all rooms

◇ Restaurant, bar; conference facilities (max 12 people non-residential, 8 residential); fishing, golf, mountain biking, other sports nearby

⊖ No wheelchair access; dogs by arrangement only

▭ Access, Visa

£ Single occupancy of twin/double £30, twin/double £49; deposit required. Alc L £5, D £10

LLANSANFFRAID GLAN CONWY GWYNEDD   **MAP 6**

Old Rectory

LLANRWST ROAD, LLANSANFFRAID GLAN CONWY, GWYNEDD LL28 5LF
TEL: ABERCONWY (0492) 580611   FAX: (0492) 584555

Excellent food and wine, comfortable rooms and superb views.

'Superior accommodation in every way', 'we were delighted with every aspect', 'meticulously run', 'the highest standards of comfort and service' – these are just some of the praises that readers have lavished on Michael and Wendy Vaughan's Georgian Wolsey Lodge this year. The interior is elegant – antique china, polished tables, piano and harp in the dining-room, pine panelling and plenty of comfortable seating in the drawing-room. Bedrooms have antique half-tester beds, concealed 'ironing centres' and maybe a corner bath. Two additional rooms in the coach-house in similar style were added last year.

Plaudits for Wendy's cooking continue to roll in. 'We could not fault the food, from the excellent hot canapés to the delicious petits fours. The fillet of local Welsh black beef was outstanding, full of flavour; we now judge all beef against this standard of slow-maturing breed.'

◑ Closed 20 Dec to 1 Feb

⤵ On the A470, ½ mile south of the junction with the A55. Private car park

🛏 2 twin, 2 double, 2 annexe rooms; all with bathroom/WC, exc 1 double with shower/WC; TV, room service, hair-dryer in all rooms

◈ Restaurant, lounge; ironing

facilities; golf, fishing, other sports nearby

⊖ No wheelchair access; no children under 5; dogs and smoking in coach-house bedrooms only

▭ Access, Amex, Diners, Visa

💷 Twin/double £59 to £97; deposit required. Set D £26 (8pm). Special breaks available

---

LLANTHONY GWENT   **MAP 6**

Abbey Hotel

LLANTHONY, NR ABERGAVENNY, GWENT NP7 7NN
TEL: CRUCORNEY (0873) 890487

Unusual atmospheric rooms among abbey ruins.

It would be difficult to imagine a more atmospheric setting, for this ancient hostelry lies within the ruins of a twelfth-century Augustinian priory. Entry is via the basement bar, a whitewashed vaulted den of a place selling real ale and lunchtime soups and ploughman's as well as evening specials such as abbot's (beef) casserole and bean goulash. Residents have a separate dining-room (formerly the prior's outer parlour) with large wooden communal tables and Gothic display cases. From here a narrow winding spiral staircase leads up to the bedrooms – beware of encumbering yourself with too much luggage, especially if you're ascending to Middle Tower or Top Tower rooms. Rooms are small, though they manage to accommodate four-posters and half-testers, and have superb views of the abbey ruins (slightly spooky at night). Facilities are basic – two toilets and one bath shared among five rooms – but the novelty of the position and the reasonable rates seem to outweigh any desire for *en-suite* comforts.

◑ Open Apr to end Nov; weekends and holidays only Nov to end Mar

⤵ From A465 take road signposted Llanthony Priory. Adjacent car park

🛏 3 twin/double, 2 four-poster; 2 public bathrooms

◈ Dining-room, bar; fishing, riding, water sports nearby

⊖ No wheelchair access; no dogs in

public rooms and in bedrooms
with own bedding only

▭ None accepted

£21, double £41 to £48, four-
poster £41 to £48; deposit
required. Alc L from £4, D £11.
Special breaks available

£€ Single occupancy of twin/double

LLANWDDYN POWYS · MAP 6

Lake Vyrnwy Hotel

LAKE VYRNWY, LLANWDDYN, POWYS SY10 0LY
TEL: LLANWDDYN (069 173) 692   FAX: (069 173) 259

A sporting hotel that provides comfort and sustenance.

Perched well above the lake, the partly half-timbered Victorian sporting-lodge offers many varied country pursuits. Our complaints last year about the downmarket tavern next door have been taken to heart: the jukebox and pool table have been removed and a more genteel lounge with terrace has been added to the slate-floored public bar. When we visited, work had almost been completed on the new conference room and eight new bedrooms. The older bedrooms vary in size and décor: those at the back without lake views usually have some other feature as compensation, such as a four-poster bed or whirlpool bath. The new conference facilities mean that the elegant drawing-room in blue, gold and yellow in the original part of the house can be reclaimed by non-conferring guests; the bar lounge, with deep leather scroll-armed sofas and bay windows facing the lake is also very comfortable.

The food is good – five choices at each stage, with much home-grown produce in evidence. A terrine of lemon sole, salmon and spinach garnished with smoked salmon and olive oil dressing might be followed by grilled medallions of beef with madeira sauce and an onion tartlet and rounded off with Welsh whisky and chocolate chip ice-cream with blackcurrant sauce.

◑ Open all year

⤢ From Shrewsbury take the A458 road to Welshpool and turn on to the B4393 signposted 'Lake Vyrnwy 28 miles'. Turn left after Llanfyllin. Hotel is 200 yards past the dam. Private car park

🛏 2 single, 29 twin/double, 2 four-poster, 2 family rooms, 2 suites; all with bathroom/WC, exc 1 double with shower/WC; TV, room service, hair-dryer, baby-listening in all rooms; no tea/coffee-making facilities in rooms

◈ Restaurant, 2 bars, 2 lounges, drying room, conservatory; conference facilities (max 30 people residential, 120 non-residential); fishing (Mar to Oct), shooting, tennis, bicycles, canoeing, sailing, abseiling at hotel, other sports nearby; babysitting by arrangement. Wheelchair access to restaurant and public areas only

⊖ No dogs in public rooms; no smoking in part of restaurant

▭ Access, Amex, Diners, Visa

£€ Single £56, single occupancy of

twin/double from £56, twin/
double from £70, four-poster
£94, family room £83, suite

£119. Set L £10.50, D £21.50;
Sun L £12. Special breaks
available

LLANWRTYD WELLS POWYS   **MAP 6**

Carlton House

DOLYCOED ROAD, LLANWRTYD WELLS, POWYS LD5 4SN
TEL: LLANWRTYD WELLS (05913) 248

Excellent-value family-run hotel with oriental touches.

The Edwardian bay-windowed house is in the centre of Llanwrtyd
Wells. The interior is unexpectedly sophisticated – strong colours, a vast
accumulation of chinoiserie collected by Mary Ann Gilchrist's parents
during their time in the Far East, lots of glossy magazines, and bookshelves of interesting volumes. Bedrooms also have oriental touches, like
Chinese prints and lacquer boxes and, in Room One, some extraordinary
1920s chinoiscrie furniture.

Downstairs, the dining area and lounge are in one split-level room
separated by raffia screens. The short set menu, with two choices of
starter and main course, is excellent value – perhaps watercress soup
followed by Thai-baked salmon with coriander and fresh vegetables.
Lemon tart produces a touch of performance art at the table as Alan
caramelises the crust in front of you with a blowtorch. Retiring back
down to the lounge fire for coffee and home-made sweeties, you are
likely to be welcomed by George the lugubrious bassett hound, who can
scent a dish of fudge at 100 paces and whose waistline discloses evidence
of previous successful forays.

◐ Open all year, exc Xmas and
New Year

⊿ In the centre of Llanwrtyd Wells.
On-street parking

🛏 3 twin, 2 double, 1 family room;
1 with bathroom/WC, 1 with
shower/WC, 2 public bathrooms;
TV in all rooms; hair-dryer on
request

⬦ Dining-room, bar, lounge; fishing,
riding nearby

⊖ No wheelchair access; no dogs in
public rooms

▭ Access, Visa

£ Single occupancy of twin/double
£20, twin/double £34 to £40,
family room £44; deposit
required. Set D £12; alc D £16.
Special breaks available

Cwmirfon Lodge

LLANWRTYD WELLS, POWYS LD5 4TN
TEL: LLANWRTYD WELLS (05913) 217

A welcoming family home in the heart of Wales.

Andrew and Sheila Swindale started having people to stay at their attractive Victorian home in 1990. In true Wolsey Lodge style, it's like staying in a family house more as friends than as guests. Sheila has no set menus but cooks 'according to guests' taste, availability and my mood' – perhaps stuffed tomatoes followed by salmon and cucumber sauce and spiced pear pie.

The house is comfortable and relaxing, filled with smart but unostentatious antiques and with rugs on the parquet floors. The bedrooms in the house feature large, luxurious bathrooms. There are also five self-catering cottages for rent behind the house, named after birds.

◗ Open all year, exc Xmas

🔁 From Builth Wells take the A483 to Llandovery. At Llanwrtyd Wells turn right by the Drover's Rest, signed Abergwesyn. After 1 mile pass church on left and bear right. Cwmirfon Lodge is 2 miles further on the left, just after a farm. Private car park

🛏 1 twin, 1 double, 5 self-catering cottages; all with bathroom/WC, TV, room service, hair-dryer on request

◈ Dining-room, lounge, drying room; fishing (May to Sept) at hotel, river swimming, riding nearby

⊖ No wheelchair access; no guests under 16; no dogs; no smoking in bedrooms and discouraged in rest of hotel

▭ Access, Visa

£ Single occupancy of twin/double £36 to £42, twin/double £48 and £56; cottage rates £138 to £316 per week (2 to 5 people); deposit required. Set D £15

LLANYCHAER DYFED **MAP 6**

Penlan Oleu ☆

LLANYCHAER, FISHGUARD, PEMBROKESHIRE SA65 9TL
TEL: PUNCHESTON (0348) 881314

A remote but comfortable farmhouse.

'Absolute peace and quiet – only sound that of munching sheep,' enthuses a reader's recommendation. This is a lovely spot, within sight of the coast and views of St David's. The whitewashed farmhouse is simplicity itself; the Stuart-Lyons have been here for 12 years, giving up previous careers as an accountant and a catering lecturer. Ruth's culinary skills have been praised as 'excellent'. Menus include four or five choices at each course: a typical meal might consist of mushrooms with garlic, steak au poivre, and ginger and cream basket. There is also a separate bar, with cushioned high-backed benches as well as easy chairs.

The bedrooms are simply and prettily furnished, with flowery duvet covers and small *en-suite* bathrooms.

◗ Open all year, exc 25, 26 Dec

🔁 From Fishguard take the B4313 signed Maenclochog; follow the road for 2½ miles and go

through Llanychaer to the top of the hill. Turn right signposted Puncheston and follow signs to hotel. Private car park

🛏 1 single, 2 twin, 2 double; most with bathroom/WC, some with shower/WC; room service and hair-dryer on request

◈ Dining-room, bar, lounge, conservatory; fishing, golf, other sports nearby. Wheelchair access to hotel (1 step), dining-room and WC (unisex), 2 ground-floor bedrooms

⊖ No children under 11; no dogs; no smoking in dining-room

▭ Access, Visa

£ Single £18, single occupancy of twin/double £20, twin/double £36; deposit required. Alc L, D £14 to £16

LLECHWEDD GWYNEDD   **MAP 6**

Berthlwyd Hall ☆

LLECHWEDD, NR CONWY, GWYNEDD LL32 8DQ
TEL: ABERCONWY (0492) 592409   FAX: (0492) 572290

Victorian manor with some interesting bedrooms and a strong French influence.

A Victorian manor, the hall retains many of its original features, such as a galleried staircase, lots of stained glass and oak panelling in the entrance hall. At one stage it was converted into holiday flats; the Griffins, Brian and Joanna, have reconverted it, creating some huge bedrooms, like Room One, with its half-tester bed and bathroom adorned with plates. Other bedrooms are smaller but have distinctive features of their own – for example Number Three, with a Victorian bath inside the bedroom, or Room Four, with a bathroom tiled in original green Victorian tiles.

Downstairs, the accent is more French – wine posters adorn the walls, and a 140-year-old wine press stands in the dining-room. The menu also has a Gallic twist, with offerings like snails, and lamb with rosemary and minted claret sauce. The bar, cheerfully decorated with potted plants and plates, is more downmarket, with a pool table and buttonback chairs.

◐ Open all year

⤴ Entering Conwy over the bridge on the A55, go into the centre and take a left turn on to the Sychnant Pass. After 1 mile follow signs to the hall, Private car park

🛏 2 twin, 4 double, 1 four-poster, 1 family room, 1 suite; all with bathroom/WC, TV, room service, hair-dryer; trouser press, baby-listening

◈ 2 restaurants, 2 bars, lounge, games room; conference facilities (max 30 people non-residential, 9 residential); heated swimming-pool, croquet at hotel, fishing, golf, other sports nearby; babysitting

⊖ No wheelchair access; no dogs in public rooms; no smoking in 1 restaurant and some bedrooms

▭ Access, Diners, Visa

£ Single occupancy of twin/double £43, twin/double £50 to £75, four-poster £95, family room from £75; deposit required. Cooked B £4; set L £16.50, D £18.50; alc L, D £18 to £25. Special breaks available

LLWYNDAFYDD DYFED   **MAP 6**

Park Hall

CWMTYDU, LLWYNDAFYDD, NR NEW QUAY, DYFED SA44 6LG
TEL: NEW QUAY (0545) 560306

A friendly Victorian guesthouse in a peaceful part of Wales.

If you don't like Victoriana, avoid Park Hall like the plague. This remote Victorian gentleman's residence, with views of the sea peeking between the hills, has been restored in traditional style by Pete and Christine McDonnell. Original features such as gleaming fireplaces, polished wood and encaustic tiled floors are played up, while collections of wall-hung plates and old sewing machines evoke the Victorian magpie tendency. Boldly patterned papers and strong colours complete the picture. Dinner is taken in the conservatory dining-room; the four-course no-choice meal may comprise cream of vegetable soup with a hint of curry served with a cheese scone, and kebab of Welsh lamb with cranberry sauce, followed by a choice of desserts.

Bedrooms have brass beds or wooden four-posters and lacy throw-overs; Room Four also has an original Victorian bath. Christine is a warm, chatty hostess who used to be a florist; Pete was a hairdresser. Mr Smith is the old English sheepdog.

◖ Open all year

↗ Take A487 Aberystwyth to Cardigan road; at Synod Inn head towards Cardigan for 1 mile, turn right at crossroads to Llwyndafydd and Cwmtydu, follow for 2½ miles; at crossroads turn left to Llwyndafydd, turn right between the Crown and the shop; after 1½ miles Park Hall is on the left. Private car park

🛏 1 twin, 3 double, 1 four-poster; some with bathroom/WC, some with shower/WC; TV, room service, hair-dryer in all rooms

◈ Dining-room, bar, lounge, TV room; conference facilities (max 25 people non-residential); fishing, tennis, other sports nearby

⊖ No wheelchair access; smoking restricted

▭ Access, Amex, Diners, Visa

£ Single occupancy of twin/double £43, twin/double/four-poster £78; deposit required. Set D £14.50, alc D £17.50. Special breaks available

LLYSWEN POWYS   **MAP 6**

Llangoed Hall

LLYSWEN, BRECON, POWYS LD3 OYP
TEL: BRECON (0874) 754525   FAX: (0874) 754545

Beautifully restored country house with self-assured style.

Since buying Llangoed Hall, Sir Bernard Ashley has certainly lavished time and money on his dream. The house, redesigned by Clough William-Ellis, 1912, is a stylish place. An excellent personal art collection includes works by Dame Laura Knight, Augustus John and Whistler. A butler greets you as you arrive, and carries your bags to your room. The lounges are large enough to allow guests their own groupings of sofas and chairs round afternoon tea served on mahogany tables. Style and furnishings are kept within the family – Laura Ashley chintzes in self-assured good taste, nothing too flamboyant. Bedrooms are similar, and generally large, with room for items like a Georgian dining table and chairs.

For dinner there is a choice between a five-course set meal and the carte. One dinner in May consisted of quail with spinach, lentils, and port and grape sauce; fish with saffron butter sauce; passion-fruit sorbet; guinea-fowl with potato wafer, celeriac and coriander purée; and orange crème brûlée. Breakfasts also show adventure, with crab and laverbread fishcake and a muffin with grilled smoked salmon, poached egg, and hollandaise sauce.

◑ Open all year

⤴ 1½ mile north of Llyswen on the A470 towards Builth Wells. Private car park

🛏 2 single, 13 twin/double, 8 four-poster (inc 4 suites); all with bathroom/WC, TV, room service, hair-dryer, baby-listening; tea/coffee-making facilities on request

◈ 2 dining-rooms, 2 lounges, games room, library; conference facilities (max 23 people residential, 30 non-residential);

fishing, tennis, croquet at hotel, riding nearby. Wheelchair access to public areas only

⊖ No children under 8; no dogs (but kennelling available); no smoking in dining-rooms

▭ Access, Amex, Diners, Visa

£ Single £95, single occupancy of twin/double £95 to £185, twin/double £140 to £185, suites £185 to £285; deposit required. Set L £16.50, D £36.50; alc D £40. Special breaks available

---

MILEBROOK POWYS   **MAP 6**

Milebrook House

MILEBROOK, KNIGHTON, POWYS LD7 1LT
TEL: KNIGHTON (0547) 528632   FAX: (0547) 520509

An excellent base for exploring the Marches.

The small country house, a mixture of grey stone and red brick, has been in Rodney and Beryl Marsden's hands for eight years now, and their tender loving care shows in the pretty flower gardens to one side of the house and the kitchen vegetable gardens to the other. Inside, the predominant colour schemes are peach and blue, with flounced blinds in the dining-room and cushioned cane chairs in the bar. Bedrooms are a good size, with stripped pine furniture and reasonably sized bathrooms. One has an Edwardian brass bed.

Rodney runs the front-of-house and is hospitable to a fault, seeing to drinks and welcoming new arrivals with genuine warmth on a busy Sunday lunchtime. Beryl offers a choice of two dinner menus at different prices; cooking is mostly traditional with modern touches – for example, warm salad of scallops and bacon, chicken with mushrooms and tarragon, or duck breast with blackcurrant and green peppercorn sauce. If you need some exercise after wading through pudding as well, Offa's Dyke is only a mile or so up the road.

◑ Open all year

↗ 2 miles east of Knighton, Powys on the A4113. Private car park

🛏 2 twin, 4 double; all with bathroom/WC; TV in all rooms

◇ Dining-room, bar, lounge, drying room; conference facilities (max 20 people non-residential, 6 residential); trout fishing at hotel, other sports nearby

⊖ No wheelchair access; no children under 8; no dogs; no smoking in some public rooms and bedrooms

▭ Access, Visa

£ Single occupancy of twin/double £44, twin/double £62; deposit required. Set D £16; alc L £11, D £19 (prices till end 93). Special breaks available

---

MONMOUTH GWENT   **MAP 6**

Riverside Hotel ☆

CINDERHILL STREET, MONMOUTH, GWENT NP5 3EY
TEL: MONMOUTH (0600) 715577/713236

A larger-than-average pub-hotel with better-than-average facilities.

'Riverside' is perhaps stretching it a bit, for between the hotel and the river is a busy road and a car park, completely obscuring any views of the Monnow. Never mind – double-glazing manages to block out most of the traffic noise, and a real effort has been made to revamp the interior. The airy conservatory, with cane chairs, plenty of plants and botanical prints, contrasts with the olde-worlde air of the low-ceilinged restaurant, lit by brass carriage lamps and a couple of freestanding mock lampposts. The bar is clubbier. Bedrooms, both in the old part and the new extension, are very similar: reasonable size, pastel blues and pinks, smallish bathrooms.

The restaurant menu is fairly short, featuring staples such as Welsh lamb and salmon as well as nods in the direction of other influences – for example, duck with strawberry and brandy sauce. You can also eat more informally in the bar. Service is young, friendly and efficient.

◑ Open all year

↗ At the west end of town at the Rochfield Road at the bottom of the High Street by the Ancient Bridge. Private car park

🛏 9 twin, 6 double, 2 family rooms; most with bathroom/WC, remainder with shower/WC; TV, room service, hair-dryer, baby-listening in all rooms

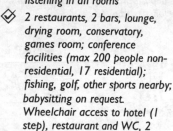 2 restaurants, 2 bars, lounge, drying room, conservatory, games room; conference facilities (max 200 people non-residential, 17 residential); fishing, golf, other sports nearby; babysitting on request. Wheelchair access to hotel (1 step), restaurant and WC, 2 ground-floor bedrooms specially

equipped for the disabled

⊖ No dogs in public rooms and in lobby of ground-floor bedrooms only; no smoking in restaurant

▭ Access, Amex, Visa

£ Single occupancy of twin/double £46 to £49, twin/double £59 to £66, family room rate on request; deposit required. Set D £13; alc L £4 to £15, D £4 to £25. Special breaks available

---

NANTGWYNANT GWYNEDD   **MAP 6**

Pen-y-gwryd Hotel

NANTGWYNANT, GWYNEDD LL55 4NT
TEL: LLANBERIS (0286) 870211

A small but popular landmark in climbing history.

The fortieth anniversary of the ascent of Everest was celebrated with much gusto at Pen-y-gwryd, for this is where Hillary and Tensing stayed when they were training for their great expedition. The hotel certainly feels a little isolated, huddling in the shadow of Snowdon. If it's lots of home comforts and facilities you're after, steer clear, for this is very much a walkers' and climbers' haunt. One bar is done out like a log cabin; old walkers' boots hang from a beam in another. It is all tempered with stylish touches like Welsh quilts thrown over the old wooden beds in the guest rooms.

The dining-room is quite smart in its simplicity, with upright leather chairs and white cloths; hearty dinners to satisfy the appetite of ravenous walkers might include potted shrimps followed by soup, lamb cutlets with vegetables, peach crumble and cheese. After dinner it's back to the panelled inner sanctum to swap climbers' tales.

◐ Closed Nov to New Year, and weekdays during Jan and Feb

↗ From Betws-y-coed take the A5 west to Capel Curig. Turn left at Capel Curig on to the A4086 — the inn is 4 miles further on at a T-junction, with Pen-y-gwryd lake in front. Private car park

🛏 3 single, 9 twin, 7 double, 1 four-poster/family room (with bathroom/WC); 4 public bathrooms; no tea/coffee-making facilities in rooms

◇ Dining-room, bar, lounge, games room, drying room; conference facilities (max 20 people non-residential and residential); unheated swimming-pool at hotel, other sports nearby. Wheelchair access to hotel, dining-room and WC (M,F), 1 ground-floor bedroom specially equipped for disabled people.

⊖ Dogs by arrangement; no smoking in dining-room

▭ None accepted

£ Single £19 to £23, single occupancy of twin/double £19 to £23, twin/double £35 to £46, four-poster/family room £46; deposit preferred. Set D £12; bar lunches from £3

NEWPORT DYFED   MAP 6

Cnapan

EAST STREET, NEWPORT, PEMBROKESHIRE SA42 0SY
TEL: NEWPORT (0239) 820575

Smart yet friendly family-run hotel, good for families.

This Georgian house has been run by Michael and Judy Cooper, plus Judy's parents John and Eluned Lloyd, for the past 10 years. The former doctor's house is halfway between Fishguard and Cardigan. Mother and daughter work together in the kitchen, conjuring up delights such as salmon and smoked fish mousse with melon, breast of duck with soya sauce, honey, ginger and apricot sauce, and bread-and-butter pudding with crunchy nutmeg crust – they're also open for morning coffee, light lunches and afternoon tea. Michael runs the bar, while John takes the role of *maître d'*.

The wall opposite the jolly rainbow-patterned bathroom is covered in family photos stretching back to the year dot. The general style is quite homely, with lots of china, pictures and other knick-knacks, but also smart, with careful colour co-ordinations and solid furnishings.

◐ Closed Feb, also 25, 26 Dec; restaurant closed Tues eve Mar to Oct

🔼 Centrally located on Newport's East Street (A487). Private car park

🛏 3 twin, 1 double, 1 family room; all with shower/WC, TV, room service, hair-dryer, baby-listening

◈ Restaurant, bar, lounge; fishing, golf, other sports nearby.

Wheelchair access to restaurant and WC (unisex) only

⊖ No dogs; no smoking in restaurant and discouraged in bedrooms

▭ Access, Visa

£ Single occupancy of twin/double £29, twin/double £48, family room £64 (4 people); deposit required. Alc L £8.50, D from £14

NEWPORT GWENT   MAP 6

Celtic Manor

COLDRA WOODS, NEWPORT, GWENT NP6 2YA
TEL: LLANWERN (0633) 413000   FAX: (0633) 412910

A business hotel given a touch of style by its nineteenth-century origin.

Thinly screened from the M4 by a veil of trees, the original building dates from 1863, with all the elaborate plasterwork ceilings and grandiose marble fireplaces that typify the period. The favourite tables in the oak-panelled restaurant are by the stained-glass windows, lit from behind at night so that you can gaze at the scene of the Prince of Wales's investiture while you dine on lamb's sweetbreads with deep-fried vegetables or grilled cod fillet with herb crust and shellfish sauce. If you prefer something less formal, the airy Patio Restaurant in the conservatory extension serves pasta, pizzas and grills.

The modern part of the hotel includes the lobby and the bedrooms, which are all of standard business layout and style. Because of its size, the hotel is a popular venue for wedding receptions and parties.

◑ *Open all year*

⤢ *Leave the M4 at Junction 24 and take the A48 towards Newport. The hotel is 500 yards along this road on the right. Private car park*

🛏 *1 single, 25 twin, 36 double, 2 four-poster, 4 family rooms, 6 suites; all with bathroom/WC, TV, room service, hair-dryer, trouser press; some rooms air-conditioned; baby-listening by arrangement*

◈ *2 restaurants (1 air-conditioned), 2 bars, lounge; conference facilities (max 300 people non-residential, 75 residential); riding, sauna/solarium, heated swimming-pool, gym at hotel, other sports nearby; babysitting. Wheelchair access to hotel (ramp) and restaurant, 16 ground-level bedrooms*

⊖ *No dogs*

▭ *Access, Amex, Diners, Visa*

£ *Single £85, single occupancy of twin/double £85, twin/double £99, four-poster £125, suite £150, family room £99. Continental B £6, cooked B £9; set L £14, D £20; alc L, D £25. Special breaks available*

NORTHOP CLWYD   **MAP 6**

Soughton Hall

NORTHOP, MOLD, CLWYD CH7 6AB
TEL: NORTHOP (0352) 840811   FAX: (0352) 840382

A stylish hotel in a well-restored, slightly eccentric bishops' palace.

It's worth pausing a moment in front of the Hall, a curious but not inelegant amalgam of Islamic turrets, Gothic tracery, quoined corners and mullioned windows. Inside, the Rodenhurst family has done an excellent restoration job, making the most of features such as the buffed walnut floors, elaborate baroque fireplaces and the magnificent high beamed ceiling with sunken frescoes in the dining-room. For relaxing, you can choose from a series of small rooms on the ground floor, from the library with Chinese-style wallpaper and Japanese prints to the entrance hall hung with family photos and tapestries. The drawing-room on the first floor is truly stately in its proportions, with a Chinese carpet, light wood panelling and a gilt mirror above the fireplace. Bedrooms are individually furnished; the top of the range Mahogany Room has half-tester drapes in rosy chintz, an antique wardrobe and dressing-table.

The table d'hôte menu has only two choices of starter and main course – perhaps black pudding with apple compote and mustard sauce followed by seafood on cucumber with lemon butter sauce and tomatoes. Service is efficient but can be cool.

◑ *Open all year, exc first half Jan; restaurant closed Sun eve*

↗ *3 miles north of Mold. Take the A5119 from Mold or Northop; the Hall is off this road. Private car park*

🛏 *5 twin, 6 double, 1 four-poster; all with bathroom/WC, TV, room service, hair-dryer, trouser press*

◈ *3 restaurants, bar, 3 lounges, breakfast room, library; conference facilities (max 50*

people non-residential, 12 residential); tennis, at hotel, other sports nearby

⊖ *No wheelchair access; no children under 12; no dogs*

▭ *Access, Amex, Visa*

£ *Single occupancy rate on request, twin/double £80 to £99, four-poster £99 to £150; deposit preferred. Set L £16.50, D £24.50; alc L, D £18 to £35. Special breaks available*

PENALLY DYFED   **MAP 6**

Penally Abbey

PENALLY, NR TENBY, PEMBROKESHIRE SA70 7PY
TEL: TENBY (0834) 843033   FAX: (0834) 844714

Elegant country house with lovely views and friendly hosts.

'We try to make the guests feel more as if they are at a house party rather than staying at a hotel,' say Steve and Elleen Warren, and the atmosphere at this unusual eighteenth-century country house is certainly relaxed – breakfast is served until 11am. The main building has a lot of character, thanks to the unusual Gothic ogee-shaped doors and windows, elegant white pillars, an original Adam fireplace in the lounge, and shiny polished marquetry tables in the restaurant and some of the bedrooms. It is very much a hands-on affair: Elleen makes most of the decisions about décor, and indeed many of the furnishings, such as curtains, herself. She also does the cooking, in a fairly traditional vein, with dishes such as crab thermidor and breast of chicken with grapes, tarragon, cream and wine.

The nicest bedrooms are at the front of the house – four-posters, most of them – with superb views of the golf course and the sea.

◑ *Open all year*

↗ *1½ miles from Tenby, just off the A4139 Pembroke coast road Private car park*

🛏 *1 twin, 4 double, 7 four-poster, family rooms available; all with*

bathroom/WC, TV, hair-dryer, baby-listening

◈ *Restaurant, bar, lounge, drying room, games room, conservatory; conference facilities (max 14 people non-residential, 12* residential); heated swimming-pool at hotel, other sports nearby. Wheelchair access to hotel (1 step), restaurant and 2 ground-floor bedrooms

⊖ No children under 7 in restaurant eves; no dogs; no smoking in bedrooms

▭ Access, Visa

£ Single occupancy of twin/double £84, twin/double/four-poster £84, family room £94; deposit required. Set L £12, D £22; alc L £12, D £22

PENMAENPOOL GWYNEDD   MAP 6

Penmaenuchaf Hall ☆

PENMAENPOOL, DOLGELIAU, GWYNEDD LL40 1YB
TEL: DOLGELLAU (0341) 422129 (and fax)

Comfortable new country-house hotel in a tranquil spot.

Once the home of a Victorian cotton magnate, Penmaenuchaf Hall is a new addition to the clutch of Welsh country-house hotels. In the hall, proprietor Mark Watson has followed the increasingly popular idea of dispensing with a reception desk, and a real fire glows invitingly on cold days. The lounge and small library show more obvious traces of a designer hand, with seagrass matting on the floor and lots of bound sets of the classics. A Van Gogh copy hangs above the fireplace. Bedrooms are a good size and highly individual, but large beds, firm mattresses and hand-crafted furniture seem common to all.

Our inspection meal in the small panelled dining-room started with a 'risotto' of Thai and wild rice – a delicious mound of grains spiked with Chinese mushrooms and surrounded by a creamy herb sauce. A duo of sorbets was followed by goose roasted in honey and a slightly flavourless strawberry gratin and coulis.

◑ Open all year

⤴ Turn off the A470 at the Dolgellau bypass on to the A493 Tywyn road. The hotel entrance is 1 mile on the left. Private car park

🛏 5 twin, 7 double, 1 four-poster, 1 suite, family rooms available; all with bathroom/WC, TV, room service, hair-dryer, baby-listening; mini-bar in some rooms

◇ 3 dining-rooms, bar, 2 lounges; drying room, library, conservatory, games room, boot/rod/gun room; conference facilities (max 70 people non-residential, 14 residential); snooker at hotel, fishing, golf, other sports nearby

⊖ No wheelchair access; dogs in hall only; no smoking in some public rooms

▭ Access, Visa

£ Single occupancy of twin/double £48 to £95, twin/double £95 to £140, four-poster £140, family room rate from £140, suite £140; deposit required. Set D £21.50; alc L £12.50. Special breaks available

PONTFAEN DYFED   **MAP 6**

Tregynon Farmhouse

GWAUN VALLEY, NR FISHGUARD, PEMBROKESHIRE SA65 9TU
TEL: NEWPORT (0239) 820531   FAX: (0239) 820808

Good-value rustic accommodation and excellent food.

This collection of sixteenth-century farm buildings can certainly prove mysterious to find – owners Peter and Jane Heard had a long battle for permission to erect even the limited signs that there are. However, they send you detailed instructions when you make a booking, and if you get lost any farmer in the area can point you in the right direction. The once-derelict buildings, parts of which are constructed from the same stone as Stonehenge, have been sturdily renovated. The interior is cosily rustic, with low beams and arrangements of corn dollies and dried flowers. Bedrooms in the main house are cheaper – and smaller – but many regulars prefer the rooms in the separate cottage, with their high mansard ceilings and bigger bathrooms.

Jane does the cooking, and the menus feature products from the Heards' own smokehouse – smoked gammon steaks with mushroom and white wine sauce, and home-smoked bacon. 'Delicious and highly imaginative' is how one guest described the food, though she also felt that it was 'rather hard to escape fellow guests and there is a slight sense of keeping everyone up if you don't go to bed by 10pm.'

◑ *Open all year; exc 2 weeks in winter*

⤢ *At intersection of B4313 and B4329, take B4313 towards Fishguard, then take first right and follow signs. Private car park*

🛏 *4 double, 4 family rooms (inc 1 four-poster); most with bathroom/WC, some with shower/WC; TV, hair-dryer, baby-listening in all rooms*

◈ *2 dining-rooms, bar, lounge; conference facilities (max 20*

people non-residential, 8 residential); golf, fishing, other sports nearby. Wheelchair access to hotel and restaurant, 8 ground-floor bedrooms

⊖ *No children in dining-room eves; no dogs; no smoking in dining-rooms and bedrooms*

▭ *Access, Visa*

£ *Single occupancy of double £23, double/family room £45 to £64; deposit required. Set D £14. Special breaks available*

 Denotes somewhere you can rely on a good meal – either the hotel features in the 1994 edition of our sister publication, The Good Food Guide, *or our inspectors thought the cooking impressive, whether particularly competent home cooking or more lavish cuisine.*

PORTFIELD GATE DYFED MAP 6

Sutton Lodge

PORTFIELD GATE, HAVERFORDWEST, DYFED SA62 3LN
TEL: HAVERFORDWEST (0437) 768548   FAX: (0437) 760826

Elegant cooking and solicitous bonhomie *in peaceful spot.*

Paul and Stan have been running this elegant Victorian restaurant-with-rooms for five years now. Paul runs the front of house with cheerful joviality; Stan works more behind the scenes, tending the fruit trees and herbs in the garden, or watering the myriad plants in the conservatory. Most importantly, he also cooks, and his no-choice dinners are real labours of love. He describes over drinks at 8pm what he has in store for you – perhaps tomato and pine kernel soup, oriental filo chicken, and black and white chocolate mousse. The tiny dining-room contains the original Victorian range and black and terracotta encaustic tiles. Colours and furnishings throughout are in strong colours, complemented by interesting paintings and other pieces of art.

Bedrooms are comfortable, with firm beds and fluffy rugs, and good-sized bathrooms. Rooms at the front have window seats built into the bay, from where you can admire the surrounding countryside.

◑ Closed Jan to Mar, and Sept; restaurant closed Sun eve

⤢ From Haverfordwest take the B4341 Broad Haven road to the village of Portfield. Take the road to Sutton where directions are signposted. Private car park

🛏 1 single, 3 double; all with bathroom/WC, TV; hair-dryer on request

◈ 2 dining-rooms, lounge, drying room, conservatory; golf, tennis, other sports nearby

⊖ No wheelchair access; no children under 14; no dogs; no smoking in dining-rooms and discouraged in bedrooms

▭ None accepted

£ Single and single occupancy of twin/double £41, twin/double £82; deposit required. Set D £22

PORTHKERRY SOUTH GLAMORGAN MAP 6

Egerton Grey

PORTHKERRY, NR CARDIFF, SOUTH GLAMORGAN CF6 9BZ
TEL: RHOOSE (0446) 711666   FAX: (0446) 711690

Self-assured country house with huge original Edwardian baths.

The lovely Edwardian country house, partly castellated, has glimpses of the sea through the arches of the viaduct. Inside, original features such as oak panelling are complemented by a host of antique display cabinets, original oils and glossy magazines; in the drawing-room, with its blue and white coved ceiling, there is a grand piano, a large marble fireplace and racehorse prints. Bedrooms are named after their previous function (Nursery, for example). Bathrooms have huge Edwardian baths.

The dining-room's intimacy is enhanced by candlelight; families have a choice of eating separately in the library. Food is hearty and tasty: a spring inspection meal consisted of creamy potato, dill and chive soup, followed by noisettes of lamb with a mint, parsley and honey glaze, and good Welsh cheeses.

◑ Open all year

🔁 Leave M4 at Junction 33 and follow signs to airport past Barry. Turn left at small roundabout at airport and left again after 500 yards. Private car park

🛏 1 single, 2 twin, 3 double, 1 four-poster, 2 family rooms, 1 suite; all with bathroom/WC exc 1 single with shower/WC; TV, room service, hair-dryer, trouser press in all rooms

◈ 2 restaurants, 2 lounges, library, conservatory; conference facilities (max 40 people non-

residential, 10 residential); tennis, croquet at hotel, other sports nearby; babysitting by arrangement. Wheelchair access to restaurant and WC (M, F) only

⊖ No dogs in public rooms; no smoking in 1 restaurant

▭ Access, Amex, Diners, Visa

£ Single £50, single occupancy of twin/double £70, twin/double £75, four-poster £120, family room £95, suite £120; deposit required. Set L £19.50, D £22.50. Special breaks available

PORTMEIRION GWYNEDD MAP 6

Hotel Portmeirion

PORTMEIRION, GWYNEDD LL48 6ET
TEL: PENRHYNDEUDRAETH (0766) 770228   FAX: (0766) 771331

A comfortable, unique hotel in an extraordinary setting.

The stunning and highly individual restoration of the building after the fire that gutted it in 1981 is worth seeing. The Mirror Room, originally the drawing-room, now feels more rococo than Victorian, painted a pale turquoise with gilded coving and mirrors and Regency-style chairs. The great limestone fireplace in the hall is a copy of the original, and the ornate wooden arches and architraves in the library were saved from the fire and restored. A newer scheme can be seen in the Jaipur Bar, with its elephant prints and carved wooden and brass chairs and doors.

The bedrooms (known as Houses) take inspiration from all round the world: House Five has an Indian-style four-poster bed and crewel-work rug; House One (no sea view) has a Chinese-style blue and white colour scheme.

The dining-room is based on the design of a 1930s ocean liner, with curving windows overlooking the estuary and columns rescued from a wrecked ketch. One reader complained of a choice of only three main courses at dinner, but on our inspection visit there were seven on offer, including brill grilled with aubergines, sun-dried tomatoes and olive oil, and loin of Welsh lamb with a tagliatelle of leeks and roast radish.

◐ Open all year, exc 9 Jan to 5 Feb

⬈ Mid-way between Penrhyndeudraeth and Porthmadog. Leave the A487 at Minffordd. Private car park

🛏 11 twin, 7 double, 2 four-poster, 4 family rooms, 10 suites (most rooms in village); all with bathroom/WC, TV, room service, hair-dryer; tea/coffee-making facilities in village rooms

✧ Restaurant, 2 bars, 3 lounges; conference facilities (max 100 people non-residential, 35 residential); tennis, croquet,

heated outdoor swimming-pool (May to Sept) at hotel, other sports nearby; babysitting

⊖ No wheelchair access; no dogs; no smoking in some public rooms

▢ Access, Amex, Diners, Visa

£ Single occupancy of twin/double £80 to £102, twin/double £96 to £112, four-poster £107 to £123, family room £111 to £123, suite £96 to £112, village room £56 to £67; deposit required. Continental B £6, cooked B £8.50; set L £13.50, D £25. Special breaks available

PRESTEIGNE POWYS   **MAP 6**

Radnorshire Arms

HIGH STREET, PRESTEIGNE, POWYS LD8 2BE
TEL: PRESTEIGNE (0544) 267406   FAX: (0544) 260418

An old coaching-inn with a characterful bar.

The Radnorshire Arms used to belong to Sir Christopher Hatton, friend and courtier of Elizabeth I. The pretty half-timbered building, with lawns and well-kept gardens behind, certainly has character: the bar, with sloping beams and leaded windowpanes, has brass warming pans and shiny copper-topped tables; the small lounge has its original Jacobean panelling. The dining-room has a higher ceiling and a large stone fireplace. Here you can dine on dishes such as avocado, apple and walnut salad and steamed halibut with lemon and basil sauce. Alternatively, if you're reluctant to leave the cosiness of the bar, there are daily specials chalked up, which come in hearty portions.

Bedrooms in the main building are suitably done out in heavy wooden furniture and half-tester beds. Most of them, however, are in a chalet-like annexe across the way; these are more functional, with dark reproduction furniture.

◐ Open all year

⬈ In the centre of Presteigne. Private car park

🛏 8 twin/double, 8 annexe rooms; all with bathroom/WC, TV, hair-dryer, trouser press, baby-listening

✧ Restaurant, bar, lounge; conference facilities (max 20 people non-residential); fishing, golf, other sports nearby; babysitting by arrangement

⊖ No wheelchair access; no dogs in public rooms; no smoking in some bedrooms

☐ Access, Amex, Diners, Visa

£ Single occupancy of twin/double
£65, twin/double £75; deposit

required. Continental B £6,
cooked B £8.50; set L £9/£10,
D £16

PWLLHELI GWYNEDD   **MAP 6**

Plas Bodegroes

NEFYN ROAD, PWLLHELI, GWYNEDD LL53 5TH
TEL: PWLLHELI (0758) 612363   FAX: (0758) 701247

Excellent restaurant-with-rooms that pays as much attention to accommodation as food.

Christopher Chown and his Faroëse wife Gunna have been running this restaurant-with-rooms for seven years; the pretty cream Georgian house and enormous old beech trees have been here for considerably longer. The six acres of gardens and woodland are also well-established. Inside, the house has a modern feel: plain carpets, original paintings, clear colours and fresh flowers are the form. The restaurant is the best example, with its light parquet floor and powder-blue walls hung with paintings. Christopher's food does justice to the setting: five finely judged courses are on offer. A warm salad of monkfish, Parma ham and mushrooms might be followed by steamed fillet of brill with cucumber and crayfish sauce, and then roast guinea-fowl with mango and sweet-corn on home-made noodles. The small lounge has peachy chintz sofas.

Bedrooms are furnished with antiques; one small double has white tent-like drapes hanging from the ceiling, others have pine, brass or four-poster beds.

◑ Closed Nov to Feb and Mons
(exc public hols)

↗ From Bangor take the A487 and
A499 to Pwllheli. Plas Bodegroes
is on the A497 Nefyn road, one
mile west of Pwllheli. Private car
park

🛏 1 single, 2 twin, 3 double, 2
four-poster; all with bathroom/
WC, TV, room service, hair-
dryer, baby-listening; no tea/
coffee-making facilities in rooms

◇ Restaurant, breakfast room, bar,
lounge; conference facilities

(max 15 people non-residential,
8 residential); fishing, golf, other
sports nearby. Wheelchair access
to restaurant and WC (unisex)
only

⊖ No dogs in public rooms;
smoking in lounge only

☐ Access, Amex, Visa

£ Single £45 to £50, single
occupancy of twin/double £55 to
£65, twin/double £60 to £95,
four-poster £80 to £115; deposit
required. Set D £30. Special
breaks available

We mention those hotels that don't accept dogs; guide dogs, however, are almost always an exception. Telephone ahead to make sure.

REYNOLDSTON WEST GLAMORGAN　　　　**MAP 6**

Fairyhill Country House

REYNOLDSTON, GOWER, SWANSEA, WEST GLAMORGAN SA3 1BS
TEL: GOWER (0792) 390139　FAX: (0792) 391358

*Superb seclusion and hard-working hosts on the lovely Gower
Peninsula.*

The Fraynes have now been here for nearly 10 years, and the restoration
goes on. You have to look at the before-and-after pictures in the
photograph album to appreciate the amount of work that has gone into
the place. The resulting plainness of the public rooms may appeal to
some, prove off-putting to others. The Welsh dresser loaded with plates
in the lobby and a similar piece of furniture that belonged to John's
grandmother take pride of place in the kitchen of one of the converted
stable cottages. The bedrooms, too, are homely rather than swanky; 211
is huge, with a green and white décor and lovely views over the gardens.
The former billiard room is now a restaurant, with dinner choices such as
grilled goats' cheese salad with bacon and pine nuts and sautéed rabbit in
Marsala with pesto noodles. The food seems to be well appreciated, as
resident Welsh sheepdog Celyn has grown fat on the chocolate truffles
proffered by satiated guests. If you prefer to do your own thing, the
cottages might be the answer.

◖ Open all year, exc 23 Dec to 1
Jan

↗ Leave the M4 at Junction 47 and
follow sign to Swansea. At the
second roundabout take right
turn and follow signs to
Gowerton. At the lights in
Gowerton turn right and take the
B4295 North Gower road
through to Oldwalls. After
passing the Greyhound Inn,
Fairyhill is 1 mile further on.
Private car park

⇌ 3 single, 8 double, 4 cottages;
some with bathroom/WC, most
with shower/WC; TV, hair-dryer
in all rooms; trouser press in 1
room

◈ 2 dining-rooms, bar, lounge,
conservatory, drying room;
fishing at hotel

⊖ No wheelchair access; no
children under 5 in dining-rooms
eves; no dogs in public rooms; no
smoking in dining-rooms

▭ Access, Visa

£ Single £65, single occupancy of
twin/double £65, twin/double
£75 to £85, cottage £120;
deposit required. Sun L £13; alc
D £22

---

*Where we know an establishment accepts credit cards, we list them. There
may be a surcharge if you pay by credit card. It is always best to check
whether the card you want to use is acceptable when booking.*

ROSSETT CLWYD   **MAP 6**

Llyndir Hall

LLYNDIR LANE, ROSSETT, CLWYD LL12 0AY
TEL: CHESTER (0244) 571648   FAX: (0244) 571258

A pleasant and comfortable business hotel with fitness facilities.

Llyndir Hall is an ideally positioned business hotel with good facilities. The original cream-coloured building dates from 1810, with the long windows almost reaching ground level being a particular feature. A newer extension holds more bedrooms. Inside, the furnishings are good-quality, ruched and swagged chintzy fabrics. A conservatory addition to the Garden Restaurant lightens the room; here you can dine on dishes such as sole and salmon terrine with coriander dressing and duck with apples and champagne sauce.

The atmosphere is noticeably more casual in the 'trimnasium', where you can work off the stress of the rat race on the weights, in the pool or on the sunbeds. There is also an informal bar with wicker chairs and tables. Bedrooms have every comfort, occasionally eschewing business-formula pastels and chintzes for colour schemes of a brighter hue. Service is very helpful.

◐ Open all year

⤢ From Chester take the A483 towards Wrexham. At the junction with the A55, follow signs to Pulford. Continue through Pulford to Rossett and follow signs for the hotel on the right. Private car park

⇌ 6 single, 16 twin, 15 double, 1 suite, family rooms available; all with bathroom/WC, TV, room service, hair-dryer, trouser press, baby-listening

◈ Dining-room, 2 bars, snack bar, lounge; conference facilities (max 150 people non-residential, 38 residential); leisure club, gym, heated swimming-pool, sauna/solarium at hotel, other sports nearby. Wheelchair access to hotel (2 steps) and dining-room, 10 ground-floor bedrooms, 1 specially equipped for disabled people

⊖ No dogs

▭ Access, Amex, Diners, Visa

£ Single £74, single occupancy of twin/double £74, twin/double £110, suite £155. Cooked B £7, continental B £4.50; set L £12.50, D £17.50; alc L, D £25.50. Special breaks available

---

RUTHIN CLWYD   **MAP 6**

Gorphwysfa

8A CASTLE STREET, RUTHIN, CLWYD LL15 1DP
TEL: RUTHIN (0824) 702748

A friendly bed and breakfast in an ancient, characterful house.

Castle Street is apparently the oldest street in Ruthin, lined with neat but crooked buildings leading up from the town centre. Walter and Eleanor Jones have lived in their half-timbered fifteenth-century house since 1989.

The large, galleried entrance hall is panelled and carved with rabbits and horses' heads. Equally atmospheric is the breakfast room, with a huge inglenook and a large print of the Waterloo Cup, a coursing event that used to be held outside Liverpool. The lounge, at the front of the house, is plainer, with a high beamed ceiling and wooden shutters. There is also a small reading area off the hall with sofas, a fireplace and plenty of books. Of the three bedrooms, one is vast, running the full length of the house – 'more like a dormitory', comments a reader. It manages to hold three armchairs in addition to the bed. The other two bedrooms are smaller and simpler and share a bathroom. Only bed and breakfast is on offer, but the town centre isn't far away.

◐ Open all year

⤴ In the centre of Ruthin. Castle Street runs between the Nat West bank and an estate agents. On-street parking between 6pm and 8am; public car parks nearby

🛏 1 twin, 1 double, 1 family room; family room with bathroom/WC

◈ Breakfast room, lounge; golf, riding, other sports nearby

⊖ No wheelchair access

▭ None accepted

£ Single £15, double/family £29 to £32

ST BRIDE'S WENTLLOOG GWENT   **MAP 6**

West Usk Lighthouse

LIGHTHOUSE ROAD, ST BRIDE'S WENTLLOOG, NEWPORT, GWENT NP1 9SF
TEL: NEWPORT (0633) 810126/815860   FAX: (0633) 815582

Offbeat, quirky accommodation.

Owners Frank and Danielle Sheahan have installed a flotation tank, a darkened chamber where you are buoyed up by nine inches of water saturated with Epsom salts, in their lighthouse home. Other options include aromatherapy and meditation. Even if you don't fancy these modish delights the location gives a great feeling of escape.

If you are expecting one of those tall red and white stripy columnar jobs you'll be disappointed, but the two floors of this 50-foot-diameter building come with a staunch historical pedigree. Wedge-shaped bedrooms contain evidence of Frank's previous existence in the music business – a guitar in one, hi-fi in another – and are decked out with wicker and pine furniture and dried flowers. Evening meals – lasagne, steak, moussaka and vegetarian options – are served on request; service is friendly and very casual.

◑ Open all year

⤴ Leave the M4 at Junction 28 and take the B4239 to St Bride's. Turn left into private road at sign 'unique B&B'. Private car park

🛏 3 double, 1 four-poster, 1 family room; all with shower/WC, TV, trouser press; hair-dryer on request

◈ Dining-room, bar, lounge, lamp room; conference facilities (max 15 people non-residential, 6 residential); fishing, flotation tank at hotel, other sports nearby

⊖ No wheelchair access; dogs by arrangement only; no smoking

▭ Access, Visa

£ Single occupancy of twin/double £25 to £35, twin/double £42, four-poster £50, family room rate on request; deposit required. Set L, D £6.50. Special breaks available

---

TALSARNAU GWYNEDD   **MAP 6**

Hotel Maes-y-Neuadd

TALSARNAU, NR HARLECH, GWYNEDD LL47 6YA
TEL: HARLECH (0766) 780200   FAX: (0766) 780211

A well-converted manor house run with friendliness and flair.

The plaudits continue to roll in for this 'mansion in the meadow': 'remains a delight', 'very peaceful', 'most enjoyable'. The Horsfall and Slatter families are celebrating their twelfth year here, and their sympathetic treatment of this old Welsh slate and granite mansion earns grateful appreciation from guests: a graceful skylight brightens the lobby considerably, and the four bedrooms in the converted coach-house are a model of their kind, with exposed beams and wood-burning stoves in the upper suites. The long, low drawing-room has a very mixed collection of work by local artists adorning its walls. Bedrooms like Meirion and Artro look across to the coast.

The menu, changed daily, is technically a set five-course affair, though the dessert stage comprises three sweets plus cheese. On our inspection in late May dinner started with salmon and chive yogurt with cucumber and mixed salad, followed by leek and potato soup, halibut and wild mushroom baked in filo pastry on a bed of creamed leek, pork parcels stuffed with apricots and sage wrapped in courgette on a pool of apple jus, and then diverse desserts.

◑ Open all year

⤴ 3½ miles north of Harlech. Leave the B4573, take the right turn with the hotel sign on the corner. Follow this lane for ½ mile to hotel. Private car park

🛏 1 single, 4 twin, 6 double, 1 four-poster, 2 annexe rooms, 2 suites; all with bathroom/WC, exc single with shower/WC; TV, room service, hair-dryer in all rooms; no tea/coffee-making facilities in rooms

◈ 2 restaurants, bar, lounge, drying room, conservatory; conference facilities (max 50 people non-residential, 16 residential); croquet at hotel,

other sports nearby. Wheelchair
access to hotel (1 step),
restaurant and WC (M,F), 3
ground-floor bedrooms

● No children under 7 in
restaurant eves; no dogs in
public rooms; no smoking

▭ Access, Amex, Diners, JCB, Visa

£ Single £48, single occupancy of
twin/double £89, twin/double/
four-poster from £99, annexe
room from £99, suite from £119;
deposit required. Set L £11.50, D
£20. Special breaks available

TALYLLYN GWYNEDD   **MAP 6**

Minffordd Hotel

TALYLLYN, TYWYN, GWYNEDD LL36 9AJ
TEL: CORRIS (0654) 761665   FAX: (0654) 761517

Small and friendly family-run hotel with excellent home cooking.

A low white seventeenth-century drovers' inn, Minffordd has a small lily
pond at the entrance, a paddock of sheep next to the garden, and Cader
Idris rearing up behind. Inside, the public rooms are informal and
unpretentious, in keeping with the management style. Some are a little
dark – the wicker-chaired sun room is more uplifting. The restaurant is
small but has well-spaced tables. Jonathan's food is good home cooking
along traditional lines, with only two or perhaps three choices. On one
evening in May, for example, you could choose Welsh onion soup, hot
prawn creams or ogen melon, followed by beef Wellington with mushroom wine sauce or poached salmon with Lady Llanover sauce. Desserts
are the likes of Bakewell tart and Sussex pond pudding.

Bedrooms are simply decorated, all with Welsh quilts. Some are quite
small, but make full use of all nooks and crannies.

◑ Closed Jan and Feb and
weekdays in Nov and Dec

↗ At the junction of the A487 and
B4405, mid-way between
Dolgellau and Machynlleth.
Private car park

🛏 3 twin, 3 double; all with
bathroom/WC, exc 1 double
with shower/WC; room service,
hair-dryer in all rooms

◇ Dining-room, bar, lounge, sun

room, drying room; fishing, other
sports nearby

● No wheelchair access; no
children under 3; no dogs;
smoking in bar only

▭ Access, Diners, Visa

£ Single occupancy of twin/double
£59, twin/double £98 (rates inc
dinner); deposit required. Set D
£17 (1993 prices). Special
breaks available

THREE COCKS POWYS MAP 6

Three Cocks Hotel

THREE COCKS, NR BRECON, POWYS LD3 0SL
TEL: GLASBURY (0497) 847215

Continental flavours and a warm welcome in a restaurant-with-rooms at the foot of the Black Mountains.

'A lovely welcome and every attention,' reports one satisfied reader on this 550-year-old ivy-clad hostelry. For Michael and Marie-Jeanne Winstone produce restaurant menus featuring dishes such as Ardennes ham with onions pickled in honey as well as classic combinations, maybe asparagus and smoked salmon mousse. Fish comes fresh from Cornwall. Dinners have been praised as 'outstanding', with extra helpings of everything on offer: 'Marie-Jeanne also found time to introduce me to the delights of Belgian beers, of which they have an extensive selection available.'

The residents' lounge (wood panelling, squashy sofas) is more elegant than the rustic restaurant (unplastered walls hung with tapestries); there's another lounge downstairs should numbers spill over. Bedrooms are simpler, with lots of uneven walls and ceilings, beams, and heavy wooden and brass beds covered in pretty patchwork-style quilts.

◑ Closed Dec and Jan; restaurant closed Tue eve

▧ On the A438 between Brecon (11 miles) and Hereford (27 miles). Private car park

🛏 3 twin, 4 double, family rooms available; all with bathroom/WC; hair-dryer on request; no tea/coffee-making facilities in rooms

◈ Restaurant, bar, lounge, TV room, drying room

⊖ No wheelchair access; no dogs

▭ Access, Visa

£ Single occupancy of twin/double £36 to £60, twin/double £60. Set L, D £23. Special breaks available

TINTERN GWENT MAP 6

Parva Farmhouse

TINTERN, CHEPSTOW, GWENT NP6 6SQ
TEL: TINTERN (0291) 689411   FAX: (0291) 689557

A friendly small hotel with good river views.

This seventeenth-century farmhouse was bought five years ago by Dereck and Vickie Stubbs. By adding an extra floor to increase the number of bedrooms they changed the emphasis from restaurant-with-rooms to more of a fully fledged hotel. Dereck does the cooking: his menus are largely traditional, along the lines of chilled melon with port and kiwi fruit, followed by half a duck with brandy and black cherry sauce. Local salmon crops up quite a lot.

The lounge, with armchairs and chesterfield sofas, has a cosy wood-burning stove and an honesty drinks trolley. The bedrooms vary in size, outlook and facilities: Number Three has a four-poster bed plus a single; from Number Five you can watch the river drift past.

◑ *Open all year*

↗ *On the northern edge of Tintern village on the A466, 50 yards from the banks of the River Wye. Private car park*

🛏 *2 twin, 3 double, 2 four-poster, 2 family rooms; most with bathroom/WC, some with shower/WC; TV, room service, hair-dryer, baby-listening in all rooms*

◇ *Restaurant, bar, lounge; drying facilities; conference facilities (max 15 people residential and*

non-residential); cycle hire at hotel, fishing, riding, other sports nearby

⊖ *No wheelchair access; no dogs in public rooms*

▭ *Access, Visa*

£ *Single occupancy of double £32 to £39, double £48 to £58, four-poster £68, family room rate on request (children under 12 free if sharing parents' room but meals charged as taken); deposit required. Set D £16.50; alc D £16. Special breaks available*

WELSH HOOK DYFED   **MAP 6**

Stone Hall ☆

WELSH HOOK, WOLF'S CASTLE, PEMBROKESHIRE SA62 5NS
TEL: LETTERSTON (0348) 840212   FAX: (0348) 840815

Peaceful restaurant-with-rooms in the best French tradition.

The whitewashed house was originally part of a large estate covering 15 parishes; now it's down to 10 acres, including plenty of woodland. Inside, there's a mixture of periods and styles. The oldest (600 years) and most traditional part is the restaurant and bar, where you'll find stone- and slate-flagged floors, low wooden beams and a huge fireplace and range; after this the high ceiling and airy spaciousness of the breakfast room, added in Victorian times, comes as quite a surprise.

Bedrooms contain a mixture of furniture both old and new and are fairly plain but comfortable; one has an interesting circular window, others have views of the pretty gardens. The food, betraying Martine Watson's French origins, is hearty bourgeois cooking, with dishes such as snails with mushrooms, garlic and cream sauce, or confit de canard.

◑ *Open all year, exc 2 weeks late Nov/early Dec; restaurant closed Sun and Mon eves*

↗ *Take the turning west off the A40, 8 miles north of Haverfordwest. Welsh Hook is*

1½ miles from the A40. Private car park

🛏 *2 single, 1 twin, 2 double; some with bathroom/WC, some with shower/WC; TV, room service in all rooms; hair-dryer on request*

Restaurant, dining-room, bar, lounge; conference facilities (max 30 people non-residential, 8 residential); fishing, riding, other sports nearby

● No wheelchair access; no dogs

▭ Access, Amex, Visa

£ Single £46, single occupancy of twin/double £52, twin/double £63; deposit required. Set D £6; alc D £20. Special breaks available

---

WHITEBROOK GWENT   **MAP 6**

Crown at Whitebrook

WHITEBROOK, NR MONMOUTH, GWENT NP5 4TX
TEL: MONMOUTH (0600) 860254   FAX: (0600) 860607

A peaceful restaurant-with-rooms in the best French tradition.

The brochure sums it up reasonably well: 'Romantic auberge for French cuisine in the Wye Valley.' In true auberge tradition, the emphasis is on the food, prepared with a French flavour by Sandra Bates. The menu includes dishes such as smoked sewin (a local variant of sea trout) served with pickled cucumber ribbons and horseradish sauce, rack of Welsh lamb topped with a kidney, covered in puff pastry and served with madeira sauce, and baked Alaska to finish. The three-course lunch is good value, and can be eaten outside on the small patio during the summer. Coffee is taken in the low-ceilinged rustic lounge, in deep reds and blues with plentiful chairs. Bedrooms, ranged along the two floors above, are bigger up top, but all have lots of facilities. The best room, Manor, also has a whirlpool bath and a chunky four-poster.

◐ Open all year, exc 25, 26 Dec

↗ 5 miles south of Monmouth between the A466 and B4293. Turn west immediately south of Bigsweir Bridge. Private car park

🛏 3 twin, 8 double, 1 four-poster; all with bathroom/WC, TV, room service, hair-dryer, baby-listening; trouser press in some rooms

◇ Restaurant, bar, lounge, terrace; conference facilities (max 24 people non-residential, 15 residential); fishing, riding, other sports nearby; babysitting by arrangement

● No wheelchair access; no dogs in public rooms; smoking discouraged in restaurant

▭ Access, Amex, Diners, Visa

£ Single occupancy of twin/double £50 to £70, twin/double £80 to £120, four-poster £94 to £134 (rates inc dinner). Set L £14.50, D £24.50. Special breaks available

CHANNEL ISLANDS

ROZEL BAY JERSEY **MAP 10**

Château La Chaire

ROZEL BAY, ST MARTIN, JERSEY, CHANNEL ISLANDS JE3 6AJ
TEL: JERSEY (0534) 863354   FAX: (0534) 865137

A memorable country-house hotel run with flair.

The attractive terraced gardens were designed by the botanist Samuel Curtis, a one-time curator of Kew Gardens. The public rooms are sumptuously decorated, especially the elegant drawing-room, with its chandelier, cherubs' heads, Corinthian pillars and rococo plasterwork. An incongruous electric fire squats in the fireplace – 'They certainly spoiled the ship for a ha'porth of tar on that,' observed one guest. The panelled dining-room is resolutely English, though the food served both here and in the airy conservatory extension is French. The short table d'hôte menu is a real bargain; your meal might be chicken livers and crisp bacon with cashew nuts and balsamic vinegar, followed by vichyssoise, breast of duck with orange sauce, and cheese.

Bedrooms are luxurious and tastefully designed in a modern country-house style and the list of extras goes on and on.

◖ Open all year

↗ Approach Rozel village on B38, take first turning on left; hotel is 100 yards further down the road. Private car park

🛏 12 double, 1 four-poster, 1 suite; all with bathroom/WC, TV, room service, hair-dryer, trouser press, mini-bar in some rooms; no tea/coffee-making facilities in rooms

◈ Dining-room, bar, lounge, conservatory; fishing, golf, other sports nearby

⊖ No wheelchair access; no children under 7; no dogs

▭ Access, Amex, Diners, JCB, Visa

£ Single occupancy of twin/double £57 to £100, twin/double £82 to £110, four-poster £104 to £130, suite £150 to £180; deposit required. Set L £12.50, D £22.50; alc L £16, D £30. Special breaks available

ST AUBIN'S JERSEY **MAP 10**

Old Court House Inn

ST AUBIN'S HARBOUR, JERSEY, CHANNEL ISLANDS
TEL: JERSEY (0534) 46433   FAX: (0534) 45103

A venerable building with bags of character.

The old court house of the title is of 1450 vintage and is tucked away at the rear of the building, where it now houses the restaurant. The gleaming white frontage that the hotel presents to the world is that of a seventeenth-century merchant's homestead. Wandering from room to room, you'll find it hard to decide whether you are in a castle or on board a ship. The latter comes to mind when you bag a berth in the Mizzen Mast Bar, whose panelled walls create the illusion that you're on an old galleon offering superb views over the yachts tied up in St Aubin's Bay and a choice of bistro food from a blackboard menu. The restaurant is more medieval, with stone walls, beams and an enormous inglenook fireplace inscribed 1611 – the date the court house was restored. Book in advance, because the seaside specialities – Jersey oysters, crab Creole, local sea bass, and of course lobster – are much in demand.

Bedrooms have recently been refurbished with style and flair. Bathrooms vary.

◑ Open all year

⤴ At St Aubin's on the harbour front. On-street parking difficult

🛏 2 single, 6 twin, 1 suite; all with bathroom/WC, TV, room service, hair-dryer, baby-listening

◈ Restaurant, 3 bars, lounge; fishing, golf, other sports nearby

⊖ No wheelchair access; no children; no dogs

▭ Access, Amex, Diners, Visa

£ Single £30 to £40, twin/double £60 to £80, suite £90 to £140; deposit required. Sun L £11.50; set L £8.50, D £14.50; alc L, D £20 to £30. Special breaks available

ST BRELADE JERSEY   **MAP 10**

La Place Hotel

ROUTE DU COIN, LA HAULE, ST BRELADE, JERSEY JE3 8BF
TEL: JERSEY (0534) 44261   TELEX: 4192522 LAPLAZ G
FAX: (0534) 45164

A converted farmhouse now operated as a well-run roadside hotel.

The old creeper-draped house is joined to a largely clean-shaven modern extension. Green canopies crown the ground-floor windows, and the cartwheel motif of the eponymous restaurant adds a touch of *Bonanza*.

Reception has a business-like grey and red carpet, marquetry tables, baroque mirrors and elaborate flower arrangements. The sitting-room has wing-backed and Queen Anne-style chairs, tied-back curtains and autumnal tones of a country-house drawing-room, while the peach, green and light wood cocktail bar conveys metropolitan chic. The restaurant combines exposed stone walls with painted-on Tudor strapping and cowboy-look cartwheels studded with lamps suspended from the ceiling. The food is ambitious: perhaps quail's egg salad with a wholegrain mustard dressing followed by seafood brochette, steamed red mullet with a warm salsa, pudding and cheese.

Bedrooms are well-equipped and daintily decorated with modish fabrics and wallcoverings.

◑ Closed Nov to Mar

⤴ 4 miles from St Helier, off the

B25 to St Aubin Bay. Private car park

🛏 36 twin/double, 1 four-poster, 2 family rooms; all with bathroom/WC, TV, room service, hair-dryer, trouser press, baby-listening; no tea/coffee-making facilities in rooms

◇ Restaurant, bar, 2 lounges; conference facilities (max 40 people residential and non-residential); sauna, outdoor heated swimming-pool at hotel, golf, water sports nearby; babysitting (at a charge). Wheelchair access to hotel and restaurant, 11 ground-floor bedrooms

⊖ No children under 7 in restaurant eves; no dogs in public rooms

▭ Access, Amex, Diners, Visa

£ Single occupancy of twin/double £65 to £75, twin/double £90 to £110, family room rate on application; deposit required. Set L £9, D £18 & £20 (Sat), Sun L £10.50

Sea Crest

PETIT PORT, ST BRELADE, JERSEY, CHANNEL ISLANDS JE3 8HH
TEL: JERSEY (0534) 46353 FAX: (0534) 47316

A smartly refurbished hotel, carefully run by diligent hosts.

Sunday lunch at Sea Crest is something of a local institution, and no wonder. Julian Bernstein, smart but not formal in blazer and slacks, carries off the front-of-house rituals with considerable aplomb. All the staff, from the bar workers and waiters to the gardeners maintaining the terraced gardens and planting vegetables, seem to take their lead from him. This is a very tightly run ship, smart but welcoming and unpretentious.

The restaurant, open-plan from reception, is a large, bright room with baby-blue Regency-style chairs and ruched and pleated drapes at patio doors. A long à la carte menu is supplemented by an ambitious seasonal table d'hôte; you might find duck liver terrine studded with pistachio nuts on a bitter orange confit, followed by sorbet, pan-fried baby monkfish tails on a pink and green peppercorn sauce, and pudding.

Bedrooms have a bright, modern feel with lemon wallpaper, white bedding and blue and yellow drapes.

◐ Open all year, exc Feb; restaurant closed Mon eve

↗ Five minutes' drive from the Red Houses shopping centre, near the Corbière lighthouse. Private car park

🛏 5 twin, 2 double; all with bathroom/WC, TV, baby-listening; room service, hair-dryer on request

◇ Air-conditioned restaurant, bar, lounge, conservatory; unheated swimming-pool at hotel, other sports nearby

⊖ No wheelchair access; no dogs

▭ Access, Amex, Visa

£ Single occupancy of twin/double £48 to £53, twin/double £75 to £86; deposit required. Set L £12, D £19; alc L £20, D £26

ST BRELADE'S BAY JERSEY   **MAP 10**

Hotel L'Horizon

ST BRELADE'S BAY, JERSEY, CHANNEL ISLANDS
TEL: JERSEY (0534) 43101   TELEX: 4192281 ORIZON G
FAX: (0534) 46269

A comfortable modern sea-front hotel with excellent food.

The building is a long, undistinguished-looking box, but the Clipper Hotel group invest it with a sense of style and accomplishment that you might not expect.

What you'll find inside is basically a business hotel by the sea, with high-level facilities bolstered by friendly staff and the added attraction of the leisure club. It's not without its faults – corridors are a little the worse for wear and bedrooms, while spacious, have rather dated décor. Sea-facing rooms have balconies and wonderful views; soft furnishings co-ordinate and bathrooms come complete with robes.

The Star Grill is the intimate, top-of-the-range option with a striking bird frieze and rattan-sided chairs. The Crystal Room is the standard option, a large room, rather plain but for its chandeliers. Seafood is the acknowledged speciality in both. More informal dining takes place in the Brasserie, which overlooks the leisure club's large indoor pool.

◑ Open all year

⤴ A 10-minute drive from Jersey Airport. Private car park

🛏 10 single, 89 twin, 4 double, 1 four-poster, 3 suites; all with bathroom/WC, TV, room service, hair-dryer, trouser press, baby-listening; no tea/coffee-making facilities in rooms

◈ 3 restaurants, 3 bars, 2 lounges, library, business centre; conference facilities (max 180 people non-residential, 100 residential); heated swimming-pool, gym, hair and beauty salon, sauna, motor yacht at hotel, golf, tennis, riding nearby; babysitting on request. Wheelchair access to hotel, restaurant and WC (M,F), 16 ground-floor bedrooms and a lift

⊖ No dogs; 1 restaurant is non-smoking

▭ Access, Visa

£ Single from £75 and £85, twin/double from £150 and £170, four poster £170, suite from £210 to £230; deposit required. Set L £14.50, D £24.50; alc L £25, D £35 (prices till Apr 94). Special breaks available

---

ST JOHN JERSEY   **MAP 10**

Idlerocks Hotel

BONNE NUIT BAY, ST JOHN, JERSEY, CHANNEL ISLANDS
TEL: JERSEY (0534) 861633   FAX: (0534) 864800

A modest but friendly clifftop hotel in an unspoilt part of the island.

The lay-out is confusing as much of the hotel is on the cliffside, hidden from the entrance level above it. Public rooms are decorated in a traditional style, and while no design statements are being made, everything is neat and gleaming. The little TV lounge has embossed wallpaper and red velour sofas. There are Coronation mugs and other family treasures in the panelled bar to make it cosy. Red velveteen Regency stripes add dignity to the dining-room, which overlooks the little harbour. Dinner is included in the tariff, and you'll be asked to choose your four courses from the short menu after breakfast. It's traditional fare for the most part – perhaps pâté followed by roast pork, raspberry cheesecake and cheese and biscuits. Service is chatty and friendly.

Bedrooms are simply but very comfortably furnished and decorated in a bright modern style.

- ◑ *Closed 15 Oct to Easter*
- ⤢ *To the north of the island. Near television mast. Take the A9 to Bonne Nuit Bay. Private car park.*
- 🛏 *1 single, 8 twin, 5 double, 1 family room; half with bathroom/ WC, half with shower/WC; TV, room service in all rooms*
- ◈ *Dining-room, bar, lounge, drying room; heated swimming-pool at*
- *hotel, fishing, tennis, riding nearby*
- ⊖ *No wheelchair access; no children under 4; no dogs; no smoking in dining-room*
- ▭ *Access, Amex, Visa*
- £ *Single £33 to £38, twin/double £66 to £76, family room rate on request (rates inc dinner); deposit required*

ST MARTIN'S GUERNSEY · **MAP 10**

Idlerocks Hotel

JERBOURG ROAD, ST MARTIN'S, GUERNSEY, CHANNEL ISLANDS
TEL: GUERNSEY (0481) 37711   FAX: (0481) 35592

Stunning views and good food in this tasteful clifftop hotel.

The brochure claims that this hotel has the finest position of any hotel in the Channel Islands, and it is very difficult to disagree. Public rooms lack any depth of character, but are nevertheless faultless in their modern good taste. Fabrics and wallcoverings are bright and modern, and the array of rattan gives a smart colonial feel. The residents' lounge combines neat reproduction furniture with crisp yellow and white striped wallpaper and a Chinese-style cabinet; a bookcase offers a good selection of second-hand books available for sale. Raffles Bar has huge picture windows that make the most of the spectacular cliff views and an informal dining area with light wood-panelled walls and cheerful gingham tablecloths. In the more formal Admiral's Restaurant, a pretty pink room with ruched blinds, staff efficiently serve dishes from an à la carte and a short but very good-value set menu. A spring menu included smoked chicken with lemon and walnut, kiwi-fruit sorbet, julienne of pork satay with egg noodles and fresh fruit salad.

Bedrooms are neatly and stylishly furnished and views are wonderful.

◑ Open all year

⤴ 10 minutes' drive from the airport and St Peter Port. Private car park

🛏 2 single, 14 twin, 5 double, 1 four-poster, 5 family rooms, 1 suite; most with bathroom/WC, some with shower/WC; TV, room service, hair-dryer, trouser press, baby-listening in all rooms; mini-bar in some rooms

◈ Restaurant, dining-room, bar, lounge, cocktail lounge, conservatory (by 94); conference facilities (max 100 people non-residential, 60 residential);

heated swimming-pool, fishing at hotel, golf, other sports nearby

⊖ No wheelchair access; no dogs in public rooms; no smoking in bedrooms

▭ Access, Amex, Diners, Visa

£ Single £23 to £43, single occupancy of twin/double £32 to £47, twin/double £44 to £74, four-poster £55 to £99, family room £69 to £129, suite £100 to £180 (rates inc dinner); deposit required. Set L £9.50, D £12.50; alc D £18. Special breaks available

---

ST OUEN JERSEY   **MAP 10**

Lobster Pot

L'ETACQ, ST OUEN, JERSEY, CHANNEL ISLANDS
TEL: JERSEY (0534) 482888   FAX: (0534) 481574

The food's the thing at this well-established restaurant-with-rooms.

This converted farmhouse of rough mellow stone looks very attractive. Inside, the décor undoubtedly takes second place to the food; there are some seascapes lining the walls between reception and the bedrooms, but you can look at the real thing from front-facing rooms if the urge takes you.

Bedrooms are spacious, which is just as well as it's unlikely that you'd want to leave yours for the staid little lounge with rather elderly chairs. Much better is the bar, which has the cosy feel of an old English pub. Décor in the popular restaurant has a simple appeal, with rough walls, beams and wood panelling, plus crossed cutlasses, wall-mounted guns, lobster pots and copper kettles which give a magpie impression. The long set menu, offering dishes such as mushrooms viennoise, consommé julienne, pasta with prawns and a dessert of fruit salad, is good value. Breakfast disappoints, with packet orange juice, a rather basic platter and packaged preserves, though good hot toast comes in a paper tent.

Bedrooms have simple décor but lots of extras. Our inspector's twin room was undeniably comfortable, although the beds would have been too soft for many.

◐ Open all year

⤢ From St Helier take the A2 to Beaumont roundabout. Take the A12 to St Ouen's parish hall, then a left-hand turn on to the B64 and at the fork in the road take the B35. Private car park

⛉ 3 twin, 9 double, 1 family room; all with bathroom/WC, TV, hair-dryer, trouser press, mini-bar

◇ 2 restaurants (air-conditioned), 2 bars, lounge, drying room; golf, water sports, other sports nearby. Wheelchair access to restaurant and WC (M, F) only

⊖ No dogs

▭ Access, Amex, Diners, Visa

£ Single occupancy of twin/double £46 to £64, twin/double £71 to £97, family room rate on request; deposit required. Set L £10, D £14.50. Special breaks available

---

ST PETER PORT GUERNSEY   **MAP 10**

La Collinette

ST JACQUES, ST PETER PORT, GUERNSEY, CHANNEL ISLANDS GY1 1SN
TEL: GUERNSEY (0481) 710331   FAX: (0481) 713516

A smashing family-oriented hotel with good facilities and a cheerful atmosphere.

The Chambers family have run their smart-looking white hotel above St Peter Port's old town for nearly 35 years and it shows, not just in the attention to detail but also in the relaxed, informal attitude that pervades the hotel. There is a positive attitude to children, for whom there is a games room and play area and a six o'clock high tea. There are also a number of family suites.

Adults are well-catered for, too. The pleasant Regency-style lounge has plasterwork picked out in gold and leather chesterfields. The Bear bar is fun, with the stuffed creature presiding over a cheerful tartan-carpeted room with piano, sporting trophies, cricket photos and a 'Twit of the Day' hat. The large, rather plain split-level dining-room serves food from a good-value set menu; perhaps fresh Guernsey crab sesame toasts followed by mango sorbet, roast farmhouse chicken with bread sauce, and pudding. Bedrooms are bright and attractively decorated.

◐ Open all year exc 2 to 31 Jan

⤢ Short walk from the centre of town. Private car park

⛉ 2 single, 11 twin, 5 double, 5 family suites, 7 cottages; all with bathroom/WC, TV, room service, hair-dryer, trouser press, baby-listening

◇ Restaurant, bar, lounge, games room, drying room; conference facilities (max 40 people non-residential, 30 residential); sauna/solarium, heated swimming-pool, spa at hotel, other sports nearby; babysitting. Wheelchair access to hotel,

restaurant and WC (M, F), 6
ground-floor bedrooms

⊖ No dogs; no smoking in
restaurant

▭ Access, Amex, Diners, Visa

£ Single £19 to £38, single

occupancy of twin/double £48,
twin/double £38 to £75, family
suite £57 to £113, cottages
£115; deposit required. Set L £9,
D £12; alc L, D from £9. Special
breaks available

Midhurst House

CANDIE ROAD, ST PETER PORT, GUERNSEY, CHANNEL ISLANDS GY1 1UP
TEL: GUERNSEY (0481) 724391   FAX: (0481) 729451

*A popular guesthouse with comfortable rooms and warmly
sympathetic hosts.*

Brian Goodenough and his wife Jan have used their long experience in
the catering industry to create a gem of a guesthouse. Everything about
the place sparkles, and Jan has an eagle eye for a doortop that has not
been dusted or a pillow that has not been plumped. Best of all, there are
no pretensions at all about the place.

The stylish open-plan lounge area has a classic black and white tiled
floor, lots of plants, comfortable green velour chairs, chunky glass-
topped tables and a wooden Adam-style fireplace. Meals are taken in a
neat but windowless pastel blue room with deep red chairs. A typical
spring menu offered cream of asparagus soup, chicken cooked with red
wine, shallots and mushrooms, lemon syllabub and cheese. Everything is
freshly prepared and expertly cooked – and remarkable value for money.

Bedrooms vary in size from the bijou to the generous. Comfort takes
precedence over style, so you'll find lots of Anaglypta and velour
headboards as well as some splendid old furniture.

◑ Closed mid-Oct to Easter

↗ The hotel is adjacent to Candie
Gardens and the Beau Séjour
leisure centre. Private garaging
and on-street parking

🛏 3 twin, 4 double, 1 family room;
some with bathroom/WC, most
with shower/WC; TV, room
service in all rooms

◈ Dining-room, lounge, drying

room; fishing, golf, other sports
nearby

⊖ No wheelchair access; no
children under 8; no dogs; no
smoking in public rooms

▭ Access, Visa

£ Single occupancy of twin/double
£31 to £40, twin/double £42 to
£66; deposit required. Set D
£8.50; alc D from £14

Moore's Hotel ☆

LE POLLET, ST PETER PORT, GUERNSEY, CHANNEL ISLANDS GY1 1WH
TEL: GUERNSEY (0481) 724452   FAX: (0481) 714037

A bustling town-centre hotel with smart public rooms.

There have been a lot of changes at Moore's recently – at the time of our inspection glamorous new suites were four days away from their inauguration, and although things were chaotic the signs looked good.

Moore's has a large non-resident turnover, thanks to its several attractive public areas. The Library Bar and Carvery is a competent, rather glitzy, modern rendition of an old English pub with a gleaming brass-railed bar, traditional wallpaper and ceiling fans. It is a popular lunchtime venue, serving hearty made-to-order sandwiches and pub classics such as lasagne and carvery dishes. Next door, the garden-style La Patisserie is a light-lunch brasserie with white trellises draped with fabric roses. It serves open sandwiches and a luscious array of (very good) gâteaux. Service is friendly and efficient.

Inside the hotel proper the plaster ceiling of the formal lounge has been restored to its former glory, making it a smart and elegant, if slightly dark, room. The bright Conservatory Restaurant serves good-value table d'hôte dinners (with pricier dishes available on payment of a supplement). One May evening it offered smoked trout and mackerel platter, minestrone soup, mushroom Stroganoff with rice, apple strudel with brandy sauce and a cheeseboard.

Bedrooms vary from the refurbished pleasant but bland to the comfortable but dated.

◑ Open all year

↗ In the town centre, ½ mile from the harbour. Free public parking nearby

🛏 3 single, 24 twin, 20 double, 3 family rooms, 2 air-conditioned suites; all with bathroom/WC, TV, room service, hair-dryer, trouser press

◇ 2 restaurants (1 air-conditioned), 2 bars, 2 lounges, coffee shop, ironing room; conference facilities (max 20 people residential and non-residential); fishing, golf, other sports nearby

⊖ No wheelchair access; dogs by arrangement only; some public rooms non-smoking

▭ Access, Amex, Diners, Visa

£ Single £27 to £39, single occupancy of twin/double £32 to £59, twin/double £44 to £77, family room £60 to £89, suite £150 to £170; deposit required. Set L £12.50 to £14; alc L from £5.50, D from £12.50

St Pierre Park

ROHAIS, ST PETER PORT, GUERNSEY, CHANNEL ISLANDS
TEL: GUERNSEY (0481) 728282   TELEX: 419162 STPPRK G
FAX: (0481) 712041

A massive resort hotel with splendid facilities but patchy service.

The mixed signals sent out by this enormous business-class but leisure-oriented hotel are hard to decipher. If all the staff were as professional as the elderly porter who takes your bags, chats amicably, sees you settled in and then refuses a tip this would be a glowing endorsement. The hotel certainly has a lot going for it: reliably comfortable, well-equipped bedrooms decorated in a pleasant, modern, undemanding style; 45 acres of parkland and a range of sporting facilities. Tariffs reflect this.

Service, however, can let the side down. An ordered morning newspaper failed to appear but was charged for on the bill, although staff in the premier Victor Hugo Restaurant, a pink fondant fancy of a place, were solicitous in their service and mixed the best Singapore Sling this side of the South China Sea. One off-season visitor on half-board terms was outraged to find that because the main La Fontaine Restaurant was closed he was forced to eat à la carte because the short table d'hôte menu was unchanging for the duration of his four-night stay. Nevertheless, for those staying for a night or two the 'Menu of the Week' in the Victor Hugo Restaurant represents excellent value. Canapés are served with your aperitif and an inspection meal of venison terrine with port sauce, pear sorbet with blue Curaçao, excellent strips of Scotch beef fillet with tarragon sauce, and fresh fruit salad was enjoyable and well-cooked.

◑ Open all year

🏄 The hotel is a few minutes' drive westwards from central St Peter Port. Private car park

🛏 1 single, 53 twin, 73 double, 1 family room, 7 suites; all with bathroom/WC, TV, room service, hair-dryer, trouser press, baby-listening

◈ 3 restaurants, 3 bars, lounge, snooker room; air-conditioned public areas; conference facilities (max 200 people non-residential, 135 residential); golf, tennis, sauna/solarium, heated indoor swimming-pool, gym, spa bath/ steam room, croquet at hotel; babysitting. Wheelchair access to hotel (ramp), restaurant and WC, 18 ground-floor bedrooms, 2 specially equipped for disabled people

⊖ No dogs

▭ Access, Amex, Diners, Visa

£ Single and single occupancy of twin/double £75 to £95, twin/double £130 to £135, family room £165 to £170, suite £215 to £220; deposit required. Set D £15; alc L from £4, D £25. Special breaks available

ST SAVIOUR GUERNSEY   **MAP 10**

La Hougue Fouque Farm

LES BAS COURTILS, ST SAVIOUR, GUERNSEY, CHANNEL ISLANDS GY7 9YF
TEL: GUERNSEY (0481) 64181   FAX: (0481) 66272

A traditional, reliable hotel that elevates comfort above style.

This roadside hotel has the vaguely Teutonic look of a ski lodge. Behind it you'll find a neat whitewashed building with a sun-trap courtyard and a pleasant garden with a kidney-shaped pool surrounded by loungers.

Things are more traditional indoors, where stuffed ducks, horns and still lifes decorate a rather masculine bar with a blackboard menu

offering reliable bar food such as moules marinière and smoked mackerel and English mustard sauce. In the half-panelled and beamed
restaurant you could dine on generous portions of seafood salad, cream
of chicken soup, baked ham steak with pineapple, and pudding. In the
long, narrow lounge the rustic wood-framed chairs are joined by a baby
grand piano. Bedrooms are simply decorated but comfortable and have
some surprising extras.

◗ *Open all year*

↗ *Near Little Chapel (Les Vauxbelets) heading towards Strawberry Farm. Private car park*

🛏 *4 twin, 4 double, 4 family rooms, 3 suites; all with bathroom/WC, TV, baby-listening; trouser press, mini-bar in some rooms*

◈ *Restaurant, bar, drying room; heated outdoor swimming-pool at hotel, golf, other sports*

nearby. Wheelchair access to hotel, restaurant and WC (M,F), 2 ground-floor bedrooms

⊖ *No dogs*

▭ *Access, Amex, Diners, Visa*

💷 *Single occupancy of twin/double £24 to £39, twin/double £48 to £56, suite £68 to £76, family room £60 to £70; deposit required. Set L £8.50, D £13.50; alc L, D £15 to £20*

ST SAVIOUR JERSEY   **MAP 10**

Longueville Manor

LONGUEVILLE ROAD, ST SAVIOUR, JERSEY JE2 7SA
TEL: JERSEY (0534) 25501   FAX: (0534) 31613

An assured country-house hotel with pretty grounds and luxurious bedrooms.

This is a top-of-the-range country-house hotel and the tariff forcefully
reflects this. Nevertheless, the much-extended manor house has lots of
friends who are happy to pay the premium price demanded. What visitors
remember are the overstuffed sofas, the restful colour schemes, the
blazing fires and the dazzling craftsmanship of a glorious Jacobean-style
overmantel. There's more indulgence in the panelled, very traditional
Oak Room where horse brasses and copper add a homely note, and the
dark antiquity of the room contrasts starkly with the cheerful colours of
the garden which it overlooks. A short set dinner menu in May offered
carpaccio of beef with pickled vegetables and fresh Parmesan, followed
by pink champagne sorbet, poached fillet of salmon with stewed pepper
and an olive cream, and bitter chocolate gâteau on an orange confit.

Bedrooms are positively sumptuous, the enormous, light and airy
garden suites with their bold, almost overwhelming décor being particularly memorable.

◗ *Open all year*

↗ *Take the A3 from Georgetown to Longueville. The hotel is 1 mile*

on the left-hand side. Private car park

🛏 *29 twin/double, 1 four-poster, 2*

suites; all with bathroom/WC,
TV, room service, hair-dryer; no
tea/coffee-making facilities in
rooms

 Restaurant (air-conditioned), bar,
2 lounges; conference facilities
(max 30 people non-residential
and residential); heated outdoor
swimming-pool (May to Oct),
tennis at hotel, fishing, golf,
other sports nearby. Wheelchair
access to hotel, restaurant and

WC (M, F), 8 ground-floor
bedrooms

⊖ No children under 7; no dogs in
public rooms

▭ Access, Amex, Diners, Visa

£ Single occupancy of twin/double
£110 to £170, twin/double £140
to £210, four-poster £165 to
£185, suite £250 to £300;
deposit required. Set L £17.50, D
£28.50; alc D £37. Special
breaks available

Les Piques Farm

ST SAVIOUR'S, GUERNSEY
TEL: GUERNSEY (0481) 64515   FAX: (0481) 65857

A charming rural guesthouse with lovely rooms and friendly staff.
Great value.

Unless you know the byways of Guernsey's rural backwaters, finding Les
Piques Farm can be a nightmare – it's probably worth phoning for
directions. What you'll find when you arrive is as pretty as a picture; a
white reception building bedecked with colourful hanging baskets plus
an extension of new traditional low-slung cottages, all in an attractive
garden.

The prevailing style is cottagey; a comfortable but rather staid lounge
with a lovely chess set is the only disappointment. The bar is cosy and
atmospheric, with beams, tiles, stone walls and horse brasses. You'll find
more brass and copper and a large inglenook fireplace in the traditional
restaurant, which is now supplemented by a lovely bright conservatory
with pretty white chairs, terrazzo tiles and views over the garden. There
is an à la carte menu as well as a limited-choice set affair that might offer
prawn bisque, fillet of bream hollandaise, dessert and cheese. Staff are
friendly, chatty and without airs.

Bright, cheerful bedrooms are individually and attractively decorated
with lots of light pastels and co-ordinating chintz.

◑ Open all year

⤢ Head in direction of Strawberry
Farm and Woodcarvers, both of
which are signposted; Les Piques
is very close by. Private car
park

🛏 2 single, 7 twin, 11 double, 2
suites; most with bathroom/WC,
some with shower/WC; TV in all
rooms; hair-dryer, trouser press

in some rooms

 2 dining-rooms, bar, lounge,
conservatory

⊖ No wheelchair access; no
children under 12; no dogs

▭ Access, Visa

£ Single £23 to £33, twin/double
£42 to £66; deposit required. Set
D £10; alc D £10 to £20

SARK CHANNEL ISLANDS MAP 10

Le Petit Champ

SARK, VIA GUERNSEY, CHANNEL ISLANDS GY9 0SF
TEL: SARK (0481) 832046   FAX: (0481) 832469

Friendly hosts at a traditional hotel in a quiet corner of the island.

Many of the qualities that make Le Petit Champ attractive to its regulars are timeless: the sea views of the island's west coast, the birdwatching possibilities, the well-kept gardens, the sense of being on a very special island with a unique way of life. Few, it must be said, can come for the décor which, with its swirly carpets and heavily patterned wallpapers, also seems to exist in a time warp. The Robins have yet to put their stamp on the place and it's unlikely that they'll introduce any radical changes, though a new blue staircarpet suggests that things are moving in the right direction. However, the homeliness of the place is part of Le Petit Champ's special attraction, and there's no denying that the bedrooms are comfortable and the bar is cosy.

Food in the three-sectioned dining-room comes from bilingual à la carte and table d'hôte menus. When we inspected the set menu offered dishes that included smoked chicken and apricot salad, kiwi-fruit sorbet, poached fillets of plaice filled with prawns and dill served with a Pernod cream sauce, and cheese.

◐ *Closed Oct to mid-Apr*

⤢ *On the western coast of Sark. No cars allowed on Sark*

🛏 *3 single, 8 twin, 3 double, 2 family rooms; most with bathroom/WC, some with shower/WC; no tea/coffee-making facilities in rooms*

◇ *3 restaurants, bar, 3 lounges, TV room, drying room, library; heated outdoor swimming-pool at hotel; fishing, tennis, other sports nearby*

⊖ *No wheelchair access; no children under 7; no dogs; no smoking in certain public rooms*

▭ *Access, Amex, Diners, Visa*

£ *Single £40 to £45, single occupancy of twin/double £57 to £72, twin/double £75 to £96, family room £99 to £146 (rates inc dinner); deposit required. Sun L £9.50; set D £16.50; alc L £11, D £15.50*

La Sablonnerie

SARK, VIA GUERNSEY, CHANNEL ISLANDS GY9 0SD
TEL: SARK (0481) 832061   FAX: (0481) 832408

A memorable experience – good food, convivial company and glorious isolation.

First there's the adventure of getting here – the boat trip from Guernsey, the tractor that brings your luggage (and you too, if you don't mind getting dusty), the horses and carriages and all the other timeless elements that make this carless (but tractor-ridden) island a magical place. Even better is the realisation that La Sablonnerie is insulated from all but the most determined of the day-trippers who haunt the island's tiny downtown area.

La Sablonnerie attracts a certain type of visitor. There can't be many hotels where after dinner a regular stands up, glass in hand, and recites verses composed in honour of the island and his hosts, yet this is what happened during our inspection. Yet outsiders are made to feel welcome, both by Philip, who presides over the bar like an elder statesman, and by Elizabeth, the brisk and efficient châtelaine. Friendly, energetic serving staff encourage the flow of conversation between tables at dinner. There is lots of choice on the set menu, and food is accomplished and inventive; your dinner might consist of sesame prawn toast with savory salad, crab and sweetcorn soup, tagliatelle niçoise, banana torte, and a cheeseboard that includes a local cheese with peppers and garlic. 'All items were very good and the ingredients superb. The taste was excellent, as was the presentation,' wrote one guest.

◑ Closed mid-Oct to Apr

▰ At the southern end of the island. No cars allowed on Sark

🛏 6 single, 8 twin, 8 double; most with bathroom/WC, some with shower/WC; room service, baby-listening in all rooms; no tea/coffee-making facilities in rooms

◈ 2 restaurants, 2 bars, 2 lounges, conservatory; fishing, tennis, riding nearby

⊖ No wheelchair access; no dogs in public rooms and in some bedrooms by arrangement only

▭ Access, Amex, Visa

£ Single £44 to £50, twin/double £88 to £99 (rates inc dinner); deposit required. Set L from £18, D from £21 (10% service charge added)

Hotels from our Visitors' Book

Here is a collection of hotels that are worth considering but which we think do not yet merit a full entry. They are marked on the maps at the back of the *Guide* with an open triangle. Please note that towns marked with a ◪ symbol contain one of our 'Visitors' Book' hotels as well as at least one full entry. Hotels marked with an asterisk are new to the *Guide* this year. Not all counties (or regions in Scotland) are represented.

The price given for each hotel is the standard cost of a twin-bedded or double room, and is the latest available as we go to press. Prices may go up sometime in 1994.

We would be particularly pleased to receive reports on these hotels.

LONDON

MAP 11

WC2 **The Waldorf*** Aldwych   071-836 2400
A grand Edwardian hotel, famous for its tea dances in the magnificent Palm Court; boldly refurbished bedrooms. From £180

SW1 **Wilbraham** Sloane Street   071-730 8296
Brightly decorated old-timer with helpful staff, which gives good value for its location, on a quiet street five minutes from Sloane Square. From £62

ENGLAND

Avon

MAP 9

Badminton **Petty France Hotel*** Dunkirk   (0454) 238361
Roadside hotel with a pretty garden. Bedrooms vary in quality of furnishings and size. Stable block rooms are the least attractive. £85 to £98

Bath **Bath Spa Hotel** Sydney Road   (0225) 444424
Plush Forte hotel a ten-minute walk from city centre. Four-poster bedrooms and suites available – at a price – and the Vellore restaurant cannot fail to impress. From £160

Bath **Cliffe Hotel** Crowe Hill   Limpley Stoke   (0225) 723226
New owners for this hotel. Popular summer cream teas by the outdoor swimming-pool. From £77

Bath **Leighton House** 139 Wells Road   (0225) 314769
Tastefully furnished, friendly B&B with good-sized rooms and award-winning garden. £56 to £58

Bath **Meadowland** 36 Bloomfield Park   (0225) 311079
Several readers have praised the high standard of bedrooms in this welcoming suburban B&B. Downstairs rooms are plainer and less stylish. Secluded garden. Non-smoking house. From £50

Bathford **Old School House** Church Street   (0225) 859593
Comfortable small hotel with friendly hosts. £60 to £64

Bristol **Avon Gorge Hotel** Sion Hill   Clifton   (0272) 738955
Spectacular views of the gorge from this comfortable but anonymous hotel. £85

Bedfordshire   MAP 9

Bedford   **Bedford Swan** The Embankment   (0234) 346565
Business-neutral bedrooms in large extension. Riverside position.
£50 to £76

Leighton Buzzard   **Swan** 50 High Street   (0525) 372148
Old coaching-inn in town centre. Reasonable accommodation in well-kept
rooms.   From £56

Woburn   **Bell Inn** 21 Bedford Street   (0525) 290280
Neatly kept and reasonably sized bedrooms in a Georgian house across the
road from the cosy pub.   £65 to £68

Berkshire   MAP 9

Donnington   **Donnington Valley Hotel*** Old Oxford Road
(0635) 551199
Modern golfing hotel with stylish public rooms and luxurious bedrooms.   £89

Hurley   **Ye Olde Bell*** High Street   (0628) 825881
Old-world country pub with some smart comfortable accommodation above the
bars and in three annexe buildings. Pretty gardens.   £85 to £95

Windsor   **Aurora Garden** 14 Bolton Avenue   (0753) 868686
Suburban hotel with bright public rooms and spacious bedrooms.   £72

Windsor   **Sir Christopher Wren's House** 52 Thames Street
(0753) 861354
Red-brick Georgian façade and modern refurbished public areas. Bedrooms are
showing signs of wear and tear, though are comfortable; other rooms and
corridors in need of sprucing up.   £69 to £99

Buckinghamshire   MAP 9

Medmenham   **Danesfield House*** (0628) 891010
Immaculate and luxurious Victorian house with castellations and candy-twist
chimneys. Formal gardens overlooking the Thames.   £150

Cambridgeshire   MAPS 5/8/9

Cambridge   **Cambridge Lodge** Huntingdon Road   (0223) 352833
One mile from the city centre. Co-ordinated bedrooms and serene public
rooms.   £65

Cambridge   **Regent Hotel*** 41 Regent Street   (0223) 351470
In central Cambridge with adequate if institutional bedrooms.   £73

Cambridge   **University Arms Hotel** Regent Street   (0223) 351241
Busy, central hotel – a good choice for sightseeing or for parents visiting
students.   £110

Gamlingay   **The Emplins** Church Street   (0767) 650581
A large, half-timbered, fifteenth-century hall with unostentatious rooms.
Home-made dinners around a communal table.   £50

Holywell   **Ferry Boat Inn** (0480) 63227
Relaxed, riverside inn on the Great Ouse with pretty garden and serviceable
rooms.   From £50

Six Mile Bottom   **Swynford Paddocks**   (0638) 70234
Too much emphasis on Byron connections and not quite enough on standards of public rooms and food. Good-sized bedrooms but mediocre décor.   £107

Wansford   **The Haycock**   (0780) 782223
Conveniently located business hotel, just off the A1. Although pricey, the rooms are beautifully presented; service is friendly and efficient.   £85 to £98

Cheshire   MAP 5

Chester   **Cavendish Hotel*** 42–44 Hough Green   (0244) 675100
Newly converted Georgian hotel in residential area. Fresh, pretty en-suite bedrooms of varying size. Candlelit basement dining area for residents only.   £50

Chester   **Chester Grosvenor*** Eastgate Street   (0244) 324024
Expensive luxury in Chester city centre. The Arkle Restaurant is highly acclaimed for grand, gourmet dining.   £150

Macclesfield   **Chadwick House** 55 Beech Lane   (0625) 615558
Friendly, modest town B&B on the road the by-pass by-passed. Sky TV but no radios in rooms. Non-smoking house.   £55

Sutton   **Sutton Hall** Bullock's Lane   (0260) 253211
Traditional Tudor inn with rooms. A popular local with a wide choice of bar food.   £85

Cornwall   MAP 10

Crantock   **Crantock Bay Hotel*** (0637) 830229
Friendly family hotel with excellent swimming-pool and wonderful views. The refurbished second-floor bedrooms are best.   £27 to £46

Golant   **Cormorant Hotel** (0726) 833426
Wonderfully situated purpose-built hotel overlooking the Fowey Estuary; public areas are disappointingly old-fashioned.   £36 to £45

Little Petherick   **Old Mill Country House** (0841) 540388
Small, friendly hotel with comfortable rooms in an old watermill which still turns during dinner.   £46 to £49

Newlyn   **Higher Faugan*** (0736) 62076
Attractive Edwardian building in extensive grounds, with games room, tennis court and several very pleasing bedrooms.   £76 to £94

Newquay   **Harbour Hotel*** North Quay Hill   (0637) 873040
Inexpensive spick-and-span hotel overlooking the harbour. Pleasant new owners.   £40

St Keyne   **Old Rectory** (0579) 342617
Attractive eighteenth-century hotel in a quiet setting but with slightly old-fashioned furnishings.   £50

St Mawes   **Rising Sun** The Square   (0326) 270233
Despite its attractive harbourside setting and good bar meals the public areas are disappointing.   £79 to £90

Tintagel   **Old Millfloor*** Trebarwith Strand   (0840) 770234
An old watermill in an exquisite valley setting approached via steep paths. None of the rather basic bedrooms has en-suite facilities.   £32

Cumbria
MAP 4

Ambleside   **Three Shires Inn** Little Langdale   (05394) 37215
Hearty meals are served in this popular pub in the heart of the Lake District.   £64

Coniston   **Old Rectory*** Torver   (05394) 41353
Good home-cooked dinners in modernised, homely house on National Trust farmland.   £50 to £66

Elterwater   **Britannia Inn**   (05394) 37210
Traditional and popular village pub with village-green position.
£59

Maryport   **The Retreat*** Birkby   (0900) 814056
Light, bright bedrooms in nineteenth-century sea-captain's house. Downstairs lacks character, but restaurant has a popular local following.   £60

Near Sawrey   **Buckle Yeat***   (05394) 36446
B&B in well-restored, pretty cottage in Beatrix Potter village. Friendly atmosphere, good breakfasts but plain bedrooms.   £37

Watermillock   **Wreay Farm Guesthouse**   (07684) 86296
Relaxing atmosphere and a warm welcome in a bright, unpretentious guesthouse with splendid views.   £74 (rate inc. dinner)

Windermere   **Hawksmoor Guesthouse** Lake Road   (05394) 42110
Pleasant and well co-ordinated rooms in a cheerful guesthouse with a good central location for the Lakes.   £40 to £59

Derbyshire
MAP 5

Buxton   **Coningsby Guesthouse** 6 Macclesfield Road   (0298) 26735
Friendly well-kept guesthouse in spacious Victorian house in centre of Peak District National Park. Simple dinners. Non-smoking house.   £36 to £40

Devon
MAP 10

Chagford   **Gidleigh Park**   (0647) 432367
Exclusive and expensive country-house hotel with exquisite food from Shaun Hill, but run with a touch of arrogance.   £260 to £360 (rate inc. dinner)

Clawton   **Court Barn**   (0409) 27219
Quiet Victorian hotel in pretty gardens; rooms on the cluttered side.
£68 to £80

Croyde   **Croyde Bay House*** Moore Lane   (0271) 890270
Seaside hotel on a rocky promontory, with slightly old-fashioned décor.
£58 to £79

Dartmouth   **Townstal Farmhouse** Townstal Road   (0803) 832300
Clean, well-kept small hotel in a sixteenth-century farmhouse, with a variety of attractive rooms.   £36 to £45

Gittisham   **Combe House**   (0404) 42756
Splendid Elizabethan mansion in extensive grounds, showing its age in places.   £92

Holne   **Church House Inn***   (0364) 3208
Stunning black and white half-timbered pub/hotel in a quiet, off-the-beaten-track village. Sadly, the rooms lack the character you might anticipate.   £45

Knowstone   **Masons Arms**   (03984) 231/582
Village-centre pub with good food and five bedrooms; can be noisy.
£46 to £100

Lustleigh   **Willmead Farm**   (064 77) 214
*Pretty thatched and oak-beamed farmhouse with ducks and chickens running
in the yard but very basic bed and breakfast facilities only.*   £46

Lydford   **Moor View Hotel*** Vale Down   (082 282) 220
*Small, cluttered hotel on the outskirts of Lydford with moor views and a menu
featuring good, old-fashioned English food and home-made puddings.*   £50

Lynton   **Combe Park** 2 Hillsford Bridges   (0598) 52356
*Victorian house surrounded by National Trust estate. Popular for country
pursuits but a little old-fashioned.*   £60

Salcombe   **Marine Hotel** Cliff Road   (0548) 844444
A large hotel with spectacular views over Salcombe Estuary.   £140 to £160
(rate inc. dinner)

Totnes   **The Old Forge*** Seymour Place   (0803) 862174
*A working forge offering bed and splendid breakfasts in rooms with sometimes
fussy décor but all the comforts.*   £50

Dorset   **MAP 9**

Blandford Forum   **La Belle Alliance** White Cliff Mill Street
(0258) 452842
Excellent restaurant with serviceable rooms.   £62 to £66

Evershot   **Rectory House*** Fore Street   (093 583) 273
B&B with spacious rooms and memorably large bathrooms.   £60

Farnham   **The Museum***   (0725) 516261
*Pub/restaurant in pretty village with real ale, good wines and interesting food.
Small rooms in converted stables have pine furniture hand-made by local
craftsmen.*   £50

Shaftesbury   **The Grosvenor** The Commons   (0747) 52282
*Standardised bedrooms in Forte heritage hotel near the 'Hovis ad' hill. Do not
miss the extraordinary Chevy Chase sideboard in the residents' lounge.*   £75

Sherborne   **Quinns*** Marston Road   (0935) 815008
B&B in a modern house five minutes from the centre of lovely old town.   £45

Co Durham   **MAP 3**

Durham   **Royal County Hotel** Old Elvet   091-386 6821
*Pleasant, riverside position for this city-centre hotel with comfortable
corporate-style rooms.*   £110

Greta Bridge   **Morritt Arms**   (0833) 27232
*Old-fashioned wayside inn with interesting public rooms and rather dated
bedrooms.*   £68

Headlam   **Headlam Hall**   (0325) 730238
*Interesting Jacobean mansion, with some bedrooms in need of a revamp. The
hotel's function trade may encroach on the enjoyment of some residents.*   £70

East Sussex   MAPS 8/9

Alfriston   **George Inn** High Street   (0323) 870319
*Unpretentious accommodation and good-value food in a timber-framed
fifteenth-century inn in the centre of town.*   £60

Brighton   **Grand Hotel** King's Road   (0273) 321188
*Grandiose Victorian landmark; the seafront rooms are the best, though pricey
and a little noisy.*   £140 to £160

Brighton   **Hospitality Inn** King's Road   (0273) 206700
*Modern atrium hotel on seafront. Make sure you ask for a refurbished
room.*   £98 to £135

Herstmonceux   **Cleavers Lyng*** Church Road   (0323) 833131
*Rural attractive red-brick, cottagey building with lattice windows, and pub-
like atmosphere inside. Undergoing refurbishment on inspection.*   £40

Rye   **Old Vicarage Hotel*** 15 East Street   (0797) 225131
*Not to be confused with the Old Vicarage just round the corner (see full entry),
this is a more upmarket hotel-cum-restaurant with some comfortable, nicely
furnished bedrooms. We found breakfast and service slightly disappointing –
more reports, please.*   £56 to £76

Ticehurst   **Spindlewood Hotel** Wallcrouch   (0580) 200430
A lovely garden setting and good set menu but old-fashioned décor.
£63 to £78

Essex   MAP 8

Coggeshall   **White Hart Hotel** Market End   (0376) 561654
*High-street hotel in a quiet East Anglian village. Rooms are comfortable if
predictable.*   £82

Southend-on-Sea   **Mayflower Hotel** 5/6 Royal Terrace   (0702) 340489
*Pretty Georgian terraced house that doesn't quite live up to its initial promise.
Some rooms have large windows and sea views, others are somewhat
faded.*   £40

Gloucestershire   MAP 9

Cheltenham   **Abbey Hotel** 16 Bath Parade   (0242) 516053
*Small bedrooms are the drawback to this friendly family hotel, which is
otherwise charming.*   £54

Cheltenham   **Hotel on the Park*** Evesham Road   (0242) 518898
*Smartly furnished villa. Current building work should give it more space. Let
us know.*   £89

Cheltenham   **Stretton Lodge** 8 Western Road   (0242) 528724
*Very efficiently run and welcoming guesthouse, but a little overpriced, even for
Cheltenham.*   £45 to £55

Chipping Campden   **Noel Arms*** High Street   (0386) 840317
*Old coaching-inn with good bedrooms but unimaginative public rooms. Fair
value.*   £78

Chipping Campden   **Seymour House*** High Street   (0386) 840429
*A good reserve option in Chipping Campden, comfortable but lacking character
in lounge and some bedrooms. Ask for a refurbished room.*   £55

Lower Swell   **Old Farmhouse Hotel** Stow-on-the-Wold
(0451) 830232
Old-fashioned and a little worn. Good food.   £89 to £93

Tewkesbury   **Puckrup Hall** Puckrup   (0684) 296200
Comfortable but rather bland hotel, heavily used by golfers and with a new leisure centre (and more rooms) being added.   £80

Upper Slaughter   **Lords of the Manor***   (0451) 820243
Stunningly beautiful Cotswold manor, but with some bedrooms not worth the high tariff, and furnished with a rather bland luxury.   £98 to £185

Upton St Leonards   **Hatton Court*** Upton Hill   (0452) 617412
Views, loos and bathrooms of exceptional standard in this large, pleasant hotel. Otherwise a bit conventional and a bit pricey.   £90

Greater Manchester   MAP 5

Bury   **Normandie*** Elbut Lane   Birtle   061-764 3869
Extensive views over Pennine foothills from hotel attached to serious French restaurant. Rooms in newer extension more attractive than older, standard rooms.   £69 to £79

Manchester   **Granada Hotel*** 404 Wilmslow Road   Withington
061-445 5908
Inexpensive, small hotel with simple, neat rooms and modern en-suite bathrooms. Good Armenian restaurant in basement.   £35 to £45

Hampshire   MAP 9

Basingstoke   **Audley's Wood** Alton Road   (0256) 817555
Slightly impersonal Victorian country house with many mod cons; in quiet grounds by the M3.   From £105

Langrish   **Langrish House**   (0730) 266941
Seventeenth-century manor house in a quiet valley.   £59 to £65

Lyndhurst   **Parkhill Hotel** Beaulieu Road   (0703) 282944
Small Georgian country-house hotel set in parkland on the edge of the New Forest. Rooms full of antiques.   £47 to £59

Milford on Sea   **Westover Hall*** Park Lane   (0590) 643044
Late-Victorian mansion looking across to the Needles; possesses a stunning oak and stained-glass interior.   From £64

Rotherwick   **Tylney House***   (0256) 764881
Turn-of-the-century country house with grandiose public rooms, many leisure facilities and 66 acres of beautiful grounds which are gradually being restored.   From £114

Sparsholt   **Lainston House** (0962) 863588
A beautiful corporately owned William-and-Mary house in fine gardens on the Hampshire Downs.   £120

Hereford and Worcester   MAP 9

Broadway   **Leasow House** Laverton Meadow   (038 673) 526;
changing to (0386) 584526 in Nov 93
A B&B not far from Broadway. Friendly isolated farmhouse.   £48 to £60

Knightwick   **The Talbot**   (0886) 21235
Old pub on the River Teme. Comprehensive bar menu.   £53 to £57

Tenbury Wells   **Corndene***   (0584) 890324
A guesthouse beautifully done up for disabled guests. Cheerful and bright.   £34 to £37

Walterstone   **Allt-yr-Ynys***   (0873) 890307
Smart family hotel in an old house hidden away near Welsh border. Aimed at the business trade, but could make a good hideaway.   £70 to £90

Hertfordshire   MAP 9

Tring   **Rose & Crown** High Street   (0442) 824071
Reasonable overnight accommodation in Tudor-style, turn-of-the-century building in the centre of Tring.   £66 to £81

Humberside   MAP 5

Driffield   **The Old Mill*** Mill Lane   Langtoft   (0377) 87284
Good food and neat rooms with a high level of facilities in the Yorkshire Wolds.   £65

Isle of Wight   MAP 9

Chale   **Clarendon Hotel & Wight Mouse Inn**   (0983) 730431
Seventeenth-century coaching hotel with smart, richly decorated bedrooms and fine views; the busy pub in the annexe can be intrusive.   £56

Isles of Scilly   MAP 10

Bryher   **Hell Bay Hotel**   (0720) 22947
A comfortable base with good-sized if slightly bland bedrooms.   £48 to £65

Tresco   **New Inn**   (0720) 22844
Popular local near the quay with fresh, simple bedrooms and good food.
£76 to £112 (rate inc. dinner)

Kent   MAP 8

Canterbury   **Thanington Hotel** 140 Wincheap   (0227) 453227
Smart modern bedrooms and an inviting indoor swimming-pool. Set back from the main road to Ashford.   £55 to £60

Chartham Hatch   **Howfield Manor** Howfield Lane   (0227) 738294
Small manor house with plain décor and grounds but helpful service and well-presented food.   £79

Sevenoaks   **Royal Oak** Upper High Street   (0732) 451109
Good central location; bedrooms are nicely decorated and comfortable but the ones at the front are noisy. Public rooms are definitely striking with heavy greens, blues and yellows.   £80 to £85

Tunbridge Wells   **Spa Hotel** Mount Ephraim   (0892) 520331
Despite its proud and grand exterior this hotel is a little tired and dated. Rooms are being refurbished and the new décor should give it a new lease of life.   From £100

Westerham **King's Arms** Market Square   (0959) 562990
Georgian coaching-inn with noisy streetside rooms and a pleasant dining-room serving good English food. £70

Lancashire   MAP 5

Morecambe **The Elms*** Bare Village   (0524) 411501
Long-established business hotel that is being updated. Modernised bedrooms are more attractive than the public rooms would suggest. Particularly popular for sequence dancing weekends. £70

Leicestershire   MAP 5

Castle Donington **Donington Thistle Hotel** East Midlands
International Airport   (0332) 850700
Modern hotel in airport complex, with good leisure facilities and comfortable rooms. From £100

Dadlington **Ambion Court Hotel** The Green   (0455) 212292
Attractive and well-equipped rooms in friendly guesthouse on village green. Straightforward, inexpensive food. £50 to £65

Melton Mowbray **The Harboro** Burton Street   (0664) 60121
Inexpensive rooms in busy Forte hotel with Harvester restaurant. Rooms rather cramped and bathrooms basic. From £42

Oakham **Whipper-In Hotel** Market Place   (0572) 756971
Well-furnished town-centre hotel near Rutland Water showing signs of wear. Friendly helpful service. From £80

Lincolnshire   MAP 5

Belton **Belton Woods**   (0476) 593200
Expensive, modern country-club hotel with good facilities. £115

Grantham **Angel & Royal** High Street   (0476) 65816
Revamped coaching-inn with fine old dining-room, popular public bar and friendly atmosphere. From £80

Lincoln **White Hart** Bailgate   (0522) 526222
Large characterful Forte hotel in city centre. Friendly staff. Superior rooms are worth the supplement. From £90

Merseyside   MAP 5

Southport **Crimond Hotel*** 28–30 Knowsley Road   (0704) 536456
Cheery, family-run hotel near Marine Drive. Bedrooms gradually being updated, so some variance in quality. £59

Norfolk   MAP 7

Erpingham **The Ark*** The Street   (0263) 761535
Friendly, family-run restaurant lying well off the beaten track, with three spacious and inviting rooms. £95

Holt **Lawns Hotel*** 22 Station Road   (0263) 713390
An imposing, red-brick Georgian house. Bedrooms are reasonably comfortable and the lounge is relaxing. £58

South Wootton **Knights Hill** (0553) 675566
Large, village-like business hotel with conference and banqueting centre set in 11 acres of parkland. £70 to £85

Thorpe Market **Green Farm** North Walsham Road (0263) 833602
Typical Norfolk flint building with bar and stone-flagged lounge. Rooms are on the cramped side. £65

Wolterton **Saracen's Head*** (0263) 768909
Two rooms only, but both are attractively furnished in pine. Convivial atmosphere and a good choice of food. £45

Northamptonshire
MAP 9

Wellingborough **The Hind** Sheep Street (0933) 222827
Large Moat House hotel in town centre. Good pub. Hotel service can be unhelpful. £60 to £87

Northumberland
MAP 3

Allendale Town **Bishop Field** (0434) 683248
Comfortable family-run hotel deep in attractive, unspoilt countryside. Phone for directions. £76

Bellingham **Westfield House*** (0434) 220340
Informal country guesthouse in a part of Northumberland that deserves to be better known. Non-smoking house. £50

Berwick-upon-Tweed **Old Vicarage** 24 Church Road (0289) 306909
Tastefully furnished, popular Victorian guesthouse in a quiet position in this bustling border town. £22

Wylam **Laburnum House Restaurant** (0661) 852185
Highly regarded French restaurant with comfortable rooms. £50

North Yorkshire
MAPS 3/5

Bilbrough **Bilbrough Manor** (0937) 834002
Exclusive turn-of-the-century manor house with interesting antiques.
From £100

Clifton **Grange Hotel** (0904) 644744
Regency house near the centre of York with high level of facilities and better-than-average food. Housekeeping and some bedroom décor could be improved upon. From £98

Gayle **Rookhurst** West End (0969) 667454
Austere-looking house which revels in its old-fashioned lack of co-ordination. Some fine features. Friendly hosts. £84 to £112 (rate inc. dinner)

Jervaulx **Jervaulx Hall** (0677) 60235
Elegant but expensive country-house hotel in memorable setting. £130 (rate inc. dinner)

Ripley **The Boar's Head** (0423) 771888
Fine-looking traditional inn opposite pretty cobbled village square, but let down by a scruffy bar. £98

Oxfordshire   **MAP 9**

Kingham   **Mill House Hotel**   (0608) 658188
Sympathetically extended Cotswold stone mill house. Comfortable and efficient, though bedrooms lack character.   £90 to £108

Lew   **Farmhouse Hotel**   (0993) 850297
Seventeenth-century Cotswold stone farmhouse on working farm. Neat, spotless bedrooms. (Previously known as **University Farm.***)*   £52

Oxford   **Bath Place** 4 & 5 Bath Place   (0865) 791812
Restored seventeenth-century cottages turned restaurant-with-rooms in the centre of Oxford. Food is good but accommodation suffers from a lack of space in bedrooms and bathrooms. Parking a short walk away.   From £85

Shipton-under-Wychwood   **Lamb Inn**   (0993) 830465
A popular pub and restaurant-with-rooms tucked away from the main street of this Cotswold village.   £65

Thame   **Thatchers** 29–30 Lower High Street   (0844 21) 2146
Restaurant-with-rooms in thatched beamed cottage with uneven floors and varied rooms; some in a small annexe to rear have windows on to a covered passageway.   £70

Woodstock   **The Laurels** Hensington Road   (0993) 812583
No-smoking, good-value B&B in Victorian guesthouse near Blenheim.   £42

Woodstock   **Star Inn** 22 Market Place   (0993) 811373
Comfortable rooms with some antiques above a central pub.   £45

Shropshire   **MAP 5**

Brockton   **Brockton Grange**   (074 636) 443
A peaceful, pampering B&B in a quiet valley with private fishing lake and a pretty garden.   £46 to £48

Dorrington   **Country Friends**   (0743) 718707
A restaurant-with-rooms. The restaurant is excellent, the rooms suffer from early-morning traffic noise. Very friendly.   £45

Ludlow   **Number Twenty Eight*** 28 Lower Broad Street
(0584) 876995
A neat and friendly guesthouse with charming hosts.   £45

Somerset   **MAPS 9/10**

Cannington   **Malt Shovel Inn** Blackmore Lane   (0278) 653432
Friendly family-run pub/restaurant with four fairly basic rooms, one for families.   £36

Castle Cary   **Bond's*** Ansford   (0963) 50464
Comfortable and pretty rooms in a small Georgian house; good reports on food.   £60 to £80

Exford   **The Crown**   (064 383) 554
Attractively situated village pub/hotel with stables, currently undergoing refurbishment.   £50

Hatch Beauchamp   **Farthings**   (0823) 480664
Small Regency house with five comfortable rooms, one with a spiral stairway to its en-suite bathroom. A little expensive.   £85

Holford **Combe House*** (0278) 741382
Large, picturesque converted watermill in remote setting; but the old-fashioned décor doesn't match up to the promise of the exterior. £64 to £76

Montacute **Milk House*** The Borough (0935) 823823
Honey-coloured fifteenth-century licensed restaurant close to Montacute House. The food receives rave reports but there are only two bedrooms. £48

Porlock Weir **Anchor Hotel & Ship Inn** (0643) 862636
The Ship, used in winter, is all fifteenth-century oak beams; the Anchor, used all summer, has spacious nineteenth-century elegance. From £60

Shipham **Penscot Farmhouse Hotel** The Square (0934) 842659
Quiet village hotel with attractive Barn Restaurant on site of maypole. Midway through refurbishment; the redecorated rooms are best. £50

West Bagborough **Higher House*** (0823) 432996
A pleasant, part-seventeenth-century house in a quiet village overlooking the Quantocks with three rooms for B&B (dinner on request). Two recently refitted self-catering cottages overlook an outdoor swimming-pool. £35

Williton **White House** 11 Long Street (0984) 632777
Friendly mixture of Sixties' psychedelia and elegant Eighties' interior design, recently refurbished with some novel fixtures and fittings. £68 to £78

Staffordshire   MAP 5

Blore **Old Rectory** (033 529) 287
Wolsey Lodge in peaceful situation with friendly and relaxed hosts. £70

Butterton **Black Lion Inn** (0538) 304232
Eighteenth-century inn with great views over the Peak District National Park, though the basic bedrooms overlook the car park. £40

Lichfield **Swinfen Hall** Swinfen (0543) 481494
Stately eighteenth-century house with formal public rooms and good-sized if rather under-furnished bedrooms. Business-orientated. £85

Stoke-on-Trent **Haydon House** Haydon Street Basford
(0782) 711311
Friendly family-run hotel in convenient suburban street between Hanley and Newcastle-under-Lyme. Rooms look a bit tired and there is some traffic noise. £50

Stone **Stone House Hotel** (0785) 815531
Much-extended Edwardian house, now a business hotel. Pricey but decent bedrooms. £81

Suffolk   MAPS 7/8

Long Melford **The Bull** Hall Street (0787) 378494
An historic old pub with good though pricey rooms. Comfortable lounge. From £85

Lowestoft **Ivy House Farm*** Ivy Lane Oulton Broad (0502) 501353
Peaceful farmhouse in 30 acres of land with large, inviting rooms. £49

Surrey
MAP 9

Bagshot **Pennyhill Park** London Road (0276) 471774
Corporately owned Victorian manor house and country club with fine grounds and opulent bedrooms. From £138

Dorking **Burford Bridge** Box Hill (0306) 884561
Comfortable Forte hotel with beautiful gardens. From £85

Sanderstead **Selsdon Park Hotel** Addington Road 081-657 8811
Huge red-brick Victorian mansion with a golf course and a host of other sporting facilities. From £100

Tyne & Wear
MAP 3

Newcastle upon Tyne **Waterside Hotel** 48/52 Sandhill Quayside
091-230 0111
Thought and care has gone into furnishing the bedrooms, but noisy location and service occasionally lacks attention to detail. £45 to £73

Warwickshire
MAPS 5/9

Abbot's Salford **Salford Hall** (0386) 871330
Lovely Tudor manor, now a functional hotel. Comfortable well-equipped bedrooms. £85 to £105

Atherstone **Chapel House** Friars' Gate (0827) 718949
Good-value accommodation in fine Georgian house in market town. £55

Berkswell **Nailcote Hall** Nailcote Lane (0203) 466174
Elizabethan manor house between Birmingham and Coventry with intimate feel. Most bedrooms in new wing. £115

Claverdon **Ardencote Manor** Lye Green Road (0926) 843111
Conference-dominated hotel in rural location. Good leisure facilities. £82

Coleshill **Coleshill Hotel** 152 High Street (0675) 465527
Mid-size hotel on the outskirts of Birmingham, with plain well-equipped rooms and popular public bar. £67 to £75

Oxhill **Nolands Farm** (0926) 640309
Immaculate bedrooms and rustic restaurant on working farm. £36 to £40

Stratford-upon-Avon **Welcombe Hotel** Warwick Road (0789) 295252
Jacobean manor in country setting just outside Stratford. Splendid public rooms with formal atmosphere. £145

West Midlands
MAP 5

Stourbridge **Talbot Hotel** High Street (0384) 394350
Business-orientated pub accommodation in heart of old town. Popular watering-hole for locals. £43 to £50

West Sussex
MAP 9

Amberley **Amberley Castle** (0798) 831992
A glorious medieval castle, complete with suits of armour; most rooms are in modern style in a converted annexe. £95 to £225

Climping **Bailiffscourt** (0903) 723511
A secluded and highly romantic folly behind Climping beach, now showing some signs of wear and tear. £80 to £150

Slinfold **Random Hall** Stane Street (0403) 790558
Attractive sixteenth-century farmhouse with dark oak beams and open fires; next to a busy A-road. From £75

West Yorkshire MAP 5

Linton **Wood Hall** Trip Lane (0937) 587271
Attractive Georgian pavilion-style mansion in peaceful location. Its special magic has been compromised by recent developments which have doubled the number of rooms, added a leisure club and propelled it firmly into the business and corporate league. £89

Wiltshire MAP 9

East Knoyle **Milton Farm** (0747) 830247
Inexpensive B&B in elegant Queen Anne farmhouse on working farm. Excellent breakfasts and friendly welcome but bedrooms need some updating. £38

Ogbourne St George **Parklands*** High Street (0672) 841555
Small hotel and restaurant converted from country pub. Bland, modern bedrooms all with en-suite shower cubicles. Reasonable prices. £50 to £65

Purton **Pear Tree at Purton** Church End (0793) 772100
Popular restaurant and business hotel. Well-equipped bedrooms but dull public rooms. 'Learn to drive a steam locomotive' weekend breaks. £92

Salisbury **Old Mill*** Town Path, West Harnham (0722) 327517
Old mill and warehouse converted into pub and restaurant. Rooms have river views. Steep stairs. Near cathedral. £65

Zeals **Stag Cottage** Fantley Lane (0747) 840458
Small, simple rooms above teashop in seventeenth-century thatched cottage. No en-suite facilities. £26

SCOTLAND

Central MAP 2

Kinbuck **Cromlix House** (0786) 822125
Grand country house has been an acclaimed hotel and restaurant. Reports please on the promising new owner and staff. From £125

Dumfries & Galloway MAP 2

Beattock **Auchen Castle** (068 33) 407
Ebulliently run traditional hotel in lovely grounds, let down by motel-style annexe and patchy food. £52 to £70

Grampian MAP 1

Aboyne **Hazlehurst Lodge** Ballater Road (033 98) 86921
Artistic exuberance animates a comfortable guesthouse/hotel. £54

Ballater **Darroch Learg*** Braemar Road (033 97) 55443
Good-value but rather bland country house on the outskirts of town; successful and adventurous cooking. £74

Highland
MAP 1

Ardvasar **Ardvasar*** Sleat (04714) 223
Old coaching-inn overlooking the Sound of Sleat. Fresh bedrooms but gloomy public rooms. £56

Aviemore **Stakis Aviemore Four Seasons Hotel*** Aviemore Centre (0479) 810681
An unsightly tower block, though the most comfortable hotel in Aviemore. Excellent indoor leisure club. £83

Glencoe **Clachaig Inn*** (085 52) 252
A busy, efficiently run inn that's popular with climbers. Simple but adequate bedrooms. £52

Grantown-on-Spey **Garth Hotel** The Square (0479) 2836
Old-fashioned Scottish hospitality in a traditional hotel with modest but comfortable rooms and enjoyable food. £72

Kentallen **Holly Tree*** by Appin (063 174) 292
Smartly furnished and imaginatively designed hotel in old railway station; reports on new management, please. £75

Kinlochbervie **Kinlochbervie Hotel** by Lairg (0971) 521275
Reliably comfortable but slightly soulless hotel above a busy fishing harbour. Good base for wildlife enthusiasts. £84 to £104

Tain **Morangie House Hotel*** Morangie Road (0862) 892281
Turn-of-the-century mansion with welcoming owners and wide-ranging menus. £65

Lothian
MAP 2

Edinburgh **Caledonian Hotel** Princes Street 031-225 2433
Confidently refurbished city-centre hotel of the grand, old school. A good bet for a weekend break. From £165

Haddington **Browns' Hotel*** 1 West Road (062 082) 2254
Fine Georgian house with a good restaurant and elaborate old-fashioned sitting-room and dining-room. Dated individual bedrooms. £78

Humbie **Johnstounburn House** (087) 553696
Country house dating from the seventeenth century with some lovely period features; part of the Thistle chain. £125

Kirknewton **Dalmahoy Hotel** 031-333 1845
Eighteenth-century mansion converted to meet the needs of twentieth-century leisure seekers. Good for golfers. £125

Strathclyde
MAPS 1/2

Dervaig **Druimard Country House** (068 84) 345
New confident and friendly owners for this small hotel next to the UK's smallest professional theatre. Reports please, especially on the food. £77

Glasgow   **The Devonshire*** 5 Devonshire Gardens   041-339 7878
*Small and exclusive hotel with extravagantly designed rooms (next to and
similar in style to One Devonshire Gardens – see main entry).*   From £120

Glasgow   **Glasgow Hilton*** 1 William Street   041-204 5555
*Stylish leisure centre and themed bars and restaurants in this new tower block
hotel on edge of city centre. Friendly but imperfect service.*   From £115

Isle of Arran   **Auchrannie Country House** Brodick   (0770) 302234
*Reliable hotel in wooded grounds, conveniently located for beach and golf
course.*   £88

Isle of Colonsay   **The Hotel**   (09512) 316
Attractive, friendly eighteenth-century inn. A good base for walkers.   £116
(rate inc. dinner)

Oban   **King's Knoll Hotel** Dunollie Road   (0631) 62536
*Inauspicious-looking small hotel on outskirts of Oban, but friendly and with
smart little bedrooms.*   £50

Port Appin   **Invercreran Country House** Glen Creran
(063 173) 414
*Stunning views and fine food at this unusually modern-looking family-run
hotel.*   £88 to £108

Port Appin   **Stewart Hotel** Glen Duror   (063 174) 268
*Attractive public rooms, good food and a peaceful location offset characterless
motel-like bedrooms in an impressive former hunting-lodge.*   £80

Salen   **Glenforsa***   (0680) 300377
*Small and friendly log-chalet hotel furnished Habitat-style. Comfortable but
dark bedrooms.*   £59

Tarbert   **West Loch Hotel**   (0880) 820283
*Budget accommodation for travellers en route to Jura, Islay and Gigha.
Simple rooms and hearty food.*   £50

Tobermory   **Linndhu House***   (0688) 2425
*Victorian dower house in fine grounds. Once recommended for its dinners, but
now B&B only. Bedrooms comfortable but less elegant than public
rooms.*   £55 to £90

Troon   **Marine Highland Hotel** Crosbie Road   (0292) 314444
*Chain hotel with public rooms and an excellent leisure complex; overlooking
Royal Troon golf course.*   £138

Tayside   MAP I

Dunkeld   **Stakis Dunkeld House**   (0350) 727771
*Tracksuits and suits to the fore at this country-house hotel set in a 280-acre
estate.*   From £92

Kinclaven   **Ballathie House Hotel***   (0250) 883268
*Finely furnished Best Western hotel by the River Tay with facilities for
outdoor pursuits. Cheaper bedrooms may disappoint but one reader
compliments the hotel's food and comfort.*   £119 to £156

Western Isles   MAP I

Lochcarnan   **Orasay Inn** South Uist   (08704) 298
Peaceful cosy guesthouse with fine views. Ideal for birdwatchers.   £50

Stornoway **Arlonan*** 29 Francis Street (0851) 703482
Well-established B&B a short walk from the centre of town. Thoughtfully furnished bedrooms share good bathrooms. From £32

WALES

Clwyd

MAP 6

Llangollen **Bryn Howel*** (0978) 860331
Late-Victorian manor with newer additions. Characterful old bar. £38 to £85

Wrexham **Llwyn Onn Hall*** Cefn Road (0978) 261225
Informal, understated country-house-style hotel on outskirts of town. £72

Dyfed

MAP 6

Cardigan **Crychdu** Nr Bronwydd (0267) 253640
Isolated farmhouse with good-sized bedrooms and friendly owners. £30

Cardigan **Penrallt Ceibwr Farm** Moylgrove (023 986) 217
Working farm and nursery in beautiful location. £37

Pembroke **Hollyland Country House** Holyland Road (0646) 681444
Good-value hotel just outside Pembroke. £50

Pontfaen **Gelli Fawr*** (0239) 820343
Former farmhouse amid bluebell woods serving interesting food. £54

Pumpsaint **Glanrannel Park*** Crugybar (0558) 685230
Peaceful, rather old-fashioned hotel overlooking lake and 23 acres of grounds. £62

Saundersfoot **St Brides Hotel*** St Brides Hill (0834) 812304
Half-timbered hotel with attentive staff and panoramic views from restaurant. £87

Tresaith **Glandwr Manor Hotel*** (0239) 810197
Unusual building, reputedly designed by Nash; handy location for exploring this lovely stretch of coast. £46 to £52

Wolf's Castle **Wolfscastle Country Hotel** (0437) 87225
Creeper-covered hotel near busy road; rooms in the newer extension are lighter with better views. £65

Gwent

MAP 6

Pontypool **Pentwyn Farm** Little Mill (0495) 785249
Pink-washed sixteenth-century Welsh longhouse with communal dining. £34

Gwynedd

MAP 6

Betws-y-coed **Ty Gwyn Hotel** (0690) 710383
400-year-old inn packed with antiques; comfy but small bedrooms. £54

Bontddu **Bontddu Hall*** (034 149) 661
Interesting Victorian Gothic mansion overlooking Mawddach Estuary. £90

Dyffryn Ardudwy   **Cors-y-Gedol Hall**   (0341) 247230
Superb Elizabethan house with real character amid 3,000 acres of land.   From £32

Ganllwyd   **Dolmelynllyn Hall Hotel**   (034 140) 273
Largely Victorian country house with pretty, formal gardens and good food.   £80 to £100

Harlech   **Castle Cottage*** Pen Llech   (0766) 780479
Restaurant with six rooms done out in simple pine furniture and pretty florals.   £48

Nefyn   **Caeau Capel Hotel*** Rhodfarmor   (0758) 720240
Friendly holiday hotel with views of Anglesey and spotless rooms.   £49

Penmaenpool   **George III Hotel**   (0341) 422525
Old pub on Mawddach Estuary with newer, larger bedrooms in separate lodge.   £88

Talyllyn   **Tynycornel Hotel** Tywyn   (0654) 782282
Great location overlooking 222-acre lake popular with fisherfolk and walkers who like to be comfortable.   £80

Powys   MAP 6

Caersws   **Maesmawr Hall**   (0686) 688255
Attractive half-timbered building with functional bedrooms. Service rather slow.   £55 to £60

Llangurig   **Old Vicarage**   (055 15) 280
Good-value Victorian guesthouse on edge of village in attractive part of mid-Wales.   £39

Llanwrtyd Wells   **Lasswade Country House** Station Road   (059 13) 515
Friendly unpretentious hotel in mid-Wales countryside.   £55

Llyswen   **Griffin Inn** Brecon   (0874) 754241
Atmospheric old fishing inn; bedrooms have less character.   £50

Pencelli   **Cambrian Cruisers Marine** Ty Newydd   (0874) 86315
Eighteenth-century farmhouse next to small but busy marina; friendly owners.   £34

Trecastle   **Castle Hotel**   (0874) 636354
Pub with good-sized bedrooms. Handy for exploring the Brecons.   £48

South Glamorgan   MAP 6

Llantwit Major   **West House Country Hotel** West Street
(0446) 792406
Friendly family-run hotel in attractive seaside village.   £58

Thornhill   **Manor Parc Country Hotel** Thornhill Road
(0222) 693723
Pretty white country house near Cardiff with elegant restaurant and blander bedrooms.   £85

West Glamorgan
MAP 6

Swansea   **Beaumont Hotel** 72–73 Walter Road   (0792) 643956
Unprepossessing exterior on busy road hides nicely furnished Victorian-style interior. £60

Swansea   **Windsor Lodge Hotel** Mount Pleasant   (0792) 642158
Georgian building handy for town centre; individual and bold décor. £56

CHANNEL ISLANDS
MAP 10

Fermain Bay (Guernsey)   **La Favorita**   (0481) 35666
The extension to the old manor house is ugly, but this is a well-cared-for hotel in splendid location, with new pool, sauna and Jacuzzi complex. Bedrooms are well-equipped but bland. £78

Herm   **White House Hotel**   (0481) 722159
Attractive public rooms let down by spartan bedrooms and sloppy housekeeping on our inspection. Restaurant service is efficient and courteous. £100

St Anne (Alderney)   **Inchalla**   (0481) 823220
Spotless, slightly bland modern hotel with pleasant, comfortable bedrooms and generous hearty food. Proprietors are friendly and helpful. £56 to £73

St Brelade's Bay (Jersey)   **St Brelade's Bay Hotel**   (0534) 46141
The sitting areas are formal and gracious, but the friendly staff are very good with children, for whom the hotel caters well. Hearty, unexciting food is served in a drab restaurant. £82 to £156

St Helier (Jersey)   **The Grand** The Esplanade   (0534) 22301
Traditional seaside grand hotel in enormous fin de siècle building with a nod to American West-Coast Victorian style. Comfort triumphs over a characterless refurbishment. £120

St Martin's (Guernsey)   **Bella Luce**   (0481) 38764
Spruce and comfortable hotel with an attractive pool. Carefully managed with almost military precision by an unflappable host. £81

St Peter Port (Guernsey)   **Pandora Hotel** Hauteville   (0481) 720971
Reassuringly traditional and unmodish hotel with good views and pleasant gardens. Bright chintzy bedrooms and large popular restaurant. £58 to £72

St Peter's Valley (Jersey)   **Greenhill Country Hotel**   (0534) 481042
Traditional hotel in a rural location with tasty food and attentive staff. Bedrooms are well-equipped but have very simple décor. Popular with older guests. £60 to £80

Your rights in hotels

A few days away at a hotel is a special treat for many of us, so we don't want anything to spoil it. And when we're travelling on business we don't want any hotel hassles that might distract us from clinching that important deal. But sometimes things do go wrong, and the hotel doesn't live up to expectations.

Below we set out your rights in dealing with hotels and answer some of the questions regularly asked by our readers. This should help you put things straight on the spot, but if it doesn't, we suggest ways to go about claiming your rights.

When I arrived at the city-centre hotel where I'd booked a weekend break I was told that they had made a mistake and the hotel was full. Due to a popular conference, the only other room I could find was in a more expensive hotel at the other side of town, so I'm out of pocket. What are my rights?

The hotel accepted your booking and was obliged to keep a room available for you. It is in breach of contract and liable to compensate you for the additional expenses arising out of that breach – the difference in cost between what you were expecting to pay and what you ended up having to pay, plus any travelling expenses. You should write first to the hotel manager explaining what happened, and enclosing copies of receipts for your additional expenditure. (See also Points 1–5 overleaf.)

After booking I found that I had to cancel. I immediately wrote to advise the owners, but they refuse to return my deposit, and say they expect me to pay additional compensation.

When you telephone to book a room and the hoteliers accept your booking you enter into a binding contract with them – they undertake to provide the required accommodation and meals for the specified dates at the agreed price, and you commit yourself to paying their charges. If you later cancel or fail to turn up, the hotel may be entitled to keep your deposit to defray administrative expenses, although it should be possible to challenge this if the deposited amount is a very high proportion of the total cost.

If a hotelier is unable to re-let the room you have booked – and he or she must try to do so – he or she can demand from you the loss of profit caused by your cancellation, which can be a substantial proportion of the total price. It's important to give as much notice as possible if you have to cancel: this increases the chances of your room being re-let. If after cancelling you find that the full amount has been charged to your credit card you should raise the matter with your credit card issuer, who will ask the hotel whether the room was re-let, and to justify the charge made.

When I phoned to book a room the receptionist asked for my credit card number. I offered to send a deposit by cheque instead, but the receptionist insisted on taking the number.

Hotels increasingly adopt this practice to protect themselves against loss when guests fail to turn up. It's reasonable for hotels to request a deposit, and where time permits a cheque should be acceptable.

After a long drive I stopped off at a hotel and asked for a room for the night. Although clearly not full the owners refused to give me a room. Can they do this?
Hotels and inns are not allowed to refuse requests for food and shelter providing accommodation is available and the guest is sober, decently dressed and able to pay. If you meet these requirements and are turned away by a hotel with a vacancy you are entitled to sue for damages. If proprietors want to be able to turn away casual business, or are fussy about the sort of people they want in their establishment, they are likely to call it 'guesthouse' or 'private hotel'. In any event, it's illegal to exclude anyone on the grounds of race or sex.

When I called to book they told me I would need to pay extra if I wanted to pay by credit card. Is this legal?
Yes. Dual pricing was legalised early in 1991 and some hoteliers have elected to charge guests who pay by credit card extra to recover the commission payable to the card company. You can challenge this if you're not told when you book, or if it's not indicated on the tariff displayed in reception.

I arrived at a hotel in winter and found I was the only guest. Both my bedroom and the public rooms were distinctly chilly. I was uncomfortable throughout my stay and asked the management to turn up the heating, but things didn't improve.
It's an implied term of the contract between you and the hotel that the accommodation will be of a reasonable standard, so it should be maintained at a reasonable temperature. You can claim compensation or seek a reduction of the bill. You were right to complain at the time. You are under a duty to 'mitigate your loss' – to keep your claim to a minimum. The most obvious way of doing this is to complain on the spot and give the management a chance to put things right.

I was very unhappy when I was shown to my room. It hadn't been vacuumed, the wastebins were full, the towels hadn't been changed and I found dog hairs in the bed.
You are entitled to a reasonable standard of accommodation having regard to the price paid. But no hotel, however cheap, should be dirty or unsafe. Ask for things to be put right, and if they're not, ask for a reduction of the bill.

While I was in bed a section of the ceiling caved in. I was injured, but I could have been killed.
Under the Occupiers' Liability Act hotel owners are responsible for the physical safety of their guests. You have a claim for compensation, and would be wise to seek legal advice to have it properly assessed.

The hotel brochure promised floodlit tennis courts. When we arrived the lawns had been neglected and the nets were down. We couldn't play.
A hotel must provide advertised facilities. If it doesn't you can claim compensation, or ask for an appropriate deduction from your bill in respect of the disappointment suffered. You might also want trading standards officers to consider bringing a case against the hotel under the Trade Descriptions Act.

While I was staying at a hotel my video camera was stolen from my room.

Hotel owners owe you a duty of care and must look after your property while it is on their premises. They are liable for any loss and damage as long as it wasn't your own fault – you would be unlikely to succeed if you left it clearly visible in a ground-floor room with the door and window unlocked. However, under the Hotel Proprietors Act, providing hotel owners display a notice at reception, they can limit their liability to £50 per item or £100 in total. They can't rely on this limit if the loss was caused by the negligence of their staff, although you will have to prove this.

My car was broken into while parked in the hotel car park. I want compensation.

The Hotel Proprietors Act doesn't cover cars. Your claim is unlikely to succeed.

My dinner was inedible. Do I have to pay for it?

The Supply of Goods and Services Act obliges hotels to prepare food with reasonable skill and care. The common law in Scotland imposes similar duties. If food is inedible, you should tell the waiter and ask for a replacement dish. If things aren't put right you can ask for a reduction of the billed amount. If you pay in full, possibly to avoid an unpleasant scene, write a note at the time saying that you are doing so under protest and 'reserving your rights'. This means that you retain your right to claim compensation later.

Getting your rights

1 Always complain at the time if you're unhappy. It's by far the best way, and necessary to discharge your obligation to mitigate your loss.

2 If you reach deadlock you can deduct a sum from the bill in recognition of the deficient service received. Remember that the hotel might try to exercise its right of 'lien' by refusing to release your luggage until the bill is paid. It's probably easier to pay in full, but giving written notice that you are paying under protest and reserving your rights to claim compensation through the courts.

3 Legal advice is available from a number of sources. Citizens Advice Bureaux, Law Centres and Consumer Advice Centres give free advice on consumer disputes. In certain cases your local Trading Standards Department might be able to help. If instructing a solicitor be sure to sort out the cost implications at the outset. Or you can write to Consumers' Association's Legal Department at 2 Marylebone Road, London NW1 4DF.

4 Once you know where you stand, write to the hotel setting out your claim.

5 If this fails to get things sorted out and you feel you have a strong case, you can sue for sums of up to £1000 under the small claims procedure in the county court. In the Sheriff Court in Scotland the limit is £750. You shouldn't need a solicitor.

Index

All full entries are indexed below. Visitors' Book entries are listed on pages 817 to 835. An asterisk indicates a new entry.

Maps

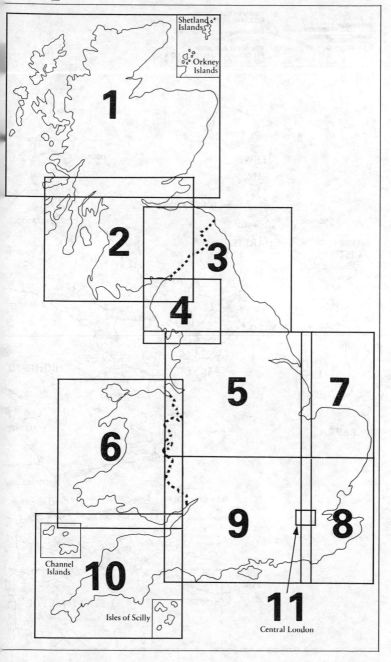

MAP 1

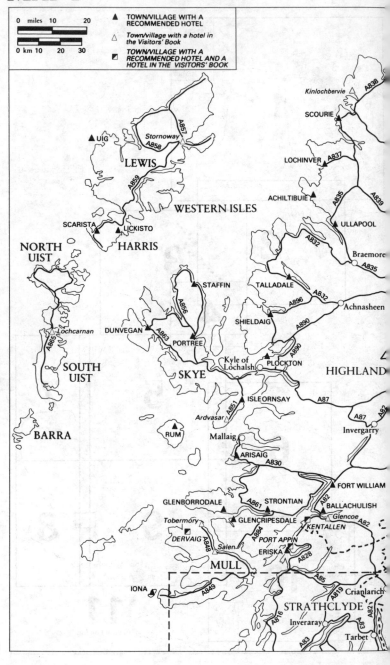

▲	TOWN/VILLAGE WITH A RECOMMENDED HOTEL
△	*Town/village with a hotel in the Visitors' Book*
◪	TOWN/VILLAGE WITH A RECOMMENDED HOTEL AND A HOTEL IN THE VISITORS' BOOK

0 miles 10 20
0 km 10 20 30

Kinlochbervie △ A838

SCOURIE ▲

▲ UIG *Stornoway* A857 A858

LEWIS A859

LOCHINVER ▲ A837 A839

ACHILTIBUIE ▲ A835

WESTERN ISLES

ULLAPOOL ▲

SCARISTA ▲ ▲ LICKISTO A832 Braemore ○ A835

NORTH UIST

HARRIS

Lochcarnan A865

▲ STAFFIN TALLADALE ▲ A832 Achnasheen ○

A856 SHIELDAIG ▲ A896 A890

DUNVEGAN ▲ A863 PORTREE ▲

SOUTH UIST SKYE Kyle of Lochalsh ○ PLOCKTON ▲ A890 HIGHLAND

ISLEORNSAY ▲ A87 A87 A82

Ardvasar △ A851 Invergarry ○

BARRA ▲ RUM Mallaig ○

▲ ARISAIG A830

FORT WILLIAM ▲

GLENBORRODALE ▲ A861 STRONTIAN ▲ BALLACHULISH ▲ A82

Tobermory ▲ GLENCRIPESDALE ▲ *Glencoe* A82

◪ DERVAIG A848 *Salen* A884 *Port Appin* KENTALLEN ▲

ERISKA ▲ A828

MULL A85

IONA ◪ A849 A819 Crianlarich ○

STRATHCLYDE A82

A816 Inveraray ○ A83

Tarbet ○

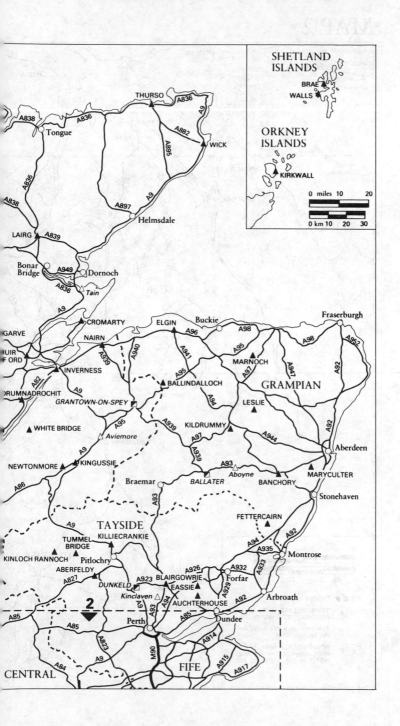

MAP 2

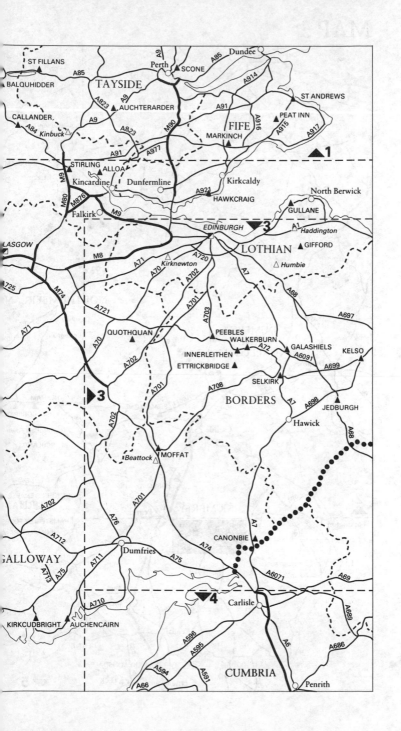

MAP 3

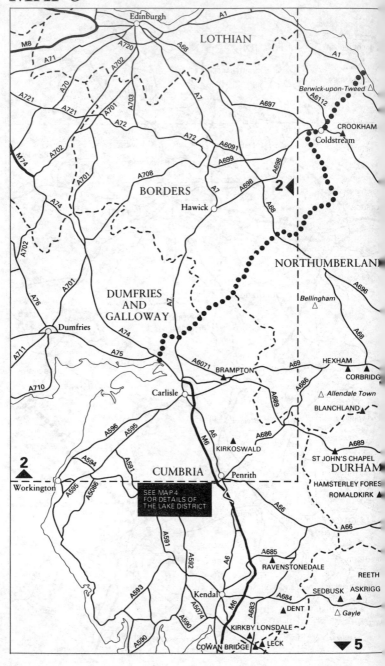

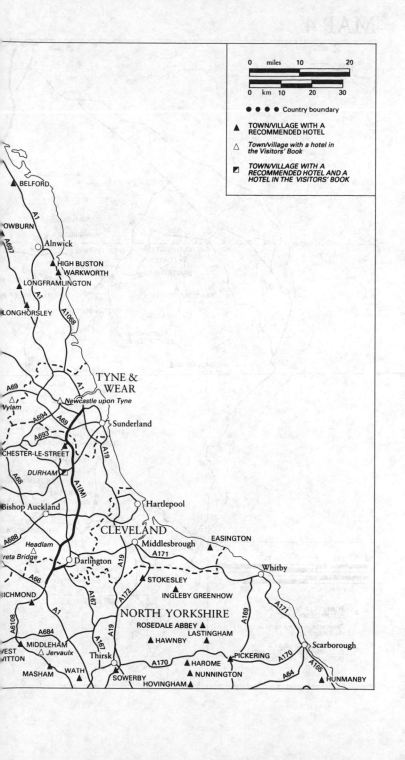

MAP 4

0 miles 10 20

0 km 10 20 30

● ● ● ● Country boundary

▲ TOWN/VILLAGE WITH A RECOMMENDED HOTEL

△ *Town/village with a hotel in the Visitors' Book*

◨ **TOWN/VILLAGE WITH A RECOMMENDED HOTEL AND A HOTEL IN THE VISITORS' BOOK**

▲ BELFORD

◦OWBURN

◦ Alnwick

A697

A1

▲ HIGH BUSTON
▲ WARKWORTH

LONGFRAMLINGTON

A1068

LONGHORSLEY

A1

TYNE & WEAR

A69

△ *Vylam*

Newcastle upon Tyne

A694 A69

◦ Sunderland

A693

A19

CHESTER-LE-STREET

A68

DURHAM ◨

A1(M)

◦Bishop Auckland

A688

Headlam △

reta Bridge - -

◦ Darlington

◦ Hartlepool

CLEVELAND

EASINGTON ▲

◦ Middlesbrough

A171

A19

RICHMOND ▲

A1

A66

A6108

A684

MIDDLEHAM ▲
△ *Jervaulx*

WEST
WITTON

MASHAM ▲

A167

A172

▲ STOKESLEY

▲ INGLEBY GREENHOW

NORTH YORKSHIRE

ROSEDALE ABBEY ▲
LASTINGHAM ▲
▲ HAWNBY

A19

A167

Thirsk ◦

WATH ▲

SOWERBY

A170

▲ HAROME
▲ NUNNINGTON

HOVINGHAM ▲

A169

Whitby ◦

A171

PICKERING

Scarborough ◦

A170

A165

A64

▲ HUNMANBY

MAP 4

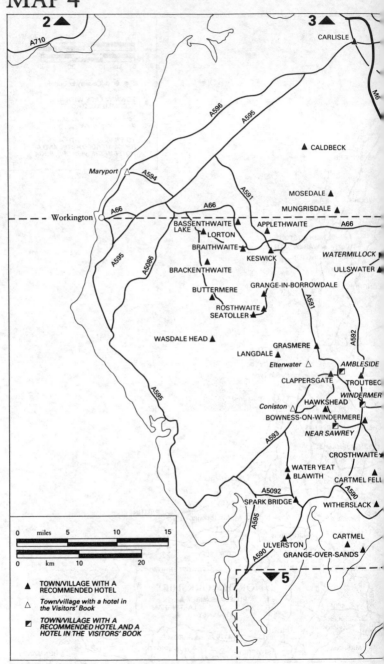

3▲

NORTHUMBERLAND

A689

A686

A686

A68

DURHAM

PENRITH

A66

A66

CUMBRIA

M6

A685

SEE MAP 3
FOR DETAILS OF
THIS AREA

3▶

A591

A6

A685

A683

A684

KENDAL

Hawes ○

A5074

NORTH YORKSHIRE

5▼

A687

A65

A683

LANCASHIRE

Lancaster ○

MAP 5

MAP 6

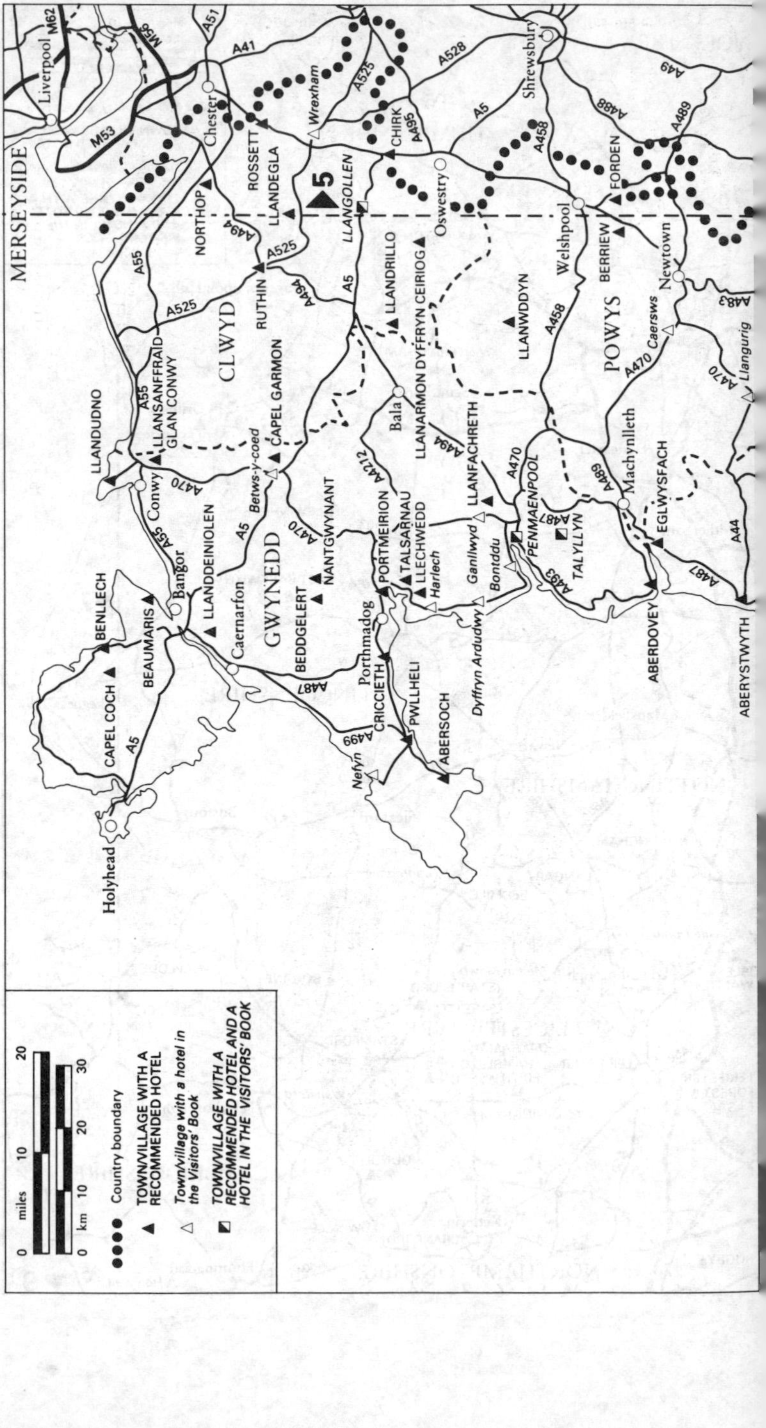

Key / Legend:

| | miles | 0 | 10 | 20 |
| | km | 0 | 10 | 20 | 30 |

- ●●● Country boundary
- ▲ TOWN/VILLAGE WITH A RECOMMENDED HOTEL
- △ Town/village with a hotel in the Visitors' Book
- ◨ TOWN/VILLAGE WITH A RECOMMENDED HOTEL AND A HOTEL IN THE VISITORS' BOOK

Place names shown on map:

MERSEYSIDE
Liverpool
M62, M63, M53, M56
A51, A41
Chester
Wrexham
A525, A528
Shrewsbury
A49, A5
CHIRK
A495
Oswestry
A458
FORDEN
A488, A489
NORTHOP
ROSSETT
LLANDEGLA
△5
▲LLANGOLLEN
LLANDRILLO
Welshpool
POWYS
BERRIEW ▲
Newtown
A483
A525
RUTHIN
A494
A5
A542
A543
A494
CLWYD
LLANARMON DYFFRYN CEIRIOG ▲
LLANWDDYN
A470
Caersws
Llangurig △
A44
LLANDUDNO
A55
LLANSANNFRAID GLAN CONWY
Betws-y-coed △
CAPEL GARMON △
Bala
LLANFACHRETH ▲
A458
A470
A489
Machynlleth
A470
A487
Conwy
A470
LLANDEINIOLEN
Bangor
A55
Caernarfon
GWYNEDD
BEDDGELERT ▲
NANTGWYNANT ▲
PORTMEIRION ◨
A4212
TALSARNAU ▲
LLECHWEDD
Harlech △
Ganllwyd △
Bontddu △
PENMAENPOOL
A487
TALYLLYN △
A493
EGLWYSFACH ▲
ABERDOVEY ▲
A44
ABERYSTWYTH
BENLLECH ▲
CAPEL COCH ▲
BEAUMARIS ▲
A5
Holyhead
Porthmadog
CRICCIETH ◨
A497
A499
PWLLHELI
ABERSOCH ▲
Nefyn ○
Dyffryn Ardudwy △
A481

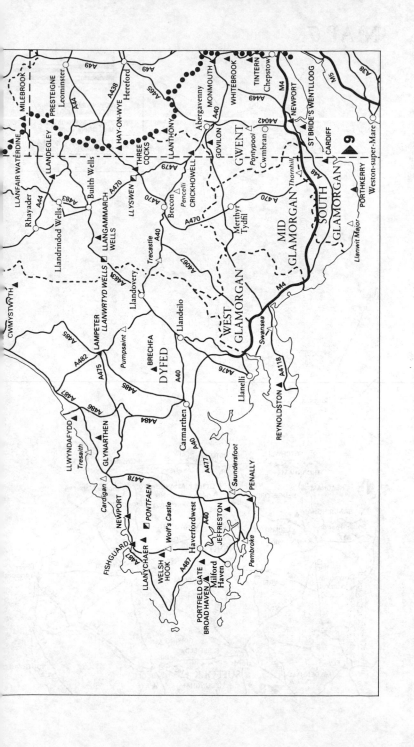

MAP 7

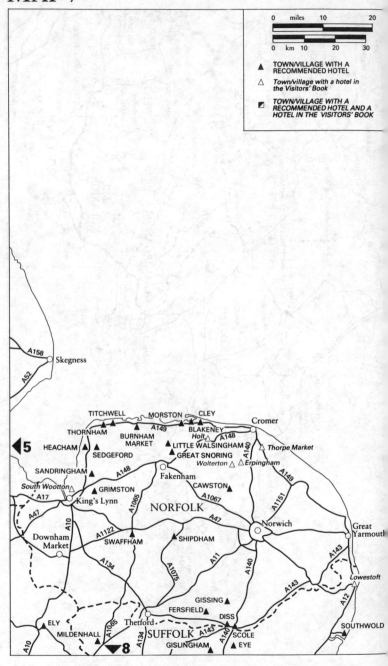

| 0 | miles | 10 | | 20 |
| 0 | km | 10 | 20 | 30 |

▲ TOWN/VILLAGE WITH A RECOMMENDED HOTEL

△ *Town/village with a hotel in the Visitors' Book*

◩ *TOWN/VILLAGE WITH A RECOMMENDED HOTEL AND A HOTEL IN THE VISITORS' BOOK*

A158
A52
○ Skegness

◀ 5

TITCHWELL ▲
MORSTON ▲ CLEY ▲
A149
BLAKENEY ▲
THORNHAM ▲ *Holt* △ A148
BURNHAM MARKET ▲ LITTLE WALSINGHAM ▲
HEACHAM ▲ ▲ SEDGEFORD GREAT SNORING ▲
SANDRINGHAM ▲ *Wolterton* △ △ *Erpingham*
South Wootton △ ▲ GRIMSTON Fakenham ○ CAWSTON ▲
A17 ○ King's Lynn A148 A1067
A47 A1065 NORFOLK A47
Downham Market ○ A1122 SWAFFHAM A11
A10 A134 A1075
ELY A1065 GISSING ▲
MILDENHALL ▲ Thetford ○ FERSFIELD ▲ DISS ◩
▼ 8 A134 SUFFOLK A143 SCOLE ▲
GISLINGHAM ▲ A140 EYE ▲

Cromer
△ *Thorpe Market*
A140
A149
A1151
○ Norwich
Great Yarmouth
A143
Lowestoft
A12
SOUTHWOLD ▲
SHIPDHAM ▲

MAP 8

SUFFOLK

Newmarket
BURY ST EDMUNDS
OTLEY
ALDEBURGH
Cambridge
Six Mile Bottom
BRADFIELD COMBUST
NEEDHAM MARKET
CAMPSEA ASH
LAVENHAM
LONG MELFORD
IPSWICH
DUXFORD
Sudbury
HINTLESHAM
LITTLEBURY GREEN
STOKE-BY-NAYLAND
DEDHAM
Felixstowe
BROXTED
GREAT DUNMOW
Coggeshall
COLCHESTER
HARWICH
ESSEX
Clacton-on-Sea
WEST MERSEA
Chelmsford
Basildon
ROCHFORD
HORNDON ON THE HILL
Southend-on-Sea
ISLE OF SHEPPEY
Margate
Rochester
BAPCHILD
Ramsgate
Sevenoaks
Westerham
Maidstone
BOUGHTON STREET
Chartham Hatch
Canterbury
KENT
CHARTHAM
BOUGHTON MONCHELSEA
SMARDEN
BOUGHTON LEES
ST MARGARETS AT CLIFFE
Tunbridge Wells
Ashford
DOVER
CRANBROOK
GOUDHURST
BETHERSDEN
HARTFIELD
BIDDENDEN
Folkestone
BENENDEN
TENTERDEN
Ticehurst
UCKFIELD
NETHERFIELD
RUSHLAKE GREEN
BATTLE
RYE
EAST SUSSEX
Herstmonceux
Newhaven
Hastings
Alfriston
Eastbourne
WESTDEAN

| | 0 | miles | 10 | 20 |

| | 0 | km | 10 | 20 | 30 |

▲ TOWN/VILLAGE WITH A RECOMMENDED HOTEL

△ *Town/village with a hotel in the Visitors' Book*

◩ *TOWN/VILLAGE WITH A RECOMMENDED HOTEL AND A HOTEL IN THE VISITORS' BOOK*

MAP 9

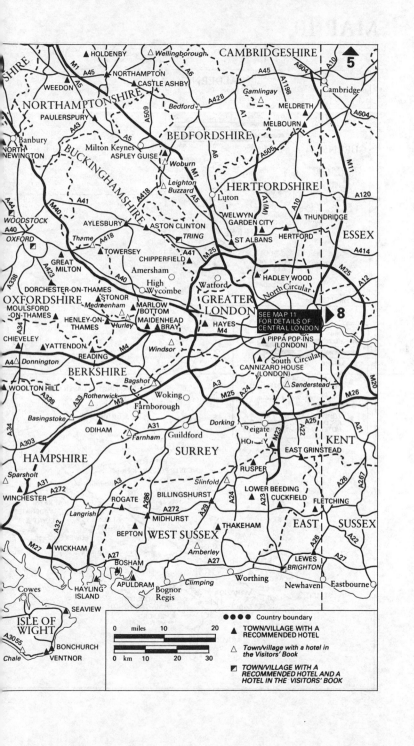

MAP 10

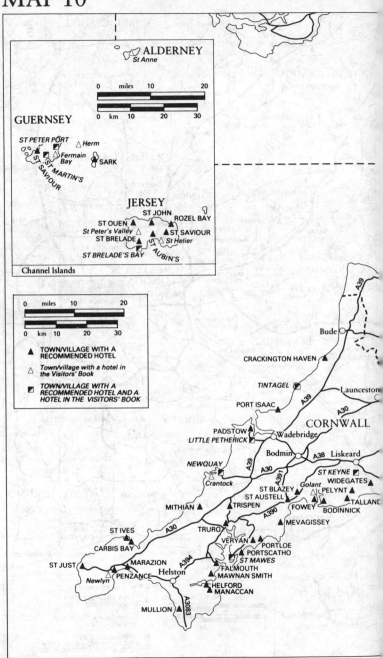

ALDERNEY
St Anne

miles 0 10 20
km 0 10 20 30

GUERNSEY

ST PETER PORT
Herm
Fermain Bay
SARK
ST MARTIN'S
ST SAVIOUR

JERSEY
ST JOHN
ST OUEN
ROZEL BAY
St Peter's Valley
ST SAVIOUR
ST BRELADE
St Helier
ST BRELADE'S BAY
ST AUBIN'S

Channel Islands

miles 0 10 20
km 0 10 20 30

▲ TOWN/VILLAGE WITH A RECOMMENDED HOTEL

△ Town/village with a hotel in the Visitors' Book

◪ TOWN/VILLAGE WITH A RECOMMENDED HOTEL AND A HOTEL IN THE VISITORS' BOOK

CORNWALL

Bude
CRACKINGTON HAVEN ▲
TINTAGEL ◪
Launceston
PORT ISAAC ▲
A30
A39
PADSTOW ▲
LITTLE PETHERICK ◪
Wadebridge
Bodmin
A38 Liskeard
NEWQUAY
Crantock
ST KEYNE ◪
WIDEGATES ▲
Golant
PELYNT ▲
St Blazey
ST AUSTELL
FOWEY
TALLAND
BODINNICK
MITHIAN ▲
TRISPEN
A390
MEVAGISSEY ▲
TRURO
VERYAN ▲
PORTLOE
ST IVES
CARBIS BAY
PORTSCATHO
ST MAWES
MARAZION
FALMOUTH
ST JUST ▲
PENZANCE
Helston
MAWNAN SMITH
Newlyn
HELFORD
MANACCAN
A394
A3083
MULLION ▲

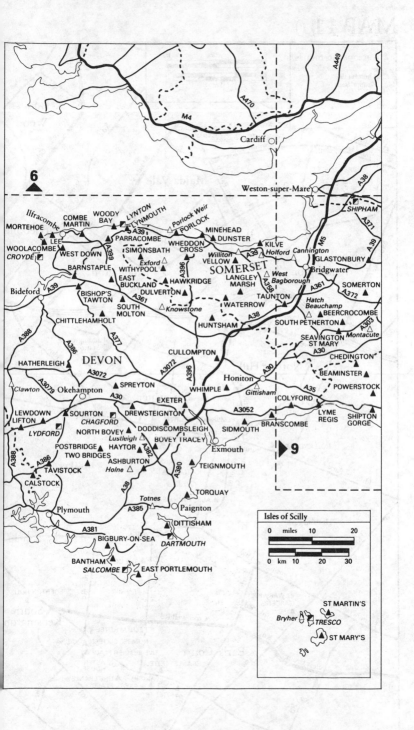

MAP 11

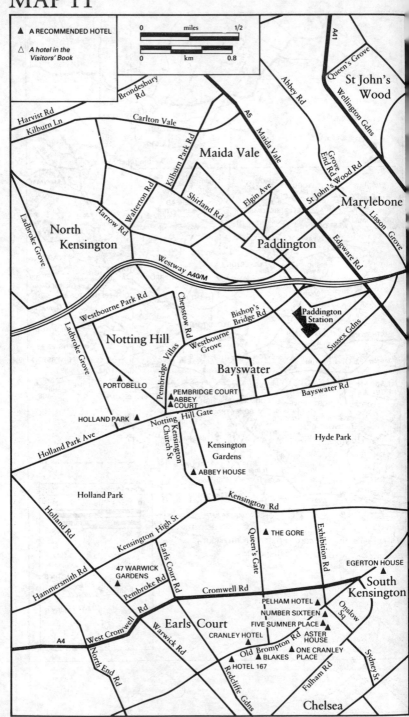

▲ A RECOMMENDED HOTEL

△ A hotel in the Visitors' Book

miles 0 — 1/2
km 0 — 0.8

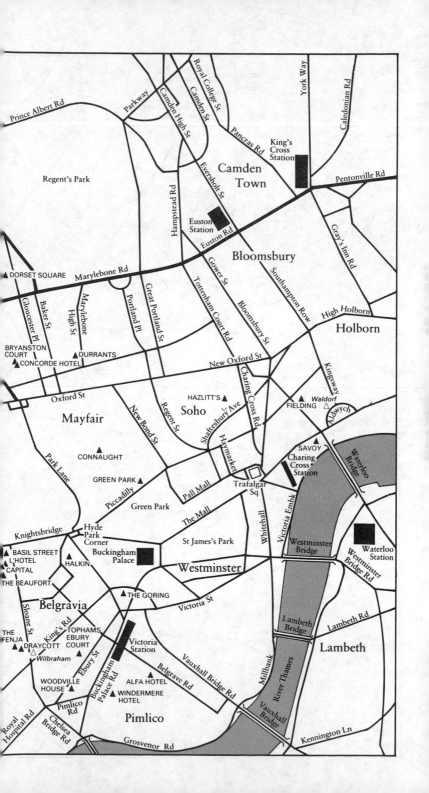

Report form

Please tell us about a stay at any hotel in Britain, whether or not it appears in this *Guide*. Write a letter if you would prefer, and send brochures or other material too. Send your forms to: The Editor, *The Which? Hotel Guide*, FREEPOST, 2 Marylebone Road, London NW1 1YN

Name of hotel

Address

I visited this hotel on:

My report is:

(Continue overleaf)

My name is:

Address:

Report form

Please tell us about a stay at any hotel in Britain, whether or not it appears in this *Guide*. Write a letter if you would prefer, and send brochures or other material too. Send your forms to: The Editor, *The Which? Hotel Guide*, FREEPOST, 2 Marylebone Road, London NW1 1YN

Name of hotel

Address

I visited this hotel on:

My report is:

(Continue overleaf)

My name is:

Address: